CONTENTS

CONTENTS

INTRODUCTION

This volume is the first of what will be a biennial series. It is customary, in an introduction, for the editor to review relevant events since the last edition. Since this book is the first of the series and necessarily includes most of the naval weapons systems developed since World War II, this review will deal with the current and likely future state of the art, as well as with the politics and economics driving that future state.

Politics and economics must come first. 1989 has been the year that the U.S. defense budget began to shrink, to meet the requirement for deficit reduction and also to mirror the apparent reduction in the Soviet threat. Other Western defense budgets have already contracted, after the steady growth of the early 1980s. By the time this book appears, it will be clearer whether the U.S. government interprets Mr. Gorbachev's peace initiatives as meaning that military vigilance can be relaxed everywhere. The editor suggests that the Third World is, and will continue to be, sufficiently unstable to justify continued U.S. military (particularly naval) presence, whatever the future of Soviet foreign policy. One might even suggest that aggressive Third World leaders would find greater room for maneuver in a world in which the Soviets were much less active.

For many countries, the most important economic issue is the future of the world arms market. Until quite recently, the market in the Third World has been dominated by Western Europe (and, to a much lesser extent, Israel), a dominance mirrored in these pages. However, several Third World countries see the arms market as a means of gaining the wherewithal to modernize. That idea is not new; countries like Britain and France developed their industrial bases partly by arms export in the late nineteenth century. At present the most important Third World exporters are China (PRC), South Korea, and Brazil. China has developed a very wide range of systems, and her export ambitions show in the extent to which she is willing to publish her systems' specifications. South Korea builds warships, but they carry Western weapons systems; she exports land combat weapons. Brazil exports land weapons and is beginning to build her own warships.

Meanwhile, India is beginning a naval arms industry to parallel her very considerable land combat weapons industry. At present she produces only for herself, but that situation may change. Taiwan manufactures some of her own naval weapons, but, again, apparently only for her own use.

The Third World producers enjoy two important commercial advantages. One is that these governments, unlike their Western counterparts, harbor no illusions that arms sales can (or should) carry political advantages; these producers will sell to virtually anyone with sufficient cash because none of them can imagine becoming any other country's dominant supplier. Nor will the average Third World producer be very deeply concerned with protecting the secrets of his military technology. Third World products also tend to be much less expensive (but also much less sophisticated) than those of the West, and probably also those available from the Soviet Union. These considerations proved extremely important to both sides in the Iran-Iraq War. If, as this editor would suppose, the Third World will continue to be the venue of future warfare, these factors can only grow in importance, particularly as the Western suppliers seek to damp conflicts by means of arms embargoes.

For any Western naval force that has to operate in the Third World, the Third World suppliers pose an interesting problem. Western intelligence agencies tend to concentrate on the Soviet Union; therefore, Western warships tend to be equipped to deal with Soviet weapons and sensors. To a limited extent, the experiences of the Falklands and then of the Gulf War have inspired interest in those Western systems, such as Exocet, that have been widely exported. Third World producers have received much less attention. The problem is not that their products are overwhelmingly deadly or that they embody new physical principles, but rather that many countermeasures, especially electronic ones, are most effective if they are tailored fairly closely to the systems they must counter. For example, any reader of the descriptions of electronic support measures in this book must be impressed by the extent to which such systems depend upon libraries of radar and other electronic signatures. If no one has inserted the appropriate data into the threat library, even the best systems will not recognize what is happening. This problem is complicated by the emergence of radars whose signals can be modified by programming. In recent years suppliers of electronic-support-measures systems, at least in the United States, have been asked to develop generic sensors that will recognize that, say, an attack radar (of whatever characteristics) has been locked on. If that capability is indeed practical, it may solve much of the problem.

The reader will notice that the quality of descriptions of Third World–originated systems varies radically. Some nations, such as China, export their equipment and, therefore, have to advertise (indeed, to a degree inconceivable a decade ago). Others such as India, however, produce only for a home market and, therefore, need not publish very much. One would assume that, given the enormous load imposed on intelligence services by the attempt to collect Soviet data, very little information is obtained on Third World weapons systems produced only for home consumption.

From this point of view, perhaps the most interesting potential development of Mr. Gorbachev's shift in Soviet foreign policy would be a much greater willingness to export weapons. After all, the Soviets need hard (i.e., foreign) currency badly, and their main product is arms. If Mr. Gorbachev is counting on a decade or so of peaceful relations with the West, he can afford to compromise the security of the current run of systems, on the theory that their sales will finance development of a later generation, for possible use when the era of good feeling runs out. The lease of one or more nuclear submarines to India might be a precursor of such a policy. From a Western point of view, the main consequence of wider Soviet exports would be that Western forces dealing with Third World states would be facing much more sophisticated opposition.

This survey cannot entirely avoid the questions surrounding Japan. For many years Japan has avoided any arms sales, on the grounds that such transactions are constitutionally prohibited. The bar seems more a matter of interpretation than of actual constitutional language, and it is conceivable that with the death of Emperor Hirohito that prohibition will be reevaluated. Japan has consistently preferred home development of missiles and torpedoes (among other naval systems) to import or license production of U.S. or other foreign equipment; it would appear that there is a national policy of maintaining a strong indigenous development and production base. Such a base could be expanded further by export. At present, running at very uneconomical rates, the current policy greatly increases the price Japan pays for its current level of defense. The situation should not be taken as a clear indication of Japanese intent ultimately to export arms; the Japanese defense industry does have a considerable (and valuable) mobilization potential.

Another political development deserves comment here. For about a decade and a half, it has become increasingly apparent that neither superpower is particularly enthusiastic about the prospect of nuclear war. For example, Soviet material recently released by the U.S. government indicates a virtually absolute unwillingness to release tactical nuclear weapons during a European war (unless NATO's nuclear weapons have been entirely eliminated beforehand); this unwillingness is based on the judgment that the introduction of nuclear weapons by both sides will not really alter the outcome but will merely make that outcome much costlier. If this account of Soviet thinking is accurate, it means that, should NATO actually succeed in stopping some future Soviet assault, the war will almost inevitably be drawn out into something more like World War I than like any of the war scenarios popular over the last few years. Not only will navies be extremely important in such combat, but they will also certainly exhaust their prewar stockpiles of such advanced weapons as antiaircraft missiles and homing torpedoes. Much will, therefore, depend upon the ability to mobilize the massive civilian industry of the West.

If nuclear war on land has become almost impossible, what of nuclear war at sea? For some years it has been apparent that Western navies, which are intended to secure the free use of the surface of the sea, would find naval nuclear warfare distinctly to their disadvantage. On the other hand, the Soviets, who consider naval operations much less important than operations on land, would not lightly initiate nuclear war at sea for fear of initiating use on land as well. The United States has already abandoned one category of naval nuclear weapons, the nuclear torpedo (ASTOR, the Mark 45), and is about to give up two more (SUBROC and the nuclear antiaircraft missile). On the other hand, the Royal Navy stoutly resists any attempt to abandon its nuclear weapon, the nuclear depth bomb, on the grounds that such weapons may be the only reliable counter to fast, deep-diving submarines.

The current NATO doctrine is to present the Soviets with a nuclear challenge, in the event that conventional forward defense fails. The usual expectation is that the nuclear "shot across the bows" would be a very limited attack on a land target. Any such attack would surely cause serious collateral damage and as such it might be vetoed by the NATO government on whose territory the weapons would fall. However, there is one sphere in which NATO could fire a nuclear warning shot without any fear of tearing up NATO territory—the sea.

The analyst is led to ask whether some bright spirit within a land-oriented NATO might not see naval nuclear weapons as the ideal means of presenting an advancing Soviet army with a nuclear challenge—and thus of initiating naval nuclear warfare without any threat of escalation onto the land, somewhat naively accepting the problems inherent in the asymmetry between NATO's and the Soviet bloc's use of the sea. The logic of this problem suggests that it is very much in NATO's interest to eliminate naval tactical nuclear weapons, perhaps even if the Soviets refuse to eliminate their own. The Soviets would presumably be reluctant to begin nuclear use at sea for fear that the nuclear exchange would spread to the land (via NATO retaliation) and thus raise the cost of the land campaign. NATO would be prevented from blundering into a nuclear exchange limited to the sea. These remarks do not apply to strategic (land-attack) nuclear weapons based at sea, since their use would not be limited to the sea itself. Carrier-based nuclear bombs are admittedly a complicating factor in any such calculation.

The NATO navies would very much want to retain nuclear weapons intended to strike land targets, partly because those weapons might be the bulk of the NATO nuclear weapons surviving the early phase of a conventional war (and because the existence of these weapons might keep the war from going nuclear). The U.S. Navy also gains considerable prospective tactical benefit from forcing the Soviet fleet to come out (i.e., expose itself to destruction) and try to attack U.S. nuclear platforms. The Soviets clearly would like to eliminate Western sea-based land-attack weapons and have made the elimination of nuclear sea-launched cruise missiles (SLCMs) a major objective of arms control. For its part, the United States sees far too much potential in future highly accurate nonnuclear long-range cruise missiles to be willing to eliminate these weapons as a category.

A general reduction in the perceived nuclear threat might have considerable implications for naval tactics. For example, formations might be grouped much more tightly, for better antiaircraft coverage (and, incidentally, to avoid the use of high-frequency communications).

In a larger sense, a shift away from concepts of nuclear blitzkrieg back to an expectation that war, should it come, would be protracted would bring back an emphasis on warship (hence weapons-system) survivability. The expectation that any future war would be extremely short has translated into a belief that any ship that would require more than, say, a week to repair could be written off for the course of the war. If the expected term of the war is measured in years, then even a year's repair (as in the case of USS *Stark*) is better than waiting two or three years for a new ship. Moreover, a lengthy war would see many ships lost and would, therefore, require a massive replacement program. No Western nation can afford to maintain a peacetime fleet large enough to see through a multiyear war.

An emphasis on survivability must, of course, address the weapons systems carried on board ships. At present, most warships are built around a single concentrated computer center, the destruction of which eliminates their fighting capacity. This computer in turn is hard-wired to the various weapons and sensors, and replacement of the wiring itself is a major contributor to the cost and duration of damage repairs. However, as computers become both more powerful and much less expensive, it is possible to distribute computing power through more of the volume of a ship. It is also possible to connect computers and sensors to one or more data buses, just as the electrical appliances in a home are connected to power cables. For the ship, the key is that the data bus must be so capacious that it can carry all the ship's essential combat data, each computer (or weapon or sensor) stripping off what it needs. The simpler the ship, the easier to implement this type of architecture because the smaller the data load and the easier it is to provide duplicate computers. No matter the size of the ship, the direction of development seems clear (as, incidentally, it is in aircraft as well as in ships). Moreover, as standard general-purpose computers take over more and more tasks, the computers can be modified by changes in software rather than by physical replacement.

The improving computer and electrical technologies have revolutionary implications. At present, one of the main costs of construction is wiring (for data rather than for power). Data buses should be much easier to install and, incidentally, to protect. That ease in turn should make wartime mass production more practical and should also make repairing battle damage much simpler, since damaged equipment can more easily be unplugged and discarded, and a concentrated (but damaged) data bus should be easier to replace than a mass of dispersed wiring. Moreover, if the combat system can be dispersed through the length of a ship, the system should become much more survivable. We will be back to the past's ideal, which envisaged a ship fighting almost until the seas closed over her. At present, hulls are much more survivable than the combat systems they carry, the *Stark* being a good example. Most of her repair bill was for rewiring and replacing the equipment in her burnt-out CIC. Her hull itself was relatively intact. For the U.S. Navy, these ideas are reflected in the new *Arleigh Burke*–class destroyers. Some other navies have gone much further; the Danish Standard Flex 300 is probably the most impressive example.

These projections may seem irrelevant, given Mr. Gorbachev's very conciliatory position. The current situation between the superpowers is less new than it may seem. In retrospect, major war has not been very close at any time since at least the early 1960s, partly because of NATO's readiness to fight in the event the Soviets wanted to try their luck. The future may be rather more unhappy than we expect. The most realistic war scenarios begin, not with planned Soviet aggression, but rather with unexpected crises, generally within the communist world. Mr. Gorbachev will almost certainly generate just such crises as he tries to shift his rather fossilized system into something approaching fluidity. Dormant tensions, not only within the Soviet Union but also among the satellite states of eastern Europe, are becoming much more overt. It would, therefore, be extremely unwise to assume that he, or his conciliatory position, is permanent. It is still quite possible to imagine conflict, particularly over the long term; NATO's level of preparedness can still make such conflict less likely.

One more point is very important: demographics. In all the Western countries, the population of military age is shrinking. That trend is probably the inevitable result of urbanization and prosperity: couples have fewer children, on average, because it costs a great deal to provide a child with the advantages the couple can hope to provide. Having too many children means descending into a much less pleasant existence. Military forces will have to shrink or else pay much more for their manpower. Competition with the civilian sector will become more intense.

Any development, such as greater reliability, that reduces the requisite numbers of nonfighting personnel (e.g., technicians) will make a considerable difference. Fortunately, it appears that Western military technology has reached just the point of development that is so badly needed for the 1990s.

At least in the West, modern electronic systems finally work: when the button is pressed, the radar lights off, the missile fires as expected, the torpedo pings as it should. For the first decade and a half after World War II, the emphasis was on stretching the maximum performance of systems. Not very much has happened in that area since about 1960. Mach 2.5, for example, is still the maximum speed of many surface-to-air missiles. But the systems, particularly the automatic systems, of 1960 very rarely worked even ten percent of the time. In 1964 the U.S. Navy was forced to shut down development of its next-generation antiaircraft system, Typhon, in favor of making its existing "3-T" (Talos, Tartar, and Terrier) work reliably. The Standard Missile was one fruit of this effort.

This reliability also shows in the performance of computers and radars. Many readers take for granted the reliability of their small (but powerful) home and office computers, forgetting that only about a decade ago computers were almost invariably attended by large numbers of carefully trained troubleshooters. The performance of modern military systems reflects the same sort of development in micro-electronics that has rendered so many of these people jobless and that has made the modernization of the past decade, especially in the United States, a particularly potent force. Many weapons and platforms, which show little nominal performance improvement over their predecessors, now can achieve that performance all or most of the time. The successors will do even better. In theory, the new generation should require many fewer technicians (who will be in increasingly short supply over the next few years) and also fewer spare parts. As a result, it should be possible to design tighter warships carrying larger weapons loads on much the current displacements.

This sort of reliability may have important implications for Third World states. Traditionally, one characteristic of the Third World has been its relative lack of technicians. Existing sophisticated weapons systems require considerable care and, therefore, may not approach optimum performance in Third World hands. However, to the extent that future systems, like current personal computers, need virtually no care, the advantage enjoyed by First World operators may decline sharply. The Soviets have already learned as much in Afghanistan: no army of technicians was needed to make the Stinger antiaircraft missiles work. The West will still enjoy important advantages, but in future they may come to be more in scale of organization (including intelligence) and in tactical skill than in operational readiness.

Performance and reliability need not equate to combat effectiveness. In 1986, in Libya, precision-guided bombs sometimes could not be launched because the political constraints entailed in the desired "surgical strike" were beyond the bombs' technical capabilities. In 1988, in the Persian Gulf, a U.S. Aegis cruiser shot down an Iranian airliner because the airplane blundered into a combat situation and did not identify itself properly. In each case, the context demanded more than the designers had put into the system or, indeed, could have been expected to provide. For example, as many news writers were astounded to learn, the radar did not display an image of the airliner. No radar in existence could have given that image, and no system in existence could have probed the airliner pilot's mind to establish his intentions.

The past three or four decades have been devoted to making sure that a given weapon performs as expected, i.e., to achieving with high-performance weapons the sort of reliability that was expected, in the past, of guns and iron bombs and straight-running torpedoes. Now that this reliability has been achieved, navies can concentrate much more on tactics and on the sort of weapons characteristics that those tactics require.

For example, until very recently the great achievement aimed at in antiship missiles was the ability to hit a moving target. More recently designers have added special maneuvers to evade or overwhelm terminal defenses. That capability is a designer's sort of development, not a tactician's. The tactician must soon ask just how to be sure, from well beyond the horizon, that the weapons have done the job. After all, the enemy does have terminal defenses and may even have ships designed to survive battle damage. Current weapons can probably knock out a ship's combat system, but the reason is that the system is heavily interconnected, not that the weapons impose damage over the whole length of a target.

At least in the West, designers have avoided the crucial question of whether their weapons can impose damage so catastrophic that an observer at a great distance can tell as much. Because Western ships tend to carry relatively few antiship missiles, and because commanders may well choose to keep firing until they are sure they have disabled their enemies, this issue is very serious. It is not that the designers have been fools: they are limited in the size and weight of their weapons by the very reasonable requirement that they fit existing platforms. Most designers have assumed that a ship that suddenly produces a column of smoke, or whose electronics have gone off the air, is dead. However, the tactician will know that another tactician may well choose to play dead, and modern radars can be switched on and off quite easily (whereas their predecessors could not).

In the next stage of development, the user, sure of the performance of the weapons, can drive development to meet tactical objectives.

The tactical situation seems much less satisfactory in ASW. Current Western systems are intended to detect and attack a submarine at considerable range, well beyond the range at which she can hope to fire her missiles or torpedoes. However, many submarine commanders maintain that they can generally penetrate the screening ships, that submarines will be detected only when they fire, either by the sound of firing or by the effect of their fire. This situation is aggravated by the appearance of significantly quieter Soviet submarines. That situation is not new. In the past, it has given rise to considerable interest in countermeasures capable of destroying incoming torpedoes, just as current close-in weapons are intended to destroy incoming missiles. It is possible that, in the West, antitorpedo measures have received less support because Soviet torpedoes are, for the most part, much less publicized than Soviet antiship missiles.

In the AAW arena, the main question for the next decade is probably the impact of stealth. Far too little information has been released for the analyst to be able to say whether stealthy aircraft and missiles will appear in numbers or just how difficult they will be to detect. Possible counters might include longer-wave radars (e.g., on board airships) or a higher degree of interconnection among the ships of a fleet. The latter would make sense if, as seems likely, a stealthy airplane or missile is not equally stealthy in all directions. Thus it might be spotted and tracked by a ship located well away from the direction of flight, or by an upward- or downward-looking conventional radar (or chain of radars).

How do the Soviets fit into this picture? It is notorious that the Soviet computer industry lags far behind that of the West, not only in the capacity of individual machines but more importantly in the mass output of machines. For example, a recent article on expanding Sino-Soviet trade in the Far East suggested that Chinese (PRC) Great Wall computers, which are primitive by Western standards, were highly prized in Siberia. One would have to suspect that Soviet naval combat systems are much less highly automated than those of the West. Reportedly, manual vertical plots are still common, even in classes that appeared in the 1970s. Combat systems built around such plots are relatively easy to overwhelm. Presumably they have been succeeded by computer systems in later classes, but it seems likely that the Soviets are still in the era of unreliability and massive numbers of technicians. Unfortunately for them, they are also in an era of shrinking demographics, partly for reasons similar

to those that affect the West and partly because of the demographic echoes of World War II and of the prewar mass killings.

These considerations make it particularly difficult to evaluate any Soviet weapons system. It is easy enough (at least in theory) to say that some particular missile, flying at Mach 3.5, has a 75-percent chance of destroying a Mach 1.3 airplane flying at 5,000 feet and capable of making 2-G turns. However, that evaluation leaves out the ship's ability to detect the airplane in the first place and then to react promptly and properly. Delays and inefficiencies in the operation of the ship's radars and of her combat command center may well delay the firing of the missile for so long that the unopposed airplane can attack and destroy the ship.

There is, as yet, no well-understood measure of the overall effectiveness of a naval combat system. One measure that was developed by the U.S. Navy some years ago was to estimate the delay between approach and successful engagement of an incoming airplane, counting not only radar and weapons performance but also the delays inherent in the functioning of the combat system. The only problem was that this delay was very difficult to compute, depending, as it did, upon quite detailed characteristics of the ship and her combat information center. One incidental benefit of this approach was that it emphasized the effect of ship's geometry, such as the delay due to turning the ship into position to engage after a target had been detected.

Hopefully this book will provide a reader with some measure of what would go into the appropriate calculation.

This handbook of naval weapons and their associated sensor and direction systems includes, so far as is possible, all the systems currently in service in navies throughout the world, either on board ships or in coast defenses or on board antiship or antisubmarine aircraft. Because arms transfers often go unreported, it is not certain whether some of the many systems developed for export in the last few decades have actually found buyers, or which buyers they have found. These systems have, therefore, generally been included. This same philosophy applies to obsolescent or obsolete mines and torpedoes, which may well survive as war reserves despite their age. Some of the abortive Western systems may show characteristics similar enough to those of existing Soviet bloc systems (whose characteristics cannot be available on an unclassified basis) to serve as useful models of those systems.

Systems proposed over the last few years have generally been included, whether or not they have achieved known sales. These systems may suggest useful ideas for future naval weapons.

It is striking that so few of the weapons and associated systems developed since World War II have disappeared. Indeed, some of the wartime weapons are still in service. Thus this book is very nearly a catalog of the development of naval weapons and weapons systems from about 1945 to the present, albeit with some important exceptions (such as early naval strategic weapons).

This book is broken down into warfare areas: surveillance and control; strategic warfare; strike/surface warfare; antiaircraft warfare; antisubmarine warfare; and mine warfare. Inevitably, there is some overlap, but maintaining this functional arrangement is important. In some cases, related weapons have been grouped together. As a result:

All shipboard and shore-based *radars* have been grouped under antiaircraft warfare because many surface-search sets are also useful to detect low fliers.

All *optronic systems* have also been grouped under antiaircraft warfare. This category necessarily includes submarine periscopes.

All shipboard *guns* have been grouped under antiaircraft warfare, again because very few of them are really limited to antiship use.

All *RPVs*, including long-endurance types which may be used for AAW surveillance, are included under strike/surface warfare (as reconnaissance/surveillance systems).

All *aircraft* ECM, whether to protect strike aircraft or for self-protection against other aircraft (or for surveillance), is in the strike/surface warfare section.

All *shipboard* ECM is in the antiaircraft section, because most such systems are for protection against aircraft or airborne missiles. However, torpedo decoys (acoustic ECM) are all in the antisubmarine section.

All *torpedoes*, whether primarily antiship or antisubmarine, are in the antisubmarine section.

All *mines*, including ASW mines, are grouped together in the mine warfare section.

This book emphasizes that naval weapons and their associated equipment are *systems*. Although the word "system" has been much overworked, it is still very useful as a reminder that none of the missiles or guns or torpedoes stands alone. Each is part of a larger entity that carries out three distinct functions: the *detection* of possible targets, the *decision* as to which to engage, and then the *engagement* itself. Success or failure depends on the proper functioning of the system as a whole.

From another point of view, the system as a whole can be frustrated either by destroying the weapon (in flight or before flight) or by attacking its other elements. For example, although in the past there was no way of shooting down a naval shell in flight, the overall naval gunfire (antiship) system could be defeated by measures taken against the range finder (which made it impossible to locate the target properly) or by violent maneuvers (which frustrated the decision–fire control part of the overall system). In general, hard-kill countermeasures address the weapon proper; soft kill addresses the detection and decision process. For example, a jammer may make detection impossible, and a deceptive countermeasure will frustrate decision-making.

This breakdown into processes is useful because individual weapons tend to be associated with specific decision (combat) systems and with particular sensors (detectors). Consequently, when the parameters of some of the elements of the overall system have not been published, a reader can estimate overall performance in terms of the restrictions imposed by particular system elements, e.g., sonars and radars.

Natural phenomena may also limit the system's effectiveness. For example, some writers have for many years suggested that U.S. and Soviet land-based ballistic missiles fired over the Arctic may be ineffective because their guidance has not been corrected to take account of special magnetic and gravitational effects (they have generally been tested only on east-west trajectories).

In practice several equipments may form a single element of the weapons system. AAW systems, for example, commonly employ a broad-beam search radar cueing a more precise fire-control sensor, both feeding into a combat system that actually decides when (or whether) to fire. In the case of an antiship missile, some of the decision-making elements of the system may reside in the missile itself.

The single most important trend in naval warfare has been to mechanize (and then to automate) each function, and then to integrate all the functions electronically. First there was engagement itself. The great development of the age of sail was the replacement of men (who boarded ships and defeated their crews) by guns; but men alone determined the accuracy of the guns. Only in this century was range finding mechanized, followed by mechanization of the calculation/decision process in fire control. Automatic range finding, by radar, came later, but it was generally still a man, a radar operator, who decided that a particular target was worth investigating (i.e., was real).

Only very recently, and only in a few cases, have the decision functions been automated. The driving forces have generally been the pressures of time and numbers. An example from air defense can illustrate the force of numbers. It is impossible for a manual plot to keep track of many more than ten distinct targets. A semimanual or semiautomatic plot keeps track of the targets, but men must identify them. That method can cope with the numbers, but it cannot match the accuracy of the radar data. The next step, then, is for the search radar itself to decide

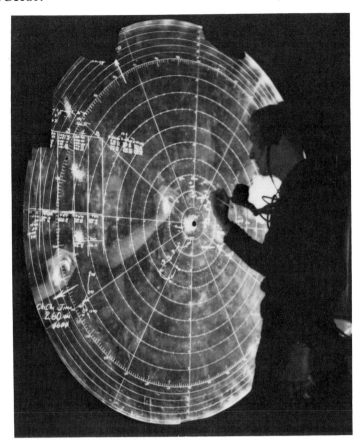

Data integration in a manual CIC, World War II. As operators saw blips painted onto their radar scopes, they called out target locations; and plotters, such as this man, wrote the targets onto a vertical plot. Because one vertical plot showed all contacts (including nonradar information), it served to integrate all available data. Strings of individual plots formed target tracks, from which a target's course, speed, and intentions could be deduced. This type of plot could not keep track of the very numerous and very fast aircraft targets encountered postwar. Probably the single greatest development in naval weapons systems during the first three postwar decades was the automation of the CIC, first of the plotter and then of the act of target detection. Note that, as in a modern automated CIC, the writing on the vertical plot—on the decision display—is processed, rather than raw, radar data, what would now be called processed video. (U.S. Navy)

which targets are real and which are false, and to set up track files for the real ones.

Time pressure forces integration, since the overall reaction rate of the weapons system is limited by the rate at which information flows from the detectors through the decision-makers to fire control. If the system is broken into distinct blocks, and if operators have to intervene between them, time is lost. To the extent that information is passed automatically, the system can function more quickly. For example, the U.S. Phalanx antimissile gun incorporates all elements of the overall system in a single stand-alone device that can automatically engage a target. The human operator can veto an engagement, but time is much too short for him to decide whether to initiate one.

Automation and integration carry an important potential drawback. Although integrated weapons systems operate much faster and, perhaps, much more reliably than manual ones, the integrated systems are also much more dependent on their built-in assumptions (the software). Software errors can, therefore, be crippling. A system's elements that were not originally designed together may function very poorly when they are grouped in an ad hoc system, to the extent that a ship's actual capabilities may not even remotely resemble her supposed combat capacity. This problem occurs frequently with analog systems that are integrated into digital systems using analog-to-digital converters, which may not be altogether compatible with other digital equipment. In combat, the lack of human interaction with integrated systems makes it possible for an enemy

Automation of radar detection: the scope in this Grumman Hawkeye (E-2C) shows processed video, the radar's deductions from the echoes it receives, rather than the indications of the echoes themselves. As in the manual CIC of World War II, once raw video has been turned into such data, it can be melded with the processed outputs of other sensors and used for decision-making. This Hawkeye crew member is using a light pen, a feature of many modern naval command/control systems, to communicate with the airplane's central tactical computer. (Grumman Aerospace)

aware of some subtle software error to disable that system altogether, or even to turn it against its owners.

In practice, automation and integration are inescapable, given the higher speeds and great numbers of modern weapons. Early, terrifying experiences with ad hoc integration have led the U.S. Navy, and presumably others as well, to test complete systems on land before sending them to sea, largely to ensure overall software compatibility.

Clearly it is impossible to provide measures of the overall system's capabilities in a book like this. However, readers may reflect that a weapons system's response times are probably a good measure of the overall system's integration, and that such information may be available from observations of the system's at-sea performance. That information in turn may be a useful correction to the weapon's maximum speed and capacity, which describe only part of the overall system's performance, particularly in AAW.

Dimensions are given, wherever possible, as diameter × length (wing- or fin-span as a separate item). In the case of a radar, the first dimension is the horizontal one, which determines the horizontal beam-width. Dimensions are generally in the units (English or metric) used by the country of origin. Where that is metric, English units are given in parentheses. Note that dimensions for some Soviet systems are given in

English units (feet and inches) even though the weapons have certainly been designed in metric terms; that is because the published data come from U.S. sources, and are surely approximate rather than precise. Ranges are in meters and yards (sometimes in thousands of yards, or kiloyards, abbreviated kyds). Although a nautical mile is 6080 ft (6053 ft in British measurement), it is commonly approximated to 2000 yards, so that a missile range of 17.5 nm is probably actually 35,000 yards.

An important note on sources. Readers should keep in mind, above all, that this is an UNCLASSIFIED book, a compilation of information from the open literature, from declassified documents, and from brochures provided by the manufacturers of the equipment. Data have been chosen on the basis of the plausibility of the source, and also on the basis of their conformity to the known characteristics of similar weapons for which data are better established. Note that, when they are declassified, official documents generally do not become available for some considerable time, typically at least twelve (U.S.) but often as much as thirty (Britain) years. Because systems are improved over time, data, correct at the time the documents were compiled, are often only approximately correct when the documents are declassified. Data should, therefore, be taken as typical rather than precise. Virtually all unclassified data on Soviet systems are limited both in accuracy and in completeness. Hopefully, readers with access to better data may find comparisons with Western systems useful.

ACKNOWLEDGMENTS

This book could not have been written without considerable assistance. I am particularly indebted to A. D. Baker III, the editor of the companion volume to this book, *Combat Fleets of the World*; to Chuck Haberlein; to David Isby; to Steven J. Zaloga; to Raymond Cheung; to Dr. Tam Melia; to Lon Nordeen; to Fu S. Mei; to Alan Raven; to Captain Philippe Roger (Armament Corps, French Navy); to Dr. R. S. Scheina; to Captain Lin Welles, USN; to Mark Wertheimer; and to C. C. Wright. The staffs of the U.S. Navy Operational Archives and of the British Public Record Office provided invaluable historical material, which remains relevant because a great number of the systems described here have been in service for so long. Many of the manufacturers represented here have been extremely generous with material, both factual and photographic. I hope I have described their products fairly and accurately.

Many people at the Naval Institute contributed to this project. I particularly wish to thank my in-house editor, Anthony F. Chiffolo; Moira Megargee for her design and her treatment of graphics; and Linda Cullen for finding many photos. As the first volume of a biennial series, this book presented special problems, in its design and because of the sheer volume of material involved; I am extremely grateful to the Naval Institute Press's staff for their willingness to accept and to incorporate late additions to the book.

I could not have compiled this book without the support, love, and assistance of my wife, Rhea.

Any book of this type is necessarily incomplete and necessarily somewhat inaccurate. Corrections and additions are most welcome; they should be submitted to the editor c/o Naval Institute Press, Annapolis, MD 21402. The next (1991–92) edition will be compiled during 1990.

PREFATORY NOTES

RADAR

Radar is described at the beginning rather than in one section of this book because radars appear in both the surface and air warfare sections.

Radars are generally described by their frequency bands, peak power, pulse width, and pulse repetition frequency (PRF).

Frequency (which is inversely proportional to wavelength) determines how precise the radar beam can be, since beam width (in radians) is approximately equal to the inverse of the antenna size in wavelengths. The larger the antenna, the narrower the beam. Moreover, the larger the antenna, the higher the gain: the larger the fraction of the returning echo the radar will detect. Frequency (or wavelength) also determines the kind of technology required to produce the radar signal, and the extent to which that signal will be absorbed by the atmosphere, e.g., by rain.

There are two quite distinct systems of coding frequency bands. One, developed during and after World War II, describes the physical characteristics of the signals, and is almost certainly mnemonic. It is used in this book. A second, more recent system is a more systematic division of the possible radar bands. It was developed for electronic intelligence, and it reflects the fact that other nations (particularly the Soviets) use radar frequencies very different from those common in the West. It is used in this book primarily to describe ECM equipment. Details of both systems are given in Table 1.

The original wartime radar-band system consisted of a metric P-band (P for pulse, as in the U.S. APS and SPS designations), and an S-band for short (or centimeter) wavelengths (about 10 cm). An X-band (for exotic) was added during World War II for a newer generation of 3-cm radars. After the war, the P-band was temporarily abandoned in favor of a long centimetric wavelength (L-band, about 20 cm), and a new compromise band (C, about 5 or 6 cm) was developed. The advantage of the C-band was that it could be used in conjunction with a small antenna (like X-band) but could penetrate rain better than X-band. There was also K-band (about 1 cm), a designation left over from an

Table 1: Radar Frequency Designations

The boundaries between bands in the classic radar system have changed over time, but the approximate positions of the bands do not. Note that 1000 MHz is 1 GHz, and that older references use cycles rather than Hertz, i.e., Mc/s instead of MHz.

Frequency	U.S. Radar Designations	ECM Bands
30–250 MHz		A
100–150	I-band	
150–225	G-band (World War II IFF)	
225–390	P-band	
250–500		B
390–1550	L-band	
500–1000		C
1000–2000		D
1550–3900	S-band	
2000–3000		E
3000–4000		F
3900–6200	C-band	
4000–5000		G
5000–8000		H
6200–10,900	X-band	
8000–10,000		I
10,000–20,000		J
15,250–17,250	Ku-band	
33,000–36,000	Ka-band	
20,000–40,000		K (K-band embraces Ku through Ka)
36,000–46,000	Q-band	
40,000–60,000		L
46,000–56,000	V-band	
56,000–100,000	W-band	
60,000–100,000		M

NOTE: In radio parlance, HF extends up to 30 MHz; VHF is 30–300 MHz; UHF is 300–3000 MHz; SHF is 3000–33,000 MHz. These boundaries approximate wavelengths of, respectively, 10 meters, 1 meter, 10 cm, 1 cm, and 1 mm.

abortive wartime attempt to rationalize band designations. Some radars are also characterized as UHF, meaning a frequency range somewhat higher than P but lower than L (the term UHF is used slightly differently in radio).

Naval radar operation is much affected by the fact that signals reflect off the sea. At low frequencies (e.g., P-band), reflected and direct signals interfere constructively and destructively, forming a lobe pattern. The lowest lobe can be at an elevation angle well above the sea surface; as a result, P-band radars generally cannot detect low-altitude targets. On the other hand, at higher altitudes, interference can be constructive, and radar range can be greater than it might be in free space (or, for that matter, over land). The lobing phenomenon itself causes targets to fade in and out of detection as they approach; the ranges at which fading occurs are a crude measure of target altitude. At higher frequencies, lobing is much less significant because the areas of constructive and destructive interference are very narrow and tend to wash out as a ship rolls.

The naval environment poses a special problem for the operation of radars. Because a ship is relatively small, and because it must carry numerous antennas in close proximity to its superstructure, its radars may often be affected by reflection off both the ship and other antennas. The effect is particularly noticeable in the sidelobes. For example, a whip antenna vibrating near a radar antenna may impose a modulation on the radar signal. Such effects may limit the extent to which a naval radar can rely on, for example, doppler information extracted from the details of returning echoes.

Quite aside from lobing, radars are affected by back-scatter off the sea, particularly when they are used to detect low fliers. At zero elevation, with a beam of 2 degrees and a pulse of 2 microseconds, the radar typically sees a patch of sea about 0.05 square nautical miles at 10 nm. Backscatter, in square meters per square nautical mile at 8–10 nm is:

RADAR BAND

Sea State	P	S	C	X
0	—	.003	.005	.01
1	—	.03	.05	.1
2	—	.1	.25	1
3 (moderate)	.001	.3	2	10
4 (rough)	.003	5	20	100

Thus in a rough sea, an S-band radar will see 5 square meters of backscatter at 8–10 nm, and any radar return from a small sea-skimmer (typically of 0.1 square meter radar cross section) will be altogether swamped.

At very high frequencies, molecules (mainly oxygen and water) in the atmosphere absorb most radiation. There are, however, three windows:

    35 GHz (8-mm wavelength) — Ka band
    94 GHz (3.2-mm wavelength) — M band in the ECM system
    140 GHz (2.3-mm wavelength).

The current upper limit on reasonable radar power generation is probably 94 GHz. Millimeter-wave radar touches the far infrared part of the spectrum. In the infrared, which is closer to light, there are windows at

    8–14 micrometers (0.008–0.014 mm) and
    3–5 micrometers (0.003–0.005 mm).

(The term micron is typically used instead of micrometer, i.e., one-millionth of a meter, or one-thousandth of a millimeter.)

Visible light wavelengths are an order of magnitude smaller, around 0.5 micrometers, or 0.0005 mm.

Radar power determines how well the radar is able to detect an individual echo. Because detection is cumulative, a large number of relatively weak echoes will have the same net effect as a small number of strong ones. Moreover, the detectability of an individual echo depends not only on its peak energy but also on how long it lasts. Thus maximum radar range is commonly equated to average radiated power, i.e., to the product of peak power, pulse duration, and pulse repetition rate or frequency (PRF). The product of pulse duration and PRF is the duty cycle, the amount of time, as a fraction or percentage of the total time, that the radar is transmitting. For example, a radar transmitting pulses of one microsecond at a PRF of 500 pulses per second has a duty cycle of 0.0005; if peak power is 1 megawatt, average power is 500 watts.

The radar's ability to distinguish objects at different ranges depends very much on pulse width (pulse duration) and on PRF. Because a radar measures distance by measuring the time between sending and receiving a pulse, it cannot distinguish a distant echo, returned after the next pulse has been sent, from a close-in echo, returned soon after that next pulse has gone out. Because of this second-time-around (STA) problem, unambiguous or maximum radar range is commonly equated to half the time interval between pulses, i.e., to the inverse of the PRF. This is not the same as the range the radar will actually achieve on a given target, but it is often the figure listed as radar range. Since the radar designer maximizes the probability of detection by maximizing PRF, a designer will generally try (but possibly fail) to match PRF-range with a realistic range on the target of greatest concern.

Note that some radars eliminate many second-time-around echoes by jittering the PRF around an average value. The apparent range of STA echoes will vary with PRF. Thus, such echoes can easily be eliminated. Jittering cannot, however, eliminate the second-time-around echoes of large objects, such as land masses. So PRF remains a measure of effective range.

Radar signals travel at about 186,000 mi/sec (about 162,000 nm/sec, or 300,000 km/sec), so the unambiguous range for a 1000 pulse/sec radar is about 81 nm (162 nm between pulses, for a pulse to go out and return). Thus 2000 pulses/sec corresponds to about 40 nm, and 500 pulses/sec to about 162 nm.

There is one important exception to this idea. Pulse-doppler radars use very high PRFs and typically detect targets at ranges considerably beyond their unambiguous range (because actual detection range depends on the average power sent out, i.e., on the product of peak power, pulse width, and PRF). In effect, pulse-doppler radars compromise between operating at a pure frequency (i.e., in a continuous wave, CW, mode) and pulsing. They use variations in the frequency of the target echoes to measure target velocity. Range cannot be measured so easily because the radar must operate at a very high PRF. Some pulse-doppler radars use computer processing to overcome range ambiguities resulting from the STA problem, rejecting those possible range solutions that correspond to nonphysical target motion.

Just as a pulse radar can be limited in its unambiguous range, a pulse-doppler radar is limited in its range of unambiguous velocities. The radar signal is a mixture of pure signals of different frequencies spaced around the nominal radar frequency; each such subsignal is doppler-shifted by the velocity of the target toward or away from the radar (radial velocity). The shift in frequency is given by target radial velocity as a fraction of the speed of light. The different subsignals are separated in frequency by the pulse repetition frequency (PRF) of the radar. Just as the radar cannot distinguish echoes that return after the next signal has been sent (i.e., whose delay times exceed the pulse repetition interval), a pulse-doppler radar cannot recognize velocities whose doppler shifts exceed the PRF. For example, a velocity of 1000 km/hour (620 mph, 540 kts) shifts an X-band signal (10,000 MHz) by about 9200 Hz. Typically the first speed that cannot be distinguished is called the first blind speed. These considerations explain why doppler radars often use extremely high PRFs, e.g., 20 kHz (corresponding to an unambiguous range of only 4 nm).

Variation in PRF can be used to resolve doppler speed ambiguities, just as jittering the PRF can resolve range ambiguities. Typically the radar is switched between two nearby PRFs, and a change is observed in the doppler shift. The true doppler shift will be the observed shift plus some multiple of the varying PRF.

High PRF is attractive partly because it can give a high probability of target detection even at a relatively low peak power. (Radar detection is a cumulative process, each pulse having some probability of being picked up, so detection depends on average power, not peak power, and average power can mean many relatively weak pulses per second). Since counterdetection generally depends on the strength of the particular pulse picked up by the target's radar detector, the high-PRF/low–peak power solution may amount to a somewhat stealthy radar.

Anywhere near the ground an airborne radar will pick up the echo of its sidelobes (and, in cases in which the radar points down, its main lobes). Suppression of this clutter becomes a major radar design objective, particularly for radars intended to operate over land (which scatters much more of the signal back toward the radar; the sea tends to scatter the signal forward, away from the radar). Because the main lobe looks toward the ground, it encounters very strong second-time-around echoes, which can entirely overshadow the echo from a target. The target echo can, however, be separated out by means of its doppler shift, since the ground (as seen by the airborne radar) may have a very different doppler shift, reflecting its very different velocity.

The ground will reflect a variety of radar lobes, both main and side. For a radar pointing down at a shallow angle, the sidelobes all see the ground at relatively short range. The main lobe sees the ground at a much greater range, closer to the range of any potential target. Thus a radar giving unambiguous range information (i.e., at low PRF) can exclude much sidelobe clutter by avoiding short-range targets, but the radar may not easily distinguish the strong echo of the main lobe from a real but very low-flying target (this distinction depends on pulse width, i.e., range resolution).

The alternative is to use relative doppler shifts. The sidelobes, striking the ground at different angles, give different radial-velocity components, corresponding to a range of doppler shifts, from very low frequency (associated with the lobes pointing almost directly at the ground) up to the main lobe, whose image of the ground may show a shift corresponding to a large fraction of the airplane's speed over the ground. The shift will be strong but relatively narrow in frequency. The sidelobe clutter will be weaker, but it will extend over a very wide range of frequencies, corresponding to everything between zero and the actual velocity of the airplane over the ground.

An airplane flying nose-on toward the radar will have a very high relative velocity and a large corresponding doppler shift, well away from the shifts of the ground clutter. The plane can, therefore, be detected at long range. On the other hand, an airplane flying away will have a very small relative velocity, hence a small doppler shift, and that plane may be swallowed in the ground clutter. Modern fighter radars typically operate at very high PRFs (often hundreds of kHz) so that they can effectively and unambiguously detect nose-on (closing) targets. At very high PRFs, it is difficult to resolve range ambiguity, and available methods reduce the detection range. For this reason, for example, the longest-range mode of the AWG-9 radar (used to control the Phoenix missile) is velocity, i.e., doppler search.

A medium-PRF mode is often available as a compromise to permit detection of tail-aspect (low–relative velocity) targets. Both range and doppler are ambiguous. The strong main lobe peaks in frequency are far enough from one another (because the PRF is great enough to keep the signal components well apart) that target signals can be distinguished. On the other hand, there is still enough range precision to separate the close-in sidelobe clutter. Range measurement in general is easier than with high PRFs. Both high- and low-speed targets still have to compete with sidelobe clutter, and the only real solution is constant switching between PRFs. That switching limits maximum range because there is never very much time to integrate over numerous pulses.

Most shipboard radars exemplify the low-PRF case, and the big airborne early-warning radars also employ low PRFs, for long unambiguous range. Fighters generally use high-PRF transmitters that can switch to medium PRF.

Pulse width determines resolution, the ability to distinguish between two targets that are close together. Radar signals travel at about 300,000 km/sec, so a pulse length of one microsecond corresponds to a distance of about 300 m. Resolution is generally slightly greater than the length associated with one pulse length, since the radar cannot quite distinguish two pulses end-to-end.

Waveguides and other radar components can carry only a limited amount of energy. If that limit is exceeded, they break down. For example, an overloaded coaxial or waveguide may arc (spark), so that no signal at all is transmitted. Since radar range depends on average power rather than on peak power, one alternative is to spread that power over a pulse varying in frequency (a chirp). The returned echo can be compressed ("pulse-compressed") into the equivalent of a very energetic short pulse. Pulse coding is another approach to the same problem. Different portions of the extended pulse are differentiated, e.g., by polarization. The resulting pulse bears, in effect, a coded signature that can be distinguished from the surrounding noise. In either pulse compression or pulse coding, the key is that the radar can distinguish between different parts of the long returning pulse, so that it can be made equivalent to a much shorter pulse.

Pulse compression or coding has another advantage: stealth. A pulse-compression radar spreads its energy over a series of frequencies, using a short pulse in each. Although total average energy may be considerable, there may be relatively little peak energy in any one pulse; therefore, a countermeasures receiver may find such pulses difficult to detect. The longer the train of pulses, the lower the peak power (for a given average power, i.e., for a given detection range). Recent pulse compression radars with very low peak power, such as the new Canadian SPS-503 and the French DRBV 26C, are designed specifically for low probability of intercept. Ultimately the pulse train (extending across different frequencies) could occupy nearly all the time between initial pulses. Such a radar could be described as frequency-modulated continuous wave (FMCW) or as spread-spectrum (for low probability of intercept), and the only current public example is PILOT (see Sweden in the Antiaircraft Warfare section).

Radar beam dimensions are horizontal × vertical; the horizontal dimension measures how accurately the radar can locate a target in bearing without concentrating on that particular target (e.g., by beam switching or monopulse techniques). Antenna dimensions are, similarly, width × height. Scan rate or data rate is the rate at which the antenna spins, and, therefore, the rate at which data about the location of any particular target are renewed. The faster the scan, the higher the target speed with which the radar can cope. On the other hand, the faster the scan, the shorter the time during which the radar dwells (stares) at any particular target, and, therefore, the lower the probability that a target will be detected.

Data about a target's speed can be extracted from the doppler frequency shift in the target's echo. The purer the frequency of the radar pulse, the more precise the doppler data that can be extracted. However, the length of the pulse (i.e., the precision with which the radar can measure distance) depends on the extent to which different wavelengths (i.e., different frequencies) are mixed. Thus there is a natural compromise between range precision and doppler (track) data. Airborne fire-control radars tend to choose the doppler characteristics (and are described as pulse-doppler), but shipboard search radars tend to have the pulse features.

Typically, a distinction is drawn between search and tracking radars. A search radar scans continuously. A pure tracking radar follows a particular target, using some technique of beam switching or beam comparison (e.g., monopulse) to detect target motion. Any scheme for associating successive target locations (as detected by a search radar) to establish an approximate target track blurs this distinction. The quicker the scan, the more accurate the track. Very quick scanning radars with the appropriate associated memory are, therefore, described as track-while-scan (TWS) radars. As more and more search radars are associated with computers for automatic detection and tracking (ADT), and as more information is extracted from radar echoes, TWS operation is becoming more universal.

Some further points deserve brief mention here. Radar tracking generally requires the radar to compare several beam positions, i.e., to measure when it is off the correct direction. One method is conical scanning (conscan), in which the beam spins. Each position of the spinning beam is somewhat off the proper radar direction, but the beam is symmetrical about the direction at which the radar antenna is pointed. Thus, if the radar return is constant while the beam spins, the radar is pointing right at the target. If one beam position shows a higher return, then the radar is pointing off, and the point in the scanning cycle at which the return is greatest can be used to show the appropriate correction. The two-dimensional equivalent of conscan is a nodding radar, pointing its beam alternatively to left and right (or above and below) the target. Conscan is simple to design, but it is subject to a relatively simple countermeasure. If a strong signal is sent back out of sequence, the tracker may pick it up in a side-lobe. In this way a jammer mounted on the target can appear to the tracker to be well off to one side; it can capture the tracker and lead it astray. This technique is called angle-stealing or angle-gate pull-off.

The usual counter is monopulse, a technique in which the radar continuously and simultaneously puts out multiple beams, continuously comparing their signals. Since there is no cycle associated with this sampling, there is no way that a point jammer can insert a deceptive signal out of sequence. The tracker can be led astray only by signals from several distinct sources, separated in location, a technique called "cross-eye."

Three current technical developments deserve brief mention here. One is the rise of solid-state transmitters (see, for example, the French DRBV 26C, the British AWS-7, and the U.S. SPS-40). This trend is distinct from the much earlier movement from vacuum-tube to solid-state technology for radar control and data processing. That left one big vacuum tube, the radar transmitter, which had to be cooled and protected. Now solid-state transmitters are powerful enough to be used, in combination, in place of the tubes. The solid-state transmitters are more reliable; they require less power (and emit less heat); and they cannot burst. Moreover, since numerous transmitters are used together, the failure of any one of them does not put the entire radar out of action. For the U.S. Navy, the first major solid-state transmitter is that replacing a klystron in some SPS-40 radars. This transmitter is expected to achieve a mean time between failure (MTBF) of 10,000 hours, and it will probably be followed by an SPS-49 solid-state transmitter. The SPS-40 unit uses 112 2500-watt modules, each of which uses eight 400-watt peak-power transistors working in parallel.

A second major technical development is the appearance of better and less expensive means of electronic beam forming and movement. In the past, phase shifters were expensive and unreliable, and many electronically scanned radars used frequency-scanning (in one dimension) instead. That method was effective, but it limited the extent to which a radar could hop among frequency bands, since the angle of elevation of the radar beam depended entirely on the wavelength of the signal. Now phase shifters are much less expensive, and newer radars tend to employ them rather than the older technology of frequency-scanning. The next step is the active-array radar, in which the elements of the antenna themselves transmit the signal. There would then be no need to apply a phase shift to a signal produced by a separate unitary transmitter. No active-array radar is currently in naval service, but the experimental British MESAR is an example of this idea.

A third development is software-controlled transmission. In most radars, pulse characteristics are determined by hard wiring. They are extremely difficult to change. There may be special wartime operating characteristics, but they, too, are hard-wired; and, even when compromised, they cannot easily be changed. However, a number of current airborne radars, such as APG-65, are software-controlled, so that their signal characteristics are quite easily changed. This ability will potentially allow the system to counter current methods of radar recognition by pulse analysis. It may still be possible to recognize a radar by the detailed structure of its pulses, but that type of recognition is several orders of magnitude more difficult.

ECM

Electronic countermeasures figure in several sections of this book, and these notes will be limited to items common to all warfare areas. ECM splits into passive devices, electronic support measures (ESM), intended to detect and identify characteristic emissions, and countermeasures (ECM), intended to disrupt hostile sensors or communications. Some of the basic alternatives are worth mentioning.

An ESM device has to determine the main parameters of the emitter: direction, intensity, frequency, pulse width, PRF, and scan rate or pattern. There are several approaches to this problem.

One is the broad-band (crystal video receiver or CVR) receiver, which can respond to any of a very wide variety of signals within its bandwidth. It identifies a signal by frequency band, but it cannot tell where in the band that signal is located. CVRs are relatively simple and lightweight, and they are normally used in radar-warning receivers (RWRs) and in small ships' ECM systems. They may be matched with devices that detect and measure the pulse width and PRF, and that use that data to identify an emitter.

A second approach is the tunable receiver (scanning superheterodyne receiver or SHR). A narrow tuning band sweeps through the receiver's bandwidth. If the sweep is very rapid compared to the duration of the signal, then such a receiver will probably detect and identify the signal. However, if the signal is brief enough, the tuner may well miss it. Typically, a mechanical tuner may sweep a few GHz per second, and an electronic tuner may improve this to a GHz per microsecond. However, typical radar pulse widths are also on the order of microseconds. SHR performance can be improved by breaking down any given frequency band into narrower channels.

Finally there are instantaneous frequency measurement (IFM) receivers, which have a high probability of intercepting a signal because they are always open to the entire frequency band. They tend to be less sensitive than the SHR because they have to respond to so broad a range of frequencies. IFM is becoming common in shipboard systems, but it is rarely used in aircraft. The main drawback of IFM is that it may be unable to deal with several signals in close succession, since it requires a finite time to process each signal. This is not an unsolvable problem, but it does increase the complexity of the equipment.

The most important distinction within ECM is probably the difference between simple noise jamming, which seeks to blot out a signal, and deception. Noise jamming can cover a wide range of frequencies (barrage jamming), or it can be directed to a particular, narrow frequency band (spot jamming). The best counter to noise jamming is frequency agility (the signal's frequency moves away from the jammer's). Note too that the higher the basic frequency, the broader the range of frequencies a barrage jammer must cover.

Because radars have finite side-lobes (i.e., cannot concentrate all of their energy or their reception in one direction), jamming signals can always enter via those side-lobes and appear (to the radar) to be coming from the direction in which the radar is pointing.

Deception generally depends upon some measurement of the radar PRF, scan rate, and pulse width, since the jammer must send back a false echo. The echo may confuse the radar in range (e.g., range-gate pull-off) or in bearing (via the side lobes). Consequently, jittered or varied PRF is a counter-countermeasure because the radar may reject signals which do not conform to the precise pattern of its variation in PRF.

IFF

Because IFF (identification, friend or foe) applies to so many radar systems, it seems best to treat it here. Since the middle of World War II, the standard system, both in the West and in the Soviet Union, is the interrogator-transponder. A radar is fitted with, or associated with, an interrogator with approximately the beamwidth of the main radar. The interrogator sends a coded pulse or pulse train in approximately the same direction as the main radar, but at a different frequency. The transponder on the target sends back a reply, at a third frequency. Generally, the reply is coded to indicate the details of the target's identity. Over the years, frequencies have increased, and interrogators have become more directional; in some cases, the text gives details for the interrogators associated with particular radars.

All of the many interrogators on board a single ship (not to mention in, say, a fleet) are entirely independent, so that all may interrogate the same incoming target. As a consequence, the transponder of any particular target may be unable to reply to all of them, since it can only send its code to one interrogator at a time. The only current exception to this problem is the single integrated IFF antenna used in conjunction with the U.S. SPY-1 radar (see that entry in the Antiaircraft Warfare section): it limits a single ship's interrogations.

Moreover, the interrogator-transponder system can be a liability in combat, since an enemy with access to the interrogation codes can use them to trigger transponders aboard approaching targets and thus can use IFF itself to track targets. That makes the coding of interrogators particularly important, and this requirement in turn makes for relatively complex systems.

Note that this is not a universal identification system; it is a means of positively identifying some radar targets, leaving all others unidentified (and hence either neutral or foe). Moreover, because a potential target may not reply to a particular interrogator (for example, because it is replying to others at the same time), IFF errors can occur even for friendlies. Additionally, the more complex the coding for security, the better the chance of error. It is commonly assumed that in wartime large numbers of aircraft will fall victim to IFF errors, on both sides of any conflict.

There is also a danger that a nearby ship will receive the reply intended for another, either through the main lobe or through a side lobe. Such false replies are called "fruit," and they are eliminated or "defruited" by assigning each interrogator its own pulse repetition frequency (PRF): special circuits eliminate any reply with a different PRF. It is also possible for a single target to receive interrogations from two radars in line, so that the reply intended for one is received by the other, and thus is associated by the other radar with an entirely different, nonreplying target. Multiple interrogation signals can also overlap and confuse a transponder.

The current NATO system, Mk 10, interrogates at 1030 MHz and replies at 1090 MHz. This system is used for both military and civil aircraft, and the responses typically carry coded information. Civil aircraft provide flight call sign and altitude. Military aircraft provide a basic IFF response plus other data. In all, 4096 identification codes are available. Mode 3 is military, Mode A is joint military/civil (often called Mode 3/A), Mode B is civil (identification), and Mode C is civil (altitude reporting). A further Mode D is not currently used, but is available for expansion of the system.

Mk 10A increased the number of code combinations.

In the newer Mk 12 system, adopted by the United States, the interrogator as well as the transponder is coded, to prevent an enemy from tracking by interrogator. Mk 12 has never extended throughout NATO, partly because it is much more expensive than Mk 10 and partly because its greater degree of coding makes the system as a whole more vulnerable to jamming, which might confuse the codes.

In the early 1970's, NATO set up a working group to define a NATO Identification System (NIS) which would replace Mk 10/12. By 1981 Britain, West Germany, and the United States were all developing prototypes. Britain and West Germany favored a higher-frequency (S-band) system, the United States and France an L-band system compatible with Mk 10/12. In April 1985, NATO agreed to adopt the U.S. solution. Britain and Germany had claimed that L-band was too crowded but accepted the L-band system when the United States agreed to add a radar interrogator mode (i.e., interrogation at radar frequencies in the S- and X-bands to supplement the previous standard of 1090 MHz; however, as at present, responses would still be at the standard frequency of 1030 MHz). This scheme meets a requirement stated by the European NATO partners, allowing interrogation by a radar not fitted with a separate interrogator.

In a larger sense, identification must be based not only on electronic replies but also on observed behavior. For example, schemes for air operations in Europe commonly involve special corridors, including altitude, along which returning strike aircraft can expect to return without being shot down. To avoid funneling enemy strikes into the same areas, the corridors are changed very frequently. Similarly, a fighter returning to a carrier would not only "squawk" or send the proper IFF reply but would also behave in a particular preassigned way. Otherwise, the fighter would probably be shot down. Systems based on flight profiles can help to allow for possible electronic failure or battle damage, but they cannot be perfect.

These inherent problems have prompted considerable work on non-cooperative means of identification, using the physical characteristics of the approaching target. In the past, at least in the United States, the most popular have been the measurement of the rates of rotation of jet engines' compressor blades (since the blades make prominent radar returns), and the direct imaging of an approaching airplane. Neither has ever been implemented.

A third alternative is positive tracking of all the aircraft in an area. That was done in the Gulf of Tonkin during the Vietnam War, when a computer-equipped ship tracked literally all air contacts. In theory, much the same thing could be done by an Aegis ship in, say, the Mediterranean. However, identification by tracking requires the cooperation of neutrals, who in effect must identify themselves when they take off. If they do not, identification must fall apart—as in the *Vincennes* incident of 3 July 1988.

The shooting down of the Iranian airliner by the USS *Vincennes* illustrates these points. Because the airliner was not a U.S. military aircraft, it could not send an appropriate IFF signal. The signals it did send seemed to correspond to those that the Iranians had used earlier for F-14s, but that was a deduction from observed Iranian behavior, not necessarily a positive identification. After all, the Iranians might well change their own IFF codes quite often. Thus the captain of the *Vincennes* could not be sure what the IFF return meant. He tried to contact the airliner by radio but received no reply, and the airliner itself did not swerve away, as Iranian airliners had in the past. He did not shoot, however, since the negative information he was receiving did not necessarily mean that the airliner was hostile. Then he was told (incorrectly, as it turned out) that the aircraft had begun to descend, to dive. To the captain, that was a positive signal of hostile intent. This reading in turn was based on a series of known Iranian threats and an expectation that the Iranians might well try a suicide attack. Apparently, the error in reporting the height was partly caused by an inconsistency in the display of target data: height was given in digital (numerical) form, whereas the track of the airplane (range and bearing) was shown graphically. Under the stress of combat (the ship was swerving to keep her after 5-inch gun bearing on two Iranian gunboats), it was apparently too easy to misreport numbers.

The incident well illustrates the central problem of identification: one might be able to determine the physical character of an approaching target, but how can one interpret the intent of the target's operator? Although Captain Rodgers undoubtedly believed he was facing an Iranian F-14, in fact his ship could have been crashed just as effectively by an airliner. A system that merely told him what type of airplane was approaching could not have sufficed. This problem will most likely recur in other areas, where several countries might be operating the same or similar equipment.

MISSILE GUIDANCE

There are three basic types of missile guidance: inertial, command, and autonomous.

Inertial guidance systems measure the motion of a missile through space, sensing and integrating accelerations to find the missile's velocities. Inertial systems were initially used only in long-range ballistic missiles, because these systems were so expensive. There are two types: a hard-wired system, in which the missile attempts to fly a precomputed path, correcting whenever the missile deviates; and a computer-based system, which constantly recomputes the necessary flight path based on the actual flight of the missile. The latter requires less fuel for correction, and thus is suited to greater ranges. It allows for operational flexibility, since only the launch location and the target need be entered into the computer. In the absence of such a system, a missile must be fired at a single preassigned target from a preassigned site.

In recent years inertial sensors, such as gyros, have become much cheaper, and some form of mid-course inertial guidance is now quite common. Often it is described as strapdown, which means that the inertial sensor lacks the full range of measurement, i.e., cannot measure pitching motions. That is acceptable in a short-range missile, or in a missile constrained by a radar altimeter to fly a flat path.

Command guidance may be of several forms: commands may be sent through a wire or fiber-optic cable or a radio link; or the missile might be a beam-rider, controlled by the movement of a radar beam (in at least one case, a laser beam). The basic attraction of command guidance is that the intelligence of the weapons system can be concentrated in a director that need not be limited in size or cost, rather than in an expendable missile of very limited size. The main limitation on command guidance is the loss of accuracy as the range increases. An advantage of beam-riding is that it is somewhat difficult to jam: the missile's antenna that senses the beam faces rearward instead of forward, toward the target. The jammer must, therefore, concentrate on the more distant (and more sophisticated) tracker, rather than on the nearby missile. That is why Bofors advertises its laser beam-rider, RBS 70, as unjammable.

Much depends on whether the beam tracks the target itself. In most early beam-riders, such as the British Seaslug and the U.S. Terrier, a single tracking radar generated the beam, and the missile, therefore, continuously pointed at its target. Because it had to follow target maneuvers, it could lose a good deal of its energy along the way. On the other hand, in the contemporary U.S. Talos (now extinct), the beam motion was programmed so that the missile flew along an energy-efficient up-and-over path. It homed semiactively only as it approached the target.

Autonomous or self-sensing guidance takes many forms. It does make the missile more accurate as it approaches its target; on the other hand, the missile seeker is of limited size, and it may not be able to deal with countermeasures. Moreover, it may be difficult to design a seeker that can distinguish some kinds of targets.

Usually missiles incorporate some compromise between these elements. In the case of antiaircraft fire, semiactive homing is quite widely used. Semiactive homing is a type of command guidance, to the extent that the missile director tracks the target. However, the missile actually tracks the radiation reflected from the target (usually radar, sometimes laser). The missile's estimate of target position, therefore, becomes more accurate as it approaches the target. The greatest drawback to semiactive homing is that the tracking radar must be powerful enough to provide the missile with sufficient reflected illumination from the moment that it is launched. This requirement

limits effective range. One alternative is to use command guidance or inertial guidance (i.e., a preset autopilot) to bring the missile relatively close to the target before turning on the semiactive seeker. That is the solution chosen in the U.S. Aegis and Phoenix systems.

Missile guidance determines missile flight path. Here command guidance has an advantage, since it can bring the missile along the most efficient flight path possible. Any form of full autonomous homing or semiactive homing results in a less energy-efficient path and, therefore, in a shorter range for a given missile.

The simplest and least efficient path is pursuit because the missile turns to fly along the line of sight to the target. The missile's rate of turn equals the rate of turn of the line of sight, and quite violent maneuvering may be required as the missile approaches its target. Pursuit is effective against slow targets, or against targets approached from the rear (e.g., by IR-guided missiles). It is also effective at very short range. Missiles using command-to-line of sight guidance (such as the French Crotale Navale and the British Seawolf) follow pursuit paths that limit the system's effective range. For missiles launched from shipboard, command-to-line of sight is effective for point defense but not really for defense against crossing targets. To the extent that major Soviet systems such as SA-N-1 and SA-N-3 appear to employ command-to-line of sight guidance, they are effective for the defense of individual ships but not of formations of ships.

Proportional navigation requires the missile to measure the rate of change of the line of sight and to maneuver at some fixed or variable multiple of that rate of change. The navigation ratio may change during flight to optimize missile performance. Proportional navigation systems require the missile to compare the direction to the target wih the direction in which it is flying. That is sometimes done by a doppler comparison between the reflected energy from the target and a broad reference beam from the launcher. In such cases the missile requires a set of rearward-facing reference antennas. The reference beam has to be broad because the missile generally is not in the tracking beam itself. Proportional navigation improves missile range performance, and also improves performance against a maneuvering target, since the missile need not maneuver violently to follow the details of target motion. In effect, proportional navigation aims the missile not directly at the target but at a computed interception point ahead of the target.

In contrast, command guidance generally involves some quite different flight path. The main alternatives are:
  — A constant-bearing or collision course, which requires the missile to be fired with a sufficient lead angle to meet the predicted position of the target.
  — A fixed lead angle path.
  — A line of sight path, which requires the missile to follow the line of sight from launcher to target (as in a beam-rider).

These concepts apply not only to missiles flying through the air but also to torpedoes. A straight-running torpedo is inertially guided. Lightweight torpedoes are self-guided, although they may have inertial (preset) run-outs before their homing devices are activated. Most heavy torpedoes are command (wire) guided, until they reach a homing basket. In a few cases they are wire guided all the way.

DESIGNATION SYSTEMS

AUSTRALIA

Australia uses the U.S. triservice (AN) designation system, but numbers are in an 800 series, e.g., the Barra sonobuoy is SQQ-801.

CANADA

The Canadian Government uses the U.S. triservice (AN) designation system, but numbers are in a 500 series. Thus SPS-501 is the first, not the 501st, Canadian naval radar.

FRANCE

The French government uses a unified triservice electronic designation system, similar in spirit to the U.S. AN system. Each piece of equipment is designated by four letters (the quadrigramme) and a number, with a letter suffix to indicate modifications. The first letter indicates the main function; the second, the process employed; the third, the normal mode of installation; and the fourth, the particular function of the system. In contrast to the AN system, the third and fourth letters can change depending upon the main function.

In addition, in at least some cases, letters are assigned in blocks that further describe the equipment.

Radars in the 10–19-block are X-band; the 20–29-block indicates either L- (20 cm) or P- (2 m) band; the 30–39-block indicates X-band; and the 50–59-block indicates C-band (5 cm).

Sonars in a 20-series are hull mounted; sonars in a 40-series are towed fish; sonars in a 60-series are towed arrays.

MAIN FUNCTION LETTERS (FIRST LETTER)

A electronic warfare
B test equipment
C switchboard (commutation)
D detection
E transmitters (emitters)
F electric generators
G mine countermeasures
H not used
I information processing
J imagery (electro-optics)
K not used
L not used
M measurement
N navigation
Q miscellaneous, not covered in other categories
R receivers
S fire-control systems
T transceivers
V guidance (for weapons)

PROCESS LETTERS (SECOND LETTER)

A artillery (fire control)
B chemical energy (batteries, etc.); ballistic missiles (fire control)
D doppler
E wind generators; electricity (measurement)
F wire (fil, in French)
G gyroscopic; gas generators
H magnetic
I infrared and light intensification
J inertial; bombing (fire control)
L laser; mechanical generators
M mixed; missiles (fire control)
N nuclear and radioisotope
P fluidic, hydraulic
R radio-electric or electronic
S sound; solar generators
T thermal generators; television and CRT; torpedoes (fire control)
U ultrasonic; electric
X other processes
Z satellite communication

SPECIAL PROCESS LETTERS FOR INFORMATION PROCESSING (SECOND LETTER)

A analog
B magnetic band
C magnetic card
D magnetic disk
E magnetic memory element
G magnetic drum
K punched card
M analog/digital
N digital (numerical)
O microfilm; optical memory
P paper
R punched tape
S semiconductor memory
T cathode-ray tube

MODES OF INSTALLATION (THIRD LETTER)

A aircraft
B surface ship (bâtiment)
C man-carried (cadre)
D vehicles and man-portable
E missile
F fixed
M mobile
N surface ships and submarines
P man-portable (portatif)
R submerged
S semifixed
T portable
U submarine
V vehicle

PARTICULAR FUNCTIONS (FOURTH LETTER)

A analysis (identification); countermeasures; signalling device; attack (sensors and imagery); in generators, 400 Hz; self(auto)-protection (mine warfare); measurement of voltage and current; landing (atterrisage) in navigation; amplification; direction (asservisement) in fire control
B jamming; in generators, direct current for battery-charging; in mine warfare, buoys; non-electrical measurements (e.g., accoustic); information processing (fire control)
C multiplex; fire control; generator control; in mine warfare, classification; calculation (computing); positioning in curvilinear coordinates (navigation) (i.e., Loran-like systems); vector control (fire control)
D surveillance—alert; detection; power distribution; in mine warfare, sweeping (dragage); coding (computing); detection (imagery); distance measurement (navigation)
E listening; emission (in test equipment and in guidance); scouting; in generators, 50 Hz for electronic equipment; writing-recording (computer); standards of measurement; illumination (navigation); engagement (fire control)
F frequency measurement; facsimile; telephone-telegraph (test equipment)
G direction-finding (goniometry); graphics; in generators, 50 Hz for general use; mine warfare (test equipment); signal generators (measurement); electrical distribution (fire control)
H radio; in generators, 60 Hz for general use; printing (impression) for computers; hyperfrequency measurement (spectral analysis, envelopes, noise factors, etc); vertical measurement (navigation)
I identification
J interception; information transmission; in mine warfare, immunization; accelerometry (navigation)
K calculator; radioactivity (sensors and imagery); in generators, energy conversion; data conversion (computers); guidance (including autoguidance and wire guidance) in fire control
L deception; security; in mine warfare, localization; reading (computers); measurement of semiconductor tube and crystal characteristics; localization and pursuit in fire control
M mixed; also mines; in mine warfare, mine-hunting; input/output (computers); oscilloscopes (measurement); modems (miscellaneous equipment); management (fire control)

N   navigation; also teletype; in mine warfare, neutralization; bearing measurement (navigation); control of nuclear explosives (fire control)
O   in mine warfare, obstruction (antisweep)
P   telephony; in generators, production of direct current for various purposes; perforation (computers); pursuit (imagery); bridges for electrical measurement; position in polar coordinates (navigation)
R   localization, reception; missile guidance (sensors and imagery); reproduction (computers); marking (navigation); reception (fire control)
Q   indicators for measurement (galvanometers, magnetometers, etc.)
S   weapons system; also position—altitude (sensors and imagery); translation (computers); analysis of low-frequency signals (measures of distortion, phase, wave analysis, etc.); altimetry (*sondage*; navigation)
T   transceiver; teleprinters; terrestrial objects (sensors); sorting (triage) for computers; marking (imagery); test or multifunction equipment (measurement); position in geographical coordinates (navigation); launching or firing (fire control)
U   regulation of direct current; general functioning (fire control)
V   guidance (command); television; surveillance (*veille*, in sensors); in mine warfare and in computers, imaging (visualization); speed measurement (navigation); display of the tactical situation (fire control)
W   propulsion, energy; visiphone; meteorology; in mine warfare, surveillance; verification (computers); power measurement (wattmeter)
X   special; testing (fire control)
Y   teletype; information storage (computers); miscellaneous, special (fire control)
Z   training

GERMANY (WEST)

West Germany follows the U.S. AN designation system for shipborne sonars, except that all are prefixed D (Deutsch), as in DSQS-21. The serially-assigned numbers do not coincide with U.S. numbers, and are assigned in blocks (e.g., in sonars, the 11-series for minehunting sonars and the 21-series for search sonars).

ITALY

For naval radars, Italy uses the U.S. triservice (AN) system of designators, with the prefix MM (Marine Militare), with a 700-series, e.g., MM/SPS-768. There are also company designators. It appears that blocks of numbers within the overall series are reserved for special applications, as some of the numbers are too high to reflect a single sequence. It also appears that all naval radars and other electronic equipment, whether air- or shipborne, are in the same single numerical sequence.

Air force electronic equipment is designated in a 200-series.

JAPAN

Japan uses the U.S. triservice (AN) system of designators, except for different ship platform letters:
E   other
H   aircraft (sonobuoy and dipping sonar applications)
L   land-based fixed
O   surface ship
R   small, portable
Y   general use
Z   undersea (submarines, but also minehunting surface ship sonar)
The prefix N (as in NOLR-1) indicates a combination of other equipment. In many cases with electronics, the U.S. system is used with the prefix J, as in JVRC or JAN/GRC for a radio transceiver. In some cases U.S.-supplied (or license-built) equipment retains its U.S. designation; in others, it is redesignated with a J prefix.

In some cases a Type number system is used, e.g., Type 1 fire-control system. However, most Type numbers indicate the date of designation (not production) in terms of Japanese Fiscal Years. Thus Type 63 is a designation adopted during Japanese Fiscal Year 1963. The Japanese Fiscal Year runs from 1 April to 31 March and is designated by the calendar year in which the FY begins (e.g., JFY63 began on 1 April 1963). This system corresponds to British practice and is six months away from the U.S. Fiscal Year (which runs from 1 October through 30 September).

Finally, equipment under development is given a serial designation, with a prefix: G for torpedo, K for mine, S for sweep gear. Thus a torpedo developed as G-9 was adopted for service as Type 73.

NETHERLANDS

Dutch naval electronic systems are generally developed by Hollandse Signaal Apparaten (HSA), and it is not altogether clear whether the HSA designations are imposed by the Royal Netherlands Navy. Radars are divided into
DA   target indication (*doels aanwijzing*)
LW   air search (*lucht waarschuwing*)
ZW   sea search (*zee waarschuwing*)
Fire-control systems, both for surface ships and for submarines, are designated by the letter M and by a number; in some cases the combination WM is used. The numbers are not in sequence of development, but often indicate alternative (and roughly contemporary) levels of capability.

TAIWAN (GRC)

Taiwan uses the U.S. AN system, except that equipment is prefixed CS, as in CS/SPG-24; CS stands for the equivalent of the U.S. Defense Advanced Research Projects Agency.

USSR

All Soviet equipment is developed by design bureaus, and each bureau maintains an internal designation series. In addition, equipment accepted for service use is given a service designation. The chief example is aircraft designations. Published histories of Soviet aircraft design provide numerous examples of internal (bureau) and service designators, e.g., Tu-95 and Tu-20 for the same bomber (Bear). A recent Polish history of the MiG bureau provides a few internal numbers for air-to-surface missiles, and there is reason to believe that the practice is universal. Many Soviet weapons seem to have acquired names, either as covers for designations or as popular references. Finally, Soviet economic planning requires that each product within the economy be assigned what amounts to a national part number, identifying the item by producing ministry. Few of these numerical designations have ever been made public.

Very few of these internal Soviet designations, of whatever type, have become public knowledge. Typically, therefore, NATO has assigned reporting names and numbers. The numbers are in a NATO-generated sequence and may not include prototypes or, in some cases, weapons fielded in small numbers or covertly. Since they reflect the dates on which weapons are first observed, the sequence of the numbers may not reflect the development sequence. The chief series are:
AAM   air-to-air missiles
ASM   air-to-surface missiles (both strategic and tactical)
SSM   surface-to-surface missiles (both strategic and tactical).
Some reporting designations may or may not reflect Soviet practice. For many years Soviet unguided antisubmarine rockets have been designated RBUs, the number indicating the nominal range. These are probably actually the Soviet designators. The few reported Soviet torpedo designators seem to reflect Soviet

rather than NATO practice, but some of them do not really fit any obvious system.

NATO's reporting names for Soviet electronic equipment often reflect either signal characteristics or physical appearance. For most naval systems, they combine an animal's name with some physical characteristic.

UNITED KINGDOM

The Royal Navy uses a Type Number system, originally adopted for radio sets. Equipment is designated in blocks, e.g., 900 for naval radars (1945–1965, roughly). There is some evidence of blocks within these series, so that the numbers are not sequential. In addition, some numbers are left blank, either to allow for improvements or for security purposes. When a block is exhausted, another is designated.

Some aircraft-related systems are designated in the NATO triservice AN series, in a 900-block (e.g., the AQS-903 acoustic processor).

The chief current blocks are:

0–100 radios, etc., through about 1945
100 sonars, up through the 1960's
200 World War II naval radars and IFF
600 radio transmitters and jammers
700 hydrophones
900 radars, post-1945
1000 radars, from the 1950's on
2000 modern sonars.

Electronic subsystems (outfits) are designated by three-letter combinations. Examples of the first letter are A for antenna (as in ANU) and D for computer (as in DBE, for an action automation system).

In addition, special designations are used for systems, most notably missile (GWS) systems. They are blocked by type. Aside from GWS.1 (Seaslug), which is now obsolete, GWS systems fall into series: GWS.20 for point defense, GWS.30 for area defense surface-to-air, GWS.40 for ASW, GWS.50 for surface-to-surface. For example, all versions of SeaCat and SeaWolf fall into the GWS.20 series, and Exocet is GWS.50.

The main command/control series are:

GSA   gun system automation
GDS   gun direction system (now extinct)
GWS   guided weapon system
LRS   long range (gun) system (now extinct)
MRS   medium range (gun) system (e.g., MRS 3)
TCSS   torpedo control system (submarine), now superseded by computer systems.

Electronic warfare systems fall into a special series. The direction-finding (D/F) sets' series are FH for HF/DF, FM for MF/DF, and UA for SHF/DF, in each case with a numerical suffix.

Electronic outfits use three-letter designators: A for antennas, D for combat-control systems (both submarine and surface ship), U for ESM/ECM, and Y for subsystems. Some examples are indicated in the text. Recent ECM systems are code-named, and it is not always clear whether there is any associated designator.

Most British weapons have names rather than numerical designators. However, some are described by their Naval Staff Requirement (NSR) or Air Staff Requirement (ASR) designator, generally a four-digit figure. Reportedly, these numbers are applied randomly; presumably, they are required for computerized accounting.

UNITED STATES

U.S. electronic equipment is designated by three letters in an AN (triservice, originally army-navy) series. The first indicates the platform, the second the type of equipment, and the third the function. Numbers run in sequence within each designation, so that there can be both an SPS-49 radar and an SQS-49 sonar. In each case, the full designation is prefixed by the letters AN (multiservice), e.g., AN/SPS-49; the first two letters will generally be omitted. In a very few cases, examples of an earlier system survive: Mark numbers applied to fire-control radars (e.g., Mk 13 on board the battleships). These numbers fit the postwar SPG-series, with Mark 49 becoming SPG-49, for example. However, they were never retroactively identified within the AN series.

Modifications of a system were formerly indicated by letter, as in SPS-6C. More recently they have been indicated by a number following (V), as in SPS-49(V)5. The intent may be to reserve letters for major system changes.

Individual components receive two-letter designations, e.g., CP for a computer or TB for a towed body. In some cases the designation is written out to include the designator of the associated system, e.g., TB-12/BQQ is a towed body which is part of a BQQ series submarine sonar.

U.S. missiles and rockets are also designated within a triservice (three-letter) system, but in this case each number is used only once. In some cases, such as Harpoon, the three-letter designator is actually changed to reflect a different application of the same basic weapon. Note that in recent years weapons' designators often have not been made public until very late in the development process (for example, veterans of the Sea Lance program cannot recall ever having seen a standard designator). This practice may have been adopted to conceal gaps in the list denoting highly classified ("black") programs such as stealth weapons. Code names are published, for budgetary reasons, but without any indication of their significance, and one name may cover several weapons (or vice versa).

U.S. aeronautical equipment (such as bomb guidance units, missile launchers, and warheads) is designated within a system developed by the U.S. Air Force in 1960. Although it superficially resembles the missile designation series, that Air Force system is entirely different, having been designed to embrace not only equipment carried on board aircraft but also ground-based materiel such as tractors and fuel tanks. This system does not include jet and rocket engines or photographic equipment. As might be expected of so broad a system, it is cumbersome (the air force initially wanted to expand the AN system to cover all aeronautical items, but the Office of the Secretary of Defense rejected that as unwieldy). Equipment is denoted by an initial letter A/, then by a three-item code. Aircraft components are designated by three letters, the last of which is K. Aircraft-associated units are designated by three letters, the last of which is U. In the case of ground equipment, the designator consists of a letter indicating the type, a two-digit number, and a letter indicating function, e.g., A/S32P-5, the fifth self-propelled (S), mechanical (32), protective (P) device (in this case, a fire truck). The only example in this book is A/N37U, a sweep-control device.

In the case of aircraft or missile units, the first two letters form a code, and designations include a letter after a slash to indicate the installation. The most important two-letter codes and installation codes are indicated below.

This system was not applied retroactively, so designations such as Bomb Mk 82 survive.

Finally, in accordance with older procedures, U.S. naval weapons (and many systems' components) other than missiles themselves are organized by Mark number. Marks are applied, for example, to fire-control systems (and, separately, to gun directors), to gun mounts (in sequence whatever the caliber), to missile-launching systems (and, to add to the confusion, to the launchers proper), to rocket motors, to torpedoes, to warheads, and to weapons systems (built around unified control systems) as a whole. Examples of the latter are Mk 7 for Aegis and Mk 15 for Phalanx (see the table below). In at least some cases, Mark series were blocked to differentiate underwater from surface systems, e.g., Mk 101 was an underwater fire-control system, not the 101st fire-control system. However, when the original series reached 100, it continued interleaved with the special underwater series.

In addition, all U.S. nuclear weapons are assigned Mark numbers (by the Department of Energy, formerly the Atomic Energy Commission). Any application of a weapon is indicated by a prefix letter, e.g., the B77 bomb would be a bomb version of the Mk 77 warhead, and W77 would be the same weapon configured as a missile warhead. Similarly, all reentry vehicles seem to have Mark numbers in a single series.

1. ELECTRONICS (THE "AN"-SERIES):

♦ Platform Letter

A	airplane
B	submarine ("boat")
C	air-portable (obsolete)
D	missile ("drone")
F	fixed
G	ground use (general)
K	amphibious
M	ground-mobile
P	man-portable
S	ship (or water surface)
T	ground-transportable
U	universal (land/water)
V	ground (vehicular)
W	waterborne (surface/submarine)
Z	piloted and pilotless airborne vehicle combination

♦ Type of Equipment

A	infrared
B	pigeon (obsolete)
C	carrier (wire)
D	radiac
E	nupac (obsolete)
F	photographic (not for U.S. use)
G	telegraph, teletype
I	interphone or public address
J	electro-mechanical or inertial wire covered
K	telemetry
L	countermeasures
M	meteorological
N	sound in air
P	radar (pulsed)
Q	sonar and underwater sound
R	radio
S	special, magnetic, etc. (or combination)
T	telephone (wire)
V	visual
W	weapons
X	facsimile or television
Y	data processing (integration of sensors)

♦ Function

A	auxiliary equipment (e.g., antennas, displays)
B	bombing
C	communications (transceiver)
D	direction-finding, surveillance
E	ejection or release
G	fire control (gunnery) and searchlight direction
H	recording/reproducing
K	computing
L	searchlight control (obsolete)
M	maintenance and/or test
N	navigational
P	reproducing (obsolete, use H)
Q	multifunction or special
R	receive (passive detection)
S	search
T	transmit (e.g., jam)
W	weapons control
X	identification (IFF)
Y	multifunction (phased-array radar)

2. MISSILE-ROCKET DESIGNATIONS:

♦ Launch Environment

A	airplane
B	multi-environment
C	coffin
F	infantry
H	silo-stored (fired from surface)
L	land (fixed silo)
M	mobile
P	soft pad
R	ship
U	underwater

♦ Function

D	decoy
E	special electronic
G	surface attack
I	intercept (antiaircraft)
Q	target drone
T	training
U	underwater attack
W	weather

♦ Type

M	missile (guided)
N	probe
R	rocket

3. AIR EQUIPMENT DESIGNATIONS:

♦ Two-Letter Code

BB	explosive items (not warheads)
BD	bombs, simulated (dummy)
BL	bombs, aircraft (live)
BN	buoys
BR	bomb racks, shackles
BS	munitions stabilizing and retarding devices
CB	cluster bomb unit, consisting of a clustering device or dispenser (SUU) and bomblets (BLU or BDU); may function on board the airplane or after it is dropped
CD	clustering device containing bomblets to be dispensed from an SUU; may or may not be required to make the BLU/BDU compatible with the dispenser (SUU).
CP	computer
CY	cartridge case
DS	target detector (e.g., in proximity fuze)
DT	timing device (e.g., intervalometer)
FM	fuze, munitions
GA	gun, aircraft (e.g., in gun pod)
GB	guided bomb
GD	dummy guided missile (for training)
GP	gun pod (GA plus SUU)
GT	gun turret (excludes gun pods)
GU	guns, non-aircraft
KA	unfilled clustering device
KB	simulated cluster bomb unit
KD	simulated clustering device
KM	miscellaneous kits (used for early "smart" bombs)
LA	launcher, aircraft (e.g., missile rails)
LK	links, ammunition
LM	launching mechanism, ground
LU	illumination (light) (e.g., searchlight)
MA	miscellaneous armament
MJ	countermeasures munitions (e.g., bombs containing chaff or flares)
ML	miscellaneous live munitions
PA	external munitions dispensers (e.g., pods, tanks, clip-ins or other devices mounted externally)
PG	gun ammunition
PJ	projectiles
PW	internal munitions dispensers

RB   rocket and launcher units (combination of LAU and conventional rockets, RLU; excludes CBU)
RL   rocket, live (e.g., FFAR, HVAR)
RV   reentry vehicle (dummy or practice type)
RW   reentry vehicle (live)
SA   sights, gun-bomb-rocket
SP   self protection (as in the SPU-1/W Magnetized Orange Pipe for aerial minesweeping)
SU   suspension and release unit stores (munitions dispenser); may provide a clustering device (CD) to provide compatibility with the ordnance being transported; also may be a CBU less its BLU's.
TD   target devices
WA   warhead section
WB   body section
WC   control section
WD   loaded warhead
WE   empty warhead
WG   guidance section
WP   propulsion section
WT   training or dummy warhead

◆ **Application Code**

A   aircraft or missile
B   aircraft or missile transported (mission expendable)
C   combined air and surface
E   ground (not fixed)
F   ground (fixed)
M   ground movable
N   aircraft or missile transported (not mission expendable)
P   personal use
S   ground, self-propelled
U   multi-installation
W   waterborne (surface or submerged)

4. WEAPON SYSTEM MARK NUMBERS

Mk 1   Weapons Control System (Typhon; abortive)
Mk 7   Aegis
Mk 15   Phalanx (CIWS)
Mks 20–24 TAS (Target Acquisition System; only Mk 23 entered service)
Mk 31   RAM (RIM-116 missile)
Mk 32   Tomahawk (ABL launcher)
Mk 34   DDG 51 class 5 inch gun system
Mk 35   SEAL boat gun system (abortive; for SWCM boat)
Mk 36   Tomahawk submarine-launched missile system
Mk 37   Tomahawk vertically-launched missile system

ABBREVIATIONS

A-Scope   radar display (range only)
AA   antiaircraft, also active adjunct (sonar)
AAC   antiaircraft common (ammunition)
AAM   air-to-air missile
AAW   antiaircraft warfare
ABF   advanced bomb family (U.S.)
ABM   anti–ballistic missile
ABRS   assault ballistic rocket system (U.S., by LTV)
ACINT   acoustic intelligence
ACLS   automatic (aircraft) carrier landing system
ACM   antiarmor cluster munition
ACQ   acquisition
ADA   new U.S. standard military computer language
ADAC   French airborne radar designation; also U.S. all-digital attack center (in submarines)
ADAR   adaptive receiver for horizontal line array (HLA) sonobuoy (U.S.)

ADAWS   action data automation weapons system (British)
ADF   auxiliary detonating fuze
ADI   air-defense initiative (U.S.), complement to SDI
ADT   automatic detection and tracking
ADVCAP   advanced capability (version of EA-6B aircraft)
AE   active enhancement (U.S. sonobuoy program)
AEM   adaptive energy management
AERP   active emission receiver processor (U.S., for sonar)
AEW   airborne early-warning
AGC   automatic gain control (ECCM measure)
AGPB   advanced general-purpose bomb
AGPO   angle-gate pull-off (ECM technique)
AI   artificial intelligence
AIMS   IFF Mk XII system (U.S.); also advanced integrated MAD system (Canadian)
AIO   action information organization (British term for CIC)
AIWS   advanced interdiction weapons system (U.S.)
AJ   antijam (communications)
ALCM   air-launched cruise missile
ALFS   airborne low-frequency sonar (U.S. program)
ALWT   advanced lightweight torpedo (U.S. Mk 50)
AM   amplitude modulation (as opposed to FM)
AMCM   airborne mine countermeasures
ammo   ammunition
AMRAAM   advanced medium-range air-to-air missile (U.S. AIM-120)
AMTI   airborne moving target indication
AM-X   joint Italian-Brazilian attack aircraft
ANL   automatic noise leveling (ECCM technique)
AP   armor piercing
APAM   antipersonnel/antimatériel
APDS   armor-piercing discarding sabot
APFDS   armor-piercing fragmenting discarding sabot (ammunition)
APFSDS   armor-piercing fin-stabilized discarding sabot (ammunition)
APHE   armor-piercing high-explosive (ammunition)
API   armor-piercing incendiary (ammunition)
API-T   armor-piercing incendiary tracer (ammunition)
approx   approximately
ARBS   angle-rate bombing system (U.S. AN/ASB-19)
ARE   Admiralty Research Establishment (British)
ARM   antiradar missile
ARP   antiradar projectile
ASAM   advanced surface-to-air missile, generic U.S. term
ASALM   advanced strategic air-launched missile (U.S.)
ASAT   antisatellite (weapon)
ASLCM   advanced sea-launched cruise missile
ASM   air-to-surface missile
ASMD   antiship missile defense
ASMP   French air-launched strategic cruise missile
ASP   airborne signal processor; also advanced signal processor
ASPJ   airborne self-protection jammer (U.S.)
ASROC   antisubmarine rocket (U.S.)
ASSM   abortive multinational antiship missile project of the 1970s, forerunner of the current ANS project
ASTAB   automatic status board

ASUW	antisurface (ship) warfare
ASW	antisubmarine warfare
ASWS	advanced standoff weapons system (U.S.)
ATA	advanced tactical aircraft (U.S. A-12)
ATB	advanced technology bomber (U.S. B-2)
ATD	automatic target detection
ATF	advanced tactical fighter (U.S. F-22 or F-23)
ATI	airborne tracker-illuminator
ATLIS	French laser designation pod
ATT	automatic target tracking, also acoustic target tracker
AUWE	Admiralty Underwater Weapons Establishment (British)
B-Scope	radar display (rectangular plot of range vs. bearing)
BAC	British Aircraft Corporation
BAe	British Aerospace
BB	bottom bounce (sonar)
BBC	broad-band chaff
bbl	barrel (e.g., of a gun)
BDF	base-detonating fuze
BDI	bearing-deviation indicator (for target following in sonar)
BGAAWC	battle-group AAW coordination (U.S.)
BHP	brake horsepower
BIT(E)	built-in test (equipment)
bit	binary digit (0 or 1)
BL&P	blind-loaded and plugged (inert target ammunition)
BPDMS	basic point-defense missile system (U.S.: Sea Sparrow)
BT	bathythermograph, to obtain a temperature profile of the sea
BVR	beyond visual range (in air-to-air combat)
byte	hexadecimal digit (four bits, i.e., base-16)
ca.	circa
C2	command and control (C-squared)
C3	command, control, and communications (C-cubed)
C3I	command, control, communications, and intelligence
CAAIS	computer-assisted action information system (British)
CAD	computer-aided design
CAINS	carrier aircraft inertial navigation system
CAIR	countermeasure, airborne, IR
CAM	computer-aided manufacture, often combined with CAD (in CAD/CAM)
CANE	computer-aided navigational equipment (British)
CANCASS	Canadian command-activated sonobuoy (CASS)
CASS	command-activated sonobuoy system
CATIC	China Aero-Technical Import and Export Corp.
CBU	cluster bomb unit
ccd	coupled charge device (electronic component)
CCS	combat-control system
CCTV	closed-circuit television
CDC	command-display console
CEM	combined effects munition
CEP	circular error probable (half of all shots will fall within this radius)
CFA	crossed-field amplifier (radar transmitter)
CFAR	constant false-alarm rate (in radar)
CIC	combat information center (U.S.; equivalent to operations room [British])
CIGARS	console internal generation and refresh system, modification to U.S. UYA-4 console of NTDS system

CIWS	close-in weapons system
CLOS	command to line of sight (missile guidance)
CNO	chief of naval operations (U.S.)
CO	commanding officer
CODAR	correlation display analyzing recorder (ASW), to obtain position data by correlating the outputs of two or more passive sonobuoys
COMINT	communications intelligence
conscan	conical scan (in radar)
COOP	craft of opportunity program (generally in minesweeping)
CORT	coherent receive/transmit (in radar)
CPIC	coastal patrol and interdiction craft (U.S.)
CPMIEC	China Precision Machinery Import/Export Corp.
CRBFD	close-range blind-fire director (British)
CRT	cathode-ray tube (display)
CRZ	controlled-reaction zone
CP	command-plotting/plotter
csc2	cosecant-squared, a typical vertical shape for radar beams; it provides constant power at a given altitude at all ranges. The expression "30 deg csc2" means a beam that has cosecant-squared shape up to 30 degrees of elevation
CSDC	combat system display console (U.S.)
CSEDS	combat system engineering development site (U.S.)
CSLC	coherent sidelobe-canceling receiver
CSU	compact sonar for submarines (U-boats) (German)
CU	control unit
CVR	crystal video receiver
CVT	controlled variable time, for a fuze
CW	continuous wave (non-pulsed)
CWAT	CW acquisition and tracking
CWI	continuous wave illuminator/injection
CZ	convergence zone (sonar)
DARPA	Defense Advanced Research Projects Agency (U.S.)
DASH	drone antisubmarine helicopter (U.S. QH-50, obsolete)
dB	decibel, a measure of relative size; it is 10 log (base 10) of a ratio. Thus 3 dB is a factor of about 2, and 10 dB a factor of 10; −3 dB is about a half. The reference value in the ratio is often implicit, as in radar, when it is the performance of a notional antenna radiating power equally in all directions.
dBm	decibel-milliwatt (measure used in ECM)
DC	direct current, also depth charge
DCAN	Direction Construction Armes Navale (French)
DCN	Direction Construction Navale (French)
DCU	distributed computing unit
DECM	defensive (also deceptive) electronic countermeasures
deg	degree
DELEX	destroyer life-extension program (Canadian)
DEMON	demodulated noise (ASW signal-processing technique)
DF	direction finding
DFT	discrete Fourier transform
DICANCASS	Canadian DICASS sonobuoy (ASW)
DICASS	directional command-activated sonobuoy (ASW)
DIFAR	directional LOFAR (in ASW)
DIGISMAC	digital scene-matching (cruise-missile guidance); also abbreviated DSMAC
DIMUS	digital multibeam steering (ASW)

DLC	down-link communications
DMCC	dual maintenance of close contact (sonar)
DME	distance-measuring equipment (passive; U.S.)
DMT	dual-mode tracker
DMTI	digital MTI
DND	Department of National Defence (Canadian, Australian)
DoD	Department of Defense (U.S.)
DP	dual-purpose
DRAI	dead reckoning analyzer/indicator (submarine)
DRARM	dual-role ARM
DRT	dead-reckoning tracer
DSARC	Defense System Acquisition Review Council (U.S.)
DSCS	Defense Satellite Communications System (U.S.)
DSMAC	see DIGISMAC above
DT	directional transmission (in sonar)
DTCN	Direction Technique Construction Navale (French)
EAC	equal angle coverage
ECM	electronic countermeasures
ECCM	electronic counter-countermeasures
EDATS	extra-deep armed team sweep (British)
EDM	engineering development model
EEZ	exclusive economic zone (defined by Law of the Sea Treaty)
EFA	European fighter aircraft (multinational project)
EHF	extremely high frequency
ELF	extremely low frequency
ELINT	electronic intelligence
EMCON	emissions control (electromagnetic silence)
EMATT	expendable mobile ASW training target (U.S.)
EMI	electromagnetic interference; also the name of a British electronics manufacturer
EMSP	enhanced modular signal processor (U.S.)
EMP	electromagnetic pulse
EO	electro-optical
EPROM	erasable programmable read-only memory
ERAPS	expendable reliable-acoustic-path sonobuoy
ERDL	extended-range data link
ESF	electronically set fuze, replacing mechanically set fuzes
ESM	electronic support (surveillance) measures
ESS	enhanced Sea Sparrow (U.S. missile project)
ESR	equivalent service rounds, measure of gun wear
est	estimated
ETF	electrical time fuze
EW	electronic warfare; also early warning
FA	frequency agility
FAC	fast attack craft
FAE	fuel-air explosive
FCS	fire-control system
FDALE	frequency domain adaptive line enhancement (sonar technique)
FET	field effect transistor
FEWSG	Fleet Electronic Warfare Support Group (simulating enemy jamming for training) (U.S.)
FFAR	folding-fin aircraft rocket (2.75-inch caliber)
FFT	fast Fourier transform
FIAR	Fabbrica Italiana Apparecchiature Radio-elettroniche (Italian manufacturer)
FIR	finite impulse response (type of radar receiver, for ECCM)

FLIR	forward-looking infrared
flop	floating-point instructions per second (measure of computer speed, as in 1 Mflop, i.e., 1 million flops per second)
FM	frequency modulation (as opposed to AM)
FMC	U.S. defense manufacturer, formerly Food Machinery Corp.
FMCW	frequency-modulated continuous wave
FM/FI	fault monitoring/fault isolation
FMS	foreign military sales (U.S.)
FOV	field of view
FPB	fast patrol boat
FRAM	fleet rehabilitation and modernization (U.S. program, applied to many destroyers now serving in foreign navies)
FRESCAN	frequency-scanning (electronic scanning technique in radar)
FSD	full-scale development
FSED	full-scale engineering development
ft	foot/feet (12 inches)
FTC	fast time constant (radar ECCM technique)
FY	fiscal year (U.S.: 1 October–30 September)
FYDP	five-year defense program (U.S., compiled annually)
G	force of gravity
g	gram
GAO	General Accounting Office (U.S.)
GDS	gun direction system
GE	General Electric Company
GERDSM	French ASW and mine warfare development establishment
GFCS	gunfire-control system (U.S.)
GHG	Gruppen-Horch Geraet (array listening system), the wartime German low-frequency passive sonar from which several postwar systems were derived.
GHz	gigahertz (thousands of MHz)
GMFCS	guided-missile fire-control system (U.S.)
GP	general-purpose (as in bomb)
GPS	global positioning system
GRP	glass-reinforced plastic (construction material)
HALE	high-altitude long endurance (drone)
HARM	high-speed antiradar missile (U.S. AGM-88)
HBX	high explosive (more powerful than TNT)
HC	high capacity (as in a shell)
HCER	high-capacity extended-range
HCHE	high-capacity high-explosive (ammunition)
HDW	Howaldt, a German shipbuilder
HE	high explosive
HEAT	high-explosive antitank (shaped charge)
HEER	high-explosive extended-range
HEI	high-explosive incendiary
HF	high frequency
HLA	horizontal line array (U.S. sonobuoy)
HLASM	helicopter-launched air-to-surface missile
HOTAS	hands-on throttle and stick
HP	horsepower (or high power or high pressure or horizontal plotter)
hrs	hours
HS	ASW helicopter squadron (U.S. Navy)
HSA	Hollandse Signaal Apparaaten (also known as Signaal)
HTP	high-test peroxide (concentrated hydrogen peroxide)
HUD	heads-up display
HUMINT	human intelligence
HVAR	high-velocity aircraft rocket (5-inch caliber)
Hz	hertz (cycles per second)
IADT	integrated automatic detection and tracking
IAI	Israel Aircraft Industry

IAM	inertially aided munitions (U.S.)
IC	internal communication (circuit) in U.S. usage; also integrated circuit
ICW	interrupted continuous wave
IFF	identification friend or foe
IFM	instantaneous frequency measurement (in ESM)
IIR	imaging infrared
ILS	instrument landing system, often as VOR/ILS
in	inch
INS	inertial navigation system
IOC	initial operational capability
IR	infrared
IRDS	infrared detecting set
IRGP	infrared guided projectile
IRST	infrared search and track (or target designation)
IRU	inertial reference unit
ISAR	inverse synthetic-aperture radar
ISUS	integrated-sensor underwater system (German)
ITAWDS	amphibious warfare data system (U.S.)
ITSS	integrated tactical surveillance system (U.S.)
IUSS	integrated undersea surveillance system (U.S.)
JCS	Joint Chiefs of Staff (U.S.)
JDF	jamming direction-finder
JFY	Japanese fiscal year
JMSDF	Japan Maritime Self-Defense Force (navy)
JSCAMPS	Joint-Service Common-Airframe Multiple-Purpose System (U.S. RPV program)
JTIDS	joint tactical information distribution system (U.S., NATO)
k	kilo, thousand. In electronics, a kilobit (or -byte) equals 1024 rather than 1000 bits (bytes).
K	degrees Kelvin (i.e., above absolute zero)
kg	kilogram, 2.204 lbs
KDA	Oerlikon gun designation (Swiss). The first letter, K, indicates that the weapon is a gun (mounts are prefixed G); the second letter indicates the caliber (A for 20 mm, B for 25 mm, C for 30 mm, D for 35 mm); the third letter is a modifier (for guns, typically A, B, or C). Other typical gun designations are KAA, KBA, and KBB.
K-Kill	catastrophic kill, as opposed to mobility or firepower kill
km	kilometer
kT	kilotons, thousands of tons (equivalent TNT)
kts	knots (nautical miles per hour)
kW	kilowatt
kyds	kiloyards, thousands of yards
LAMPS	light airborne multipurpose system (U.S. helicopter)
LANTIRN	low-altitude navigation-and-targeting IR system for night (U.S.)
lbs	pounds
LCAC	landing craft air cushion (U.S.)
LCS	low-cost sonobuoy (U.S.); also low-cost seeker
LED	light-emitting diode (for electronic displays)
LF	low frequency
LFDM	low-flier detection mode (in radar)
LGB	laser-guided bomb
LLLGB	low-level laser-guided bomb
LLLTV	low-light-level television

LNFE	low-noise front end
LOAL	lock-on after launch
LOBL	lock-on before launch
LOCWS	laser obstacle and cable warning system
LOFAR	low-frequency analysis and recording (ASW)
LOVA	low-vulnerability ammunition
LPI	low probability of intercept
LRCCM	long-range conventional cruise missile
LRDMM	long-range dual-mode missile
LRU	line-replaceable unit
LSI	large-scale (electronic) integration
LST/SCAM	laser spot tracker/strike camera
LTV	Ling-Temco Vought, U.S. manufacturer
LWIR	long-wave infrared
m	meter
M	Mach (number), multiple of speed of sound
MAD	magnetic-anomaly detector (in ASW)
MAP	military assistance program (U.S.)
MARV	maneuverable reentry vehicle
MASC	multi-array signal conditioner (U.S., in sonar)
max	maximum
Mbit	Megabit, million bits (approximate)
Mbps	Megabytes per second (measure of data rate)
Mbyte	megabytes, million bytes (approximate)
MCAR	multiple channel aural reception (sonar)
MCC	maintenance of close contact (sonar)
MCM	mine countermeasures
MCOPS	million complex operations per second
MDC	mine-destruction charge
Megaflop	million floating point operations per second (measure of computing speed)
MEKO	modular frigate (by Blohm & Voss)
MEL	British and Canadian electronic manufacturer
MEM	maximum energy management
MF	medium frequency
MFCC	multifunction common console
MFCS	missile fire-control system
MFR	multifunction radar
MG	machine gun (also motor-generator, to transform AC to DC current)
MGC	manual gain control (in radar)
MHC	minehunter, coastal
MHz	megahertz (millions of cycles per second)
microsec	microsecond, millionth of a second
MIDAS	mine detection-and-avoidance system (U.S.)
min	minute or minimum
MIPS	million instructions per second
MIRV	multiple independent reentry vehicles
Mk	mark (number, for designations)
mm	millimeter
MMW	millimeter-wave (length)
MNS	mine neutralization system (U.S.)
MoD	Ministry of Defence (e.g., British)
Mod	modification to equipment of a given Mk number, as in Mk 46 Mod 5 torpedo
MOP	magnetized orange pipe (U.S. mine sweep)
MOSS	mobile submarine simulator (U.S.)
MoU	memorandum of understanding
mph	miles per hour
mrad	milliradian (thousandth of a radian)
MRBF	mean rounds (fired) before failure
MR-RPV	mid-range RPV (U.S.)
MRV	multiple reentry vehicle
msec	millisec, thousandth of a second
MP	medium power
MPA	maritime-patrol aircraft
MPC	multipurpose console
MSB	minesweeping boat
MSC	minesweeper, coastal

MSD	minesweeping drone
MSI	medium scale integration, as opposed to LSI and VLSI; also minesweeper, inshore
MSL	minesweeping launch
MSO	minesweeper, ocean
MSOW	modular standoff weapon (NATO)
MT	Megatons, millions of tons (TNT equivalent); also mechanical time, for a fuze
MTBF	mean time between failure
MTI	moving-target indicator (or indication)
MTT	moving-target tracker
MTTR	mean time to repair (also multitarget tracking radar)
MW	Megawatt, million watts
NADGE	NATO air-defense ground environment
NAVAIR	Naval Air Systems Command (U.S.)
NAVSEA	Naval Sea Systems Command (U.S.)
NDB/NSB	nuclear depth bomb/nuclear strike bomb
NEL	Naval Electronics Laboratory (U.S.)
NIS	NATO identification system (IFF)
nm	nautical mile, 6080 ft
NMR	nuclear magnetic resonance
NOSC	Naval Ocean Systems Center (U.S.)
nsec	nanosecond (billionth of a second)
NSR	Naval Staff Requirement (British)
NSSMS	NATO Sea Sparrow missile system
NSWC	Naval Surface Warfare Center (U.S.)
NST	Naval Staff Target (British)
NTDS	naval tactical-data system (U.S.)
NTU	New Threat Upgrade (U.S. program)
NUSC	Naval Underwater Systems Center (U.S.)
NVG	night vision goggles
ODT	omnidirectional transmission (sonar)
OFD	optical fire director
ONI	Office of Naval Intelligence (U.S.)
OPV	offshore patrol vessel
OR	Operational Requirement (U.S.)
ORDALT	ordnance alteration (U.S.)
ORTS	operational recording and testing system (U.S.)
OSD	Office of the Secretary of Defense (U.S.)
OTC	officer in tactical command
OTCIXC	OTC information exchange channel
OTH	over the horizon (in radar); OTH-B is OTH by means of backscatter (off the ionosphere). A forward-scatter OTH system uses a beam that scatters off the target, then goes beyond to a separate receiver. OTH-B uses transmitter and receiver close together, bouncing the reflected wave back off the ionosphere between target and radar.
OTH-T	over-the-horizon targeting (U.S. term)
PACS	plotting and combat summary display (U.S.)
PADLOC	passive-active detection and localization (sonar, U.S.)
PAIR	performance and integration refit (conversion of SQS-23 sonar to SQQ-23)
PAL	permissive action link (in nuclear systems, to prevent unauthorized use)
PD	probability of detection; also point detonating (fuze)
PDD	point detonating delay (fuze)
PDF	point (instantaneous) detonating fuze
PDMS	point-defense missile system (U.S.)
PEAB	Philips Elektronikindustri AB (Swedish manufacturer)
PFHE	prefragmented high-explosive (ammunition)
PGM	precision guided munition ("smart weapon")

PI/DF	passive identification direction finding
PK	probability of kill
POM	program objective memorandum (U.S. defense plan)
PPI	plan-position indicator (maplike radar display)
PPS	pulses per second
PRC	People's Republic of China
PRF	pulse repetition frequency
PSP	programmable signal processor
PTA	passive-tracking algorithm; also proposed technical approach, in U.S. procurement
PUFFS	passive underwater fire control (U.S.)
QRC	quick reaction contract, a U.S. procurement technique used during the Vietnam War
RAAF	Royal Australian Air Force
rad	radian, measure of angle (1 radian is about 57.3 degrees)
RAF	Royal Air Force (British)
RAM	random access memory (in computers); also rolling airframe missile (U.S.)
RAN	Royal Australian Navy
RAP	rocket-assisted projectile (shell); also reliable acoustic path (ASW)
RBOC	rapid-blooming off-board chaff (U.S.)
R&D	research and development
RDF	Rapid Deployment Force (U.S.)
RDT	rotationally directed transmission (sonar)
RDT&E	research, development, testing, and engineering
RDX	high explosive (more powerful than TNT)
RF	radio frequency
RF/IR	combined radio (or radar) and IR
RFA	Royal Fleet Auxiliary (British)
RFP	request for proposal
RGPO	range-gate pull-off (ECM technique)
RLO	radar lock-on
RHAW	radar homing and warning
RHI	range-height indicator (for radar)
rms	root-mean square
RN	Royal Navy (British)
rnds	rounds
RNEE	Royal Naval Equipment Exhibition
RNTF	Royal Navy Torpedo Factory (now closed)
ROM	read-only memory (in computer)
ROV	remotely operated vehicle (generally underwater)
RPC	reflected power canceler or remote power control (British: guns)
RPG	rocket-propelled grenade (antitank weapon)
rpm	revolutions per minute
RPV	remotely piloted vehicle; see also UAV
RSLS	receiver side-lobe suppression
RTLOS	remote track launch on search (missile tactic)
RTN	Italian (Selenia) radar designator
RTV	recoverable test vehicle
RV	reentry vehicle (for a missile)
RVC	radar-video converter (to digital data)
RVP	radar video processor
RWR	radar-warning receiver
SACLANT	Supreme Allied Commander Atlantic
SADARM	sense and destroy armament (submunition)
SADS	SubACS acoustic detection system (U.S.)
SALGP	semiactive laser-guided projectile
SAM	surface-to-air missile
SAP	semi–armor-piercing
SAR	synthetic aperture radar; also search and rescue

SCCS	submarine combat-control system
SCEPS	stored chemical energy propulsion system (for torpedoes; see U.S. Mk 50)
SCI	special compartmentation information (generally information outside the usual classification system; information is often "sanitized" to remove SCI so that it can more freely be used by operating forces) (U.S.)
SDC	sensor-data converter
SDI	strategic-defense initiative (U.S.): defense against ballistic-missile attack
SDT	steered directional transmission (sonar)
SEAL	Sea-Air-Land (U.S. Navy special forces)
SEC	second
SEM	standard electronic module (U.S.)
SEPADS	sonar-environment prediction-and-display system
SFCS	submarine fire-control system
SHAB	steerable hull array beam-former (U.S.)
SHF	super high frequency
SHINPADS	shipboard integrated processing-and-display system (Canadian)
SHP	shaft horse power
SHR	superheterodyne receiver
SIAC	submarine integrated attack center
SIDS	sensor interface data system (U.S.)
SIGINT	signals intelligence
SIMAS	sonar in-situ mode assessment system
SINS	ships' inertial navigation system
SLAM	standoff land attack missile (modified harpoon)
SLAT	supersonic low-altitude target; also surface-launched air-targeted
SLB	side-lobe blanking (in radar)
SLBM	sea-launched ballistic missile
SLC	side-lobe cancellation (in radar)
SLCM	sea-launched cruise missile
SLEP	service-life extension program (U.S.)
SLMM	submarine-launched mobile mine
SMA	Segnalamento Marittimo ed Aero (Italian manufacturer)
SNIA	French rocket motor manufacturer
SOR	specific operational requirement (U.S.)
SOSUS	sound surveillance system (U.S. and NATO)
SPAT	self-propelled acoustic target
SRARM	short-range ARM (U.S.)
SRBOC	super rapid-blooming off-board chaff (U.S.)
SRDT	steered rotationally directed transmission (sonar)
SRSSM	short-range surface-to-surface missile
SS	submarine
SSB	single sideband (radio); also diesel-powered ballistic-missile submarine
SSBN	strategic ballistic-missile submarine (nuclear powered)
SSI	sector scan indicator (sonar, for target tracking)
SSK	ASW submarine (nonnuclear)
SSLV	standard small launch vehicle
SSM	surface-to-surface missile
SSN	nuclear submarine
SSPK	single-shot kill probability
SSTx	solid-state transmitter
STA	second time around, referring to radar pulses arriving back at the radar after the next pulse has been sent
STAE	second-time-around echo (radar)
STC	sensitivity time control (ECCM technique)
STIR	separate track and illumination radar (U.S.); also Signaal track and illumination radar

	(Dutch); also surveillance and target indication radar (British)
SURTASS	surveillance towed-array sonar system
SWCM	special warfare craft, medium (SEAL craft, U.S.)
SYS	sensor (radar) integration computer (U.S.)
3P-HV	programmed-proximity prefragmented high-velocity explosive (Bofors ammunition)
TABP	towed-array broad-band processor (U.S.)
TACAN	tactical air navigation beacon (U.S.)
TACCO	tactical coordinating officer
TACSIT	tactical-situation display (in U.S. submarines)
TACTASS	tactical towed-array sonar system
TADIL	tactical digital link (U.S. and NATO)
TAO	tactical action officer
TAPS	towed-array broad-band processing system (British)
TARP	towed-array range processor/processing (for U.S. long thin array)
TAS	target acquisition system (U.S.); also tactical Arctic sonobuoy (U.S.)
TASP	towed-array signal processor
TASS	towed-array sonar system
TB	towed body (U.S. designation)
TCSS	torpedo control system, submarine (British)
TDD	target-detection device (proximity fuze)
TDHS	tactical data handling system (ASW)
TDI	target doppler indicator (sonar, for target tracking)
TDS	tactical-data system
TDT	target designation transmitter
TELCOM	two-way wire guidance for Mk 48 torpedo (U.S.)
TENCAP	tactical exploitation of national (intelligence) capabilities (U.S.)
TERCOM	terrain comparison (cruise missile guidance)
TG	transmitter group (in sonar)
TI	target indication (British)
TMA	target-motion analysis (for ASW ranging and fire control)
TMAD	target-motion analysis display
TOR	Tentative Operational Requirement (U.S.)
TOW	tube-launched optical wire-guided missile (U.S., antitank)
TP	target practice (ammunition)
TP-T	target practice tracer (ammunition)
TPX	explosive (torpex, more powerful than TNT)
TRAM	target recognition and attack multisensor
TRDT	tribeam rotationally directed transmission (sonar)
TRIASP	tri-advanced signal processor (U.S., in sonar) (three ASP packaged together, for the BQQ-5C sonar)
TRUMP	Tribal-class modernization program (Canadian)
TSC	tactical support center (U.S., for ASW)
TSS	tactical surveillance sonobuoy (U.S.)
TT	torpedo tube
TVM	track via missile (guidance technique)
TWS	track-while-scan
TWT	travelling wave tube (radar transmitter)
UAV	unmanned air vehicle (this more general term is replacing RPV in many cases)
UDACS	Universal Display and Control System (Boeing ASW system)
UEP	underwater electric potential

UHF	ultra-high frequency
ULC	up-link communications
VA	attack squadron (U.S. Navy) (with a number)
VAB	variable-action button (of a console)
VDS	variable-depth sonar
VECG	video extractor and control group (in radar)
VF	fighter squadron (U.S. Navy) (with a number)
VGPO	velocity-gate pull-off (ECM technique)
VHF	very high frequency
VHSIC	very high speed integrated circuit
VIS	visual
VLA	vertical-launch ASROC (missile) (U.S.)
VLAD	vertical line array DIFAR (U.S. sonobuoy)
VLF	very low frequency
VLS	vertical launch system
VLSI	very large scale integration (of electronic circuits)
VOR	VHF omni-range (for air navigation)

VP	patrol (ASW) squadron (sometimes used for patrol aircraft) (U.S. Navy)
VQ	ECM squadron (U.S. Navy)
VSTOL	vertical/short take-off and landing
VT	variable time (proximity), used for a fuze
VTOL	vertical take-off and landing
VAW	AEW squadron (U.S. Navy) (with a number)
VX	test squadron (U.S. Navy) (with a number)
WAA	wide-aperture array (U.S.)
WBL	wide-band limiting (in radar)
WCS	weapons-control system (U.S.)
WDC	weapons-delivery computer
WDS	weapons-direction system (U.S.)
WP	white phosphorous (shell)
WPB	wide pulse blanking (in radar)
WRA	weapons replaceable assembly
XBT	expendable bathythermograph
yds	yards

SURVEILLANCE AND CONTROL

A fleet's visible elements are its ships, submarines, and aircraft. These elements are tied together by communications links, many of them satellite-borne. Increasingly, a fleet's operations are motivated by external sources of operational intelligence data. Many of the sources and systems involved are sensitive and so cannot be described. Much of the West's knowledge of the Soviet systems, for example, has been obtained by careful sifting of intelligence obtained at great cost, and this information is by no means publicly available. Thus the systems described in this section should be considered samples of a larger whole, indications of the very important invisible elements of modern navies.

Such systems are not nearly as new as they may seem. Before World War II, for example, the U.S. Navy operated a Strategic High Frequency Direction Finding system around the rim of the Pacific, specifically to track the Japanese Fleet. The system fed information to naval headquarters in Washington, D.C., which in turn would have directed the CinC U.S. Fleet in Pearl Harbor into position to deal with his enemies. With the success of Allied code-breaking during World War II, centralized operational intelligence became more common and more important. It remains important now, although, of course, the degree of success with which we track, say, Soviet submarines must be a matter of speculation in any unclassified discussion of the subject.

The central question in the design of all such systems has always concerned the amount of raw data a deployed commander should be provided. In World War II, it was obvious that the deployed commanders required a great deal of raw data, and great pains were taken to protect the channels by which those data were transmitted. Afterward, as the United States and her allies came to believe that a major war, if it ever occurred, would soon escalate to a nuclear exchange, the operational aspect of intelligence seemed less and less important. Systems with an operational potential, such as SOSUS, were valued primarily for their war-warning potential, their data prepared primarily for the National Command Authority. Now it seems clearer that a war might remain nonnuclear for quite some time, perhaps throughout its course. In that case, tactical war-fighting becomes more important; and some of the same intelligence systems built up for the National Command Authority are being turned, in part, to the needs of the deployed commanders. This development explains such systems, discussed below, as OSIS (the Ocean Surveillance Information System) and the TFCC (Tactical Flag Command Center).

In the case of the United States, the investment in existing intelligence-gathering systems is so large that new tactically oriented systems cannot likely be built, at least in the short term. Instead, existing systems are being used, where they are appropriate. Note that these systems do *not* include such classic intelligence-gatherers as photographic satellites, which cover only very limited areas at any one time, or deep-space nuclear-detonation detectors.

The other key question for the United States is to what extent fixed, as opposed to mobile (i.e., integral with tactical formations such as battle groups), intelligence systems should be supported. If the United States had to face only the Soviet Union, there would be no question: full coverage of northern waters would have the highest priority, and nowhere else would full coverage be particularly valuable. However, the single greatest asset of sea power is its mobility, its ability to deal with the unexpected—which, since 1945, has usually meant conflict in the Third World. The question of mobile surveillance has not yet really arisen, but that is only because the United States' Third World enemies have not yet had serious naval forces requiring the use of more than existing fleet assets. That may well not be the case in the future, and the United States may even have to face the Soviets outside their home waters. This issue affects systems such as SOSUS (the Sound Surveillance System) and ROTHR (the Relocatable Over-the-Horizon Radar).

For the Soviets, the situation is rather different. Much of the Soviet intelligence program, including at least some (and perhaps all) space and long-range direction-finding assets, is concentrated in the hands of the GRU, the intelligence arm of the General Staff. It is unlikely that the GRU would ever have thought in other than operational terms; the Soviets may well rely on agents in place in other countries for such purposes as war-warning. In any case, the Soviets seem much more willing than the Americans to use intelligence data for operational purposes, whereas in the West, the emphasis has been much more on protecting invaluable sources (including technical ones) to avoid losing war-warning capabilities.

On the other hand, the Soviets concentrate much more power in the hands of their central command structure, so that deployed commanders, in the Western sense, probably do not exist at all. Intelligence assets, such as most satellites, report to the central command. Deployed forces are ordered into position to attack on the basis of these reports, in some cases using satellite or other off-board data as a basis for attacking. This organization relies heavily on long-haul communications, and the Soviets are well known for their redundant command links.

From a technological point of view, perhaps the most important development has been the changing fortune of HF radio. HF communications have very long ranges because HF signals bounce off the ionosphere, but a long range subjects an HF system to intercept and to direction-finding (DF). HF also suffers in practice from the vagaries of the variable ionosphere.

During World War II, Allied forces came to rely more and more on higher-frequency (VHF, then UHF) radio for communicating within task forces or with other naval formations because these signals propagate in approximately straight lines and may not, therefore, pass much beyond the horizon. HF remained, however, the only means of long-haul communication.

Tactically, then, a fleet could be detected at long range only when it communicated with its home base. The fleet could maintain radio silence (with respect to hostile HF/DF stations) while communicating among its own units on VHF or UHF radio. During the 1950s, however, HF was revived even for intrafleet communications because fleets had to disperse in the face of the new nuclear threat: a single bomb could not destroy an entire fleet spread over many thousands of square miles of ocean. Thus, the United States chose HF for the NTDS data link. Even if the nuclear threat becomes less credible in the future, dispersal may still be valuable because it greatly complicates the analyst's task of trying to discern a coordinated fleet from a picture of individual, widely separated ships. Thus, the need for long-haul tactical communications is likely to remain.

Nor are VHF and UHF as safe as they once were. All antennas, however directional, have sidelobes, so that some energy propagates in other directions—for example, straight up. Satellites can, then, intercept VHF and UHF (and higher-frequency) signals, nominally limited to line of sight. A group of satellites operating together can locate the transmitter by measuring the time of arrival of the same signal at different points in space (interferometry). Satellites do differ in one important, disadvantageous way from big fixed HF/DF sites. The ground sites can pick up all signals in their vicinity, out to ranges of hundreds or thousands of miles, and are always listening. Satellites, however, can hear only those signals in a finite swath below, so knowledge of the satellites' characteristics and orbits (these satellites probably cannot be so far away as to be in fixed orbits) tells a communicator when it is safe to transmit.

Satellite interception is, moreover, limited by the strengh of the sidelobes: the more directional the transmission, the less probable the interception. Most UHF antennas are very nearly omnidirectional because they are intended to transmit to any nearby units rather than to one specific ship. These antennas are, therefore, quite vulnerable to interception. The potential for satellite ESM thus makes very directional communications links much more attractive.

Satellite communication can help solve some of these problems. In theory, a ship can send radio signals up in a tight UHF or even SHF (super-high-frequency) beam, which can be intercepted only by a satellite virtually on that beam. The satellite can then relay the message along a broad downward-looking beam. Thus, a ship using a satellite system can transmit directionally (i.e., with reduced probability of interception) without losing the ability to broadcast to many other ships, even to those well beyond the horizon. The satellites are vulnerable, however, to failure as well as to hostile fire. Alternatives may include such "poor man's satellites" as high-altitude airplanes, RPVs, and airships. Of course, the satellite up-links that are not narrow beams can be intercepted by DF devices, and satellite communications are valued primarily for their reliability and for their message capacity.

The effect of external command/control and intelligence is to extend the horizon of an individual ship. However, most of the information so obtained is given in terms of geographical (i.e., earth-oriented) coordinates: the incoming force of bombers is in this position, flying this course, at this speed. Only if a ship at sea has reasonably accurate navigational data can it take full advantage of such information. Thus, this section includes some specialized navigational systems, such as the U.S. global positioning satellites. When these devices provide really accurate information, they can be used to guide weapons, such as cruise missiles, to specific points on the earth. The question then is whether the intelligence systems providing initial targeting data are nearly as precise as the navigational systems exploiting them. For example, it is not too useful to guide a missile to within a foot of a presumed target when the actual target is a mile away. Not knowing the target's location precisely enough is a central problem in all long-range ballistic-missile firings.

Accurate navigation is also essential to successful mine countermeasures. The minehunter or sweeper must know precisely which channel her predecessors have cleared and precisely where she goes from there. This section, therefore, also includes accounts of the standard in-shore precision-navigation systems now in use on board Western mine-countermeasures ships. Soviet systems are presumably roughly equivalent.

The big fixed systems share and sift information so that it can be fed to ships at sea. Ships have analogous combat systems, such as the British ADAWS series, the French SENIT, and the American NTDS, whose function is to coordinate information available on board ship (including that provided by external sources) and then to present all the information in a form suitable for decision making (including weapons assignment and control).

Like the big external systems, the on-board combat system is by no means a new idea. The classic warship information center consisted of the plot, a presentation of the situation around a ship: information was provided by lookouts and signals from other ships. During World War II this idea was extended and elaborated as the British and American Navies developed the AIO (Action Information Organization)/CIC (Combat Information Center). Perhaps the most important difference between a CIC and a classic plot is that the CIC must handle data that change very rapidly (such as fast air contacts); CIC must also integrate more different kinds of data (radar, visual, ESM).

The most important of CIC's functions is to filter data, deciding which information is likely to be accurate and which information is relevant.

The output of an AAW CIC is a plot showing tracks, i.e., the directions and speeds and histories of the targets the radar detects. That display is quite different from the instantaneous picture of target positions that a radar itself sees at any one time. ASW displays show a similar difference between tracks and individual contacts. Decisions are based on these tracks since they indicate which targets are of greatest concern and which ones are within engagement range. Track plots also make it possible to assign dedicated gun, missile, or fighter control trackers to the individual targets selected for engagement. One role of the other (nonradar) information in an AAW CIC is to identify the tracks, so that the ship does not try, for example, to shoot down friendly aircraft. Identification is partly a function of the IFF systems, but also a matter of observing the target's behavior and of recording or deducing the track's origin. For example, during the Vietnam War, U.S. ships in the Tonkin Gulf were able to avoid firing on a scheduled Tokyo-Manila airline run by tracking the airliner from its point of origin.

The advent of the CIC brought into question the classic way of fighting a ship. A plot, which was usually adjacent to the bridge, was a convenient source of information for the captain stationed on his bridge or in his conning tower. However, the CIC provided that captain with information on events far beyond visual range. Captains, therefore, either commanded from the bridge (and left a senior subordinate, the CIC Evaluator, in CIC) or commanded from CIC. As CICs have become stations for weapons control, their importance has increased; in current U.S. practice, the Tactical Action Officer, who actually fights under the captain's direction, is stationed in CIC. In the future, at least in the U.S. Navy, captains will generally be expected to fight their ships from CIC.

Wartime and early postwar experience showed that a manual CIC, in which radar contacts are plotted sweep by sweep for each radar, cannot handle very large numbers of tracks. The picture loses accuracy and then begins to miss tracks. As a plot of any one target becomes less accurate, moreover, the plotters may erroneously associate it with a plot (detection) of another target, and so produce a misleading track leading to wrong decisions (e.g., to assignment of the few available fighters to nonexistent targets).

The solution was the most important postwar shipboard command-and-control development, the automated CIC. Examples include the British ADAWS and the U.S. NTDS. These systems began as computerized track-keepers. In a manual plot, a man at a radar scope sees what is called raw video, or blips on a screen. He reads the position of a blip off the screen so that it can be entered into the plot. The first step toward automation was for the radar-display operator to enter blip positions directly into a computer, which in turn fed an electronic summary display. The first two such systems were the British CDS (Comprehensive Display System) and the U.S. EDS (Electronic Display System). The CDS computer had 24 or 48 track "stores" or electronic registers. The radar operator entered a blip position by moving a cursor (a "hook") over the blip. This position was then entered in the next empty store, and a tracker assigned to that target. The tracker was then responsible for entering successive target positions. These positions formed a track, and the summary display showed all the tracks, as a basis for command decisions. The details of the summary display could be transmitted to other ships equipped with CDS by means of a digital data link, DPT (digital plot transmission).

In this system (and in EDS) the computer did not process the track data. For example, the decision to engage one target or another was based on the CIC officer's perception of the summary plot. Compared to a manual CIC, CDS or EDS had the important advantage of reducing errors in transferring blip positions from radar scope to summary plot, but these systems did not exploit the full power of digital computing.

The next step, then, was to process the track data, to treat tracks as computer files. The computer could then calculate fighter intercept vectors and could decide which targets deserved particularly urgent attention. The U.S. NTDS is typical of this stage of development. Operators still enter targets manually, but there are no dedicated trackers. Instead, the computer forms a track based on a sequence of entered blip positions. The computer then projects target position ahead (the successive positions imply a target course and speed), and the radar operator monitors this projection to catch any change in course and speed.

When NTDS was conceived, the technology of automatic radar detection was in its infancy. A radar can decide that a particular echo represents a real target by checking whether it reflects a set number of pulses per scan; the required number is generally set to keep the expected number of false alarms below some preset criterion. The British equivalent to NTDS, the big ADA (Action Data Automation) system installed onboard HMS *Eagle*, did employ automatic radar detection, and ADA used its track data for automatic computation of fighter interception vectors. The U.S. Navy limited automatic detection to a few ships, using the semiautomatic (rate-aided) system in most cases. ADA was designed slightly later than NTDS, and ADA's successor, ADAWS, employs automatic radar detection (which the British call radar plot extraction).

The great advantage of the automatic systems is that they are always alert; they never grow tired, and they never become fatigued in the face of intense operation. On the other hand, the greater the range, the lower the probability that a particular radar signal will be reflected, so the automatic-detection threshold has to be set lower.

Typically, automatic detection uses a Radar-Video Processor (RVP) to turn analog radar data into digital data suitable for a computer. The RVP generally provides only a static position. However, modern coherent radars can also measure a target's radial velocity by analyzing the doppler shift in the radar echo; in principle, these data, too, can be recovered for computer analysis. In the end, the object is to determine the target's track, either by associating successive echoes or by combining this association with doppler data. Radars or systems that combine detection and tracking are denoted ADT, automatic detection and tracking; detection alone is ATD, automatic target detection.

The effect of converting raw radar video into target position (i.e., into processed video) is to make the outputs of dissimilar radars compatible. Their data can then be entered into and summarized by a single track-keeping computer. Moreover, if these data are precise enough, they can feed directly into weapons-assignment and -control devices. The NTDS, for example, typically connects with a Weapons Designation System (WDS).

Tactical data systems of this type are limited by computer capacity. The maximum number of separate track files a computer can process is determined by its word length, since each file must be designated by a computer word. Thus an 8-bit computer has an 8-bit word, and the maximum number of distinct words of this type is 256 (each bit is 0 or 1, and 256 is 2 raised to the 8th power). This limit will be familiar to users of home computers. A 16-bit computer has a potential limit of 65,536 files. However, it may be a functional replacement for an earlier 8-bit machine. Software production is so serious a problem that the more powerful machine may be designed to use programs written for the simpler machine. In that case the 16-bit machine may not be able to go beyond the 256-file limit inherent in the earlier device. These considerations explain why tactical data systems are so often described as limited to 128 (7 bits) or 256 tracks.

These figures are entirely independent of the overall size of the computer's memory, the maximum size of which is determined in part by word length (for example, an 8-bit machine is limited to 64K bytes). A computer's memory limits the complexity of the programs the machine can apply to the tracks in its file, and also the complexity of data in each track file itself. A computer's speed, of course, determines how well the computer system can respond to a rapidly changing tactical situation.

Automation can be difficult. When most modern weapons and sensor systems were designed, there was no national or international standard for their operation. Thus a casual review of current computers and weapons reveals a wide variety of operating-clock speeds and even of word lengths (16, 24, and 32 bits are all quite common). Linking together such dissimilar equipment is by no means a trivial exercise. For example, one of the United States' early fully computerized nuclear cruisers went to sea on its first trials and discovered that its entire weapons system could not function because of software (data-handling) problems. The lesson learned was that combat systems had to be duplicated ashore, and software tested and modified until it could indeed make disparate elements of the system work together properly. This problem will persist for many years because the existing equipment, including the crucial analog-to-digital converters that permit weapons and sensors to communicate with computers, was developed at different times and for different purposes. This question of compatibility is just the problem faced by the buyers of personal computers who try to use items from different manufacturers. The different pieces are intended to be, but cannot always be entirely, compatible.

The second very important postwar development in internal ships' systems was the data bus. Initially the individual elements of each system were wired together, and data generally transferred from system to system by hand or voice. For example, a World War II–era CIC had a series of radar displays, each wired to a specific radar. Men at the displays called out contacts to be plotted in the summary plot used for decision making, e.g., for fighter control. There was, then, no physical connection between a search radar, a plot, and a radar used to track targets for fighter control. When systems were automated, the links between individual radars and the central computers were still specialized, and ships had to be rewired when equipment was changed.

Specialized links were required because the amount of data a single link could carry within a ship was limited. However, as links with much greater capacity have become available, it has become possible to feed all the data from the sensors, for example, into a common bus from which computers can strip what they need. Ultimately, the use of data buses has two consequences. One is that computers and display consoles can be added or subtracted from a system without rewiring, since each is linked only to the common bus. A second is that weight and space can be saved, since each console and each computer does not need a separate data cable. Instead, each is plugged into a common bus, just as each is plugged into a common electric-power grid. The success or failure of such systems depends on the carrying capacity of the bus, and it can be argued that some systems, like some in the U.S. Navy, do not use buses because the available buses have insufficient capacity.

There is a basic architectural question: to what extent must the combat system be centralized if it is to make the appropriate decisions in a timely manner? A central computer that processes all raw data will generally be slower to react than a central computer whose data processing is done mostly by smaller computers closer to the weapons and sensors. It can also be argued that the more the processing is distributed through a ship, the less vulnerable that ship is to localized damage. Systems employing distributed preprocessing of data are generally termed federated.

In a typical fully distributed system, there is no centralized computer at all. Instead, each weapon and each sensor have an associated processor that feeds into (or draws from) a data bus, which in turn carries a common data base giving target and track data (as divorced, for example, from the raw video from which the data are derived). This data bus can also accept information from external sources. Decisions are made at a series of command consoles (e.g., AAW, ASW, ASUW), which take data from the sensor bus and feed into a command bus. Sensing and command data may actually share the same data bus. Typically, the data base is duplicated within each console and updated when any sensor provides new information. The alternative, having a single, central data base, is generally rejected because the consoles would have to refer to it too frequently.

Because the full data base is replicated in all the consoles of the system, a commander looking at, say, the ASW picture can switch his console to show other aspects of the full picture, instead of having to move to another display. Moreover, because each console holds the full picture, the data base is not lost with the loss or shutdown of any one console.

Data busing is already quite common in Western businesses' computer systems, which link individual processors to Local Area Networks (LANs). A bus-linked combat data system is analogous to an LAN and its work stations, plus, perhaps, a powerful central computer or minicomputer. Of current interest is the extent to which systems developed for specialized naval computers should be able to interface with off-the-shelf commercial equipment.

A great deal depends on the topology of the data bus, which may be in the form of a ring or a star or may be linear. In a standard ring or linear system, the failure of any one element in the system generally causes the entire system to fail; it can be resurrected only after the failed element has been disconnected or fixed. That arrangement limits the system's ability to tolerate combat damage. A star arrangement can tolerate the failure of any element except the key element at the center of the system. All of these arrangements are associated with software systems that allow the different devices on the bus to enter their data without interference. The main alternatives are to use a master scheduler, which determines which device is entering its data, or to use a "token-passing" protocol, in which a particular device transmits as long as it has priority, then passes priority to the next device. Token-passing generally requires a ring topology. The other major consideration is whether the system as a whole replicates its data base in many places, or whether the system uses a single master device for data-base storage, other devices (such as fire-control consoles) requesting data as needed.

The best-known Western data bus is MIL-STD-1553B, which was defined in 1978 (1553A dates from 1975). It is a single twisted-cable pair carrying data in 16-bit words (with a parity-checking bit and two synchronization pulses) at up to 50K words/sec (800 k bits/sec) at a frequency of 1 MHz. The maximum length of the cables is 100 m, and a terminal can carry up to 32 stubs (input/output points), one of which is allocated to a bus controller; the bus controller keeps signals from different systems separate. It is rare for the cables to approach the maximum length or for the terminal to have all 31 stubs. The 1553B bus is standard on board many NATO aircraft, where it is used to control underwing stores.

In British service, MIL-STD-1553B is called DEF STAN 00-18.

The standard French system is DIGIBUS (Dassault), which is related to the Bus Standard Marine of the French Navy. DIGIBUS operates at 1 MHz and has a 40K-words/sec capacity (16-bit words).

Signaal has developed a 10-Mbits/sec system, which can use up to four triaxial cables in parallel. It is based on a commercial Ethernet LAN. Signaal has suggested that military buses may actually be less demanding than their civilian counterparts because the devices connected to military buses have much more predictable bus loadings. Perhaps many current civilian LANs can easily be militarized.

The newest British official system is DEF STAN 00-19, previously known as ASH or the ASWE (Admiralty Surface Weapons Establishment) Serial Highway. At present it is limited to British surface warships. The transfer rate is 1.5 Mbits/sec (16-bit words), using a screened single twisted-cable pair. Up to 63 computers can be accommodated in a total length of 300 m.

Racal offers a naval version of PLANET (Private Local Area Network), which can communicate both voice and digital data. The data interchange rate is 19.2 kbits/sec (normally 9.6 kbits/sec). The company, however, claims that PLANET easily carries digitized voice data at 64 kbits/sec.

The newest U.S. system is USQ-82, the Shipboard Data Multiplex System (SDMS), which can use up to five buses in parallel. FMC has produced UDICON, which is rated at 10 Mbits/sec using a single twisted-cable pair.

The most likely future data bus technologies are fiber-optic cables, which are already in widespread use ashore in telephone networks, and microwave waveguides.

The systems described here are general-purpose and found on board surface ships. Pure AAW combat systems and pure submarine combat systems are described, respectively, in the AAW and ASW chapters.

SURVEILLANCE/CONTROL

Surveillance Systems

USSR

◆ SOSS

Soviet Ocean Surveillance System is the generic Western name for the integrated system the Soviets use to detect, track, and target Western ships. SOSS is a natural outgrowth of the Soviet coast-defense system built up from before World War II. A combination of intelligence and passive sensors (originally, primarily HF/DF) detect ships approaching Soviet waters, and active sensors (mainly aircraft radars) are used as a follow-up for targeting. The passive sensors are supplemented by human agents (HUMINT or human intelligence), by intelligence-gathering ships (AGIs) operating near Western bases, and by warships (tattletales) that often trail Western naval formations. In recent years, SOSS has been supplemented by both passive and active satellites, but the principle of operation remains the same.

SOSS is designed to detect and target ships approaching the Soviet Union, rather than to protect a moving Soviet naval formation from the approach of hostile ships or aircraft. The system, therefore, feeds a central naval command-authority, which in turn directs Soviet ships, aircraft, and missiles to intercept the approaching enemy force. The home-defense, rather than the formation-defense, role of SOSS is probably reflected in its criterion for target detection. Since there is considerable sea space beyond Soviet frontiers, the system can afford a low probability of detection on a day-by-day basis. In contrast, a surveillance system protecting a moving naval force cannot afford leaks.

Before the advent of satellites, SOSS's direction-finders were mainly land-based. The Soviets now operate both passive (EORSAT, Electronic Ocean Reconnaissance Satellites) and active radar (RORSAT, Radar Ocean Reconnaissance Satellites) satellites, which should, in theory, represent a global capability. However, the EORSATs still almost certainly report only to the central naval command in the Soviet Union. The RORSATs can link down to attacking units, but they are not the primary search sensors of the system.

For example, a carrier's transit from a U.S. base to a forward area would probably first be detected by a human source in or near the U.S. base. The carrier would be seen as it left its base by an offshore AGI and might be picked up by an offshore submarine tattletale, although the Soviets do not have enough fast submarines to use as regular tattletales. The next detection would be of the carrier's electronic emissions, picked up either by a shore-based HF/DF station or, perhaps, by an ESM satellite. This detection would necessarily be passive; any active sensor would be overloaded with data because there are just too many ships at sea at any one time. However, once the passive sensors had reduced the area of interest to the one around the carrier, it would be worthwhile to send out reconnaissance aircraft to confirm the carrier's position, course, and speed and, if necessary, to provide targeting data. Once the carrier was located, it could be trailed by a tattletale. The latter's mission would be not so much to confirm the carrier's movements as to confirm which ship within the battle group was the high-value target; the Soviets would view the others as missile absorbers.

Once the tattletale had joined, an attack could be mounted, using either a radar-equipped reconnaissance airplane followed by ASM-armed bombers, or a Bear-D providing over-the-horizon data to a submarine or surface ship, or a RORSAT in a similar role.

The Soviets captured the German Wullenweber HF/DF systems at the end of World War II and about 1952 began producing a Soviet version, KRUG, an array about 115 yards in diameter, consisting of 120 equally spaced monopole antennas. Direction finding accuracy is reportedly about 1 degree, over a range of 6 to 20 MHz. The HF array was later supplemented by an inner concentric ring of monopoles that extended coverage into the VHF range.

The Soviets reportedly also use a somewhat less accurate land-based HF/DF antenna, Fix-24, consisting of 24 monopoles located at 15-degree intervals around a 150-meter circle.

Since HF/DF is used by all the Soviet services, it is not clear from the unclassified literature to what extent, if any, particular networks are intended primarily for naval purposes. Because the Soviets take service unification seriously, through their unified General Staff (and its specialized intelligence branch, the GRU), one might speculate that there is no particular net reserved for the navy, but rather that the unified GRU net filters naval data down to naval headquarters. However, each of the four Soviet fleets reportedly has its own SIGINT (signal intelligence) collection site(s). Presumably, the GRU can also draw on HF/DF sites abroad, in Soviet client states.

UNITED STATES

◆ ACS

Afloat Correlation System is an automated system that assembles off-board surveillance data for the battle group and composite warfare commanders. ACS feeds the TFCC (see entry below) and uses data from OSIS (see entry below), TADIXS B, and tracks generated within the ship's combat direction system (ACDS, see entry under tactical systems, below). ACS also provides battle-group track data back to OSIS to help ensure that the larger system carries the same tracks as the fleet at sea. That input helps solve the ocean-wide gridlock problem and helps avoid wasting scarce resources.

TADIXS, the tactical information exchange data system, is a one-way satellite link transmitting ocean surveillance information from the FCC (see entry below) to operational units at sea.

ACS might be considered the operational outgrowth of the Outlaw Shark/Outlaw Hawk programs described below under the TFCC.

◆ OSIS

Ocean Surveillance Information System (OSIS) is the combination of all the U.S. Navy's existing operational intelligence systems, joined to support tactical operations. Although tactical support might seem to be an obvious idea, in fact until the mid-1970s most intelligence was collected and disseminated for strategic purposes such as war-warning and for analysis. In the late 1970s, the information began to be exploited for tactical purposes, under a program called TENCAP (Tactical Exploitation of National [Intelligence-Gathering] Capabilities). Examples included Outlaw Hawk (1974–75) and Outlaw Shark (1975–76), which collected and collated intelligence-grade data to provide the commander of a ship (in these cases, respectively, the carrier *Kitty Hawk* and a submarine) with a reasonably complete picture of naval activity around him, beyond the immediate range of his sensors.

The object of Outlaw Shark was to provide a useful means of targeting long-range over-the-horizon antiship missiles, such as Tomahawk. The flow of operational intelligence between FOSIF Rota and the carrier *John F. Kennedy* was tapped at Naples, and edited material sent to the submarine via a special data link. Because timeliness was important, the intelligence data was sent event by event rather than by the usual scheduled broadcast, and the messages themselves were streamlined accordingly. Some arrived only six minutes later than the events they described, an important advantage for a missile, like Tomahawk, with a finite seeker-window.

OSIS represented a conscious choice to exploit existing sources of data (designed for quite different purposes) rather than to develop entirely new surveillance systems, such as the Soviet-style active-radar satellites. The choice was logical because U.S. naval requirements could not justify full and continuous surveillance of the surface of the seas, but the fleet needed information about enemy warships in its vicinity, particularly to use long-range antiship missiles effectively. The strength of OSIS is the ability to maintain large volumes of data at the analysis (data-processing) nodes and to transmit information quickly and securely. The system was initially constructed in the 1970s, and late in 1982 TRW was given a contract for an OSIS baseline upgrade.

OSIS assets include a ground HF/DF system, Bulls Eye (and a shipboard adjunct, Classic Outboard), EP-3 aircraft, and the White Cloud satellite described below, as well as SOSUS and its adjuncts (described below).

OSIS employs six major sites: the Naval Ocean Surveillance Information Center (NOSIC) at Suitland, Maryland; three Fleet Ocean Surveillance Information Centers (FOSICs) at the CINCLANTFLT, CINCPACFLT, and CINCUSNAVEUR headquarters (Norfolk, Pearl Harbor, and London); and two Fleet Ocean Surveillance Information Facilities (FOSIFs) at Rota, Spain, and at Kamiseye, Japan, to support the two forward-deployed fleets. OSIS collects surveillance data from the variety of naval and national intelligence systems and correlated these data to provide a picture of all naval movements at sea.

OSIS is being updated through an OSIS Operational Baseline Upgrade (OBU), which is being installed in the FOSICs and FOS-IFs. The object of OBU is to improve OSIS's timeliness to nearly real time (to 95-percent accuracy) without heavy investment in new sensors, by updating the OSIS data base with each satellite pass and each new sensor reading. Given the degree of noise in existing data, this goal is probably somewhat unrealistic.

◆ FCC

Flag Command Center is the shore station of the commander of the Atlantic or Pacific Fleet. In theory, FCC is his wartime battle station. The FCC communicates directly with the TFCC on board the flagship of a deployed battle group and receives data from the national World Wide Military Command and Control System (WMCCS) and from national-level elements of the Navy Command and Control System (NCCS), such as OSIS. An FCC includes a special decision area arranged to display all-source intelligence information, with desks for intelligence and operations officers. The CNO approved development of an automated Integrated Information Display (IID) for FCCs in 1981, to replace the mass of wall charts, maps, viewgraphs, and plots currently used. In theory, the FCC performs the same role as a ship's CIC, though on a much grander scale, integrating available sensor data obtained both throughout the navy and by national means (TENCAP).

In wartime the FCCs would also control some national ASW forces via ASWOCs (ASW Operations Centers), and submarines through the fleet SUBOPCONCENs (Submarine Operational Control Centers).

FCCs are being provided for the two fleet commanders, at Norfolk and at Pearl Harbor. In theory, the commander of the Atlantic Fleet has two operational subordinates, commanders of the Second and Sixth Fleets (the former based in Norfolk); commander of the Pacific Fleet has the Third and Seventh Fleets. However, the situation is rather more complex. The commander of the Atlantic Fleet is also the commander of the Second Fleet, and in wartime he would transform Second Fleet into the main component of the NATO Striking Force Atlantic. Similar arrangements presumably apply in the Pacific.

In each case, the fleet commander, going from a strategic to an operational role, would have to decide whether to try to command from the shore. Opinions on this point have been very mixed, individual admirals feeling very strongly either for or against command from on shore. For example, as commander, Atlantic Fleet, Admiral H. C. Mustin argued that in wartime long-haul communications (on which the FCC concept depends) would not be reliable; he expected to ride into battle on board one of the carriers of his battle force.

The issue of FCC viability is tied to the question of whether the United States will build battle-force capable flagships for the four numbered fleets. It might be argued, for example, that in wartime such a fleet might include up to four carriers, and that coordination of their hundreds of aircraft might require a substantial data-handling capacity outside the carriers themselves. The earlier flagships were retired because their cruiser hulls wore out, and there was insufficient money at the time (late 1960s and early 1970s) for replacements.

◆ TFCC

Tactical Flag Command Center, developed by Lockheed Electronics, supports a battle-group commander and his composite warfare commanders, providing them with relevant material, developed by the U.S. Navy's world-wide intelligence systems, on a timely basis. Ideally, TFCC should provide a commander with the location, speed, and identification of all forces within any potential battle space around him. Thus, TFCC's capacity (and the related capacity of OSIS) should, in theory, increase with increases in a potential enemy's speed and numbers. The alternative is to provide the battle group itself with more integral assets, such as long-range electronic-surveillance aircraft.

The system operates by maintaining a current data base, the computerized FDDS (Flag Data Display System), which provides easy and secure access. The data base in turn must be supported by secure communications from the global OSIS intelligence system (see above). FDDS is designated USQ-88(V).

TFCC has a lengthy history. It was inspired by a Grumman study of command requirements (1968–72, for NEL [Naval Electronics Laboratory], San Diego). The then Naval Electronic Systems Command prepared RFPs (Requests for Proposal) in 1972–73, formulating the TFCC concept: ocean surveillance information would be provided to the fleet from a fusion center on shore. An interim TFCC was demonstrated on board the carrier *John F. Kennedy* in 1975–76 (see the discussion of Outlaw Hawk and Outlaw Shark under OSIS, above). Development was slow, partly because senior officers could not agree on standardized operating procedures, partly because funds for command-and-control developments were very limited, and partly because system requirements expanded suddenly from one command team (battle-group commander) to four (commander plus three composite warfare commanders). Martin-Marietta won the design competition in 1975–76 and built a prototype. However, the program was too expensive, and the contract was canceled in 1978.

In August 1979, the Chief of Naval Operations, Admiral Hayward, broke the project into three increments: (1) preparation of TFCC spaces, using existing equipment; (2) installation of the special command-and-control displays; (3) enhancements. The development cycle was accelerated in March 1980 when a ruggedized version of the Outlaw Shark terminal, USQ-81(V), was chosen as the baseline. Three were temporarily installed to gain operational experience, on board the carriers *Midway* (June 1980) and *America* (January 1981) and the cruiser *Josephus Daniels* (February 1981). The carriers operated in the Indian Ocean with their interim TFCCs, and the cruiser tested procedures for over-the-horizon targeting. *America* called her TFCC-equipped CIC a Combat Direction System (CDS) and established a supporting plot (SupPlot), an intelligence fusion center manned 24-hours-a-day by intelligence personnel, that had some ability to look up emitter data for passive identification. SupPlot sanitized intelligence data for tactical use.

TFCC had to be supported by a special high-information-density radio-net, designated the OTC (Officer in Tactical Command) Information Exchange Channel (OTCIXC). The fleet's normal radio broadcast net carried 75 baud data; OTCIXC carried 2400. A second special net carried sensitive intelligence data.

The product of all of these data was displayed on a large-screen plot, which might show an area out to 1500 nm. Such a display was, moreover, more and more valuable as speeds increased and the battle space enlarged. For example, an attack had to be identified as much as 450 nm away if fighters were to be vectored to intercept at about 200 nm.

In January 1981, the CNO decided to buy six systems (three for each coast), after limited operational experience, for the carriers *America* (completed 15 May 1983), *Constellation* (completed 15 July 1983), *Nimitz* (completed 15 September 1983),

Midway (completed 15 October 1983), *Ranger* (completed 15 February 1984), and *John F. Kennedy*. All would have large-screen displays. At that time Increment 1 included special intelligence capability, a 20 × 20 foot TFCC space, NTDS, a dead-reckoning tracer (DRT), voice communications, a central console, and dedicated plots. Increment 2 included the Lockheed FDDS to correlate off-board and organic (battle group–generated) tactical data. Note the need for high-capacity communications, because the TFCC itself could not maintain the data base of the overall system. That data base had to be stored elsewhere (OSIS).

By 1983, TFCC was planned for 15 carriers, four *Belknap* class cruisers, the *Long Beach,* and, if possible, the two amphibious flagships, a total of 20 or 22 ships. This figure was later reduced to 18 flagships (15 carriers, the *Belknap,* and 2 amphibious flagships).

With six Increment 1s ready to install, the question in 1984 was whether to extend the system immediately to the remaining sixteen ships or to redesign it to use the new UYK-43/44 computers. Apparently the choice was to install TFCC Increment 1 during carrier SLEP (Service-Life Extension Program) modernizations. Some problems were encountered in operational tests. The first Increment 2 (FDDS) installation, on board the carrier *America,* was scheduled for 1988.

TFCC uses the Afloat Correlation System (ACS), an automatic information-management system, to integrate the contact and threat warning-data received from sources outside the battle group with the group's organic data, for over-the-horizon combat. Both sensitive intelligence information (SCI) and normally classified information (GENSER) are fed into the TFCC, but only sanitized (GENSER) information is released to the Combat Direction Systems (CDS) of the battle group. ACS is to be installed in 1990–1996. The prototype uses the Prototype Ocean Surveillance Terminal (POST), which is now being integrated with the Electronic Warfare Coordinating Module (EWCM), for completion by the end of FY90.

Satellite Sensor Systems

USSR

◆ EORSATS

EORSATS is the generic designation for the Soviets' ESM Ocean-Reconnaissance Satellites, which presumably detect radar-frequency (line-of-sight) emissions from the sidelobes of surface ships' radars. The first of these passive naval satellites was Cosmos-651, launched in May 1974. It and its successors were launched into circular orbits at 65 degrees of inclination, maintaining a 93.3-minute orbital period.

In 1986 the Soviets launched the first of a new generation of EOR satellites, Cosmos-1735, described at the time (by U.S. officials) as the first new design in 15 years. It works in conjunction with Cosmos-1834, launched in the spring of 1987, which has a 259 × 250 mile orbit inclined at 65 degrees. Both orbits are unusually low, and together the two satellites provide coverage of every part of the world every three days, compared with every four days by earlier systems.

EOR satellites typically provide their data, probably not precise enough for targeting, to a central naval command, which then tasks Soviet naval forces to intercept and identify the contacts.

◆ RORSATS

Radar Ocean Reconnaissance Satellites, nuclear-powered, can supply data either to a central naval command-authority or directly to a submarine or surface ship. The submarine terminal uses the Punch Bowl antenna.

These satellites are normally launched in pairs in circular orbits 155 to 175 miles high (to maintain constant position relative to the targets) at an inclination of 65 degrees, the pair being 6 degrees apart for cooperative tracking. Each is about 14 m long and weighs about 4950 kg; power is supplied by a small 150-kW nuclear reactor (with 50 kg of U-235 fuel). Normally, the satellite is boosted into a very high orbit when its fuel has

been exhausted; but in two cases (Cosmos-954 in 1978 and again in 1988), boosting has failed, and the satellite has crashed to earth. Useful life is reportedly 60 to 80 days.

Reportedly, the radar is a side-looking type that uses a slot antenna in the side of the satellite and scans a swath about 400 to 500 km wide. The radar probably operates at relatively high frequency, since it is reportedly ineffective when the target area is obscured by bad weather.

The first operational RORSAT, Cosmos-198, was launched in December 1967, the first test vehicle having been launched in 1965. From 1967 to 1975, ten out of the twelve Soviet naval satellites launched were RORSATs; but since 1975, passive satellites have predominated. Even among the RORSATs, orbital lifetime was quite limited until 1972 — suggesting that the program was not entirely satisfactory. For example, a satellite launched in 1970 during the Jordanian crisis did not survive for a day in orbit, and another, during the Angolan War in 1975, lasted only one day. However, in 1972, average lifetimes as great as four months were observed. Both active and passive satellites supported the 1975 Soviet naval maneuvers. RORSAT launches were suspended in 1978 after the Cosmos-954 failure but resumed in April 1980.

UNITED STATES

◆ White Cloud

White Cloud is a passive ocean-surveillance satellite-system employing clusters of satellites and functioning as the overhead part of the Classic Wizard ocean-surveillance system. Each satellite is reportedly equipped with IR and mm-wave scanners and with receivers for intercepting radio transmissions. Each cluster of three satellites (plus a mother) orbits at an altitude of about 700 nm and can detect emissions from ships 2000 nm away. The cluster is used so that emitters can be located by interferometry, using the distance between the satellites as a baseline.

The first cluster was launched in 1976, and the fifth cluster was placed in orbit in June 1983.

White Cloud seems to have been conceived as an intercept system to detect and catalog Soviet emitters so that units equipped with tactical ESM devices could identify those emitters. The location capability was necessary to pair the emissions with particular Soviet platforms. However, this capability could also be turned around to track known Soviet platforms, under TENCAP and related programs.

This type of system should be able to detect even line-of-sight systems such as short-wave radars by picking up their sidelobes. Interferometry is limited in its precision; in the late 1970s, a program called Clipper Bow proposed to combine White Cloud with an active radar that could locate emitters more precisely. Congress killed Clipper Bow in 1980, ordering the navy to participate instead in similar air force and CIA projects (thus far unannounced).

It should be emphasized that no very limited constellation of satellites (such as White Cloud) can provide continuous coverage of the world's oceans. Instead, the partial coverage that can be obtained can be combined with other sources of information to give reasonably full information on the movements of ship-based emitters. Although the localization of targets is imprecise, the system is effective because of the limited speed of surface ships. No such system can be effective against fast-moving emitters such as aircraft. For these reasons, active radars are required to track Soviet naval bombers, and very large numbers of satellite radars would be required to provide solid coverage.

Surface Radar/ELINT (Electronics Intelligence) Systems

AUSTRALIA

◆ Jindalee

Jindalee is the Australian project, for sea and air surveillance, that consists of three over-the-horizon radars. Jindalee also monitors sea-state and wind direction and is currently being used to provide wind- and sea-state maps for the area north of Australia.

The name, meaning "bare bones," originally applied to an experimental over-the-horizon radar at Alice Springs. This experimental radar was conceived as the culmination of the earlier Project Geebung, which investigated HF propagation via the ionosphere, between Woomera and Broome. Since this type of propagation is the basic mechanism for over-the-horizon radar, project Geebung was, in effect, a feasibility study for such a system. In 1974, the study built Jindalee Stage A at Alice Springs; this system projected a single pencil beam toward Derby to obtain basic performance data, testing the reliability of ionospheric radar-propagation near Australia. The radar was able to detect, for example, civil aircraft at Singapore. Jindalee A became operational in 1978. Its success led to Stage B, at Alice Springs, in 1979. Two beams were steered within a quadrant looking northwestward. Stage B attained "minimum capability" (about 50 percent) in 1982, and this experimental program was completed at the end of 1985. Experimental targets included Mirage III, F-111, HS 748, and Pilatus Porter aircraft, as well as ships as small as patrol craft.

Target resolution is reportedly 20 to 40 km. Range may be as long as 4000 km. Propagation is normally off the F-layer of the ionosphere (about 350 km high), but range may be shorter when the E-layer (150 km high) is used, as is sometimes possible. Frequency is about 30 MHz, and transmitter power is about 400 kW. The frequency must be selected to avoid multipath (bouncing off more than one layer) propagation, and also to avoid interference (e.g., with the Milky Way, at about 20.5 MHz). One result of the early studies was the discovery that the ionosphere, at least over Australia, is substantially more stable than had previously been thought.

The Stage B transmitter was built at Harts Range, with the receiver located about 100 km away at Mount Everard, both north of Alice Springs. The transmitter consists of a large array of log-periodic antennas each about 30 m high, radiating over a cleared area covered with a reflecting wire-mesh mat. The receiver is 2.8 km long, consisting of 492 elements (each a twin in-line broad-band monopole). Beams are reportedly formed by a set of networks of cables cut to precise lengths. That characteristic presumably limits the extent to which the radar can shift frequencies, since the direction of a beam so formed depends on frequency (operation is equivalent to that of a frequency-scanned radar). The equipment was upgraded during 1986, and operations began in January 1987.

Jindalee reportedly incorporates special locally developed software for automatic detection and tracking. The main means of detecting aircraft is doppler; but other methods were developed for ships, and the Australians claim that the latter represent a major advance in over-the-horizon radar technology. Given Australia's reported exchanges with the United States, it may be presumed that these concepts are incorporated in the U.S. ROTHR (see below).

In July 1988, the Australian government announced that it planned to acquire four airborne-early-warning aircraft to fill the gaps in Jindalee's coverage. The probable implication is that Jindalee will provide early warning in a band about 3000 km distant and that the aircraft will track targets and manage the air battle at shorter ranges.

UNITED STATES

◆ ROTHR (TPS-71 [XN-1])

ROTHR is the Relocatable Over-The-Horizon Radar, a system built by Raytheon after that company defeated General Electric in a 1986 competition. ROTHR is intended primarily to provide a fleet commander with early warning of the approach of Soviet antiship bombers; ROTHRs are to be emplaced so that their beams sweep the likely paths along which the bombers may fly. It is clear that those paths may change with major shifts in the political situation. A fleet's surveillance assets should be able to shift with the fleet; ROTHR approaches that ideal by being

The ROTHR receiving array. (Raytheon)

relocatable over a period of weeks or months. ROTHR will also be able to detect ships. ROTHR was chosen as preferable to a much more expensive alternative, a system of radar satellites that would have provided continuous coverage of the entire globe.

Like other OTH radars, ROTHR operates by bouncing its HF beam off the ionosphere. Ionospheric conditions vary from place to place in the world. To be truly relocatable, therefore, ROTHR incorporates a quasi-vertical incidence (QVI) sounder and a radar-backscatter grounder for propagation management assessment (PMA), which provides automatic adjustments according to changing ionospheric conditions. Transmission is FMCW at an average power of about 200 kW, for a reported range of 1600 nm on ships and aircraft.

The system consists of three separate sites: a transmitter (about 1200 ft long) 50 to 100 nm from a receiver, and an Operations Control Center (OCC) at the receiver. The transmitter consists of a series of wires strung from short masts; the receiver is a double array of dipoles about 8500 ft long. Beams are formed digitally in the signal processor, roughly as sonar beams are formed digitally in a DIMUS sonar.

Full-scale tests began about April 1987. The receiver was located at the Naval Security Station at the North Carolina border, near the Dismal Swamp, and the transmitter was about 25 miles east of Richmond (Whitehouse, Virginia), i.e., 75 to 100 nm apart. About ten ROTHRs will be built, beginning with three under the FY88–89 budget. The test unit is emplaced at Amchitka, in the Aleutians; of the other three, one will go to Guam, one probably to Amchitka (each covers a 60-degree sector, so more than one can usefully be employed at a given site), and one to Virginia (for operational evaluation and training). The operational ROTHR at Amchitka entered service in 1989. Each ROTHR costs $65–85 million.

The Soviets have their own OTH radars (as does, for that matter, the U.S. Air Force); all these systems have been omitted because they are probably designed to track airborne traffic without reference to purely naval requirements. For example, if the waveforms are specially selected to track aircraft or missiles, such radars may be unable to detect ships or may tend to reject ships as valid targets because of doppler filtering.

Strategic Underwater Sensor Systems

UNITED STATES

◆ FDS

Fixed Distributed System is an alternative to, and possible successor of, SOSUS. The name implies the use of a large number of elementary detectors, fixed in place, as compared to the small number of big beam-formers used in SOSUS. It is presumed that FDS would employ individual reliable-acoustic-path (RAP) units, with an individual range on the order of 12 nm. Reportedly they would be linked with a shore station by fiber-optic cables.

Compared to SOSUS, FDS would cover a much smaller area, but with a much higher probability of detection. FDS would, therefore, be laid in a strategic strait or choke point.

FDS was announced in 1984. In 1989 the navy issued an RFP for the FDS shore station and information processor, to be awarded on a competitive basis.

◆ RDSS

Rapidly Deployable Surveillance System was an abortive means of extending SOSUS coverage to meet contingencies. It was an outgrowth of the early 1970s MSS (Moored Surveillance System) studies, which envisaged an air-dropped system forming a deep-water barrier that would last about six months. General Electric was selected as contractor in 1976, after which the project was redefined; the moored buoys would have DIFAR/VLAD features. As a result, the MSS project grew too expensive, and it was replaced by RDSS.

RDSS was begun in 1978, and full-scale engineering development was approved in July 1981. A contract was awarded to Sanders that August but was canceled in December 1984. RDSS was resurrected briefly but finally canceled in 1987. It was reported that RDSS could not deal with the new generation of very quiet Soviet submarines. RDSS was intended for deployment in areas of fleet operation, such as the Indian Ocean, where no permanent surveillance system had been established. The buoy was about the size of a Mk 46 torpedo and was moored to the bottom by an anchor containing the battery pack. The mooring line, which could be 20,000 ft long, carried a vertical-line array giving good medium range detection and having the capability of rejecting most shipping noise. Data would be stored by the buoy and retrieved on command by an airplane overhead.

At the U.S. Navy League show in March 1989, Honeywell displayed a sketch of an air-delivered bottom surveillance system, consisting of a string on upward-looking sensors. It appeared that the system would be monitored from the air. No

A possible configuration for a future RDSS-type surveillance array, as envisaged by Honeywell. The upward-looking sensors are all connected by cable (presumably fiber-optic) to an anchored data collection-and-transmission device. (Honeywell)

program name was associated with the sketch, and it was not clear whether it represented an internally funded project.

◆ SOSUS

This system of large fixed underwater-arrays has been in service since about 1955, increasing in extent and sophistication over time. SOSUS was apparently inspired by the discoveries, just after World War II, of the deep sound-channel and of the convergence-zone effect. SOSUS was originally suggested as a means of detecting submarine operating areas, so that coastal convoys could be rerouted. However, it was later discovered that, with appropriate signal processing, a system of SOSUS arrays could cover much of the North Atlantic and North Pacific Oceans and thus could be used to cue patrol aircraft. Only in the late 1960s did then–Secretary of Defense Robert S. McNamara explicitly connect SOSUS with the P-3 Orion program.

The role of long-range submarine-detection has changed over time. In the late 1950s, SOSUS was valued as a means of detecting Soviet strategic submarines that, it was assumed, would have to approach American waters in order to fire. Later, it was assumed that the Soviets would surge large numbers of submarines into the North Atlantic just before attacking Western Europe: SOSUS was, then, primarily a war-warning sensor. However, it was also a means of tracking attack submarines in the open ocean and, therefore, a means of cueing patrol aircraft to deal with them. SOSUS could provide at least an approximate picture of Soviet submarines' patrol areas and could, therefore, also be used as a guide for evasion, whether by convoys or by naval forces.

The overall effectiveness of the SOSUS/P-3 combination depends upon several connected factors: first, the probability of detection by SOSUS; then, the size of the areas in which SOSUS locates a submarine; finally, the ability of the P-3 to redetect the submarine within that area. SOSUS is a passive system, but it uses several arrays whose beams should cross to locate a contact within a limited area.

In the current system, raw data is initially processed by NAVFACs (Naval Facilities), which pass their products to Regional Evaluation Centers (RECs: one each for Atlantic and Pacific) and then to Main Evaluation Centers (MECs), which have access to information from other sources. In 1974, it was announced officially that there were 22 SOSUS arrays; there has been some speculation that this total includes only arrays off the coasts of the continental United States.

It now appears that SOSUS was the first application of the Lofar narrow-band signal-processing technique. The prototype array, at Eleuthera in the Bahamas, was about a thousand feet long and consisted of 40 hydrophones forming beams about 5 degrees wide. When the array was first built, about 1952, each beam had to be processed separately, and detection/classification took about five minutes. The beam could then be shifted to another bearing, using delay lines. At this time the goal was to achieve detections at 50 to 500 miles. It is clear that these specifications no longer even vaguely apply, but they indicate the likely improvements in SOSUS: beam preforming capabilities, so that all beams can be sampled simultaneously; larger arrays at greater depths, to make better use of propagation within the deep sound-channels and to achieve greater gain; and low-loss transmission lines, to send data back to the shore stations. Note that the original installation was designed to detect snorkelers: in 1952, such submarines were quite loud by current standards.

One improvement to SOSUS has been publicly described. In common with the airborne Lofar systems of the 1950s and 1960s, SOSUS used a time-compression (analog) method, Deltic, to build up the signatures the system recognized. That scheme was effective as long as the threat consisted of relatively noisy diesel submarines and then noisy first-generation nuclear submarines. However, the signatures of second-generation nuclear craft (Charlie, Victor, and Yankee classes) were more subtle. A Canadian company, Computing Devices of Canada (CDC), introduced digital acoustic analysis in the 1960s, applying fast Fourier transforms to extract spectra from sampled inputs. When the original FQQ-1 processor was replaced by a new FFT processor, SPEAR, it was reportedly possible to recognize the new signatures by analyzing their fine structure. CDC later provided recorders to supplement SPEAR analyzers, and these systems were reportedly installed throughout the U.S. and Canadian SOSUS system.

Lofar, i.e., detection by signature, allows different SOSUS stations to be sure that they are detecting the same submarine (so that they can cross beams to provide range as well as bearing). Moreover, given the signature of the submarine, an airplane using Lofar buoys should have a better chance of redetection, comparing the known signature to the received signal. This combination (SOSUS plus patrol aircraft) was first extensively tested during the Cuban Missile Crisis in 1962, proving spectacularly successful.

The viability of such long-range passive detectors has been called into question as submarines have become much quieter. The usual alternative has been a low-frequency active system. One, called LORAD, was tested in the late 1950s. It would have reached out to about five convergence zones (about 165 nm in mid-Atlantic), and a scaled-down transducer of this type was installed in the tanker *Mission Capistrano*. LORAD would have been deployed on board special mid-ocean pickets, probably converted Victory ships. Improved SOSUS apparently solved the problem. Note that LORAD was suggested at about the same time as the Julie active-passive sonobuoy system (see the ASW section of this book): Julie was abandoned in favor of a better passive detector, Jezebel (airborne Lofar).

A major SOSUS upgrade program was reportedly ordered in 1971, including sensors moved forward into the deep ocean basins. That move seems to reflect a belief that prospective Soviet silencing would reduce effective ranges. The projected deep-ocean sensor was SASS, the Suspended Array Subsystem, a tripod, six miles on a side, that supported a directional array in the deep sound-channel, in water 18,000 feet deep. SASS was never built (presumably improved signal processing and delays in Soviet silencing solved the problem).

About 1971, a Computer-Assisted Array Processing project was started, to deal with the mass of raw data provided by the big low-frequency arrays. SOSUS reportedly detected both the loss of the U.S. submarine *Scorpion* and the loss of the Soviet Golf-class submarine off Hawaii in 1968, but operators did not notice either (transient) event until the SOSUS tapes were reviewed later, after other indicators had shown that something had indeed happened. The implication is that the operators concentrated on particular spectral lines (as would be natural in a Lofar-based system), and that transients received little attention.

More recently, SOSUS's effectiveness has been called into question as the Soviets have built quieter submarines. One solution seems to be FDS (Fixed Distributed System), which would cover a smaller area more thoroughly. It is also possible that, in analogy to the active adjuncts proposed for towed arrays, active very-low-frequency pingers could be integrated with the existing passive SOSUS arrays.

SOSUS has two other major drawbacks, both connected with the sheer size and sophistication of the arrays. First, although the arrays' locations are classified, they probably have not changed very much over the three decades of the system's existence, and the Soviets presumably know most or all of them. The arrays have to be located in relatively quiet areas, so there will not be so much local shipping noise as to overwhelm the faint sounds of distant submarines. The arrays and their shore connections may, therefore, be relatively easy to sabotage or attack early in a war. Second, because SOSUS is fixed, it cannot support U.S. ASW operations in areas other than those for which it was laid down, i.e., in areas other than (probably) the North Atlantic and North Pacific. Like other fixed sensors, then, it cannot react to political surprises, such as crises in the Indian Ocean.

The solution to both problems is a portable equivalent of SOSUS. One such is SURTASS, the towed surveillance array (see below). Another, which did not succeed, was RDSS, an air-deployed surveillance system. The requirement for a system like RDSS would seem to persist, and some form of long-range battle-group sensor, such as an air-deployed/retrieved array, may eventually enter service.

Note that the designation SOSUS (Sound Surveillance System) has been applied both to a particular deep-water system and also to the full array of fixed detectors, including several technologies, that the United States and her allies possess.

♦ SURTASS (UQQ-2)

Surveillance Towed-Array System, using specially designed towing ships (T-AGOS) and a very long array, is a backup or gap filler for SOSUS. SURTASS replaces the six SQR-15 towed arrays deployed in the 1970s. Signals from the array are partially processed on board the towing ship, but most of the work is done at a shore station after the signals have been transmitted by satellite (DSCS) link. The ships are designed to steam 1500 nm to a patrol area, where they tow their arrays at 3 kts. The arrays are 8575 ft long, towed at a depth of 500–1500 ft; the tow cable is reportedly 6000 ft long.

A total of 24 to 26 SURTASS ships is planned.

In June 1988, it was reported that the U.S. Navy was considering an active adjunct system, in which a big SWATH (reportedly of 5000 tons) would carry a very large very-low-frequency active transducer and would tow an array as a receiver. The Navy bought some British ATAS active towed arrays from British Aerospace in November 1987, "for evaluation purposes in the development of new active sonar systems," which might mean as a scale model of the projected SURTASS active system.

An indication of the trend in surveillance array technology is shown by a comparison between early, 1980s, and future arrays, done in 1985 by Whitehall, which is responsible for UQQ-2.

Date	Diameter	Length (ft)	Channels
Early	1.75 in	2500	8
Current (1980s)	3–3.5 in	15,000	250–500
Future	Smaller	–	1000 +

TACTICAL COMMUNICATIONS SYSTEMS

Radio Systems

Long-haul naval communications may be by low frequency (LF, using a ground wave, up to 300 kHz) or by medium/high frequency (MF/HF, up to 30 MHz, using a combination of ground waves and sky waves bounced off the ionosphere). Higher frequencies are inherently limited to line of sight, although most antennas are not directional. One important potential exception is bridge-to-bridge communications between two ships in contact. Such communications would be highly directional, and the antennas used might be the sort otherwise used for surface search or navigational purposes, outwardly indistinguishable from the radars' antennas. All navies use a combination of MF/HF and shorter-wave, higher-frequency communications, and only a few systems can be listed here. UHF is generally used for ship-to-aircraft and aircraft-to-aircraft, and for short-range ship-to-ship (line of sight). UHF and higher frequencies are generally used for satellite up-links.

Perhaps the most important recent development is the increasing interest in antijam and anti-intercept communications, focusing largely on frequency-hopping. Another effort is the attempt to overcome the vagaries of the ionosphere, which is affected by, among other things, the 11-year solar cycle. For HF radio, these two developments are linked because the appropriate transmission frequency depends on ionospheric conditions. In the past, finding the appropriate frequency and making contact was sufficiently laborious that frequency-hopping was inconceivable. Now the radio can automatically repeat the usual manual steps, and it can often achieve a connection in as little as 10 seconds. The logical extension of automatic connection is automatic frequency-hopping, typically 10 to 20 hops per second (less than 7 milliseconds per hop). Hopping is unlikely to be fast enough to frustrate interception (hence, HF/DF will remain), since the existing wide-open intercept systems will probably pick up even very short snippets of message. However, hopping can frustrate jamming, since it takes some time for an enemy to retune his jammer from one bit of message to the next.

Examples of modern HF systems are the French SPIN and the British ASSAT (Advanced Ship-to-Shore Automatic Telegraph). SPIN emphasizes ECM resistance by frequency-hopping; ASSAT seems more oriented towards reliable long-haul transmissions. In ASSAT, the shore station transmits a standard message for several seconds on each available frequency, and the shipboard receiver measures the signal-to-noise ratio for each and calculates the best frequency to use; this evaluation continues throughout the transmission. ASSAT is currently being tested.

Another approach is to use the ionization from meteor bursts: meteors leave trails of ions that reflect electromagnetic energy, and there are always, it seems, enough meteors to provide sufficient (if intermittent) communications paths. Because the paths are intermittent, messages may be broken up, and they must, therefore, be quite redundant; the redundancy can be achieved by modern computer-coding techniques. The frequency band is usually 40–50 MHz, although 20–120 MHz can be used. Thus far, meteor burst has only been used for land communications, but it has obvious naval application.

FRANCE

♦ Syracuse

This system employs repeaters (7-8 GHz) in the two French Telecom 1 satellites reserved for military, primarily naval, use, under an agreement made in 1980. The two repeaters are horn antennas; the civilian antennas are dishes (14/12 GHz for French industry and for video transmission, covering France, and 6/8 GHz for telephone and television traffic between France and some overseas territories; there are also two 40-MHz repeater channels). Ground coverage extends from the West Indies to the Reunion Islands.

The associated naval system uses a pair of 1.5-m stabilized antennas in radomes, located so that one will always have a clear line of sight to the satellite. The antennas track either using preprogrammed satellite data or homing on the satellite's beacon. The terminals are interchangeable; about twenty ships are, or will be, fitted with terminals.

The two satellites will last until about 1992. The follow-on, Syracuse II, may be either another add-on to a future civilian satellite or a dedicated satellite.

INTERNATIONAL

♦ NATO Satellites

There is a family of NATO communications satellites (Phases I, II, III) covering the northern hemisphere. NATO III has a maritime role. Both the satellites and their ground stations are managed by Ford Aerospace. The program was conceived in 1965–67; and in 1988 NATO had 22 fixed ground terminals, one mobile terminal, and two active satellites in orbit. As formally proposed in 1966, the program consisted of three Phases: I, for experiments and training; II, for reliable voice and code communications among the NATO countries' military and political headquarters; and III, for much of the capacity of the NATO Integrated Communications System (NICS), with access by mobile users. SATCOM III was one of the first all-digital communications satellites.

NATO IIIA, IIIB, and IIIC were placed in geostationary orbit over the North Atlantic in 1976–78; and NATO IIID was added as an in-orbit spare in November 1984, partly because the Phase IV characteristics had not yet been determined. Nine new Phase III terminals have been built, and twelve Phase II terminals modernized to Phase III standards. These satellites operate at 7–8 GHz and are compatible with the U.S. DSCS and with the British Skynet 4 systems. Each satellite operates two beams simultaneously: one for North America, one for Western Europe.

Skynet 4 has now been selected for Phase IV, with the first launch scheduled for 1990.

♦ NATO Data Links

These digital links were originally developed by the United States, but they are now used throughout NATO and thus are best listed as an international standard.

Link 1 — Data link within NADGE (NATO Air Defense Ground Environment) radar chain. It is comparable to, but not compatible with, Link 11. In 1978, the U.S. Marine Corps obtained an interface, MANTA, to pass Link 1 data into its own tactical data system, which uses Link-11 formats for air information. The U.S. designation is TADIL B.

Link 4 — Data link for controlling aircraft, used between airborne controllers and fighter aircraft and also between carriers and their aircraft, replacing voice radio. The current U.S. version is Link 4A, and the U.S. designation is TADIL C. This link is not encrypted, nor is it jam-resistant.

Link 10 — British tactical digital data link, equivalent to (but not compatible with) Link 11. This system is built by Ferranti and probably corresponds to the Digital Plot Transmission (DPT) conceived as part of the original British naval tactical data system, CDS (Comprehensive Display System). CDS preceded ADA, which in turn preceded ADAWS (see below under tactical data systems). Link 10 is used by the Belgian, Dutch, and Royal Navies. As of 1978, HMS *Bristol* was unique in her ability to pass data from Link 11 into a Link 10 format. The three British aircraft carriers, which are also command-and-control ships, presumably have a similar capability. Link 10 is subject to NATO STANAG 5510. Operating range is reportedly 150 to 180 nm.

Both Links 10 and 11 use about 3 kHz of bandwidth, and both use ground-wave propagation to avoid errors due to multipath sky-wave effects. Link 10 operates at up to 1200 bits/sec, using frequency-shift keying. The system structure as a whole is based on a series of computer-allocated time slots, and each station is allocated a number of slots based on projected needs.

Link 11 — Digital encrypted HF or UHF link for the U.S. Navy Tactical Data System. This link is TADIL A (Tactical Data Link A) in U.S. terminology. Compared to Link 10, Link 11 carries three times the data per target and requires about four times the dedicated computing power. Link 11 is subject to NATO STANAG 5511.

System architecture is based on a roll-call mode, with each station being called in turn and transmitting data into the network. One designated station controls the entire network. The Link 11/NTDS network operates with very short time delays between transmissions by different stations; the end of one message signals the next transmitter to start. The transmitter sends a series of synchronizing pulses then starts sending data. One technical problem in the early versions of the system was that the receiver of the unit that had just transmitted could not start up quickly enough to receive the synchronizing pulses of the next transmission. Because time delays would be so destructive, it is not possible to transmit Link 11 data through a satellite. Even a distance such as that between Rome and Brussels is reportedly too great, in terms of the resulting time delay.

Link 11 uses both the upper and lower sidebands of the radio signal to achieve a degree of diversity; and in the ground-wave mode, the system can reach a range of about 300 nm. Data is transmitted at 1364 or 2250 bits/sec, using frequency-shift keying. Phase is also used to add data-modulation.

The current Link Eleven Model Five (LEMF) improvement program adds new waveforms and protocols and is intended to be jam-resistant in HF. A full-scale engineering-development contract for the Link 11 Improvement Program was let in 1987.

The Royal Navy has a receive-only Link Eleven (ROLE) in some ships. As of 1987, the U.S. Navy was developing its own receive-only Link 11 to enable Aegis ships to control the firing of missiles by non-Aegis ships. Techeval/opeval was scheduled for completion in June 1988.

Besides the long-range HF, there is a line-of-sight UHF Link 11 for use between nearby ships and AEW aircraft (E-2Cs and some E-3A AWACS).

Link 14 — Teleprinter data link between ships not equipped with NTDS.

Link 16 — Link associated with JTIDS, the U.S. Joint Tactical Information Distribution System; it is also called TADIL J. This is the planned replacement for all existing U.S. airborne high-capacity data links. Since the system entails the transmission of common synchronizing pulses, and since the time of arrival of messages can be precisely measured, JTIDS is also, in effect, a tactical navigational system (pulses can be used to measure distance). In theory, JTIDS will also provide highly reliable identifications.

JTIDS operates in Lx-band (960 to 1215 MHz), hopping frequency randomly over a bandwidth of several hundred MHz on a pulse-to-pulse basis. A JTIDS net is defined by a particular sequence of hopped frequencies. Subscribers in the net are assigned transmission slots within the 12.8-minute cycle; each slot is 7.8125 msec (1/128 second) long, so that the cycle contains 98,304 slots. One subscriber is the designated time reference, responsible for maintaining the timing of the net. Within each slot, every other message pulse is redundant, so that messages can be reconstructed even if they are badly jammed. There is also a jitter period at the beginning of each slot, so the actual beginning of the transmission of data varies. The data rate can be doubled (at a price in terms of ECCM), first by eliminating the redundant data (packed-2 structure), and then again by eliminating the jitter (packed-4 structure). This scheme is described as Time Division Multiple Access (TDMA).

The navy developed a higher-capacity system, Distributed TDMA (DTDMA), which permits the operation of several concurrent independent nets (6, 8, or 16; only 1 with TDMA). The navy argued that operating multiple nets was essential because a fleet must operate simultaneously in several dimensions, and each composite warfare commander (AAW, ASW, ASUW) needs his own net. The air force developed the single-net system because it generally operated in a more centralized way. In 1985, faced with the high cost of developing two parallel systems, Congress mandated the choice of a single triservice system, and the navy cancelled DTDMA in favor of the existing air force-army TDMA system. This form of JTIDS is also being adopted by some NATO allies.

JTIDS line-of-sight range is about 300 nm, a figure probably limited by the time of transmission (which must be allowed for in the slot's length: 300 nm equates to about 1.6 msec); it can be extended to 500 nm. From a user's point of view, JTIDS provides all subscribers with a common tactical picture, much as NTDS does.

Link 16 is intended to replace Link 4A and to complement (but not replace) Link 11. It is included in both the E-2C update plan and the F-14D program.

Links W, X, and Y — European proprietary data links, used, e.g., for shipboard helicopters.

USSR

◆ Molniya

The Molniya satellites in high elliptical orbits cover the northern latitudes. They have been launched since 1965: Molniya 1, 33 satellites; Molniya 2, 15 satellites, from 1971; and Molniya 3, 4 satellites, from 1974. Orbital period is about 12 hours, with perigees of about 500 km in the southern hemisphere and apogees of about 40,000 km in the north. The arrangement was

Before the advent of reliable satellite communications, the Soviets relied heavily on HF radio. Fleet flagships are provided with characteristic vee-shaped antennas; the command cruiser *Zhdanov* shows Vee Cone on her new mainmast. (U.S. Naval Institute)

The command cruiser *Zhdanov* shows two Big Ball satellite communications antennas just abaft the after funnel. (U.S. Navy)

initially 120 degrees apart (so that three satellites could cover the Soviet Union for nine hours each day); but Molniya 2 and 3 were 90 degrees apart, and Molniya 1 satellites were moved to positions between the Molniya 2 and 3 satellites in 1976. Molniya 1 is UHF; Molniya 3 and later satellites operate in the SHF range.

The first synchronous satellite, Cosmos-637, was launched in 1974, and Molniya 1S was placed in synchronous equatorial orbit that year. It was followed by a series of about 11 Raduga/Gorizont satellites, operating in SHF. In 1980, the Soviets launched the first of their Volna geostationary communications satellites.

Note that the Soviet Union evidently employs numerous data links, e.g., that connecting a Bear-D with the submarine or surface ship for which the aircraft furnishes targeting data. However, apart from some identifications of the antennas involved, details have not been made public.

UNITED KINGDOM

◆ Skynet

Skynet is the British military/naval communications satellite system, begun in 1967 with the trials of the NEST ship terminal. Skynet 1 and 2 cover longitudes east from Britain to Australia. Skynet 2B was launched in 1974. The program's sponsor is the Royal Air Force, but the Royal Navy is the chief user.

The current version, Skynet 4, was first launched in 1986. It has 300 times the power of its predecessor and provides two UHF and four SHF channels, and beamwidths down to 3 degrees. There is also a single experimental EHF up-link.

The associated ship's terminal is SCOT, operating in the 7-to-8 GHz (SHF) band (chosen to avoid radar and cosmic interference). Frigates and destroyers use a SCOT 1 (1.1-meter dish); larger ships use SCOT 2 (1.8-meter dish). An enhanced SCOT 1A was ordered in 1984 for delivery beginning in 1986: it provides a 1.2-meter dish for both classes of ships and the equivalent of four secure-voice communications channels. Bandwidth is 500 MHz, compared to 50 MHz for SCOT 1; the 1A terminal can be tuned to any 50-MHz channel. All 17 remaining units of the original 21 SCOT 1 terminals are being brought up to SCOT 1A standards. The larger SCOT 2 terminals are also being modified for greater bandwidths. As of 1985, the Royal Netherlands Navy planned to buy SCOT terminals, and the U.S. Navy wanted eight of them as an alternative to its more expensive WSC-6. For example, USS *Enterprise* had SCOT antennas in 1986. The German Navy was also considering SCOT.

Note that SCOT is not far from the X-band missile-seeker and fire-control-radar frequencies, so that it may be necessary to shut down nearby ESM equipment when SCOT is in use. Reportedly, that interference contributed to the loss of HMS *Sheffield* in the Falklands. In the future these systems will move into the EHF band.

UNITED STATES

WSC-3 is the U.S. Navy's standard satellite-communications terminal. It is also the standard line-of-sight radio transmitter/receiver, in part because its modular design made modifications simpler. V(2) and V(3) were the original FLTSATCOM terminals. V(6) and V(7), the next to be produced in quantity, were line-of-sight radio terminals. V(8) was a coast guard radio, remotely controlled. V(9) was compatible with AFSATCOM's 5-kHz-channel spacing. V(10) and V(11) are Have-Quick upgrades of V(6) and V(7). V(12) is a V(2) adapted for Trident submarine use. V(13) operates from a 400-cycle power supply, and V(14) has an interface compatible with MIL-STD-1553. RT 1217

AS-3018A/WSC-1, the standard U.S. UHF satellite communications antenna. It is also used for a directional line-of-sight ship-to-air and ship-to-ship link, and many NATO navies use the antenna for that purpose. This one was photographed in 1988 on board HMS *Bristol.* The antenna is 54 inches in diameter. (A. Wetback)

is a line-of-sight WSC-3 for the Danish and Norwegian Navies. RT 1217-2 is the relevant Have-Quick version. RT 1244 adds a fast frequency-hopping synthesizer to the WSC-3 used by the Australian and New Zealand Navies.

◆ AFSATCOM

Air Force Satellite Communications system includes among its users the navy's TACAMO (strategic submarine control) aircraft. The other users are the air force strategic bombers (B-52 and B-1), the RC-135 reconnaissance aircraft, and the E-4B strategic command-and-control aircraft. AFSATCOM operates in UHF and can link to FLTSATCOM, DSCS III, and SDS (a satellite system linking the satellite command center in California with remote satellite ground terminals).

◆ AJACS

Antijam Advanced Communications System by E-Systems and Rockwell is offered as an alternative to Have Quick. AJACS is a frequency-hopping two-channel TDMA line-of-sight radio based on the WSC-3 satellite communications-antenna. With AJACS, a single radio can receive antijam communications in one time slot and retransmit in another.

◆ DSCS

RCA's Defense Satellite Communications System is the main high-volume system for the Defense Department and for diplomatic communications. DSCS serves users such as the fleet commanders, the National Command Authority, and the major U.S. defense agencies. MILSTAR should take over the strategic circuits, with DSCS remaining as the link between fixed tactical users.

Phase II, the current system, consists of four satellites in geostationary orbits plus two in-orbit spares, all built by TRW. Each has four transponder channels, and most of the terminals are fixed on land. Seven DSCS II satellites had been launched as of 1985; estimated service life was five years. All DSCS satellites have a small propulsion plant on board, so that they can be repositioned to meet contingencies.

DSCS III (General Electric) will consist of four active SHF (7–8 GHz) satellites and two in-orbit spares, each carrying a six-channel transponder (compared to one channel in AFSATCOM). There are four Earth-coverage horns (two transmitting, two receiving); a 61-beam waveguide lens receiving-antenna; two 19-beam waveguide lens transmitting-antennas; a gimballed dish-transmitter for selecting the area of coverage; and UHF transmit-and-receive antennas. These satellites should have higher power and, thanks to their movable beams, should be more difficult to jam. As of 1985, the planned total procurement was fourteen, with seven having been included in the Defense Department's explicit plans.

One DSCS satellite was procured in FY88 and two were scheduled for FY89.

◆ FLTSATCOM

FLTSATCOM is a UHF (244–400 MHz) fleet-communications system that provides worldwide high-priority communications between aircraft, ships, submarines, ground stations, the Strategic Air Command, and the National Command Authority. The system, managed by the Air Force System Command (Space Division), uses three-axis body-stabilized satellites in geosynchronous orbit. Each satellite has an 8-foot hexagonal body (50 in high), with an 18-turn-helical UHF receive-antenna and a 16-foot-parabolic UHF transmitter-antenna. The satellites are powered by two 7 × 13 ft solar panels, and they weight 4250 lbs (5100 lbs for satellites 7 and 8). Each supports more than 30 voice and 12 teletype channels or, alternatively, 23 high-capacity channels (one for fleet broadcast; nine (7 low- and 2 high-power) for navy relay; 12 (all low power) for air force narrowband; and one for DoD wide-band). Hydrazine engines are used to maintain stability and also to relocate the satellites as required.

The contract for the system's development was awarded to

TRW in November 1972, and the first launch was made on 9 February 1978. As of 1988, the four oldest (of a total of seven launched) have already exceeded their five-year design-lives. Satellite 5 was damaged during launch (6 August 1981) and thus could not perform satisfactorily. Satellite 7 was launched on 4 December 1986 (actually the sixth launch), but Satellite 6 (seventh flight) had to be destroyed soon after launch on 26 March 1987. An eighth satellite has not yet been launched, and satellites 7 and 8 incorporate an experimental EHF package as a prototype for future systems. Thus in 1988 five were operational, with four in use and a fifth designated as an in-orbit spare.

The navy issued a request for proposals for a UHF follow-on satellite in November 1987, and the contract was to be awarded in July 1988. The RFP called for a 39-channel capacity using demand-assigned-multiple-access (DAMA) technology; the satellites are to be fully compatible with FLTSAT and LEASAT, and they will use existing ground terminals (and hence will require one SHF up-link to supplement their UHF capability). As an example of this type of system, TRW's proposal called for three times the capacity (28 low- and 10 high-power navy relay, 40 high-power air force narrow-band, but no DoD wideband and no fleet broadcast channels) and twice the lifetime of the existing FLTSATCOM. It is presumed that this program is affected by the loss of launch capacity as a result of problems with the space shuttle and with the major launch boosters.

The Hughes HS-601 satellite was selected at the end of July 1988, six weeks after Australia had chosen that same design. The contract called for one satellite plus options on nine more; these satellites will replace both FLTSAT and LEASAT. The first should be launched in mid-1992, the second late in 1993, two in 1994, three in 1995, and three in 1996, either by shuttle or by expendable launcher. Each satellite will weigh about 2300 lbs (FLTSAT weighs about 2200) and will have double the capacity of the earlier vehicle: 21 narrow-band channels (5-kHz bandwidth), 17 relay channels (25-kHz bandwidth), and one fleet broadcast channel (25-kHz bandwidth). All but the fleet broadcast channel use UHF up- and down-links (the fleet channel uses SHF, 7–8 GHz).

◆ Have Quick

Have Quick was originally the air force's program, now adopted by the navy, for providing antijam communications, primarily by frequency-hopping across the radio net. The primary piece of hardware is the Have Quick A20 control module, which contains the processor, memory, signal interface, and controls. The air force's version applied to airborne ARC-164 UHF radios. The navy's contracts, awarded in 1981, applied to airborne ARC-182 radios and shipboard WSC-3s.

Under this program, the Navy has adopted the ARC-182 combination radio (low and high power VHF/FM, VHF/AM, UHF/FM, and UHF/AM) with frequency-hopping filters and broad-band antennas. The army's Single Channel Ground and Airborne Radio System (SINCGARS) will be adopted for shipboard use, with airborne UHF relay pods and VHF relay pallets ("poor man's satellites") for communications within the battle group (to limit intercept range). The pod uses four ARC-182s, two of them modified to carry Link 11. Development of the pod was completed during FY87.

◆ Leasat

The U.S. Navy leases some commercial satellites to fill gaps in national systems, e.g., to support operations in the Indian Ocean. Examples are the Comsat General Gap-filler (now obsolete), which provided limited UHF cover of much of the eastern hemisphere from 1976 on, and the Hughes Leasat, a four-satellite system (orbited 1984–85). Unlike military satellites, these commercial types almost certainly are not hardened against attack (e.g., against EMP). However, their use indicates the number of U.S. communications satellites that can be turned to military use in an emergency.

Leasat is to be replaced by Hughes's UHF Follow-On Satellite (see FLTSATCOM).

◆ Lightsat

Lightsat is the Defense Advanced Research Projects Agency's austere lightweight satellite, conceived as a wartime gap-filler and replacement for destroyed satellites. Lightsat would also be launchable from mobile facilities, since permanent satellite launchers might well be destroyed or disabled in wartime. As initially conceived, Lightsat would be launched by a booster about the size of a Pershing missile (70,000-lb class). The interim goal is to be able to put a 400-pound satellite into a 400-mile polar orbit, with an eventual goal of a 1500-lb payload in a 400- to 500-mile orbit, using a booster now called the standard small launch-vehicle (SSLV). There has been some speculation that Trident missile tubes might be used to launch lightweight communications satellites in wartime.

◆ Milstar

Milstar is the all-service U.S. military communications satellite system, to enter service in the 1990s. It is the first U.S. millimeter-wave (EHF) communications satellite system (44-GHz up-link, 20-GHz down-link), and the system is to have a minimum of seven operational satellites at any one time (at first there will be four synchronous satellites, one of them an in-orbit spare, with all four in inclined polar orbits). Milstar was considered important enough to receive overriding (Brick Bat) priority. The advantages of going to EHF include escape from the crowded lower-frequency bands, better resistance to ECM (because there are more frequencies and because beamwidths are very narrow), and reduced terminal size (or, for a given size, a narrower, and hence less easily intercepted, beam).

Lockheed was awarded the prime satellite contract in 1983.

◆ Satellite Information Exchange System

The U.S. Navy communications satellites carry a combination of fleet broadcast and other nets. The naval communications system as a whole employs a combination of HF radio and UHF/SHF satellite broadcast, plus automated facilities that assemble and retransmit the broadcasts. The chief nets supported by the satellite information exchange system are:

CUDIXS, the Common User Digital Information Exchange System, carrying general service (GENSER) messages to and from ships.

SSIXS, the Submarine Satellite Information Exchange System, carrying carrying the submarine broadcast messages in unformatted text, plus targeting information in formatted computer-readable standard message formats (RAINFORM formats).

OTCIXS, the Officer-in-Tactical-Command Information Exchange System, the battle group's command-and-control channel, carrying RAINFORM messages (at 2400 baud), teletype (75 baud), and narrow-band secure voice (2400 baud).

TACINTEL, the Tactical Intelligence Network, exchanging special intelligence data, using the USQ-64(V)5, and carrying both RAINFORM and unformatted messages.

TADIXS, the Tactical Digital Information Exchange System, a one-way satellite link, carrying ocean-surveillance data from the FCC to deployed forces.

Narrow-band secure-voice channel supporting the High Command Net, linking fleet commanders with battle group commanders. There is also a Fleet Tactical Net.

Submarine Communications Systems

A submarine's radio communications with surface ships and aircraft are inherently limited because seawater is a barrier to most signals. The primary communications choices for submarines are currently surface radio (HF and above), periscope-

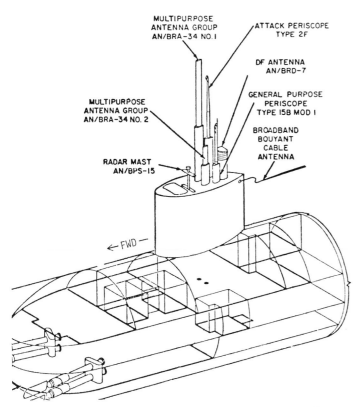

MULTIPURPOSE
ANTENNA GROUP
AN/BRA-34 NO.1

ATTACK PERISCOPE
TYPE 2F

DF ANTENNA
AN/BRD-7

GENERAL PURPOSE
PERISCOPE
TYPE 15B MOD 1

MULTIPURPOSE
ANTENNA GROUP
AN/BRA-34 NO. 2

BROADBAND
BOUYANT
CABLE
ANTENNA

RADAR MAST
AN/BPS-15

←FWD—

Typical U.S. submarine communications antennas, on board a *Los Angeles*-class submarine. The sail also carries WLR-9, an acoustic intercept receiver. This drawing does not show the ELF trailing-wire receiver now standard in attack submarines. (*Principles of Naval Weapons Systems*, vol. 3, Annapolis: Weapons Systems Engineering Dept., U.S. Naval Academy, 1979)

depth radio (LF and VLF), and ELF (extremely-low-frequency) radio. Conventional antennas can transmit signals down to VLF, although VLF antennas can be quite large. For example, the airborne VLF antennas used as back-ups for communicating with strategic submarines are several thousand feet long and must be trailed from a considerable altitude. The sheer sizes of LF and VLF antennas make it impossible for submarines to transmit at these frequencies; LF and VLF are usable only for communication to submarines.

Only ELF penetrates to great depths, but it requires very large land-based transmitters (which in turn require favorable geological conditions) and has a limited capacity for carrying information. Moreover, because ELF has so great a range, it is subject to jamming, intentional or otherwise, by other nations' ELF systems. The U.S. ELF system was originally conceived as a means of alerting strategic submarines, using transmitters so large and so redundant that they might well survive an initial nuclear attack. A test installation opened at Clam Lake, Wisconsin, in 1969; it was given a message handling capability in 1976, and functioned successfully through 1978. The project was opposed on political (nominally environmental) grounds, and it was cancelled by President Carter in 1978. It was revived, in limited (and vulnerable) form, by the Reagan Administration and is now in service. ELF has been extended to all U.S. submarines. The operating frequency is 76 Hz; wavelength is then about 2500 miles. The antenna at Clam Lake, Wisconsin, is 28 miles long, and the one on the upper peninsula of Michigan is 56 miles long. The current system became operational in 1987.

Submarines monitoring ELF broadcasts must trail a long neutrally buoyant wire antenna, but the submarine need not approach the surface. The first major submarine-ELF-receiver contract (with GTE) was announced in 1988, the receiver having been tested successfully in the Pacific Fleet in May 1985. A total of 137 (to equip attack as well as strategic submarines) are to be delivered in 1989–1992.

In mid-1987 the British announced that they were building

an ELF site in Scotland (Glen Gally Forest, near Fort William). A French ELF system, Astarte (with a transmitter at Rosnay), is to enter service in 1988–89.

The Soviet Union has the type of geology needed for ELF transmission; the basic idea is very well known, and the technology involved is not very complicated. In 1987 it was reported that the Soviets were building an ELF station.

Deeply penetrating land and waters, ELF is always receivable. It acts as a bell-ringer, informing a submarine commander that he must come near the surface to receive a more conventional message, e.g., by HF or satellite link.

Although an ELF transmitter, with its very long buried antenna, could in theory be hardened against nuclear attack, existing ELF systems are generally not so protected. For example, the U.S. system was initially conceived as a hard communications device, but only the soft demonstrators were actually built.

A submarine must put an antenna either through or very near the surface to receive all of the usual long-haul naval signals (HF or satellite-transmitted SHF, UHF, or EHF). For example, many submarines are equipped with buoys containing wrapped-wire HF antennas. Higher line-of-sight frequencies are useful either for air-to-submarine communications or for submarine-to-satellite communications. One advantage of very short wavelengths (such as SHF or EHF) is that the antennas can be so small that they can be housed atop periscopes.

At lower frequencies (VLF), radio waves can penetrate the water's surface down to 10–30 ft. Typically, reception requires either a wire loop (which may be in a towed buoy) or a towed linear floating antenna. Using a towed wire limits the submarine's depth, speed, and course. Moreover, any method of communicating requires the submarine to place an object near the surface, where the antenna is more visible and marks the submarine's position.

GTE, the supplier of current U.S. submarine strategic-communications equipment, has proposed a compromise radio system, SubTACS (Submarine Tactical Communications System), operating at low frequency (but not quite ELF frequency), with a higher data rate (about 15 words/min, 300 times that of ELF). Like ELF, SubTACS employs a trailing-wire (rather than a floating-wire) antenna, and the existing standard ELF receiver can be modified to accept SubTACS's signals. Effective range is 1000 + nm, and a submarine can listen at any speed and at keel depths of about 250 feet. These range and penetration figures are far beyond those of a conventional VLF (periscope-depth) system. Compared to ELF, SubTACS is a transportable system, requiring no special geological conditions; its antenna is an insulated 12-km-long antenna cable laid on the surface of the earth. That characteristic makes the system a candidate for the U.S. requirements for reconstitutable strategic communications (i.e., for systems that can be reassembled in the event of a nuclear attack). Alternatively, the transmitter and antenna can be adapted to installation on surface ships. Signals can penetrate sea water, ice, and also the earth itself.

SubTACS is a GTE private-venture (IR&D) program, begun late in 1987, with some U.S. Navy support. As of March 1989, the company hoped to conduct a demonstration experiment late in 1989 or early in 1990.

One alternative that has been proposed in recent years is the use of blue-green lasers. Such lasers penetrate to substantial depths (they were once proposed as antisubmarine sensors, but did not penetrate quite well enough for two-way use), and they can carry considerable amounts of information. Effective information transmission is limited, however, because the laser must scan its relatively narrow beam over the wide area in which a submarine may be located, repeating the message frequently enough for any submarine touched by the beam to receive all of the information. No operational blue-green-laser communications system currently exists, but the U.S. Navy and the U.S. Defense Advanced Research Projects Agency have been developing a suitable space-based laser, which was tested (in airborne-form) in 1987.

This test, called "Project Y," showed that clouds did not prevent transmission to a submarine at operational depth. The navy is also conducting "Project Lambda" (i.e., upside-down Y) to investigate laser-communications up-links from submarines, although it is difficult to imagine that such up-links could not be intercepted easily.

Plans for the U.S. Navy's laser-communications satellite, SLCSAT, were reportedly abandoned because of cuts in the FY89 budget. However, navy-funded SLCSAT studies have continued.

CANADA

♦ WQC-501

This new underwater telephone was first fitted in the modernized *Oberon* class (SOUP program). WQC-501 is manufactured by Safare-Crouzet, which makes the French TUUM-2. Transmission is omnidirectional, with a rated range of 20 km. This range can be reduced, for greater security, by reducing the power output. Operating modes are voice, key, transponder, and automatic transmission. The standard submarine outfit includes both an omnidirectional transducer and four directional transducers, plus a transducer-switching unit and a power amplifier. The frequency used is the NATO standard.

FRANCE

♦ ERUS-2A/B

The emergency underwater telephone, made by Safare-Crouzet, is for divers. It operates at high frequency (AM transmission), has a range of 800 to 1000 m, and is omnidirectional.

♦ ERUS-3

The emergency battery-powered submarine underwater telephone, made by Safare-Crouzet, operates on standard NATO frequency with a range of 6 km. This range can be reduced by reducing power.

♦ TUUM-2

The standard underwater telephone, made by Safare-Crouzet, has a range of 10 km (20 km with a 1-kW amplifier). The basic design operates at standard NATO frequency, but the unit can be modified to operate at alternative frequencies. Characteristics are similar to those of the WQC-501 (see above), but there is no transducer-switching unit. The customer decides whether he wants directional or omnidirectional transducers.

Strategic Communications The current command link for SSBNs uses the VLF (20 kHz) transmitters at Kerlouan and Rosnay, which were built specifically for the strategic submarine program. An airborne VLF system, Astarte (*Avion station relais de transmissions exceptionelles*), analogous to the U.S. TACAMO, is based on four Transall aircraft. Astarte is being developed and was scheduled to enter service in 1988–89. It will be hardened against EMP.

ITALY

♦ TS-200/TS-510

These underwater telephones operate at NATO standard frequency (8.3–11.1 kHz), with a single sideband and CW transmission. TS-200 has two modes: omnidirectional (vertical beamwidth of 90 deg), and directional (about 28 degrees of vertical beamwidth).

TS-510 is a smaller omnidirectional unit with a smaller transducer.

USSR

♦ Whale Tongue

Whale Tongue is the standard Soviet acoustic-communications device, used for submarine-submarine and submarine-surface ship communications. Whale Tongue is fitted to all destroyers and larger surface combatants and to all Soviet submarines.

A Victor-I-class submarine displays her Park Lamp antenna (open loops on the aftermost mast). Although possibly usable for direction-finding, Park Lamp is almost certainly primarily a VLF receiver, usable at periscope depth, analogous to the U.S. Navy's loop antennas (originally radio direction-finders) of World War II. (U.S. Naval Institute)

For many years, the Soviets have been credited with superior, and probably covert, means of coordinating their submarines and surface ships. The Soviet style of naval command-and-control requires considerable direction from above and would demand an effective system for communicating with submarines. At the same time, because the Soviets tend to use stereotyped tactics, they might be able to tolerate a very low information rate, or a very limited repertoire of messages, so that developing a satisfactory secure and covert underwater communications system would be easier. The U.S. Navy appears to have been far less successful in this endeavor, perhaps because the more flexible U.S. tactics require much greater information exchange.

Radio Links Submarines currently rely on VLF. The standard mast-mounted VLF/LF receiving-antenna is Park Lamp (which is often described as an ECM or navigational antenna). In addition, strategic and some tactical missile-submarines (Charlie-II, Oscar) tow buoys, which are often carried in prominent housings. Of the new classes of attack submarines, Akula seems to be unique in towing a communications buoy. Victor-III, Akula, and Sierra all have a prominent housing atop the tail fin, probably for a towed communications-array (although some have argued that the housing contains a towed acoustic-array). The same array may be associated with the pipe emerging from the top of the tail fin of the Oscar, Delta-IV, and Typhoon-class strategic submarines. Many submarines (including all strategic submarines) also have satellite antennas (Pert Spring). Subma-

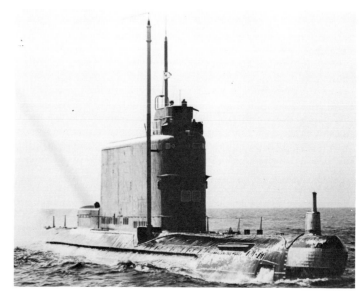

A Golf-II-class ballistic-missile submarine shows her communications-buoy housing, abaft her sail. The tall sonar dome forward is an underwater telephone. (U.S. Navy)

A Typhoon missile submarine displays two of her communications systems: two buoys under doors and a towed antenna (which is deployed through the pipe atop her tail fin). (U.S. Department of Defense)

rines operating the SS-N-12 and SS-N-19 missiles have been equipped with a radar satellite down-link antenna (Punch Bowl).

Bear-J aircraft function as strategic communications links analogous to the U.S. TACAMO. These aircraft entered service in 1985.

UNITED KINGDOM

Underwater telephones are listed under sonars; no details are available.

UNITED STATES

◆ BRC-6 (XSTAT)

The Expendable Submarine Tactical Transceiver, a two-way expendable buoy for UHF communication between a submarine and an airplane, is produced by Sippican. XSTAT is launched from a submarine signal ejector. After launching, a lifting body separates from the buoy, remaining attached to the submarine (and, therefore, to the terminal) by a 40-foot tether cable. Very fine wire (0.008-inch diameter, up to 10,000 ft long) unreels from the flying body, maintaining a connection to the rising buoy. When the buoy reaches the surface, it deploys an antenna for two-way radio voice communication. The buoy normally receives; it is placed in a transmit mode by keying the microphone on the submarine. The antenna itself is a quarter-wave ground-plane with four radials. It feeds from a battery useful for 45 minutes, but the life of the system is really controlled by the length of fine wire, which unreels as the submarine steams away from the nearly stationary buoy. Typically the wire lasts for 8 minutes at 10 knots, or for 20 minutes at 4 knots.

This form of operation contrasts with that of the air-launched communications buoys described below, which are essentially transponders, converting a submarine's acoustic signals into radio signals for air transmission, and vice versa.

◆ SLOT (AN/BRT-1)

Sippican's submarine-launched one-way transmitter, a buoy launched through the submarine's signal ejector, carries a 4-minute tape-recorded message (either voice or CW) and a radio transmitter. The message is recorded using a BRM-2 test set and can be checked by playing back through the buoy transmitter. SLOT can be set to delay transmission either by 5 minutes or by one hour, giving the launching submarine time to clear the datum created by the buoy. The buoy can function in sea-states up to 5, and it rises at 2 m/sec. Transmission is by VHF (on a sonobuoy frequency), and an aircraft or surface ship can com-

mand the buoy to turn off by using a UHF signal. The buoy then floats until sunk by its scuttle timing unit; selectable lifetime is 1, 3, or 8 hours. Dimensions are 3 × 39.12 inches, and weight is 7.25 lbs.

BRT-2 is a SLOT buoy manufactured by Electrospace.

◆ BRT-6

Hazeltine's one-way UHF satellite communications system for submarines, consisting of a buoy launched from a standard 3-inch signal ejector, carries a tape-recorded message and is usable up through sea-state 5. The satellite channel can be preselected (between 290 and 315 MHz in 25-MHz increments). Data are transmitted digitally into the SSIXS system, and 1–15 transmissions can be made. The buoy is normally preset for 2400 bits/sec; alternatively, 75, 300, 600, 1200, 4800, or 9600 bits/sec can be selected. As with BRT-1, a message transmission delay can be selected (in this case in 5-minute increments), with output selectable between 25 and 100 watts. The buoy scuttles within 30 minutes after its final transmission. Dimensions are 7.6 × 103.1 cm, and weight is 4.4 kg.

This device was technically evaluated on board USS *Baltimore* and operationally evaluated on board USS *Sea Horse*; approval for full production (AFP) was granted in 1983.

There is also a Hazeltine submarine-launched one-way satellite relay UHFSATCOM buoy (BRT-6). Work on a tethered two-way UHFSATCOM buoy, comparable in concept to XSTAT (BRC-6), began under the FY89 program.

◆ OUTPOST

This Sippican-developed two-way communications buoy uses a 20-km fiber-optic link in place of the fine wire of BRT-1. OUTPOST is now in advanced development at NUSC New London.

◆ SLATE

This submarine-launched UHF expendable transceiver buoy is launched through a 3-inch signal ejector and connected to the submarine by a fine wire. SLATE is presumably an earlier alternative to BRC-6.

◆ SSQ-71

The air-dropped two-way air-submarine acoustic-communications buoy (ATAC) can be tuned to one of 3 radio channels. It is in current production. This "A"-size buoy weighs 25 lbs.

◆ SSQ-86

This "A"-size communications buoy (25 lbs) is tunable to one of 99 RF channels.

◆ SUS

Sound Underwater Signal is a small device dropped by an airplane to send signals to a submarine. For example, SUS can indicate an emergency, telling the submarine to stay down; ask an unknown submarine to surface for visual identification; or act as a bell-ringer, asking the submarine to establish radio communications. The current version is the Sippican Mk 84 Mod 1, replacing the earlier Mk 64. Note that an earlier version of SUS was the sound source in the Julie explosive echo-ranging system (see the ASW section).

Mk 84 can be launched at 100–10,000 ft, at speeds of 30–380 kts. It sinks at 14.5 ft/sec, spin-stabilized by its canted tail fins. The signal, which lasts 45–128 seconds, consists of two tones (3.5 and 2.95 kHz), coded by pulsing for either 0.5 or 1.5 sec. The tones may alternate at two different pulse lengths, for four signals, or the SUS can transmit steadily at 3.5 kHz, for a fifth signal. The signal's source level is 160 dB. The desired signal is selected before launch by using a switch on the side of the SUS. Dimensions: 3 in × 15 in (6.5 lbs).

◆ TACAMO

The national command link to strategic submarines is currently operating on board the EC-130G/Q aircraft; but the TACAMO's electronics are being transferred to the E-6As because they are hardened against EMP (electromagnetic pulse). The communications suite is designated USC-13; it receives over the VLF-to-UHF range and transmits in VLF, using a dual (long and short) trailing antenna. Messages are received from the navy's shore bases and from airborne national command posts (ABNCPs), via satellite and other emergency radio links.

The long trailing antenna is half the wavelength of the transmission; the short antenna, which is the active one, is trailed at a length tuned to that of the long reflector. About 35,000 ft of long and 5,000 of short antenna are available, but typically the long antenna is unreeled to a length of 16,000 to 20,000 ft. The signal is vertically polarized and can penetrate the sea's surface. Transmitting frequencies are 14–30 kHz.

The term TACAMO derives from the order to a submarine commander to "Take charge and move out."

◆ WQC-2A

The underwater telephone operates at 1.45–3.1 and 8.3–11.1 kHz, with an auxiliary mode of 100 Hz to 13 kHz. The low-frequency range is used for long-range communications at a relatively low data rate; the high-frequency range is effective at shorter range and has a higher data rate (i.e., is less garbled). Power output is 600 W at low frequency, 450 W at high frequency, in each case at the center of the band.

A variety of attempts to develop a covert, encrypted underwater-communications link, dating back at least to the early 1960s, has apparently failed, as have attempts to develop underwater forms of IFF.

TACTICAL DATA SYSTEMS

CANADA

◆ Shinpads

Shipboard Integrated Processing and Display System was developed as the result of a 1974 study of alternative architectures for combat systems. SHINPADS was one of the earliest fully distributed (data bus) systems, chosen because digital equipment was no longer so expensive that all processing had to be concentrated in a single central computer. All users have access to the entire data base, and consoles are interchangeable (for graceful degradation in case of damage or breakdown). The data bus itself was designed to be transparent to standard NATO interfaces; thus, existing equipment could be connected to the bus.

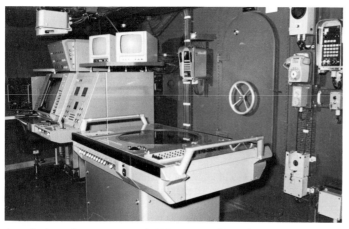

A typical, modern, automated CIC in a small combatant. The vertical console in the background is fed by a sensor (or connected to a weapon). The console in turn is connected to the horizontal summary display in the foreground. The captain or executive officer can use this display to see the tactical picture and to assign weapons to targets. Note the trackball toward the front of the display: such communication is almost completely electronic, targets being entered by ball and keyboard. (CMN)

Distribution is on three levels: by location throughout the ship (for survivability), by function, and by control. All of the minicomputers of the system can be applied to any one role, e.g., to processing an array's data. The only difference between, e.g., a fire-control computer and an engine-control computer is the software that they are executing. All of the computers are UYK-20s.

The data bus is designed to accommodate up to 256 users, with a maximum length of 300 m. Up to 16 users can be given priority access, if their functions are particularly time-critical. For example, fire-control equipment requires updated information about every 50 milliseconds (i.e., about twenty times per second). That rate can be achieved because the average user's access time is less than 100 microseconds. An analysis of typical frigate requirements showed that the data bus would have to pass at least 3 million bits/sec, and the design capacity is over twice that rate [actually 8 million bits/sec (10 MHz clock rate)] to prevent delays. The standard message may have as many as 254 16-bit words, although a special block mode allows much longer messages to be sent.

The bus uses a pair of triaxial cables but is compatible with a future upgrade to fiber optics. One to four additional bus cables can be added for redundancy, to ensure survivability. Any two of the cables can then be selected as the operating or primary bus. Bus control can be assigned to any node (user interface); if the control node fails, another can replace it.

Messages are sent broadcast, i.e., through the entire data bus, and addressed so that each user can pick off its own messages. Messages intended for several users do not, therefore, have to be retransmitted. There is also a point-to-point signal mode, in which a message is sent to a specific user.

◆ CCS-280

CCS-280 is the *Tribal* (DDH 280) class's command-and-control system, now being superseded as the ships are rebuilt. These ships were intended as squadron flagships and as such can send and receive Link 11 messages as well as Link 14. CCS-280 is built around a single Litton USQ-501 (L-304F) computer, connected to seven multifunction situation-display consoles (SDC) in the operations room (CIC), connected in series, i.e., sharing the same data base held by the main computer. One console is used for command; the others can shift in role from situation to situation. Typically one is used for air and one for surface detection and tracking. One might be used to control the ship's helicopter; others might be used for target evaluation, intercept direction, weapons coordination, and engagement monitoring. There are separate dedicated consoles for sonar (feeding the ASW computer), for fire control (feeding a fire-control computer, for the 5-inch gun and the Sea Sparrow missiles), and for electronic warfare (feeding a data processor). Link 11 also feeds directly into CCS-280, as do the main navigational sensors (gyro and log). The 32-bit computer has a capacity of 40K words (expandable to 80K), and the displays can show objects at ranges of up to 152 nm. This system was one of the earliest applications of fault-isolation software.

The consoles show both raw and synthetic video. Operators communicate with the consoles via light pen, keyboard, and track ball. Tracking is manual with update (i.e., rate-aided), and the system can handle surface-target speeds of up to 64 kts and air-target altitudes up to 64,000 ft. CCS-280 can store up to 237 tracks (of which 50 may be targets). Like NTDS, CCS-280 conducts threat evaluation and weapon assignment and also directs interceptions (in this case by both aircraft and the assigned ASW helicopter). The system can also display alternative tactical options.

CCS-280, then, is a small-ship NTDS equivalent, roughly contemporary with the German SATIR. The Canadian Navy described CCS-280 as the first operational micro-electronic tactical data system for shipboard situation assessment and control. CCS-280 is probably the end result of a Canadian program for a small-ship tactical data system, DATAR, which was conducted in parallel with the U.S. NTDS and the British ADA/ADAWS. The Canadian system was projected for installation on board a class of eight projected ASW destroyers, announced in 1960 but canceled in 1963. However, this basic design became the basis of the *Tribal* class, work on which began in 1965.

CCS-280 was installed on board the two *Annapolis*-class frigates as part of their DELEX (Destroyer Life Extension) modernization.

◆ ADLIPS

Automatic Data Link Plotting System, a "poor man's NTDS," was developed as part of the Canadian DELEX (Destroyer Life Extension) program. Like NTDS, ADLIPS integrates shipboard sensors and provides both Link 11 and Link 14 capability. Until ADLIPS had been installed, only the four *Tribal*-class destroyers had Link 11 capability. Thus the older ships could not rapidly exchange ASW data, nor could these ships fully integrate with the *Tribals*. The ADLIPS contract was awarded to Litton of Canada.

Like NTDS, ADLIPS displays both raw radar data and synthetic video, including data received over Links 11 and 14; it also replaces existing obsolete electro-mechanical plotting tables (such as dead-reckoning tracers). ADLIPS was developed using only existing components, which had to be integrated with the existing sensors.

The central computer is the standard U.S. UYK-20(V) minicomputer, rather than the UYK-7 used in contemporary versions of NTDS. The key system decisions seem to have been to minimize the actual computing load (e.g., in target evaluation), and also to distribute that load (e.g., to rely on the existing computerized electronic warfare and ASW systems. The only weapons directly controlled by the UYK-20 are the gun and any missile the ship might carry (the ships involved carry only ASROC).

Link 14 data is entered directly (which is unusual in NTDS systems) through a special interface. There is an analog-to-digital converter for radar, log/gyro, and sonar data (the converter transmits data to the gun), and the UYK-20 connects directly to the Canadian ASW Data System (ASWDS), where that system has been installed. A similar computer-to-computer channel connects the ship's EW system with ADLIPS. Finally, Link 11 and other encrypted digital data links feed directly into the computer via a modem and a decrypter.

The UYK-20 in turn feeds a variety of displays, including two plasma displays (for synthetic video, in the EW room and on the bridge), a plotter, and two 20-inch horizontal CRTs (in situation information displays, SIDs) each of which communicates with the UYK-20 via three sets of keyboards and trackballs. Each of the three positions at an SID is also provided with quick-action buttons to inject data and instructions. The CRTs can also be fed directly with raw radar video.

ADLIPS can process and display up to 140 objects (100 moving, 40 static), plus track histories (6 positions each) for 25 targets and velocity vectors for up to 100 tracks. As in NTDS, the operators at the consoles detect the targets, so that each SID can insert three targets into the system simultaneously.

The Canadian government hoped that other navies would find ADLIPS an attractive way of modernizing pre-NTDS combat systems, but no foreign sales seem to have materialized. The Canadian Navy bought a total of nineteen systems, three for its Fleet School and 16 for installation in the *St. Laurent* (two SIDs, two plasma displays), Modified *Restigouche* (two SIDs, two plasma displays), *Mackenzie* (one SID, two plasma displays), and *Annapolis* (two SIDs, two plasma displays) classes. Installation required only about ten weeks.

DENMARK

◆ StanFlex 300 System

Standard Flexible 300 is the first combat information system designed specifically for rapid reconfiguration. StanFlex 300 consists of three standard two-position multipurpose consoles (each including its own ruggedized commercial-type VLSI computer) on a data bus that also connects the consoles to modular weapons and sensors. The latter can be replaced, using only dockyard cranes, in 24 hours, and the system reconfigured by software substitution. Up to three additional consoles can be added to control additional weapons or other systems. All weapons control is centralized in the Operations Room (there is no local control at all in a classical sense). This type of operation requires very high computing capacity at each machine; the Danish Navy states that the total computing capacity of a StanFlex is 30,000 times that of the first Danish small-ship system, which entered service as recently as 1978. A fiber-optic data bus was considered and tested, but instead a conventional 10-Mbit/sec shielded cable has been used. The bus is duplicated to ensure its reliability.

It was originally expected that the machinery would be monitored and controlled from the single data bus, so that the ship could operate with an unmanned engine room. The full integration of machinery with the command-and-control system proved too difficult, and instead the machinery forms a separate subsystem that feeds into the main data bus.

The StanFlex program began as a feasibility study in 1982; project definition followed in 1983, and funds for seven ships were approved in 1984. The first ship, *Flyvefisken*, was delivered in December 1988. The number "300" is the nominal displacement of the ship (actual displacement depends upon which weapons and sensors are installed at any one time). The Royal Danish Navy hopes to fit a similar system to a frigate-sized ship. As an indication of the degree of flexibility built into StanFlex, the same ships are intended to function as missile- or torpedo-armed fast attack craft and also as minehunters, roles that in the past have been absolutely incompatible. In this case, mine-hunting is possible only because the ship can deploy and control remotely operated vehicles, such as the Swedish SAM and the German Troika, and submersibles comparable to the German Pinguin. The towed minehunting sonar is likely to be an adapted U.S. AQS-14, which has proven successful in trials in the Baltic.

Terma was responsible for the basic system, which employs a Swedish (PEAB 9LV200 Mk 3) fire-control system.

FRANCE

◆ SENIT

The standard French naval tactical information system, *Système d'Exploitation Naval des Informations Tactiques*, is equivalent to the U.S. NTDS. SENIT was conceived as part of the *Suffren*-class *corvette* design in 1962, and development began the following year.

SENIT 1, with three computers, is on board *Suffren*, her sister *Duquesne*, and the cruiser *Colbert*, for fleet air defense. All of these ships are armed with Masurca area-defense missiles. SENIT includes a video extractor for the three-dimensional DRBI-23 radar for automatic tracking, and a digital link to Masurca. The version for the flagship *Colbert* established a data link with other SENIT-equipped ships.

Developed in cooperation with the West German Navy, SENIT 2 is found on board the two carriers and the *Kersaint*-class destroyers (and in *Duperre*, which has a two-computer version). SENIT 2 has one computer but two versions: one version was for the air defense of a naval force, and the other was for radar-picket contributions to the French national air defense system (information fed by teletype to the STRIDA system). SENIT 2 was installed on board eight destroyers: three modified radar pickets (*Surcouf* T53 class), four destroyers fitted with the Tartar antiaircraft missile (*Surcouf* T47 class), and the ASW-destroyer *Duperre*. The Tartar refit included replacement of analog fire-control computers with digital units adapted to SENIT. The Tartar ships had three computers.

Clemenceau was fitted with the SENIT 2 system taken from the inactivated destroyer *Jaurreguibery* during a September 1977–November 1978 refit. *Foch* was fitted with the SENIT 2 system of the inactivated destroyer *Tartu* during a July 1980–December 1981 refit. SENIT 2 was also planned for the helicopter carrier *Jeanne d'Arc*, but by 1987 this project had been dropped.

SENIT 3, using two computers with memory extensions, is in the destroyer *Aconit* and in the three *Tourville*-class vessels. This system was designed primarily for ASW but could also handle the tactical air situation and the air defense of the ship. There are eight tactical consoles, which correspond to the various sensors; weapons are controlled from separate consoles, and there is a computer-driven plotting table. This system, which uses two Univac 1230 computers, is on board the *Aconit* and the F67 (*Tourville*)-class. The 1230 is a 30-bit computer (capacity 32K words) with a 1.0-MHz clock rate.

SENIT 1, 2, and 3 were built with U.S. equipment (Univac computers and Hughes displays, the latter built under license by Thomson-CSF). Each version is built around a single central processor.

SENIT 4 is a large-ship version that uses French equipment, conceived by the French Navy's programming center and built around the Iris 55M computer (256 to 512K capacity) and the new Vizir display. Iris 55M is a 16-bit machine (32-Kbyte capacity) with a 1.0-MHz clock rate. There are ten consoles, each of which can display 130 tracks. SENIT 4 is in the *Georges Leygues* class of ASW frigates. SENIT 4 was planned for the carriers, but SENIT 2 was installed instead (see above).

SENIT 5, announced in 1976 (developed in 1975), is intended for ships of about 2000–6000 tons, with long-range air-search radars; it can also fit a fast patrol boat that controls a whole formation. The computer was initially to have been IRIS 35M (16 to 256K), with five Vizir consoles (using two sensors). Each console could carry 40 tracks. The system was later described as capable of carrying up to 60 target tracks simultaneously and passing this data to weapons controllers. It can also communicate with other SENIT platforms using Link 11. This system was planned for the Type A-69 avisos (*D'Estienne d'Orves* class), but apparently it was not installed.

Unlike earlier SENITs, SENIT 5 uses multiple computers in a network, and the basic machine is the 64K CII 15M. There is also an automatic radar-plot extractor.

SENIT 6 equips the *Cassard* (Type C70AA) frigates. It uses the 15M/125X microprocessor (1 Mbyte of memory, speed 1 Megaflop). There are twelve one-man consoles and one two-man console. All of the operators' consoles and tactical plotting positions are linked (via the display bus) to a single central display computer, which carries the tactical picture and which is linked to the system bus that is connected to the weapons and the sensors. Much of the processing for each weapon and sensor is done locally, outside the system bus. Each of the two buses has an autonomous bus controller to supervise its operation, and there is also a simulation bus for training.

◆ SISC

Système d'Integration du Système de Combat was developed for the new *Charles de Gaulle*–class carrier. It is presumed that SISC corresponds to TAVITAC 2000 (see below).

◆ TAVITAC

Traitement Automatique et Visualisation Tactique, a Thomson-CSF (Thomsea) modular action-information system, is also known as Vega IIIC. Its 15M/125F-processor (128K, expandable to 512K) is also used in SENIT; one version of TAVITAC is the export version of SENIT 6. Existing systems for frigates include up to five displays (16–32 target tracks each, air or surface), and each system has a built-in simulator for training. Tracking is automatic, using radar-video processors (with manual or automatic track initiation), but targets can also be tracked manually (rate-aided). The system makes provision for non-NATO data links. The extended version, equivalent to large-ship SENIT, can engage targets automatically. TAVITAC can be built in a

A TAVITAC command-and-control console with random-scan CRT. (Thomson-CSF)

TAVITAC CIC, showing the command-and-control consoles in place. The original photo is in color. (Thomson-CSF)

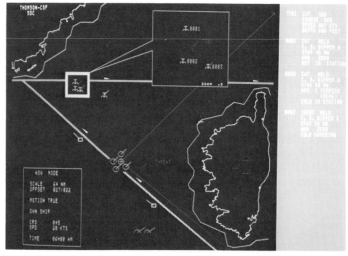

Typical TAVITAC display (western Mediterranean). (Thomson-CSF)

large-ship version with ten or more consoles, each of which can handle up to 200 tracks.

This system is installed on board the Saudi Arabian *Madina*-class frigates and has also been sold to Colombia and to Tunisia.

TAVITAC 2000 is the next-generation development. It uses a distributed architecture (local area network), standard multipurpose display consoles, and the ADA computer language. TAVITAC 2000 consists of a central computer with a hard disk, for integrating data from the sensors and for managing the display, and of more than ten multifunction consoles. The main computer has 6 Mbytes of active memory and accommodates two 40-Mbyte hard-disk units; the display is a 19-inch high-resolution CRT (1024 × 1280), and the computer can carry up to 800 tracks in an area with a radius of 512 nm. Up to 32 ESM contacts and up to 5 local sonar tracks can be carried and displayed as processed video. Each console can handle the entire track file, and the tactical picture is updated through a double buffer so that the picture need not wait while data is sent into the system. A full picture (300 tracks, 30 circles, 30 ellipses, 500 vectors, 2000 shoreline elements, and 2000 characters) can be built up in less than 0.3 seconds. Radar video can be superimposed on the processed-video display, with priority accorded to the graphics.

GERMANY (WEST)

◆ AGIS

This command-and-control system for fast attack boats (*Automatische Gefechts und Informations-system Schnellboote*) uses a data link to exchange data with shore stations, with SATIR-equipped surface ships, and with surveillance aircraft. The shipboard end of the system employs two programmable computers, one to generate and utilize the tactical situation and to assign targets to the various units of the flotilla, and the other to regulate fire control for the ship carrying the system. AGIS supports two torpedo-control consoles, one gun-control console, a horizontal tactical display, and a vertical plot. It was designed specifically for Type-143 boats, which were intended to act as flotilla leaders for Type 142 and 148; hence the need for sophisticated data processing, including input from external command systems (via Link 11).

AGIS entered service in 1976, providing a link with the central German maritime headquarters (MHQ) ashore. That link in turn permitted MHQ to form mixed battle groups, including both fast attack craft and aircraft, because MHQ could be sure of the precise location of each during combat. Otherwise, the aircraft might well have killed the fast attack boats by mistake.

The original Type-143 boat carried two torpedo tubes aft and required a pair of specialized torpedo-control consoles to control their wire-guided weapons. A modified Type 143A lacks the torpedo tubes (which, with the after 76-mm gun, are replaced by a RAM defensive missile launcher). The space freed by the elimination of the two torpedo-control consoles is used to expand AGIS into a Mk-II configuration; a multifunction display console is installed. It in turn makes possible combined helicopter–attack boat operations, and this installation of AGIS II is associated with the program to modify German Sea King helicopters to fire antiship missiles. Boats fitted with AGIS II have active and passive ECM integrated into their combat systems.

The German Navy plans ultimately to convert all Type-143 boats to AGIS-II configuration, with improved air defense (RAM and ECM). These boats will cooperate with 20 Sea Kings, converted from the search-and-rescue (SAR) role to the surface-attack role, using new radars and carrying Sea Skua missiles. The helicopters will also provide over-the-horizon targeting for attack boats using Link 11.

From 1982 on, the older Type-148 boats were fitted with PALIS, the passive-active link data transmission (and sharing) system. It had been developed during the AGIS program and was intended to unify the tactics of the German fast attack boats. With PALIS, any fast attack boat could cooperate with other units, even dissimilar ones such as destroyers, and with

MHQ. Given this system, Link 11 information for the construction of a current tactical picture could be relayed, stored, and correlated with own-ship data as well as with own-ship sensor information. By using electronic data processing, reaction time could be drastically reduced.

◆ SATIR

System zur Auswertung Taktischer Informationen auf Raketenzerstoren is a command-and-control system for the three German *Lutjens*-class missile destroyers and for the Type-122 *Bremen*-class frigates. As originally developed for the *Lutjens* class (which entered service in 1969–70), SATIR is a more compact substitute for NTDS, which in the U.S. Navy was limited to much larger ships. SATIR in turn inspired a U.S. project to extend NTDS to such ships and thus indirectly led to the RVP installation in Australian missile destroyers (see RVP under U.S. radar systems in the Antiaircraft Warfare section). SATIR employs U.S. hardware (UYK-7 computer and UYA-4 displays, as in NTDS, albeit on a more compact scale) and is based on experience with NTDS and with its French equivalent, SENIT. SATIR was the first NTDS-like system on a destroyer, proving sufficiently successful for the German Navy to choose a derivative for its *Bremen*-class (Type-122) frigates. The Type-122 version differs from the original SATIR in using digital links to sensors, weapons, integrated navigation system, and CIC display. Presumably this integration includes automatic radar target detection (ATD) to feed targets into the combat system.

When the *Lutjens* class was modernized in 1983–86, a U.S.-type SYS-1 radar integrator was fitted. These ships also have an NTDS data link designated SATIR-1, presumably equivalent to Link 11.

ITALY

◆ SADOC/IPN Series

SADOC (*Systema Direzione della Operazioni di Combattimento*) was the first Italian naval combat system. SADOC 1 was the U.S. NTDS adapted to the *Doria*-class missile cruisers. SADOC 2 is a small-ship modular system, developed for the

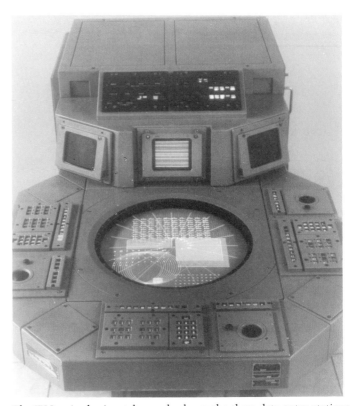

The IPN series horizontal console shows the three data entry stations with their keypads and trackballs. (Selenia)

Maestrale- and *Lupo*-classes, that uses Italian equipment and ideas. It has been widely exported under the designation IPN-10. The current large-ship system is SADOC 3/IPN-20, in the *Garibaldi,* the *Animoso*-class, and the modernized *Audace*-class missile destroyers.

SADOC 2/IPN-10 is a Selenia-Elsag modular distributed combat system that uses a 10 Mbit/sec data bus. SADOC 2 employs two types of multifunction consoles, a single-operator vertical console with a 16-inch CRT and a multi-operator horizontal console with a 22-inch CRT and three control positions. The consoles are linked to the sensors and the weapons by a central computer (which presumably maintains the system's data base), and each console contains its own NDC 160/E 16-bit minicomputer (replaced in newer versions by the MARA 286 computer, programmed in ADA). There are up to five consoles in the export version; SADOC 2, for the Italian Navy's *Lupo-* and *Maestrale*-class frigates, has a sixth. SADOC 2/IPN-10 is also installed on board the private-venture *Saettia*-class patrol boat and on board the *Minerva*-class corvettes. This system was ordered for the Indian Navy's aircraft carrier *Vikrant* and frigate *Godavari.*

SADOC-3/IPN-20 was designed for the carrier *Giuseppe Garibaldi.* As fitted to that ship, SADOC 3 includes two multi-operator horizontal consoles (supervision, command-and-control) and nine single-operator vertical consoles (EW, track management, air operations control). In the *Garibaldi,* SADOC 3 supports Links 1 (to NADGE, the NATO shore-based air-defense system), 11, 14, and 16; the NADGE link permits the ship to control shore-based aircraft.

SADOC succeeds two earlier Selenia naval tactical data systems, SES, for missile cruisers (contract awarded 1958, produced 1961–65), and SIDA (naval integrated defense system, 1963–66).

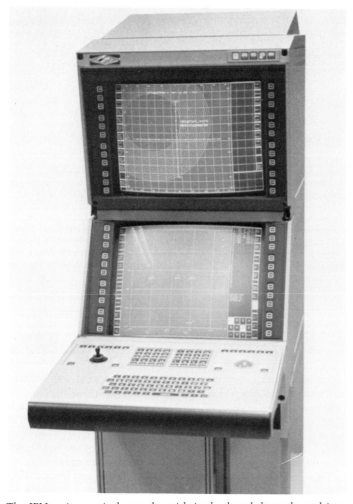

The IPN series vertical console, with its keyboard, keypads, and joystick. (Selenia)

♦ **SEN Series**

The Selenia-Elsag small-ship combat systems were announced in 1984.

SEN-100 is based on the Elsag NA18 optronic director, expanded to provide some command-and-control facilities. Intended for small craft of up to about 200 tons, SEN-100 controls two guns of different calibres. As of 1984, this system had been offered to Indonesia for use on board four projected fast patrol craft (it is presumed that they were the German Lurssen PB 57 type ordered in 1982, two of which were completed in 1985–86 and two of which have not yet been completed). The system is built around a single one-man vertical console, which normally shows radar PPI data but which can switch to a fire-control display.

The SEN-200 designation was reserved for ships of up to about 600 tons, but no such system was designed.

SEN-300 is intended for ships of up to about 1000 tons, to control a surface-to-air missile and two guns of different calibres. SEN-300 is based on Dardo E (an antiaircraft fire-control system, described in the AAW section) and on the Selenia IPN-10 command-and-control system; the associated search radar will be based on the Orion RTN-30X electronics. The system uses one horizontal (tactical) and one vertical multipurpose console, thus requiring a minimum of two operators for all functions, including both active and passive surveillance.

♦ **TBA**

The Selenia-Elsag combat system based on SEN-300, for larger ships (about 1000 tons and up), is effectively a modernized version of the *Maestrale/Lupo* system (SADOC 2/IPN-10).

JAPAN

Japanese naval tactical data systems (combat direction systems) are designated in an OYQ series:

OYQ-2 was described as a Weapon Entry System (WES); it was fitted to the destroyer *Asakaze.* WES succeeded Weapons Direction Equipment (WDE) on board the first Japanese area-defense destroyer, *Amatsukaze.*

OYQ-3 was originally installed on board the *Haruna* but has now been replaced by OQS-6. OYQ-3 was described as a Tactical Data Processing System (TDPS).

OYQ-4 Mod 1 is found in the *Hatakaze*-class area (Standard Missile) air-defense ships. All air-defense sensors (radars and ESM) feed into the OYQ-4, which also receives Link 11 and Link 14 data directly. Only the sonar, OQS-4, bypasses OYQ-4, to feed directly into the underwater fire-control system (SFCS-6A), which controls ASROC and Type-68 12.75-inch torpedo tubes. In contrast to U.S. systems, there is no Weapons Direction System as such embedded in the tactical data system; the OYQ-4 communicates directly with the missile fire-control system (Mk 74 Mod 13). Earlier Japanese area-defense missile destroyers (*Tachikaze* and *Amatsukaze* classes) are not credited with tactical data systems, and in this sense correspond to the U.S. *Charles F. Adams* class. Presumably OYQ-4 is approximately comparable to the German SATIR. OYQ-4 is described as a Combat Direction System (CDS).

OYQ-5 in the *Asagiri, Hatsuyuki,* and *Shirane* classes uses the U.S. UYK-20 computer. This system employs U.S. NTDS-type (OJ-194B) consoles; see the entry on NTDS for details. A block diagram of the *Asagiri* class's weapons system shows all the radars feeding into OYQ-5. However, sonar data is fed separately into an underwater fire-control system (SFCS-6B), which receives heading and gyro data from OYQ-5. Although the NOLR-6C ESM system feeds OYQ-5, the other major ESM sensor, OLR-9B, feeds directly into a jammer (OLT-3), and does not feed into the main combat system's computer at all. OYQ-5 controls guns and antiaircraft missiles through their respective fire-control systems (FCS 2-21A and 2-12, respectively). The only associated data link is Link 14. However, the *Shirane* class has Link 11 as well as Link 14. OYQ-5 is described as a Tactical Data Processing System (TDPS).

OYQ-6 in the *Haruna* class, replacing OYQ-3, uses the U.S. UYK-20A computer. OYQ-6 is described as a Combat Direction System (CDS).

Tactical Data Systems are also designated in a Type series, so that, as modernized, the *Takatsuki*-class destroyer has TDS 3-2 with provision for Link 14.

Submarine combat data systems are designated in a ZYQ series.

NETHERLANDS

◆ DAISY/FORESEE

DAISY consists of a computer plus the CDIS (Combat Information Display System) and is the basis of SEWACO (see below). DAISY accepts and processes raw sensor data, using a radar-video processor and a Signaal SM-R computer. Both horizontal and vertical displays are available, and DAISY is designed to communicate with a data-bus system by means of a commercial computer-communications system, Ethernet. Up to four buses may be used in parallel, with a total capacity of 40 Mbits/sec.

SM-R was the standard Signaal computer of the 1970s. It used a 24-bit word (maximum capacity 64K words), and clock rate was 1.0 MHz. The first 64K machine was delivered in 1970, and the first application (to a SEWACO system) was in 1973. Signaal also offered a smaller SMR-S, with half the clock speed (capacity 4 to 64 K rather than 8 to 64 K).

Systems of this type have been sold to the Argentine, Belgian, Canadian, Dutch, Greek, Indian, Indonesian, Thai, Turkish, and Peruvian Navies.

◆ SEWACO

SEWACO is Signaal's Sensor, Weapon, and Command System for corvettes and frigates. Seven versions were developed: SEWACO I, for the *Tromp* class; SEWACO II, for the Dutch "Standard" frigates; SEWACO III, a Signaal configuration (using ZW-06 and LW-08 radar, a WM-25 fire-control system, an SQS-505 sonar, and guns, Exocet, and NATO Sea Sparrow) for which no user was found; SEWACO IV, for the Belgian *Westhinder* class; SEWACO V, for the mid-life modernization of the six *Van Spejk*-class ASW frigates; SEWACO VI, for the two *Jacob van Heemskerck*-class AAW frigates; and SEWACO VII, for the new *Karel Doorman* class. SEWACO systems have also been ordered for Turkish and Portuguese MEKO frigates. SEWACO is based on a single DAISY computer, which interfaces with both the sensors and the weapons, using 24-bit input/output channels. The system was centralized in this way so that the ship would be able to concentrate her full firepower on the single most threatening target. All of these systems use Signaal SM-R computers.

SEWACO III had twelve operator consoles: command/control; air and surface situation displays; electronic warfare/data link control; weapons direction; helicopter control; ASW; hull sonar; variable-depth sonar; sonar signal injector; weapons control; and television. Other versions are simpler. SEWACO V has four horizontal tactical displays and a plotting table. SEWACO VI has six vertical consoles, two horizontal consoles, and a sonar display console. SEWACO VII is described as a next-generation system, with a higher degree of automation and integration.

NORWAY

◆ MSI-80S

MSI-80S is the combat system made by Kongsberg for the Norwegian *Hauk*-class missile/torpedo attack boats. MSI-80S uses twin Decca TM 1226 radars and an optronic tracker (TV tracker, laser range-finder, and IR scanner). Some of the software is based on that developed for the MSI-70U submarine system (see the ASW section). There is a single three-man console (tactical operator, weapon control operator, and passive sensor operator). The officer in tactical command occupies a fourth position. Both raw and processed video are shown together on a horizontal 23-inch CRT; a 12-inch CRT shows alphanumeric data and can be used to back up the larger CRT.

◆ MSI-3100

Kongsberg's (now NFT's) combat system for the updated Norwegian *Oslo*-class frigates (contract awarded 1985) is also installed in other types of ships. It employs the BUDOS data bus (see NAVKIS, below) and a radar-plot extractor (REX II). As in the case of NAVKIS, the system is split between a two-CRT Tactical Control Console and a two-CRT Weapons Control Console. The radars feed both consoles in parallel, and both communicate via the data bus. There are no dedicated fire-control systems as such because all directors feed the Weapons Control Console, which in turn connects to the guns and missile launchers.

The first MSI-3100 system, in the operations room of HNMS *Trondheim*, September 1988. The console on the left is for weapons control (with one position for above-water warfare and the other for gun control); that on the right, for tactical control. The tactical-control console is responsible for surveillance and for target tracking (i.e., for evaluation of the tactical situation) and also for underwater warfare. Tracking can be manual (via a trackball) or automatic. Both consoles are connected by a data bus. Each screen is a 20-inch (diagonal) multicolor digital raster (television-like) display; the two to the left show a combination of raw and processed video. As a whole, the system can handle up to 99 self-generated and 48 link-reported tracks. (NFT)

◆ NAVKIS

Kongsberg's (now NFT's) Navigation Command Control and Information System is installed in the *Nordkapp*-class coastal-patrol ships (EEZ enforcement ships). The system was ordered in November 1978. Priorities were (i) accurate navigation, so that the borders of the EEZ could be maintained; (ii) command/control; (iii) air surveillance and gun control. Each function is served by its own console (two in the case of navigation: one in CIC and one on the bridge), and the consoles are connected by a data bus, which also receives sonar data directly.

The main console is the Command, Control, and Information System (CCIS), which can identify and automatically track 16 targets and identify and automatically plot up to 64 fixed points. It can display the air targets picked up by the air surveillance console, and it can define and display local geography (including fishery grid, oil block, and similar data). This console is also responsible for antisubmarine weapons control (sonar input, drop-point calculation and plotting for mining, and target-intercept calculation for torpedoes), and it provides a navigation back-up (correlates data from the ship's sensors with known geographical points in the display of navigation data). The air-search radar feeds into the CCIS console, as does the ESM receiver.

Navigation was considered particularly important because radio-navigational-aid coverage of the Norwegian Sea is relatively poor. The ships, therefore, use three-axis main gyros, two-axis secondary gyros, a passive log, TRANSIT (satellite), Decca, Loran C, an echo-sounder, X-band navigational radars, and GPS. A navigational computer monitors the receivers and sensors, filtering their data to produce a best estimate of ship's position. The navigational computer also has access to surveillance radar, LLLTV, and optical sight data normally fed to the CCIS console.

Finally, the air-surveillance and gun-control console directly controls air engagements and the ship's helicopter. Up to eight air, surface, or subsurface targets can be tracked manually, and the air display includes IFF data. This console receives data from the air-search radar via a radar switchboard, which also feeds data to the CCIS.

The data bus is BUDOS, operating at about 30 MHz (bandwidth 10 MHz), with a capacity of 1 to 3 Mbit/sec.

SPAIN

◆ SCPVZ

Bazan's *Sistema de Combate para Patrullero de Vigilancia de Zona* is a new EEZ–patrol boat combat system, based on a Cor-monet data bus. Typically SCPVZ is expected to control 76/62 and 40/70 guns, but it is designed to accept other devices such as electronic warfare units and surface-to-surface missiles. The gunfire control portion of the system was tested in 1985. No sales have been reported.

SWEDEN

◆ CEPLO/MARIL/MARIS 880

CEPLO is a DataSAAB (now Ericsson) tactical system, for Danish frigates, corvettes, and fast attack boats. It was originally developed by DataSAAB as CCIS (Command and Control Information System), employing a combination horizontal and vertical display. The 16-inch-diameter horizontal PPI display was used for target detection and tracking, three operators using their roller balls and keyboards. The 24-inch vertical (command decision) display shows only synthetic video. Tracking can be automatic or rate-aided. The system uses two Censor 900 32-bit computers in parallel, each of which is sufficient to run a two-console system.

The consoles themselves are designated EPLO (Electronic Plotting System). Target positions are updated cyclically, every 2 minutes for 24 tracks, or every 30 seconds for 6 tracks. In the semiautomatic (rate-aided tracking) mode, the operator can correct the estimated target position by means of his trackball; the PPI then shows the new position plus a track history. All targets are generally shown with vectors (course and speed). EPLO is designed to accept data both from own-ship sensors and from external digital data links (see MARIS 880, below).

CEPLO exists in two forms: a single-console version for fast attack craft (in the Danish *Willemoes* class completed in 1976–78) and a four-console version (with two summary synthetic displays physically removed from the horizontal displays) for corvettes and frigates. CEPLO was installed on board the two *Peder Skram*–class frigates when they were modernized in 1977–79 and was initial equipment for the three *Nils Juel* class, completed in 1980–82. In the four-console version, the horizontal multifunction displays would typically be used for local

air, surface, and subsurface plots, and for weapons coordination and control.

The EPLO console forms the basis of two Swedish fast attack boat combat systems: MARIL, for the *Stockholm* class (which uses a Censor 932E computer); and MARIS 880, for the *Spica-II* class. MARIS 880 can accept targeting data from helicopters, for over-the-horizon attacks.

UNITED KINGDOM

◆ ADAWS

The Action Data Automation Weapons Systems incorporate video extractors that enable the system to automatically recognize a valid radar echo and enter it into a track-keeping computer as a plot. This automatic update may be a follow-up to a plot initiated by an operator, or the plotting may be wholly automatic. Tracking is based on the association of successive plots rather than on the processing of individual echoes (e.g., for doppler). Depending upon plot quality, the system may automatically control weapons. Thus, with the advent of ADAWS, ships no longer have separate fire-control systems. Instead, at least in theory, all weapons control is exercised by the integrated control system.

ADAWS 1 was fitted to the "County"-class missile destroyers *Glamorgan, Fife, Norfolk,* and *Antrim.* It used two Ferranti Poseidon computers and fed its processed data to the Seaslug and Seacat missiles and to the 4.5-inch guns. Computers also tested whether targets could be engaged by the missile system. Sensor data and target allocation could be exchanged within a task force via an associated digital data link.

Note that, although the weapons were primarily controlled by ADAWS, all of them retained their older analog controls as back-ups. This system had eight twin-display consoles. Unlike the original British ADA (Action Data Automation) system installed on board the old carrier *Eagle,* this system included ASW contacts and was connected to EW receivers. It employed a new radar-target extraction device, SPADE. This device generated processed rather than raw video (i.e., tracks rather than a series of raw blips).

ADAWS 2 was designed for the next-generation missile destroyer, HMS *Bristol,* introducing the Ferranti FM 1600 computer (192K words), two of which were used. In this system, the central computer took over the entire fire-control task; in ADAWS 1 weapons control was still carried out by specialized analog machines. This pattern of centralization was followed in later ADAWS systems. ADAWS's tasks included not only the control of shipboard weapons (4.5-inch gun, Sea Dart, Ikara) but also the calculation of air intercepts.

ADAWS 2 introduced limited-area automatic (plot) extraction. Instead of processing all radar signals, the computer examined only a limited window around the last plot, a system called Limited-Area Extraction (LAX), which was also used in later versions of ADAWS. This design limited computer effort and also helped ensure that tracks were limited to targets behaving more or less realistically. Typically, an operator initiated a track by identifying the blips of interest (using a roller ball), and he was alerted to resolve ambiguities, e.g., two tracks that seemed to merge. Once the computer was tracking, it placed a letter at the end of the track: P for a track passing through a predicted position, M for a missed target (on that radar sweep), and C for a confused target (the computer followed the plot closest to the predicted position, unless otherwise instructed).

ADAWS 3 would have been in the abortive carrier CVA.01.

ADAWS 4, in Type 42 destroyers, controls both Sea Dart missiles and the 4.5-inch gun. Development began in 1967. ADAWS 4, virtually ADAWS 2 with the Ikara-missile capability deleted, employs Link 10. As modernized in 1988, the ADAWS 4 of HMS *Birmingham* now has a separate computer display for the captain, so that he no longer has to interrupt the principal warfare officer (PWO, presumably equivalent to the U.S. TAO or tactical action officer) to see his summary display. The modernized software reportedly gives better threat evaluations in terms of the ratio between rate of approach and range, and the ship can now transmit on three data links (presumably 4, 10, and 11) simultaneously.

ADAWS 5 is in *Leander*-class frigates fitted with Ikara missiles. This system uses only a single FM 1600 series computer (64K, later increased to 128K words; designated Computer Outfit DAE-1). Eight systems were manufactured. This system is a subset of ADAWS 2.

ADAWS 6 is the *Invincible*-class system, using two FM 1600's.

ADAWS 7 is in Type 42 Batch 2 destroyers. It was developed in parallel with ADAWS 6. Improvements included the switch to Link 11.

ADAWS 8 is in Type 42 Batch 3 destroyers. It is a modified ADAWS 7: the principal change was to accommodate the Type 2016 sonar.

ADAWS 9 was not used; presumably it was planned for the abortive Type 43 double-ended missile destroyer.

ADAWS 10 is in HMS *Ark Royal*.

These systems are all descended from the digital automated action-information organization first installed on board the carrier *Eagle* (Action Data Automation, ADA) using three Ferranti Poseidon computers. In the *Eagle*'s system, targets were automatically detected by a special-purpose computer, which processed video from the Type 984 3-D radar, and this data (plus other data from other sources) was injected into a track-keeping computer. The hope that the system could also provide automatic fighter control apparently proved impractical because the input data were not accurate enough. However, ADA could keep up with large numbers of targets, and it could help prioritize them. Becoming operational in 1964, ADA must have had one of the very first automatic radar-target detection (ATD) systems in naval service. It had sixteen twin-display consoles.

ADA in turn replaced CDS (Comprehensive Display System), a track-keeping system intended to replace manual CICs (AIOs, Action Information Organizations, in British parlance), which could not keep up with large numbers of fast aircraft. CDS was first installed on board the carriers *Eagle* and *Hermes* in the late 1950s to support their Type 984 radars. It was a manual rate-aided system, i.e., it still required operators to input radar-detection data. Its intercept computers (for fighter control) used analog data processing. CDS was designed in three versions: 24-, 48-, and 96-tracks. ADA was intended to increase the number of tracks that could be maintained, while reducing crew size.

FM 1600 and FM 1600B introduced integrated circuits, replacing the earlier Poseidon. FM 1600E (large) and FM 1600D (smaller) are corresponding computers using medium scale integration. They are small enough to be integrated into the display consoles themselves, so there is no longer any need for a separate computer room.

FM 1600 and its successors are all 24-bit computers. FM 1600 could accommodate up to 131,062 words (or twice that if a reduction in speed was accepted). FM 1600B was a fifth of 1600's size but had about half its computing power (clock rate 3 MHz, up to 65,536 words' capacity). FM 1600D uses 24- or 48-bit words (but calculates in 8-bit words to achieve higher speed). Its capacity is that of FM 1600B.

◆ CACS

Computer Assisted Command System is the successor of ADAWS. Much less centralized than the earlier system, CACS uses three Ferranti FM1600E computers (one is a running spare that carries the operating program) as well as twelve Argus M700 miniprocessors that handle displays, sensors, and fire controls. The system can, therefore, be divided into modules. CACS is intended to integrate, for the first time, passive sonar and ESM data into the action information system. However, CACS has encountered serious developmental problems. CACS 1 cannot handle both air and towed-array-sonar pictures simul-

taneously, so Type 22 frigates using it must still process their towed-array data separately and input the results manually.

CACS 1 originated in a 1977 Ferranti study of the proposed mid-life refit improvements to the AIO (CIC) of the Type 21 frigates. Late in the study, the project was extended to Type 22 frigates. CACS 1 is in HMS *Boxer, Beaver*, and *Brave*. Trials began in 1984 and were completed in 1986, but even in 1988 the system is described officially as "not fully operational." Since Type 22s have gone into the Persian Gulf, it is presumed that CACS can handle air but not underwater threats. Current forecasts of the date of completion vary between 1989 and 1991.

CACS 2 and CACS 3 were projected as updates for the Type 42 destroyers and HMS *Invincible*. They were canceled as part of the 1981 Defence Review cuts, as a presumed consequence of the cancellation of Sea Dart Mk 2.

CACS 4 was the version proposed by Ferranti for Type 23 frigates. CACS 4 used two data buses, a Combat System Highway and a Command Display Highway. There were seven displays, one for the maintainers and six for the operators and the commander. Ferranti's design proved unsuccessful, and the first four Type 23s will have to go to sea without a computer combat system. CACS 5 was also affected. Bidding was, therefore, reopened. The two alternatives are Ferranti and Dowty-CAP, and the choice is to be made early in 1989.

CACS 5, a modified CACS 4, is to equip Type 22 Batch 3 frigates (*Cornwall* class). First-of-class harbor trials were completed in 1988, and the system should be fully operational by 1992, several years after the ships intended to carry it have entered service.

◆ CAAIS (DBA)

Computer-Assisted Action Information System was less comprehensive (i.e., more distributed) than ADAWS. It was designed for ships retaining separate fire-control systems (Type 21 frigates, Exocet and Seawolf *Leander*s, Batch 1 Type 22 frigates, and the carrier *Hermes*). The first CAAIS systems used the Ferranti FM 1600B, a smaller version of the FM 1600 used in ADAWS systems. The displays were commercial Decca units. FM 1600B was comparable in power to the Poseidon of the original ADA and ADAWS but cost about 10 percent as much. FM 1600B has in turn been succeeded by a more powerful, and less expensive, FM 1600D (used in Nimrod ASW aircraft and in some EW equipment).

In contrast to ADAWS's organization, CAAIS's central computer sends data to radar-tracker fire-control computers that actually control the weapons; the system is decentralized. CAAIS is, in effect, confined to AIO functions. A separate weapons-control system is required. In Type 21 frigates, that system is the WSA 4 (see below).

Because the FM 1600B computer is fairly large, processing cannot be distributed among the consoles. All are, therefore, connected to a data bus that is itself connected to the computer. The computer is fed directly by the various sensors and by the ship's data link, connecting directly with the associated WSA 4 weapons-control system.

A smaller version of CAAIS equips "Hunt"-class minehunters.

The operational requirement for CAAIS was laid down in 1966, and final development was carried out by Ferranti, with Decca (for displays) as principal subcontractor. Two versions, DBA 1 and 2, entered production in 1969. Note that DBA is the *computer* outfit:

DBA 1, for *Leander* Batch 2s, using a 32K FM 1600B.

DBA 2, for Type 21 frigates.

DBA 3, for *Hermes* as modernized (now the Indian *Viraat*).

DBA 4, for "Hunt"-class minehunters (special low-magnetic system).

DBA 5, for *Leander* Batch 3s and Type 22 Batch 1s, to control Seawolf missiles (GWS 25) and Type 2016 Sonar. The computer is a 48K FM 1600B.

◆ CANE

Decca's Computer-Aided Navigational System is essentially a combat system for patrol craft and minecraft. In its simplest form, CANE is an automated plot, in which a spot of light is projected upward onto the back of a chart to show the ship's own position. The spot is controlled by a Decca Automatic Plotter fed by a Decca Navigator and Loran C. Other ships are detected by radar or sonar and are automatically shown by other points of light, and these contacts can easily be plotted on the chart. A Track Management Unit tracks up to ten surface targets simultaneously, using rate-aided tracking. The operator initiates a track with the usual tracker ball and assigns a number through a keyboard; detailed track data can be seen on an adjacent display.

CANE I was used on board British "Island"-class offshore patrol vessels and was installed on board the hydrofoil *Speedy*. CANE II, which can track 38 targets simultaneously, was evaluated in 1980 and was installed on board the two "Castle"-class offshore patrol vessels; CANE II also replaced CANE I on board the earlier "Island" class.

◆ WSA 4/401/402/403 (GSA 4/GWS 22)

WSA 4 (Weapon System Automation 4) controls the 4.5-inch gun and the Seacat missile on board Type 21 frigates. WSA 4 is built around a single Ferranti FM 1600B computer, and all functions are centralized in the CIC (AIO in British parlance). There are two identical consoles, for gun and Seacat control, and both are linked to a one-man horizontal console of the CAAIS automated AIO, manned by the missile-and-gun director. Note that this system is sometimes denoted GSA 4/GWS 22 for its separate gun and missile elements.

From his console, the single gun controller can track targets on two Type 912 (Orion RTN 10X) radars, see them on television, and fire as many as twenty rounds from the Mk-8 gun. The Seacat controller next to him can fire as many as four Seacats (without reloading). Both are supervised by a missile-and-gun director at a CAAIS display a few feet away. CAAIS compiles the surface and air picture, and the director designates targets to WSA 4 using a tracker ball and marker. CAAIS also assigns the relevant tracking radar. The gun controller initiates the fire-control calculation and orders the gun or missile to aim and fire. Normally, the director receives the WSA 4 track data before fire begins, but in special cases the gun controller can open fire on his own by closing the safety switch and pressing the firing pedal.

There are also emergency control (back-up) operating modes for the gun and missile launcher. The 4.5-in gun is then directed by the lookout-and-aiming sight, and the Seacat by the pedestal sight operator. Both would otherwise send their data to the WSA 4 computer rather than to the weapons.

The two-man WSA 4 console has two main Electronic Data Displays (EDDs) with light pens, each showing data in graphical and alphanumeric form on a page-by-page basis. The correct page is chosen by light pen, using a list running along the bottom (TCD, WCD, NGSA, NGSB, WIND, SEACAT, for Target Control Display, Weapon Control Display, Naval Gunfire-Support Channel A and B, Wind, and Seacat, respectively). TCD, for example, shows the status of the two trackers, the track number of the target, the weapons mode (e.g., GAA, for Gun Antiaircraft), and the target's heading, range, speed, and height.

The WSA 4 computer itself stabilizes the tracking radar antennas and also helps reduce tracking errors by predicting future target position. The computer considers all gun ballistics. Because the combination of computer and radars acts like a track-while-scan radar, shifting from target to target while firing at both is relatively easy; and spotting corrections from both targets can be applied. In essence, the computer executes two fire-control solutions simultaneously. This technique takes advantage of the shell's 30-to-50-second time of flight to provide the equivalent of two gunfire channels. Splash spotting is semiautomatic, with the gun controller entering splashes via a track-ball applied to a B-scan scope. For indirect fire, the ship's and the target's coordinates are entered into the computer in metric grid form; and the computer automatically tracks the ship, using log and compass data and tidal data. During surface fire, if the director calls for antiaircraft fire, the system can shift over within a few seconds.

The computer permanently holds basic range tables, and information such as mean sea level pressure, mean equivalent winds, and muzzle velocity (gun wear/ammunition temperature) are entered by light pen.

The WSA 400 series is an expanded version, developed for the ASW version of the Brazilian *Niteroi*-class frigates. WSA 401 controls the Bofors 375-mm rocket launcher and the 4.5-inch gun. WSA 402 controls the Ikara and Seacat missiles. Similar systems are used in the general purpose version of the frigate. See also the WSA 420 series below.

◆ CAAIS 400

CAAIS 400 is Ferranti's commercial CAAIS, for the Brazilian *Niteroi*-class frigates. The corresponding weapons-control system is the WSA 400 series.

◆ CAAIS 450

Ferranti's automated AIO (CAAIS), corresponding to the WSA 420-series, provides for data-link operation, for presentation of a unified tactical picture (with indications of the most threatening target), for control of ECM, and for navigational assistance.

◆ NAUTIS

Naval Autonomous Information System is Plessey's private-venture, integrated naval command/control system. NAUTIS is based on Plessey's NAUTIC autonomous work stations (consoles), which are connected by a command system highway (data bus). There is no single central computer, but NAUTIS can be added to an existing command system. NAUTIS-M is currently in production for British minehunters, and it is planned for the updates of the amphibious assault ships.

Versions:

NAUTIS-A	assault ships and auxiliaries
NAUTIS-D	destroyers
NAUTIS-F	frigates
NAUTIS-L	logistics landing ships
NAUTIS-M	minehunters and minesweepers
NAUTIS-P	patrol vessels, strike craft, corvettes

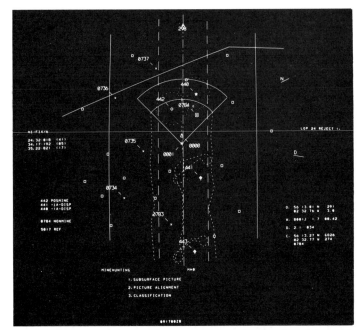

NAUTIS-M tactical display during sonar search, showing the search plan, the history of the ship's track, and sonar coverage with sonar contacts. (Plessey)

◆ WSA 420-Series

Ferranti's private-venture, weapons-control systems for fast patrol craft are built on WSA 4 experience. The simplest version, WSA 421, has two optronic trackers (with laser range-finders and closed-circuit television) and (as an option) a range-only radar; and WSA 421 controls two guns. It can maintain three simultaneous tracks (two tracks queued). One man can operate the system in cruising condition and two in action stations (four for a double version).

WSA 422 adds surface-to-surface missile capability. In each case the computer is an FM 1600D. WSA 422 is also described as WSA 421 plus a one-man CIC console. 422 can handle 10 to 12 tracks for weapons direction, with an overall system capacity of 60.

WSA 423, with an FM 1600E computer, is more powerful and can employ a tracking radar to give full blind-fire capability. There are two complete fire-control channels, one using the tracker radar and the other the optronic/range-only radar or laser or perhaps a TWS radar. In this version, too, an AIO console is added to the basic system. This system can handle 128 tracks (up to 100 automatically generated). Production began in 1980.

For a larger ship, the fire-control system, which is built around a single console, can be connected to an automated AIO. The system would also have a data link, allowing individual units to operate in radio and radar silence.

◆ WS500/CS500/MC500 (System 500)

Ferranti announced these combat systems in 1987, following three years of development: WS500 for weapons control (to supersede the WSA 400 series), CS500 for command, and MC500 for mine countermeasures. All are built around distributed processors using a special computer operating system, which Ferranti calls its virtual system environment suite (VSE500). The basic idea of the virtual system is not new to computers: it is interposed between applications programs (such

as trackers) and the basic hardware of the system. The applications program does not have to be closely coordinated with the details of the machine; the virtual system is responsible for that coordination. Many readers will be familiar with the operating systems of personal computers, such as the Disk Operating System (DOS), which carry out this task for them.

The great virtue of VSE500 is that programs to run individual weapons and sensors can be inserted relatively easily so that it is unnecessary to build up a single massive program for a ship's command system, a program that is difficult to modify when changes are made in the associated hardware. Much of the effort of development has, therefore, gone into a new method of creating operating software, using the ADA language. The combination of hardware and software modularity should make it relatively easy to assemble a system optimized for any given collection of weapons and sensors. One might see in the modular command program a software parallel to the hardware modularity of the very successsful German MEKO frigate, which caters to different navies' great differences in hardware choices.

Moreover, modular programming makes modification much easier and safer, since changes in one module need not affect the others. The potential for modularity is a direct consequence of increased computing power. Veteran programmers will recall that in the age of relatively slowly rotating magnetic drums it was essential for the programmer himself to time his arithmetic operations so that the numbers required would come toward the reading head of the drum about when they were needed (so that searching for them would not itself add major delays). Later, when memories could be accessed on a random basis, sheer computer memory capacity made it essential that programs be very tightly written, with the shortest possible routes between different instructions. Once computers are fast enough, procedures that emphasize ease of reliable software production over efficient computer operation become very attractive since they reduce the cost and danger of rewriting portions of each program.

System 500 is designed to employ an FDDI 1 data bus (a fiber-optic local area network) and numerous (typically over 100) Motorola 68020 processors (68030 and 68040 can be substituted as they become available) in standard multirole consoles, each of which carries the full program load of the system, but 500 runs

Ferranti's System 500 synthetic video display shows the effect of windowing (sonar-performance parameters are shown on the same screen as the tactical situation). (Ferranti)

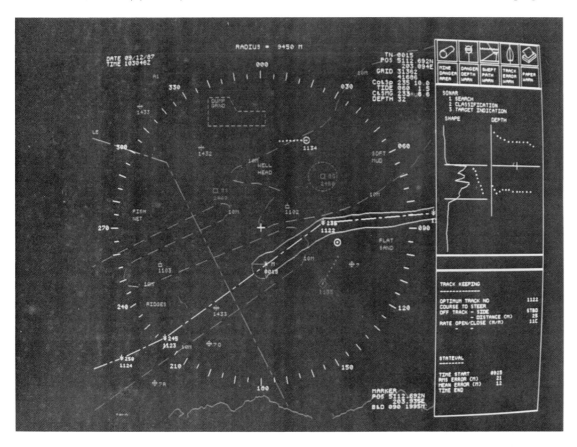

only those processors needed to perform a particular task. As in existing computers ashore, the CRTs of the consoles can be windowed to show several sensor or other device displays simultaneously, and the CRTs can also show closed-circuit television pictures, e.g., from the bridge or from a remotely piloted vehicle. In this sense these CRTs are equivalent to the multipurpose CRT displays of the new "glass cockpits" of aircraft.

In CS500, the track table employed in earlier tactical data systems is replaced by a relational data base catering, in the larger versions of the system, to thousands of tracks. For each track the system carries a long-term history and comprehensive identity data, the latter making it possible to apply artificial intelligence techniques for tactical decision making. Because all the tracks are carried in comparable form, the system can correlate tracks from different sources to avoid duplication and clutter. This correlation is presumably equivalent to current U.S. measures to ensure gridlock (see ACDS and BGAAWC in the Antiaircraft Warfare section). Moreover, because all radar tracks (taken from ADT sets) are carried together, the system can automatically select the best sensor track for each target; the operator does not shift, for example, between search radars. An associated multilink processor uses correlation techniques to reduce duplication among received tracks before these tracks are correlated with those produced by own-ship sensors.

The main track data base includes sonar and EW data.

Relational data-base techniques were used to achieve very fast reaction time, the Ferranti development team using a new solid-state relational processor (in effect, parallel processor), the first of its kind. Such a processor has the advantage of searching equally quickly through its data base for single or multiple attributes (e.g., looking for all incoming tracks that are at altitudes below 500 ft and at speeds of Mach 1 or more, a combination of three attributes that a normal processor would search out one by one).

The program includes sufficient artificial intelligence for threat evaluation and weapons (or countermeasures) assignment (TEWA), according to preselected rules. The program also provides maneuvering advice, which is important if the appropriate systems are to bear, and also if the ship is to present a minimum cross section to the approaching threat. Generally the operator is provided with a veto; he does not initiate action. Command-by-negation is necessary for short-range systems facing very high speed or pop-up threats.

The weapons-control applications of System 500 incorporate new types of prediction (software) based on target profile matching, target maneuver forecasting, and spread fire techniques. Earlier systems, based on linear or simple curve prediction, did not have the information capacity to adjust their methods to particular targets, even though intelligence on the characteristic flight or ballistic paths of those targets might well be available in paper form. This type of direct application of intelligence data is possible in systems with really large memories and is likely to become increasingly common in the future.

Although the system is primarily software, Ferranti's favored application employs 20-inch full-color CRTs with touch-sensitive screens, capable of rewriting a 1000-track picture within 80 milliseconds; color provides the operator with much more information than a monochrome display. Menus are used to assist the operator in manual inputs. Each console can display both raw and processed video, and resolution is sufficiently good to display navigational charts. The standard console (workstation) carries a large CRT and two interchangeable electroluminescent panels, plus a trackball and keyboard. Ferranti also offers a simpler console (e.g., for damage control, hydrography, or a port headquarters) without the two electroluminescent panels.

Ferranti has offered a version of CS500 for the Royal Navy Type 23 command system competition, employing 13 workstations (consoles). A variant, with six workstations, has been offered for the new AOR; presumably both share the software needed to control vertically launched Sea Wolf missiles. Ferranti estimates that 40 workstations would be required for a

carrier. As of late 1988, System 500 was being proposed for the Australian ANZAC frigate, for a proposed refit of New Zealand *Leander*-class frigates, and for the West German Type-123 program. Ferranti expects to employ a System 500–type open architecture as its contribution to one of the NATO AAW system proposals (see the Antiaircraft Warfare section).

UNITED STATES

◆ Aegis

See Radar Integration in the Antiaircraft Warfare section.

◆ ACDS

Advanced Combat Direction System, the successor to NTDS (see below), uses Link 16 for data transmission and exploits the capabilities of the UYK-43 computer (which replaces the earlier UYK-7). ACDS Block 0, the interim system, covers installation of the new hardware, including the new UYQ-21 display. The associated software is a direct continuation of existing NTDS software, and Block 0, therefore, shows only modest improvements in capability compared to NTDS. ACDS Block 0's software is designated CDS Model 4, and the carrier and cruiser versions are quite different (the carrier is modular, the cruiser restructured). ACDS Block 1 uses CDS Model 5 software.

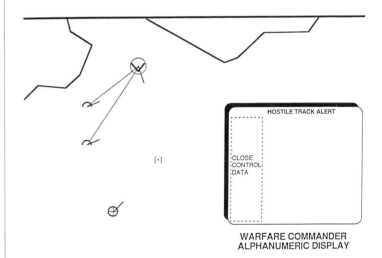

WARFARE COMMANDER
ALPHANUMERIC DISPLAY

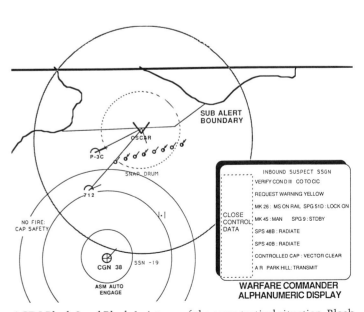

WARFARE COMMANDER
ALPHANUMERIC DISPLAY

ACDS Block 0 and Block 1 pictures of the same tactical situation. Block 0 is equivalent to current NTDS; the diagram shows one hostile submarine (the "v") and two friendly aircraft (the semicircles), plus a ship (the circle) at the bottom. Interpretation is entirely the responsibility of the CIC personnel. Block 1 shows the effect of providing extensive on-line data bases, displaying weapons capabilities and threats. (Hughes)

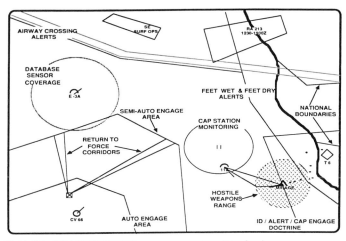

The effect of ACDS Block 1 zone processing. (Hughes)

Block 0 begins a transition from AAW orientation in NTDS towards multiwarfare orientation; Block 1 is structured specifically to support composite warfare commanders (CWCs). This evolution is essential because the threat is no longer easily divisible into the traditional categories. For example, a missile-firing submarine may be tracked by ASW sensors, but it is really an AAW threat. Unless the portion of the combat system that is normally devoted to ASW recognizes a launcher's sound (a transient) as an AAW cue, the AAW part of the system will not be ready to look for a missile emerging from the water near the detected submarine.

Like NTDS, Block 0 is limited in track capacity, range, and "vocabulary" (the ability to describe tracks in greater detail than air/surface/subsurface and friendly/unknown/enemy); Block 0's ability to gridlock is limited to self-correlation, and it has very limited capabilities to integrate ESM and ocean surveillance data, even though those types of data are becoming much more important. Like NTDS, Block 0 is not designed to automate the decision to engage a target and, thus, does not really greatly reduce a ship's reaction time.

From a maintenance point of view, Block 0 shares the basic problems of NTDS: the program's logic is relatively inflexible, and system updates are difficult because the programming is not sufficiently modular. These problems in turn make it attractive to add stand-alone systems to ships, rather than to integrate the systems with the basic combat system. Such stand-alones, however, tend to be relatively ineffective because they cannot benefit from the ship's main sensors. Quick-reaction ECM systems suffered from that particular problem.

Block 1 marks a departure in system philosophy. NTDS was primarily a display system, the tactical action officer (TAO) using his experience to add the information needed for decisions. In this sense NTDS is semiautomatic. For example, it shows but does not particularly highlight potential threats, and it is not intended to suggest appropriate courses of action. The sole current exception is the command and decision (C&D) processor in the Aegis system, which the ship's commanding officer feeds with a series of doctrinal rules (including rules of engagement) and which does indeed suggest courses of action. For Aegis, the weapons-assignment role has been melded with the NTDS role to create something new, a combat direction system (CDS). This change, from pure information coordination to combat direction, is reflected in a change from the existing CIC designation to a new CDC (combat direction center) designation for the central command-and-control space of a ship.

Compared to NTDS, ACDS Block 1 offers expanded surveillance coverage, automated sensor processing, and expanded data exchange, both within a battle group and between the battle group and external sources of information.

Block 1 is already planned for all carriers (to enter service beginning in 1992) and may be extended to pre-Aegis cruisers (NTU ships) and to the major amphibious units. The lead ship is USS *Carl Vinson* (CVN 70), which is currently equipped with

NTDS Model 4.0. Block 1 (Model 5.1) adds a second UYK-43 computer, plus entirely new software to fully exploit the new hardware. On board a carrier, ACDS Block 1 receives battle-force tactical data from the command-and-control processor (C2P, a third UYK-43), which receives the tactical data links (and, in future, the remote satellite links, OTCIXS and TADIXS). ACDS receives all shipboard data directly: ESM data from SLQ-32 and from the Tactical Signals Exploitation System (TSES); SYS-2 radar tracks; beacon video; information from the ASW module; information from the TAS Mk 23 target acquisition system; and information from the interim afloat correlation system/POST (which receives TADIXS B information from intelligence centers ashore). In future it should also receive data from the big intelligence processing systems, such as the Flag Data Display System (FDDS) in the TFCC (see above).

Compared to NTDS, Block 1 operates over four times the range (for 16 times the surveillance volume, maximum altitude being fixed). Block 1 can handle four times as many track files and adds auto-identification of tracks (7 levels, compared to three levels of manual track identification in NTDS). Link 16 provides ten times the throughput of Link 11. Given much more data, it is possible to correlate tracks automatically and thus to maintain gridlock automatically. The only existing track correlator of this type is SGSAC, a manual system implemented in Aegis ships. On-board and remote ESM can be fully integrated because the system is fed by a highly secure data link (Link 16) that can carry ESM data. By way of contrast, NTDS ships have to rely on a separate secure data link (Park Hill), and their off-board ESM data are, therefore, processed outside the automated ship's combat system.

In particular, there is now enough information in the system to correlate ESM data for targeting. Such correlation requires special knowledge of individual sensor and emitter characteristics and exchange of data on emitter parameters among several ships, so that the correlator knows which ships are detecting the same emitter. The battle group command system must, then, associate individual intercepts of what seems to be the same emitter to obtain positions good enough for targeting.

The most visible impact of ACDS Block 1 is in graphics, which are much more detailed than those of NTDS or Block 0. The improved graphics are supported by the second UYK-43, the decision support processor. As in NTDS, the first is primarily a track manager. Graphics are much more than simply a decision aid. Graphic processing, which is already quite common ashore, makes it easy to exploit the position of a point or a track in relation to a preassigned zone of the space in which the system works. For example, it is relatively easy to make the system reaction to a track depend on whether the track is or is not within a zone (say, the 12-mile limit) surrounding some coast. The alternative, to test the track against the entered zone boundary, is time-consuming and is probably outside the power of earlier combat system computers. Zone processing complements the system architecture designed to accept doctrinal rules ("if . . . then" statements) and to present the operators and the TAO with the immediate operational implications of those rules.

This doctrinal processing can be used to create automatic combat system checklists (ACSCLs). The CO and his staff create the checklists to cover specific situations; each checklist is a series of actions and operating modes that should be optimum for that situation. Each list can also be reviewed and revised at will. All the checklists are carried as computer files, and the CDS automatically implements them when it detects the appropriate conditions. Its action includes display of the checklist itself so that the operator has, in effect, a veto in the event the system has somehow used an inappropriate ACSCL. This type of automation seems essential as threat-warning time shrinks and is an extended equivalent of the auto-engagement capability that is increasingly common.

Block 1 is the first CDS to incorporate an on-line intelligence data base; it can be used for realistic threat evaluation and weapons assignment (TEWA). By way of contrast, NTDS had to base its assessments entirely on target speed, course, and range (which, even so, was better than the situation before NTDS). This function seems like what Ferranti is now promising in its System 500 (see above) and will probably be characteristic of future tactical data systems using very powerful computers.

As an indication of the new level of data available on any particular track (i.e., detected target), one can compare data available from Block 0 (i.e., NTDS) and Block 1:

	Block 0	*Block 1*
Track Identifier	4 values	8 values
Track Category	4 values	8 values
Primary ID Amplifier	16 values	—
ID Amplifier	144 values	—
Platform	—	504 values
Platform Type	—	4095 values
Type Modifier	—	32 values
Nationality	—	country codes
Alliance	—	alliance codes
Unit	—	256 values/type

For example, the same ship might be described as:

Block 0	**Block 1**
Hostile	Hostile
Surface	Surface
Destroyer	Destroyer
Missile Platform	Krivak-II
	ASW/Targeting
	USSR/Warsaw Pact
	Hull No. 539

Given this specific data, the system evaluates the threat presented by the target (based on its known weapons characteristics, which are stored as a data base), provides alternative methods of engagement, and displays alternative engagement capabilities.

Link 16 is essential for this type of detailed processing because of its precision and its great information capacity. Thus, the Block 1 program is being paralleled by programs to place Link 16 on board E-2Cs and F-14s.

Unlike NTDS, ACDS will have an integrated ESM interface because Link 16 is secure enough to carry intelligence and ESM data. Bearings can, therefore, be shared rapidly among ships for better targeting. NTDS had to use a separate ESM/intelligence facility using a dedicated secure signals system, Park Hill. Moreover, because ESM data are integrated with other sensor data, the system as a whole can choose between ESM and weapon responses to particular threats.

One advantage of the much more powerful graphic processing capability is that the format in which information is presented can easily be changed. The data base is object-oriented, so screen data structures are easy to change without recompiling basic computer code. This capability is important because users have such different desires (and needs) for interface formats. Given flexible formats, individual commanders can choose what they want, and the choice of format does not delay overall system development.

Automated status boards (ASTABs) complement the usual graphic displays, showing threat summary, task organization, and combat system summary. All ASTABs can be displayed on either the dedicated ASTABs or on CRTs in the combat direction center, and the system operators can request ASTABs as desired. ASTABs can be defined as multipage electronic documents, one page being displayed at a time, but the overall computer system keeps the entire ASTAB up to date, to be called up as desired. There are 60 predefined formats (own-ship and force data) plus 20 user-defined formats. All of this information can be pulled from the full ACDS data base, including the track file and the intelligence data. For example, an operator might define an ASTAB listing ASW threats, giving for each threat platform its track number, its category (submarine, surface, air), its range, its ASW sensor, and its ASW weapon. Another page

of the display (which could be called up as desired) might associate each threat with its lethal range. An ASTAB on force status might, for example, list the ships with the status of their ASW systems or their roles (e.g., picket, pouncer).

Hughes Ground Systems is responsible for ACDS Block 1. In contrast to recent modular command-and-control systems such as the Ferranti Series 500, Block 1 cannot be decentralized, partly because the data base is much too large to fit anything short of a very large central computer. In commercial terms, Block 1 corresponds to a system based on a mainframe with computer terminals, rather than to a decentralized local area network (LAN) using individual workstations, each embodying the computing power of the system. Presumably it will take at least a further generation of higher-density computers, and a much more capacious data bus, to permit the U.S. Navy to pass from a centralized NTDS-type system to something decentralized.

ACDS is based on the new UYK-43 computer, which is manufactured by Unisys and which supersedes the UYK-7 on which current versions of NTDS are based. The instruction set of the new computer includes the instructions of the UYK-7, so that UYK-43 can run UYK-7 programs relatively easily; that capability explains why ACDS Block 0 is so similar in performance to NTDS. However, UYK-43 is much faster, with two central processors each capable of 2.45 MIPS (million instructions/second) and two input/output controllers each with a throughput of 3 MIPS. Total semiconductor memory is 1024K (expandable to 2048K), plus 32K cache memory (16K for instructions, 16K for data). UYK-43 uses VLSI technology. Estimated MTBF is 56,000 hours, i.e., one failure in six years. On this basis, Unisys claims that UYK-43 is the most reliable militarized computer ever built. However, this remarkable figure should probably be seen more as heralding a generation of extremely reliable equipment, requiring far less maintenance than its predecessors.

◆ NTDS/CDS/ATDS/MTDS

The U.S. Navy Tactical Data System is the oldest such system still in use, albeit greatly updated. NTDS was the world's first shipboard tactical data system based on programmable solid-state computers and using multiple computers in a distributed tactical-data processing system. It was also the first in the world to use automatic computer-to-computer data exchange, and the first naval implementation of an "expert" computer system in the form of a threat evaluation and weapon assignment (TEWA) system.

NTDS was conceived as a means of automating the World War II–era vertical plot (the grease pencil, i.e., manual display of available radar data from all ship radars) to deal with the increasing number and speed of modern aircraft. After several experimental systems had been designed, a set of technical specifications was written in 1955. NTDS was conceived both as a single-ship system and as a means of exchanging information throughout a task force. NTDS was, therefore, based on standard computers, display terminals, and communications links; and although it was conceived initially for AAW, it was designed so that it could easily be extended to other warfare areas. Each ship would have data links connecting it to other ships, to aircraft, and to a compatible Marine Corps system on shore. Each ship could control the entire NTDS net, so that on a fleet-wide basis the system would degrade gracefully in the event of battle damage. The original NTDS concept also called for the use of programmable solid-state computers, to limit shipboard space requirements and to allow for future change. Some of these decisions were quite farsighted in 1955; for example, at that time it would have been much simpler to hardwire the computers than to make them programmable. Many contemporary systems did use special-purpose computers that, it turned out, froze system design much too early.

The data link chosen was phase-modulated HF (HF was chosen so that ships in the net could be widely dispersed, to minimize losses in the event of a nuclear attack). Message standards

TACTICAL DATA SYSTEMS

31

HF discone data-link antenna (AS-2865) for NTDS, USS *Mississippi,* June 1988. (Stefan Terzibaschitsch)

and protocols were first set by BuShips in July 1957 and later adopted by a Canadian-British-U.S. Tactical International Data Exchange (TIDE) Committee, and then by NATO as a whole. This message standard became Link 11. An alternative UHF link, Link C, was studied but rejected because of its limited range. The current system does use UHF links to nearby ships and to (and via) some aircraft.

All data had to be converted from analog to digital form. Two standards were imposed: on-line for such essential data as primary radars, gyros, and pit logs; and off-line (keyboard) for other sensors. However, the technology of radar-video extraction was relatively new at the time, and in 1955–57 it was considered impractical to provide radar-video processors (RVPs) for all the existing fleet radars. Therefore, NTDS was given a manual, rate-aided tracking capability. This manual data insertion was also available as a back-up against the failure of those RVPs that were later installed, e.g., for SPS-33 on the nuclear ships *Enterprise* and *Long Beach* and more conventional radars on the carrier *Oriskany.* Only much more recently have RVPs become the rule, sometimes via an integration system such as SYS-1/2.

In the manual system, an operator (detector/tracker) detects a target (i.e., enters it into the computer) by moving a cursor over a blip; the computer acknowledges by superimposing track symbols on the indicated position. The detector/tracker then indicates the position he associates with the same target on a later (hopefully, on the next) radar scan by moving a "ball tab," a small circle on his PPI, over that location. On each subsequent scan, the operator again corrects target position by ball tabbing the new blip (video) position and pressing a "position correction" button. After three such target confirmations, the computer begins to project the target's position, based on the target's course computed from the three positions. The operator is then responsible for checking whether the target does indeed follow this steady course and speed.

The action of the operator converts the raw analog video data into digital (position) data suitable for computer operation. In practice, the accuracy of the subsequent track projection is often reduced, as operators hit the "position correction" button three times for the same blip position, to be sure that it is entered

into the computer as a valid target. Operators are likely to be particularly tempted to do so when targets are approaching at high speed at low altitude, and thus when they are first detected at fairly close range by a radar that may well take 4 seconds or more to look again in their direction.

This rate-aided system projected a target's course and speed based entirely on the initial entry, without being able to check (except by operator intervention) whether the target continued at a steady course and speed. In theory, the operator would detect any changes by comparing the target's actual position with the projected position, but verification was not always practical when many targets were present.

Rate-aided projection was not a new idea; it was employed by several earlier systems. However, earlier rate-aided trackers were analog devices, in which a strobe could be positioned over a particular blip and then made to move to match the next appearance of the same target. Strobe position and rate of growth could be extracted from a radar console. In NTDS, a digital computer compared successive target positions and generated an estimated target position, which it sent back up to the detector/tracker's screen. Thus the detector/tracker could insert numerous targets, all of whose positions the computer would project ahead. The earlier analog trackers were limited to a single target.

With manual blip entry, many target detections were missed; and in many cases subsequent blips were missed, so that track files were not constructed or could not be maintained. Hence the importance of RVP (see Radar Integration in the Antiaircraft Warfare section).

Automation of combat data allowed for the passing of that data directly into the ship's combat system. Automation was first realized in the cruiser *Wainwright,* fitted with NTDS and WDS (Weapon Direction System) Mk 11 in 1966.

The original NTDS computer was the Univac CP-642 or USQ-20 (USQ-17 was used for development and programming), which fed a Hughes SYA-1 analog-digital display (succeeded by UYA-1). The CP-642A computer of 1960 was replaced in 1963 by CP-642B (USQ-20B), and in 1971 by the current UYK-7. UYK-7 is a 32-bit computer (storage capacity 16K, expandable to 512K) with a cycle rate of 0.6 MHz.

In contrast, USQ-20 had a capacity of 32k words (each de-

NTDS consoles on board the missile cruiser *Wainwright,* 1968. Each console has a trackball that the operator uses to position a cursor over the blip he wants to enter into the system; one such ball is visible on the table in the foreground, and one is being manipulated by the second man from the right. (U.S. Navy)

scribed as consisting of 30 bits, but more likely 32, including two parity check bits), and a repertoire of 62 instructions. The computer could use half-words for faster operation; with full words, average instruction-execution time was 13 microseconds. There were twelve input and twelve output channels, plus two input and two output channels for data transfer with another computer. There was also a 16-word auxiliary memory to store critical instructions so that the system could automatically recover in the event of program failure or for initial program loading. The earliest NTDS installations employed these machines in groups, four for a carrier and two for a large destroyer (cruiser). UYK-7s were so powerful that they could be employed individually.

The earliest remaining NTDS display, SYA-4, was designed about 1960. Using discrete transistor technology, it consisted of NTDS display consoles, special-purpose readouts, radar azimuth conversion equipment, a radar data switchboard, a pulse amplifier, and a symbol generator. There were separate consoles (with rotary switches for 22 operating modes) and communications consoles (for communication within the ship). About 1965 the current standard UYA-4 was designed. Using integrated circuits, UYA-4 was so compact that using two separate types of consoles was no longer necessary; only one designated OJ-194/UYA-4 was used. The latest version of the console is computer-driven, and it provides the operator with descriptions, such as land clutter or jamming, and automatically selects the best possible fix. Up to 1000 characters can be generated. The next stage, UYQ-21, is one of a family of advanced modular displays. Using UYQ-21, the baseline NTDS configuration is at least two computer display consoles (TDS consoles, each containing one display indicator and one digital display indicator) and a central equipment group (central data buffer, sensor converter group, and sensor data distribution switchboard). Like its predecessors, UYQ-21 can show both raw and processed video and can be used to control weapons systems. Up to 4000 characters can be displayed. Compared to UYA-4, UYQ-21 is larger (17 inches on the diagonal vs. 12 inches in diameter), has a shorter minimum range scale ($\frac{1}{2}$ vs. 1 mile), and can display much more data by using color (its 3 colors convey 8 times as much data as the single-color UYA-4).

Typically, NTDS automatically incorporates information from a ship's own sensors and similar information inserted by other ships of a force into a computer data base in the form of a map of the space around the force. Electronic intercept data is collated separately (in special secure spaces), and a sanitized version is entered manually into the data base by keyboard. The basis of the system, then, is the detector/tracker at his CRT. An analogous role is played by a separate beacon video processor tracker, who uses the TACAN air navigation beacon and IFF transponders to track friendly aircraft.

The minimum NTDS installation, then, consists of four consoles: two for the detector/trackers (one for air targets, the other for surface/subsurface targets), a summary console for the CIC supervisor, and a console for the weapons control officer (WCO). The tactical action officer (TAO) who fights the ship from CIC (under the general orders of the commanding officer) does not man a console but has access to one, to gain an overview of the tactical situation. This minimum is acceptable only for a highly automated system, employing ADT radars. In most cases there is a considerable degree of track supervision, to ensure that the detector/trackers do not miss targets that deviate from the rate-aided projections the NTDS computer assigns to them. In general, too, there is at least one detector/tracker console per search radar. Radar data are merged (in the form of processed video) in the summary consoles, such as those for the WCO and the CIC supervisor.

Generally the surface tracker/detector is also responsible for inserting sonar data, which is not entered automatically. This split between radar and sonar data reflects the AAW origin of the NTDS system.

The TAO sets target priorities (generally by exception rather than positive direction). The WCO designates assigned targets

to the weapon direction system (WDS) embedded in the NTDS. Ideally, the WDS compares target parameters with preset and entered thresholds and recommends an engagement sequence. The WCO actually selects weapons and fires them. In the *Perry* class the expectation was that some targets, such as pop-up missiles, would arrive too quickly for this sequence to work in time. The ship's NTDS was, therefore, designed for automatic engagement, the WCO having only a veto. However, that level of automation proved less than popular and was rarely, if ever, implemented. It may become more reliable as the frigate's radars are tied together using a SYS system (see the Antiaircraft Warfare section) in an ongoing current program. One advantage of full integration is that there are many fewer false targets, so a ship's commander can have more confidence in a fully automatic engagement system.

A ship controlling aircraft will often have separate consoles for air controller(s) and for intercept controller(s), and one console will be devoted to IFF. There may also be multiple consoles for each of the roles listed. For example, in the minimum installation, the air detector/tracker has to compromise in his choice of range scale. In a larger installation, there may be separate long-range and short-range air detector/trackers.

The issue of minimum NTDS requirements arose in the design of the *Perry*-class frigate. Although nominally not an NTDS ship, the frigate was designed for highly automated operation and was, therefore, provided with what amounted to a single-ship NTDS system. The ship was designed in 1972 with four consoles (UYA-4s), but that fall it was proposed that the number be cut to three, to keep the ship within her cost target. That cut would have required the amalgamation of two functions, e.g., supervisor and long-range air detector/tracker, proving unacceptable. As it was, the reduction to only four consoles was practicable only because the ship employed automatically detecting radars. In the *Perry* class's design, the division between air and surface detector/trackers was relatively easy because one could monitor the SPS-49 radar and the other the SPS-55 or Mk 92. Ideally there would have been at least one other console, so that the SPS-55 and Mk 92 data could have been monitored separately.

In the *Perry* class's CIC, the surface detector/tracker and WCO consoles (both UYA-4s) flank a CIC supervisor (horizontal operational summary display) console. The air director/tracker's UYA-4 is on one side of CIC, flanked by a weapons control console (WCC) and an ECM console; there is also a second weapons control console. A tactical coordinator (TACCO) operates a fourth UYA-4 (actually the fifth NTDS console in CIC). The NTDS computers are backed by a classical grease-pencil vertical plot, standing behind the three main consoles (WCO, CIC supervisor, and surface detector/tracker). The sonar equipment (including the LAMPS helicopter processor) is in an adjacent space. Like other CIC arrangements, this one was developed from a mock-up emphasizing quick communication between men at nearby displays. The CIC also includes other equipment, such as a separate radar display (SPA-25) for helicopter control and a dead-reckoning tracer to assist in antisubmarine attacks. Full integration would eliminate both, except as backups.

Because she was designed to cost, *Perry* was not provided with Link 11; however, space was provided for the necessary UYK-7 expansion, which is now being accomplished.

Some typical NTDS configurations are listed on the next page. The data are as of 1979, but (apart from NTU modernization) they are almost certainly still valid.

These figures understate the number of computers on board ships. For example, the destroyer *Mahan* (DDG 37), a very early NTDS ship, has a second USQ-20 computer for her SPS-48 radar. The missile cruiser *Texas* employs four additional UYK-7s, one each for fire-control systems Mk 74 and Mk 116, one for electronic warfare, and one for her radars. In addition to the UYA-4 displays listed, she has two operational summary UYA-4 displays and two OJ-200 displays. CG 28 (*Wainwright*) was the first ship completed with NTDS integrated with her

Equipment	FFG 7	CG 28	CG 24	DDG 37	CGN 39	CV 41	CV 59	CVN 68	DD 963
UYK-7	1	–	–	–	2	–	1	–	3
USQ-20	–	1	1	1	–	1	1	1	–
CP-642A	–	3	3 (642B)	3 (642B)	–	4 (642B)	4	11 (642B)	–
UYA-4	4	2	16	14	17	24	2	24	10
SYA-4 (INPUT)	–	7	–	–	–	–	10	–	–
SYA-4 (USER)	–	6	–	–	–	–	13	–	–

weapons direction system (WDS); CG 24 (*Reeves*) typifies refits in which NTDS was installed.

Of the carriers, CV 41 (*Midway*) was an early installation. She required an additional CP-642B computer to handle her Ships Inertial Navigation System (SINS). *Forrestal* had, in addition to the computers listed above, two CP-642Bs for her radars and one CP-642B for her SINS. Presumably the two CP-642Bs handled the SPS-58 interface with NATO Sea Sparrow and the SPS-48 radar.

The listing for the *Nimitz* (CVN 68) is somewhat deceptive because only four of the CP-642B computers were devoted to NTDS itself. The presence of seven others shows the extent to which modern combat subsystems require their own computer support: one for SINS, one for SPS-48, one for NATO Sea Sparrow, and probably at least one to manage ECM. In the next carrier, *Dwight D. Eisenhower*, one UYK-7 was combined with one USQ-20 and ten CP-642Bs, four of which were dedicated to NTDS.

Finally, the listing for the destroyer *Spruance* shows that even a non-AAW form of NTDS could be quite complex. Of the three UYK-7s listed, one was a three-bay (i.e., expanded memory) type, to support ASW operations.

Operational experience with NTDS ships showed that they could handle much more complex situations than their predecessors. However, the central computer system was responsible for virtually all shipboard functions, so that there was no usable backup combat mode. NTDS operation depended upon computer viability, which in turn depended upon factors such as providing sufficient chilled water to keep the computers from overheating. Newer computers, such as UYK-43, are much more reliable than their predecessors and use technology (such as VLSI) that is more tolerant of higher temperatures and thus less liable to fail if a ship loses some of her auxiliary systems.

CDS, the Combat Direction System, is the successor to NTDS and is currently used on board Aegis ships. In effect, CDS is the form of NTDS adapted to Aegis.

ACDS is the Advanced Combat Direction System. Block 0 is a restructured NTDS with new software, entering service in FY87. Block 1 incorporates the Joint Tactical Information Data System (JTIDS) and has improved high-data-rate networking.

ATDS is the Airborne Tactical Data System, carried on board the E-2 radar aircraft. Its air-to-air link to fighters is Link 4 (now Link 4A). ATDS had an impact comparable to that of NTDS, although it has received much less publicity. The last pre-ATDS AEW airplane was the Grumman WF-1 (E-1B), which carried an airborne CIC. It was comparable in character to contemporary shipboard CICs: it was credited with a capacity to maintain 4 to 6 tracks, and its two radar operators could arrange no more than two simultaneous intercepts, using voice radio. In contrast, even before the first E-2A had flown in 1960, it was expected that computerization would increase the number of tracks to 250 and the number of simultaneous intercepts to 30, all conducted by automatic data link. The drastically different architecture of the E-2A system is reflected in the very different arrangement of the crew: one radar operator instead of two, an air control operator, and a combat information center operator. The E-2A's new APS-96 radar automatically detected targets. Newer versions of the E-2, with better computers, can handle many more tracks and many more simultaneous engagements (see APS-120 and successors in the Antiaircraft Warfare section). This drastic improvement in AEW capacity might be likened to the impact of NTDS on a missile ship otherwise limited by her

Weapons Direction System (WDS; see the Antiaircraft Warfare section).

MTDS is the analogous Marine Tactical Data System. Its roles include bringing in fire support to protect Marines in forward positions.

Note that until about 1968 the U.S. Navy also used an analog tactical data system, the Electronic Data System (EDS), comparable to the British CDS of that period. EDS was replaced by NTDS. A total of twenty EDSs were bought, and they were installed on board four radar picket destroyers, as well as on missile cruisers (none of which has survived).

Perhaps the greatest problem of NTDS operation has been gridlock, the means of assuring that all ships in an NTDS net use the same coordinates to identify the same points in space, i.e., truly share a common grid. If the units do not, then the same target detected by two ships may be counted as two different targets, and thus assigned two (of a limited total number of) tracking and engagement channels. The gridlock problem has now, finally, apparently been solved, initially using Aegis hardware.

NAVIGATIONAL SYSTEMS

FRANCE

◆ Syledis

Syledis is a precision hyperbolic navigation system used by French Tripartite Minehunters, operating at VHF frequency. See Decca (below) for an explanation of hyperbolic navigation. Syledis was developed specially for the Tri-Partite program. The minehunters were also fitted with Thomson-CSF TSM 5700 doppler sonars to measure velocity (both fore and aft and lateral) over the ground.

◆ Toran

Toran is a precision circular navigation system used by French Tri-Partite Minehunters, operating at HF frequency. Distances to two transponder beacons are compared, and position is found by triangulation. The Toran shore system is operated by the French lighthouse and navigational beacon authority.

◆ Trident III

Trident III is a three-beacon position-fixing system developed by Thomson-CSF and installed on board some export mine-countermeasures craft.

USSR

There are two major satellite navigational systems, one comparable to the U.S. Transit and the other to the U.S. Global Position Satellite (GPS). The Transit equivalent consists of six satellites in 60-degree orbits and six in 30-degree orbits. GLONASS is reportedly comparable to GPS, the first three satellites having been orbited in October 1982.

There are also several surface systems. One of them, ALPHA, is similar to the U.S. Omega. It is not clear whether the designation is Soviet.

UNITED KINGDOM

◆ Decca

This navigational system was developed by the Admiralty Signals Establishment from 1937 on; Decca was first used to guide small craft and minesweepers during the Normandy Invasion in 1944. The Decca Navigator Company was founded to further develop the system after the war, and to operate the associated system of transmitters. Although not as accurate as such higher-frequency systems as Hi-Fix/6, it is still used as a back-up in mine countermeasures and would be available in wartime to guide merchant ships through cleared minefields. Decca is effective at short and medium ranges; Loran and Omega are long-range systems.

Like Loran, Decca uses master and slave stations and measures position by forming a hyperbolic grid. All such systems are based on the geometric fact that all points for which the difference between the distances to two fixed points is the same form a hyperbola between them. A series of differences defines a series of hyperbolas, and in theory a user can determine on which hyperbola he lies. A second pair of stations provides a second series of hyperbolas, and position is determined by the intersections between the two series.

Decca operates at low frequency, 70–130 kHz, with a nominal maximum range of 240 nm. Average maximum position errors at this range are 150 yds by day and 1200 yds by night; at 100 nm from the master station, the average errors are 30 and 100 yds, respectively. Typically a chain consists of a master and three slave stations. The signals are all CW, distances being measured by comparison in phase between master and slave signals. Because phase changes are cyclic, position can be measured only within one 360-degree cycle, which is called a lane. Special supplementary signals are transmitted so that a receiver can determine in which lane it is located.

♦ Hi-Fix/6

Hi-Fix/6 is a Racal Marine Systems (formerly Decca) precise navigation system, operating at 2 MHz, essentially a higher-frequency equivalent of Decca. Hi-Fix/6 and the earlier Hi-Fix are used by some mine-countermeasures craft (such as Belgian and Dutch Tripartite Minehunters and by British craft). Hi-Fix/6 is now being superseded by Hyperfix (see below).

♦ Hyperfix

Hyperfix is a Racal Marine Systems precise navigation system, superseding the earlier Hi-Fix/6. Like Decca and Hi-Fix, Hyperfix uses phase comparison. The system operates at 2 MHz (actually the 1.5–3.5 MHz band), with a repeatable accuracy of 5 m at 250 km at night (500 km in daytime), described as 20 times better than earlier 2-MHz systems. Ranges as great as 700 km are available much of the time, depending on ionospheric conditions. Accuracy is often between 1 and 2 m.

Each station in the chain transmits signals at two frequencies about 1 percent apart. As in Decca and Hi-Fix, phase comparison is used to determine position within a lane. The lane is determined (within a group of about 100) by comparison between the phases of the two signals. At the frequency used, a lane is about 75 m wide at the baseline. Resolution is 0.001 lanes (but the display is not fine enough to fully exploit this accuracy).

Hyperfix has been deployed in chains of remotely controlled stations around Britain. The system has been adopted by Canada and at present is being supplied under contract to the U.S. Navy. Twenty-four stations are being supplied in the Persian Gulf under Japanese contract.

♦ Micro-Fix

Micro-Fix is a new Racal 5-GHz line-of-sight system with an accuracy about 1 m out to 80 km. The ship transmits a signal that is returned from two or more portable shore stations for triangulation. Racal claims that this system is unique in being continuously self-compensating. The company is now developing a nonradiating hyperbolic variant.

UNITED STATES

♦ GPS (NAVSTAR)

Global Positioning System will be completed by 1990. It will fix position within about 16 m (spherical accuracy), and velocity within 0.1 m/sec. With such accuracy, GPS becomes a means of guiding weapons against fixed targets, and several recent weapons, such as SLAM, are to incorporate GPS receivers.

A user automatically chooses the four most suitably located satellites and locks onto their navigation signals, obtaining a pseudorange (time difference) to each. These four pseudoranges in turn figure in four simultaneous equations, which the specialized Navstar computer solves for user position.

The first series, whose launchings began in February 1978, cover the continental United States and are intended primarily for test and validation. Ultimately, an 18-satellite constellation will provide global coverage. Satellites orbit at 10,898 nm, with a 12-hour period. Each weighs 1020 lbs and is expected to last 5 years (carrying 7 years' worth of consumables, primarily booster fuel).

Including in-orbit spares, the total system consists of 28 satellites.

♦ Loran/Omega

Long Range Navigation system was originally devised during World War II and is now quite common on a worldwide scale. Omega is a variation. The basic unit consists of a "master" emitting timed pulses and a transponder ("slave") some distance (usually about 500 nm) away. A ship equipped with Loran listens for both master and slave pulses. The time difference between the two indicates the difference in path between the two stations, since the slave emits only after the master pulse has traveled the distance between master and slave stations. This time difference in turn defines a hyperbola on which the listener must be located. By listening to two pairs, the ship can locate itself on two intersecting hyperbolas (the system is often called hyperbolic navigation or hyperbolic fixing). Accuracy depends on the ratio of ship's distance from the baseline to baseline length; the longer the baseline, the better. Therefore, the tendency in Loran has been toward lower frequencies that propagate better over greater distances.

The original Loran-A operated at 1850–1950 kHz with a range of about 450–800 nm by day and 1400 nm by night, using ground wave transmission. Loran-A was very widely deployed in the North Atlantic and North Pacific between 1955 and 1970. Loran-B was an abortive attempt to achieve greater range by reducing frequency. Stations proved difficult to synchronize, and the ground and sky waves interfered. Loran-C solved these problems by using synchronized pulses for both time-difference and phase comparison, and -C became operational in 1957. As coverage expanded, -C superseded Loran-A, which was largely abandoned in 1977. Loran-C operates at 90–110 kHz. Ground wave range is 1200 nm, but signals can also propagate by sky wave (range with one reflection from the ionosphere is about 2300 nm, and with two reflections about 4000 nm; the latter can be received only at night).

The purpose of the master/slave combination is to synchronize signals from the two stations of the hyperbolic pair. During the late 1960s, atomic time standards that made for simpler operation were developed. Pulses were synchronized by time standard. The secondary (formerly slave) station transmitted upon receiving the master pulse but did not have to retransmit the original pulse. The system uses a form of pulse compression to achieve very long range and compares details of the pulse to avoid confusing ground and sky waves.

Omega operates at 10–14 kHz. At such very low frequencies, signals penetrate the sea surface and can be used by submarines operating at periscope depth. By using atomic time standards to synchronize very distant stations, Omega can exploit base lines as long as 5000–6000 nm; a total of eight stations (the last of which, in Australia, entered service in 1982) cover the entire globe, three and usually four stations being usable from any position. As in Decca, phase difference is used for positioning, each lane being 8 nm wide on the baseline. Lane identification is by phase comparison of three auxiliary signals multiplexed with the basic 10.2-kHz signal. A ship finds her approximate position by some other means, to within about 50 nm, and then uses Omega to obtain a better fix. Once an initial fix is obtained, a receiver can count lanes crossed to maintain an accurate fix. Positions can be obtained within 1 or 2 nm.

◆ PINS (SSN-2)

The Magnavox PINS (Precise Integrated Navigation System) is installed on board the new U.S. *Avenger*-class minesweeper/hunters, following tests on board the older minesweeper *Pluck*. PINS was designed to operate with or without the assistance of shore-based fixed reference systems, and also in very deep water, integrating all available references: Loran-C, Raydist, Transit (and then GPS) navigational satellites, and a doppler bottom log effective to depths as great as 20,000 ft. The bottom log measures true ship's speed, so that position can be measured accurately between satellite passes. PINS is also used to record mine contacts and the ship's track through an area.

◆ Raydist

The Hastings Raydist "T" is a commercial hyperbolic (phase comparison) navigational system broadly comparable to Decca and its successors, originally adopted for the sweeping of Hanoi-Haiphong in 1973 and still in use as a U.S. alternative to other fixed systems. In 1972 the United States had no such system, and navigational accuracy was no better than 100 to 250 yds; a more precise system had been sought for a quarter-century. Two ground networks and 33 receivers were purchased in October 1972 and installed on board the sweeping helicopters, the mine clearance ship MSS 2, and two ocean sweepers. Each ground network consisted of two CW and two single-side-band (SSB) transmitters. During the 1973 clearance operation, average navigational error was reduced to 10–20 yards.

◆ SINS

SINS stands for Ship's Inertial Navigation System; it is presumed that the Soviets have an analog. SINS is the basic sensor of the U.S. Navy's ballistic missile program (Polaris, Poseidon, Trident) since SINS is the nonemitting submarine position-and-motion indicator. In practice, SINS data are updated every so often by using Transit or some alternative navigational satellite, but any such update requires the submarine to put a detectable radio antenna through the surface. SINS's performance is measured in terms of the required reset interval to determine position to within a given error. Perhaps the major source of error is drag exerted on the main SINS gyro by its supporting structures.

Compared to the inertial sensor of a missile, SINS must function over much longer periods at much lower velocities. Otherwise, it is identical in concept: measured submarine acceleration is integrated to provide submarine velocity and then integrated again to provide submarine position. The missile's fire-control system requires not only the absolute position of the submarine (latitude and longitude) but also its heading, speed (north and east components), roll, pitch, and vertical velocity (heave), a total of eight parameters.

Work on SINS began in 1954, based on the research done for the inertial navigation system of the air force's Navaho cruise missile. The first unit, installed in the USS *Compass Island* and the USS *Nautilus*, was a modified missile N6A, with a gas spin gyro bearing. Mk 2 Mod 0 was introduced in the *George Washington*–class ballistic missile submarines, with a total of 56 being built (3 per submarine). Installation of a new stable platform-housing with fewer temperature gradients and airflow variations converted these units to Mod 4. A new SINS, Mod 2, was introduced to support the longer-range Polaris A-3. It incorporated a new gyro with greater angular momentum (i.e., less affected by unwanted torques). Mod 2 was installed in the *James Madison* class. Mod 3 introduced an additional monitor gyro, identical to the main gyro, that compensated for drift in the two leveling gyros. Mod 3 was installed in all ballistic missile submarines but the *George Washington* class. For Poseidon, with its greater range (2600 nm), Mod 3 was modified to a new Mod 6 configuration.

A new electrostatic-gyro-support technology was developed for Trident submarines, although early units have the earlier Mk 2 SINS.

SINS is installed on board carriers, where it provides initial data to aircraft navigation systems (CAINS, the carrier aircraft inertial navigation system).

◆ TACAN

Tactical Air Navigation system is a transponder that provides aircraft with accurate distance and heading information. The antenna rotates within a radome, producing a series of coded pulses: bearing relative to magnetic north, beacon identification, and beacon distance. Equipment on board the aircraft processes these pulses to provide location data. Because TACAN is a transponder, it is somewhat more discreet than the earlier beacons, which emitted whether or not they were required. Current U.S. TACANs operate on 252 channels (evenly divided for reception and transmission) in L-band (1025–1150 MHz for reception, 962–1024 and 1151–1213 MHz for transmission). TACANs can communicate with up to 100 aircraft within a 300-mile radius. Ships generally carry a single TACAN antenna, mounted at the masthead. There are four standard antennas, URN-20, URN-25, SRN-6, and SRN-15, all of which provide the same type of pulse train.

The Soviet equivalents are Top Knot, in the *Kiev*-class carriers, and various versions of Round House, which are always mounted in pairs, either fore and aft or athwartships.

◆ Transit

Transit was the first U.S. satellite navigation system, developed by the Applied Physics Laboratory (APL) to exploit the doppler effects of passing emitting satellites like the first Soviet Sputnik. APL used doppler data to measure the Sputnik's orbit but then realized that, given a known orbit, doppler data could be used to measure position on the ground. Transit was proposed in 1958, primarily to support the Polaris submarine program, and was placed in full-time service in 1964, becoming the first U.S. operational satellite system. It was made available for commercial use in 1967.

The current Transit system consists of six 100-pound solar-powered satellites in 600-nm orbits, each carrying a precise crystal clock and emitting orbital signals. Accuracy at a fixed site is about 100 ft.

STRATEGIC STRIKE SYSTEMS

CHINA (PRC)

◆ C-SS-N-3

Dimensions: approx 1.5 × 10 m (60 in × 33 ft)
Weight: approx 14,000 kg (30,000 lbs)
Warhead: one (reports vary on yield)
Range: est 2700–3600 km (1750 to 2300 nm)

C-SS-N-3. (*Ships of the World*)

The first submerged launch was carried out on 12 October 1982 by the single Golf-class trials submarine, at a range of 1600 km. The missile has two solid-propellant stages. Twelve missiles can be carried by Xia-class submarines; in 1988, two such submarines had been completed and two were under construction. Reportedly this weapon was developed in part from the CSS-2 (DF-3) land-based ballistic missile, which has a range of 2700 km and which carries a single 1-to-3-MT warhead (and, in its newer version, three Multiple Reentry Vehicles (MRVs), 50–100 kT each). This missile was first fired by a Xia-class submarine during July 1988. The Chinese designation is Ju Lang 1 (JL-1).

An improved C-SS-NX-4 is currently under development; reportedly this improved version carries a 2-MT warhead.

FRANCE

◆ M20

Dimensions: 1.5 × 10.4 m (5.2 m first stage, 2.6 m second stage) [59 in × 34.1 ft; 17.1 ft, 8.5 ft]
Weight: 21,000 kg (46,300 lbs)
Warhead: megaton range (TN-60); later replaced by an improved TN-61
Propulsion: solid-fuel rocket: Type 904 first stage, Rita IIP6 second stage. Burn duration: first stage 50 sec (45,000-kg thrust); second stage 52 sec (32,000-kg thrust). [99,200/70,500-lbs thrust]
Range: 3000 km (1900 nm)

M20 was the second-generation French naval ballistic missile, succeeding the original M1 and the longer-range M2. M20 is an M2 with a megaton warhead accompanied by penetration aids (decoys); it is intended specifically to penetrate the missile defense around Moscow. The thermonuclear warhead is hardened

A Chinese Xia-class submarine armed with C-SS-N-3 missiles. (*Ships of the World*)

against ballistic-missile defenses, presumably such radiation effects as neutrons and EMP. This missile may also be designed to use a steep energy-inefficient trajectory that limits exposure to defensive radars by reducing time spent in their beams.

The M20 missile is cold-launched by compressed air and is aerodynamically unstable. Note that the second stage and the warhead are the same as those of the S3 ground-launched strategic missile. M20 became operational in 1977 (on board the submarine *Indomptable*). Only one submarine, *Le Redoutable*, still carries this missile; all of the other submarines have been converted to fire the newer M4.

◆ M4

> **Dimensions:** 1.93 × 11.05 m (76.0 in × 36.2 ft)
> **Weight:** 35,000 kg (77,140 lbs)
> **Warhead:** six 150-kT TN-70 (MIRVs)
> **Propulsion:** two-stage rocket with powered MIRV bus. first stage: Type 401(P10), 71,000-kg thrust; second stage: Type 402(P6), 30,000-kg thrust; third stage: Type 403, 7000-kg thrust. (156,500/66,100/15,400-lbs thrust)
> **Range:** 4500 km (2900 nm)

M4 is the multiple-warhead (MIRV) successor to M20. Almost twice as heavy as M20, M4 is designed to fit the launch tubes of existing French strategic submarines. Exploiting French research into small thermonuclear warheads, the French government decided to proceed with M4 in December 1974. Compared to M20, M4 is an all-new missile with new first- (401), second- (402), and third- (403) stage motors. The latter powers the warhead-dispensing bus.

The M4 missile is launched by a powder charge; M4 can be fired at greater depths than M20 and can be fired in closer sequence than the earlier weapon. The six TN-70 warheads are spread over a 150 × 350 km (97 × 227 nm) area.

M4 was first fired at sea on 10 March 1982 and became op-

erational in 1985 on board the submarine *L'Inflexible*. M4 now arms all earlier strategic submarines except *Le Redoutable*; conversion of that ship would have required the installation of new (rather than modified) launch tubes.

Delays in M5 development have led to a new program for an interim weapon, M45, which is to enter service in 1994 on board the submarine *Le Triomphant*, the first of a new generation. M45 can carry a TN-71 warhead to a nominal range of 5000 km (3200 nm); however, an M45 carrying a single warhead reached 6000 km on 4 March 1986. Operational M45s will carry six new TN-76 "stealth" warheads, presumably to evade Soviet ballistic-missile defenses.

◆ M5

The M5 missile is under development for projected second-generation strategic submarines (the first missiles will go to sea in the third submarine of the class). Design requirements include a range of 3240 nm and eight to twelve TN-75 MIRV warheads; radar signature may be reduced, and penetration aids added, to counter Soviet ballistic-missile defenses. This weapon was initially described as M4C.

The French submarine-launched ballistic missile M5 emerging from the water. (Armées d'aujourd'hui–SIRPA)

◆ ASMP

> **Dimensions:** 0.30 m × 5.38 × 0.96 m over fins (11.8 × 211.8 × 37.8 inches)
> **Weight:** 840 kg (1851 lbs) **Warhead:** 300-kT
> **Propulsion:** integral rocket-ramjet; maximum speed Mach 3.5
> **Range:** 80+ km at Mach 2, low altitude; 250+ km at Mach 3, high altitude (52 and 162 nm)

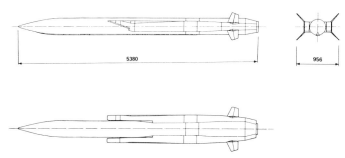

ASMP. The dimensions are in millimeters. (Aerospatiale)

A medium-range nuclear standoff missile, ASMP (*Air-Sol Moyenne Portée*) is designed for use against both tactical and strategic targets. ASMP is carried by 24 (of a total of 55) Super-Étendard carrier attack aircraft as well as by French land-based tactical (Mirage 2000N) and strategic (Mirage IVP) aircraft. Note that in French official parlance the word "tactical" was changed to "prestrategic" before the ASMP went into service, to em-

ASMP under the wing of a Super-Étendard. (Aerospatiale)

phasize French reliance on deterrence through the threat of escalation. In the case of the Super-Étendard, ASMP replaces a standard nuclear gravity bomb (the 60-kT AN-52, first deployed in 1977). This program began in March 1978 after a government decision to proceed with an aircraft-carried standoff weapon for attacking hardened targets. ASMP was, therefore, primarily a way of extending the usefulness of the French strategic air arm.

The carrier *Foch* was refitted in 1987–88 to carry ASMP in place of the earlier AN-52 bombs. However, her sister, *Clemenceau*, is not being refitted because she is to be replaced by the new nuclear carrier *Richelieu* about 1996. It is reported that the French Navy wanted a lower-yield version for antiship attack, but finances precluded development of two versions of the basic weapon.

The size of the missile was limited so that it could be carried by a Mirage 2000N. The missile design has some stealth features, including some radar absorbing material. In addition, ASMP is hardened against EMP.

ASMP's aerodynamic design is unusual, having two prominent angled air intakes, whose fairings lead back to the after end, but no wings as such. At very high speeds, the intakes and fairings provide sufficient lift, and the only special aerodynamic surfaces are the four fins at the tail. The intake fairings carry such auxiliary equipment as the actuators for the fins. The air intakes are modeled on those of the Concorde airliner.

There are three alternative flight modes: high-altitude/terminal dive, low-altitude terrain following, or low-altitude with terminal pop-up for air burst (against naval targets). In the latter case, the missile would be targeted for specific radars, attacking from relatively short range (effective range is limited to about 60 km (39 nm) by the radar horizon of a low-flying attack aircraft). All three flight modes include preprogrammed evasive maneuvers.

The engine is probably the most interesting feature of the missile. The initial choice, a solid-fuel rocket, was rejected because it would have been much too heavy, resulting in an unacceptable 3-to-4-ton missile. Instead, a solid-fuel booster is used to accelerate the missile to Mach 2, at which speed the main ramjet is efficient. The rocket burns out in about 5 seconds, and about 1/20 second later the nozzle is ejected. The burnt-out booster becomes the combustion chamber, a "swirl type" developed since 1972. There can be no conventional flame holder (since all the volume of the chamber is occupied by the solid booster), so the flame is stabilized by the two jets of air from the air intakes, forming what amounts to a fluid flameholder. The fuel is conventional kerosene rather than the denser Shelldyne used in U.S. cruise missiles, the former fuel being much better known in France when ASMP was designed. However, a second-generation cruise missile will use denser fuel.

ASMP first flew on 23 June 1983 and was the first European missile to shift automatically from rocket to ramjet mode. The missile became operational on 1 May 1986 on board Mirage IVP bombers of the FAS (*Forces Aériennes Stratégiques*). Total planned production is about 100 weapons.

USSR

♦ SS-N-3 Shaddock

See the surface-strike section for the strategic version of this tactical missile.

♦ SS-N-5 Sark (R-21)

> **Dimensions:** 4 ft × 42 ft   **Weight:** 36,700 lbs
> **Warhead:** 1 × 800-kT   **Propulsion:** liquid-fuel rocket
> **Range:** 900 nm (originally 750 nm)   **CEP:** 3000 m [3280 yds]

Soviet SS-N-5 missiles on parade. (*Ships of the World*)

This is the main survivor of a large naval strategic program that included the earlier SS-N-4 ballistic missile and the strategic version of SS-N-3. SS-N-4 was the first Soviet missile that could be fired from a submerged submarine. It is carried by 13 Golf-II-class submarines (6 in the Baltic, 7 in the Far East). SS-N-21 and SS-N-6 (now that most remaining Yankee-class SSBNs are operating in European and, presumably, Asian, waters) may be the functional successors, as the Golf boats wear out.

SS-N-5 entered service in 1963. R-21 was the Soviet designation (design bureau designation D-4), the earlier SS-N-4 being R-13. Initial tests began in 1961, the test platform firing at depths of 65–100 ft. The missile was propelled to 100 ft above the surface by compressed air. SS-N-5 was reportedly designed by the Yangel bureau, which was also responsible for the first Soviet naval ballistic missile, a navalized Scud, and for SS-N-4.

SS-N-4 in turn succeeded a navalized Scud (SS-1B), which the Soviets had designated R-11FM. Two such missiles were mounted in the sails of six modified Zulu-class (Zulu-5) submarines. These missiles had to be lifted to the top of the sail before they could be fueled and fired, and firing could be done only in calm seas. Reportedly dissatisfaction with the system and limits on Soviet fissionable materials caused the Soviet Navy to use only conventional warheads on its R-11FMs.

♦ SS-N-6 Serb

> **Dimensions:** 72 × 396 in   **Weight:** 41,600 lbs
> **Warhead:** one 650–700-kT in Mods 1 and 2; two 350-kT RV in
>   Mod 3.   **Propulsion:** two-stage liquid rocket
> **Range:** 1300 nm (Mod 1); 1600 nm (Mod 2); 1600 nm (Mod 3)
> **CEP:** 1 nm

SS-N-6 was the first modern Soviet sea-launched ballistic missile, enough smaller than SS-N-4/5 that a useful number (sixteen) could be carried by one submarine. This ship, a Yankee-class submarine, was designed to carry SS-N-6. From 1967 until the advent of Typhoon in the 1980s, all Soviet ballistic-missile submarines were direct developments of this one. SS-N-6 could be carried in numbers because it was so much shorter than SS-N-5, which filled not only the depth of the submarine hull but also the height of its sail. SS-N-6 required only a small protrusion above the submarine hull. (U.S. Navy)

This was the first modern Soviet naval ballistic missile, carried on board Yankee-I-class submarines. It is reported that about 1000 were built. Because range was only 1300 nm at first, submarines carrying Serb had to approach the U.S. coast to fire. That range reflected the secondary role assigned to Soviet naval forces when the weapon was conceived (probably about 1960) and deployed (1968). Official doctrine then was that submarines would remain in reserve while the land-based strategic rocket force engaged targets in North America; the submarines would be used either for terminal bargaining or for a second-phase attack. The surge requirement explains the Western assumption that the contemporary Victor-class ASW submarine was conceived as a Yankee escort.

In practice, Yankees patrolled off the U.S. coast during the 1970s and 1980s; some analysts assumed that the assigned role of these submarines was to destroy key U.S. command-and-control facilities at the outbreak of war. The Soviets would certainly not have expected these boats to survive very long after the outbreak of war, in waters dominated by the U.S. Navy. By 1988 the Yankees had been withdrawn to European waters, perhaps to replace the SS-20 land-based missiles scrapped under the new Intermediate Nuclear Forces treaty. Yankees returned to the U.S. east coast during the summer of 1988, after the treaty had been ratified.

SS-N-6 is liquid-fueled, the fuel being replaced periodically and the missile refurbished. Possibly because of problems with missile fuel, a Yankee-class submarine suffered a missile tube explosion in the Atlantic, ultimately sinking on 6 October 1986 off Bermuda. It is difficult to avoid concluding that these weapons are deteriorating despite maintenance and, therefore, that the force as a whole may be losing its effectiveness.

All operational missiles are SS-N-6 Mod 3, carrying two MRVs.

SS-N-6 was reportedly designed by the Chelomei bureau, which was also responsible for some cruise missiles. This missile reportedly shared some characteristics of the earlier land-based SS-11, which Chelomei also designed, and was reportedly developed as part of Khrushchev's seven-year plan (1959–65), the tactical-technical requirement having been drafted in 1958. According to a former Soviet naval officer involved in missile development, the original requirement was for a single-stage underwater-launched missile 180 × 1000 cm (71 × 394 inches, i.e., 4 m [157 inches] shorter than the existing SS-N-4), with a maximum weight of 19 metric tons, a range of 2400 km (1300 nm), and a CEP of 1 km (0.54 nm); the missile would carry a single 0.7-MT reentry vehicle. The rival Yangel bureau had just completed work on the SS-N-5 (1300-km [700-nm] range) and was concentrating on land-based missiles (SS-9). SS-N-6 was first flight-tested in 1966, and it entered service in 1968. Mod 2 was an interim longer-range version, developed by the Chelomei bureau while work proceeded on SS-N-8; Mod 2 provided 550 km (300 nm) more range, partly by reducing warhead weight (to 650-kT yield).

◆ SS-N-8 Sawfly

Dimensions: 5.3 ft × 42 ft   **Weight:** 30,000 kg (66,000 lbs)
Warhead: one 1.2-MT (Mod 1) or two 800-kT (Mod 2)
Propulsion: liquid-fuel rockets
Range: 4240 nm (Mod 1); 4950 nm (Mod 2)
CEP: 0.84 nm (Mod 2)

SS-N-8 symbolized a shift in Soviet strategic doctrine: the navy achieved parity with the strategic rocket force. Submarines had to be able to fire at any time after the outbreak of war. This missile, therefore, was given sufficient range for it to be fired from its peacetime operating area, i.e., from a sanctuary (bastion) area dominated by the Soviet Navy. SS-N-8 incorporated stellar-inertial guidance, in hopes of achieving useful accuracy even from the bastions. Reportedly the stellar-inertial system was not always reliable, and initial reports of spectacular accuracy were exaggerated. The maximum range achieved during testing has been 9200 km, which is the longest of any current naval strategic missile.

Delta, carrying the SS-N-8 missile, is essentially a Yankee (SS-N-6) with longer missile tubes. The original Delta, shown here, even retained the lower after end of the missile tube section, and the difference in height is a measure of the difference in missile length. (U.S. Navy)

Sawfly is carried by Delta-I- and -II-class submarines and by the sole experimental Golf-III, which was presumably the test ship. This weapon entered service in 1973. This missile's design is reportedly based on the SS-N-6's.

◆ SS-N-17 Snipe

Dimensions: 5.3 ft × 36.3 ft (approx)   **Weight:** approx 45,000 lbs
Warhead: one 800-kT or two 500-kT
Propulsion: solid-fuel rocket
Range: 2000 nm (also given as 2500 nm)   **CEP:** 1400 m (1500 yds)

This was the first Soviet solid-fueled naval ballistic missile. It is carried by a single Yankee-II-class submarine, apparently a system test ship. SS-N-17 was first tested in 1975 and appeared at sea in 1977. This missile reportedly uses some SS-16/20 technology and itself led to SS-N-20.

◆ SS-N-18 Stingray (RSM 50)

Dimensions: 6 × 46 ft   **Weight:** 34,000 kg (75,000 lbs)
Warhead: three 200-kT MIRV (Mod 1), or one 450-kT (Mod 2), or seven 200-kT MIRV (Mod 3)
Propulsion: liquid-fuel rockets (two stages)
Range: 3530 nm (Mod 1 or Mod 3) or 4350 nm (Mod 2)
CEP: Reported as 875 or 1200 yds

The height of the missile section of this Delta-III is a measure of the great length of its SS-N-18 missile; the sail proper, at the forward end of the missile section, is the same height as that of a Yankee. (U.S. Navy)

SS-N-18 was the first Soviet naval MIRV missile, using storable liquid propellant as in SS-N-6/8. Mod 1 was introduced in 1977 and Mod 2 in 1979. SS-N-18 is carried on board Delta-III-class submarines. When SS-N-18 entered service, it was the

No photo of SS-N-21 has been released, but in connection with the Intermediate-Range Nuclear Forces Treaty the Soviets did release this photograph of its land-based version, SS-C-4. (Department of Defense)

largest naval strategic missile in the world. This missile was first flown in 1976.

◆ SS-N-20 Sturgeon (RSM 52)

Dimensions: 7.2 × 49 ft   **Weight:** 60,000 kg (132,200 lbs)
Warhead: six to nine 100-kT MIRV
Propulsion: solid-fuel (three stages)
Range: 4300 nm   **CEP:** 550 to 650 yds

SS-N-20 is a solid-fueled missile, carried by Typhoon-class submarines. It was first tested, unsuccessfully, in January 1980, but successful tests were reported in 1981; and in October 1982, four were launched by a submerged submarine. Reportedly problems with this weapon delayed the Typhoon program, the submarine being ready well before the missile had become sufficiently reliable.

This missile reportedly embodies SS-N-17 technology.

◆ SS-N-21

Dimensions: 51 cm × 8.09 m (canister: 65 cm × 8.39 m) (span approx 300 cm) [20.1 × 318.5/25.6 × 330.3 inches]
Weight: 1700 kg (2440 kg with canister) [3747/5378 lbs]
Propulsion: Turbojet with rocket booster   **Range:** 1600 nm

SS-N-21 is the Soviet equivalent of the U.S. Tomahawk strategic cruise missile. There are two other versions: the land-based SS-C-X-4 and the air-launched AS-15 (KENT). Details were taken from the Soviet description of SS-C-X-4, released as part of the Intermediate Nuclear Forces treaty. SS-C-X-4 is carried in a 65-cm canister; it seems likely that the naval version is carried similarly. It follows that the weapon can be fired only from a 65-cm torpedo tube. Reported speed is Mach 0.7.

Yankee-class submarines are being converted to carry this missile, in a new midships section with horizontal launching tubes. The estimated capacity is 20–40 missiles.

The Soviet designation of the associated land-based weapon (SS-C-4) is RK-55.

◆ SS-N-23 Skiff

Dimensions: 6 ft × 46 ft (approx)   **Weight:** 40,000 kg (88,000 lbs)
Warhead: seven MIRV
Propulsion: liquid-fuel rockets (three stages)
Range: 5000 nm   **CEP:** estimated 900 m (980 yds)

SS-N-23 is the weapon carried by Delta-IV-class submarines. It is similar in size to SS-N-18 but has greater throw weight and is more accurate. Flight tests began in 1983, and the missile entered operational service in 1986.

◆ SS-N-24

Dimensions: approx 1.25 × 12 m; span 5.9 m (49 × 472 × 232 inches)
Propulsion: jet; supersonic   **Range:** 2200 nm

SS-N-24 is a very large, new cruise missile; range estimates are as great as 4000 nm. This missile may correspond to SS-N-21 as SS-N-8 corresponds to SS-N-6, i.e., SS-N-24 may be a strategic cruise missile that can be fired from within a bastion. The only published sketch suggests that this missile is launched

SS-N-24 cruise missiles being fired by a converted Yankee-class submarine. (Department of Defense)

without any canister, spreading its wings after emerging from the water. The only launch platform to date is a modified Yankee-class submarine.

There are also land- and air-launched versions.

UNITED STATES

◆ Polaris (UGM-27C)

Dimensions: 54 in × 387.5 in   **Weight:** 35,000 lbs
Warhead: six 150-kT (three 200-kT in U.S. version)
Propulsion: solid-fuel rocket (first stage thrust, 36,000 kg)
Range: 2500 nm

Although no Polaris missiles remain in U.S. service, this weapon equips the four British strategic submarines, under the 1962 Nassau Agreement. Britain maintains a facility capable of manufacturing and servicing Polaris missiles, and her weapons are armed with a British multiple warhead, Chevaline. Chevaline was developed as a penetration aid, and it is described as a compromise between the multiple (but cotargeted) warheads of U.S. Polaris missiles and the fully independently targeted warheads of Poseidons.

The British version is designated A-3TK. Chevaline entered service in 1982. Except for the warhead description, the data are for the U.S. version, Polaris A-3.

◆ Poseidon C-3 (UGM-73A)

Dimensions: 74 × 408 in   **Weight:** 65,000 lbs
Warhead: up to 14 MIRV to 2500 nm or ten 50-kT RV (Mk 3) to 3200 nm   **Propulsion:** two-stage solid-fuel rocket
Range: 2500 or 3200 nm

This Lockheed weapon was the second-generation U.S. submarine-launched strategic missile. In twelve *Lafayette*- and *Benjamin Franklin*-class submarines, it was replaced by Trident C-4, which fits the same launch tube. This replacement program was completed in December 1982. Some remaining Poseidons are being "uploaded" with more powerful warheads.

Poseidon flight tests began in August 1968, the first submarine to deploy with the new weapon being USS *James Madison*. Although fourteen RVs can be carried, the usual load is ten. CEP has been reported as about 600 yards, although the missile was more commonly regarded as a relatively inaccurate soft-target killer. In fact, during the 1970s, the navy was prohibited from developing either a new stellar-inertial guidance system or a new high-yield warhead on the grounds that with either, the weapon would become a viable hard-target killer. Both decisions were reversed in the development of Trident.

◆ Trident C-4 (UGM-96A)

> **Dimensions:** 74 × 408 in   **Weight:** 70,000 lbs
> **Warhead:** eight 100-kT Mk-4 MIRV   **Propulsion:** solid-fuel rocket
> **Range:** 4350 nm   **CEP:** 1500 ft

Trident C-4 (right) compared to Trident D-5 (left). Note the aerospikes. (Lockheed)

Trident I is Poseidon's successor, designed to fit existing tubes and to achieve 4000 nm range without losing the accuracy of the predecessor. Its post-boost vehicle (MIRV bus) incorporates a stellar sensor for positional corrections, thus achieving greater accuracy. This missile became operational in 1978.

Compared to Poseidon, Trident I was conceived as a longer-range missile with about the same throw weight. Trident I achieves greater range partly by increasing its effective length, extending an aerospike at launch. The spike is credited with reducing frontal drag by 50 percent, i.e., with adding 300 nm to the missile's range. The aerospike also made it possible to use a very blunt nose that could accommodate a third rocket stage together with the warheads. C-4 also benefits from advances in propellant chemistry, making fuller use of its fuel. Instead of blowing open ports (and thus neutralizing thrust) at a precalculated point in second-stage flight, it burns all its fuel and then calculates the appropriate third-stage trajectory. The new high-energy fuel is credited with about 40 percent of the range

Polaris A-3, as currently used by the Royal Navy. (U.S. Navy)

Poseidon C-3 (right) compared to Polaris A-3. (Lockheed)

Trident C-4 launching, with the aerospike extended. (U.S. Navy)

improvement, another 35 percent being credited to the use of improved chamber material (Kevlar), which allows increased propellant loading and higher operating pressures.

C-4 uses the stellar-inertial-update guidance proposed for Poseidon to help overcome the effects of uncertainty in a submarine's position. The missile is credited with a CEP of 500 yds (eight Mk-4 RVs with W76 100-kT warheads), and in 1982 it was stated that improvements in guidance optics could reduce CEP to 250 yds. The Mk 500 Evader MARV (Maneuverable Reentry Vehicle), carrying a 100-kT weapon, was developed by Lockheed as an alternative warhead but has not been procured.

Lockheed received the C-4 contract in 1974, and the first missile was launched in January 1977. *Francis Scott Key* was the trials ship, beginning her first Trident patrol in October 1979. The entire twelve-ship Poseidon-to-Trident conversion program was completed in March 1982. The C-4 procurement objective was 570; procurement ended in FY84 (72 in FY83, 52 in FY84).

◆ Trident II (D-5)

Dimensions: 83 in × 528 in   **Weight:** 130,000 lbs
Warhead: eight to twelve Mk-5 RV (300-to-475-kT warheads) or fourteen 150-kT MIRV or seven 300-kT MARV (Maneuverable RV); initially D-5 will use the Mk-12A RV of the Minuteman and MX land-based missiles (475-kT)
Propulsion: three-stage solid-fuel rocket; burn time about 65 secs for each of two lower stages, and 40 secs for the third stage.
Range: 6000 nm   **CEP:** 400 ft

The first submarine to be equipped with this weapon will be SSBN 734. The missile was to have entered service in late 1989 on board a submarine originally equipped with Trident I; the first submarine to be completed with the new missile would have been the twelfth Trident. However, early in 1982, the schedule was changed so that Trident II would go into the ninth submarine (USS *Tennessee*), thus avoiding the cost of replacing Trident I in three ships. Submarine construction costs rose slightly but were balanced by the elimination of the retrofits.

The fire-control system on the submarine matches that of Trident I but adds a gravity sensor and a new navigation sonar. The missile itself uses a new epoxy case for all three stages and a new high-energy propellant similar to that of the land-based MX. As of early 1988, the first full system tests (submarine launches) were scheduled for March 1989.

Production of the first 21 missiles was authorized under the FY87 program (66 under each of FY88/89); the total objective (1988) is 845 missiles (for 19 SSBNs, with 30 missiles for testing). Alternative loads: 10 to 15 MIRV, or 11 to 13 Mk-4 RVs, or 6 to 9 Mk-5 RVs. Guidance is stellar-inertial, for a reported CEP of 400 ft (1500 ft for Trident I). The Mk-5 vehicle/W87 combination was selected in October 1982. All missile tests up to September 1987 used eight warheads; in September 1987, a D-5 was tested with ten smaller warheads. However, in December 1987, President Reagan and the Soviet General Secretary Mikhail Gorbachev agreed that, for arms-control purposes, the missile would carry no more than eight warheads.

Britain has chosen Trident D-5 for her next-generation *Vanguard*-class strategic submarines. They will carry British warheads; but the missile bodies will be maintained by a U.S. facility, the Royal Navy turning missiles in for maintenance and drawing refurbished ones (which the British will then arm with their own warheads). Critics of the British Trident program have derided this practice as "rent a missile." The Anglo-American agreement was signed on 14–15 July 1980; 80 missiles will be acquired (16 per submarine plus enough spares to fill another submarine).

◆ Tomahawk (including non-nuclear versions)

Dimensions: 20.9 × 252 in   **Weight:** 3181 lbs
Warhead: 200-kT (W80 warhead)
Propulsion: F-107 turbojet sustainer
Range: 1350 nm (250 nm for TASM, 675 nm for the conventional land-attack weapon, and 472 nm for the land-attack sub-munition weapon)

Tomahawk programmed conventional air burst over a revetted bomber, demonstrating the ability to attack large aircraft. (General Dynamics)

Tomahawk attacking multiple targets using submunitions. (General Dynamics)

Tomahawk was conceived as a weapon not covered by existing arms-control treaties and, therefore, as an initiative the United States could take to counter growing Soviet strategic forces. The initial Defense Department cruise-missile studies were ordered in 1973, and it is reported that then Secretary of State Henry Kissinger favored the weapon as a bargaining chip in SALT II negotiations. Tomahawk then acquired a life of its own, and critics of arms procurement have cited cruise missiles as examples of how a bargaining chip can become a permanent fixture of military forces. The Carter Administration resisted deploying this strategic cruise missile for fear that it would breach the observability requirement built into the SALT II treaty. Late in 1980, however, the decision to deploy the tactical version of Tomahawk opened the way to deployment of the strategic version.

The navy had been very interested in a small and easily deployed strategic weapon before 1973 as a way of spreading U.S. strategic firepower over a much larger number of platforms. One advantage of such dispersal for the U.S. is that the Soviets, preoccupied with nuclear weapons, must dissipate their own efforts by targeting (hence tracking) a much larger number of U.S. ships and submarines. This U.S. strategy is a form of ju-jitsu: if the war is unlikely to turn nuclear, it is a way of using the existence of nuclear weapons to gain decidedly non-nuclear ends (greater survivability of individual valuable ships, such as aircraft carriers). The idea of reversing the significance of nuclear forces can also be seen in more recent maritime strategic approaches to Soviet bastions: threatening Soviet nuclear forces there will, it is hoped, concentrate Soviet naval attention away from the sea lines of communication, at least early in a war.

Tomahawk can be dated to a 1971 internal navy study of basing options for a future U.S. sea-based cruise missile. The two alternatives studied at the time were a 2000-nm weapon, six of which could fit a standard Poseidon tube (and which could be ejected together), and a 1500-nm torpedo tube–launched weapon. The latter was adopted, and the SLCM (sea-launched cruise missile) program formally approved on 2 June 1972. On 6 November the SLCM project was merged with a program for a 300-nm submarine-launched tactical (antiship) missile, STAM, which had originally been conceived as an extended-range Harpoon.

General Dynamics won a fly-off against LTV's ZBGM-110; more recently, McDonnell Douglas has been selected as a second source, for competitive annual bidding. The first guided Tomahawk flight was in December 1976.

Note that missile diameter is slightly less than the 21 inches usually quoted: the missile in its canister fits the standard 21-inch torpedo tube. The data above, except for range, are for the strategic version. Quoted ranges differ widely, figures as great as 2000 nm being claimed for the strategic missile and 400 nm for the tactical version armed with a Bullpup warhead.

Both strategic and tactical versions are in service. Under the Intermediate Nuclear Forces treaty, land-based Tomahawks in Europe (operated by the U.S. Air Force) are being destroyed. This does not affect the naval versions. Air-launched versions, both long- and medium-range, have been proposed, but they have not entered service. Soon, then, Tomahawk will exist only in surface ship and submarine versions. The planned total naval procurement is 3994. Surface ships carry Tomahawk in 4-missile armored box launchers and (in the future) in the Mk-41 vertical launcher. Submarines carry Tomahawk either in torpedo tubes or in special vertical tubes.

The effective range of the antiship version is limited by the need to search for the target at the end of what may be a lengthy flight. Land-attack range is limited by the weight of the warhead. Guidance is by terrain-matching (TERCOM) and inertial navigation, a system designated TAINS (TERCOM-Aided Inertial Navigation System). Unlike a ballistic missile, a TERCOM-guided cruise missile can attack only over suitable (and suitably mapped) territory, and that requirement in turn may somewhat limit Tomahawk operations. Tactical versions use DSMAC (Digital Scene-Matching Correlation), in which the scene viewed optically is compared to an on-board digital map. In a 24 April 1988 night test, the optical viewer was assisted by a strobe light. The antiship version of Tomahawk incorporates Passive Identification/Passive Direction Finding (PI/DF) equipment intended to enable the missile to discriminate among potential targets, presumably on the basis of their characteristic emissions. The four antennas are flush-mounted on the missile skin, feeding a microwave receiver.

Versions (navy procurement goal in parentheses): BGM-109A, nuclear land attack (758); BGM-109B, antiship (593); BGM-109C, conventional land attack (2643, of which 1486 are Block IIA with Bullpup unitary warheads and 1157 are Block IIB with bomblet warheads); BGM-109D, land attack with bomblets (0); BGM-109E, antiship (0); BGM-109F, land attack, antiairfield (560); BGM-109G, ground-to-ground nuclear, with variable yield (0). AGM-109C was the abortive medium-range air-to-surface (MRASM) terrain-following missile; AGM-109I was a proposed MRASM with an infrared seeker, and AGM-109J was a proposed MRASM carrying bomblets. The Tomahawk land-attack missile with a nuclear warhead is sometimes denoted TLAM-N; the Tomahawk antiship missile is TASM; and the Tomahawk conventional land-attack missiles are often denoted TLAM-C (unitary conventional warhead) and TLAM-D (bomblet dispenser).

TLAM-C Block IIA, which carries out an optional terminal maneuver (pop-up and dive), was approved for production during FY86. The terminal maneuver is selectable before flight. Other improvements are provisions for a mobile launch point and for alternative selection of over-water waypoints. A programmable warhead detonation (PWD) for this version has been tested.

TLAM-C Block IIB is the bomblet version, tested in FY86. It carries 166 Aerojet Ordnance BLU-97/B combined-effect bomblets in 24 packages, 22 of them holding seven bomblets each (six each in the other two). Each bomblet (2.5 × 6.6 in, 3.4 lbs) carries an incendiary fuze, a fragmenting case, and a shaped charge. The missile can eject bomblets to hit several targets per pass; in a November 1987 test, a submarine-launched Tomahawk dropped bomblets on three targets and dove on the fourth.

An Improved Sea Skimming Variant (ISSV) was operationally tested in December 1985 through May 1986.

A Block 3 Improvement Program, now in development, will enter production in FY91. Changes include an improved turbofan engine (19 percent more thrust, 3 percent less fuel consumption), GPS, an improved form of DSMAC, and improvements for better coordination with tactical air strikes.

The supporting weapon system is Mk 36/37 (submarine/surface ship vertical launcher). It is being modified (Block II) to accept data from fleet intelligence sources and sensors, presumably as an outgrowth of Outlaw Shark (see OSIS and TFCC under Surveillance and Control).

Late in April 1988, the navy briefed contractors on requirements for a stealthier next-generation sea-launched cruise missile, with better accuracy and greater range. The navy was expected to decide by December 1988 whether to proceed with a new missile or to press for a modified version of the existing Tomahawk.

♦ Excalibur

Excalibur is a navy project for a long-range highly accurate cruise missile, a Tomahawk successor, which might be used to deliver nonnuclear warheads. A bidders' conference was held in May 1988, but as of late 1988 bidders had not yet been selected. The missile will presumably exploit new high-accuracy technology that was first publicly described in the summer of 1987 and that may use lasers for very accurate map-reading. Some have suggested that long-range conventional cruise missiles can take over some roles currently reserved for strategic nuclear weapons, and that, therefore, such missiles may have a revo-

General Dynamics's version of Excalibur. (General Dynamics)

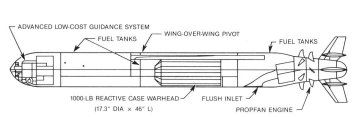

McDonnell-Douglas's version of Excalibur. (McDonnell-Douglas)

lutionary impact on future warfare. In particular, in 1987 both the Blue Ribbon panel on a new U.S. national strategy (which conceived the concept of "discriminant deterrence") and a Defense Science Board study of Strategic Nonnuclear Capabilities (SNNC) pushed for the development of what they called Long-Range Conventional Cruise Missiles (LRCCM). The air force requested $50 million to begin development in FY89. Ultimately the program was moved into the Joint (i.e., air force and navy) Stand-Off Weapons program, which also includes the AIWS and MSOW described in the Strike/Surface Warfare section of this book.

Excalibur is a navy LRCCM program proposed as an alternative to the JSOW weapon; the navy proposal for development during FY90–94 reportedly includes ship-, submarine-, and air-launched versions. The key difference between a navy-developed LRCCM and an air force-oriented weapon would almost certainly be the navy requirement that the weapon fit a standard submarine torpedo tube, whereas the dimensions of the air force weapon would probably be limited by those of the standard bomber rotary launcher. Because of just these requirements, Tomahawk is so different from the contemporary air force ALCM.

In November 1988 the Naval Air Systems Command awarded Lockheed Missiles and Space Company a contract to study guidance, mission planning, and survivability for an Advanced Sea-Launched Cruise Missile (ASLCM) to replace Tomahawk. The ASLCM is to have a greater range. The Lockheed study will concentrate on the surface-launched version. Lockheed suggested that the contract might lead to hardware design and construction and then to demonstration validation flights.

Three companies exhibited alternative long-range conventional cruise missiles at the U.S. Navy League show in March 1989: Boeing, General Dynamics, and McDonnell-Douglas. Each missile was powered by an unducted-fan (propfan) jet at its tail, driving contra-rotating propellers of the type also proposed for full-scale aircraft. The program is entering the concept definition stage, and the navy is expected to request bids during FY90. At this writing the final designation of the program is uncertain. Excalibur is a name used within the navy. The original ASLCM designation was succeeded by LRCCM, then by LRCSOW (long-range conventional stand-off weapon), and then by LRCSW (long-range conventional standoff weapon).

At least three alternative guidance techniques are being investigated: laser radar scene-matching (CMAG, cruise missile advanced guidance, developed as an air force program since about 1983), imaging infrared, and a synthetic aperture radar (SAR). Loral exhibited its own SAR at the 1989 show. Besides the terrain comparison navigation used by the current Tomahawk, a very precise future cruise missile might employ feature

Boeing's proposal for Excalibur. (Boeing)

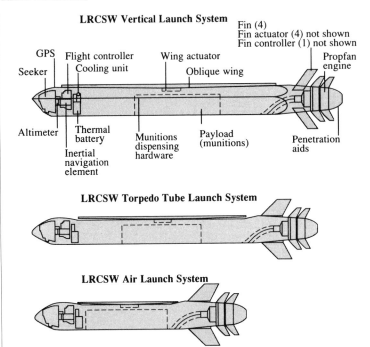

Boeing's modular conventional cruise missile family. (Boeing)

navigation (i.e., comparison with the relative positions of features on the surface, such as crossroads, rather than with the absolute height of terrain). In theory, feature navigation data might be derived from conventional maps and so might permit the use of long-range missiles against targets for which special terrain-contour maps had not been prepared.

Loral displayed its autonomous SAR seeker at the Navy League show; this device is probably typical of those being considered for LRCSW guidance. It is 15 inches in diameter and 23 inches long, weighs 74 lbs, and requires 392 watts of power. This seeker employs a conventional-looking flat plate array antenna, which can swivel to the side (for SAR) or can look straight ahead. The seeker can, therefore, be used for conventional terrain avoidance and even terrain height matching as well as for scene matching by imaging. Typically the radar would be used for at least one mid-course match with some prominent terrain feature and then would produce a series of target images of successively finer resolution as the missile approached. Compared to the current height-matching system, a SAR is much easier to program since it needs only a series of images of terrain. Loral claims that missions can be planned (i.e., weapons programmed) in minutes rather than hours at the squadron level.

This type of SAR is the outgrowth of a long series of systems; Loral provided a table of SAR's evolution:

Date	System	Volume	Weight	Power	Cost
1970	UPD-4	20 cu ft	620 lbs	2.7 kW	$2.5M
1981	SLASH	16 cu ft	675 lbs	2.2 kW	$450,000
1986	LASS	2 cu ft	135 lbs	392 W	$100,000
1990	FSED	1 cu ft	65 lbs	225 W	$ 65,000

Here LASS and FSED (full-scale engineering-development model) are cruise-missile guidance packages, and costs are in terms of a 10,000-unit production run (in, respectively, FY84 and FY86 dollars). This advance is a result of improvements in the computers processing the synthetic aperture radar's data:

Date	System	Volume	Throughput (millions of operations per second)
1975	SAPPHIRE	*	5000
1981	SLASH	8 cu ft	480
1986	LASS	0.25 cu ft	120
1990	FSED	0.1 cu ft	120

*Five standard electronic cabinets, costing $6 million. SAPPHIRE was, therefore, a ground-based processor for an airborne system.

The three proposed weapons differ in configuration. Boeing showed a missile with a single wing pivoted along its upper surface; after firing, the wing would turn into an oblique position. General Dynamics showed two forward-swept wings, carried internally, that would pop out after firing; its missile also showed small canard foresurfaces. McDonnell-Douglas showed two pivoting wings (carried one over the other) below the upper surface of the missile; these wings would also pop out after firing. McDonnell-Douglas's and Boeing's configurations leave considerable space under the wing for a submunition-dispensing warhead (although McDonnell-Douglas's sketch showed a 1000-lb unitary reactive case warhead, 17.3 inches in diameter and 46 inches long). Boeing emphasized commonality between dif-

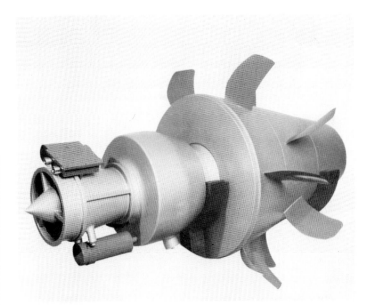

A possible Excalibur power plant is this new propfan engine by Teledyne-CAE. Total length is 35.53 inches, and diameter, with the blades folded, is only 16 inches. The entire engine weighs 150 lbs. In comparison, the Harpoon missile's J402-CA-400 sustainer, which was the first to be designed for "wooden round" use, weighs 101.5 lbs and is 29.2 inches long, with a maximum diameter of 12.5 inches. Teledyne also offers a bypass turbojet for next-generation cruise missiles, presumably a rival to the propjet. This turbojet would weigh 135 lbs, with a diameter of 13.2 inches, and would produce a thrust of 1100 lbs (compared to 660 for the Harpoon engine), with a specific fuel consumption of 0.9 lbs/hr/lb-thrust (compared to 1.2 for the Harpoon engine). (Teledyne-CAE)

ferent LRCSW versions, for vertical launch, torpedo-tube launch, and air launch; Boeing had already conducted a study of a propfan derivative of its air force air-launched strategic cruise missile (AGM-86B).

Since a major LRCSW application is submarine launch, the missile is probably limited by the torpedo tube's dimensions, which include a 21-inch maximum diameter. McDonnell-Douglas showed a length of 235 inches, which is presumably the maximum allowable.

Several companies at the Navy League show displayed cruise missile propfan engines; Allison has several in the 500–1000 HP range, all using folding blades with high tip sweep and thin sections, and all using geared drives. All should be substantially more economical than current turbofan cruise missile engines, providing either more range with current warheads or larger warheads. The existing Tomahawk makes its long range only in its nuclear version, and in that case the warhead weighs less than 300 lbs. Tomahawks carrying substantial nonnuclear warheads cannot carry enough fuel to go nearly as far, yet the hope of the LRCSW is that it can reach full Tomahawk ranges and still carry large conventional warheads (and achieve virtually zero CEP).

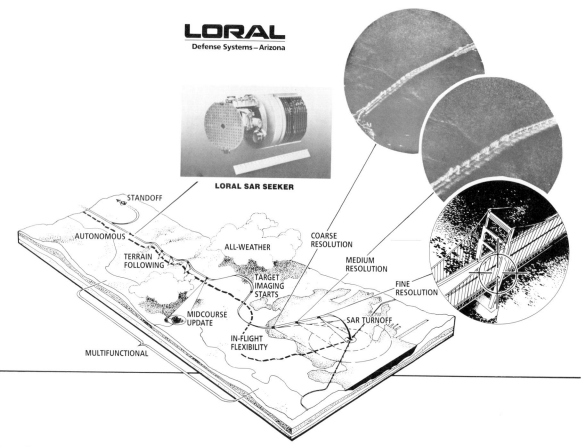

A synthetic-aperture seeker for advanced cruise missiles. (Loral)

STRIKE/ SURFACE WARFARE

This section includes all weapons and fire-control systems intended primarily for antiship or ground attack. The two applications are often extremely difficult to distinguish, as many weapons, such as cluster bombs, intended primarily for use against land targets have important antiship applications. For example, during the fighting in the Persian Gulf in 1988, U.S. A-6 Intruders used Paveway laser-guided bombs to attack Iranian ships, while cluster bombs were used during attacks on Libyan ships in March 1986. The Maverick ground-attack missile has reportedly been used by Iran to attack tankers, and indeed the U.S. Navy uses a special antiship version of Maverick.

From a missile's point of view, ships and land targets all move relatively slowly; therefore, they impose very similar loads on propulsion and aerodynamics: hence, the dual-purpose weapons. However, a ship almost always presents great contrast to its surroundings and, therefore, is a relatively easy target for a fire-and-forget weapon. Most land targets show much less contrast with their surroundings and, therefore, must be identified by eye, at least at present. In some cases, there is sufficient contrast for an autonomous seeker, but in most an artificial signature must be imposed. Hence, the widespread current use of laser designators and the considerable interest in imaging infrared seekers (which allow an operator to designate a target for a missile or guided bomb). The great drawback of the laser is that its designation platform must remain in position while the weapon is in flight. Note that, even in the case of ships, the situation may not be very simple. The target ship may well be part of a formation, and other, lower-value parts of the formation may be larger radar targets.

Weapons characteristics largely shape attack tactics. The issue for the designer is how best to penetrate terminal defenses. The techniques, very broadly, are speed, saturation, and stealth. Very high speed penetrates by limiting the number of shots a defense can fire while the attacker passes through that defense's effective-range band. Examples include most recent Soviet antiship missiles, which fly at about Mach 2.0. Alternatively, an attacker may fire numerous weapons at the target, preferably from many different directions. Several recent antiship missiles, such as current versions of Harpoon, incorporate programming for way points. The missile is fired along a course away from the target and then turns sharply into the target. This maneuvering has two effects. First, it limits the value of early-warning since the missile does not remain on its initial course long enough to be engaged. Second, the maneuver enables a single attacker to execute a coordinated multidirectional strike, with missiles appearing on target from several angles at once. Waypointing may allow an attacker to overwhelm the limited number of defensive channels that most ships have. Finally, there is stealth, the best-known example of which is the use of sea-skimming trajectories that limit detection time (as long as the defender has no airborne radar). The desire for stealth affects the choice of missile seeker (e.g., IR rather than radar, or one type of radar rather than another) and of targeting device (the presence of a radar platform may warn a target that it is about to be attacked, even when the attack itself is stealthy). Generally, stealth limits the defense's reaction time.

These techniques work not only for attacks on shipping but also for other forms of strike warfare. For example, a pilot attacking a concentration of vehicles on land can probably make a single successful pass if he approaches at very low altitude because he would enjoy the advantage of surprise—in effect, the benefit of stealth. However, if he has to use that pass merely to decide which vehicle to hit, he may well die on the second pass, when the defense is alerted: hence, the advantages claimed for current single-pass/multiple-shot systems (e.g., for Maverick). Similarly, modern attack tactics often envisage several aircraft suddenly appearing on radically different bearings, a single formation having split up beyond the target's radar horizon. That is saturation. Note that, as a target's defensive capacity increases (in terms of the number of defensive channels), the attacker is forced to allocate more weapons per attack, in turn reducing the lethality of those weapons that do penetrate. Similarly, an attacker forced to use faster weapons may not be able to fly those weapons at very low altitude, and the weapons themselves may emit so much infrared radiation that the target enjoys earlier warning.

This section includes airborne surface-search radars, although some of them are intended primarily to detect submarines. This section does not include standard shipboard surface-search and navigational radars. They are described in the Antiaircraft Warfare section of this book. Some of the radars listed are intended primarily to help enforce Exclusive Economic Zones, particularly in the Third World. Such radars, because they can detect and locate small surface craft (such as those used by smugglers), have an important potential either for direct targeting or for directing other missile-bearing aircraft. In the Falklands War, for example, an Argentine Neptune with a long-range APS-20 radar reportedly directed Exocet-carrying Super-Étendard fighters, which had only to pop up briefly to fire and could thus avoid extended exposure to British detection. The standard U.S. airborne early-warning radar (APS-120 series) has the same capability but is listed in this book under AAW because air-to-air detection is that radar's primary role.

Probably the most important current antiship-sensor development is inverse synthetic aperture radar (ISAR). An airborne synthetic aperture radar (SAR) achieves its very high resolution (sufficient for imaging) from the motion of the airplane along a straight and level course. High resolution would normally require a very large antenna. A conventional radar scans as it moves, so that by the time it has moved a significant distance, the radar is no longer looking at the same scene. By way of contrast, a SAR does not scan. Since it is constantly staring in the same direction, pulses emitted at any one point along the SAR's path and received later on contribute to the overall radar picture. A SAR's effective aperture (antenna size) is the distance the radar travels while those pulses build up, the product of the aircraft's speed (along the straight flight path) and the period of time during which pulses build up in a coherent way (the integration time). The latter depends in part on the amount of memory built into the SAR system, since the radar has to remember earlier echoes to compare them with later ones, taken further along the flight path. A SAR can achieve very impressive resolution but can look only to the side. Targets are more often straight ahead.

ISAR solves this problem by using the motion of the target (roll, yaw, or pitch) rather than that of the airplane. The resulting image generally lacks the quality associated with SAR but may suffice for crude ship recognition and for attack assessment (comparison of before and after images). The radar may be able to measure target course relative to the radar, reassembling what amounts to a target silhouette; and crude recognition may be automated. In this form ISAR may be applicable to future antiship missiles.

The key is that the angular velocity of the target as a whole equates to different linear velocities (e.g., in ft/sec) at different distances from the distant radar. Each such linear velocity (in the direction of the radar) causes a doppler shift in reflected radar echoes. Thus different doppler shifts are associated with different distances from the line about which the target is moving (for example, its centerline in the case of rolling motion). The line about which the target moves becomes a reference line, and an image of distances can be built up. In the case of roll, with the radar abeam, a plan image of a ship results. Similarly, the doppler frequencies associated with the pitching of a ship give the heights of points along its length, so that a series of measurements by a radar pointing bow to stern gives a target silhouette. Since the target is unlikely to be either directly in line with the radar or directly abeam of it, the ISAR should be able to produce a nearly three-dimensional image.

This section also includes infrared detectors. They fly on board all ASW aircraft and on board many attack aircraft; some are intended primarily to detect hot snorkel exhausts, and others are primarily for land attack. All have some capability to detect and image (and hence to help classify) surface targets; therefore, they are included here.

The central distinction in classifying weapons, whether they are attacking fixed or moving targets, is between point-attack and area-attack weapons. Improved technology makes it possible for weapons to be delivered with extremely small errors (CEPs, or circular errors probable, of ten feet or less are now quite common). Some analysts have, therefore, suggested that the future of munitions lies with relatively small numbers of essentially zero-CEP devices, some of them perhaps deliverable from extreme distances. However, the efficacy of such weapons depends in turn upon how well the targets can be located. Therefore, this section also includes some tactical reconnaissance systems. The ones listed should be taken as typical rather than comprehensive; but the reader should be aware that, no matter how precise the weapon, it cannot reach a valuable target unless that target can be located in the first place. That makes it difficult, for example, to attack individuals who may not be home when the missiles arrive to greet them.

The alternative is to cover a suspected target area with large numbers of relatively imprecise weapons. Area-attack has certainly been the approach in the past, and at present this approach is represented by bomblet-dispensing munitions such as the U.S. Rockeye and, presumably, also by fuel-air explosives. Area-attack is useful not only because targets may not be precisely located but also because the targets themselves may be spread out over a considerable area. For example, it may be impossible to fire a separate long-range weapon at each of numerous troops dug-in around a target area; however, area-attacks on the troops may kill many of them and may so demoralize the rest as to make them ineffective.

It is common, then, to distinguish between "dumb," "smart," and "brilliant" weapons. A "dumb" weapon is entirely unguided after release; all the intelligence in the system is concentrated in the launch vehicle, be that an airplane or a ship. A "smart" bomb attacks a target designated by the launcher, homing on some element of the target's signature picked out in advance or on a signature, such as a laser spot, imposed by the launch vehicle or by some cooperating platform. Finally, a "brilliant" weapon will choose its own target. No "brilliant" weapons are currently in service, but many analysts have suggested that these weapons are the future of guided munitions.

There are several major ground-target categories. In amphibious operations, it is essential to neutralize troops and coast-defense weapons (such as truck-borne antiship missiles) dug-in at the objective area. There is some hope that modern high-mobility amphibious forces can evade such fixed defenses altogether, although evasion may not be possible when geography clearly dictates the choice of landing zone. Generally, it will be important to disable opposing enemy air forces and air defenses. Once amphibious forces have landed, an enemy will try to counter them with mechanized troops, tanks, and perhaps attack helicopters. Thus, antiarmor/antivehicle weapons are extremely important. Naval forces may also be called upon to execute classical, deep air strikes, e.g., at enemy industrial targets, air bases, roads, highways, and bridges, as in Vietnam. Given sufficient lifting capacity, the naval air-to-ground arsenal is not so different from that available to the land-based tactical air force, and many of the weapons listed here are air force types.

The major problem in ground attack is that the targets (which may be both small and camouflaged) must be distinguished from considerable ground clutter and then must be designated to a bomb or other munition. The pilot's eye is likely to be more effective than any automated system, but the pilot may be subject to antiaircraft fire as he chooses his targets. The longer the pilot takes to make up his mind, the more vulnerable he is. In theory, a pilot can designate a target to a purely ballistic system. However, a bomb, rocket, or cannon shell that is unguided after launch will probably miss because of such random factors as windage between release and impact. The closer the pilot to the ground at the time of release, the more accurate the delivery, but also the greater the danger to the airplane.

The next step, then, is to provide some sort of post-release guidance. A bomb can be made to home on a laser spot on the designated target, and the laser can be manipulated either by the pilot or by someone on the ground. An alternative is to direct the bomb to home on some feature of the target as it is seen from the airplane, using either optical or infrared wavelengths, so that the pilot need not wait for the bomb to hit; but the target may have insufficient contrast for homing. In both cases, homing must be continuous after the bomb begins to approach its target, and experience shows that homing may be thrown off completely by the dust and debris thrown up by an earlier bomb, by clouds, or by smoke. If laser homing is used, an enemy who is aware of which laser wavelengths are in use may be able to provide alternative targets.

Moreover, if the attacking pilot has to keep a laser on the target during the missile's flight, he must remain within the target area, and that is quite dangerous. However, few ground targets show sufficient contrast for autonomous television (electro-optical) homing.

A variation on these themes is to provide the missile with an optical or infrared seeker and a data link to the launch airplane. The missile can then be fired at a target that the pilot cannot see but that he can designate via the data link once the missile spots the target. The U.S. Navy developed just such a weapon, Condor (AGM-53); but the jam-resistant data link proved extremely expensive, and the project had to be abandoned. More recent (and less ambitious) data-link projects have, however, survived, as in the case of Walleye. Note that, as with laser designation, the data-linker must remain in a restricted air space and, thus, may himself be vulnerable to enemy attack. On the other hand, he is further from the enemy than he would have been had he fired a lock-on-before-launch missile. This situation is not very different from that of a Soviet submarine or surface ship firing an SS-N-3 or SS-N-12 antiship missile. Indeed, it is sometimes suggested that the latest Soviet air-launched antiship missiles incorporate data links that permit them to lock the missiles on after, rather than before, they are launched.

One other possibility has recently arisen, inertial guidance: the pilot designates his target as a point in space, and the bomb or missile flies itself into that point, without reference to the ground. In principle, this is precisely what a long-range ballistic missile (which is, after all, a ground-attack weapon) does, but in this case over a much shorter distance and a much shorter time.

Another important near-term improvement is millimeter-wave (MMW) homing. Millimeter-length radiation is at the long-wave end of the infrared spectrum, short enough to provide some imaging, but long enough to cut through such natural obstacles as smoke. Millimeter-length radiation can also be generated by extremely high-frequency radar techniques. There is some hope that MMW will make direct (fire-and-forget) homing on tanks and other vehicles possible. At present there is no really effective means of homing on such objects, unless they are generating considerable heat against a cool background. Most "brilliant" antiarmor submunitions (weapons intended to be carried within larger warheads) now under development in the United States seem to use some type of millimeter-wave homing. In the absence of such techniques, antiarmor munitions depend either on continuous guidance by the operator (e.g., wire guidance, as in the TOW missile) or on a percentage chance of hitting (as in bomblets).

Somewhat further in the future are imaging techniques using artificial intelligence (AI) to enable an incoming weapon to decide for itself which target to hit. These techniques are unlikely to end the story because, just like a human eye, a mechanical sensor can be misled by clever forms of camouflage and decoying. It is not at all clear, either, whether future "smart" or "bril-

liant" antiarmor weapons will be cheap enough to apply on a large scale.

All of these techniques are applicable to shells, and laser-guided artillery shells now exist.

For simplicity of reference, torpedoes are all included under ASW weapons, although in many cases torpedoes are intended for use against only surface targets. Similarly, antiship mines are listed separately in the Mine Warfare section. Guns are all listed in the AAW section; note that in some cases their anti-aircraft capability may be marginal.

RECONNAISSANCE SYSTEMS

Aircraft-Carried Sensors

UNITED STATES

◆ ATARS

The joint-service Advanced Tactical Air Reconnaissance System will be the first airborne reconnaissance system to replace film with electronic data storage (as currently used in satellites) so that information can be data-linked back to base while the ATARS platform is still airborne. Because there is no need to store large quantities of film, the system can fit in an RPV. Reportedly, the greatest technical challenge in the project is the very-high-data-rate digital recorder required.

The sensors will all, therefore, be electro-optical: as in TARPS (see below), two visual for daylight (low-altitude/wide field of view and medium altitude/stand-off) and one IR (night).

This program is air force led, and the first application will be to existing RF-4Cs. The initial navy application will be to the mid-range RPV (MR-RPV), and the marines will use ATARS on board F/A-18Ds. ATARS will also replace TARPS pods on board F-14Ds.

Bids were submitted in July 1987, and Control Data Corporation was chosen as manufacturer in May 1988. Initial flight tests, on an air force RF-4C, are scheduled for the fall of 1990. ATARS-equipped RPVs will also be used.

◆ TARPS

Tactical Air Reconnaissance Pods can be carried by F-14 and F/A-18 fighters. Currently, two F-14As in each carrier air wing are fitted to accept these pods, and three aircrew are trained to use TARPS. All new F-14Ds will be wired to accept TARPS.

TARPS replaces the specialized equipment built into such aircraft as the RF-8 and RA-5C and was bought as an alternative to a new specialized reconnaissance airplane, which would have been a modified F-4 Phantom (the marines did buy a specialized RF-4B). The pod is conceived primarily as a strike-planning and battle-damage-assessment system, and TARPS was widely used during the operations off Lebanon in 1983–84.

The pod carries two cameras (Fairchild KA-99 low-altitude panoramic, with 9-in focal length; and CAI KS-87B frame camera with 12-in focal length) and an infrared line scanner (Honeywell AAD-5A, with both wide and narrow fields of view). Total weight is 1700 lbs.

TARPS was developed by the Naval Air Development Center and is produced by the Naval Avionics Center. The system is to be replaced by the new ATARS.

The marines have not followed the same development path. Instead, they are developing an internal reconnaissance pallet for two-seat F/A-18D fighters, about one-third of which will be wired to accept the pallet. Installation of the pallet requires removal of the internal 20-mm cannon of the F/A-18, and the pallet can accept any two of the three TARPS cameras.

◆ UPD-4/9

UPD-4 is a Goodyear synthetic aperture radar, used on Marine Corps RF-4Bs. When these aircraft retire, their F/A-18 successors will carry a podded UPD-9, similar to the air force UPD-8. UPD-9 adds a data link so that the radar image can be received on the ground before the airplane returns. Data-link range is about 200–250 nm; radar range is about 50 nm. The pod, which can be carried by the F/A-18D, weighs less than 1500 lbs and is cooled by ram air. At least some of the new marine pods are repackaged UPD-4s. The pods are about the same size as the standard 330-gallon centerline fuel tank and weigh about 1500 lbs each.

Production development of the pod began in July 1987; by that time the prototype had already flown on board an RF-4.

RPVs

CANADA

♦ CL-227 Sentinel

Engineering development of this small helicopter RPV began in 1977, with the first systems-test vehicle flying in 1980. In 1985, the Canadian government agreed to support the final development phase, so that fully militarized aircraft were available from late 1987 onwards. CL-227 consists of a pair of turbine-driven contraprops with bodies above and below; guidance is based on a strapdown inertial sensor. Sentinel can fly at the end of a 200-m (655-ft) tether; powered by a Wankel engine, the prototype made its first flight on a tether on 25 August 1978. Most of the flight experience has been gathered with a slightly enlarged Phase 2 RPV powered by a 32-HP Williams International WR34-15-2 engine, which first flew untethered on 14 December 1981. The current Phase 3 version is slightly larger yet (details below).

The Sparton dwarf buoys (described in the ASW section) and their related seeder magazine were intended specifically for the Sentinel RPV. The magazine, 50 × 36 cm (30 kg), carries 20 miniature LOFAR omnidirectional buoys, or four DIFARs, or four SSQ-529 DICANCASS buoys. The DICANCASS transducer would be lowered into the water while the RPV hovered, functioning as a miniature dipping sonar.

Dimensions: rotor diameter 2.80 m (9 ft 2.25 in); height, including landing gear 1.64 m (5 ft 4.5 in); maximum take-off weight 190 kg (419 lbs), including 88 kg (194 lbs) payload (up to 54 kg [119 lbs] fuel and up to 45 kg [99 lbs] disposable payload).

Performance: maximum air speed 130 km/hr (84 kts), ceiling 3000 m (9840 ft), climb rate 3 m/sec at 1500 m (9.8 ft/sec at 4920 ft); endurance 4 hours at 1000 m (3280 ft).

The CL-227 program began in 1964 and was substantially reoriented in 1968. Customer flight trials began in 1980. The current $60-million program, including production of ten ve-

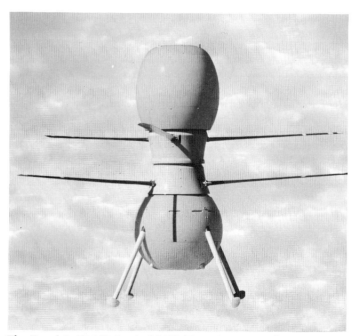

The Canadair CL-227 Sentinel RPV. (Texas Instruments)

hicles, is supported in part by the Canadian government (agreement announced 7 May 1985) and began in 1986. The first full production prototype flew on 20 November 1987.

♦ CL-289 (AN/USD-502)

A surveillance RPV designed initially for land use but proposed for the U.S. MR-RPV (see below), CL-289 was derived from CL-89, a joint Canadian-German project begun in 1961 and first flown in 1964. Production of CL-89 began in 1967, and as of 1987 more than 500 had been delivered to the British, German, French, and Italian armies. CL-289 was conceived as a corps-commander support-device, i.e., for area surveillance over ranges greater than those achieved by CL-89. CL-289 is a joint Canadian-German project; work began in July 1976, and France joined the program in March 1977. CL-289 first flew on 3 March 1980, and full-scale production began in 1987, initially for the French and German armies. The RPV is powered by a KHD T117 (240-lb thrust) turbojet. Speed is described as considerably more than that of CL-89, which achieves 400 kts. Dimensions: 1 ft 3 in × 11 ft 6.5 in (plus 3 ft 9.5 in booster); span is 4 ft 4 in.

GERMANY (WEST)

♦ Maritime Aerodyne

Maritime Aerodyne was a Dornier RPV, which resulted from a 1971 study in collaboration with Hawker Siddeley Dynamics and was used for reconnaissance, ASW, ECM, and forward missile guidance. Maritime Aerodyne had one engine and twin side-by-side ducted propellers and could carry two lightweight torpedoes. The basic configuration has been tested successfully on land, and a shipboard vehicle of this type was proposed in 1975–76, for over-the-horizon targeting. The project was killed in 1977, but it is the sort of vehicle that might now be revived for the NATO PRIAMOS naval RPV (see below). Dimensions: 9 ft 10 in wide (overall) × 16 ft 9.25 in × 8 ft 6.25 in (height). Weight: 3000 lbs. Performance: 329 kts at sea level, service ceiling 22,000 ft, hover ceiling 3940 ft (1200 m). With a 100-kg (220-lb) payload, range was 809 nm at maximum level speed, and endurance was 3 hr 20 min (1 hr 20 min with 880-lb payload).

♦ PRIAMOS

Dornier's helicopter RPV, proposed for the NATO maritime role, is based on the earlier Argus. Work began in 1986, and the first flight was scheduled for 1987. PRIAMOS will be a modified U.S. QH-50D (see CH-84 under the U.S. entry) carrying a French Orchidée II battlefield-surveillance radar and powered by a 330-SHP Boeing T50-BO-12 turboshaft. A specially designed vehicle may follow later. PRIAMOS means *Primarauflarungsmittel und Ortungssystem* (primary reconnaissance and direction system).

INTERNATIONAL

A NATO study group on RPVs for small ships was formed in December 1986 to establish a two-year program to develop requirements because an earlier study (1985) had shown that there were no funded national programs for maritime-suitable RPVs. The U.S. Navy is chairing the group, which includes representatives of Canada, France, Italy, Spain, West Germany, and the United Kingdom. Four ship categories are involved: 500-ton fast patrol boats (as in the German Navy); corvettes; frigates; and 5000-to-8000-ton surface warships. RPVs had to be operable in 85 percent of weather conditions, which meant launch/recovery at: (figures for frigates, with FPBs in parentheses) pitch 4 (5) degrees, roll 10 (15) degrees, acceleration at the bow 9 (5) m/sec. The required radius of action was 35 nm for a fast patrol boat and 75 nm (100 nm desired) for a larger ship. Fuel had to be compatible with the host ship (JP-5 preferred), and the controlling data link had to be difficult to jam and to intercept.

Typical missions included

Early detection of an air threat along a known axis, using ESM, focal planar array, IR search-and-track: endurance 1 hour, radius 40–60 nm.

OTH area reconnaissance/missile damage assessment, day/night imaging system: endurance 1 hour, radius 75–100 nm.

Gunfire-support targeting, day/night imaging plus laser range-finder/designator: endurance 3 hours, radius 30 nm.

Electronic warfare, ESM, active/passive ECM, decoys: endurance 2 hours, radius 75–90 nm.

Communications Relay, two VHF/UHF radios back to back: endurance 3 hours, radius 80 nm.

ASW, sonobuoys and/or dipping sonar: endurance 3 hours, radius 60 nm.

Initially, the greatest interest was shown in vertical take-off RPVs such as the Canadair CL-227 Sentinel, the British Sprite, and the U.S. Pointer. There was also a Dornier design study, PRIAMOS.

As of mid-1988, Canadair was scheduled to demonstrate its CL-227 on board a frigate in September 1988. M. L. Aviation (Great Britain) was scheduled to demonstrate its Sprite RPV helicopter from a "Castle"-class OPV in November 1988, and there were tentative plans for a demonstration on board a German fast patrol boat. The Bell-Boeing Pointer tilt-rotor RPV was scheduled for demonstration on board a U.S. ship by the NATO group's December 1988 deadline.

ISRAEL

◆ Pioneer

The U.S. Navy bought this Israeli RPV to satisfy a requirement, stated in mid-1984, for a mini-RPV, for both the marines and for naval gunfire support (spotting). The RPV was probably based in part on experience with an Israeli RPV, Mastiff (a design predecessor of Pioneer), which was bought by the United States in January 1984 to support the marines in Lebanon. Mastiff was flown on board the helicopter carrier *Guam* on 26 March 1984. In July 1984 Secretary of the Navy John Lehman directed the Naval Air Systems Command to achieve a minimum operational capability as soon as possible, i.e., to buy an existing RPV. He was later credited with having accelerated the program by at least two to three years. The navy, therefore, opened the competition to any manufacturer that could participate in a fly-off by the spring of 1986, the winner to provide three years of technical-support services. Only Lockheed and Mazlat could be ready in time, and in 1985 Lockheed withdrew

Pioneer control antenna (at the forward end of the funnel, in the radome), USS *Iowa*, 1988. (A. Wetback)

from the competition, leaving only the Mazlat Pioneer. Canadair, which demonstrated its CL-227 to the U.S. Navy in 1984, could not be ready in time. The navy bought three Pioneer systems in 1986 (two shipboard and one Marine Corps, ordered 7 January 1986, with options for two more, exercised in February 1987), and four more in FY88. Successful tests during 1987 led to a decision to seek full-scale production under the FY89 program. In June 1988 the U.S. Navy ordered four more Pioneer systems, each including several RPVs. The ultimate navy requirement is 43 RPV systems, each consisting of eight aircraft and a control unit.

The manufacturer, Mazlat, is a subsidiary of Tadiran/IAI, and the U.S. agent for Pioneer is AAI.

Pioneer was tested on board an LHA in June 1986 and became operational on board the battleship *Iowa* in December 1986 (installed June–December), carrying out reconnaissance over Central America. Pioneer was rocket-launched by the battleship and recovered in a net; the guidance transmitter was in a radome on the second funnel of the ship. Teething troubles caused the loss of four of the first five, three to crashes on the ship and one to engine failure. The two major problems in the RPV itself were insufficient data-link range and an unreliable engine. The required 100-nm range could not be met, but range did increase from 50–67 km (32–43 nm) during tests. A ground-based version could be controlled at 165 km (107 nm), presumably by using a taller antenna.

Pioneer is powered by a 26-HP Sachs gasoline engine, and the U.S. Navy wants to replace this engine with one running on JP-5, the standard (and considerably safer) Navy-wide gas-turbine fuel. The sensor is a television camera.

In April 1988 it was reported that Pioneers had flown without mishap for 207 hours (70 sorties) from the battleship *Iowa*, during a Mediterranean and Gulf of Oman deployment.

Dimensions: span 5.15 m × 4.26 m length overall × 1 m height (16 ft 10.75 in × 13 ft 11.75 in × 3 ft 3.25 in); maximum payload 45 kg (99 lbs); maximum take-off weight 195 kg (430 lbs). Maximum level speed is 48–70 kts; ceiling is 4575 m (15,000 ft), radius 100 nm, and endurance 6–9 hours. Fuel capacity is 11.1 U.S. gallons.

In June 1988 Mazlat announced that it was designing a VTOL RPV for small ships but would not undertake full-scale development until finding either a foreign partner or a launch customer.

ITALY

◆ Mirach

Mirach is a family of RPVs manufactured by the Meteor company. The propeller-driven Mirach 20 (carrying either an IR sensor, with a range of 32 km, or a radar) was proposed for the U.S. Navy's short-range RPV (Pioneer was chosen). Mirach 20 was displayed at the Italian naval exhibition, *Mostra Navale*, in 1986. Mirach 20 is powered by a 26-HP Herbrandson Dyad two-stroke flat-twin engine, and the airframe is built mainly of Kevlar. Dimensions: span 3.83 m, length 3.62 m (12.5 × 11.9 ft); weight 95 kg empty, 197 kg max at launch (210/434 lbs); maximum internal combat load 20 kg (44 lbs). Maximum level speed is 108 kts, and maximum endurance is 3 hours. Maximum rate of climb at 1000 m is 240 m/sec (3280 ft: 787 ft/sec).

There is also a larger Mirach 100, proposed for the MR-RPV, powered by a 400-lb-thrust NPT 401 turbojet. Mirach 100 is currently in production, over 150 having been built by early 1987. Users include Libya and Iraq, so that Mirach may well have seen combat service. Mirach is built under license in Argentina as MQ-2 (Bigua). In the U.S. MR-RPV contest, Mirach was offered with a Pacific Aerosystems Mizar data link. Dimensions: 1.8 m span × 3.94 m (71 × 155 inches); weight 210 kg empty, 310 kg loaded, internal combat load 70 kg (463/683/154 lbs); maximum level speed 458 kts (Mach 0.92); maximum endurance 1 hour. The normal one-way penetration range is 485 nm. Mirach can be preprogrammed, e.g., to loiter over a battle area.

UNITED KINGDOM

◆ Sprite

M.L. Aviation demonstrated this helicopter RPV to the U.S. DoD in May 1985. In British tests, Sprite has successfully landed on a rolling platform in gusty winds of up to 20 kts. Overall weight is 88 lbs (40 kg), and endurance (depending on payload) is over two hours. Rotor diameter 1.6 m, body diameter 0.65 m (5 ft 3 in/2 ft 1.5 in). Payload is 12 kg, typically 6 kg of fuel and 6 kg of sensors (26/13/13 lbs). The power plant is two 6-BHP Kolbo D238 2-cycle gasoline engines, or two 7-BHP Piper 2/80 2-cycle gasoline engines. Cruise speed is 60 kts, and climb rate (at 45 kts) is 1200 ft/min. Normal operating altitude is 250–500 m, ceiling 3000 m (820–1640, 9800 ft).

Sprite was developed as a private venture and first flew in January 1983.

UNITED STATES

◆ RPV Master Plan

In 1988 the Department of Defense constructed an RPV Master Plan in response to congressional directives. RFPs for a baseline family of RPVs are to be issued in 1990, with evaluation and testing to begin in FY92. There will be at least three separate RPVs: close-air support, short-range shipboard, and deep operations. Existing programs may be curtailed to fund the baseline RPVs; and as of August 1988, FY88–89 RPV funds had been frozen. There has been some concern, both in Congress and in the Defense Department, that the delay involved in restarting the program will be excessive.

This freeze was not the first restructuring of the RPV program. Secretary of the Navy John Lehman significantly accelerated the navy program late in FY85, and in FY87 Congress demanded increased use of RPVs, probably as a reaction to the loss of an airplane and its crew during the Libyan raid. Secretary Lehman's directive was to use, wherever possible, existing equipment. The navy requirement was broken down into short range (Pioneer), medium range (MR-RPV), and long range (high altitude, in combination with the army and DARPA). A reconnaissance version of the existing BQM-74C Chukar target drone was tested during FY86.

◆ Amber

This long-endurance reconnaissance RPV was developed as a classified program by the Defense Advanced Research Projects Agency. Amber is propeller-driven (pusher engine), and the fuselage's length can range from 13 to nearly 20 ft (payload volume 5 to 15 cubic feet, capacity 150 to 300 lbs). It was announced in May 1988 that the U.S. Navy planned to buy 96 Ambers, which are suited to ship or ground launch, for radio relay, surveillance, and signals intelligence. At that time ten had been turned over to the navy. Operational trials are scheduled for late 1989, and the system could become operational in 1990.

As of early 1988, Amber had flown continuously for 31 hours, at altitudes of up to 23,000 ft. In the basic high-altitude Amber 1 configuration (450A45), the power plant is a 65-HP pusher (KH-800) engine, length is 14.3 ft, wing span is 28.4 ft, and gross take-off weight is 750 lbs (empty weight 280 lbs). The manufacturer is Leading Systems. Two alternative payloads are being developed: one for radio relay, the other with an electro-optical sensor (as in Pioneer) and a signals intelligence package.

Amber was conceived as a successor to the air force's manned TR-1 and is separate from the HALE program of the Naval Air Development Center.

◆ HALE Projects

HALE is an acronym for High Altitude Long Endurance, and there are persistent reports of U.S. Navy interest in such devices, Amber (above) being a case in point. HALE reconnaissance vehicles were successfully used in Vietnam, and the new technologies of very lightweight aircraft construction and also of lightweight sensors make HALE vehicles quite attractive.

The current definition of long endurance seems to be about a week, so that a few HALE could support a deployed surface action group without requiring integrated launch-and-recovery facilities. The current HALE program is described as an investigation of a large unmanned aircraft of extremely long endurance.

In December 1986, the Naval Air Development Center issued an RFP for a HALE for wide-area surveillance and OTH targeting; responses were due by 6 February 1987. Requirements included an endurance of 120 hours at a cruising speed of 116–161 kts, and a service ceiling of 65,000–90,000 ft. The required payload was 7500 lbs, and wingspan could exceed 61 ft. The RPVs described here are generic HALEs and were not specific responses to this RFP. They indicate the sort of capabilities that are now available.

In 1983 Lockheed-California announced a twin-engine HALE powered by two turbofan/turboshaft engines (driving 14.3-m-diameter propellers, which would be locked for take-off), with a wingspan of 84.1 m. Endurance was 24 hours at 27,400 m.

About 1985 Teledyne Ryan announced Spirit, with an endurance of 80 hours at an altitude of 15,850 m to 160 hours at an altitude of 6100 m. Span was 85 ft and overall length about 40 ft (depending on payload); height at the tail was 14 ft (propeller diameter 20 ft). Weight was 4500 lbs, and payload 300–1200 lbs (depending in part on fuel load, which could be as much as about 900 lbs). Cruising speed was 130 kts, and operating altitude 52,000 ft (absolute ceiling 75,000 ft). The power plant was a single flat-six pusher engine. Spirit probably flew in 1986.

At about this time, too, E-Systems tested L450F, based on a Schweitzer sailplane and powered by a Pratt & Whitney PT6A engine.

Boeing Electronics rolled out a very large twin-engine RPV late in March 1986 (about 60 ft long and about 18 ft high at the tail), powered by two Teledyne Continental liquid-cooled piston engines driving three-bladed propellers.

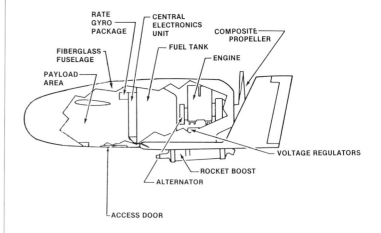

For a time, a version of the Boeing Brave 200 vehicle was being developed as a loitering decoy. (Boeing)

◆ MR-RPV

The RFP for a medium-range RPV with a target variant was issued in August 1986, and one of two finalists was to be chosen late in 1988, with production to begin in 1989. The program

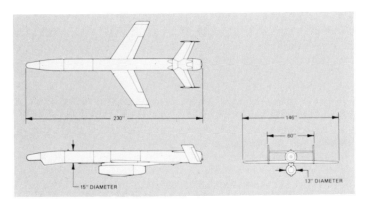

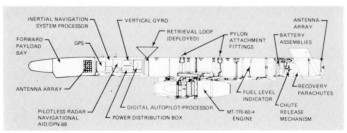

The Martin-Marietta/Beechcraft proposal for the MR-RPV. (Martin-Marietta)

The Teledyne-Ryan Model 350 RPV and its progenitor, the Model 324 Scarab (right). (Teledyne-Ryan)

was restructured as a navy-air force program in 1988, new RFPs being scheduled for April of that year. At that time the Navy planned to buy 31 mid-range systems, each including 5 to 8 RPVs. Funds were frozen in March 1988, pending creation of a joint-service RPV office, to comply with a congressional directive. Industry meetings were held in August 1988 to discuss the restructured program, and at that time it was not clear just when money would be available or just how well the program would be supported; reportedly there was some official skepticism about the value of such long-range RPVs. As of 1988, the program has been renamed JSCAMPS (Joint-Service Common-Airframe Multiple-Purpose System). The new multiple-purpose designator covers alternative use as a target drone. The new request for proposals was issued by the Naval Air Systems Command on 28 June 1988; proposals were due 60 days later.

As of 1986, the specified operating radius of the MR-RPV was 350 nm. Other reported requirements were 2-hour endurance with a 250-lb payload, a speed of at least Mach 0.90, ceiling of at least 40,000 ft, and maximum weight of 2000 lbs. The baseline missions were:

— Air launch from an A-6E/G, to fly over an airfield 350 nm away, determining the type, number, and location of aircraft there. The notional field is assumed to be defended by ZSU-23 cannon, with SA-6 and SA-9 missiles nearby. Image data must be available to the battle-group commander within two hours. The RPV data link might be jammed in the target area. The RPV would be recovered from the water by helicopters, or directly by a destroyer with a landing device.

— Deck launch by a destroyer, to locate a three-ship surface action group about 175 nm (accuracy of location assumed to be 15 nm) away, finding type, course, and speed of each enemy ship. Target data would be transmitted to friendly forces, and the RPV would remain in the target area to conduct damage assessment. The RPV would be recovered from the water.

— Ground launch by a Marine field unit, to provide images for strike planning against three widely separated, defended targets (e.g., bridges, fuel-storage areas, truck/tank parks), 150 nm from the launcher; total flight would be 450 nm. A similar air force mission would involve a target 350 nm away, data to be transmitted in real-time by data link (see ATARS above).

— Air launch by an RF-4C or F-16, for the 350-nm mission.

The MR-RPV ground station must be compatible with that used by the shorter-range Pioneer, which the new RPV will complement.

The original competitors included the Canadair CL-289, the Meteor Mirach (see above), a Martin-Marietta/Beechcraft RPV based on the BQM-126, the Northrop NV-144, and the Teledyne Ryan Model 324 Scarab.

The Beechcraft was designed to replace the earlier Firebee I (BQM-34) drone and flew in March 1984. Martin-Marietta was to have been responsible for the reconnaissance payload. Power was provided by a Microturbo J403-MT-400 engine (899-lbs thrust), and dimensions were 15 in (diameter) × 230 in (span 146 in); weight was 670 lbs (1398 lbs including booster and 424 lbs of usable fuel); maximum load was 100 lbs internally or 220 lbs externally. Maximum speed was 580 kts, service ceiling 40,000 ft, and typical endurance 1 hour 36 minutes.

The Northrop NV-144 has a range of over 950 nm. Dimensions: 20 in × 19 ft 5.5 in (span 10 ft 8.5 in); weight 950 lbs empty or 1500 lbs loaded, including a maximum payload of 300 lbs; maximum fuel load 400 lbs. Performance: maximum speed Mach 0.975, 580 kts at sea level, 300 kts economical cruise at 37,500 ft; service ceiling 42,500 ft. Range at Mach 0.8 at 15,000 ft is 380 nm; maximum range at 50,000 ft is greater than 960 nm; and endurance is 2 hrs 45 min. Flight can be either preprogrammed or remotely controlled.

The Scarab, which is already active in Egyptian service, is a surface-launched RPV, 20 ft long with a 12-ft wingspan and a 250-lb payload; nominal range is 1400 nm. The power plant is a Teledyne CAE 373-8C (Mach 0.8), and the RPV takes off with the aid of a modified Harpoon missile booster.

In August 1988, Ryan displayed Model 350, a candidate for the reopened MR-RPV competition, based on Model 324. It is 44 in shorter than Scarab, with an overall length of 16.3 ft and an 11-ft wing span, and with a weight of 1400–1800 lbs. The proof-of-concept prototype is powered by a Teledyne CAE 373-8C (970-lbs thrust) engine, and the airframe is built entirely of fiberglass-epoxy composites. Estimated cruising radius is 450 nm. Maximum speed is Mach 0.91, and ceiling is 45,000 ft. Carrying a 307-lb payload, Model 350 weighs 1825 lbs and has a cruising endurance of 2.5 hours and a range of 1000 miles. The Model 350 prototype flew for the first time on 22 October 1988, being launched by an F-4C at 15,000 ft. The flight lasted half an hour, the RPV reaching 27,500 ft and Mach 0.75. It was recovered by parachute.

Prototype contracts were awarded to Martin-Marietta and Northrop in September 1987 for a fourteen-month prototype construction phase. As of late 1988, however, Teledyne-Ryan was still in competition for the restructured program.

Boeing has proposed its own Brave (Boeing Robotic Air Vehicle) 3000 for essentially this requirement. Like Boeing's version of the conventional cruise missile (Excalibur; see the Strategic Strike Systems section), Brave 3000 uses a wing that lies lengthwise along the body of the vehicle then pivots for flight. Brave is designed primarily for use by land forces, but the company points out that Brave is compatible with Harpoon launchers. It can carry a warhead or dispense submunitions; Brave can also carry electronic warfare, reconnaissance, or decoy payloads (up to 185 lbs over a 200-km range, loitering more than 30 minutes in the target area). Dimensions: 11.6 × 11.8 in cross section, wing span 89 in, length 135.5 in (excluding rocket booster); launch weight 525 lbs plus 104-lb booster; payload (including fuel) 290 lbs. Maximum cruise speed is 380 kts; loiter speed is 245 kts; ceiling is 25,000 ft; and maximum range is 224 nm (with 105 lbs of fuel). Initial rate of climb at sea level is 3300 ft/min. As in the MR-RPV contestants, Brave 3000 has a pre-programmed flight pattern with waypoint navigation, based on a digital three-axis autopilot.

◆ CH-84 Pegasus

This Aerodyne Systems Engineering, Ltd., helicopter RPV is based on the old QH-50D ASW drone, the notorious DASH of the 1960s. Pegasus carries a 1000-lb payload and is powered by a 425-SHP Detroit Diesel Allison 250 C-20F/S turboshaft engine, cruising at 135–140 kts (maximum speed 140 kts), with maximum endurance of 6.5 hours at 55 kts (52 gallons of fuel internally plus an 80-gallon external tank). Empty weight is 745 lbs, and maximum take-off weight is 2600 lbs; rotor diameter is 20 ft, and height is just over 9 ft. Maximum hovering altitude is 11,000 ft.

In 1986 Aerodyne announced that it would offer CH-84 to both the army and the navy, in the latter offer to meet the MR-RPV requirement. Note that the CH-84 could not meet the high speed requirement inherent in the original MR-RPV specifications but could fit on board virtually all warships, many of which have pads (now considerably enlarged) originally designed for DASH. DASH itself was the first U.S. service RPV, intended to deliver torpedoes at maximum ship's-sonar range. DASH lacked any feedback channel and, therefore, behaved badly often enough to gain a very poor reputation. Presumably, these problems were easy to solve with current technology, and the load-carrying capability remains attractive.

◆ Design 754

Design 754 is Grumman's 1986 proposal for a long-endurance VTOL airborne early-warning RPV. The company claimed that the VTOL feature would make the RPV usable on board ships such as the *Spruances*, and the design is interesting as an approach to surface-action-group early-warning. 754 was to have used conformal-array antennas (in its wings) for its UHF radar, augmented by an ISAR nose radar. Power plant: Garrett F109 turbofan (1330-lbs thrust) plus lift engine (Rolls-Royce RB162-81 or XJ-99, 6010- or 9000-lbs thrust). Performance: maximum endurance 14 hours, range 2800 nm, cruise speed 210 kts (at 31,000 ft). Avionics payload: 1500 lbs (take-off weight 9800 lbs). Dimensions: 51-ft span × 27 ft 6 in (34 ft 8 in with wings folded); weight 9800 lbs at take-off (1500 lbs mission equipment, 3800 lbs fuel).

◆ Pointer

Bell-Boeing's tilt-rotor RPV is essentially a miniature V-22 Osprey. Pointer flew for the first time in 1988. The short-range version has a maximum speed of 160 kts and can loiter at 70 kts; ceiling is 25,000 ft and range is 220 nm (endurance 5 hours). Dimensions: 13 ft 5 in length, rotor diameter 7 ft 9 in; empty weight 395 lbs (655 lbs loaded, including 160 lbs of fuel and 100 lbs of sensors). The power plant is a 95-SHP Williams International turboshaft.

◆ Sea Ferret

Boeing's expendable low-altitude RPV was first proposed in 1983 as an electronic countermeasure (decoy) and shifted to the navy RPV program in 1985 under the Naval Air Systems Command. Sea Ferret was then canceled, presumably because of the reorganization that included the procurement of Pioneer. Sea Ferret was a version of the Boeing Brave 200 and was proposed for a variety of roles including decoy and lethal attack. Brave 200's characteristics were length 7 ft, span 8 ft 5 in, maximum fuselage depth 20 in, empty weight 154 lbs, loaded weight 265 lbs, payload about 60 lbs. Performance: cruising speed 121 kts, loiter speed 78 kts, range 434+ nm, ceiling 13,000+ ft. The power plant is a 28-HP Cuyuna two-cylinder, two-stroke engine driving a pusher propeller.

Seek Spinner, which was rejected in favor of Tacit Rainbow (which is listed as a missile under air-to-surface weapons), was another version intended for use as an antiradiation weapon.

AIRBORNE SENSORS

CANADA

◆ APS-503

> **Band:** X (9.2–9.4 GHz)   **Beam:** 4 × 5 deg
> **Peak Power:** 50 kW   **Gain:** 30 dB
> **Pulse Width:** 0.5 microsec   **PRF:** 400
> **Scan Rate:** 30 rpm   **Antenna Dimensions:** 24 × 18 in
> **Antenna Weight:** total weight 45 kg (100 lbs)

APS-503 is the sea-search radar of Canadian Sea King helicopters and is manufactured by Eaton and by Litton of Canada. The antenna is stabilized in pitch and roll and can be tilted through 8 degrees up or down.

LASR-2 is a commercial version with twice the power (100 kW peak), two pulse widths, four alternative PRFs, and three alternative scan rates. LASR-2 is broadly comparable to the APS-504.

◆ APS-504

> **Band:** X (8.9–9.4 GHz)   **Beam:** 2.3 × 5 deg
> **Peak Power:** 100 kW   **Pulse Width:** (i) 0.5 (ii) 2.4 microsec
> **PRF:** 1600, 1200, 400, 200 (range scales 20, 50, 100, 250 nm)
> **Scan Rate:** 30 or 12 rpm (or 72 deg/sec sector scan)
> **Antenna Dimensions:** 112 × 33 cm (stabilized)
> **Antenna Weight:** Under 72 kg total

APS-504 is the maritime-surveillance radar developed from APS-503 by Eaton and by Litton of Canada. In the (V)5 version, the TWT transmitter is frequency agile, and the pulses are compressed (peak power is reduced to 8 kW). In 1987, Litton Canada received contracts for a (V)5 upgrade, which could be used on board Canadian S-2 Trackers.

The Litton APS-140(V) is a derivative of APS-504, incorporating coherent TWT, pulse compression, frequency agility, and scan-to-scan integration.

◆ LN-66

See shipboard radars and fire-control systems (under Antiair Warfare section).

◆ ASP

Computing Devices Co. is conducting full scale engineering development of an Airborne Signal Processor (ASP) for a synthetic aperture radar planned for Canadian CP-140 Aurora maritime-patrol aircraft.

FRANCE

◆ DRAA-2A

> **Band:** X   **Pulse Width:** (i) 0.5 (ii) 2 microsec
> **PRF:** (i) 1300 (ii) 400
> **Scan Rate:** 6 or 8 rpm (provision for 30-deg sector scan)

The stabilized radar of the Alizé carrier-based ASW aircraft and of the Atlantique Mk 1 (DRAA-2B) has a maximum instrumented range of 60 or 200 nm (reflected in PRFs above). This radar is being superseded by IGUANE.

Note that although this radar is principally a means of detecting surface ships and snorkels, DRAA-2A can also function as a low-altitude airborne early-warning set, like the British Searchwater and the U.S. APS-20 (which, after all, was originally conceived as an airborne early-warning set). Within a French battle group, the combination of this radar and the shipboard higher-altitude sets should give effective radar early-warning out to a radius of about 100–150 nm.

Many details are not available, but note that the first prototype Alizés had U.S.-supplied APS-33s, which presumably approximated DRAA-2A dimensions and performance. APS-33 was intended for large ASW aircraft such as the Neptune. APS-33 operated in X-band and had a 3.6-degree fan beam and, with 52 kW peak power (pulse widths 0.5 and 5 microseconds, PRFs 800 and 200), could detect a surfaced submarine at 65 nm and a snorkel at 20 nm. Maximum range was 200 nm, minimum 200 yards.

A 1957 proposal to equip some Alizés with APS-20 radars for dedicated airborne early-warning was rejected. Presumably a combination of separate AEW and ASW aircraft would have displaced so many strike aircraft that the small French carriers would no longer have been viable.

◆ Agave

The multimode X-band monopulse radar of the Super-Étendard strike fighter is used to target Exocet antiship missiles, among other weapons. Scan limits are 140 × 60 degrees, and the radar can detect an airplane at 18–28 km or a patrol boat at 40–55 km. In the search mode, the radar scans over 140 degrees horizontally, and over 6–12 degrees vertically, the position of the horizontal bar being selectable through 60 degrees up or down. Typically, vertical cover is limited to a single 6-degree bar to reject low-altitude clutter; at higher elevation angles, two bars (12 degrees) are used because the single narrow bar may miss a fast target. In the autotrack (monopulse) mode, the radar can transmit data either to a missile or to a HUD. Range gates can be set at 5 to 85 nm.

Agave is a one-man radar, and its controls (antenna elevation, bearing and range markers, lock-on for autotrack) are all on a single hand grip. The antenna is an inverted Cassegrain. Total weight is 65 kg.

Agave was proposed in 1974, derived from the earlier RH 370 helicopter radar. Passing its trials in 1975, Agave entered service in 1978. Over 170 had been ordered by 1986. They have been installed on Jaguar, Mirage F1, and Mirage 50 aircraft. The Jaguar version uses a raster scan display rather than the usual PPI. Agave is to be replaced by the new Anemone radar on French Navy Super-Étendards.

Note that the original RH 370 had a peak power of 90 kW and used a 51-cm Cassegrain dish, stabilized in roll and pitch. RH 370 could detect a patrol boat at 35 nm, with an accuracy of 1 degree in bearing and 0.1 nm in range. RH 370 reached the initial evaluation stage in June 1971.

◆ AGRION 15/IGUANE/VARAN

These systems are X-band frequency-agile pulse-compression surface-search radars. Pulse compression is used partly to reduce peak power, thus making the radars less detectable. In 1982, Thomson-CSF claimed that pulse compression made for an effective pulse width only a tenth that of magnetron radars, with 35 times the equivalent peak power and that VARAN was 6 to 8 times lighter, 3 to 9 times more difficult to detect, and 6 times more discrete than any other pulse-compression radar on the market.

These radars use two pulse lengths, long (tenths of microseconds) for long-range detection of large targets and short (thousandths of a microsecond) for small targets in a rough sea. The long compressed pulse provides sufficient energy for long range. The short pulse is needed in a rough sea to limit the size of the resolution cell, so that the target stands out against the surrounding noise.

The basic unit is IGUANE, the radar for the Atlantique 2 and for the modernized Alizé. The program began in 1974, and tech-

An Atlantique Nouvelle Generation (Atlantique Mk 2) displays its IGUANE radar and its ESM systems, in the wingtips. Any radar pushed out into the airstream creates drag, but that offset from the main airframe is the only way a single reflector can cover anything approaching 360 degrees. Offset was the solution in aircraft such as the Alizé, the P-2, and the S-2. The alternative is to use two reflectors (as in the P-3) or to accept 180-degree scanning (as in the S-3, which has a nose radar). The bulge under the transparent nose contains a gyrostabilized high-resolution thermal imaging camera, Tango, with a switchable 6.45 × 4.30/2.15 × 1.43 degree field of view (the turret can turn to 110 degrees to either side of the airplane, and its elevation limits are +15/−45 degrees. The output is a 625-line television signal, 50.5 frames/second. (U.S. Naval Institute)

nical evaluation began in January 1979; IGUANE first flew in May 1981. Claimed performance: 28 nm on a snorkel, 60 nm on a fast attack boat, 130 nm on a medium-sized ship, all in sea-state 3 or 4. For target classification, the antenna is locked with its beam pointing sideways, functioning as a synthetic aperture system, while a special unit (Anaconda) forms the image. The antennas used in the Alizé and Atlantique are identical to those already in use. Total weight is 75 kg in an Alizé and about 130 kg in an Atlantique.

AGRION 15, which is used to target AS 15TT missiles, adds a monopulse tracking unit and a matched boresight-stabilized 1.3-m cheese antenna. AGRION 15 has two scan speeds and a TWS mode. This radar is used on board the Dauphin helicopters exported to Saudi Arabia.

VARAN is an IGUANE with a smaller antenna, for medium maritime-patrol aircraft to use for sea search and OTH targeting. VARAN equips French Navy Guardian maritime-surveillance aircraft.

Thomson-CSF, the manufacturer, credits all three radars with the ability to detect a lifeboat or a snorkel at 30 nm, a fast patrol boat at 60 nm, and a freighter at 120 nm.

The names of all three radars are acronyms: IGUANE is *Instrument de Guet pour Avion Navale Embarqué*; AGRION is *Appareil de Guet de Recherche et d'Identification d'Objectif Navale*; VARAN is *Veille Aéroportée Anti-Navire*. Work on IGUANE began in 1975, and the first production radars were delivered in 1980.

◆ Anemone

Anemone is the replacement for Agave, to be used in French Navy Super-Étendards now being modernized.

◆ **ORB 31 (Heracles I)**

> **Band:** X (9335–9415 MHz)
> **Beam:** (a) 4 × 7.5 (b) 3.2 × 6 (c) 4.8 × 7.5 deg
> **Peak Power:** 12 or 30 kW
> **Gain:** (a) 29.2 dB (b) 30.5 dB (c) 28 dB
> **Pulse Width:** (i) 0.2 (ii) 0.5 (iii) 4 microsec
> **PRF:** (i) 1600 (ii) 800 (iii) 400
> **Antenna Dimensions:** (a) 608 × 308 mm (b) 728 × 368 mm
> (c) 460 × 308 mm
> **Antenna Weight:** (a) 1.1 (b) 1.3 (c) 0.8 kg (ORB 31D combines re-
> flector (c) with 30 kW transmitters) (ORB 31W combines reflec-
> tor (a) with 30 kW transmitters)

The Omera-Segid helicopter sea-search radar is used in its ORB 31D version on board Super-Frélon helicopters to target the AM 39 Exocet. This radar also exists in an ORB 31W configuration, for French Navy Lynx helicopters, and in an ORB 31AS antisubmarine version, carried by Alouette-IIIs. These radars all scan through 180 degrees in bearing.

The ORB 31D and 31W versions use two transceivers, one for long range and another for short range and high resolution (and for clutter rejection). Range on a ship (1000 square meters) is 80 km (ORB 31D) or 50 nm (ORB 31W), and total weight is 75 kg (ORB 31D) or 61 kg (ORB 31W).

ORB-31 was derived from ORB-3, which is a license-built Ekco weather radar.

◆ **ORB 32 (Heracles II)**

> **Band:** X (8500–9600 MHz or 9100–9500 MHz)
> **Beam:** 2.6 × 6.2 deg   **Peak Power:** 80 kW
> **Gain:** 32 dB   **Pulse Width:** 0.25 or 2.0 microsec
> **PRF:** 1200, 600, or 300   **Antenna Dimensions:** 72 × 36 cm
> **Antenna Weight:** total weight 129 kg

The modular Omera radar for small maritime-patrol aircraft was announced in 1979. ORB 32 was developed from the ORB 31-series. Each radar consists of five main elements: an antenna (one of seven parabolic reflectors, with major axes 46 to 85 cm and minor axes 30 or 36 cm, with front or rear illumination, gains of 28.5–32 dB and beams of 2.6–4.8 × 6.2–7.5 deg); a pedestal (single- or two-axis stabilization, full or sector scan at 20 and 40 rpm); a junction box; a transmitter-receiver (four types covering both bandwidths above, all with the same peak power, PRFs, and pulse widths, but fixed, tunable, coded jump, or frequency-agile); and a PPI display. Sectors are 60, 120, 180, or 240 degrees; and all of these radars can scan the full 360 degrees. Range is 90 km on a 500 square-meter target.

Data apply to the ORB 32WAS version for the SA 321 Super-Frélon helicopter. This radar was adopted by China (PRC) for its SA321J helicopters. There is also a similar ORB 32WD reconnaissance and target designation radar, capable of tracking two ships. The Swedish government plans to buy a combined AS/WD version, ORB 32ASD.

◆ **RDX**

The Thomson-CSF pulse-doppler radar for the new Rafale fighter is to be operated by both the French Air Force and the French Navy. The air force requires simultaneous air-to-air and air-to-ground operation, including terrain-following. The navy emphasizes air-to-air detection at maximum range, for fleet air defense. The air force requirement is to be met by an electronically scanned antenna, which flew in 1987 and which will be able to generate multiple beams either simultaneously or in rapid succession. Because multiple-beam forming wastes some radar energy, the ideal Navy solution would have been a mechanically scanned antenna. Since both versions of Rafale will probably have to carry the same radar, RDX will instead add radar power to make up for the scanning losses. To meet the requirement for operations at a wide variety of ranges, RDX will operate at high, medium, and low PRF, the peak power being matched to PRF (and varying by a factor of up to ten). The transmitter will be a dual-peak-power TWT. RDX will also use a programmable signal processor capable of about 1 Megaflop within relatively small dimensions, requiring the development

of new 0.8-micron (versus the current 1.2-micron) integrated-circuit technology.

ITALY

◆ **APS-705/707/APQ-706**

> **Band:** X (dual frequency)
> **Beam:** 2 × 7 deg (AB 212); 1.5 × 10 deg (SH-3D)
> **Peak Power:** 25 kW (option: 75 kW)
> **Pulse Width:** (i) 0.05 (ii) 0.15 (iii) 0.5 (iv) 1.5 microsec
> **PRF:** (i) 1600 (ii) 1300 (iii) 1300 (iv) 650
> **Scan Rate:** 20 and 40 rpm
> **Antenna Dimensions:** 1.2-m aperture (AB 212) or 1.6-m aperture
> (SH-3D)   **Antenna Weight:** Total system weight 87 kg

The SMA TWS radar for Italian Navy AB 212 and SH-3D helicopters (surface search, periscope detection, and tracking) employs two 25-kW transceivers (one antenna) for frequency diversity. The antenna is stabilized in line of sight and can be tilted 20 degrees up or down.

APS-707 is a more austere version of APS-705. 707 is a single-channel fixed-frequency lightweight set (one 20-kW transmitter). There is also a high-powered version, using a 90-kW transmitter, which has been adopted by the Argentine Navy to replace existing APS-20 radars on board SP-2H Neptune maritime-patrol aircraft. APS-707 is frequency agile and has other ECCM features.

APQ-706 is a double-antenna radar (back to back) used to guide the Marte antiship missile (carried on board Italian Navy SH-3D Sea Kings). 706 uses two channels, one of fixed frequency and one with frequency agility, the latter to detect small high-speed targets. The fixed-frequency channel is used for navigation and periscope detection. The transmitter is the 75-kW frequency-agile unit available as an option in APS-705. The antenna is line-of-sight stabilized.

◆ **APS-784**

The EMA/FIAR X-band radar for Italian EH-101 helicopters will probably serve both for surface search (including attack against surface ships) and for some degree of airborne early-warning. The antenna will scan through 360 degrees. The transmitter will be a TWT, and pulses will be compressed. For antiship operation (such as missile target designation), APS-784 will be capable of track-while-scan operation. APS-784 will be a compact radar, using only four line-replaceable units.

SMA has offered a scaled-down version for the NATO NH.90 helicopter.

◆ **Grifetto (PA-2801) and SCP-01**

Grifetto is the FIAR radar proposed for the antiship version of the Italian-Brazilian AM-X fighter; some of this technology may be incorporated in the APS-784 radar of the EH-101 helicopter. Grifetto is part of a privately developed Grifo series of X-band radars. The simplest, PA-2801, is a small (50-kg) magnetron radar limited to antiship and close-air-support missions. It is designed to detect a frigate at a range of 55 nm. Aeritalia considers Grifetto the standard radar for the antiship version of the AM-X.

However, a more advanced radar in the same family, Grifo X, may be adopted for Italian Air Force strike versions of the AM-X. Grifo X weighs about 70 kg (165 lbs), has a 16-inch antenna, and should have useful air-to-air performance.

The most advanced radar of the series, Grifo, uses a TWS transmitter and weighs about 90 kg (about 200 lbs). The antenna is a 24-inch flat plate, and a frigate can be detected at 80 nm in sea-state 4. This radar is intended to replace existing radars on aircraft such as Mirages and Soviet- and Chinese-built fighters. The prototype was tested in 1988. Bandwidth is up to 200 MHz, with both low- and medium-PRF waveforms. Average power is up to 120 kW (up to 4 percent duty cycle).

In 1988 SMA announced an alternative AM-X radar, SCP-01 (Scipio), which SMA was developing in cooperation with a Brazilian company, Tecnasa, using Brazilian Air Force research and development funds. SMA will be responsible for signal processing. SCP-01 will presumably equip Brazilian AM-X strike fighters. Total weight will be about 80 kg; the antenna diameter is about 16 inches, and average power will be about 120 W. Estimated range on a frigate is 60 nm.

SWEDEN

◆ HERA (9HCI 100)

The PEAB-Omera frequency-agile periscope-detection and surface-search radar appeared on refurbished KV-107 ASW helicopters in 1986. HERA can detect a snorkel at 25 nm in sea-state 5, or a frigate at 100 nm, and can be used to find targets for the RBS 15 missile. A transponder allows two helicopters to coordinate their attacks.

9HCI 100 is the export designation (9HCI 200 with torpedo fire control included).

USSR

◆ Big Bulge

The Bear-D X-band surface-search radar is used to target SS-N-3 and -12 missiles. This radar, with a smaller radome, is also fitted to Hormone-A helicopters. Reported PRFs for the Hormone version are 414–418 and 621–628 pps.

Big Bulge radar on board a Bear-D bomber. (U.S. Navy)

This Hormone helicopter carries a smaller version of Big Bulge, for missile targeting. (U.S. Navy)

◆ Crown Drum

Crown Drum was the surface-search radar used by Badger-B bombers carrying AS-1 missiles; the associated beam-riding guidance radar was Komet III. This system became operational in 1957. Both radars operated at X-band. Crown Drum was also associated with the AS-3 strategic attack missile (carried by Bear-B bombers).

◆ Down Beat

The Blinder and Backfire missile-guidance radar appeared in 1959. Down Beat is associated with the AS-4 and AS-6 missiles, and it is frequency-agile, with variable PRF.

Down Beat nose radar on board a Badger. (U.S. Naval Institute)

◆ Mushroom

This X-band surface-search radar is installed in Ka-25 ASW helicopters.

◆ Puff Ball

The navigation/attack radar on Badger-C is used to target AS-2 and AS-6 missiles. Puff Ball is also carried by Badger-D, -E, -F, and -J.

Puff Ball radar under the nose of a Hormone ASW helicopter, which is dipping its sonar. (U.S. Naval Institute)

◆ Short Horn

Short Horn is a Ka-band (14–15 GHz) bombing radar and is the chin (sea-search) radar on the Bear-D. This radar is also carried by Badger-G (AS-5 and AS-6 missiles). Short Horn is frequency-agile and has both circular and sector scan. Reported characteristics: pulse width (i) 1–1.8 (ii) 0.5–1.4 (iii) 0.4–1.3 (iv) 0.01–0.9 microsec; PRF (i) 313–316 (ii) 496–504 (iii) 624–626 (iv) 1249–1253 pps.

◆ Wet Eye

The surface-search radar of May and Bear-F ASW aircraft is associated with the BM-1 and, presumably, later sonobuoy systems.

Wet Eye radar as carried by an IL-38 MAY. (U.S. Naval Institute)

UNITED KINGDOM

◆ ARI 5955/MAREC/MAREC II

Band: X **Peak Power:** 15 kW
Pulse Width: 0.5 **PRF:** 400

The Sea King X-band search radar was introduced in 1968 and has been replaced since 1982 by the MEL Sea Searcher. ARI's effective range is 50 nm, compared to over 100 nm for the Sea Searcher. ARI 5955 was originally a German Ekco radar. X-band was chosen because S- or C-band would have given insufficient definition, and Ka- and Ku-band would have been excessively affected by weather. Note that this and later MEL radars are all associated with big horizontal plotting tables incorporating backlit radar displays.

MAREC (Maritime-Reconnaissance Radar) is a developed form of ARI 5955, with a higher peak power (65 kW) and antenna gain (34.5 dB), two pulse lengths (0.5 and 2.5 microseconds), and two PRFs (200 and 400 pps). In a proposed installation on board the British Aerospace HS 748, MAREC used a 36-inch stabilized antenna (2.5-degree beam) in an under-fuselage radome. Alternative antennas were 24–48 × 12–21 inches.

MAREC was not sold successfully, but MAREC II was selected for Indian Coast Guard Do 228 aircraft and also for the Dornier Do 128 used by the Cameroons. MAREC II operates in X-band (peak power 80 kW); pulse widths are 0.4 and 2.5 microseconds (PRFs, respectively, are 400 and 200). Maximum range is about 250 nm (maximum instrumented range is 219 nm). Note that the Indian sets are being produced under license by Hindustan Aeronautics.

◆ Blue Fox

The Ferranti multimode monopulse X-band radar for Royal Navy Sea Harriers was developed from the private-venture Blue Falcon core radar of the mid-1970s. Reportedly, Blue Fox is also related to Seaspray. The antenna is a flat roll-stabilized slotted array. It incorporates an IFF interrogator.

Radar modes: (i) air-to-air/air-to-surface scanning in azimuth and/or elevation; (ii) lock-on track (one target); (iii) visual acquisition (through the HUD); (iv) air-to-surface ranging (the radar locks on the aim point to provide range data); (v) ground mapping (for navigation).

The transmitter is a spin-tuned magnetron, hopping frequency on a pulse-to-pulse basis for ECCM, for clutter rejection (the clutter characteristics vary from frequency to frequency, hence can be reduced if successive pulses are integrated), for glint reduction (again, the reflecting characteristics of a complex target will vary with the frequency, and thus can be smoothed out by frequency-hopping), and also for reduction of second-time-around errors due to detection of large reflectors (such as land masses) at a distance.

This radar is to be replaced by Blue Vixen in Sea Harrier FRS.2.

◆ Blue Kestrel

This X(I)-band radar for British EH-101 and Sea King helicopters covers 360 degrees. Blue Kestrel is a TWS radar, and its transmitter is coherent (with pulse-compression); it is also frequency-agile. This radar was derived from Seaspray (below).

◆ Blue Vixen

Ferranti's multimode coherent pulse-doppler radar for modernized Royal Navy Sea Harrier (FRS.2) is derived from the earlier Blue Fox and from Ferranti's private venture Blue Falcon core-radar project. Blue Falcon is also the basis for Ferranti's proposals for aircraft such as EFA. Blue Vixen is a response to some of the Falklands lessons and is designed to be compatible with the AMRAAM medium-range air-to-air missile. Operating modes include look up/down, TWS, single-target track, ground-mapping, air-to-surface ranging, and sea-surface search. The display can be frozen, and surface beacons can be interrogated.

Because it uses a data bus, the radar can distribute some of its components throughout the airplane. For example, the radar processor is installed in the rear fuselage.

The development contract for this radar was let in July 1983, and a prototype, which flew in a BAC 111, was delivered late in 1985 (flying in mid-1986). Limited finances forced deletion of provisions for JTIDS, although space and weight are still reserved for later installation.

Red Fox is a repackaged version offered for other aircraft.

◆ Sea Searcher/Super Searcher

Compared to the earlier ARI 5955, MEL X-band search radar for Sea King helicopters is credited with twice the range. Sea Searcher is a TWS radar that can sector-scan. There are two alternative (selectable) pulse widths, for operation in various sea states. The antenna is enlarged: sizes from 107–610 mm in horizontal aperture (42–240 inches) are available.

Super Searcher is a development announced in 1982 that uses a 42-inch antenna and has greater detection, tracking, and missile-guidance performance. A new color CRT replaces the earlier monochrome PPI. There are three selectable pulse lengths, including an ultra-short pulse for high definition in bad weather; and the CRT has freeze frame and memory storage (and MTI). This radar has TWS capability. Super Searcher is the radar of the Indian Navy Sea King Mk 428 helicopter and also of the Royal Australian Navy S-70B Seahawk.

MEL has announced Triple S (Super Searcher Skua), which was chosen in September 1987 for Royal Navy Lynx helicopters. The virtue of Triple S was that it could scan the full 360 degrees, so that a helicopter could turn away from the target after firing a Sea Skua missile. At the time of writing (1988), the future of this radar was uncertain, given cuts in British defense spending.

◆ Seaspray

Band: X **Antenna Dimensions:** 27 in × 10 in (deep)
Antenna Weight: total weight 65 kg

Ferranti's sea-search radar for the Lynx helicopter uses a Phillips frequency-agile (spin-tuned magnetron) transmitter. Seaspray is intended primarily to detect and track small fast craft, such as fast patrol boats, and can be used to guide Sea Skua missiles. It can also be used as a periscope detector. Tracking is monopulse. There are four selectable PRFs.

Ferranti announced Mks 2 and 3 in August 1982. Mk 2 had a new processor, and Mk 3 was a TWS version with a full 360-degree scan. Compared to Seaspray Mk 1, Mk 3 has full 360-degree coverage and TWS performance. The display is a television-type raster showing processed video, and the picture can be frozen if necessary. Total weight is about 140 lbs.

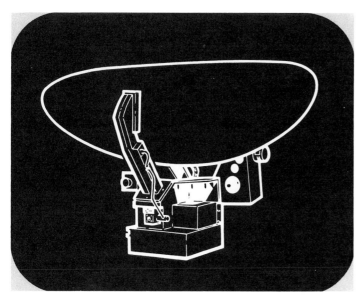

Seaspray antenna (686 mm wide). (Ferranti)

By early 1985, over 250 Mk 1s had been ordered, users including the Royal Netherlands Navy, the Royal Danish Navy, Argentina, and Brazil. In 1984 the German Navy selected Seaspray Mk 3 for the Sea King Mk 41 helicopters, to replace their existing MEL ARI 5955 radars, which could not be used to illuminate targets for Sea Skua missile engagement. In November 1984, a further version, Seaspray Mk 4, was chosen to equip Bell 212 ASW helicopters for Turkey.

♦ **Searchwater (ARI 5980)**

Searchwater is Thorn-EMI's Nimrod MR.2 X-band pulse-compression surface-search radar; Searchwater also serves as an airborne early-warning radar on board British and Spanish Sea King helicopters. This radar was the major improvement over the MR.1 version, using both a narrow beam and a short pulse

Searchwater in its airborne early-warning form, as carried by Sea King helicopters. (Westland)

to limit the patch of sea clutter surrounding a target. Pulse-to-pulse frequency agility helps eliminate sea returns, which are frequency-dependent. The radar integrates all pulses in any one beamwidth during one scan and can also integrate from scan to scan. The detection threshold is controlled to maintain a constant false-alarm rate; the associated computer produces processed video, which is what the PPI shows. Searchwater is credited with a target-classification capability based on target size and aspect. The antenna is pitch- and roll-stabilized, with controllable tilt and automatic sector scan.

The operator has A-scope, B-scope, and raster-scanned PPI displays, the A-scope being used for what appears to be ISAR.

In 1985 Thorn-EMI was awarded a contract for a color display, with which processed video could be overlaid on raw video (in the monochrome version only processed video could be displayed). That was expected to improve anticollision performance, as well as detectability of targets.

Claimed performance: 28 + nm on a snorkel, 60 + nm on a fast attack boat, and 130 + nm on a medium-sized ship.

Searchwater development began in 1972, initial tests following in 1973; the first production Nimrod 2 was delivered in August 1979.

The associated IFF is the Cossor Jubilee Guardsman.

Thorn-EMI's helicopter-borne early-warning version of Searchwater was initially developed in response to the experience of the Falklands War. The patrol version, intended for sea search, uses a fan beam; the AEW version uses a pencil beam with circular polarization provided as an alternative to the vertical and horizontal polarization of the Nimrod (patrol) version.

The AEW version has two alternative scan rates (faster to track faster-moving targets, slower for better detection at longer range) and four range scales (i.e., PRFs; pulse widths are adjusted to match range scales, presumably to maintain the same average power output). There are alternative warning and search modes optimized, respectively, for aircraft and ship detection. The antenna can also be tilted to scan for weather features, and a separate A-scope is used to assist in target classification; presumably the blips displayed on it show some structure related to the target's shape and aspect.

Targets are detected by the operator, who manually designates them on the PPI. In the warning mode, the PPI is arranged to brighten fast-moving targets. Once designated, targets can be automatically tracked. Any position of the PPI can be displayed in expanded form on a B-scope (bearing vs. range) for more accurate positioning of the target designator, a feature presumably valuable if there are many targets close together. The associated computer provides both target track data and computed range and intercept-vector data for fighters. A Sea King equipped with Searchwater controls fighters directly (as does the much more powerful E-2C) rather than merely handing target data down to a ship (as in early U.S. and all previous British AEW aircraft).

The system can track up to 16 air targets in manual control and can direct up to six simultaneous interceptions. There are two operator stations, side by side, with the tactical coordinator (in contact with the senior warfare officer on board the carrier) on the right. The tactical coordinator can track up to 40 surface targets, the helicopter providing over-the-horizon targeting support for surface ships. The officer at the left-hand display is responsible for air targets. The system is reportedly being developed to interchange data between the two displays so that fighters can be directed against designated surface targets. Work is also proceeding to increase computer capacity so that more air targets can be handled. The system currently lacks the air-to-surface data link associated with many earlier AEW aircraft (which did not themselves control fighters); reportedly, Searchwater also suffers from clutter when tracking low-flying air targets. Introduction of a coherent transmitter (as in the related Skymaster surface-search radar) would help solve the latter problem, as target doppler would be easier to extract.

Searchwater is described as noncoherent, but its manufacturer also credits the system with the capability of extracting doppler data from its pulse-compressed signals. That capability suggests that pulses are internally coded by phase rather than by frequency.

Thorn-EMI had proposed an AEW adaptation of Searchwater before the Falklands War, but this project had been rejected on the grounds that the Royal Navy would, in the future, fight only in the North Sea and eastern North Atlantic, i.e., always under the cover of long-range shore-based aircraft such as AWACS. The Falklands War demonstrated that other contingencies were very possible, and on 5 May 1982 Thorn-EMI revived its idea. The study was officially approved on 13 May, and two Sea King helicopter prototypes were ordered on 24 May; the first flew on 23 July 1982, and the prototype Sea King AEW helicopters embarked on board HMS *Illustrious* on 2 August 1982. The project survived the end of the war, and production AEW helicopters became operational in 1986. British carriers now embark a flight of three AEW helicopters. In addition, two ASW Sea Kings are fitted for, but not with, the Searchwater radar, as potential spare airframes.

This system is also employed by the Spanish Navy.

♦ ANR 360 (Navigator)

Decca's maritime-surveillance radar was developed in Norway and first flew in a Cessna 337 in mid-1979. Navigator is a standard Decca X-band (3-cm) solid-state marine radar with a 25-kW transmitter. The antenna is limited to 18-cm depth to fit under the chin of a helicopter. In the Mk 1 fitted in the Cessna, the antenna is in a standard cargo pack attached to the underside of the fuselage, using a fiberglass radome. Mk 3, planned for the Sea King helicopter, will use a chin radome for 360-degree scanning. Maximum instrumented range is 95 nm, with eight range scales from 0.5 nm up.

This radar was originally developed to meet a Norwegian requirement for a periscope detection unit, to deal with submarines in fjords. As fitted in Sea Kings, the radar will have a data link to control attacks by fast patrol boats hidden behind islands.

♦ ASR 360

> **Band:** X **Beam:** 3 × 27 deg
> **Peak Power:** 25 kW
> **Scan Rate:** 32 rpm
> **Antenna Dimensions:** 30-inch slotted waveguide

ASR 360 is Racal-Decca's surface-search marine radar, adapted for small maritime-patrol aircraft, such as converted Short Skyvans (Sultan of Oman Air Force, which bought 15 in January 1984). As of 1984, ASR 360 had also been selected by British Aerospace for a modified Jetstream 31EZ. ASR 360 was originally developed for the Royal Norwegian Navy in 1979, to be flown on board a single- or twin-engined Cessna (the first installation was a Royal Norwegian Navy Cessna 337).

UNITED STATES

♦ AAR-42

AAR-42 is Texas Instruments's pod-mounted forward-looking infrared (FLIR) detector for A-7 attack aircraft. AAR-42 is gimballed and provides a night window/bombsight; as of 1988 over 100 had entered U.S. Navy service. Early in 1985 work began on an upgrade for the Air National Guard, to include a wide-field-of-view navigation mode, DC-restored video, and a capability for hands-off operation (automatic gain/level). These improvements will be available for possible navy upgrades.

Work on the A-7 FLIR began in mid-1974, and the production award followed in 1977.

♦ AAR-50/AAQ-16

Hughes's system, AAR-50 is a navigation set, TINS (thermal imaging navigation set), for the F/A-18, derived from the earlier AAQ-16. AAR-50 provides a pilot with an image (on his heads-up display) of the terrain toward which he is flying, in either black-is-hot or white-is-hot form (the latter looks something like a conventional television image). TINS has a fixed 20 × 20–degree field of view (and thus cannot be used for target-following), occupying a pod (10 × 78 inches, 175 lbs) on a stub pod adapter on the starboard side of the airplane. Hughes claims that MTBF is greater than 410 hours (MTTR is 17 minutes, using standard WRA components). Five prototypes have been delivered; as of early 1989, first production deliveries were scheduled for that year.

The earlier AAQ-16 is intended for both the U.S. V-22 Osprey tilt-rotor aircraft and the Anglo-Italian EH-101 helicopter. AAQ-16 is a turret-mounted FLIR, with two alternative fields of view (1× and 6×), a zoom lens (1× to 10×), and an autotracker. The turret weighs 45 lbs and is 12 inches in diameter (14 in deep). Hughes claims MTBF is 400 hours.

TINS (AAR-50) mounted on an F/A-18. (Hughes)

♦ AAS-36/37

AAS-36 is the Texas Instruments infrared detecting set (IRDS) for P-3 Orions. IRDS provides a thermal image of the target on a television set, and the detector is inertially stabilized against target motion. The passive tracker can be locked onto a target of interest. The set is carried in a small turret under the nose of the airplane.

Texas Instruments began working on a P-3 FLIR late in 1974, the first production award following in mid-1977. AAS-36 was originally developed for the P-3C Update II but is now being fitted in earlier P-3Bs and -3Cs. A derivative, AAS-37, is used on board marine OV-10Ds. AAS-37 provides automatic target tracking and laser illumination for weapons such as Paveway. The AAS-36 infrared receiver is incorporated in the AAQ-15 infrared detecting-and-tracking set used on board air force HH-60 helicopters and C-130 gunships. In that application three simultaneous fields of view are presented, and there is an automatic video tracker.

♦ AAS-38

AAS-38 is the Texas Instruments/Ford Aerospace forward-looking infrared (FLIR) for F/A-18 Hornet fighter-bombers and is used primarily for attack against land targets. The system is pod-mounted and ultimately will control a laser target designator/ranger. This FLIR incorporates an automatic target tracker and automatic gain/level control for hands-off operation. The system as a whole employs 10 Weapons Replaceable Assemblies (WRAs); mean time to replace one is less than 12 minutes.

AAS-38 FLIR pod mounted on an F/A-18. (Hughes)

The pod is 13 × 72 inches and weighs 347 lbs. It is typically mounted on the lower left of the aircraft fuselage and provides the pilot with a 3-×-3- or 12-×-12-degree field of view. The pilot can move the line of sight from −150 to +30 degrees, with 540 degrees of roll freedom in either direction. Targets can be tracked at 75 deg/sec.

AAS-38 was the first navy FLIR designed for supersonic operation. This system entered service in February 1985, after more than 175 successful test flights between 1980 and 1983, a 170-flight program at NWC China Lake and NAS Patuxent River in 1984, and an operational evaluation at Patuxent River in 1985. Full-scale development of the laser tracker began in 1983, and it is scheduled for incorporation in pods delivered from 1989 onwards.

Dimensions: 13 × 72 in; weight 370 lbs (including laser ranger). Ford claims an MTBF of 80 hours for the full FLIR/laser ranger (MTTR 15 minutes).

Three major improvements are currently in production: pod boresight G-load compensation software; filtered inertial-to-sightline coordinate transformation (CSI) for better targeting accuracy; and air-to-air automatic tracking. A multifunction autotracker and an advanced air-to-air capability are under development. The multifunction autotracker automatically selects one of several possible air-to-air tracking methods (algorithms) to lock onto another airplane. The autotracker can conduct a search for an airborne target, automatically detecting it and locking on; alternatively, the autotracker can track several targets simultaneously (a FLIR equivalent of radar TWS performance).

◆ S-3 FLIRs (OR-89/AA)

The FLIRs installed in S-3s do not have separate AN designations because the FLIRs are integral elements of a larger weapons system. The first version, OR-89/AA, was also the first FLIR to be designed simultaneously with the overall airframe. The OR-89/AA is also installed on board many P-3Bs and Canadian CP-140 Auroras. Existing OR-89C/AAs are now (1988) being upgraded to OR-263/AA configuration, incorporating DoD Common Modules. The OR-263 can be operated off-line as an independent FLIR.

Both OR-89 and OR-263 are manufactured by Texas Instruments.

OR-89/AA was developed from the AAD-4 and AAS-28 FLIRs used in Vietnam. Lockheed contracted with Texas Instruments directly in August 1969, and the first prototype was delivered in March 1971. The FLIR is turret-mounted under the airplane, just abaft the cockpit. The field of view is 5 × 6.67 or 15 × 20 degrees, with azimuth coverage of 200 degrees in either direction and elevation coverage of 0 to −84 deg. Output is an 875-line television picture. About 1982, the specified MTBF, which had been demonstrated in service, was 345 hours. Turret diameter is 20.5 in.

◆ APG-65

See the Antiaircraft Warfare section; APG-65 is a dual-purpose radar.

◆ APQ-126

> **Band:** Ku (seven selectable frequencies, 600-MHz band)
> **Beam:** 2.5 × 18.4 deg (antenna tilts to cover 45 × +70/−30 deg)
> **Peak Power:** 60 kW   **Gain:** 28.5 dB
> **Pulse Width:** (i) 0.2 (ii) 1 (iii) 2 microsec
> **PRF:** (i) 3600 (ii) 720 (iii) 360
> **Scan Rate:** 90, 120, 180 deg/sec (horizontal); 150 deg/sec (vertical)
> **Antenna Dimensions:** 19.5 × 13 in
> **Antenna Weight:** 45 lbs (230 lbs total)

APQ-126 is Texas Instruments's radar for the A-7E Corsair II attack bomber. Compared to the earlier APQ-116, 126 added a third pulse mode and a terrain-avoidance mode, in addition to ground ranging, ground mapping for navigation, and blind bombing. Frequency agility (over a 30 MHz range at a switching rate of 100 Hz) is used to improve ranging accuracy and to achieve long-range target detection. APQ-139 is a later version with AMTI.

◆ APQ-148/156/APS-130

APQ-148/156 are radars for the A-6E; APQ-156 is -148 plus TRAM, the Target Recognition and Attack Multisensor, which includes a FLIR and a laser range-finder/designator. Both versions have TWS capability, and target elevation angle is obtained from a separate phase interferometer carried beneath the conventional fan-beam antenna. The interferometer consists of two rows of 32 horns each, moving with the main dish in azimuth and measuring differences in time of arrival. The interferometer produces a continuous elevation-range profile for terrain avoidance. Norden received a contract to convert existing APQ-92 radars to TWS operation in August 1969, and the APQ-148 contract the following year; a new AMTI contract followed in 1978.

The A-6E Intruder is equipped with both an APQ-148/156 radar and with a laser/FLIR turret, TRAM; the latter is visible just under the airplane's nose. (U.S. Navy)

APS-130 was a simplified version of APQ-148 for the EA-6B Prowler. Note, however, that in 1987 Norden delivered six APQ-156C radars for EA-6Bs; presumably, that delivery represents increased standardization.

◆ APQ-168/174

APQ-168 is the Texas Instruments radar selected for air force and navy versions of the Bell-Vertol V-22. APQ-168 is intended primarily for navigation and terrain avoidance and is derived from a radar developed for the LANTIRN low-level attack sensor. Flight trials on board an HH-60 helicopter began in 1988.

APQ-174 is another derivative of the same LANTIRN radar, intended specifically for combat search and rescue.

◆ APQ-173

APQ-173 is the projected radar for the canceled A-6F Intruder and is intended to replace the APQ-156 of the earlier version. The contract award to Norden was announced in 1985. The future of this radar is in doubt, given the cancellation of the A-6F and uncertainty over the A-6G (which was intended to have most of the avionics planned for the -6F, but not some other improvements). This radar may have been derived from a multimode radar developed by Norden for Israel.

APQ-173 uses doppler beam sharpening for ground-mapping and has an ISAR mode for ship classification. Reportedly, APQ-173 can acquire and track tactical targets at more than twice the range of the earlier APQ-156.

◆ APS-20

> **Band:** S (2820 MHz)   **Beam:** 3.5 × 8 deg
> **Peak Power:** 2 MW   **Gain:** 32 dB
> **Pulse Width:** (i) 0.67 (ii) 2 microsec   **PRF:** (i) 900 (ii) 300
> **Scan Rate:** 2, 4, 6, or 15 rpm; sector scan 20 to 50 deg/min
> **Antenna Dimensions:** 8 × 3 ft, parabola
> **Antenna Weight:** 180 lbs

APS-20 was carried on board Royal Navy Gannets; this 1978 photograph gives an indication of the size of the radar's antenna. (U.S. Navy)

These data apply to APS-20F. This radar was originally developed late in World War II for airborne early-warning and was carried by a variety of single-engine aircraft, including the British Gannet. APS-20 also proved very effective at snorkel detection and for that reason equipped the P-2 Neptune ASW aircraft. During the Falklands War, Argentine P-2s used their APS-20 radars to target British warships for Super-Étendards carrying Exocet missiles.

♦ **APS-80A**

Band: X (8.5–9.6 GHz)
Beam: 2.4 × 3.5 deg (3.6-deg pencil beam; 18-deg csc2) (coverage: 45 × +10/−20 deg)
Peak Power: 143 kW   **Gain:** 35 dB
Pulse Width: 2.4 microsec   **PRF:** 400
Scan Rate: 6 rpm (sector scan 48 scans/min)
Antenna Dimensions: 42 × 24 in
Antenna Weight: total weight 380 lbs

APS-80 is the radar installed on board P-3A and P-3B patrol aircraft, replaced in P-3C updates by APS-116.

♦ **APS-88**

Band: X (8.5–9.6 GHz)
Beam: 2.6 × 5.0 or 3.2 × 18.0 csc2 deg (coverage: 40 × +10/−25 deg)
Peak Power: 45 kW   **Gain:** 33.5 dB
Pulse Width: (i) 0.35 (ii) 0.8 (iii) 4.5 microsec
PRF: (i) 2000 (ii) 1025 (iii) 200
Scan Rate: 6 or 28 rpm; sector scan 36 deg/sec
Antenna Dimensions: 42 × 20 in
Antenna Weight: 61 lbs (total 228 lbs)

APS-88 is the periscope-detection and surface-search radar of S-2 Trackers.

♦ **APS-115**

Band: X   **Beam:** 2.4 × 3.6 deg
Peak Power: 143 kW   **Gain:** 34 dB
Pulse Width: (i) 2.5 (ii) 0.5 microsec   **PRF:** (i) 400 (ii) 1600
Scan Rate: 6 or 12 rpm; sector scan 36 or 72 deg/sec
Antenna Dimensions: 3.5 ft
Antenna Weight: 84 lbs (each); total system weight 523 lbs

APS-115 is the sea-search radar of the P-3 Orion. This radar is unusual because it uses two antennas, one in the nose and one beneath the tail, to achieve 360-degree coverage, without disturbing overall streamlining.

♦ **APS-116/134/137**

Band: X (9.5–10.0 GHz)   **Beam:** 2.4 × 4.0 deg
Peak Power: 500 kW   **Gain:** 34 dB
Pulse Width: (compressed) (i) .0025 (ii) 0.5 (iii) .012 (iv) .012 microsec (all pulses are transmitted at 0.5 microsec duration) (compression ratio 250:1)
PRF: (i) 2000 (ii) 400 (iii) 400 (iv) 400/2000
Scan Rate: (i) 300 (ii) 6 (iii) 60 (iv) searchlight, for ISAR
Antenna Weight: total system weight is 472 lbs

These data apply to APS-137.

APS-116 is the surface-search radar of the S-3A Viking, of the German version of the Atlantic, and of the Canadian CP-140 Aurora. Manufactured by Texas Instruments, APS-116 is a coherent (MTI) high-resolution (short-pulse) radar. For periscope detection amid the clutter of rough water, or for high-altitude surveillance, this radar rejects clutter by using pulse compression and fast-scan processing. APS-116 has track-while-scan capability but can also operate in a searchlight mode, tracking a single small target. Modes are (i) periscope and small-target detection, (ii) navigation and weather avoidance, (iii) long-range maritime surveillance, and (iv) ISAR imaging.

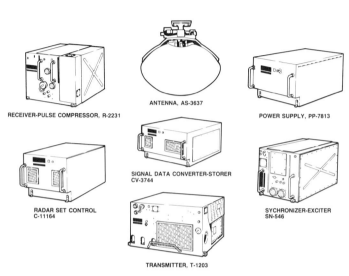

APS-137(V)1. (Texas Instruments)

Performance in test: 26-nm range on a snorkel (aircraft at 1500 ft), 33-nm on a fast attack craft (from 5000 ft), 75-nm on a destroyer (8000–10,000 ft). These are maximum ranges in sea-state 3/4, and mean ranges were shorter. For example, the average range on a snorkel was 15.5 nm. Minimum resolution is 1.5 ft.

APS-134 is the "international successor" to APS-116, incorporating the latter's less sensitive improvements. Peak power is 500 kW, with a fast-scan antenna. Modes are

(i) periscope detection in clutter, with high resolution (1.5 ft): 2000 pulses/sec, 150 rpm, 32-nm display, adjustable false alarm rate;
(ii) long-range search/navigation, with medium resolution: 500 pulses/sec, 6 rpm, 150-nm scale;
(iii) maritime surveillance, with high resolution (short pulses): 500 pulses/sec, 40 rpm, 150-nm scale. This radar was chosen for the U.S. Coast Guard HC-130.

APS-137(V) is a modified APS-116 incorporating ISAR, for the S-3B Viking; 137(V) supports the Harpoon antiship missile. In ISAR mode, the aircraft antenna does not scan the ship but points in searchlight mode, examining the different doppler shifts as the target moves.

APS-137 will replace APS-115 on some P-3s.

♦ **APS-120/125/138/139/145**

See the Antiaircraft Warfare section.

♦ **APS-124**

Band: X   **Beam:** 1.2 × 20 deg
Peak Power: 350 kW   **Pulse Width:** (i) 0.5 (ii) 2 (iii) 1 microsec
PRF: (i) 1885 (ii) 940 (iii) 470 (16-period staggered PRF)
Scan Rate: (i) 120 (for weather) (ii) 6 (iii) 12 rpm
Antenna Dimensions: 72 × 12 in planar array
Antenna Weight: total system weight is 208 lbs

APS-124 is the sea-search radar of the LAMPS III (SH-60) helicopter. Small targets are detected in the midst of sea clutter by sea-clutter decorrelation (fast scanning and scan-to-scan integration). With a low profile, the antenna can be slung under the

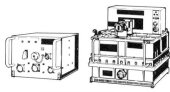

ANTENNA, AS-4035/APS-124

SIGNAL DATA CONVERTER CV-3204/A

TRANSMITTER UNITS
T-1308/APS-124
C-9889/APS-124

RECEIVER/SYNCHRONIZER
R-1979/APS-124

CONVERTER CONTROL C-9643/A

APS-124. (Texas Instruments)

AN/APS-128
MARITIME
PATROL
RADAR
Components

TRANSMITTER-RECEIVER

BRIGHT DISPLAY

DIGITAL
SCAN CONVERTER

FLAT PLATE
ANTENNA/PEDESTAL

RADAR CONTROL

APS-128. (Eaton)

helicopter, for full 360-degree coverage. The short-pulse rapid-scan mode is for weather. Estimated range on a 1-square-meter target is 16 nm, compared to 20 nm for APS-115 or -116.

The antenna is AS-4035.

◆ APS-127

Band: X **Beam:** 5 × 6 deg
Peak Power: 200 kW **Pulse Width:** (i) 2 (ii) 0.5 microsec
PRF: (i) 400 (ii) 1600 **Antenna Dimensions:** 2 × 2.6 ft
Antenna Weight: total weight 295 lbs

APS-127 is Texas Instruments's surface-search radar for small maritime-patrol aircraft, such as Danish Gulfstream IIIs. Estimated range on a 1-square-meter target is 18 nm. This radar is carried by U.S. Coast Guard HU-25A aircraft.

◆ APS-128

Band: X (9375 MHz) **Beam:** 2.4 × 9 deg
Peak Power: 100 kW **Gain:** 32 dB
Pulse Width: (i) 2.4 (ii) 0.5 microsec **PRF:** (i) 400 (ii) 1600
Scan Rate: 15 or 60 rpm **Antenna Dimensions:** 42 × 11 in

Eaton's sea-surveillance radar is for light aircraft, particularly for antismuggling and EEZ enforcement. Users are Brazil, Chile, and Gabon on Brazilian-built Emraer EMB-111 aircraft; the Japanese Maritime Self-Defense Agency on Beech 200Ts; the Royal Malaysian Air Force and Indonesian Air Force on C-130MPs; Spain and Uruguay on CASA C-212s; Spain on retrofitted C-130s; NASA on the Short Skyvan; and the U.S. Customs Service on an ILC Aerostat (balloon).

The flat plate array antenna is compensated for pitch and roll up to 20 degrees and can be tilted up to 15 degrees up or down. The transmitter is frequency agile (85 MHz peak-to-peak). Claimed mean time between failure is 442 hours in long-term use.

Unlike most radars, this one uses a television-type (raster-scan) display. The radar signal is converted into a digital signal before display, and the bright 8-inch (diagonal) tube can be shifted to display the outputs of other sensors, such as FLIRs. The display is bright enough to have signal-processing features, including target enhancement and scan-to-scan integration, so that target tracks can be generated. The radar is also fully integrated with inertial, Omega, or other navigational systems, and the display can be switched to other sensors, such as infrared.

There is a pulse-compression version for small-target detection; the manufacturer claims that resolution is five times

better than that of standard maritime radars. Frequency is selectable between 9.2 and 9.5 GHz in 20-MHz steps, and there is 100 MHz pulse-to-pulse frequency agility. Peak power is 8 kW minimum (10 kW nominal) but equivalent to 500 kW (50:1 compression ratio), for 5 microsecond pulses (compressed to 0.1 microseconds). PRFs are 2000, 1500, 800, and 400 Hz.

◆ APS-131/135

APS-131 and -135 are Motorola side-looking SAR radars used by the U.S. Coast Guard to detect ships and boats as well as oil slicks. APS-131 employs two 8-foot slotted arrays mounted back to back in a stabilized pod carried under the belly of an HU-25A aircraft. There are four range settings: 13.5, 27, 54, and 108 nm. APS-135 is a similar radar carried by Coast Guard HC-130s. Its two 16-foot antennas are mounted on the sides of the fuselage. In both cases, the output of the radar is a film image analogous to a strip map.

◆ ASQ-173

The pod-mounted F/A-18 Laser Spot-Tracker/Strike Camera (LST/SCAM) is manufactured by Martin-Marietta. The stabilized laser spot-tracker occupies the forward end of the pod. The system picks up a target designated by a ground- or air-based laser, feeding digital target data into the F/A-18 fire-control system and indicating target position on the heads-up display. The target is acquired at maximum standoff range on the first pass, reducing aircraft vulnerability; and communication between the attack pilot and the forward air controller or ground target designator is minimized. The 35-mm strike camera at the after end of the pod is gimballed so that the target can be photographed while the attacking airplane maneuvers. Dimensions: 8 × 90 in, weight 155 lbs, required MTBF at least 333 hours. This pod occupies the space on the starboard side of the F/A-18 body otherwise occupied by a Sparrow missile.

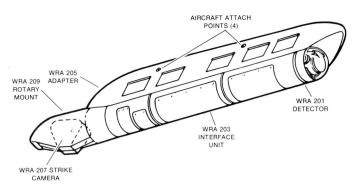

F/A-18 laser spot tracker/strike camera (LST/SCAM, or AN/ASQ-173). (Martin-Marietta)

◆ Harrier Night Attack (Cheap Night)/Real Night

From late 1989 on, Marine Corps Harriers (AV-8B) will be equipped with a special austere night-attack system, comprised of a narrow-field forward-looking infrared (FLIR) camera in the nose and a pair of night-vision goggles for the pilot. The FLIR image, with a 22-degree field of view, is presented on the pilot's heads-up display (at 1:1 scale) and can also be shown on a cockpit CRT. The goggles allow the pilot to see to the side, and they expand his field of view at minimum cost (and minimum space and weight penalty). Although the view through the goggles is not as sharp as that presented by the FLIR, pilots have found no difficulty in integrating the two. The result is much simpler and less expensive than the air force's LANTIRN, partly because the field of view of the FLIR is fixed (pointing ahead). Pilots look into a turn with their goggles, rather than slew the FLIR, which is mounted in the nose above the angle-rate bombing system. Unit flyaway cost is estimated at $1.2 million.

The goggle concept, code-named Cheap Night, evolved in 1984–85 from a proposal, presented at the navy/marine strike school, for an inexpensive night vision device to expand Harrier capabilities. GEC Avionics was chosen to supply the Cat's Eye goggles. Cat's Eye was developed as part of a continuing British program, Night Bird, begun in 1978. Quick Night (1985–86) was a follow-on to Cheap Night.

Real Night was a follow-on program in an A-6, using a CO_2 laser-scanning and obstacle-warning pod (the British-built GEC LOCWS) to paint unseen obstacles on the heads-up display projecting a FLIR image. The pod scans an 8-degree box (2 degrees up, 6 down, 4 across) in a near-vertical sinusoidal pattern at 50 kHz, building up a full frame every 1–1.5 sec. Once obstacles have been detected, they are stored and continue to be displayed even after they have moved out of the 8-degree box. Locus is designed to detect a 1-cm cable at 1.5 km in heavy rain. The first test flights were in 1986, using an A-6 carrying a FLIR with a thermal target-cuing device in an underwing pod.

As of May 1988, the U.S. Department of Defense planned to buy 600 Laser Obstacle and Cable Warning Systems (LOCWS) and 2000 Night Vision Goggles (NVGs—part of Cheap Night).

Night attack F/A-18Cs and Ds are to receive a related system using a 20-degree heads-up display.

◆ ARBS (AN/ASB-19)

Hughes's Angle Rate Bombing Set was developed for the Marine Corps, to improve the accuracy of visual bombing. ARBS automatically tracks ground targets and automatically acquires spots designated by ground-based lasers. The tracker provides the bombing (weapons-delivery) computer, an IBM System 4/Pi, with both the line-of-sight angle to the target and the rate of change of that angle. The air-data computer provides true air speed and altitude; and the weapons-delivery computer solves for the ballistic path of the bombs, providing the pilot with an appropriate course displayed on his HUD and releasing the bombs at the appropriate moment. No range measurement is required (it is implicit in the combination of altitude and line-of-sight angle). Targets are tracked by a dual-mode television/laser tracker. The weapons-data computer stores all appropriate weapons ballistic data.

Nine preproduction models were built in 1975, and tests began in the summer of 1976. ARBS was initially installed in A-4M attack bombers, which had no elaborate radar system, and was also compatible with the AV-8 Harrier, which ARBS now equips. In an AV-8B, ARBS consists of a dual-mode tracker (DMT) in the nose, a weapons-delivery computer (WDC), and control units (CUs). The DMT acquires and tracks laser-designated targets; in daytime, the pilot can also designate and track using a television. Because the television camera is located next to the laser tracker, transition from one mode to the other is very easy; the airplane can also acquire (and then track) targets designated by lasers on board other aircraft or on the ground. In addition, because the airplane is provided with an inertial navigation system, a target position can be predesignated, and the laser set to point it out when the airplane comes within range. The WDC computes weapon trajectory and filters DMT data, delivering them to the aircraft general-purpose computer, which actually flies the airplane and drops the bombs. Tracker slew angle and target designation are controlled from the aircraft stick (the AV-8B has a HOTAS cockpit); target data are presented on the heads-up display.

AIR-LAUNCHED MISSILES AND GUIDED BOMBS

ARGENTINA

◆ Martin Pescador

Dimensions: 21.85 cm × 2.95 m (span 73 cm) (8.6 × 116.1 × 28.7 in)
Weight: 140 kg (309 lbs)   **Warhead:** 40 kg (88 lbs)
Propulsion: rocket   **Speed:** Mach 2.3 (impacts at Mach 1.1)
Range: 2.5–9 km (2700 to 9800 yds)

Martin Pescador, as displayed in Argentina, 1982. (Dr. R. S. Scheina)

This radio-command-guided antiship missile was developed by the *Instituto de Investigaciones Científicas y Tecnias de las Fuerzas Armadas* (CITEFA); the name means Kingfisher (which suggests its role). It is sometimes described as a Bullpup derivative. The guidance operator follows the missile, using the tail flare. Martin Pescador can be launched from an airplane at up to Mach 0.5, or from a low-speed helicopter (in which case its effective range is 4.3 km).

Development was completed in 1979, and the missile entered service in 1982. Two or three were used, unsuccessfully, during the Falklands War. A total of 68 were reportedly manufactured between 1981 and 1984, to replace AS 11 and AS 12 missiles in Argentine service.

CHINA (PRC)

◆ HY-4, C601

See Silkworm (ship-launched version).

FRANCE

◆ Exocet (AM 39)

See ship-launched versions.

◆ ANL

ANL is the projected Aerospatiale-MBB aircraft- and helicopter-launched antiship missile (*anti-navire legère*): 200 kg (50-kg warhead), with solid-fuel ramjet propulsion (for speed greater than Mach 2) and 30-km range. Guidance will be mid-course inertial and terminal active radar.

This weapon began with a German Navy requirement for a missile for helicopters, combat aircraft, maritime-patrol aircraft, and even ships operating in narrow waters. However, ANL would also fill a potential French requirement for an AS-15TT replacement. MBB will probably collaborate with Aerospatiale on this project.

◆ ANS

See ship- and ground-launched antiship missiles.

◆ ARMAT

Dimensions: 40 cm × 4.15 m (span 120 cm) (15.8 × 163.4 × 47.2 in)
Weight: 550 kg (1213 lbs)   **Warhead:** 160 kg (353 lbs)
Propulsion: solid-fuel rocket
Speed: Mach 0.9 (supersonic in a dive)
Range: 40–120 km (43,700–131,200 yds)

This antiradar missile, carried by the Atlantique maritime-patrol aircraft, replaces AS 37 (and uses much the same airframe). ARMAT has much the same configuration as AS 37; but the motor has a much greater impulse, and ARMAT has a new seeker. This missile has been used by the Iraqi Air Force in the Gulf War (reportedly in 1984). ARMAT will be replaced by the lighter-weight STAR.

◆ AS 11

The air-launched version of the SS 11 missile is used for training with CM 175 aircraft. See the surface-to-surface version, SS 11.

◆ AS 12

This wire-guided missile is carried by French Navy and Royal Navy WG-13 (Lynx) helicopters. See also the surface-to-surface version, SS 12M.

◆ AS 15TT

Dimensions: 18.4 cm × 2.16 m (53 cm wing span) (7.2 × 85.0 × 21 in)
Weight: 96 kg (211.6 lbs)   **Warhead:** 29.7 kg (65.5 lbs)
Propulsion: rocket (boost-sustain; burn time 45.2 sec)
Speed: 280 m/sec (919 ft/sec)   **Range:** 15+ km

AS 15 TT, as carried by a Dauphin 2 helicopter, with AGRION 15 radar. (Aerospatiale)

This helicopter-fired missile first appeared in the mid-1970s as a replacement for the existing AS 11/12. AS 15TT is a sea-skimmer (altitude about 15 m, radio altimeter equipped) and

radar-beam command-guidance replaces the wire guidance of the earlier missiles. The manufacturer claims that AS 15TT is difficult to jam because it receives signals by means of a rear-facing antenna. The guidance radar, a Thomson-CSF Agrion 15 (X-band, pulse-compression), tracks both target and missile and computes the error in range and bearing between missile and target.

The impact-fuzed warhead is derived from that of the AS 12.

Current users: French Navy, Bahreini Navy (from a helicopter on board the Lurssen fast patrol boat), Saudi Arabia (helicopters flying from *Al Madinah*-class frigates). The development program was financed as part of the Saudi program; first deliveries were in March 1985.

A surface version, MM 15, was proposed for coast defense in 1979 and was shown as a ship-launched weapon in September 1984. No sales had been announced as of late 1988.

◆ AS 30

Dimensions: 34.2 cm × 3.65 m; 1.0 m span (13.5 × 143.7 × 39.4 in)
Weight: 520 kg (1146 lbs)   **Warhead:** 240 kg (529 lbs)
Propulsion: solid-fuel rocket (boost-sustain)
Speed: 450 m/sec on sustainer, after 2 second boost (1476 ft/sec)
Range: 10 km; flight time to impact approx. 21 sec; minimum range about 3 km (10,900/3,300 yds)

An AS 30L is fired; the laser illumination pod is outboard on the same wing. (Aerospatiale)

Data apply to the AS 30L laser-guided version of the basic weapon. The original AS 30 (semiautomatic-command line-of-sight guidance) was begun in 1958 and was delivered in 1964. Work on the laser-guided version began in 1974, the ATLIS designator running its trials in 1977. The laser-guided missile first flew on 4 April 1980, production beginning in 1984 (first delivered June 1984). The target is designated on the basis of a television image, the laser and television being slaved together so that the pilot can drop the weapon and break away at 4 Gs. The television automatically tracks the target during and after the break.

This weapon is in service on board French Navy Super-Étendards and on board French Air Force Jaguars equipped with a Thomson-CSF laser designator pod, for use against both ships and fixed land targets. AS 30 has also been exported to Egypt and to Iraq; Iraq reports having used it during the Gulf War.

Production: 538 were on order by early 1987, 223 having been delivered. Reportedly more AS 30L have been manufactured for export than for French service. Over 4000 of the earlier AS 30 were manufactured, for at least 7 countries. Estimated unit price in 1986 was $275,000.

An earlier radio-command guided AS 20 (25 cm × 2.60 m × 0.80 m, 140kg, range 4–8 km) is used in firing training for AS 30. (9.8 × 102.4 × 31.5 inches, 309 lbs, 4400–8700 yards)

◆ **AS 37 Martel**

Dimensions: 40 cm × 4.122 m (span 1.192 m) (15.8 × 162.3 × 46.9 in)
Weight: 550 kg (1212 lbs)   **Warhead:** 150 kg (331 lbs)
Propulsion: dual-thrust solid-fuel rocket
Speed: about Mach 1
Range: 30–60 km (32,800–65,600 yds)

Kormoran missiles carried by a German Navy Tornado. (Messerschmitt-Bölkow-Blohm GmbH)

AS 37 Martel television-guided missiles carried by an RAF Buccaneer maritime-attack bomber. (U.S. Naval Institute)

This Missile Anti-Radar Television was an Anglo-French project, originally an antiradar weapon. Separate studies conducted by Hawker Siddely Dynamics and by Matra during 1960–63 were merged in 1964. Matra was responsible for the antiradar Martel (AS 37). Hawker Siddely developed a television-guided version to meet RAF Staff Requirement AJ.168. Only the antiradar version remains in service, with the French Navy (Atlantique Mk 1) and with RAF antishipping Buccaneers. The airframe is similar to that of AS 30. The antiradar seeker is steerable.

In 1982, Martel was considered for action against Argentine radar in the Falklands, but the U.S. Shrike was chosen instead, reportedly because of skepticism that the missile could survive the very long flight from Ascension to the target. The missile was used by the French Air Force in Chad in 1987.

Hawker Siddely Dynamics (now part of British Aerospace) proposed a ship-launched version of Martel as an alternative to Exocet. The Royal Navy selected Exocet instead of Ship Martel in 1971 (reported summer 1971). There was also a proposal for a submarine-launched encapsulated Martel.

◆ **STAR**

In 1986 Engins Matra announced that it was working on a new antiradar missile, STAR (*Supersonique Tactique Anti-Radiation*). STAR is described as a 250-kg (551-lb) ramjet with a range of 150 km (164,000 yds), designed to open penetration corridors for naval attack aircraft and also to attack heavily defended targets such as high-value warships. STAR will incorporate experience with Martel and also with the ARMAT missile, manufactured since 1984. The latter is too heavy to be carried by anything short of an Atlantique maritime-patrol bomber, whereas a Super-Étendard would be able to carry four STARs.

At the Bourget Navale show in 1988, Matra described STAR as the first of a family of lightweight Mach 2.3 air-to-surface missiles, the second of which would be an antiship missile, a competitor to the Aerospatiale ANL.

Germany (West)

◆ **Kormoran (AS 34)**

Dimensions: 34.4 cm × 4.4 m; 100 cm span (13.6 × 173.2; 39.4 in)   **Weight:** 600 kg (1320 lbs)
Warhead: 160 kg; 55-kg HE (353/121 lbs)
Propulsion: boost-sustain rocket
Speed: M 0.9   **Range:** 30+ km (33,000+ yds)

Kormoran was conceived as an antiship missile that could be fired by a low-flying aircraft, popping up briefly to fire, against ships moving at up to 40 kts. Kormoran, therefore, uses inertial mid-course guidance and an active terminal seeker, approaching the target at a height of 2–5 m. Guidance modes are radar lock-on (RLO), radar acquisition (ACQ), and visual (VIS). In the RLO and ACQ modes, the missile is fired either without any use of the aircraft's radar or with a brief pop-up for acquisition. The visual mode allows firing even if the fighter's radar fails, but this mode entails considerably greater danger to the launching pilot.

The missile uses a delayed-action fuze to penetrate the target, the warhead consisting of 55 kg of high explosive surrounded by 16 projectile charges, each of which can penetrate 70–90 mm of steel. The explosive is formulated to provide an especially rapid explosion, so that the pressure wave is particularly destructive.

Kormoran firings began in 1967 with a series of booster tests from F-104G fighters. Test firings were completed in 1974 with approval for service use. At that time MBB was awarded a contract for 10 preseries and 350 production weapons. Of seven test shots between July and September 1977, all were hits. The first production missiles were delivered in December 1977.

Kormoran 2 has an improved (220-kg) warhead, increased range (55+ km), and improved ECM resistance and is designed for better target selection and for multiple launches. The missile weighs 630 kg and flies at Mach 0.95.

Kormoran began with an MBB study in 1962, a development contract following in October 1967. The design was reportedly influenced by experience in several abortive Franco-German missile projects of the 1960s; development was by Nord (now Aerospatiale) and Bolkow (now part of MBB). Drop tests were made in 1969, and a fifty-round test program was completed in 1973. The production contract, for 356 missiles and 56 installations, was let in November 1976. The missile made 7 hits out of 7 shots during German naval tests in December 1977. Italy ordered Kormoran to arm her antiship Tornadoes in 1980, and about 450 have been delivered to date.

The Kormoran 2 program began with a 1983 development contract, and deliveries to the German Navy (*Marineflieger*) are expected in 1988–89. Late in 1987, Kormoran 2 was successful in its second test flight (Sardinia range). Total production will probably be about 180, excluding export sales.

In 1987 estimated unit cost was $450,000 for Kormoran 1 and $575,000 for Kormoran 2.

INDIA

Hindustan Aeronautics Ltd is reportedly developing a Mach 4 air-to-surface missile for air force and Navy use, with a 100-km (109,000-yds) range and a 35-kg (77-lb) payload. The missile is to be launchable from 30,000-ft altitude.

INTERNATIONAL

◆ ASSM

This project for an international antiship missile is interesting because it led to the current Franco-German ANS (see above). ASSM was intended to succeed Kormoran, Exocet, Harpoon, and Sea Eagle in the early to mid-1990s. Feasibility studies were completed in November 1980 by a consortium consisting of MBB, Aerospatiale, and British Aerospace, and the three-year project definition phase was to have begun in April 1981. Britain pulled out, and the project was reconstituted as ANS.

The project covered a family of missiles, all sharing a common front end with a Ku-band incoherent seeker (with possible IR back-up). The air-launched version had to be light enough to be carried by the French Super-Étendard (and, therefore, had a short-range motor). The ship-launched version was initially to have been vertically launched, but vertical launching proved too complex; when the project was abandoned, launching was to have been at a 15-degree angle of elevation. That angle did increase expected salvo interval when missiles were fired from violently rolling ships. There was also to have been a submarine-launched encapsulated version.

Germany was the main partner, and MBB was to have provided a solid-fuel rocket-ramjet power plant (which later became an ANS alternative). Solid fuel was preferred for its high energy content (using boron as an additive) and for its simplicity. Expected maximum speed at altitude was Mach 3 to 4, and maximum range was 100+ km. Normally, the missile would sea-skim all the way to its target; alternatively, the missile could be programmed for an up-and-over flight path. Cruising at Mach 2.1 (Mach 2.3 over the last 15 km, for terminal maneuvering), ASSM was expected to be able to pull as much as 15 Gs in any plane during the terminal maneuver, compared to 3 Gs for existing subsonic missiles. The seeker was intended to select a particular target within a formation, given sufficient initial data.

Although ASSM died, these requirements presumably apply to the subsequent ANS project.

◆ MSOW

The Modular Standoff Weapon is a NATO program to develop a family of weapons of varying ranges. The program is led by the U.S. Air Force; the U.S. Navy joined when air force and navy standoff programs were merged into a new Joint Standoff Weapons Program. This merger in turn was complicated by the NATO connection. MSOW will incorporate some technology now being developed for the navy AIWS, which is also part of the joint program. The NATO partners have balked at the expense associated with adapting MSOW to the U.S. naval environment. A Memorandum of Understanding was signed on 31 July 1987, and Requests for Proposals were issued in October 1987. The two competing consortia are led by General Dynamics (which proposed a version of Tomahawk for the long-range member of the family) and Rockwell International. Demonstration and validation contracts were due late in 1988, leading to a 30-month development period. There were originally seven partners (Canada, France, Italy, Spain, the UK, West Germany, and the United States), but Canada and France withdrew in 1988, citing the rising cost of the weapon. As of late 1988, the two competing groups were General Dynamics (with Brunswick, Hunting [U.K.], Dornier, Agusta, and Sener [Spain]); and Rockwell (with British Aerospace, MBB, CASMU [Italy: an Aeritalia-SNIA/BPD consortium], and CASA [Spain]). The Rockwell group, ADC (Alliance Development Corp.), is a joint venture, whereas General Dynamics has organized in prime-subcontractor fashion. On a national level, each of the United States, United Kingdom, Germany, and Italy is to receive 22% of the work, with 12% for Spain.

As in the case of the U.S. AIWS, standoff means that the weapon can lock onto a target that the launching airplane cannot see at that moment. For example, an airplane flying below the line of sight to the target (and hence below the horizon of the antiaircraft weapons defending that target) could launch a standoff weapon that would still be able to engage the target. Almost all current ground-attack weapons, such as Maverick, must be locked onto the target at the time of launch. In the past, true standoff weapons have employed data links to transmit a target image back to the distant airplane so that the pilot could decide to engage. The data link itself became a very expensive element of the overall system. The major U.S. weapon of this type, the Condor (AGM-53A) missile, was canceled largely because its antijam data link was too expensive.

One alternative is to provide the missile with a target image, either before the airplane carrying the missile takes off, or when the airplane pops up to sight the target well outside the range of the target's defenses. Advances in electronic integration might provide the missile with a means of recognizing a fixed target by comparing it to the stored image. MSOW will probably use a new air force autonomous guided-weapon IIR seeker, embodying a stored target image, which was originally intended for use on board 2000-lb bombs, for use against fixed targets. With the cancellation of the projected AGM-130 and also of the standoff bomb, the air force was left without the 2000-lb standoff weapon. Hence, the air force's intense interest in a short-range version of MSOW. In the short term the air force is buying Have Nap, the Israeli Popeye 2 television-guided bomb.

The initial MSOW is to have a range of 30–50 km (16–27 nm); a later version will have a range of 185–600 km (100–324 nm). Both are intended to engage fixed targets, such as SAM sites and airfields, using submunitions. A future version may be able to engage mobile armored targets at ranges of 15–30 km (8–16 nm). Guidance against fixed targets might be by some form of image processing, or by inertial guidance (as in AIWS and IAM, described in the U.S. section below). The future transition to attacks on mobile targets suggests reliance on a more sophisticated form of image processing, or else the use of new "brilliant" submunitions that can themselves distinguish individual moving tanks. These versions are currently described as Variants "A" (short-range airfield interdiction), "B" (long-range vs. fixed targets), and "C" (short-range vs. moving armor).

MSOW will be powered by the same turbojet engine in all three versions (and ADC and General Dynamics will offer the same, as yet unspecified, engine). The engine will have to be optimized for the long-range version and, thus, will have features not needed for shorter ranges, but both groups argue that overpowering will leave needed room for growth. Given a common propulsion unit, the missile can be entirely modular, any one variant being convertible into another by replacing the payload (including fuel) and guidance. Maximum weight has been set at 1000 kg (2200 lbs) for the short-range version and 1600 kg (3500 lbs) for the long-range version, with unit cost limited to $500,000 (with $300,000 to $400,000 preferred). These prices can be compared to the $150,000 target of the earlier abortive Brunswick LOCPOD (low-cost powered dispenser), presumably broadly similar to the short-range version of MSOW. MSOW will use GPS for mid-course guidance, and two alternative terrain-following/terminal-guidance systems are to be evaluated during the 30-month development period (1989–1992).

In U.S. service, the Joint Standoff Weapon is intended as a long-term successor to two interim weapons, the navy SLAM and the air force Have Nap. Within NATO, MSOW replaces the earlier LRSOM (Long-Range Standoff Missile) and SRSOM (Short Range Standoff Missile). A Dornier version of SRSOM (which was being developed in collaboration with Aerospatiale) was tested beginning in May 1985. It had a maximum range of 20 km when launched at low altitude, and its configuration and performance are probably indicative of future MSOW characteristics. SRSOM was 133.8 inches long and had a wing span of 102.4 inches; the missile weighed about 1600 lbs and cruised at Mach 0.8. A larger version, which could be carried by aircraft such as the Tornado, weighed about 3000 lbs (length 169 inches) and had a range of 40 km. Each carried submunitions, and Dornier proposed a combination of mid-course and terminal guidance.

LRSOM was under development by two teams, Boeing/British Aerospace/GEC/MBB and General Dynamics/Hunting Engineering/Dornier, to meet the requirements of a British-German-American Memorandum of Understanding signed on 12 July 1984. Weight was to have been about 1600 lbs, cruising speed about Mach 0.9, and range up to 600 km (as in the long-range version of MSOW).

ISRAEL

◆ Gabriel III A/S

See ship-launched version.

ITALY

◆ Marte

See Sea Killer (ship- and ground-launched antiship missiles).

Marte Mk 2 carried by a Sea King helicopter. (OTO-Melara)

JAPAN

◆ ASM-1

Dimensions: 35 cm × 3.95 m; 120 cm span (13.8 × 156.8; 47 in)
Weight: 610 kg (1344 lbs)   **Warhead:** 250 kg (550 lbs)
Propulsion: solid-fuel rocket   **Speed:** Mach 0.9
Range: 50 km (54,680 yds)

ASM-1. (*Ships of the World*)

Mitsubishi is the prime contractor, selected in November 1973, for this Japanese Type 80 antiship missile. The missile was tested in 1977–79 (first unguided flights were December 1977), and production began in 1980. ASM-1 was announced for coastal defense in 1981 and entered service in 1982 (F-1 fighter). This missile employs inertial mid-course guidance and an active terminal seeker and approaches the target at low altitude.

Platforms: F-1, F-4EJ, F-15, F-16, and P-3; all but the F-16 (2 missiles) carry four each. In the case of the F-1, a J/ASQ-1 fire-control system is required. Estimated unit price (1987) is

$425,000. An ASM-1C version for P-3 Orions is being bought under the 1987–1990 Four-Year Defense Plan.

The Japanese FY88 budget included funds for a successor ASM-2 using an imaging infrared seeker and powered by a turbojet. The ASM-2 will be the primary antiship weapon of the new FS-X (F-16 derivative).

The SSM-1 surface-to-surface missile is a turbojet-powered version. In 1988 it was reported that Mitsubishi was beginning development of a new long-range antiradar missile specially intended to attack ships.

NORWAY

◆ Penguin

See ship-launched version.

SWEDEN

◆ Rb 04E

Dimensions: 50 cm × 4.45 m × 200 cm span (19.7 × 175.2 × 78.7 in)
Weight: 600 kg (1322 lbs)   **Warhead:** 300-kg HE (661 lbs)
Propulsion: single-stage solid rocket
Speed: about Mach 0.9   **Range:** up to 32 km (35,000 yds)

A Viggen attack fighter with two Rb 04E missiles underwing. (Swedish Navy)

Guidance for this missile is by active terminal radar following an autopilot-controlled flight. This weapon, the first Swedish air-launched antiship missile, is manufactured by Saab-Scania. Rb 04 was originally designed to meet a 1949 requirement for an antiship stand-off missile, the prototype being launched on 11 February 1955; Rb 04 became operational in 1959. Rb 04D became operational in 1972 and was followed by the current Rb 04E, which has a reduced wing span, modernized structure, better guidance, and a new rocket motor. The contract for its development was signed in 1969. Rb 04E can be launched at near-sonic speed and is carried by the AJ 37 Viggen fighter. The missile attacks at low altitude, after a programmed descent. Production ended in 1977. Rb 04E experience was exploited in the RBS 15 program (see ship-launched missiles).

◆ Rb 05A

Dimensions: 30 cm × 3.6 m × 80 cm span (11.8 × 141.7 × 31.5 in)   **Weight:** 305 kg (672 lbs)
Propulsion: liquid-propellant rocket
Speed: Supersonic   **Range:** 9 km (9800 yds)

The Rb 05A antiship missile, as carried by a Viggen attack fighter. (Swedish Navy)

This missile is radio-command guided, the operator using a joystick to line up a tracking flare in the missile's tail with the target. The Rb 05A development contract was let in 1960, followed by a production contract in 1970; production ended in 1977.

◆ Rb 15

See ship- and ground-launched antiship missiles.

USSR

◆ AS-1/SS-C-2 Kennel/Salish (Komet)

Dimensions: 115 cm × 7.9 m; span 4.9 m (45.3 in × 25.9 ft; span 16.1 ft)
Weight: 3100 kg (6800 lbs)   **Propulsion:** RD-500K turbojet
Speed: 510 kts   **Range:** 55 nm (13.5 nm for coast defense)

AS-1 being moved to its Badger bomber. (U.S. Navy)

AS-1 was the earliest Soviet air-to-surface antiship missile; SS-C-2 is the coast-defense version. The Soviet name is Samlet. SS-C-2 has been widely exported. It was initially deployed only in concrete bunkers on the Black Sea coast; in the mid-1960s a mobile system was tested. In the early 1970s these weapons were replaced, in Soviet service, by SS-C-3 (the coast-defense version of the SS-N-2). Reportedly SS-C-2 is still used by Bulgaria, Cuba, Egypt, Poland, Romania, and North Korea. The air-to-surface version is no longer in Soviet service, but a few may remain in Egypt and Indonesia, for launching from Tu-16 bombers.

The Soviet Navy initially experimented with ex-German V-1 cruise missiles, but in 1947 the MiG fighter design bureau was ordered to begin work on a new antiship missile, Komet, using a combination of beam-riding mid-course guidance and semiactive terminal guidance. The radar was a modified RPB-1 X-band bombing/navigation radar, Komet III (NATO code name Mushroom). This weapon became operational in 1958. It was limited in effective range because the bomber had to provide sufficient terminal illumination. Moreover, because the bomber had to remain near the target throughout the flight of the missile, the attack could be disrupted up to the time of impact by the destruction of the bomber. The combination of tail bulb (to receive the guidance beam) and nose radome (for semiactive terminal homing) provided evidence that the system had both beam-riding and semiactive guidance. AS-1 was typically dropped at 16,000 ft at 250 kts, to dive at about 3 degrees.

The normal warhead weight was 600 kg, but reportedly it could be increased to as much as 1000 kg.

The missile generally resembles (and reportedly is based on) that of the MiG-15 jet fighter, and reportedly AS-1 used MiG-15 jet engines with more than 5 hours of running time remaining (so that the engine could be run up and tested annually without exhausting its lifetime before operational use). Running time was 6 minutes before flight, with a flying endurance of 15 minutes.

The beam-riding guidance technique limits surface-to-surface range to line of sight. This missile was installed on board the cruiser *Admiral Nakhimov* in 1956–57, and several missiles were launched successfully. However, the system was abandoned because of the size and inefficiency of the weapon. Several Komets were reportedly test fired before Marshal Tito on the Soviet naval test range at Cape Feolent in 1958.

A coast-defense (land-based) version entered development in 1952, differing from the air-launched version by having a smaller rearward-pointing antenna. Presumably that decrease was acceptable because the range was quite limited, to about 25 km, so that the missile needed less gain to receive the guidance beam at extreme range. Tests began in 1956 at Cape Feolent, and the first missiles were deployed at Balaklava, and then at Kildin Island, in 1958, as a replacement for the existing 130-mm coast-defense gun. Missiles were fired from semifixed rails in reinforced underground bunkers, the missile rising to a preprogrammed cruise altitude of 400 m before coming under radar control. The bunkers were expensive, and they were soon replaced by a mobile launcher, a truck-borne rail. This device in turn was derived from a zero-length launcher that the MiG bureau had developed in 1956 for the SM-30 (MiG-19 derivative) interceptor. The Soviets deployed their first mobile launchers at Poti in the early 1960s. Ultimately, the Soviet Navy deployed about 19 missile battalions (3 Northern Fleet, 6 Pacific Fleet, 5 Black Sea Fleet, and 5 Pacific Fleet), but these figures probably include SS-C-1 (land-based SS-N-3) missiles. A typical mobile battalion consisted of three batteries, each with 6 launchers. The earlier fixed battalions had been only about half as large, with 2 or 3 launchers per battery.

Exports began in the early 1960s. The Polish Navy received 3 battalions, the East Germans one, and the Rumanians and Bulgarians one or more batteries each; the missile is still in service in the latter two countries. This missile was also exported to Cuba, Egypt, and Syria, Cuba receiving about 50 launchers.

There was also an army version.

In the late 1970s the Soviets began to replace SS-C-2 with a land-based version of SS-N-2 (Styx).

The Soviet designation of the air-launched version is KS-1 (industrial number 4K87, popular name Komet). The designation of the coast-defense version is S-2 (Sopka).

◆ AS-2 Kipper

Dimensions: 35 in × 31 ft, span 16 ft   **Weight:** 9250 lbs
Warhead: 1000-kg (2200-lb) HE or nuclear
Propulsion: turbojet   **Speed:** Mach 1.4 to Mach 1.6
Range: 115 nm high trajectory; 54 nm low trajectory

Kipper is a turbojet antiship missile with active radar seeker or inertial guidance (nuclear version); one missile is carried by a Badger-C or -G. Kipper entered service in 1961. Like the later AS-4 and AS-6, AS-2 locks its radar on before launch: hence the need to fly at relatively high altitude until fairly close to the target. This method of operation is ultimately limited by the launch platform's altitude; at 40,000 ft the radar horizon is about 300 nm. Note that a missile that can lock on after launch can be fired to a greater distance. For example, if the missile climbs to 80,000 ft and then scans (and locks on by data link), the radar horizon is about 480 nm.

AS-2 is typically launched at about 35,000 to 40,000 ft at 400 kts, cruising at 40,000 ft for the first 40 nm then diving until standard flight altitude is reached at about 70 nm.

Note that AS-3 (Soviet designation: K-20), a fighter-sized missile carrying a large thermonuclear bomb, is almost certainly limited to strategic attack and so is not described here. AS-3 is being replaced by the slower (but much longer-ranged) AS-15, an air-launched version of SS-N-21.

◆ AS-4 KITCHEN

> **Dimensions:** 35 in × 37 ft, span 11 ft   **Weight:** 14,300 lbs
> **Warhead:** 2200-lb HE or nuclear
> **Propulsion:** liquid-fuel rocket
> **Speed:** Mach 2.5–3.5 (1850–2590 mph)
> **Range:** 250 nm high flight profile; 150 nm low altitude

This weapon was apparently designed specifically for the Blinder bomber, itself intended as the successor to the Badger. Kitchen was first seen in 1961 under a Soviet Air Force Blinder-B, during the Tushino air display, and was later adapted for strategic bombers (Backfire-B and Bear-B and -C). AS-4 has not been seen under Soviet naval Blinders but is carried by Backfire-Bs, entering service in 1967.

AS-4 is a very difficult target to engage because, thanks to its rocket motor, it cruises at extreme altitude before diving steeply at its own target. The antiship version uses active radar guidance, but nuclear-armed versions probably are inertially-guided; in this latter form AS-4 may replace the huge AS-3 (which is essentially a jet fighter's body carrying a large thermonuclear bomb). In the nuclear antiship version, AS-4 presents a particularly difficult problem: because the missile may be intercepted only as it dives, a conventional missile kill may leave the tumbling bomb intact. This problem has made for considerable U.S. Navy interest in defensive nuclear SAMs in recent years.

There is also an antiradar version, reported in 1981.

The Soviet name is Burya. AS-6 is the successor.

◆ AS-5 Kelt

> **Dimensions:** 35 in × 28 ft; span 15.7 ft   **Weight:** 6600 lbs
> **Warhead:** 2200-lb HE   **Propulsion:** liquid-fuel rocket
> **Speed:** Mach 0.9 to Mach 1.2
> **Range:** 175 nm high-altitude flight profile; 90 nm low-altitude
> flight profile

AS-5 is a faster, one-for-one replacement for AS-1 (the Soviet Komet) and was introduced in 1965. Two can be carried underwing by Badger-C and -G bombers. J-band terminal-phase active radar homing replaces the beam-riding guidance of the earlier missile, and AS-5 has about twice the range of the AS-1. The warhead is 1000 kg (2204 lbs) of HE. Wings and tail surfaces resemble those of AS-1; the nose is similar to that of Styx (SS-N-2).

Antiradar AS-5s were fired at Israeli targets during the 1973 October War. Of 25 missiles fired, 20 were shot down by fighters or by ground antiaircraft guns. The remaining five destroyed two radars and a supply depot, demonstrating the antiradar capability of the seeker.

◆ AS-6 Kingfish

> **Dimensions:** (approx) 35 in × 34.4 ft; span 8 ft.
> **Weight:** 10,800 lbs
> **Warhead:** 1000-kg (2200-lb) conventional or 350-kT nuclear
> **Propulsion:** liquid-fuel rocket   **Speed:** Mach 2.5–3.5 (at 60,000 ft)
> **Range:** 350 nm high-altitude profile; 160 nm low-altitude

AS-6 carried by a Badger bomber. Note the absence of a big targeting radome: this missile is probably an inertially guided land-attack version. (U.S. Navy)

Carried by Badger and Backfire bombers, AS-6 is the successor to AS-4 and probably embodies some AS-4 technology. Guidance is reportedly similar. AS-6 probably has a considerably higher speed but a similar flight profile (high altitude cruise, reportedly at about 18,000 m [59,000 ft], and a steep terminal dive). First reported about 1972, Kingfish entered service about 1977.

The long range quoted recently and unofficially for the high-altitude profile would suggest that this missile can lock on after launch (LOAL). Whether Soviet air-launched weapons have this capability has long been the subject of debate, as LOAL would greatly change Soviet antiship tactics. For example, a bomber carrying a LOAL missile could approach at relatively low level before firing its weapon in a pop-up trajectory, basing the launch point on data supplied externally (e.g., by satellite). Maximum range may actually be closer to 250 nm if this weapon is not locked-on after launch.

◆ AS-7 Kerry

> **Dimensions:** 305 mm × 3.5 m; fin span 950 mm (12 × 137.8 × 37.4 in)
> **Weight:** 400 kg (882 lbs)   **Warhead:** 100-kg (220-lbs) HE
> **Propulsion:** solid-fuel rocket
> **Speed:** Mach 1   **Range:** 6 nm

AS-7 is a tactical missile carried by Forger VTOL fighters. Guidance is by narrow radar beam. Introduced in the late 1970s, this missile is roughly equivalent to the U.S. Bullpup.

The Soviet name is Grom.

◆ AS-9 Kyle

> **Dimensions:** (approx) 500 mm × 6 m (19.7 × 236.2 in)
> **Weight:** about 650 kg (1430 lbs)   **Warhead:** 150 kg (331 lbs)
> **Propulsion:** turbojet   **Speed:** Mach 3.0
> **Range:** 60 nm

This antiradar missile, carried by Badger, Backfire, and Fitter-C and -D, was introduced in the late 1970s. AS-9 may be the antiradar missile supplied by the Soviets to the Iraqis during the Gulf War under the designation X23. Reportedly AS-X-12 is a variant of this missile with a different guidance system. AS-11 is reportedly an antiradar missile carried by MiG-25 Foxbats.

◆ AS-10 Karen

> **Dimensions:** 305 mm × 3.5 m (12 × 137.8 in)
> **Weight:** about 400 kg (882 lbs)   **Warhead:** 100 kg (220 lbs)
> **Propulsion:** solid-fuel rocket
> **Speed:** Mach 0.9   **Range:** 6 nm

The AS-10 is an electro-optically guided tactical missile, derived from AS-7. Karen is carried by land-based naval Fitter-D fighter bombers. It is broadly comparable to the U.S. Maverick. A longer-range (40 km, equivalent to about 22 nm) electro-optically guided weapon, AS-14, has been reported.

The Soviets have laser-guided versions of their standard 500-, 750-, and 1000-kg bombs; it is not certain whether these versions are in naval service.

UNITED KINGDOM

♦ Alarm

Dimensions: approx 23 cm × 4.24 m; span 73 cm (9 × 166.9 × 28.8 in) **Weight:** About 200 kg (441 lbs)

Alarm antiradar missiles carried by an RAF Tornado. (British Aerospace)

Sea Eagles on board an Advanced Sea King helicopter, 1985. (Westland)

ALARM (Air-Launched Antiradar Missile) is currently being developed for the RAF; ALARM, should it enter service, will probably also be carried by Royal Navy Sea Harrier fighters. The manufacturer, British Aerospace, claims that maritime use on board RAF antiship Buccaneers is currently (1988) being studied.

ALARM differs from earlier antiradar missiles in that it can loiter above a radar, forcing its operator to shut down. The missile uses a boost-sustain motor, flying to a preset altitude and then diving or gliding. In theory, because the motor is shut down well away from the target, ALARM should not provide much of an infrared signature. The seeker is turned on soon after launch; the missile is guided toward an emitter if one is found. Published sketches of ALARM's trajectory suggest that it follows a ballistic (up and over) path rather than a direct homing path and, therefore, that the missile can function despite emitter shut-down (after launch). If the preselected target does not emit when the missile is fired, the missile hangs from a parachute over the target area, deterring an enemy operator from turning on his set.

Unfortunately, trials in the United States had to be canceled because of failures of the Nuthatch motor, and in November 1987 a new motor, developed by Bayern Chemie of West Germany, was selected. Early in 1988 there were reports that the British Ministry of Defense was considering buying U.S. HARM missiles and canceling ALARM. However, the missile flew successfully at China Lake in November 1988.

♦ Sea Eagle (P3T)

Dimensions: 40 cm × 4.14 m; span 1.2 m (15.8 × 163 × 47.3 in)
Weight: 600 kg (1325 lbs)
Warhead: approx 230 kg, aluminized RDX-TNT (about 500 lbs)
Propulsion: Microturbo/Toulouse TRI-60-1-607 turbojet engine
Speed: Mach 0.85 (cruise) **Range:** 110+ km (120,000 yds)

Sea Eagle was developed to meet British Air Staff Requirement 1226 for a replacement for both the television-guided AJ 168 and the antiradar AS 37 versions of Martel. Sea Eagle is essentially a Martel with a turbojet and a new seeker.

Sea Eagle uses inertial mid-course and active terminal-phase radar guidance and can distinguish a preferred target from among a target array (e.g., a task force or convoy). Selected target-signature data are stored in the missile's computer before flight. Reportedly, the seeker head is capable of homing on jam or homing on a specific radar emitter. The manufacturer is British Aerospace Dynamics.

The missile is designed to hit a target at or just below the waterline. The front face of the warhead is specially dished to ensure penetration at shallow grazing angles, recalling dished faces fitted to World War II air-dropped depth charges so that they would not skid on hitting the water. This warhead was developed at RARDE (Royal Armaments Research and Development Establishment) for the abortive Under-Sea Guided Weapon development of Martel.

Sea Eagle is carried by British Sea Harrier, Tornado, and Buccaneer aircraft, and in 1988 it is operational with both the Royal

Navy and the Royal Air Force; the missile has also been sold to the Indian Navy (to be carried by Sea King helicopters). Reportedly, Sea Eagle will also be exported to Saudi Arabia, to be carried by Saudi Tornado strike aircraft. There are reports that India may buy Sea Eagle for Jaguar fighter-bombers. Sea Eagle has been tested on board the Chilean CASA/Enaer T-36 trainer (2 can be carried by the A-36 attack version) and on board the Tornado.

Sea Eagle was first fired in 1981. Development of a projected Mk 2 was abandoned.

A ship-launched version, P5T, was proposed in 1981. British Aerospace claimed that three could be carried for every two MM 40 Exocets. However, the Royal Navy chose the U.S. Harpoon in place of both for the Type 22 Batch 3 and the Type 23 frigates. At that time, the major development item was the strap-on booster. However, British Aerospace had to develop the booster anyway so that Sea Eagle could be fired by Indian Navy Sea King helicopters. Thus, British Aerospace was able to develop the surface-launched version of the missile with very little additional effort. P5T was first launched in March 1987. As of 1988 no sales had been reported.

♦ Sea Skua (CL 834)

Dimensions: 25 cm × 2.5 m; 0.72 m span (9.8 × 98.5 × 28.5 in)
Weight: 145 kg (325 lbs) **Warhead:** 30 kg (9 kg RDX) (66/19 lbs)
Propulsion: boost-sustain solid-propellant rocket (boost burn-time 2 secs)
Speed: Mach 0.8 **Range:** 15 km (16,400 yds)

Sea Skuas carried by a Lynx helicopter, 1984. (Westland)

Sea Skua is a helicopter-launched antiship missile, conceived primarily as a counter to fast missile-armed patrol boats. The range was chosen so that Sea Skua could be fired from outside the lethal envelope of a Soviet SA-N-4 antiaircraft missile (located, e.g., on board a *Nanuchka*).

Guidance is by semiactive radar, typically using emissions by a surface-search set such as the Seaspray on board Lynx helicopters. The flight path is preprogrammed, with a choice of four approach altitudes (choice based on sea-state and type of target). Approach height is maintained by a radar altimeter. Typically, a Lynx shipboard helicopter carries two or four Sea Skuas.

Sea Skua replaces the French AS 12 in British service and is broadly equivalent to the French AS 15TT. AS 12 had been bought as an interim weapon that could be fired by a Wasp helicopter, and Sea Skua was inspired by evidence, e.g., in Exercise Northern Merger (1974), that such a helicopter could easily locate and attack surface ships. The Lynx, then in development, was expected to locate and identify hostile ships by both Seaspray radar and ESM. Missile weight was fixed by the requirement that three missiles and their associated equipment (but not the Seaspray radar) weigh no more than 580 kg. Frigates' space constraints limited the length of the stowage frame to 2.65 m, and wings and fins had to be detachable. The intended target set the type of warhead (30-kg SAP, for penetration).

Project definition for Sea Skua began in April 1972, and BAC formally proposed the missile in 1974. British government funds were provided in 1975 to complete the program and produce missiles. The first airborne firing of a fully guided round came in November 1979. This missile was ordered by the West German Navy in May 1984 for use on board Sea King helicopters, which are being equipped with Ferranti Sea Spray 3 radars in dorsal radomes. This program is being completed in 1989. Turkey has adopted Sea Skua for use on board her projected fleet of Agusta-Bell AB.212 helicopters, using a radar mounted above their cockpits; and Brazil plans to deploy the missile on board her Lynx helicopters.

Current work concentrates on the ship-launched (SL) version. Reportedly, several Southeast Asian and Latin American navies have shown interest, although no orders had been announced as of the fall of 1988. There is also a proposed coast-defense version, using a four-missile box launcher. British Aerospace carried out the first successful firing of the SL version in December 1988.

UNITED STATES

◆ AIWS

AIWS is a navy program for a short-range Advanced Interdiction Weapon System, to engage land targets and to replace laser-guided weapons such as Paveway, Skipper, and Maverick. These three subject the launching airplane to too great a threat; AIWS will be fire-and-forget. AIWS was one of two new air-weapon starts of the FY87 program; the other was SLAM. The program also envisaged an additional new weapon, ASWS, for use at greater ranges. ASWS and AIWS were formally proposed in February 1985 as future affordable ("bronze bullet") stand-off weapons; the interim SLAM will be extremely expensive.

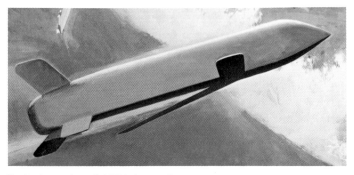

Boeing's version of AIWS. (Boeing)

McDonnell-Douglas's version of AIWS. (McDonnell-Douglas)

AIWS was conceived as a low-cost weapon with a range of somewhat over 5 nm and with a maximum weight of 2250 lbs, to carry three alternative warheads: 1000- or 2000-lb unitary warheads or a cluster of bomblets. Guidance will initially be inertial (see IAM below), although satellite navigation (GPS) may later be incorporated. Reportedly, the required baseline navigational performance is a drift of no more than 10 deg/hr, but the new ring laser gyro technology may make 1 deg/hr practicable. Press releases suggest that the "bronze bullet" concept may later be relaxed to allow for such exotica as an Israeli-developed fire-and-forget IR-imaging (as in Popeye 2) or millimeter-wave guidance, and fiber-optic-wire guidance by the launching airplane. The baseline remains a fire-and-forget weapon.

AIWS resulted from the Naval Strike Warfare Master Plan of 1985, and the Request for Proposals, originally scheduled for December 1986, was approved in March 1987 after a long study of performance vs. cost. Then Secretary of the Navy John Lehman ordered the cost limit of $50,000 just before he left office; the original expected unit cost had been $70,000 to $120,000. The production decision will probably be made about 1992, AIWS entering service about 2000.

The AIWS program was approved by the Deputy Secretary of Defense in December 1985, to make up for the lack of any true standoff naval attack weapon other than the obsolescent Walleye. The only other general-purpose naval attack weapons are general-purpose bombs (including such laser-guided variants as Skipper) and cluster weapons (Rockeye and APAM). Even guided weapons such as Skipper must be launched by a pilot who has the target in view and who is, therefore, vulnerable to antiaircraft fire.

AIWS's characteristics were developed at a May 1986 conference at NSWC. They were much affected by lessons learned both in Lebanon and in the Libyan raid. The conferees wanted a low-altitude standoff range greater than that possible with Walleye, Skipper, and LGBs; the launch itself should not reveal the aircraft's location; the weapon should be difficult to detect en route to its target; the weapon should make multiple kills per pass; and the aircrew should be provided with "last frame assurance" that the intended target had been neutralized or destroyed, so that subsequent attackers could be assured that the target was no longer a threat, and so could avoid wasting weapons on it.

The key requirement was the demand that the pilot not have to lock the missile onto the target before firing. Pilots cannot stand off at low (safe) altitude if they must have the target in sight at the moment of missile launch. The usual solution has been to provide the missile with a data link to the airplane, locking on only after the target has been detected, while the pilot looks on from a safe distance. However, long-range antijam data links are expensive, and a pilot loitering, even at a distance, to decide which of several targets in the seeker's field of view to attack may be in danger.

The AIWS solution is to allow the pilot to specify the precise location of a target during a brief pop-up at a safe distance. Target location is fed into the memory of the missile, which can, in theory, navigate to the designated target after popping up at much shorter range. "Last frame assurance" required a combination of some kind of imaging sensor and a data link, but that link would be needed for only a short time, just before the missile hit. The link could, therefore, be simpler than that used in earlier missiles, for which pilots had to use their imaging sensors to find the targets in the first place.

Quiet launch required aerodynamic performance superior to that of existing weapons, so that even when launched at low altitude the missile could coast for a time before its motor ignited (if power was required at all). Multiple kills per pass required a cluster munition. The missile could provide CEPs, at 5-nm range, of 5–7 feet. Long range suggested GPS-aided inertial guidance. The system could be either completely prebriefed, the missile flying to a predetermined target position; or the missile could be flown to a target located by the airplane. In either case, accuracy would depend on the accuracy of the aircraft's navigation. In the second case, the aircraft's survivability would depend upon how quickly the target could be located once the airplane was nearby. It would have to pop up to sight the target, and pop-up altitude would depend on terrain features.

Unfortunately, studies soon showed that within the $50,000 ceiling the weapon could not have a terminal seeker, data link, or propulsion. AIWS characteristics were, therefore, revised; the weapon would achieve a minimum operationally acceptable standoff range, a low-cost inertial guidance system (estimated guidance costs were $14,000 to $21,000), a cluster payload, and capacity for future growth to meet the initial requirements.

There were still some design problems, particularly in providing an unusually high lift-to-drag ratio (as much as 13:1). In 1988, it was estimated that the airframe would probably cost $12,000 to $20,000 (perhaps as little as $10,000 in a future automated factory). AIWS is reportedly conceived as a stealthy weapon. That characteristic is probably important for two reasons. First, unless the missile is stealthy, its appearance near the target will give away the presence of the launching airplane. Second, AIWS will enter service at about the same time as the new stealthy naval attack aircraft, the A-12 (the Advanced Tactical Aircraft). In theory, a stealthy missile could be slung from a stealthy airplane without compromising the latter's low observability, whereas conventional munitions would add enormously to the overall radar cross section of such an airplane.

Development of AIWS began in mid-April 1987. The competitors are Boeing, Grumman, McDonnell Douglas/Hughes Aircraft, and Texas Instruments/LTV. Boeing is already under contract to build ten Recoverable Test Vehicles (RTVs), which will be used to test elements that may be integrated into AIWS; the first RTV was delivered to the Naval Weapons Center in January 1988. Grumman was dropped from the program early in 1989.

◆ ASWS

The navy's Advanced Stand-Off Weapons System was conceived as the long-range complement to AIWS (SLAM successor). No details have been released.

◆ Bullpup (AGM-12)

Dimensions: 18 × 163 in; span 48 in
Weight: 1785 lbs   **Warhead:** 1000 lbs
Propulsion: storable liquid-fuel rocket
Speed: Mach 1.8   **Range:** 10 nm

Data are for Bullpup B (AGM-12C), typical of most versions.

Bullpup is radio-command guided into its target, the operator visually tracking a flare in the missile's tail. The original Bullpup A was designed in the early 1950s, entering fleet service in 1959. Bullpup B and later versions carried the heavier warhead listed above. Huge numbers of Bullpup were built, both in the United States and in Europe, and they were carried by ASW

Bullpups carried by a P-3B Orion, 1970. This missile was carried to attack surfaced submarines; it has now been superseded by Harpoon. (U.S. Navy)

aircraft (such as the P-3) as a means of dealing with surfaced submarines (e.g., providing mid-course guidance to missiles) and with small warships. In French service Bullpup was replaced by AS-12.

Although this weapon has been superseded in U.S. service by "smart" (i.e., self-guided) stand-off weapons, Bullpup is probably still in large-scale service elsewhere. The Bullpup warhead is incorporated in the Tomahawk missile and in the Norwegian Penguin and was also used in an abortive surface-to-surface derivative of Tartar developed for (but not used by) the West German Navy.

◆ HARM (AGM-88)

Dimensions: 10 in × 13 ft 7 in × 44 in wingspan
Weight: 798 lbs   **Warhead:** 146 lbs
Range: depends on launch speed/altitude
Propulsion: dual-thrust rocket motor (Over Mach 2)

A HARM (AGM-88A) missile. (U.S. Navy)

HARM, the High-Speed Anti-Radar Missile, is the current standard U.S. antiradar missile. It is supersonic (as its name implies) and enjoys a very long range and, it is claimed, low detectability. Performance objectives were a broad frequency range, an increased sensitivity, a countermeasures resistance, and a smokeless motor (for low detectability). HARM is important both as a strike-protection weapon and as an antiship weapon; HARMs could be launched as precursors of an antiship-missile attack, forcing an enemy to turn off his defensive radars before the heavier (and slower) Harpoons or Tomahawks arrive.

The missile can be fired in any one of three modes: prebriefed, self-protection, or target-of-opportunity. In the prebriefed mode, the target can be acquired by the missile after it is launched (the missile seeks out an expected signature), and the attack can be conducted from very long range. Alternatively, an attacking aircraft can fire HARM automatically on the basis of information processed by a radar-warning receiver. Finally, HARM can be fired at targets of opportunity, using the missile itself as the radar-search receiver, the weapon being fired manually.

The guidance system incorporates a strapdown inertial system; reportedly HARM can continue to fly toward a threat radar even after the radar has shut down. This capability predates the missile, having been introduced in Standard ARM during the Vietnam War.

Current tactics reportedly require that the missile be programmed with target range, bearing, and frequency before being fired. Given a preset range, the missile seeker can be set to activate 7–10 nm from the expected target position, to protect the missile from distraction by other emitters resembling the target. Current HARMs must be pointed to within 15 deg of the direction of the target (i.e., the airplane must be pointed to within 7.5 degrees of the target at the moment of firing).

Missile range is generally described as greater than 25 nm. In 1974, when HARM was first being developed, the desired maximum range was given as 100 nm. In 1988 it was reported that maximum range is 80 nm. Missiles are usually fired at 35–55 nm to ensure that their seekers acquire the targets.

HARM originated in the navy's Tactical Air Armament Study of 1969, which outlined the limitations of the existing Shrike and Standard ARM. Studies began in FY70, and a Proposed Technical Approach was published in FY71. After FY72 tests, Decision Coordinating Paper 92 of June 1972 approved development. Texas Instruments was selected on 24 May 1974. The air force joined the program in 1975. However, development proved difficult. Although 25 advanced-development missiles were tested, a DSARC II review in January 1977 ordered that the weapon stay in advanced development until demonstrating expanded frequency coverage and sufficient maneuverability. After that demonstration, full-scale engineering development was authorized in February 1978; and in November 1980 a navy SAR recommended low-rate production (80 weapons) for FY81. Operational evaluation, using 40 missiles, was begun in November 1981. It was successful, and full-scale production was approved on 20 April 1983. HARM was first deployed on board the carrier *Kitty Hawk* (carried by A-7s) on 13 January 1984 and first saw combat during the April 1986 Libyan raids, when forty HARMs, some of which had been on hand for up to three and a half years, very successfully destroyed Libyan radars.

HARM is manufactured by Texas Instruments and is employed on board U.S. naval aircraft: the A-7 Corsair II, the F/A-18 Hornet, the A-6 Intruder, and the EA-6B Prowler (first deployed August 1986). The missile would also be compatible with F-14 Tomcat fighters, although they do not currently carry it.

HARM platforms vary widely in capability. An A-7 or F/A-18 pilot will generally respond only to a preprogrammed threat. He can manually reprogram the missile; but without a sophisticated threat receiver such as the ALQ-99 of the EA-6B, he cannot expect to detect an unexpected threat. Until the mid-1980s, however, installation of HARM on board EA-6Bs was resisted, partly for fear that the missile might home on the airplane's active jammers. Installation became necessary when the navy experimented with all-Grumman (F-14, A-6, and EA-6B) air wings, since the new air wings did not include the usual HARM platforms, the A-7 and the F/A-18. It turned out that the missile could not home on the host airplane because the seeker was not turned on until well clear.

The great advantage of the EA-6B is that, using its ALQ-99, it can detect, locate, and verify a threat, reprogramming its missile to suit. A Block-86 upgrade to the EA-6B will remove the requirement that the aircraft point at the target and will also add a range-unknown firing mode. The first improvement is important for the EA-6B because otherwise it must interrupt jamming to fly toward the target before firing. Block 86 also allows the EA-6B to reprogram HARM in flight for threats not included in its preset threat library (prepared before flight by TEAMS, the Tactical EA-6B Mission Planning System). TEAMS prepares mission tapes for the ALQ-99, telling it which signals to seek. Using TEAMS, the airplane can be quickly reprogrammed on the ground to meet unexpected threats.

As of late 1988, only five EA-6B squadrons (in the all-Grumman air wings) have deployed with HARM. The navy expects to extend HARM capability to all other EA-6Bs. The bottleneck is missile-control panels, only 16 of which were available as of late 1988. Texas Instruments was to have begun delivery of 129 new panels (6 per month) beginning in November 1988.

Production of AGM-88A will continue through FY 89/90, to meet a requirement for about 15,500 missiles (7672 for the U.S. Navy and 7821 for the U.S. Air Force, down from 8054 and 9006 as stated in 1985). Procurement: FY83, 160; FY84, 381; FY85, 813; FY86, 904; FY87, 766 (total 1078 for both services, against a request for 1177); FY88, 766; FY89 (request), 1307; FY90 (plan) 200; FY91 (plan), 400. As of 1987, unit cost was about $285,000. The thousandth missile was delivered on 26 August 1986, and the 5000th missile was delivered in September 1988.

A low-cost seeker (LCS) was developed by China Lake (1986). There are two alternatives, and one of them is a seeker developed originally for the army's advanced radar projectile (ARP) (which would have to be modified to match the frequency coverage of the China Lake seeker). Because the seeker accounts for about half the overall cost of the missile, there is some hope that the new seeker will cut cost by about 20 percent. The low-cost seeker may also be installed in an alternative airframe, perhaps a Sparrow; the Senate Armed Services Committee has asked that the seeker be made generic rather than specialized for HARM. For a time, the navy was considering a low-cost ARM seeker for Skipper, the bombs to be used to saturate enemy radars. Congress has required that at least 800 of the FY89 HARMs, and at least 1200 of the FY90 missiles, incorporate low-cost seekers. HARMs with the low-cost seeker will be designated AGM-88B. Ford Instrument delivered the first six production low-cost seekers in 1987 for evaluation. The first missiles equipped with these seekers will enter service at the end of 1989. The low-cost seeker was expected to be the basis of a projected joint-service advanced ARM. However, the program was terminated as part of the 1989 budget cuts.

A proposed dual-role ARM (DRARM) would have used LCS (ARP) technology and a gimballed seeker for both air-to-air and air-to-surface attack, using a Sparrow or AMRAAM airframe. DRARM was a new start scheduled for FY89, based on brass-board work under the earlier ERASE program (with initial planning in FY86).

AGM-88B shows several major improvements. It has a programmable memory (using EPROM, electrically programmable and erasable memory chips) so that the missile can easily be adapted to changing threats, even in the air. The new warhead contains thousands of 3/16-in tungsten-alloy cubes, three times the density of the replaced steel cubes. This warhead can now do substantial structural damage to a radar station, not merely to the radar antenna proper, cutting through half-inch mild steel or quarter-inch armor. The current flyaway cost, about $200,000, is less than one-fifth the price of the original FY81 missiles, and MTBF greatly exceeds the original requirement of 200 hours. The next major hardware change, scheduled for FY89, is an engine that can better withstand flight-deck fires. It will be painted with a thermal insulation layer except for a narrow stripe. When the missile cooks off, only the stripe will ignite, and the motor will fall apart instead of exploding.

The next version, AGM-88C, will have a new seeker to deal with more sophisticated radars. Originally, Texas Instruments was to have developed this version, while Ford (having beaten out Raytheon) was to have developed an alternative low-cost seeker. The choice has been to abandon the separate low-cost effort; instead, Texas Instruments and Ford Aerospace will both produce high-end seekers, the missiles carrying these seekers being designated, respectively, AGM-88C-1 and C-2.

AGM-88B is being sold to Germany. The first letter of offer (5 April 1984) was for 866 missiles; the offer was revised in September 1985, for 944. Reportedly, West Germany wants to license-produce the weapon, requiring as many as 9000, to be carried by Tornadoes. A sale to Japan was announced in January 1987, and a sale to Spain is expected. Australia and Italy have also expressed interest, partly inspired by the missile's performance in the Libyan raids.

The U.S. budget request, as of January 1989, was for 1307 missiles in FY89, 1162 in FY90, and 1400 in FY91.

◆ Harpoon (AGM-84)

See ship-launched version.

◆ IAM

Inertially Aided Munitions, a generic U.S. program for a new type of guided bomb, was revealed in 1988. IAM began about 1984–85. A low-cost inertial sensor (strapdown gyroscope and accelerometers) is used to provide the bomb with a precise measurement of its path through space, so that, even if lofted by an airplane below the radar horizon, the bomb can guide itself into a target designated by the attacking pilot. The inertial system cancels the usual delivery errors and is expected to improve CEP by at least an order of magnitude. The bomb trajectory can be tailored to conditions, such as terminal defenses, and the sensor should be immune to countermeasures. Moreover, each of several bombs dropped simultaneously by one airplane can be aimed at a different objective. Because IAM does not emit any signals, it would seem to be an ideal complement to future stealthy attack aircraft.

The IAM communicates with and receives alignment data from the aircraft inertial-navigation system through the standard bomb data bus (MIL-STD 1760 architecture). Predesignated target coordinates are stored in the bomb's inertial reference unit (IRU), the unit being updated via the data bus during flight. The IRU in turn controls the bomb's tail fins. In this form, bombs must be pretargeted before the airplane takes off. However, an airplane equipped with a mapping radar or a laser range-finder could presumably compute target coordinates just before the moment of release, and IAM could attack targets of opportunity, as long as they did not move very much during the bomb's flight. On the other hand, a bomb aimed at a set of coordinates cannot be jammed or fooled by camouflage, as long as the airplane can bring the target within the footprint of the bomb's fall. Similarly, an IAM weapon can attack targets that are virtually invisible, such as bridges or command posts, or very small targets such as aircraft in revetments.

Captive-carry tests have demonstrated a 12-to-14-ft CEP for 20-second time of flight (low-altitude delivery) and 40-ft CEP for high-altitude delivery (50,000 ft, 60-second flight). There is some expectation that these figures can be improved by adding satellite (GPS) navigation to the airplane and, perhaps, to the bomb. Analysis suggests that kill probability may be improved by a factor of 5 or 10 because of the much improved IAM CEP. Of course, a great deal depends on just how accurately target position has been determined before attack.

Northrop (Precision Products Division) and Boeing are the contractors. As of April 1988, Northrop had built 22 Mk 82 IAM bombs.

The technology-demonstration phase of the IAM program should have been completed by December 1988. The navy included an IAM full-scale engineering-development line in its FY89 program; the air force plans to begin such development in FY90.

◆ Maverick

Dimensions: 12 in × 98 in × 28.5 in (span)
Weight: 635 lbs   **Warhead:** 300 lbs
Propulsion: Thiokol TX-481 dual-thrust solid-fuel rocket
Speed: supersonic   **Range:** about 14 nm

AGM-65F Mavericks under the wing of an A-6. (Grumman Aerospace)

Data are for the AGM-65F navy IIR version.

The Hughes Maverick is now the standard U.S. short-range tactical stand-off missile; AIWS is the planned successor. Reported average CEP is less than 4 ft; and of 100 known combat launches to date (AGM-65D version), 87 hits have been achieved. This missile has been very widely exported, combat use including both South Vietnam and the Iran-Iraq War (by Iran). By the end of 1977, a total of 5666 had been exported to seven countries: Iran (2500), Israel (600), Turkey (100), Sweden (500), Saudi Arabia (1666), South Korea (200), and Greece (100). Maverick has since been exported to Egypt, Germany (West), Jordan, Morocco, Pakistan, Singapore, Taiwan (GRC), and Yugoslavia. A European consortium, led by Selenia, manufactures the missile for Belgium, Denmark, Italy, the Netherlands, and Turkey.

Development began in 1965, the prime contractor (Hughes) being selected in 1968. The missile first flew in 1969, and procurement began in 1971; Maverick entered service with the air force in January 1973. The imaging infrared version was approved (DSARC II) in September 1976, the first successful firing being on 18 November 1975.

Versions are: AGM-65A, the original television-guided missile; -65B, the extended-range television version with scene magnification; -65C, a laser-guided version (-65E produced instead); -65D, the air force imaging infrared (IIR) version, with a 125-lb warhead; -65E, the Marine Corps laser-guided version with a 300-lb blast/penetrating warhead and a reduced-smoke motor; -65F, the navy IIR version with the -65E warhead and motor, for day/night attack against ship or shore targets; and -65G, the air force IIR version with the 300-lb warhead. AGM-65G has an improved seeker that the attacking pilot can use to aim the missile at a specific portion of a large target. The A- and B-versions weigh 462 lbs; the D-version, 485 lbs; and the E-version, 645 lbs.

The navy's purchase of laser Maverick in FY88 will keep the production line open through 1990. The FY89 budget includes only IIR Maverick.

Procurement to date: over 30,000 AGM-65A/B; 60,697 AGM-65D; 5306 AGM-65E; 7000 AGM-65F; 1800 AGM-65G.

Unit cost: AGM-65A/B, $50,000 in FY80 dollars (production ended May 1978); AGM-65D, $124,000 in FY85, $119,700 in

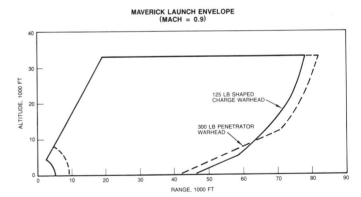

Maverick launch envelope. (Hughes)

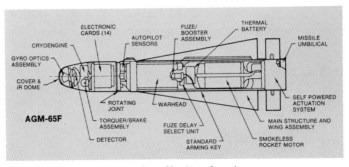

Maverick (AGM-65F) internal profile. (Raytheon)

FY86, $88,343 with competition in FY88; AGM-65E, $140,000 in FY84. Recent procurement:

	FY84	FY85	FY86	FY87	FY88	FY89
Air Force IIR	1980	2600	2240	3224	2700	2931
Navy IIR	–	–	195	248	425	731
Navy Laser	185	600	1500	–	1300	(732 re-quested)

Rapid cost escalation explains the reduction in procurement, costs later falling because of dual-sourcing and also because of the implicit threat to cut Maverick further by substituting Skipper. Note that navy laser-Maverick production was suspended in FY87 so that a new fuze could be incorporated. In September 1987 the total U.S. objective was stated as 60,697 missiles.

Other versions have been suggested. Hughes and the air force proposed Have Wedge, a dual-mode weapon (ARM in AGM-65A television missiles). The television would have allowed the weapon to remain on course to the target even if the radar transmitter shut down. An August 1984 test produced a direct hit, but the program was not carried through to production. Note that this concept might be applicable to SLAM, which uses a Maverick IIR seeker.

In April 1988 Hughes announced a new IR Maverick fire-control system, Rapid Fire. It automatically scans a target area and chooses likely targets, displaying them in the cockpit (and aiming up to six missiles for engagements). The pilot can, therefore, engage several targets during his first pass, which is all he is likely to get before defensive guns engage him. Rapid Fire uses one of the Maverick IR seekers as a sensor, so no additional aircraft sensor is needed; the system selects targets on the basis of their shape and size. The pilot can override the system's target selections. Hughes claims that Rapid Fire can fire four Mavericks in less time than one can be fired manually. Although the program is administered by the air force, Rapid Fire is applicable to navy and marine aircraft carrying this weapon. The target discriminating logic may also be applicable to other imaging IR weapons.

As of March 1989, Hughes and Raytheon, the two Maverick manufacturers, were competing for a contract to develop an Improved Maverick missile. An award was expected in the summer of 1989, leading to an 18-month demonstration-validation phase. The weapon, which is intended as a gap-filler pending the appearance of AIWS, would enter service in FY93 (the baseline AIWS, expected to enter service in FY95, will not match Improved Maverick capabilities). Improved Maverick is a short-range standoff weapon incorporating a data link (for lock-on after launch) and a new motor with more sustainer thrust (the current missile is boosted for the first half second, then the sustainer fires for $3\frac{1}{2}$ seconds, the missile reaching Mach 1.3 before coasting). The range is expected to double, perhaps even to triple.

As of March 1989, Hughes is proposing a helicopter-launched version for LAMPS helicopters, with a shaped-charge warhead, as a shorter-range alternative to Penguin at about a sixth the cost. With an imaging infrared seeker and a shaped-charge (125 lb) warhead, Maverick could reach about 6 nm from a 100-kt helicopter, and 4.5–5 nm from a hover. Use of the heavy 300-lb warhead would roughly halve these figures. Hughes argues that the shaped charge will suffice against most ships; in static tests, it cut through 45 ft of hull when exploded at a 70-degree oblique angle, generating a 4-atmosphere overpressure (and temperatures of 700 degrees C) in the area adjacent to the trajectory.

Hughes also expects to propose a Maverick using a fiber-optic data link, similar to that in the army's FOG-M lightweight missile. As of early 1989, China Lake was testing a fiber-optic guided Walleye, and the second firing, conducted while the launch airplane maneuvered freely, had been successful. Hughes uses a dual payout system (one reel in the missile, one in the airplane) analogous to that of a wire-guided torpedo. This method has been demonstrated at supersonic speed at ranges as great as 100 km and is complemented by a new proprietary method of high-speed fiber-optic inspection (by laser) for quick and inexpensive fiber winding.

The Israeli Popeye 2, which is to be carried by U.S. Air Force B-52 bombers, is reportedly derived from Maverick.

The U.S. budget request, as of January 1989, was for 731 missiles in FY89, 560 in FY90, and 2135 in FY91.

♦ MSOW

See International above.

♦ Paveway

Paveway is the standard U.S. laser-guided bomb, manufactured by Texas Instruments. Paveway II is in service; Paveway III is a new development, intended for low-level delivery, that will use a mid-course autopilot and a very sensitive seeker. Paveway is also designated LLLGB (Low-Level Laser-Guided Bomb). Paveway is a generic seeker/wing combination, which can be fitted to standard Mk 82/83/84 bombs.

In 1988, Texas Instruments claimed that 2 Paveway III bombs were equivalent to 7 Paveway II and to 1014 unguided bombs of the same type, so that destruction of a given target would cost $470,000 using Paveway III, $2.08 million using Paveway II, or $171 million using conventional weapons. It is not clear to what extent these figures included estimated aircraft losses.

The advantage of Paveway III is that it can be delivered below the flight envelopes of most surface-to-air missiles and outside antiaircraft-gun range. Texas Instruments claims that the bomb automatically compensates for varying release conditions, so that the pilot has merely to place the target in the middle of his heads-up display, minimizing his own exposure to enemy fire. The mid-course guidance allows for considerable offset from the airplane's flight path, and the bomb is designed for steep terminal trajectory. Inertial control is required for mid-course guidance, the bomb homing on a laser spot only at the end of the trajectory. Guidance is by four short wings attached to the seeker on the nose of the bomb; four big wings at the tail make for a 5:1 glide ratio to the target.

♦ Shrike (AGM-45)

Dimensions: 8 × 120 in; wingspan 36 in
Weight: 400 lbs **Warhead:** 145-lb blast-fragmentation
Propulsion: solid-fuel rocket
Speed: Mach 2 **Range:** 25 nm

The first U.S. antiradar missile, Shrike is obsolescent but remains in service (1988). Based on the Sparrow air-to-air missile airframe, Shrike was developed by the Naval Weapons Station at China Lake. The main design limitations are that the seeker must be pretuned to a set frequency (a total of thirteen different seekers have reportedly been produced) and that the seeker is rigidly mounted in the missile, so that the carrying aircraft must dive at the target, warning the radar operators to shut down. The missile then goes ballistic, as it has no memory circuits. Even so, Shrike has been widely used, in Vietnam, in the Middle East, in the Falklands, and probably in the Libyan raids of 1986, always as an interim weapon pending provision of sufficient HARMs.

A series of accidental Shrike attacks on ships in Vietnam in 1972 (most notably USS *Worden*) demonstrated that small weapons could destroy combat capability by wrecking topside antennas. Antiradar missiles were thereafter considered effective antiship weapons, with the potential for "cheap kills." Partial protection, in the form of Kevlar wrapped around some waveguides, was later provided, at least in the U.S. Navy.

Development of Shrike began in 1958 and production in 1963. About 18,500 were made. Variants included AGM-45A-1, A-1A, and A-2 (1963–66, G- to lower J-bands); A-3, A-3A, A-3B (1963–68, wider-band seekers); A-7 (lower frequencies; A-7A was canceled because of antenna-polarization problems, May 1967); A-9 and A-10 (USAF only); and AGM-45C (Shrike currently carried by Air Force F-4Gs, to suppress SA-6 guidance radars).

◆ Sidearm (AGM-122A)

Dimensions: 5 × 113 in; span 24.8 in   **Weight:** 195 lbs
Warhead: 10-lbs blast-fragmentation
Propulsion: single-stage rocket   **Speed:** Mach 2.3
Range: about 18,000 yds (high-altitude delivery)

Sidearm carried by an attack helicopter. (U.S. Navy)

Sidearm is a low-cost self-protection antiradar missile, to be carried by Marine Corps helicopters and Harriers. A converted AIM-9C (semiactive radar-homing version of Sidewinder), Sidearm was developed by the Naval Weapons Center (China Lake), which modified the original narrow-band passive seeker to broader-band purely passive operation and also modified the original target detection device for air-to-ground operation. The original rocket motor and wings were retained, but the canard fins were modified. Sidearm executes a programmed pitch-up shortly after launch, so that the missile can be carried by a very low-flying airplane.

Procurement: FY86, 885; FY87, 256; FY88, 276; none in FY89 (although continued production had been requested). In theory, Sidearm will be replaced by SRARM, a NATO weapon. However, in 1988 the future of SRARM is uncertain, and Sidearm may be revived and new copies manufactured. As of September 1988, Sidearm was being operationally evaluated, and a production decision was expected early in 1989. On 25 April 1988 a Sidearm successfully attacked an armored vehicle.

◆ Skipper II (AGM-123A)

Dimensions: 14 × 169 in; span 63 in
Weight: 1280 lbs   **Warhead:** Mk 83-5 1000-lb bomb
Propulsion: Shrike solid-fuel rocket (Mk 78-0; WPU-5/B)
Speed: transonic   **Range:** 7–9 nm

Skipper II. (U.S. Navy)

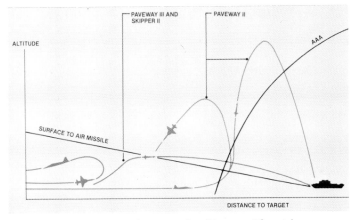

Skipper and Paveway attack trajectories. (Emerson Electric)

Skipper II was conceived as an inexpensive air-to-surface standoff missile, consisting of a Paveway II (GBU-16) laser-guided bomb with a Shrike rocket motor. Skipper, although it could not match Maverick performance, cost only about a quarter or half as much. Therefore, Skipper could be deployed in large numbers very quickly; it was certainly superior to an unguided bomb or a laser glide bomb. Because Skipper was a viable alternative to Maverick, the navy could effectively pressure the Maverick manufacturer to reduce his costs. (Cost reduction was also the effect of opening a second-source Maverick production line (Raytheon).) Skipper is much slower, unable to duplicate Maverick performance. Even so, Skipper can still follow a moving target.

Skipper was conceived in the late 1970s at the Naval Weapons Station, China Lake, but did not attract official attention until 1981. An airfoil-motor trade-off study was conducted in FY82. Prototypes were operationally evaluated in January 1983 (over 25 were launched), and FY84 funds were reprogrammed to support the weapon. The production RFP was issued 7 December 1983. Aerojet was awarded the motor contract on 24 July 1984, and Emerson received the missile contract on 5 March 1985; first deliveries followed in July 1985. Unit cost was $24,324 (FY88). Procurement: 500 in FY85, 995 in FY86, 1600 in FY87, and 1334 (2556 requested) in FY88. The FY89 POM included 1550, but the budget request deleted this weapon. The stated navy requirement had been 12,000 missiles and 15,000 bomb-modification kits ($10,000 each, for Paveway II bombs; the motor costs $5000).

There were reportedly some problems with the quality control of the Emerson guidance-and-control package, and the navy asked Texas Instruments to improve the Skipper seeker.

The navy proposed conversion of the entire air force Paveway III stock, to replace the projected Paveway III bomb (unit cost $142,000 when canceled), but the air force did not consider any of its bombs surplus for conversion.

A Skipper with a low-cost antiradar seeker was suggested by the navy as an alternative to, or complement to, HARM. A cluster-bomb version has also been suggested.

◆ SLAM

See Harpoon (ship-launched)

◆ Standard ARM (AGM-78)

Dimensions: 13.5 × 180 in; wingspan 42 in
Weight: 1356 lbs   **Warhead:** 219-lb blast-fragmentation
Propulsion: dual-thrust rocket
Speed: Mach 2.5   **Range:** 60+ nm

The two ARMs developed during the Vietnam War, and still in service: Standard ARM (foreground) and Shrike (background). (U.S. Navy)

Standard ARM is an antiradar derivative of the Standard Missile surface-to-air weapon and is designed for greater versatility than Shrike. Standard ARM can continue to home on a radar that has shut down during the missile's approach. No longer in production, Standard ARM remains in service (1988).

Standard ARM was ordered in September 1966 as an emergency replacement for Shrike, initially using the Shrike AGM-45A-3A seeker (Mod 0) but then being fitted with a Maxson broad-band seeker (Mod 1: AGM-78B) that did not have to be pretuned and that was gimballed to allow for a wider range of airplane maneuvers. There was also an impact marker, to permit follow-up attacks on a concealed target. Major variants: AGM-78A-2 (red phosphorous smoke marker), A-4 (improved seeker to counter specific early-warning and GCI radars), B (seekers for E–G- and I-bands), B-2 (unified seeker covering all bands), C-2 (more sensitive seeker, modified fuze, and rocket motor), D (General Dynamics seeker), and D-2 (final production).

Production of AGM-78A began in FY68, and the last AGM-78D-2s were delivered in August 1976, about 3000 missiles having been manufactured. General Dynamics proposed a further lightweight version, as an interim HARM, but it was rejected. In July 1986 the Israel Defence Forces released a photograph of a Purple Fist antiradar missile very similar to configuration to Standard ARM but with a reshaped nose.

◆ **Tacit Rainbow (AGM-136A)**

Dimensions: 27 × 100 in; span 61.4 in
Weight: about 1270 lbs   **Warhead:** 40 lbs (WDU-30B)
Propulsion: Williams International WR36-1 turbofan
Range: reported about 100,000 yds (endurance at least 80 minutes)

Tacit Rainbow fired by an A-7. (Northrop)

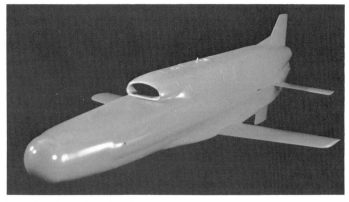

Tacit Rainbow. (Northrop)

A new type of antiradar missile developed by the Northrop Ventura Division, Tacit Rainbow can loiter in the area of a suspected (but shut-down) radar, waiting for it to be turned on. Tacit Rainbow should, then, deter the operator and, thus, turn off enemy air defenses. Conventional antiradar missiles, such as HARM, cannot loiter, and thus a radar turned off to avoid them can come back up after they have passed. Some current missiles, such as HARM, are credited with a capability to hit a threat radar even if it is turned off during their flight, but they are probably unable to deal with multiple threats. Because the operators of the several radars could not know which one(s) Tacit Rainbow had targeted, the operators would be less likely to turn their sets back on when the missile was in their area. Details have not been released, but presumably the missile can select any of a variety of threat radars for attack, automatically setting priorities, and it would appear that flight path and loiter time are preset. The missile was developed as a classified program, first revealed in 1987.

The first successful flight against an emitter was made on 10 December 1984. The first successful launch from a navy A-7 (against an emitter) was on 27 November 1985. It appears that the first successful full-up flight, in which the missile loitered, then automatically sought out and identified an emitter (which had been shut down when the missile appeared), and then attacked and destroyed that emitter, was made on 12 April 1988. It is not clear whether some of the 1984–85 flights were made with preprototypes since recent press releases refer to flight tests beginning in 1987.

The missile is stowed with its surfaces folded, the 61.5-inch wing swinging out shortly after launch.

Tacit Rainbow is expected to enter service on board navy A-6Es and air force B-52Gs, with production beginning late in 1988. Because of test problems, the House Armed Services Committee recommended a $60-million cut in FY89 funding, leaving $55 million (including $11.9 million to start second-source production). There is some hope that Tacit Rainbow can also be adapted for land use, from the current army multiple-rocket launching system.

◆ **Tomahawk**

See Strategic Warfare section.

◆ **Walleye I and II (AGM-62)**

Dimensions: 18 × 159 in; span 51 in
Weight: 2340 lbs   **Warhead:** 2000 lbs
Speed: glide bomb   **Range:** maximum 20 nm (minimum 1 nm)

Walleye. Note the television nose (covered until flight) and the windmill generator at the tail. (U.S. Navy)

Walleye. (U.S. Navy)

Data are for Walleye II. Walleye I, 1100 lbs, is 12.5 × 136 in (span 45.5 in), with a maximum range of 16 nm.

This electro-optical (television) homing glide bomb by Martin-Marietta was employed during the Vietnam War. No longer in production, Walleyes remain in storage.

The specific operational requirement for this homing glide bomb was issued in August 1962, and Walleye I entered production in 1966 and service in 1967 (production ended in 1970, 4531 having been built). Walleye I could be carried at up to Mach 1.9, and from 35,000 ft it could glide 10 nm. This version carried an 825-lb linear shaped-charge warhead. Hughes converted 1481 Walleye I to Walleye II, with a heavier warhead and a more accurate seeker, and reportedly built 529 new Walleye IIs. Walleye II enjoyed a much greater glide range. To exploit it, a better data link (extended-range data link, ERDL) was developed, so that the bomb could be locked on after launch. Most or all remaining Walleyes have been converted to Walleye II.

There was also a nuclear version, but it was acquired only by the air force.

SHIP- AND GROUND-LAUNCHED ANTISHIP MISSILES

BRAZIL

♦ Barracuda

> **Dimensions:** 30 cm × 5 m (12 × 197 in)
> **Range:** 70 km (77,000 yds)

This missile is under development by Avibras Industria Aerospacial in both ship-mounted (MM-70) and truck-mounted (SM-70) forms. Barracuda was to have equipped the projected 7th through 16th Brazilian ocean-patrol frigates to be built by Verolme do Brasil at Puerto Alegre, replacing Exocet MM 40; however, this project was canceled in the 1987 Brazilian defense cuts. Barracuda was also known as Astros II/Ms. Astros II is an unguided bombardment rocket (Artillery-Saturation Rocket System), using SS-30 (127 mm, 30 km), SS-40 (180 mm, 35 km), or SS-60 (300 mm, 60 km) rockets. Presumably SM-70 denoted a guided weapon with a 70-km range, launchable from the standard Astros truck. The existing rockets are all derived from space sounding (research) vehicles, and the launcher is modular so that rockets can be interchanged very easily.

CHINA (PRC)

♦ Silkworm (HY-2, HY-4, C601, C201)

	HY-2	HY-4	C601
Diameter	—	0.76 m	—
	—	(29.9 in)	—
Length	7.36 m	7.36 m	7.38 m
	(290 in)	(290 in)	(291 in)
Span	2.75 m	—	2.4 m
	(108 in)	—	(95 in)
Weight	2998 kg	2000 kg[a]	2440 kg
	(6608 lbs)	(4408/3834 lbs)	(5378 lbs)
Warhead	513 kg	500 kg	513 kg
	(1131 lbs)	(1102 lbs)	(1131 lbs)
Speed	M 0.9	M 0.8–0.85	—
Range[b]	95 km	150 km	95–100 km
	(104 kyds)	(164 kyds)	(104–109 kyds)

a. 1740 kg, air-to-surface.
b. Effective range 35–135 km (38–138 kyds).

The HY designation stands for Hai Ying, meaning Sea Eagle.
Silkworm (CSS-N-2) is derived from a direct copy of the Soviet SS-N-2A Styx, which the Chinese designated HY-1 (NATO designation CSS-N-1). HY-1 first appeared in 1965. Production of HY-2 (by the China Precision Machinery Import and Export Co.) began in the mid-1970s. The warhead is somewhat smaller than that of Styx so that Silkworm can carry more fuel for greater range. C601 is an air-launched version carried by Chinese-built Badger bombers (1 or 2 per airplane). FL-1 (see below) may be the shipboard version of the same weapon.

A modified HY-2, HY-4 uses a turbojet power plant and a solid booster for launch. HY-4 exists in both surface- and air-launched versions, the latter being lighter (as shown above). Flight altitude is 200 m during cruise and 70 m during homing; the missile dives steeply into its target.

Chinese HY-2 (Silkworm) coast-defense missiles. (U.S. Naval Institute)

Silkworm being launched by a Chinese Osa-class attack boat. (Naval & Merchant Ships Publishing House)

HY-2 and -4 have active radar seekers; C601 has an active monopulse seeker. HY-2A uses an infrared seeker; and HY-2G flies at lower altitude (30 m or 50 m [98 or 164 ft]), using a precision radar altimeter. The other weapons in this series fly at 100-m height. HY-2 and C601 (which is slightly more powerful) use liquid-fuel rockets and solid boosters. HY-4 is powered by a ramjet, with an air intake under the fuselage.

C201 is a revised HY-4 with better electronics. It was first displayed at ASIANDEX 1988 (November 1988).

These missiles are manufactured by the China Precision Machinery Import and Export Corporation (CPMIEC), the commercial arm of the Chinese Space Ministry.

HY-2 is carried on board Chinese Luda-class destroyers, Jianghu- and Riga-class frigates, and missile boats.

Reportedly, this missile is manufactured under license in North Korea, using Chinese- rather than Soviet-supplied technology. Reported exports: Albania, Egypt, and Pakistan. Reportedly, the Silkworms fired by Iran in the Persian Gulf (from April 1987 on) had been manufactured in North Korea; the PRC denied having provided them and announced that sales would be stopped. Reportedly, Zaire may use HY-2 as a coast-defense missile.

♦ HY-3/C101/C301

> **Dimensions:** 54 cm × 5.6 m (21.3 × 220 inches)
> **Propulsion:** two ramjets (and two solid-fuel boosters)
> **Speed:** supersonic   **Range:** 50 km (27 nm)

C101, which resembles the British Bloodhound surface-to-air missile in configuration, was announced in 1985 and will probably enter service about 1990. C101A is a proposed air-launched version. The manufacturer is CPMIEC. Note that length is also sometimes listed as 7.2 m (283 inches) and range as 70–80 km.

Launched using four boosters, HY-3 is a heavier and longer-range version of C101. Approximate dimensions are 76-cm diameter and 9-m length (29.9 × 354 inches). This missile was exhibited as C301 at ASIANDEX 1988 in Beijing (November 1988).

◆ FL-1/SY-1

FL-1 is a winged missile similar in configuration to HY-2. After launch, FL-1 rises to 100–300 m (328–984 ft), but then it descends to 30 m (98 ft), maintaining altitude with a radar altimeter. The missile has a new monopulse radar seeker, apparently operating at a higher frequency than that of the HY-2 series, and carries a 513-kg warhead. This designation may apply to HY-2 missiles carried on shipboard, HY-2 being the coast-defense version.

The FL designation stands for Feilung, meaning Flying Dragon.

The designation SY-1 has also been published. It may refer to the original SS-N-2 copy or to a simplified version of FL-1.

The SY designation stands for Shui Ying, meaning Sea Eagle.

◆ FL-2

Dimensions: 54 cm × 6 m; span 1.705 m (21.3 × 236 × 67.1 in)
Weight: 1300 kg without booster (2865 lbs)
Warhead: 365-kg shaped-charge (804 lbs)
Propulsion: solid-fuel rocket
Speed: Mach 0.9   **Range:** 50 km (55,000 yds)

This ground-launched sea-skimming antiship missile was first shown at the 1987 Paris Air Show. Externally, FL-2 broadly resembles Silkworm, but FL-2 uses solid propergol fuel; there is also a jettisonable booster. The manufacturer is the China Nanchang Aircraft Manufacturing Company (CATIC). It is possible that FL designations denote CATIC, as opposed to CPMIEC, weapons.

The manufacturer describes the seeker as an antijam type, and the radio altimeter is said to be accurate to within 0.6 m, for sea-skimming flight.

◆ FL-4

FL-4 is the ship-launched version of HY-4.

◆ FL-7

Dimensions: 54 cm × 6.6 m (21.3 × 259.8 in)
Weight: approx 1800 kg (3967 lbs)
Warhead: shaped-charge
Propulsion: liquid-fuel sustainer; solid booster
Speed: Mach 1.4   **Range:** 32 km (35,000 yds)

The manufacturer is CATIC. Externally, FL-7 appears to be a stretched FL-1/HY-2. FL-7 is described as an alternative to C801. Cruise height is 50–100 m (164–328 ft). CATIC claims a hit probability of 75 percent and states that the guidance system has ECCM features. Reportedly, this missile is intended to replace FL-1/HY-2 (Styx).

◆ C801/C802

Dimensions: 0.36 × 5.814 m; span 1.18 m (14.2 × 228.9 × 46.5 in)   **Weight:** 815 kg (1794 lbs)
Warhead: 165 kg, semi-armor piercing (364 lbs)
Propulsion: boost-sustain rocket (two motors)   **Speed:** Mach 0.9
Range: 8–40 km ship to ship; 10–50 km air to ship (8700–44,000 yds/10,900–55,000 yds)

This weapon is also called "Yinji" (Hawk Attack). It is similar in configuration to Exocet and uses a similar box launcher, but these missiles probably are not related. The missile climbs after launch then dives to cruise altitude (20 or 30 m). Diving again to 5 or 7 m, C801 turns on its active monopulse radar seeker and then dives into the target.

C801 is carried by at least one E5SG-class submarine (six missiles in tubes, fired on the surface) and Jianghu-III-class frigates. C801 has been offered for export on board a modified Hoku-class missile boat (four C801 in place of two HY-2; the boat is a steel-hulled version of the Soviet Komar). At least one Luda-class destroyer is reportedly being refitted with C801 missiles (but reports may actually reflect a Chinese proposal to build ships so armed for export), and this weapon is also being placed on board existing Chinese fast attack boats. An A-5 attack aircraft can carry two underwing. The submarine-launched version is probably designated SY-2.

C802 is an upgraded C801, first displayed at the Asiandex exhibition in the fall of 1988. Propulsion is by turbojet for a maximum speed of Mach 0.9, and maximum range is reportedly 50 nm. This missile is manufactured by CPMIEC.

FRANCE

◆ Exocet

	VERSIONS			
	MM 38	*AM 39*	*SM 39*	*MM 40*
Diameter	34.8 cm (13.7 in) all versions	34.8 cm	34.8 cm	34.8 cm
Length	520 cm (205 in)	469 cm (185 in)	580 cm (228 in)	580 cm (228 in)
Span	100 cm (39.4 in)	110 cm (43.3 in)	113.5 cm (44.7 in)	113.5 cm (44.7 in)
Weight[a]	750 kg (1653 lbs)	655 kg (1444 lbs)	666 kg (1468 lbs)	855 kg (1884 lbs)
Warhead[b]	165 kg (364 lbs) all versions			
Speed	Mach 0.93 all versions			
Range	42 km (46 kyds)[c]	50–70 km (55–77 kyds)	50 km (55 kyds)	65 km (71 kyds)

[a]1345 kg (2964 lbs) with capsule.
[b]Hexolite blast-fragmentation with a delayed impact fuze for SAP action. Explosive weight 132 lbs.
[c]Minimum range 4440 yds.

Perhaps the best-known Western ship-launched antiship missile, the Aerospatiale Exocet sank the British destroyer *Sheffield* and the container ship *Atlantic Conveyor* in the Falklands. Exocet has also been used by Iraq in the Gulf War, severely damaging the U.S. frigate *Stark* and hitting numerous tankers. Exocet exists in ship-launched (MM 38 and MM 40), air-launched (AM 39), and submarine-launched (SM 39) versions, all of them

Exocet MM 38, the original version. (U.S. Naval Institute)

Exocet AM 39 carried by a Mirage 50 fighter. (Aerospatiale)

C801 being launched by a submarine. (China Precision Machinery Import and Export Corporation)

fueled by a solid rocket, and all sea-skimmers with active-radar homing. The ANS is the projected replacement.

The operational requirement was to disable the target, the designers arguing that to guarantee sinking they would have to provide so heavy a weapon as to preclude carrying it on board anything but a large ship. They also argued that even a relatively small (700–800-kg) missile penetrating a ship at Mach 0.9 or more while carrying a 160-kg warhead would have a devastating effect on a large ship. Some have compared this missile to a 13.5-inch semi-armor-piercing (i.e., battleship) shell. In practice, when Exocets have failed to explode after impact, their unexpended solid fuel has started major fires. Because the fuel includes its own oxidizer, such fires can be impossible to smother, and the extreme temperatures generated can start fires in nearby compartments. This incendiary effect seems to have been entirely unexpected. A substantial number of duds was reported during both the Falklands War (for example, the *Sheffield* succumbed to the effects of the rocket-fuel fire, the warhead never exploding) and the Gulf War; but this problem has apparently been cured.

Range is relatively short, the designers arguing that a missile launched at very great range has to search a relatively large area of uncertainty around the target, and that the radiation of the seeker is likely to be the first warning of the missile's approach. On this basis, the original MM 38 was designed for a range of only 40 km (44,000 yds), corresponding to the radar horizon of the medium-sized warship that would be firing the missile. At so short a range, flight time is very limited, and the target cannot move very far while the weapon is in flight, i.e., there is little uncertainty. However, a shipborne helicopter can do better, and the current MM 40 has a range of 70 km. The helicopter links its data to the launch ship; the missile still operates on a fire-and-forget basis. The air-launched AM 39 has a range of 50–70 km, depending on platform speed.

Rocket propulsion makes for shorter range than a turbojet, but the designers claim that it is unnecessary to boost an Exocet to anything like the initial altitude of a turbojet missile such as a Harpoon. The surface-launched version is fired from a fixed launcher (elevated to 12 degrees), and the 2-second boost brings the missile to a maximum altitude of 30–70 meters (98–229 ft). The missile then cruises at 9–15 m (30–49 ft) in altitude. At a distance of 12–15 km (13–16 kyds) from the predicted target position, the missile descends to attack altitude (normally 8 m [26 ft], but as low as 2.5 m [8.2 ft] in a calm sea). The seeker is turned on at this point, and altitude is maintained by radar altimeter.

System reaction time is about 60 seconds (time required to warm up the seeker radar's magnetron). Prefiring information is target range and bearing, own-ship heading, own-ship speed, and vertical reference, plus manual inputs for seeker angle search, seeker turn-on range, terminal altitude, and proximity function selection (impact or pseudoproximity). There is no proximity fuze as such, but the radar altimeter can be set to burst the missile as it passes over a target. The pseudoproximity fuze works through the seeker, which calculates a "should-hit" time from the range, and detonates the weapon about 0.015 seconds after it should have hit. The missile is, therefore, vulnerable to chaff: the pseudoproximity fuze can be activated by the chaff, causing the missile to explode after entering a chaff cloud, instead of seeking a real target after passing through the cloud. Missiles can also be set to begin a target-search routine after passing through a chaff cloud without detonating and without detecting an object above the sea's surface. Aerospatiale now offers a Super ADAC seeker (with better ECCM) for backfit.

AM 39 has modified control surfaces so that it can be carried at supersonic speeds, and it has a light-steel rather than an alloy motor casing. The motor provides more thrust for greater range. The SM 39 version, which is carried by French attack and strategic submarines, is launched via a buoyant capsule (fired from the tube by a gas generator and powered underwater by a solid-fuel motor, which boosts the missile clear of the water). This version uses a waterproofed MM 40 digital computerized seeker. The capsule is powered so that it can break the surface some distance from the launching submarine, reducing the risk of detection for the submarine. Boosting from underwater also reduces the maximum altitude the missile reaches and, thus, its detectability (50 m rather than the reported 600 m of Sub-Harpoon).

MM 40 is a longer-range version in a more compact canister (possible because the wings fold; total weight is 1150 rather than the 1750 kg of MM 38, and typically two MM40s can be carried for every one MM 38). MM 40 is suitable for coast defense because this version can take a gyro angle as great as 90 degrees (MM 38 can turn only 30 degrees).

Exocet was first announced in October 1968, with an order from the French Navy. Greece followed in December (first firing July 1970), then Germany (West) in December 1970 (first firing June 1971), and the Royal Navy in June 1971 (trials, HMS *Norfolk*, April 1974). AM 39 was first tested in 1972. SM 39 was announced in 1979 and first fired by the submarine *Agosta* in mid-1981. Series production of MM 40 began in January 1981. The thousandth Exocet was delivered in October 1980. First reports of combat use in the Persian Gulf were in 1984.

Estimated unit costs as of 1986 (export price in parentheses): MM 38, $350,000 ($450,000); AM 39, $525,000 ($650,000); SM 39, $850,000 (this weapon is not available for export); MM 40, $490,000 ($600,000).

Production: total deliveries as of 1986 (total orders in parentheses): MM 38, 1262 (1575); AM 39, 714 (809); SM 39, 24 (62); MM 40, 399 (470). Orders in 1986 amounted to MM 38, 2; AM 39, 3; SM 39, 11; and MM 40, 31.

China (PRC) reportedly obtained some of these missiles in April 1985 via a third party, possibly using Exocet as a basis for her own C 801 missile, and there have been reports of Brazilian production under license. A torpedo-carrying version (as a future French ASW stand-off missile) has been proposed; it is described in the Antisubmarine Warfare section of this book.

◆ **ANS (Anti-Navire Supersonique)**

Dimensions: 35 cm × 5.7 m (13.8 × 224 in)
Weight: estimated 850 kg (1873 lbs)
Warhead: about 180-kg SAP (397-lbs)
Propulsion: rocket-ramjet
Speed: Mach 2 cruise, Mach 2.5 at high altitude
Range: 180 km (97 nm)

- AIR LAUNCH MISSILE

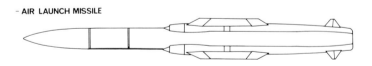

- SHIP LAUNCH AMMUNITION

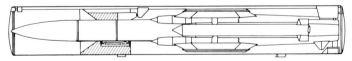

ANS. (Aerospatiale)

An ANS prototype in flight. (Aerospatiale)

SS 11 missiles carried by a French Army helicopter. (U.S. Naval Institute)

the typical unit price was $1900. This system is now considered obsolete.

SS 11 was mounted on board the French patrol boat *La Combattante* (in effect the prototype of many export missile attack boats), but the missiles have been removed. The U.S. Navy considered SS 11 for use on board small attack craft; of 54 launches at Point Mugu in 1964, only one was a failure. The U.S. Army adopted SS 11 as AGM-22B for the Huey helicopter.

◆ **SS 12M**

    Dimensions: 7.1 × 73.7 × 25.6 in   **Weight:** 165 lbs
    Warhead: 62.5 lbs. Several types, including OP3C, an SAP with a bulbous shape to aid fragmentation (actuates about 6 ft after penetration), containing about 13 lbs of TNT/RDX mixture.
    Range: 6580 yds (670 yds minimum)
    Speed: 580 ft/sec (flight time 34 secs maximum)

This projected replacement for the Exocet is currently under development by a consortium of Aerospatiale and MBB (Messerschmidt-Bolkow-Blohm). ANS is designed to make maximum use of existing Exocet fire-control (fire-and-forget) and launch facilities and will be compatible with MM 40 launchers. However, ANS is intended to reach supersonic speed (Mach 2.0) and should be able to go as far as 180 nm by flying at high altitude. Normally, ANS will fly most of the way to the target at high altitude (hence at high speed, without excessive fuel consumption), descending to sea-skimming altitude about 30 km from the predicted target position and weaving at high speed (up to 10 Gs) to avoid defensive measures. The surface-launched version will have a rocket booster; the air-launched version will use no booster at all and thus may avoid detection (at the moment of launch) by passive infrared scanners.

ANS was conceived about 1974 as an Exocet replacement, MM 100, which was intended to fly its entire flight path at sea-skimming altitude. The project then became the French/British/German ASSM/ASEM. That project collapsed in 1981, the British having withdrawn. ANS was announced in May 1981. ANS incorporates many projected ASSM features, including the ramjet with solid booster, the inertial navigation system, and the active-radar (Serge Dassault Super ADAC) seeker. There are two alternative power plants: a liquid-fuel ramjet with solid booster derived from that of the ASMP strategic missile (see the Strategic Warfare section), tested in 1985; or a boron solid-propellant rocket-ramjet proposed by MBB. In 1988 it was reported that the boron-hydride motor had been chosen.

The French-German MoU was signed in 1983, and development was completed in 1986, with the first test flight at the CEM test center in the Mediterreanean on 21 May 1987. However, at that time the choice of propulsion had not yet been made. Series production is scheduled for 1992/93, and missiles should enter service about 1994 on board ships and from 1997 on board aircraft. Unit price will probably be about $1–$1.5 million.

SS 12 M missiles on board the French patrol boat *La Combattante*, on the side of the turreted launcher amidships (the much larger launcher aft carries flares). These missiles are no longer carried by French patrol craft but survive in small numbers in some other navies. (U.S. Naval Institute)

SS 12 is a spin-stabilized missile derived from SS 11. SS 12M is the naval version. The naval users are Greece (*Kelefstis Stamou* class), Libya (*Susa*-class fast attack boats), and Tunisia (P 48-class patrol boats). The launching system was developed by Vosper (the Libyan boats' builder) and Nord Aviation. The launcher fires up to eight prepackaged missiles in succession, all the missiles occupying forward-facing fixed racks. The attack boat, therefore, has to turn toward the target at the moment of firing.

In these boats the missile aimer occupies a turret with a gyro-stabilized APX.260 sight. He uses a joy-stick to guide the missiles in flight, this optical control limiting their use to targets he can see. This system is extremely difficult to use from a moving ship or boat.

The French manufacturer also developed trainable launchers (SS 12 was compatible with the SS 11 of the patrol boat *La Combattante*). The trainable quadruple launcher weighed 6320 lbs, compared to less than 200 lbs for a fixed single launcher on board a fast attack boat, and was built only in prototype form.

◆ **SS 11**

    Dimensions: 6.4 × 47.6 × 19.7 in   **Weight:** 66 lbs
    Warhead: 16 lbs (3.5 lbs of HE)
    Propulsion: dual-thrust solid-fuel rocket (1.2-sec boost, 20-sec sustainer)
    Speed: 580 ft/sec   **Range:** 3280 yds (minimum 500 yds)

Nord Aviation's helicopter- and ground-launched wire-guided missile was originally developed as an antitank missile but employed by Sweden for coast defense. Development began in 1952, and SS 11 entered French Army service in 1956. SS 11 rolls slowly in flight, its wings being slightly offset, and the missile is controlled by vanes in the rocket thrust. Very large numbers were manufactured for several armies (French production amounted to 168,450), and SS 11 was license-manufactured by the United States, Germany (West), and India. About 1980

ISRAEL

◆ Gabriel

	VERSIONS				
	I	*II*	*III*	*IIIA/S*	*IV*
Diameter	32.5 cm (12.8 in)	35 cm (13.8 in)	34 cm (13.4 in)	34 cm (13.4 in)	43 cm (16.9 in)
Length	3.35 m (132 in)	3.35 m (132 in)	3.8 m (150 in)	3.85 m (152 in)	4.7 m (185 in)
Span	1.385 m (54.5 in)	1.385 m (54.5 in)	1.35 m (53.1 in)	1.1 m (43.3 in)	1.6 m (63.0 in)
Weight	400 kg[a] (882 lbs)	500 kg (1102 lbs)	560 kg (1234 lbs)	600 kg (1322 lbs)	960 kg (2116 lbs)
Warhead	180 kg[b] (397 lbs)	180 kg (397 lbs)	150 kg (331 lbs)	150 kg (331 lbs)	est 150–200 kg (est 331–441 lbs)
Boost Thrust	3600/3	3600/3	— (lbs thrust/duration)	—	—
Sustain	100 sec	200 sec	— (duration)	—	—
Speed	M 0.65	M 0.65	M 0.65	M 0.73	M 0.85
Range	20+ km[c] (22+ kyds)	36–40 km (39–44 kyds)	36 km (39 kyds)	60+ km (66+ kyds)	200 km (220 kyds)
Attack Altitude	4.5–6 m (14.9–19.7 ft)	2.5 m (8.2 ft)	1.5/2.5/4 m (4.9/8.2/13.1 ft)	— —	— —

[a]Gabriel I in launcher/container: 600 kg (1322 lbs).
[b]Explosive weight in Gabriel I: 154 lbs, with delayed-action fuze.
[c]Minimum range for Gabriel I: 5500 yds.

Gabriel was developed by IAI in 1966–68 as a direct counter to the Styx missiles supplied to the Arab states; and Gabriel entered service in 1972, proving successful during the October 1973 Mid-East war. Although having a much shorter range than Styx, Gabriel could lock onto a smaller target (i.e., a missile boat) and apparently could be fired much more easily.

The original concept was to use semiactive guidance, the firing boat providing illumination. In theory, such guidance uses the intelligence of the shipboard operator to overcome jamming and sea clutter. Gabriel I also has a back-up pure radio-command mode, in which the missile is steered with the aid of an optical sight, the operator tracking four tail flares. Gabriel II uses semiactive guidance, though in a more sophisticated form, and has an upgraded sustainer motor. During the 1973 war several missiles broke lock on their relatively small targets after picking up larger commercial ships. In 1980, therefore, work began on an active seeker (incorporated in Gabriel III) for better discrimination. Current Israeli tactics reportedly favor fire-and-update and mixed attacks (e.g., one active-seeker Harpoon and two semiactive Gabriels) to complicate target ECM.

Gabriel I climbs to about 100 m (328 ft) after launch then, at an estimated range (from the target) of 7.5 km (8200 yds), descends slowly to 20 m (66 ft). The missile can then be command-guided in azimuth. At a range of 1.2 km (1300 yds) from the target, Gabriel I descends to 3 m (9.8 ft), using either radio-command or semiactive-radar guidance. Later versions rise to only about 35 m (115 ft), and cruise at 17–20 m (56–66 ft).

The associated fire control is the Selenia Orion 250 (RTN-10), later replaced in at least some cases by the Israeli-built EL/M 2221.

Gabriel II carries a television camera and two-way command link, sending back an image for over-the-horizon attack. The operator presumably locks the missile on for attack.

Gabriel III has a new frequency-agile active seeker (for greater operational range) and an updated guidance computer. The missile can be fired either in fire-and-forget or in fire-and-update (mid-course data-link update) mode. The aircraft-launched III A/S version has no booster. Typically, the aircraft track-while-scan radar is used to aim III A/S; the TWS radar can cut search area by as much as 40:1, and the missile seeker can be turned on much closer to the target. This missile can be launched at 300–30,000 ft altitude by F-4, Mirage, Kfir, or A-4 aircraft. Gabriel III was announced in 1979, and development was completed in March 1980.

Gabriel IV is a new swept-wing missile, powered by an 810-lb thrust Bet Shemesh Sorec 4 turbojet, that entered service in 1987.

After the 1973 Middle East war, Gabriel I was widely exported, in characteristic sealed shipping/launching containers with a shelf life reported as two years. Known customers include Taiwan (1978), Kenya (37.5-meter boats, 1979), Ecuador (1980), Singapore, Thailand, and South Africa. Brazilian plans to acquire Gabriel (1982) were canceled to avoid problems with the Arab states buying Brazilian weapons. Reportedly, about 2500 to 3000 Gabriels have been manufactured. Estimated unit prices (1987) were Gabriel I/II, $400,000; Gabriel III, $450,000; Gabriel III A/S, $550,000; Gabriel IV, $675,000. In 1971, the quoted Gabriel I price was $85,000–$95,000 or a total of $2.5 million for six missiles plus radar and fire control.

The South African Skorpioen is a Gabriel II derivative, built under license. However, the Taiwanese (GRC) Hsiung Feng I is an unlicensed copy.

ITALY

◆ Otomat

Dimensions: 46 cm × 4.46 m; 1.35-m span (18.1 × 189.8 × 49.1 in)
Weight: 770 kg at launch; 660 kg in flight (1697/1455 lbs)
Warhead: 210-kg (463-lb) Herotol blast (132-lbs explosive)
Propulsion: Turbomeca Arbizon III turbojet and two solid-fuel boosters **Speed:** Mach 0.9
Range: 6–60 km, Mk 1; 100–180 km, Mk 2 (6.6–66 kyds/109–197 kyds) minimum range for Mk 1 is 6600 yds; maximum effective range is 64 kyds; maximum flight range is 88 kyds.

Gabriel in flight. The two dipoles visible below the missile are presumably part of its radar altimeter. (U.S. Navy)

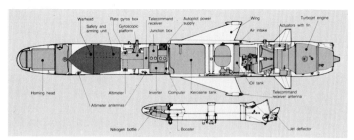

Otomat missile. (Matra)

Otomat emerges from its launcher. Note the oval-section tube, allowing two missiles to be carried in the space that formerly accommodated only one. (Matra)

Otomat. (Matra)

Otomat is a collaborative French-Italian project (OTO Melara and Matra); missiles are manufactured in both countries. Otomat uses inertial mid-course guidance and an X-band active terminal seeker. The launcher is fixed at an elevation of 12 or 18 degrees. The rocket booster carries Otomat to an altitude of 80 m (262 ft) and a sustainable speed of Mach 0.9. The missile swtiches on its seeker at an expected range of about 12 km (13.1 kyds). The missile climbs to 175 m (574 ft) at a range of 4 km (4400 yds) from the target then, at 2-km (2200-yds) range, dives at 7 degrees. That dive increases the chance of penetrating deep into a target ship but exposes the missile to hostile fire for an estimated 12 seconds. Otomat Mk 2 is, therefore, designed to sea-skim throughout its flight.

Mk 1 receives its launch data (true target bearing, own-ship heading, time of flight, and vertical reference) from the launch ship. The initial missile course can be as much as 200 degrees away from the angle of the launcher. Warm-up time is 30 seconds (gyro spin-up time). It appears that the original missile could not accept mid-course updates, but that limitation does not apply to production Mk 1s.

The French version of Mk 1 (which was apparently not successfully exported) uses the Clio fire-control system, and all Mk 1s use a three-axis Thomson-CSF Col Vert terminal seeker that scans in elevation and to 20 degrees to either side of the missile. Italian-made Mk 2s have an Italian-made SMA single-axis active seeker.

Mk 2 is designed to accept mid-course guidance from a helicopter closer to the target. There are two forms. In the Italian Teseo system, the helicopter orders the turn toward the target, so the missile is initially directed toward the helicopter. Thus, the missile flies at low altitude all the way to the target, not needing to be high enough to receive mid-course guidance from a ship. However, because the missile must fly directly to the helicopter, the system as a whole cannot engage more than one target (or a few targets very close together) at one time. Moreover, the effect of the system is to increase flight time, as the missile must follow an angled path. For example, a missile fired by a Venezuelan *Lupo*-class frigate hit a target 131.5 km (144 kyds) away, but that engagement entailed a flight leg of 85.8 km (93.8 kyds) to the helicopter, and another of 51.9 km (56.8 kyds) to the target. Typical mid-course guidance platforms are AB 212 and Sea King helicopters.

In the French ERATO (Extended Range Targeting of Otomat), mid-course corrections are transmitted directly by the launching ship. The missile must, therefore, climb to 900 m (2952 ft) altitude to remain within range of the shipboard data link. The ship tracks the helicopter, which in turn detects and tracks the target. The missile descends to 20 m (66 ft) cruise altitude after receiving final instructions by ship data link, at a maximum range of about 80–100 km (the ship's radar horizon for the helicopter). A final pop-up maneuver is possible. Maximum total range is 166 km. The helicopter need not fly near the missile's flight path, and the system as a whole can engage several targets simultaneously (up to 16 missiles at six targets with six simultaneous mid-course updates). This flexibility makes it possible for the missiles to approach one target from several different directions more or less simultaneously. Typically, this system employs an ORB 31 or 32 or Agrion helicopter-borne radar.

Mk 2 is also designated Otomat Compact; it has folding wings for more compact stowage. The original box was 1.36 m in diameter and 4.7 m long, with a weight of 850 kg empty. Otomat Compact uses an elliptical-section container with the same width, but only 0.84 m high and weighing only 595 kg. As in the case of Exocet (MM 38/MM 40), the change in launcher allows two missiles to be carried in the space (and very nearly with the weight) formerly allowed for one.

OTO Melara and Engins Matra conceived Otomat as a private venture and began studies in 1967 and development in 1969. The first unguided launching was in 1971, the first successful guided flight following in February 1972. Mark 2 trials began in January 1974. A proposed air-to-surface version was abandoned in 1976.

Otomat is in Italian Navy service and has been exported to Egypt, Iraq, Kenya (on board two Vosper-Thornycroft 56-meter attack boats), Libya, Nigeria, Peru, Saudi Arabia, and Venezuela. About 830 Otomats had been ordered by the end of 1986, and unit cost was about $350,000–$400,000. As of January 1982, 402 Otomats had been reported deployed on board 83 ships.

As of 1988, Otomat production was to continue, to be followed by a successor, the supersonic Otomach. Because the Otomach program has encountered difficulties, a Mark 3 version of Otomat may be developed with improved guidance and better flight characteristics. An ASW version (see the Antisubmarine Warfare section) was announced in October 1986.

◆ Otomach

Warhead: 100 kg (220 lbs)
Propulsion: turbojet with two strap-on solid boosters
Speed: Mach 2.0   **Range:** 193–380 km (211–416 kyds)

Otomach is a projected Otomat successor, but as yet the Italian government has not formally authorized development. Otomach was conceived by an Italian consortium headed by OTO-Melara in 1979; and a development contract between OTO-Melara and Alfa-Romeo (which, with Fiat Aviazione, is responsible for the turbojet cruise engine, based on the AR 318) was signed on 14 April 1981. Guidance will be similar to that of Otomat Mk 2, with a radar terminal seeker supplemented by IR or television.

In 1987, it was reported that Matra and OTO-Melara were working on a supersonic Otomat successor to be designated *Anti-Navire Futur* (ANF). It will compete with ANS.

◆ Sea Killer/Marte

Dimensions: Marte Mk 2: 31.6 cm in diameter; Mk 2: 20.6 cm in diameter (12.5 and 8 inches, respectively). Marte Mk 2: 4.84 m in overall length, including 1.09-m booster (191/43 inches); Mk 2: 4.7 m in overall length, or 3.64 m without booster (185/155 inches). Marte Mk 2, 98.4 cm in span (38.7 in); Mk 2: 99.9 cm in span (39.3 in)
Weight: Marte: 330 kg (727 lbs); Mk 2: 300 kg (661 lbs). Marte in shipping container: 1056 lbs. Marte Mk 2 weighs 345 kg (760 lbs).
Warhead: Sea Killer Mk 2: 70-kg (154 -lbs) Tritolital blast SAP with impact fuze; Mk 1: 75-lbs HE-fragmentation, including 35-lbs HE
Propulsion: boost: 1.7-sec burn, to 250 m/sec (820 ft/sec); sustain: 75-sec burn
Speed: Marte: 300 m/sec (984 ft/sec); Mk 2: Mach 1.9
Range: Marte and Mk 2: 20–25 km (22–27 kyds; minimum range 6 kyds; Mk 1: minimum range 3250 yds, maximum 11 kyds)

The missile is Sea Killer, the ship system is Mariner, and the helicopter system is Marte. Sea Killer can also be carried by a fixed-wing airplane, in which case the missile needs no booster (and is, therefore, 84 kg lighter). These missiles were manufactured by Sistel.

Mark 1 (Nettuno) is a surface-to-surface version of the Contraves Sea Indigo surface-to-air missile (slightly longer, with a larger diameter and greater weight). Sea Indigo was never placed in service by any navy, but Sea Killer Mk 1 was bought by Italy for fast patrol boats (installed only in the now-stricken *Saetta*). Mk 1 is no longer in service. Work was begun by Contraves Italiana SpA in 1963, the first prototype flying in 1966, and the weapon entering service in 1969; that year the missile was taken over by Sistel SpA (which was formed around the Contraves missile division).

Nettuno was designed for use with the Contraves Sea Hunter Mk 2 fire-control system. It is command guided, either beam riding or by direct radar command based on optical target tracking. In either case, the missile maintains sea-skimming altitude (6.5–33 ft) by means of a radio altimeter. This missile was fired from a trainable quintuple launcher (total weight about 10,000 lbs).

Sea Killer Mk 2 (Vulcano) is an entirely new two-stage missile designed to use the same guidance and construction techniques as its predecessor. The associated fire-control system is Sea

Hunter 4. The missile is commanded into the line of sight of the fire-control system then rides a radar beam. Corrections, a reference signal, and event commands (e.g., warhead arming signal) are sent via a command link at a frequency well removed from that of the guidance radar. Initial launch information includes roll, pitch, and own-ship speed. Flight time is input either manually or through the fire-control computer, and maximum range corresponds to about 120 seconds. The system's reaction time is about 30 seconds (to warm up the radio altimeter). The missile flies a sea-skimming (3-m altitude) course by radio altimeter; altitude can be adjusted in flight by command from the launching ship or from a helicopter. Like Mk 1, Mk 2 can also be radio-command guided (via the command link mentioned above) using an optical target tracker; the missile is made to fly down the optical axis of the tracker.

In a typical ship installation, the target-tracking radar is a Selenia RTN or a radome-mounted SPQ-711 (part of the Contraves Sea Hunter system). The bridge carries an optical tracker.

Sea Killer Mk 2 was bought by Iran (in a trainable quintuple launcher on board Vosper Mk 5 frigates). In these ships the fire-control radar is the Orion RTN-10X.

The first two successful Mk 2 launches were reported in October 1971.

In the Marte Mk 1 system, a Sea King helicopter with SMA APQ-706 radar carries two Sea Killer Mk 2 missiles. The APQ-706 radar uses two back-to-back antennas and two radar transceivers: one frequency-agile unit and one unit linked to a PPI. When the radar locks onto the target, the missile can be fired. Like Sea Killer, it is a beam-rider flying at a set altitude (between 3.4 and 5 m) above the sea.

Marte Mk 2 has a larger-diameter nose containing an Otomat active seeker for fire-and-forget operation. Reports indicate that the warhead is no heavier than that of Sea Killer Mk 2 or Marte Mk 1. The airframe and booster aft of the nose section duplicate those of Marte Mk 1. There is also a version of Marte Mk 2 intended for use by fast aircraft; it has no booster and weighs 260 kg (573 lbs).

The corresponding ship system, which has not found any buyers, would carry six missiles in tubes good for six months without maintenance.

Sea Killer began as a private-venture project in 1965, the first tests coming in 1969, and the first operational installation, on board Iranian Navy frigates, in 1971/72. The first Marte Mk 1 was delivered to the Italian Navy in 1977, and the Italian Navy selected the Mariner system in July 1979. However, no ship installations were made. Marte Mk 2 was announced in mid-1983, and the first Marte Mk 2 test was a shot from a ground launcher against a trawler at a range of 18.8 km, 23 March 1984. Marte Mk 2 entered Italian Navy service in 1987.

In 1988, AerMacchi announced plans to integrate Marte with the MB339 trainer/light attack aircraft, and this missile will probably be carried by the Italian/Brazilian AMX fighter/attack airplane (using an FIAR/ECTA Pointer radar or an SMA/Technasa Scipio for the Brazilian version, or the FIAR Grifo for the dedicated antiship version).

JAPAN

◆ SSM-1

Dimensions: 35 cm × 5 m; 116 cm span (13.8 × 197 × 45.7 in)
Weight: 661 kg (1457 lbs)   **Warhead:** 225 kg (496 lbs)
Propulsion: Mitsubishi TJM-2 turbojet, 2 boosters
Speed: subsonic   **Range:** 150 km (164 kyds)

SSM-1. (*Sea Power*)

At present SSM-1 is a truck-mounted antiship missile, for coastal defense. However, the missile is probably suitable for ship mounting. The Japanese FY88 budget included the first six six-tube truck-mounted launchers for the Ground Self-Defense Force, out of a planned total of 56 (total 384 missiles). SSM-1 is derived from the ASM-1 (see Air-Launched Missiles), with a turbojet instead of a rocket power plant. Reportedly, the ASM-2 air-launched missile will be derived from SSM-1.

SSM-1 was proposed in 1981, and development began in 1982. The prototype was completed in 1983. Japan has no test range of its own, so the first prototype SSM-1 was dropped by a T-2 over the Sea of Japan in July 1986; missiles were also test-fired at Point Mugu, California, in June 1987.

In February 1988 Kawasaki received a contract for a feasibility study of an air-launched version, to be carried by P-3C Orions.

A new ship-launched antiship missile, SSM-B (presumably SSM-1B), is to replace Harpoon in Japanese service; first trials were reportedly scheduled for 1988.

When SSM-1 was originally proposed, unit cost was to have been $385,000 (FY78 dollars), based on a purchase of 150 missiles. The purchase was increased to 250 missiles, but the current unit-price estimate is $697,000 (FY87 dollars); the prototypes cost $728,000 each (FY87).

NORWAY

◆ Penguin (AGM-119)

Dimensions: 28 cm × 2.95 m × 1.42 m span (11 in × 118 in × 55.5 in span); Mk 2 length 2.96 m (117 in); Mk 3: 28 cm × 3.20 m × 2.00 m span (11 in × 10 ft 5 in × 3 ft 3 in)

Weight: Mk 1: 330 kg; Mk 2: 340 kg; Mk 3: 350 kg, 400 kg with launcher (Mk 1: 741 lbs; Mk 2; 749 lbs; Mk 3: 771/882 lbs). Mk 3 weight has also been given officially as 820 lbs with a 265-lb warhead.

Warhead: 250-lb SAP (Bullpup Mk 19)

Propulsion: solid rocket

Speed: Mach 0.7 (Mk 2 and Mk 3: Mach 0.8)

Range: Mk 1: 20 km; Mk 2: 27 km; Mk 3: 40+ km (22/29.5/44 kyds) (Minimum range is 2750 yds in the Mk 1 version)

Penguin being test fired by a U.S. 65-foot Patrol Boat Mk 3, 1982. (U.S. Navy)

Penguin Mk 2 Mod 7 on board a LAMPS helicopter (Grumman Aerospace)

Penguin was the first infrared guided antiship missile (indeed, the first modern NATO antiship missile). It is boosted to an altitude of 80 m, cruising at 66 ft; the IR seeker is activated at a preset range. The designers chose IR homing because the prospective users, the Norwegian and Swedish navies, operate in areas of strong radar clutter dealing, respectively, with fjords and the Stockholm archipelago. IR homing also provides a target with less warning than an active-radar seeker, although requiring the missile to fly at a greater altitude. Prior to launch, the missile is provided with target bearing, target relative speed perpendicular to the line of fire, range to IR-seeker activation, and gyro-platform compensation data. Maximum flight time (Mk 1) is about 85 seconds. Total reaction time, from the off condition to firing, is about 2 minutes but can be cut to 7 seconds if seeker cooling is maintained.

The altimeter is a pulsed laser.

The warhead is a U.S. Bullpup Mk 19 with a U.S. Mk 312-2 contact fuze (delay changed from 8 to 10 milliseconds, to allow some penetration of the target). Total explosive weight is 103 lbs.

Mk 1 is carried in the fiberglass shipping container (43.3 × 43.3 × 122 in, 396 lbs) from which the missile is launched.

Mk 2 is a longer-range ship-launched version using a new launcher. However, the U.S. Navy plans to adopt Mk 2 Mod 7, a helicopter-launched version, for the LAMPS helicopters (see below).

Mk 3 (AGM-119) is an air-to-surface version that flies a preselected search pattern. The missile can be launched at altitudes of 150–30,000 ft and at speeds of up to Mach 1.2. The pilot can launch Mk 3 at up to 50 degrees off boresight. There are four trajectory options: altitude hold "on" (missile flies either at maximum cruise altitude or at launch altitude, whichever is lower, up to the waypoint); altitude hold "off" (missile descends to preset mid-course altitude); mid-course altitude high (about 300 ft); and mid-course altitude low (sea-skimming). The pilot also selects the search pattern (wide, normal, asymmetrical) before launch.

In Norwegian service the associated fire-control system is MSI-80S, incorporating twin Decca TM 1226 radars, a Marconi-Elliott low-light-level television camera/tracker, a laser range-finder, an IR scanner, and ESM. In Swedish service the missile interfaces with the PEAB 9V200 fire-control system; the Greek Navy uses Penguin with the Thomson-CSF Vega 2.

Penguin was developed in 1962–1970 by the Norwegian Ministry of Defense and Kongsberg Vapenfabrikk, with some U.S. Navy financing (which is why Penguin uses a Bullpup warhead, and why the U.S. Navy has certain rights to the missile; it has been evaluated several times in the United States). Test flights were completed in 1971, and Penguin entered service in 1972 in the Greek, Norwegian, Swedish, and Turkish navies, on board fast patrol craft and, later, on board Norwegian frigates.

The U.S. Navy evaluated Penguin on board a 65-foot patrol boat (completed April 1982). The missile seemed too heavy for that hull but was chosen for the larger special-warfare craft (SWCM, Sea Viking). Penguin was successfully tested on board the air-cushion landing craft JEFF B in October 1983 in response to a House Armed Services Committee recommendation that alternative missions be sought for the landing craft. For this test the missiles were loaded on a flatbed truck. The U.S. surface-launched Penguin program died with Sea Viking.

By 1983 the fleet had proposed both a helicopter-launched antiship missile (HLASM) and a short-range surface-to-surface missile (SRSSM). A 1983 study rejected SRSSM (for carriers, amphibious ships, and service-force ships) but did show that the combination of LAMPS III and HLASM would be worthwhile. Penguin was the leading HLASM candidate, and in April 1984 the Mk 2 Mod 7 version, with folding wings and with an improved IR sensor, was formally chosen. The program then called for 272 missiles. In 1985 $14.6 million was provided to evaluate the missile in this role, but rising unit cost led to a reduction from 272 to 192 missiles. In July 1986 the Senate Armed Services Committee objected that Penguin was too expensive, that it would equip only 33 ships (and a total of only 28 helicopters), and that it had a range of only 20 nm. As of 1988, production funds have been dropped from the FY89 budget, but the program is still alive; the first free-flight tests are scheduled for early 1989. Moreover, the missile has been proposed for Korea and for Greece on board an adapted LAMPS I helicopter (Kaman SH-2F).

In 1988, Penguin Mk 3 is in production for the Royal Norwegian Air Force, to be carried on board F-16 fighters. Turkey is reportedly showing interest in purchasing it, and the U.S. Air Force is testing it.

In 1988 estimated unit cost is $220,000 for Mk 1 or Mk 2, or $500,000–$550,000 for Mk 2 Mod 7 or Mk 3.

The U.S. budget request, as of January 1989, was for 64 missiles in FY90 and another 65 in FY91.

SOUTH AFRICA

♦ **Skorpioen**

See Gabriel (Israel).

SWEDEN

♦ **Rb 08A**

    Dimensions: 65 cm × 5.7 m; span 3.6 m (26.1 × 224 × 142 in)
    Weight: empty 1720 lbs (launched at 2645.5 lbs)
    Warhead: 250-kg (551-lbs) blast-fragmentation
    Propulsion: turbomeca Marbore IID jet (882-lb thrust) with solid-fuel booster
    Speed: about Mach 0.65   **Range:** 135 nm

This antiship cruise missile was derived from the French (Nord Aviation) CT-20 target drone and developed by Nord and CSF (later part of Thomson-CSF) under the designation M20, specifically for the Swedish Navy. Work began in 1959, and Rb 08A entered production (by Saab) in 1966; 98 were manufactured, and production ended in 1970. The missile was formerly carried by two Swedish destroyers and is now used for coast defense.

No speed data on Rb 08 were ever released; the figure above is characteristic of the similar R 20 battlefield-surveillance drone. The CT 20 target, which was lighter than Rb 08 but of about the same size, was credited with a speed of 900 km/hr at 10,000 m (486 kts at 32,800 ft).

♦ **Rb 12**

Rb 12 is the Swedish designation for the Norwegian Penguin Mk 2 (see above).

♦ **RBS 15**

    Dimensions: 50 cm × 4.35 m; span 85 cm folded/1.4 m spread (19.7 × 171 × 33.5/55.1 in)
    Weight: 598 kg (780 with boosters) (1318/1719 lbs)
    Warhead: estimated 250-kg (551-lbs) semi-armor piercing (a modified, heavier warhead is under development)
    Propulsion: Microturbo TRI 60-1-077 (370-kg thrust) with rocket boosters
    Speed: Mach 0.9 (to Mach 0.7 by 3-second booster burn)
    Range: 70 km (77 kyds) (150 km for air-launched version)

RBS 15 is a fire-and-forget weapon with an active-radar (frequency-agile) seeker. Flight parameters, such as the search pattern, are automatically selectable by the fire-control system. The mid-course inertial system can be updated by data link. PEAB claims that frequency agility in the seeker reduces glint by a factor of 2 to 4 and increases target-detection range by more than 50 percent. Frequency agility is also said to eliminate target fading during lock-on, to reduce sea clutter, and to obviate any requirement to allocate different frequencies to the different missiles of a salvo. The seeker is designed to provide home-on-jam as an option, and the missile can also be modified to maneuver evasively (using memory tracking to remain locked-on).

The seeker is designated 9GR400; it is built around the same type of PEAB spin-tuned X- or Ku-band magnetron used in the 9LV200 fire-control system. Typical pulse width is 0.2 to 1.0 microsec, with a jittered PRF of 1000–4000, a peak power of

RBS 15. (Saab)

RB 15 missile being fired from a coast-defense launcher. (Swedish Navy)

65–100 kW, and search limits of 30 degrees either side in azimuth and 15 degrees up or down in elevation.

Reportedly the RBS 15 airframe is derived from that of the earlier RB04E air-launched missile; the use of components of the earlier weapon drastically cut development time. Reportedly, too, the missile was developed at the urgent recommendation of the Swedish Aircraft Industry Committee to maintain missile design and production capability. The Swedish defense forces disagreed (presumably on grounds of cost), but were overruled: RBS 15 was chosen instead of the U.S. Harpoon or the French Exocet.

The development contract was let to Saab in June 1979, and the design was frozen in mid-1980. The first live firing was in July 1981. Initial Swedish Navy deliveries were completed in 1985. Finland ordered RBS 15 (15M version) in March 1983, and the missile entered service on 7 June 1984; Finland also uses the missile for coast defense (first delivered in April 1988). This weapon has been ordered by Yugoslavia to replace existing Soviet-supplied SS-C-3 Styx coast-defense missiles and may also be carried by new *Kobra*-class missile boats. Estimated unit cost is $479,000 (FY87).

There is also an air-launched version, RBS 15F, for use by Swedish Air Force Viggen fighters. Reportedly a vertically launched version is planned for *Vastergotland*-class submarines.

♦ **Hellfire (RBS 17)**

See U.S. section.

Hellfire (RBS 17) being fired from its coast-defense launcher. (Swedish Navy)

TAIWAN (GRC)

♦ **Hsiung Feng I/II**

Hsiung Feng I is an unlicensed copy of the Israeli Gabriel; the name originally meant Male Bee, but was changed to Proud (or Brave) Wind in 1980/81 in line with a general redesignation of new Taiwanese (GRC) systems with "Wind" names. Reportedly the developers experienced problems with the rocket motor and with the copied guidance system. The warhead is a 70-kg blast-fragmentation type. This missile is used both on board ship and in coastal batteries. Hsiung Feng may not be a true sea-skimmer, since at least some films show it flying well above the sea and then diving steeply into its target.

The associated fire-control radar is SPG-24.

Reportedly work on the Hsiung Feng I fire-control system began in the 1970s. The missile project was completed in 1977 (it was first reported in January 1977). The initial test firings were conducted on board the former torpedo boat *PT 1*. Israeli-supplied Gabriels had been mounted on board some GRC destroyers as early as 1974. In the absence of any Israeli radar, these missiles may have relied on radio-command guidance, which is a back-up control system for Gabriel I.

Hsiung Feng II resembles the U.S. Harpoon but is reportedly powered by a license-produced Turbomeca Arbizon IV turbojet, which has a somewhat greater diameter than the U.S. engine (but develops 10 percent more thrust). Film footage of the initial trial shows folding wings, and the missile appears to approach its target at very low altitude (5–7 m), using an active-radar seeker. Reports indicate that the missile can accept mid-course guidance data, e.g., from a helicopter. The data link involved is probably similar to that of Hsiung Feng I. Unlike Harpoon, Hsiung Feng II incorporates an IR sensor, officially described as Automatic Target Recognition Image Tracking Module Mk 2. The missile is carried in a fairing above the main (radar) seeker.

Presumably the combination of radar and infrared will defeat the relatively simple countermeasures currently employed on board PRC ships.

Film of test launches, shown in February 1988, appears to show a modernized *Fletcher*-class destroyer (Wu-Jin I or Weapons Improvement Mk I) launch platform. Reportedly, the Taiwan Navy will employ Hsiung Feng I and II side by side, as the Israeli Navy employs Gabriel and Harpoon.

Films of Hsiung Feng II launches from both coastal batteries and ships have been released. Reportedly air- and submarine-launched versions are under development.

Hsiung Feng being fired by a Taiwanese destroyer. (*Defense Technology*)

A Hsiung Feng I missile on parade in Taiwan. (Fu S. Mei)

Hsiung Feng I being fired from a Taiwanese destroyer. Note the command-guidance director in the foreground. The unmanned director is a U.S.-type Mk 51 controlling the twin 40-mm gun mount visible below the director to the right. (Fu S. Mei)

Hsiung Feng I being fired by a Taiwanese PSMM Mk-5 class (*Lung Chiang*-class) fast attack boat. She carries an OTO-Melara 76-mm gun forward, and the main air-search radar is the stand-alone version of the U.S. SPS-58, which is unique to the Taiwanese (GRC) Navy. The radome presumably covers a Hsiung Feng control radar of unidentified type. (Fu S. Mei)

Hsiung Feng II missiles on parade in Taiwan. The fairing above the nose carries the infrared sensor. (Fu S. Mei)

USSR

Many Soviet naval missiles have alternative nuclear warheads, as noted below. Many may also have chemical warheads; certainly chemical weapons are very common in Soviet land forces. No detailed information on naval chemical weapons has been published, and it is sometimes argued that a fleet subject to a chemical attack could steam out of the chemical cloud, relying on short-term measures such as citadels. Another view is that, since the Soviets themselves class chemical weapons with nuclear weapons as "means of mass destruction," nuclear deterrence would also deter them from using chemicals.

One can imagine an attack in which explosives or bomblets were used to open ships for follow-up chemical attack. Gas attack was taken very seriously before World War II, and no realistic solution was found at that time (in one internal U.S. document, experts suggested that a gassed battleship might as well be scuttled, since it could not be decontaminated). Western consciousness of Soviet chemical-warfare potential has increased enormously over the last few years, and numerous reports of the chemical-security measures that the Soviet Navy has taken

have been adduced to suggest that the Soviets do indeed possess naval chemical weapons. Perhaps the most important antigas devices that Western navies currently use are the gas detectors, most of which use lasers to detect poisonous chemicals in the surrounding atmosphere.

◆ SS-C-2 Salish

See AS-1/SS-C-2 under air-launched weapons.

◆ SS-N-2 Styx (and SS-C-3)

Dimensions: 30 in × 21.3 ft; span 9 ft (SS-N-2C: 31-in diameter)
Weight: 5070 lbs (SS-N-2A)
Warhead: 500 kg (1100 lbs); somewhat heavier in SS-N-2C
Propulsion: liquid-fuel rocket (solid booster)
Speed: Mach 0.9 (666 mph)
Range: 25 nm (effective to 16 nm); SS-N-2C: 45 nm

An SS-N-2 being loaded. (Siegfried Breyer)

An SS-N-2 missile being checked before loading. (Sovfoto)

SS-N-2 was the first Soviet sea-based antiship missile to enter large-scale service. Intended to replace the torpedoes of small fast attack craft, SS-N-2 is a radar- or IR-homing fire-and-forget weapon. Styx was the first antiship missile to sink a ship in combat, Egyptian Komar-type missile boats sinking the Israeli destroyer *Eilat* in 1967. Styx was also fired successfully during the Indo-Pakistani War of 1971, by the Chinese (PRC) Navy in the Paracel Islands in 1974, and, reportedly, by the Iraqi Navy during the Iran-Iraq War (1980). In 1988 Iran began to use a land-based version of the Chinese (PRC) equivalent, Silkworm (HY-2 and derivatives), against shipping in the Persian Gulf. Styx was also used, unsuccessfully, during the October War (Israel-Arab) of 1973. At that time the reported reason for the weapon's failure was the excessive time required to run up the missile's gyros before firing: the Arab missile boat crews, under attack, tended to fire before their weapons were ready. In addition, because the missile had been designed to attack large warships, its seeker could not always distinguish the small Israeli missile boats, parts of whose superstructures had been covered in radar-absorbing material.

SS-N-2 A and B (introduced 1958 and 1964, respectively) are I-band active-radar homers, the B-versions having alternative IR homing. SS-N-2B (Osa-II-class missile boats) also has folding wings and, reportedly, sea-skims on its final approach to the target. These weapons are carried by Osa- and Komar-type missile boats. SS-N-2C (originally designated SS-N-11) has a maximum range of 45 nm. Both radar and infrared homing versions are in service. A forward observer is needed to take advantage of the increased range; presumably, larger ships can accommodate the necessary communications and plotting facilities. Therefore, this weapon, introduced in 1967, is carried by Modified Kashin- and Kildin-class destroyers, by Tarantul-class missile corvettes, and by export Nanuchkas (Soviet Nanuchkas fire SS-N-9 missiles). All versions of the missile have been widely exported.

The Soviet designation is P-15 (industrial index number 4K40); SS-N-2C is P-20 and P-21. The coast-defense version, SS-C-3, is P-20/21.

Development began in 1954. Although Styx-armed missile boats entered service in 1958 or 1959, final testing (in the Northern Fleet, by two Osa-Is) was not completed until 1960–61. Reportedly, the liquid-fuel rocket was chosen over a turbojet for quick acceleration, and the weapon was not provided with a nuclear warhead because of its short range (initially 13 nm): the firing platform might have suffered damage. Initial Soviet estimates were that two hits were needed to sink a destroyer (as in the case of the *Eilat*), and that twelve missiles (three boats) had to be fired to achieve them. Boats were, therefore, organized in units of three, and standard doctrine called for the dispatch of two units to ensure that one would reach the target area. Missile installation and arming initially took 15 hours, but that period was later reduced to 12 hours, and by 1962 an Osa could be fitted with her four missiles in 4–6 hours.

Missiles are loaded with storable liquid propellant, which gradually corrodes the missile body. Weapons, therefore, tend to be expended in large numbers, the usual lifetime being about two years.

The Square Tie targeting radar of an Osa or Komar can detect a destroyer at up to 22 nm under favorable conditions (maximum theoretical radar range is 48 nm), and fast patrol boats can be detected at about 10 nm. The operator sets a range gate around the expected target position, and data for firing the missile can be computed for ranges between 3 and 15 nm. For longer ranges, at least in the original version, the appropriate firing range must be calculated manually, by plotting board, and that significantly reduces hit probability. The missile-firing platform must turn into the direction of fire. The missile is launched at a 15-degree angle to the horizon, then climbs at 45 degrees to an altitude of about 450 ft. The seeker, operating on one of 6 preset frequencies, is switched on at about 6 nm from the calculated impact point. At least in early versions, the seeker cannot distinguish fixed from moving targets and chooses the one with the strongest echo. The seeker is, therefore, quite vulnerable to deception by chaff. Altitude is preset at 100, 150, 200, 250, or 300 m (330, 500, 660, 825, or 1000 ft). Reportedly, the initial design of the missile included provisons for mid-course guidance, the weapon flying at 400 m (1300 ft) until it neared the target.

The warhead is a large-diameter shaped-charge, and the fuel tank is carried abaft the warhead, near the missile's center of gravity. In theory, then, the effect of a hit is to blast a hole deep into the target while filling it with burning fuel. Soviet doctrine is to fire 7 to 8 missiles at a cruiser, or 4 against a destroyer. Because hit probability against a fast patrol boat is limited (due to its small radar cross-section), the doctrine in this case is to fire 2 to 4.

Some major limitations in the original SS-N-2 were the minimum range of 5 nm (the homing and arming mechanisms are not activated until the missile has flown that far) and the inability to seek out the preferred target among a group of ships. Nor can targets be attacked from seaward within 4 nm of the shore, because of radar clutter. At least in its original form, SS-N-2 cannot be fired if the air temperature is below 4 degrees F or above 101 degrees F.

Although the Soviets considered SS-N-2 strictly an antiship missile, the Indian Navy very successfully used this missile against shore installations, such as refineries (which are strong radar reflectors) during the 1971 Indo-Pakistani War.

The coast-defense version, SS-C-3, was developed in the late 1970s to replace the much larger SS-C-1 (coast-defense version of SS-N-3). Meanwhile the Chinese were using essentially the same Styx missile for coast defense. However, the standard Soviet transporter carries two Styxes and a Plank Shave fire-control radar, plus a control cabin, whereas the standard Chinese launcher is a single rail. Thus, each Soviet launcher truck is, in effect, an independent fire unit, even though Soviet doctrine calls for several such units to attack most warships. Effective engagement range is limited by the performance of the truck-mounted Plank Shave, which can probably detect a target at about 35 km (38,000 yds) at maximum elevation.

Exports of this missile began in 1983–84, initially to East Germany and then to Yugoslavia, followed by Soviet clients in the Middle East. As in the case of SS-C-2, the standard organization is a 3-battery battalion, each battery consisting of six launchers.

◆ SS-N-3 Shaddock (and SS-C-1)

Dimensions: 38.3 in × approx 33 ft (SSN-3C: 39 ft); span is about 16.8 ft **Weight:** 11,900 lbs
Warhead: 1000 kg (2200 lbs; nuclear version reportedly 350 kT)
Propulsion: liquid-fuel rocket **Speed:** Mach 1.4 (1040 mph)
Range: 250 nm (400 nm for SS-N-3C)

SS-N-3 missiles in their launch tubes on board a Juliett-class submarine, being raised for firing. (U.S. Navy)

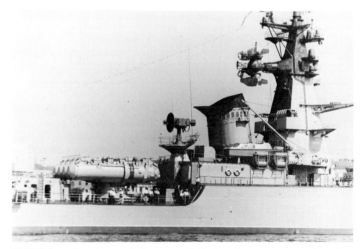

SS-N-3 launch tubes and the control device, Scoop Pair, on the after side of the mast above. There are two independent antennas, so the ship can presumably engage two targets using this director. The radomes on the side of the mast are for electronic countermeasures: the big randome is a Top Hat jammer (another pair is on the tower foremast). Above and below the jammer are smaller Bell-series radomes and the squatter, broader-diameter radome of Guard Dog. Presumably the latter is a wide-open detector, whereas the Bells contain spinning antennas for accurate direction-finding and, therefore, for directing the jammers in the Top Hats. (*C.P. Lemieux*)

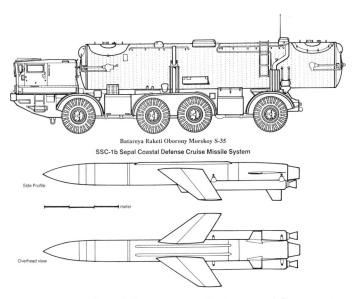

Batareya Raketi Oborony Morskoy S-35
SSC-1b Sepal Coastal Defense Cruise Missile System

Side Profile

meter

Overhead view

The SS-N-3 missile and the transporter for its coast-defense version, SS-C-1b. (Steven Zaloga)

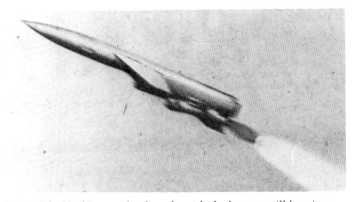

SS-N-3 (Shaddock) soon after launch, with the booster still burning.

Shaddock was the first Soviet over-the-horizon ship-launched anticarrier missile. It seems to have originated as a strategic cruise missile but is listed under antiship weapons because all of the platforms (Echo-I-class submarines and Whiskey-class conversions) designed to use the missile solely in the strategic role have either been converted to other uses or discarded. Note, however, that the nuclear-armed nonhoming strategic version remains in service. This version might also be usable against moving formations, depending upon the details of the targeting technique.

Because the homing version of SS-N-3 flies so far, i.e., spends so long in flight, the missile requires mid-course assistance to ensure that it hits the right ship within the target formation. That help generally involves a Bear-D radar-reconnaissance aircraft, which provides the firing submarine or surface ship with a radar picture of the target formation. This picture is matched against that provided by the missile itself. Hormone-B helicopters also carry an appropriate targeting radar. The firing platform uses a radar tracker/transponder: Front Door/Front Piece in submarines (Juliett- and Echo-II-classes), Scoop Pair in a Kynda- or Kresta-I-class missile cruiser. Some missile cruisers also have Plinth Net antennas (probably passive) clearly associated with this missile system; they appear to be receivers for targeting data derived from the missile seeker.

The targeting technique can be upset by the destruction of the radar platform or by an attack on the launching platform before it has locked the missile(s) onto the desired target. The high-altitude radar search by the missile itself can provide a target with useful warning. The Soviets are well aware of these weaknesses, the much faster SS-N-19 providing the ultimate solution. An interim solution would be to accept a much shorter

A Soviet submarine's missile-guidance antennas, Front Door/Front Piece, folded down inside the sail. The front and side of the sail hinge to expose the antennas. The glassy strip on the front of the sail (at left) covers a sonar; the windshield at right indicates the forward part of the manned portion of the sail.

engagement range, hence a much shorter flight time, and then to use the weapon in a fire-and-forget mode. The efficacy of such a tactic would depend upon the quality of prefiring data and upon the speed of the missile (i.e., upon flight time). The better the pretargeting data, the closer to the target the missile could turn on its seeker, hence the shorter the effective warning time.

Typically SS-N-3 climbs from its launcher at an angle of 15–20 degrees, attaining a maximum altitude of about 13,000 ft. The missile switches on its seeker when it attains cruising altitude and begins a 20-degree dive after it locks on, leveling out for the terminal run-in. In a typical attack at a range of 150 nm, the missile would attain maximum altitude about 100 nm from launch and would begin diving about 50 nm from the target. These data were compiled about 1971, at which time the missile was credited with a speed of Mach 1.2 and a maximum range of 220 nm (minimum 12 nm); operational range was about 150 nm. A submarine firing SS-N-3s would launch them in pairs. Apparently because the Front Door/Front Piece could not track two salvos simultaneously, the submarine could not fire a second salvo until the first had locked on, so the salvo interval was about 15 minutes. This limitation may explain the installation of a secondary antenna, Plinth Net, on board some surface ships armed with SS-N-3; the additional antenna might be used to communicate with distant missiles while the main guidance radar (Scoop Pair) handled a second pair of missiles, closer to the ship.

SS-N-3C, the inertially guided version, was probably actually the first developed. It appeared in 1960. SS-N-3A, fired by submarines (Juliett and Echo-II), entered service in 1962, contemporary with SS-N-3B, for surface ships (Kynda and Kresta-I).

The Soviet designation for the original strategic weapon is P-5, P-5D being an improved version with a doppler altimeter. It appears that P-6 and possibly P-7 were the submarine-launched nuclear-armed anticarrier versions, and that P-35 was the surface-ship version. S-35 is the coast-defense version. All were designed by the Chelomei bureau.

SS-C-1 is the Western designation for the coast-defense cruise-missile version.

This weapon evolved into SS-N-12 and SS-N-19.

◆ SS-N-7 Starbright

Dimensions: Approx 21–22 in × 23 ft   **Weight:** 7440 lbs
Warhead: approx 1100-lbs (500-kg) HE
Propulsion: liquid-fuel rocket
Speed: Mach 0.9   **Range:** 35 nm

SS-N-7 is an underwater-launched analog of SS-N-2, i.e., a replacement for previous submarine antiship torpedoes. Starbright is carried by Charlie-class nuclear attack submarines and, like SS-N-2, is a fire-and-forget weapon. SS-N-7 appears to exist only in a conventional version.

Charlie was apparently not a very successful submarine, and there is some question as to whether the Soviets consider the short-range fire-and-forget submarine missile a dead end. If that is true, then the 65-centimeter torpedo (see the Antisubmarine Warfare section) may be this missile's true successor, in effect functioning as an underwater cruise missile. Alternatively, the new 65-centimeter tube may provide sufficient volume for a new antiship cruise missile.

As evaluated about 1971, SS-N-7 was credited with a maximum range of 30 nm and a minimum range of 4–5 nm; probable operational range was given as 25 nm. The missile cruised at an altitude of about 300 ft and made a low-angle dive into the target.

From a Western point of view, SS-N-7 was particularly frightening when it appeared in 1968 because, unlike previous longer-range Soviet antiship missiles, it would provide very little warning. It would pop out of the water only about two or three minutes before hitting a ship. Even though it would fly high enough to be detected, such detection might not occur early enough for defenses to be activated. SS-N-7 thus inspired a variety of countermeasures, including the British Sea Wolf missile, the U.S. New Threat Upgrade (IADT), and the U.S. decision to provide the *Perry*-class frigate with a highly automated antiaircraft fire-control system, in principle capable of initiating fire against a pop-up missile. All of these measures were partly inspired by the threat of the Styx missile, which had just demonstrated its efficacy against the Israeli *Eilat*, but it seems more likely that SS-N-7, which could appear anywhere on the world ocean, was the terrifying new threat against which NTU was designed.

The missile itself is essentially a longer-range equivalent of Styx (SS-N-2) and physically may be somewhat similar to some of the Chinese Styx derivatives. SS-N-7 in turn gave way to the dual-purpose (surface- and submarine-launched) SS-N-9. When the Charlie-class submarine first appeared, it was evaluated as firing, not a winged cruise weapon, but rather an antiship equivalent of the U.S. SUBROC ASW missile—which would have been an even more difficult target for antiaircraft defenses.

There appears to be no antiship version of the SS-N-21 torpedo-tube cruise missile (see the Strategic Strike Systems section), presumably because the Soviets demand a combination of high speed and large warhead, to overcome target defenses and to damage large warships.

◆ SS-N-9 Siren

> **Dimensions:** length 8.84 m (348 in)   **Weight:** 6500 lbs (2950 kg)
> **Warhead:** 1100-lbs HE   **Propulsion:** liquid-fuel rocket
> **Speed:** Mach 0.8   **Range:** 58–65 nm

SS-N-9 launch tubes on board a Nanuchka-class missile corvette. The big radome, Band Stand, probably contains a surface-search radar and a data-link receiver that allows the ship to attack targets beyond her horizon. The gun aft is a twin 57 mm controlled by a Muff Cob director, and the back-to-back surface-search radar in front of Band Stand is Peel Pair. Forward of it is the Pop Group director of the SA-N-4 missile launcher that is located forward of the superstructure. (U.S. Navy)

Carried on board Nanuchka-class missile boats and Charlie-II-class nuclear attack submarines, SS-N-9 is a longer-range equivalent of SS-N-2. Siren may have originated in a 1961 project for a 50–70-km patrol-boat missile. Effective targeting at the ranges possible with this missile requires third-party assistance, presumably directly to the firing platform. The missile system is associated with the Band Stand radar (actually, with

Nanuchkas firing SS-N-9 missiles.

the radome; it is not certain that the same equipment always occupies it). The radome may contain a radar receiver for down-linked third-party data.

This weapon has not been exported; Nanuchkas produced for Soviet client states are armed instead with SS-N-2C. That circumstance may reflect the security of the down-link or of the inertial guidance required for long-range flight before the active seeker is switched on.

There may be a nuclear version (200 kT), as at extreme range the missile is far enough away not to damage the firing platform.

SS-N-22 is the successor weapon.

◆ SS-N-12 Sandbox

> **Dimensions:** ca. 90 cm × 11.7 m with span 260 cm (35.4 × 461 × 102 in)
> **Weight:** about 11,000 lbs   **Warhead:** 2200-lb HE or nuclear
> **Propulsion:** liquid-fuel rocket
> **Speed:** Mach 2.5 (1850 mph)   **Range:** 300 nm

SS-N-12 missile launchers on board the cruiser *Slava*, 1984. Their tracker/data-link radar, Front Door/Front Piece, is on the forward side of the foremast, below the big air-search radar. Below it is a Kite Screech fire-control radar for the twin 130-mm gun forward. The air-search radar on the foremast is Top Steer; the larger back-to-back radar further aft is Top Pair. The large fire-control radar aft is Top Dome. The small guns abaft the 130-mm turret are 30-mm Gatlings, controlled by Bass Tilt directors. (HMS *Excellent*)

Sandbox is a faster successor to SS-N-3; like the earlier missile, SS-N-12 presumably exists in both nuclear and conventional versions. Like SS-N-3, SS-N-12 requires mid-course correction.

These weapons are carried on board Echo-II-class submarines and on board *Kiev*- and *Slava*-class cruisers.

◆ SS-N-19 Shipwreck

> **Weight:** About 10,000 lbs
> **Propulsion:** liquid rocket   **Range:** 300 nm

To date, Shipwreck is the ultimate development of the SS-N-3 concept. SS-N-19 is so fast that it needs no mid-course guidance.

An Oscar-class missile submarine can, therefore, fire the missile submerged, on the basis of information provided by a radar satellite via the Punch Bowl down-link antenna. This weapon is also carried by *Kirov*-class missile cruisers.

◆ SS-N-22 Sunburn

> **Dimensions:** length about 30 ft   **Warhead:** 1000-lb HE
> **Propulsion:** liquid rocket   **Speed:** Mach 2.5
> **Range:** 55–68 nm

SS-N-22 missiles in their launch tubes on board the missile destroyer *Otchayannyy*. The Band Stand radome is like that on board a Nanuchka-class corvette. Above the radome is a Kite Screech director, controlling the twin 130-mm gun forward; note the hole in the dish for a television camera. The enclosed radome to one side of the foremast is Front Dome, to control the SA-N-7 antiaircraft missile (whose single-arm launcher is visible forward of the bridge), and the big air-search radar is Top Steer. The three surface-search radars are Palm Fronds. Note the IFF array atop the three-dimensional radar. (U.S. Navy)

SS-N-22 is the larger, faster, and lower-flying successor to SS-N-9 and thus the ultimate current expression of the Styx concept. Sunburn is similar in concept but should be more difficult to counter, although, given its sheer size, SS-N-22 probably cannot fly as low as Western sea-skimmers. At present *Sovremmenny*-class missile destroyer and Tarantul-III-class missile boats are the only platforms, although it is possible that this missile will form the battery of a Charlie successor.

◆ SS-NX-?

Late in 1988 a new East German fast attack craft, about 52 meters long, tentatively code-named BAL-COM-10, was observed on her sea trials. She carried eight missile canisters, similar in size to those used for Western Harpoon or Exocet (MM 40) missiles. Presumably each canister holds a new Soviet antiship missile. The new weapon would seem to be a considerable departure from previous Soviet practice, seeming unable to carry anything remotely like the current standard 500- or 1000-kg warhead. On the other hand, a boat carrying eight such missiles can present a Western antimissile defense system with a degree of saturation that, in the past, would have required either several boats firing together or else a large surface combatant like a *Slava*.

There are several possible explanations for this development. One is that, in the Baltic, the Soviets will generally face relatively small Western warships and, therefore, will not really need the massive warheads adopted in the past to attack carriers and other major warships. Another is that the Soviets realize that they cannot achieve much more in the way of penetrating terminal defenses unless they adopt smaller and more numerous weapons. For example, it is unlikely that a big supersonic missile like SS-N-22 can really sea-skim.

Much depends on the details of the new weapon. If it is a rocket, like Exocet, then it can saturate defenses by sea-skimming and streaming in, but it cannot execute elaborate way-point maneuvers. If the weapon uses a small turbojet, like Harpoon, it can sea-skim and then attack from many directions by using way points.

Soviet willingness to adopt smaller warheads might also point to a decision to buy smaller air-launched antiship weapons (e.g., which might be carried internally) and perhaps to adopt a 53-cm torpedo tube–launched antiship weapon (the salvo effect could be achieved by firing such weapons from several tubes, in rapid succession.

No NATO reporting number has been published. However, up to now the highest published number has been SS-N-24, so the new weapon is probably SS-NX-25.

UNITED KINGDOM

◆ Exocet (GWS.50)

See above under France.

◆ Sea Eagle

See Air-Launched Missiles above.

◆ Sea Skua

See Air-Launched Missiles above.

◆ USGW

Under-Sea Guided Weapon is a submarine-launched antiship missile. It was conceived as a Martel derivative (see air-launched missiles) with a new antiship warhead (which was used in Sea Eagle). The Royal Navy bought the U.S. Sub-Harpoon instead. USGW was announced in 1973.

UNITED STATES

◆ Harpoon (AGM-84/RGM-84/UGM-84) and SLAM (AGM-84E)

> **Dimensions:** 13.5 × 182.2 in (151.5 in long for air launch) (SLAM is 177 in long)
> **Weight:** 1145 lbs (air launch), 1439 lbs (ASROC launcher), 1500 lbs (SAM launcher), 1503 lbs (capsule/canister launcher), 1385 lbs (SLAM version)
> **Warhead:** 488.5-lbs HE (blast; semi-armor piercing)
> **Propulsion:** J402-CA-400 Turbojet (cruise) (600-lb thrust) with solid-fuel booster (12,000-lb thrust for 2.9 seconds) for ship or submarine launch   **Fuel:** 100 lbs   **Speed:** Mach 0.85
> **Range:** 75–80 nm surface-launched, 120 nm air-launched

Harpoon is probably the most widely-deployed of all modern Western antiship missiles; it is used by 19 navies (including 9 NATO navies). Originally developed for air-to-surface use, Harpoon also exists in surface- and submarine-launched versions,

Harpoon is fired from the ASROC launcher of USS *Knox* (FF-1052). (U.S. Navy)

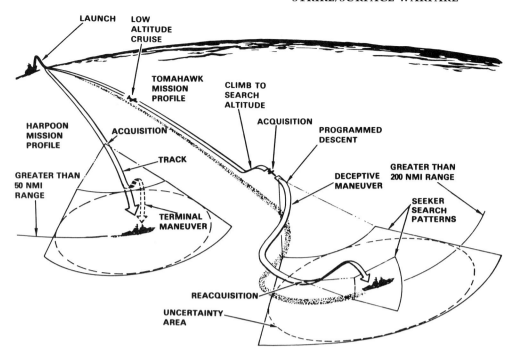

Typical mission profiles for Harpoon (left) and TASM (Tomahawk Antiship Missile). (McDonnell-Douglas)

the latter employing a buoyant capsule for launch. The object was to develop a weapon that could be carried on board virtually all naval platforms. That requirement in turn limited Harpoon's dimensions to approximately those of the Standard Missile (Surface-to-Air) so that Harpoon could be fired from the usual surface-ship launchers. Even so, most Harpoons on board surface ships are carried in canisters that, incidentally, can only be replaced in harbor.

Harpoon was originally a P-3 weapon. It is also carried by standard U.S. and foreign naval attack aircraft, and the first launch from an F/A-18 was in the summer of 1986. The U.S. Air Force currently carries Harpoon antiship missiles on board B-52G bombers (12 internal, up to 8 external) to support its maritime warfare Memorandum of Understanding with the navy; the first operational air force launch was in the Caribbean, 20 April 1986.

McDonnell Douglas, the manufacturer, has proposed Harpoon as a coast-defense weapon, analogous to an existing form of Exocet.

Harpoon first saw combat on 24–25 March 1986, when A-6Es used the missile to sink two Libyan ships. Harpoon was also successfully used during the Persian Gulf engagement in April 1988.

Harpoon was conceived in 1965 by the Naval Air Systems Command as a longer-range (25 nm) follow-on to Bullpup, to be carried by ASW aircraft attacking surfaced submarines (i.e., a harpoon to kill whales). That mission was later expanded to include antiship attack (e.g., attacks against Soviet missile-bear-

ing fast patrol boats), and the missile was being considered for ship mounting even before the *Eilat* incident of 1967 publicized the potential of antiship missiles. The project began formally in 1968, an RFP being released in 1970. McDonnell Douglas, whose in-house studies of long-range antiship missiles began about when NAVAIR became interested, was chosen as prime contractor in June 1971, flying the first missile on 17 October 1972. The requirement for long (over 50 nm) range was imposed after McDonnell Douglas was chosen, a small turbojet being substituted for the rocket envisaged in early studies. Production began in 1975, and Harpoon entered service in 1977. Overall, demonstrated flight reliability has been about 93 percent in 374 launches (100 percent since 1982).

All versions home using a Texas Instruments active Ku-band frequency-agile radar (fire-and-forget). A strapdown-inertial system is used to maintain course until the missile reaches a preset position where radar homing is turned on. Alternatively, the missile can be fired as a bearing rider, with the radar on throughout flight, to attack a target whose range is not known. Warning of the approach of the relatively small missile should be primarily by detecting its radar emission; the better the initial target position, the shorter the time the radar seeker need be switched on. Early versions flew directly toward the intended target, but later types (Blocks IB and IC) may incorporate waypoints, the missile flying an indirect course and perhaps switching the radar on intermittently. It is also possible to select either a nearly-horizontal approach to the target or a terminal pop-up (steep climb and then dive) that may frustrate many types of terminal defense.

As originally designed, the missile (when launched by a ship or submarine) was boosted ballistically to 1300 ft before diving into its cruise path. That profile would clear nearby ships, but it would also expose the missile to radar detection. In particular, submarine operators feared that the column of smoke and water coming out of the sea would disclose their position, and some versions apparently provide much less of a tell-tale signature.

The warhead is designed to survive penetration of a submarine's pressure hull or of a surface ship's hull. Reportedly, one hit should suffice to kill anything the size of a Nanuchka or smaller; two should disable a frigate (e.g., a Krivak), and four, a missile cruiser; five should disable a *Kiev*. That estimation of effectiveness does not take missile reliability and terminal defenses into account. Note that most warships carry eight Harpoons in two clusters of four canisters each.

Block IB incorporated an advanced guidance package, for the Royal Navy, which wanted a sea-skimming terminal phase for

Air-launched Harpoon, as carried by a P-3. (McDonnell-Douglas)

submarine-launched Harpoons. Deliveries to the U.S. Navy began in June 1982.

Block IC shows increased range and selectable terminal trajectory. It can also fly several doglegs to the target (way-pointing), concealing the position of the firing ship. A ship equipped with a Harpoon fire-control computer (SWG-1) can use way-pointing to arrange for several Harpoons to arrive simultaneously from different directions. IC is the current (1988) production version. Earlier versions can be upgraded to IC standard at a unit cost of about $20,000. The Royal Navy is having this work done in the UK.

McDonnell-Douglas expects to produce a Block II for the 1990s, with a range of 100+ nm, with variable mission profiles, and with improved discrimination between targets and nontargets. Range can be improved by about 15 percent by replacing the current JP-5 fuel with JP-10, and a greater improvement is possible if the fuel tank section of the basic airframe is lengthened. There is also continued interest in better target discrimination; for example, in future it may be possible to set the radar to seek out smaller high-priority targets instead of larger low-priority ones. McDonnell-Douglas has reportedly proposed modifying the overall system to feed target-signature data to the weapon before launch.

As of the fall of 1988, Block II was described as a combination of Block IC features with a new Dash-4 seeker.

The U.S. Navy and McDonnell-Douglas are currently studying an improved Harpoon, incorporating a re-attack mode; the missile tries to reacquire a target if missed on the first attempt. Reportedly, McDonnell-Douglas is also working on a supersonic Harpoon successor with twice the range of the current missile.

The navy requested, but failed to obtain, FY87 funds to start work on an extended-range Harpoon with increased maneuvering capacity. The missile would have been lengthened, the fuselage plug adding a fuel tank to double the range; minor increases in skin friction would have been more than made up for by the additional fuel.

The standard stand-alone shipboard launcher is a quartet of Mk-141 canisters, ships typically carrying two sets (although the battleships have four). The canisters cannot be reloaded at sea, and typically they are replaced rather than reloaded in port. There is no current vertically launched version, although some years ago effort in that direction was reported; the new cruisers and destroyers equipped with vertical launching systems carry canisters. As of late 1988, an armored canister was being developed. Harpoon can also be fired from the standard Mk-11/13 and Mk-26 Tartar/Standard launcher and from the standard ASROC "pepperbox," as well as from standard submarine torpedo tubes (60 percent of the U.S. attack submarine fleet was equipped to fire Harpoon as of the end of 1988). Some export customers use truck-mounted Harpoon as a coast-defense weapon.

The air force has requested a longer-range version for B-52s, with a range of over 120 nm. McDonnell Douglas has test-flown a missile with a 13-inch plug (extra fuel tankage) that reportedly almost doubled the range.

The ship-launched version was bought for the Australian, British, Danish, Dutch, German, Greek, Iranian, Israeli, Japanese, Korean, Norwegian, Pakistani, Portuguese, Saudi, Singaporean, Spanish, Thai, Turkish, and Venezuelan Navies (a Yugoslav request was turned down in 1984). The submarine-launched version is in service in the Australian, British, Dutch, Israeli, Japanese, and Pakistani Navies. Indonesia, as well as many of the navies listed above, operates the air-launched version. Note that, although Iran ordered 222 air-launched Harpoons, only a very few had been delivered at the time the United States imposed an arms embargo, and 85 of these weapons were bought in FY85 for the Air Force B-52G program, 30 aircraft being modified.

Current (1988) inventory goal is 4023, with production scheduled to continue through 1992. The 4000th missile was delivered on 17 December 1986, at which time 4800 had been ordered. The 5000th missile was delivered on 2 December 1988,

by which time more than 5400 had been ordered. As of 1988, 40 percent of production was for foreign sales. Recent U.S. procurement: FY83, 221; FY84, 315; FY85, 354; FY86, 395; FY87, 96; FY88, 124; FY89, 138. Missiles procured from FY88 onward will have an improved ("Dash-4") seeker and guidance package.

SLAM (AGM-84E) is to be a modified Harpoon (120-nm range) for long-range precision ground attack, in effect a replacement for the long-dead Condor. SLAM incorporates a Maverick IIR seeker with a Walleye II data link and a GPS satellite-navigation receiver for mid-course guidance. Condor's problem was that the jam-resistant data link was extremely complex and expensive. Presumably SLAM will fly almost all the way on inertial/GPS instructions, turning on its data link only at the last possible moment, and so avoiding jamming or interception. Although employing off-the-shelf components, SLAM is likely to be quite expensive, and it is being bought only as an interim weapon until the new ASWS (see Air-Launched Missiles above) appears. McDonnell Douglas was awarded a contract for 14 SLAM on 1 February 1988. As of 1988, procurement of only 290 missiles was planned. The first production SLAM was delivered on 3 November 1988.

SLAM land-attack missile. (McDonnell-Douglas)

SLAM under the wing of an A-6. Note the nose window for its electro-optical sensor. (McDonnell-Douglas)

SLAM was the outgrowth of a long series of IIR Harpoon experiments. In 1981 it was reported that versions of the missile had been flown carrying both the electro-optical seeker originally developed for Condor and two types of IIR seeker built by Ford Aerospace. One of the latter used a data link, the operator on the ship designating the target; the other had on-board processing. SLAM could, therefore, be delivered in fire-and-forget fashion by an A-6. In one test, the missile successfully identified its target in a harbor, commanded a 360-degree turn, and flew over the ship's funnel. Reportedly, this type of seeker could even distinguish between one ship and others, of a different type, nearby.

In the triservice Stand-Off Weapon Master Plan (1988), SLAM was selected over the air force's AGM-130.

The U.S. budget request, as of January 1989, was for 119 missiles in FY89, 190 in FY90, and 184 in FY91.

◆ Harpoon II

Reportedly, Martin-Marietta has proposed a surface-to-surface version of its Supersonic Low-Altitude Target (SLAT: BQM-127A) as a follow-on to Harpoon, with the unofficial name Harpoon II. The missile is powered by an integral rocket-ramjet; its design is based on the ASALM (Advanced Strategic Air-Launched Missile) flight-tested in 1979. As currently (1987) conceived, this missile would be dropped by an airplane at an altitude of about a thousand feet, 55 nm from the target. Descending to about 30 ft in the first 10 nm, the missile would cruise at that altitude for 45 nm at Mach 2.5, popping up over the target. The full-scale engineering-development program will also seek a capability for Mach 3 flight at altitudes over 30,000 ft. Flight tests began in the latter half of 1987.

The unique Martin-developed engine combines a solid booster with a liquid-fuel ramjet. The solid booster case becomes the combustion chamber of the ramjet once the solid fuel has been consumed; the booster accelerates the missile to Mach 2.1 in about six seconds, after which the ramjet accelerates the missile to Mach 2.5.

The SLAT full-scale engineering-development contract was awarded in September 1984; it covered 15 flight-test missiles, with navy options for 330 more. The navy has indicated a requirement for a total of 1000 operational missiles. SLAT presumably simulates the Soviet SS-N-22 missile and, therefore, would seem a natural starting point for a future U.S. supersonic antiship weapon. SLAT dimensions are 21.2 × 218.2 inches (launch weight 2445 lbs).

SLAT carried by an F-4. (Martin-Marietta)

SLAT in action. (Martin-Marietta)

♦ **Hellfire (RBS 17; AGM-114A)**

     Dimensions: 7 × 64 in; span 14.25 in
     Weight: 108.5 lbs (compared to 99.6 lbs antitank)
     Warhead: approx 20 lb   **Propulsion:** solid-fuel rocket
     Speed: Mach 1+   **Range:** 3+ nm

This U.S. Army weapon, built by Rockwell, has been adapted for coast defense by the Swedish Navy. The missile is laser-guided (semiactive homing). As of 1988, 25 battalions were scheduled for formation, to replace 32 battalions firing French SS-11 wire-guided missiles (1989–1995). The first 700 missiles were ordered in June 1987. The air-launched version, which has two shaped-charge warheads in tandem (for follow-through attack against, e.g., reactive armor) is the primary armament of army AH-64 attack helicopters and of Marine Corps AH-1W and AH-1J attack helicopters. The Swedish version has an antiship warhead (Bofors blast-fragmentation, downward-pointing) and a modified autopilot. It is fired from a portable launcher.

The missile is designed as a combination of four modules: seeker, warhead, autopilot, and motor. The standard army version uses a semiactive laser seeker, an analog autopilot, a

Hellfire (RBS 17) in its coast-defense version. The missile weighs 48 kg (with its container, 71 kg). (Bofors)

shaped-charge warhead, and a minimum-smoke motor. Rockwell offers some other options: imaging-infrared, RF/IR, or millimeter-wave seekers; a digital autopilot; a multipurpose warhead; and an extended-range (pulsed) motor.

The Swedish designation is RBS 17.

Note that Hellfire is currently carried by U.S. Marine Corps helicopters and was tested in 1987 as a possible SEAL-boat weapon. The missile entered U.S. Army service in January 1985.

Flight tests of rounds with digital auto-pilots began in early 1988. Missiles so fitted can use more maneuvering power, can dive more steeply, and can be launched from high-speed fixed-wing aircraft. Ford Aerospace and Texas Instruments are working on competitive designs for a joint-services IIR seeker that will give Hellfire a fire-and-forget capability. A version with a Marconi millimeter-wave radar has been proposed as a helicopter and fixed-wing aircraft fire-and-forget ground-attack missile.

♦ **Crossbow**

LTV's Crossbow is a stabilized pedestal-mounted stand-alone weapons platform suitable for fast attack craft. Crossbow is included in this section because the weapon's most likely application is to small antiship missiles carried on board craft in the same class as the current 65-foot Patrol Boat Mks 3 and 4. The platform has also been demonstrated on board trucks and on board wheeled and tracked personnel carriers. Crossbow carries a television camera and can accommodate a FLIR and a laser designator or range-finder. The system is designed for automatic target acquisition and tracking while the off-mount operator identifies the target, selects his weapons, and (according to LTV) optimizes his firing. The latter phrasing suggests some form of computer threat evaluation and even weapon assignment. The system automatically leads the target.

Elevation limits are +75/−10 degrees, and total weight, including up to 1500 lbs of weapons and sensors, is less than 3000 lbs. LTV lists a wide variety of missiles and guns suitable for the Crossbow pedestal, including Hellfire, the British Starstreak, TOW, the French Mistral, the U.S. Stinger, the Swedish RBS 70, a variety of unguided rockets, 0.30- and 0.50-caliber machine guns, the Oerlikon KAA 20-mm cannon, the Mauser 25-mm cannon, and the Bushmaster (Mk-38) cannon. There is an associated fire-control console incorporating a gripstick.

Acquisition and tracking tests were conducted on board the surface-effect landing craft LACV-30 at Patuxent River, as part of a PMS 300 Foreign Weapons Evaluation effort (the weapon in question was the Bofors-modified version of the Rockwell Hellfire, its foreign feature providing the occasion for evaluation). The tests are a collaborative NAVAIR/NAVSEA effort, and NAVSEA is paying for further evaluation for a near-term application to Special Warfare (i.e., to craft like the 65-footer). The Crossbow on LACV-30 managed to track surface and air targets, such as Cobra helicopters and Septar fast surface targets, in a simulated firing mode. The laser could not be demonstrated in the LACV-30 tests because of range safety limitations. The next test stage was a series of three unguided missile firings at Huntsville, Alabama, to test the ability of the launcher to overcome transient firing motions, so that its laser designator can be held on the target. Early in April 1989, Crossbow was to be tested at Yuma, firing guided weapons from a Hummer truck. A marinized mount is to be tested on board the SES-200 surface-effect craft late in September 1989.

At the U.S. Navy League show in March 1989, LTV displayed a model of Crossbow carrying a pair of Hellfires on one side, a 2.75-inch rocket pod on the other, and a 0.50-caliber machine gun.

◆ **Sea Ray**

> **Dimensions:** 8 × 118 in   **Weight:** 400 lbs
> **Warhead:** 150-lb fragmentation
> **Propulsion:** Mk 78 solid-fuel rocket motor
> **Speed:** subsonic   **Range:** ca 7 km (7700 yds)

Texas Instruments announced in 1985 that it was developing this missile for an unnamed foreign customer, most likely South Korea. The missile can be fired from shipboard, from a helicopter, or from an airplane. Sea Ray uses many existing components: the Paveway III laser and guidance unit and the Shrike Mk 78 motor. The missile flies a ballistic path until the laser designator is switched on, about 10 sec before expected impact. Texas Instruments stated that during sea trials on board the customer's ships, a round hit the target at 7-km range within 9 in of the nominal aim point.

Development began in 1981, and Sea Ray may have entered service in 1987.

◆ **Standard Missile**

See Antiaircraft Warfare section.

◆ **Tomahawk (BGM-109)**

See the Strategic Warfare section.

UNGUIDED BOMBS AND AIR-LAUNCHED ROCKETS

FRANCE

◆ **Bombs**

Super-Étendards carry 250- or 400-kg (551- or 882-lb) free-fall or retarded bombs. Typical dimensions are 273 × 2253 mm (10.75 × 88.7 in) or 324 × 2121 mm (12.75 × 83.5 in) for 250 kg, and 403 × 2195 mm (15.9 × 86.4 in) for 400 kg.

◆ **Dispenser**

The Super-Étendard can carry an Alkan 530 bomblet dispenser carrying two blocks, each with twenty 74-mm (2.9-in) Thomson-Brandt grenades or cartridges in tubes facing sideways. Each cartridge is 74 × 214 mm (2.9 × 8.4 in) and weighs 2 kg (4.4 lbs); each grenade is 70 × 190 mm (2.76 × 7.5 in) and weighs 1.6 kg (3.5 lbs). Cartridges carry chaff and IR flares. Grenades are parachute-retarded antiarmor bomblets, which can penetrate 200 mm of armor.

◆ **Nuclear Weapons**

The standard bomb carried by the Super-Étendard is the AN.52; it is now being retired in favor of the ASMP stand-off missile. Yield is probably about 15 kT, and the bomb weighs about 1300 lbs.

◆ **Rockets**

Super-Étendards carry Matra 155 pods (eighteen 68-mm [2.68-in] rockets). This pod can also be carried by British Sea Harriers.

An Étendard attack fighter displays the standard French guided and unguided weapons, including the standard rocket pods and AS 30 missiles and DEFA 552A guns. (ECP Armées)

There are two types: first-generation rockets with unitary warheads (shaped-charge, blast-fragmentation, or chaff); and second generation multidart warheads (antiarmor or illumination). Typical dimensions are 68 × 910 mm (2.68 × 35.8 in), 5 or 6.2 kg (11 or 13.7 lbs) for first generation; 68 × 1380 mm (2.68 × 54.3 in), 8.3 kg (18.3 lbs) for second generation. Range is 1000–4000 m (1095–4375 yds).

USSR

◆ **Bombs**

The Yak-38 Forger VTOL fighter can carry 250- and 500-kg (551- and 1102-lb) free-fall bombs of various types.

◆ **Rockets**

The Yak-38 Forger VTOL fighter can carry pods: UB 16-57 and UB 32-57 with, respectively, 16 and 32 55-mm S-5 series folding-fin rockets. The "57" refers to tube diameter. There are nine warheads, including HEAT, high explosive, fragmentation, and chaff. Typical burnout speed is 620 m/sec (2034 ft/sec).

UNITED KINGDOM

◆ **Bombs**

The standard Sea Harrier load is three British Mk 13/18 or U.S. Mk-83 1000-lb bombs. During the Falklands War, Sea Harriers also delivered U.S.-supplied Paveway laser-guided bombs, reportedly using hand-held laser target-designators. Note that Mk 13/18 is considerably fatter than the U.S. low-drag bombs but has a fairing for streamlining. Mk 13/18 can be fitted with a parachute retarder.

◆ **Carrier Bomb Light Stores**

Sea Harriers carry BL 755 bomblet dispensers (419 × 2451 mm [16.5 × 96.5 in], 277 kg [611 lbs] loaded), which carry 21 shaped-charge/fragmentation bomblets in each of seven compartments.

◆ **Rockets**

The standard Royal Navy rocket pod carries nineteen 2-inch rockets; Sea Harriers also carry the French Matra 155 pod and the U.S. LAU-69/A (2.75-in FFAR).

◆ **Nuclear Weapons**

For some years the British government has stated that Sea Harriers are provided with tactical nuclear weapons for delivery from the three light carriers. No other details have been given, and it is not clear whether these weapons are similar to tactical

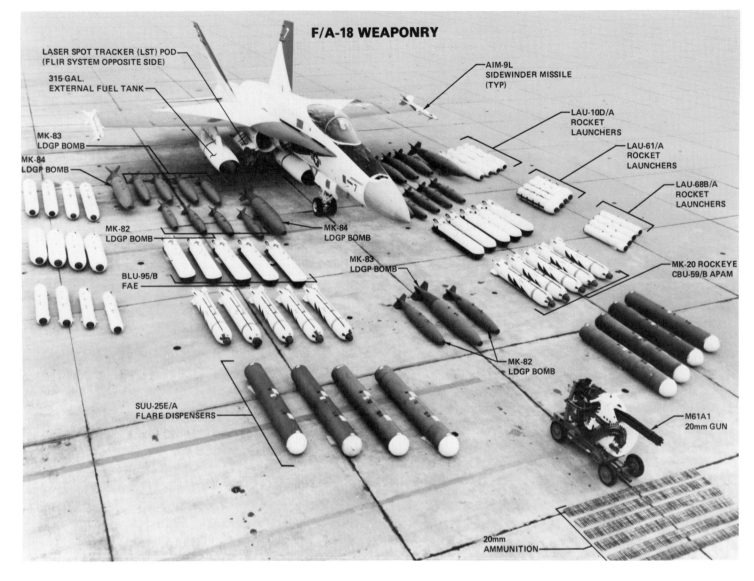

F/A-18 WEAPONRY

LASER SPOT TRACKER (LST) POD
(FLIR SYSTEM OPPOSITE SIDE)

315 GAL.
EXTERNAL FUEL TANK

MK-83
LDGP BOMB

MK-84
LDGP BOMB

MK-82
LDGP BOMB

BLU-95/B
FAE

SUU-25E/A
FLARE DISPENSERS

MK-84
LDGP BOMB

MK-83
LDGP BOMB

MK-82
LDGP BOMB

AIM-9L
SIDEWINDER MISSILE
(TYP)

LAU-10D/A
ROCKET
LAUNCHERS

LAU-61/A
ROCKET
LAUNCHERS

LAU-68B/A
ROCKET
LAUNCHERS

MK-20 ROCKEYE
CBU-59/B APAM

M61A1
20mm GUN

20mm
AMMUNITION

An F/A-18 can carry all the standard U.S. unguided weapons, which are shown here. LDGPs are low-drag (i.e., streamlined or "slick") general-purpose bombs; FAE is fuel-air explosive. (McDonnell-Douglas)

bombs carried by RAF Tornadoes or are similar to the nuclear depth bombs reportedly carried by British naval helicopters. No designations have been reported. However, in 1987 there was an official reference to WE 177 tactical nuclear weapons in the context of a navy contract. These weapons are carried by RAF Tornadoes.

UNITED STATES

◆ Bigeye

Bigeye is a new binary chemical bomb, developed about 1985 but not yet deployed. The binary weapon is safer to handle than unitary munitions since its components are not lethal until they mix in the air. They mix only after release, to produce VX nerve gas, which the bomb sprays from its nose. Critics of this program have suggested that the mixing process is so lengthy that the bomb must be released either at high altitude or in a toss maneuver; both releases increase the vulnerability of the launching aircraft. In 1986 Congress repealed a 16-year moratorium on U.S. production of chemical weapons, but only for army 155-mm shells and not for Bigeye.

In 1986 the Grumman A-6 was validated for Bigeye delivery.

◆ Fuel-Air Explosives

The standard current weapons are BLU-95(XCL-1)/B and BLU-96(XCL-1)/B, originally known as FAE I and II (500 and 2000 lbs). U.S. work on fuel-air explosives dates at least from 1966.

They dispense a fuel vapor that mixes with the air over the target; once the critical level of fuel concentration has been reached, detonators are dispersed into the cloud and then fired. The result is a shock wave reminiscent of (though much less powerful than) that of a small nuclear bomb. Weight for weight, these explosives have about 2.7 to 5 times the effect of TNT, partly because they need not carry their own oxidizers. The issue has always been whether prevailing weather conditions would make it difficult to disperse the explosives properly. Fuel-air explosives have also been suggested as a means of clearing mine fields.

Fuel-air weapons, generally CBU-55/B cluster bombs, were used in Vietnam from October 1970 onward.

◆ Low-Drag Bombs/Snakeye/Ballute

The Mk-80 series are the primary U.S. Navy bombs, developed in the late 1940s at the suggestion of Douglas Aircraft. All have the same aerodynamic shape (aspect ratio 8.5), the Mark number indicating the weight: Mk 81, 250 lbs (9 × 76.1 in); Mk 82, 500 lbs (10.8 × 90.9 in); Mk 83, 1000 lbs (14 × 110.9 in); and Mk 84, 2000 lbs (18 × 154 in). Ninety percent of navy bombs dropped in Vietnam were Mk 82s, with Mk 83s accounting for most of the rest.

The two main developments have been retarders and anti-cook-off casings. Retarders make low-level delivery practical (so the bombs will not explode directly under the airplane). The major current retarder is a set of four pop-out fins (Snakeye); but they are not always reliable, and accidents have occurred. Goodyear developed an alternative, the inflatable Ballute. Snakeyes may be designated with an R suffix, as in Mk 82R.

The effect of a fuel-air explosion, shown in a sequence of 1972 photographs of a simulated near-miss on the former destroyer escort *McNulty*. Note the dispersion of the cloud before the detonators are fired into it. The second and third photos show how the cloud envelops the ship and then goes off (note the shock wave in the water). (U.S. Navy)

An AV-8B Harrier II drops Snakeye (Mk 82) retarded bombs; note the fins opening. (McDonnell-Douglas)

general belief that guided bombs had made unguided weapons obsolete. However, a new program, for the advanced bomb family (ABF), began in FY87. These weapons are described as suitable for the Advanced Tactical Aircraft: presumably these bombs are stealthy, so that they can be carried externally without compromising the stealth of the aircraft. The bomb's stealth is more likely to be achieved by material than by shape.

◆ Napalm

The current standard weapon is BLU-27 (750 lbs, filled with 100 gallons of Napalm-B).

◆ Nuclear Bombs

The current standard strike bomb is B61. However, there is also a version of the B57 nuclear depth bomb rated as a lay-down weapon. B57 is now quite old, and it is to be replaced by a dual-purpose nuclear depth bomb/nuclear strike bomb (NDB/NSB), for which one candidate is a modified B61. The advantage of the dual-purpose weapon is that it limits the carrier magazine space that must be devoted to nuclear weapons. B61 is the current standard air force/navy bomb, development of which began in 1963. B61 was fielded in 1967. The current version, Mod 5, entered service in 1977. Dimensions are typically 13.4 in × 10 ft 11 in. Reported yields vary with the version, one unofficial claim being 10–100 kT for Mod 0/2, 300 kT for Mods 3 to 5, and 900 kT for Mod 1. There is also an earlier high-yield nuclear bomb, B43 (18 in × 13 ft 8.5 in, 2060 lbs).

◆ Rockets

The two primary U.S. air-launched rockets are the 2.75-inch folding-fin aircraft rocket (FFAR) and the 5-inch folding-fin Zuni. Both are normally carried in pods.

FFAR ("Mighty Mouse") was originally conceived as an air-to-air weapon. It is carried in expendable 7-rocket (Aero 6, then LAU-32) or 19-rocket (Aero 7, LAU-3 and LAU-69) launchers. The rocket is 47.85 in long and weighs about 18 lbs; its 800- to 900-lb thrust motor accelerates the rocket to 2300 ft/sec (1570 mph). Warhead options are blast (HBX or Composition B) and armor-piercing (HEAT). FFAR is sometimes carried by attack helicopters, and it was used against Iranian attack boats in the Persian Gulf.

Zuni replaces the earlier fixed-fin high-velocity aircraft rocket (HVAR), which may survive in some navies. It is 110 in long, weighs 107 lbs, and reaches 2370 ft/sec, about 1400 kts. It is typically carried in a four-rocket LAU-10 pod and has either a general-purpose or a shaped-charge warhead. During the Vietnam War, ship-launched Zunis were used to disperse chaff (see the Antiaircraft Warfare section).

◆ Rockeye/Sadeye/Gladeye/Gator

Rockeye is an unguided bomblet-dispenser. Unlike most such dispensers, Rockeye is dropped by the airplane carrying it, so that the airplane need not fly directly over its target. This weapon was originally developed by China Lake and was widely used during and after Vietnam. The current Rockeye II carries 247 armor-piercing bomblets in a 13.2 × 92 in (94.5 in, includ-

Anticook-off bomb casings reduce the risk inherent in flight-deck fires. A conventional Mk 82 in a fuel fire will cook off in about four minutes. A coated MK 82 will last nine minutes and will then burn rather than explode, so that it can be tossed off the flight deck.

After Vietnam, an advanced general-purpose bomb (AGPB) program was begun, to produce improved 500-, 1000-, and 2000-lb weapons. The 500-pounder was a blast-fragmentation type for close air support, fuzed for either instantaneous or delayed explosion or for air burst. The medium bomb was designed for moderate penetration (e.g., against buried ammunition). The heavy bomb was a demolition weapon for attacking bridges, roads, and deep tunnels. AGPB never received very much funding, partly because the Mk-80 series had been manufactured in such great numbers during Vietnam, and partly because of a

Rockeye (Cluster Bomb Mk 20 Mod 1). (U.S. Navy)

ing fuze cover) casing (490 lbs total). Four fins pop out of the rear end of the casing (span 17.2 in closed, 34 in open). Minimum release altitude in level flight is 250 ft, or 100 ft in pitchup (toss delivery). The typical bomblet pattern from 500 ft forms a 30,000-square-foot oval. Each bomblet has a short stand-off fuze and a shaped-charge warhead.

The basic Rockeye concept is well known, and many similar weapons are used by other forces. Chile produces its own version (Cardoen Industries).

The other major U.S. cluster bombs developed in parallel with Rockeye were Mk 15 (Sadeye) and Mk 17 (Gladeye); Rockeye is Mk 12, and Rockeye II is Mk 20. Sadeye is fin-retarded and carries 2100 bomblets. Gladeye uses two separate time-delay cartridges in a canister, which is itself carried on a standard strongback slung from a bomb rack. The strongback carries seven Gladeyes, each filled with 330 M40 antipersonnel bombs.

More recent cluster bombs are CBU-30, CBU-52, CBU-58, CBU-59, and CBU-71 (Gator). CBU-30 carries gas bomblets. CBU-59 matches Rockeye II dimensions (carrying seven antipersonnel/antimaterial [APAM] bomblets). CBU-52, -58, and -71 are 16.12 × 87.89 in (including nose fuze cap), consisting of SUU-30 with various loadings. CBU-52 carries 254 BLU-61/B fragmentation bomblets; CBU-58 carries 650 BLU-63/B fragmentation bomblets; CBU-71 carries 670 BLU-86A/B fragmentation bomblets, or Gator antitank or antipersonnel mines.

It was reported in 1988 that 40,000 of the 120,000 Rockeye II in U.S. service are to be modernized. Their filling will be replaced by insensitive explosives, and the bomblet casings will be prefragmented. This program is being conducted by the Tactical Systems Division of ISC Technologies (now Ferranti International Signal).

◆ Weteye

Weteye is the unitary chemical bomb analogous to the Mk 80 series. Weteye is currently considered unacceptable for shipboard use because of the danger of leakage; hence the need for Bigeye (see above). As of early 1985, 888 Weteyes were held in U.S. Navy inventory, for use from shore bases. The U.S. Navy also had Cluster Bomb Mk 23, Padeye, which carried fifteen gas bomblets, but it is not certain whether this weapon was ever produced in numbers.

AIRCRAFT GUNS

FRANCE

◆ DEFA 552A

Caliber: 30 mm/47 Muzzle Velocity: 815 m/sec (2674 ft/sec)
Rate of Fire: 1250 rnds/min Ammunition Supply: 125 rnds/gun
Weight: 81 kg (179 lbs)

This gun arms the Super-Étendard strike fighter (two carried). Rated barrel lifetime is 5000 rounds. DEFA 552A is a revolver cannon descended from the World War II Mauser MG213C (as is the British Aden). The ammunition is the same as that of the Aden 30-mm cannon.

USSR

◆ GSh-23L

Caliber: 23 mm (0.44-lb projectile)
Muzzle Velocity: 690 m/sec (2260 ft/sec)
Rate of Fire: Up to 3000 rnds/min
Ammunition supply: 200 rnds
Weight: approx 72 kg (160 lbs)

The podded cannon of the Forger VTOL carrier fighter is a twin-barrel gun based on the Gast principle (first tried by the Germans during World War I): the two barrels, which are connected by a rocker arm, fire alternately.

UNITED KINGDOM

◆ Aden Mk 5 Cannon

Caliber: 30 mm/36 (projectile approx 1.1 lbs)
Muzzle Velocity: 790 m/sec (2590 ft/sec)
Rate of Fire: 1200 to 1400 rnds/min
Ammunition Supply: 150 rnds/gun Weight: 87 kg (192 lbs)

A Sea Harrier shows its 30-mm Aden gun pods, as well as two Sidewinder air-to-air missiles. (British Aerospace)

Carried by the Sea Harrier fighter, in a detachable two-gun pallet, the Aden is a gas-operated revolver based on German World War II Mausers and is similar to the French DEFA 552A.

RAF Harrier GR.5s are armed with a 25-mm version first tested in the air in October 1985; as of 1986, the Royal Navy reportedly favored Aden 25 for the rebuilt Sea Harrier FRS.2. The argument in favor of Aden 25 was that the existing Aden 30 had reached a limit in rate of fire and muzzle velocity; Aden 25 is credited with 1650–1850 rnds/min and with 1050 m/sec. The new cartridge is longer and has a greater diameter, imposing greater stresses on the breech-cylinder, which is made of stronger material to keep down overall dimensions and weight (the increase is about 5 kg). Given its higher rate of fire, a twin Aden 25 matches the rate of fire of the U.S. GAU-12/A Gatling gun. Total weight, including 200 rounds, is 430 kg.

UNITED STATES

◆ Mk 12

Caliber: 20 mm Muzzle Velocity: 3320 ft/sec
Rate of Fire: 1000–1200 rnds/min
Ammunition Supply: 144 rnds/gun

This Hispano-type weapon arms the U.S.-built F-8E(FN) Crusader interceptor of the French Navy. Unlike more recent U.S. guns, Mk 12 is gas-operated. Performance in combat, in Vietnam, was somewhat disappointing, the gun showing wider dispersion (12 vs 3 mils) than its predecessors and sometimes jamming during dogfights. Some writers claim that the Pontiac M39, the U.S. version of the wartime German revolver gun (see DEFA 552A and the Aden) arms the F-8E(FN). However, M39 was limited to air force fighters, and it seems unlikely that the F-8E(FN) could have been modified so radically as to take it in place of the navy Mk 12.

◆ M61A1

Caliber: 20 mm/62 **Muzzle Velocity:** 3400 ft/sec
Rate of Fire: 4000 or 6000 rnds/min
Ammunition Supply: 570 rnds
Weight: total 841 lbs (gun 252 lbs, feed system 270 lbs, ammunition 319 lbs)

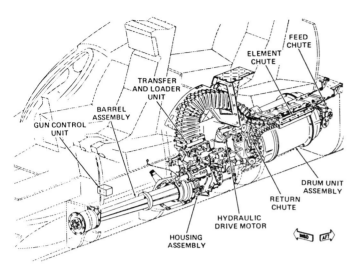

M61A Vulcan as installed in an F-14 fighter. (*Principles of Naval Weapons Systems*, vol. 3, Annapolis: Weapons Systems Engineering Dept., U.S. Naval Academy, 1979)

Data apply to the gun as mounted in the F/A-18.

General Electric's 20-mm Gatling gun is mounted in the A-7E bomber and the F-14 and F/A-18 fighters. This gun is also the basis of the Phalanx close-in defensive weapon (see the Anti-aircraft Warfare section). This gun was originally developed for the air force F-105 fighter, replacing a similar but much less reliable T-171 gun used in the B-58 and F-104. The key improvement was a powered linkless feed. The rounds are stored, nose inward, inside a cylinder on what amounts to a large worm gear. As the gear rotates, they are fed into the feed chute. Current rated barrel life is 20,000 rounds.

In 1986 General Electric announced an improved version of the basic gun, its barrels 48.3 cm (24 calibers) longer, firing improved ammunition with a more compact propellant and a better bullet shape. The muzzle velocity would increase from 1030 to 1200 m/sec. Ammunition would be wrapped in aluminum, and the barrels would be wrapped in composites to reduce total system weight from the current 360 kg to 275 kg.

The 30-mm GAU-8/A, used in both the A-10 ground-attack airplane and in the Goalkeeper (and related) close-in shipboard weapons, is an enlarged version.

With the demise of the F-4 Phantom in U.S. Navy service, all U.S. carrier fighters incorporate built-in cannon. The only major airplane lacking such a gun, the Grumman A-6 Intruder, is apparently not well suited to carrying an external gun pod and, therefore, does not carry it. These pods are, therefore, no longer in U.S. Navy service and are not described here.

◆ GAU-12/U Equalizer

Caliber: 25 mm
Muzzle Velocity: 3500 ft/sec (HEI, TP; 3400 ft/sec AP)
Rate of Fire: 3600 rnds/min **Ammunition Supply:** 300 rnds
Weight: total 900 lbs empty, 1230 lbs loaded (280-lbs gun)

General Eleleric's 25-mm five-barrel Gatling gun was developed specially for the AV-8B Harrier II attack fighter. This gun incorporates GAU-8/A (30-mm) technology. The gun is in the left-hand pod, and the ammunition on the right. The rounds are moved along a fixed track by a continuous-loop driving chain. The gun takes 0.4 seconds to reach its firing rate. Rated barrel life is 15,000 rounds (20,000 rounds MRBF), and dispersion is 1.4 mil.

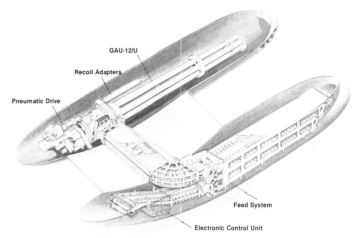

The GAU-12 gun of an AV-8B Harrier II. (General Electric)

◆ M197

Caliber: 20 mm **Muzzle Velocity:** 3400 ft/sec
Rate of Fire: 750 or 1500 rnds/min (selectable)
Ammunition Supply: 750 rnds **Weight:** 145 lbs

The armament of the Marine Corps AH-1T attack helicopter, M197 is a three-barreled version of the M61. M197 is mounted in a turret, which has also been suggested as a patrol-boat weapon, and the Japanese Maritime Self-Defense Force uses this weapon as a pedestal-mounted gun.

◆ GECAL-50

Caliber: 0.50 caliber (12.7 mm) **Muzzle Velocity:** 2900 ft/sec
Rate of Fire: up to 4000 rnds/min (3 barrels); up to 8000 rnds/min (6 barrels). In the V-22, the gun is to fire at the rate of 2000 rnds/min. **Ammunition Supply:** 1200 rnds
Weight: three barrels 66 lbs, six barrels 96 lbs

General Electric's 0.50-caliber Gatling turret-gun for the V-22 Osprey tilt-roter was eliminated from the basic design late in 1984 but was later reinstated as an option.

COAST-DEFENSE GUNS

FINLAND

◆ 130 mm

This weapon is a locally-produced (Tampella) gun, in a turret emplacement, that replaces older 152-mm guns. Range is 25 km. No other details are available.

The Finnish coast artillery forces consist of a mobile battalion in Vasa and two fixed battalions. Weapons include Soviet-supplied T-55 turrets (110-mm guns), as well as older Bofors 152-mm and 254-mm weapons. The entire force has recently been modernized.

GERMANY (WEST)

◆ 150 mm

Denmark, Norway, and Portugal use 150-mm guns, presumably of German manufacture. During World War II the Germans used a 150 mm/40 for coast defense, firing a 40-kg (88-lb) shell at 800 m/sec (2625 ft/sec) to a maximum range of 14,300 m (15,640 yds). This weapon presumably survived postwar.

The Danish weapons are 15-cm SKC/28 guns from the battleship *Gneisenau*, in two twin turrets, plus six single SKL/45 manufactured specifically for coast defense. Both types fire 45.3-kg (99.8-lb) shells to a range of 23,500 m (25,700 yds). Denmark also has a few ex-U.S. 3-in/50 naval guns in coastal mountings.

◆ 127 mm

Norway uses a 127-mm coast-defense gun, presumably an ex-German destroyer weapon. The German gun was a 127 mm/45, firing a 28-kg (61.7-lb) shell at 830 m/sec (2723 ft/sec), to a maximum range of 17,400 m (19,030 yds).

◆ 105 mm

Now in Norwegian service, this gun is presumably the standard German 105-mm/65 antiaircraft gun, firing a 15-kg (33.3-lb) shell at 900 m/sec (2953 ft/sec) to a maximum range of 17,700 m (19,360 yds). The Germans also used a variety of older lower-velocity 105-mm guns during World War II.

◆ 88 mm

Spain and Yugoslavia still use the old German 88-mm/56 gun in coast defenses, in fixed emplacements. It fires a 44-kg (97-lb) HE shell at a muzzle velocity of 820 m/sec (2690 ft/sec), to a maximum range of 14,860 m (16,250 yds).

SWEDEN

◆ Bofors 254-mm gun

This prewar weapon may survive in Finnish service; the gun was originally built for two Finnish coast-defense ships. This 10 in/45 fires a 225-kg (496-lb) shell at 850 m/sec (2790 ft/sec) to a maximum range of 30,300 m (33,140 yds).

◆ Bofors 155 mm L39 (CD77)

This mobile gun, developed specially for export, uses many Karin (see below) components. Total weight is 12 tons, and elevation limits are +70/−3 deg. Rate of fire is 10 rnds/min. Muzzle velocity (range): 827 m/sec (HEER round: 41.65 kg, 30,000 m or HE round: 42.6 kg, 24,000 m) or 700 m/sec (HCER round: 53 kg, 30,000 m). The HCER is probably the gun bought by Finland.

Sweden still uses 152-mm and 210-mm coast-defense guns, presumably prewar Bofors naval weapons.

◆ Bofors ERSTA 120 mm/62

This fixed coast-defense gun, developed about 1970, had by 1987 replaced about half the Swedish heavy coast-defense weapons, the remainder dating from the 1950s. Maximum elevation is 50 deg (limits +50/− 3 deg), to achieve maximum range. Rate of

A modern coast-defense weapon: The ERSTA 120-mm gun as emplaced in Norway. (*Ships of the World*)

fire is 25 rds/min (200 rnds in 20 min). The gun barrel is water-cooled. Total weight: 70.5 tons plus 103.5 tons of concrete. Muzzle velocity (projectile weight, range): 880 m/sec (HE: 24.6 kg, 24,000 m; HCER: 26 kg, 34,000 m). The shells are similar to those fired by the Karin gun (see below), but the cartridges are larger.

This weapon is used by the Swedish Navy and in 1980 was ordered by Norway (delivered 1987).

◆ Bofors Karin 120 mm L55 (CD80)

This mobile gun was first delivered in 1978 and has many elements in common with ERSTA. Karin has the same carriage as the FH77 155-mm field gun.

Typically, there are four guns per battery, and they can be towed by road at 70 km/hr. When the guns are emplaced, their arc of fire is 60 degrees. Each gun has its own computer. Elevation limits: +50/−3 deg. Rate of fire: 15 rds/min. Muzzle velocity (range): 790 m/sec (HE: 24.6 kg, 21,000 m) or 830 m/sec (HCER: 26 kg, 30,000 m).

◆ Bofors 75 mm L60

This weapon is a turreted gun, actually a 76/62, developed about 1960 for the Swedish Navy and exported to Norway and, probably, other customers. Elevation has been limited to 20 deg (limits are +20/−5 deg) to minimize the opening in the turret (range is limited to 11,400–16,000 m). Rate of fire is 25 rds/min. Muzzle velocity is 870 m/sec (range 12,000 m) for the 5.52-kg HE round, and 890 m/sec for the HCER round (6.4 kg, 16,000 m). Total weight is 17.5 tons.

Sweden also uses a mobile form of this gun, on a four-wheel towed carriage. She has a total of 12 mobile and 53 fixed coast-defense batteries (including missile units).

USSR

◆ 305 mm

The Soviets used both their new 305 mm/56 and their old (dreadnought-type) 305 mm/52 for coast defenses during World War II and planned to emplace twelve batteries of the new guns and eight batteries of the older ones (four four-gun in the Baltic, two four-gun in the Black Sea, and two five-gun in the Far East). Many of these weapons must have been destroyed, but some reportedly survive in active service, perhaps in the Northern Fleet. The 305 mm/56, which was designed for the abortive battle cruisers, fired a 480-kg (1058-lb) shell to 43,900 m (48,000 yds), probably at about 850 m/sec (2789 ft/sec). The older 305 mm/52 fired a 470.9-kg (1038-lb) AP shell at 762 m/sec (2500 ft/sec) to a maximum range of 24,620 m (26,925 yds).

◆ 152 mm

These guns are in Soviet, Bulgarian, East German, Romanian, and possibly Finnish service. These guns are mounted in the *Sverdlov* class, and some were mounted in Soviet coast-defense batteries during World War II. In coastal service, the 152 mm fired a 55-kg (121-lb) AP shell to 29,000 m (31,700 yds), probably at a muzzle velocity of about 885 m/sec (2900 ft/sec).

◆ 130 mm SM-4-1

This gun has been very widely adopted; reported export users are Angola, Bulgaria, Egypt, North Korea, Poland, Romania, South Yemen, Syria, and Yogoslavia. The Israelis captured some when they took Sharm el Sheikh in 1967. In addition, Soviet-type 130-mm guns (presumably of earlier type) arm Chinese (PRC), Cuban, and Finnish coast defenses. Performance approximates that of the 130-mm/58 naval gun, probably with a maximum range of about 29,500 m. Maximum elevation is 45 degrees. The APHE shell weighs 33.6 kg and is fired at a velocity of 1050 m/sec. Rate of fire is 5 rnds per minute. The gun is mounted on a four-wheel carriage (with removable axles) with a nearly vertical shield. This weapon does not fire the ammunition of the 130-mm M-46 field gun or the 130-mm KS-30 antiaircraft gun. The associated radar is ZALP-B (Long Bow).

Soviet client states first adopted 130-mm coastal guns in the early 1960s, at a time when the U.S. Navy was eliminating its heavy shipboard guns. The remaining 5-inch guns were outranged by the new 130s, and the abortive lightweight 8-inch gun program was begun as a counter to this new Soviet-bloc capability.

◆ Other Soviet Guns

122-mm guns are in Cuban, Finnish, North Korean, and possibly Yogoslav service. Finland uses T-55 (110-mm) turrets embedded in concrete and controlled from a blockhouse. Maximum range is about 15 km. Older 100-mm guns are in Bulgarian and Chinese (PRC) service. Finally, the 85-mm gun is in Yugoslav service, and also (presumably copied) in Chinese (PRC).

UNITED KINGDOM

◆ 15 in/45

Vickers Model 1926 is still in service in Spain. The AP shell weighs 859.65 kg (1895 lbs), and the HE shell 801.84 kg (1767 lbs); muzzle velocity is 2500 ft/sec (AP shell), and range is 35,100 m (38,400 yds). Guns are mounted singly, in armored gun houses. There are 12 or 16 mounts in Groupos of 4 (2 batteries per Groupo). The associated fire-control system is the Swedish 9KA 410 built in Spain.

◆ 12 in/50

Spain retains Vickers 12-in/50 guns, some of them originally built for her dreadnoughts, some specially built. The gun fires an 850-lb AP shell at 3010 ft/sec.

◆ 9.2 in

This gun is in Portuguese and Turkish service. When Britain and Canada gave up their coast defenses in 1956, they transferred their weapons to the NATO Southern Tier nations, primarily Portugal and Turkey. The standard 9.2 in/47 fired a 380-lb HE shell at 2700 ft/sec, to a maximum range of 36,700 yds.

◆ 8 in

Spain retains some British-supplied 8-inch coast-defense guns. She is alone in using this caliber. These weapons are probably Vickers 8-in/50 cruiser guns similar to those in the former Spanish heavy cruisers; the guns fire a 256-lb AP shell at 2725 ft/sec to a maximum range of 29,200 yds.

◆ 6 in/50

Vickers 6-in/50 guns, installed in 1915–25, remain in Spanish service, in both single and twin mounts. Maximum range is 21,600 m. There have been proposals to replace the gun tube with that of the Spanish 155-mm/39 howitzer, which fires standard NATO rounds. The 155-mm coast-defense gun would have a range of 22,500–24,000 m (30,000 m with enhanced-range ammunition) and fire 2 rnds/min (4 rnds/min in a burst).

Brazil and Paraguay use a 6-inch Vickers Mk V. Portugal also uses 6-in guns, presumably also of Vickers type.

BOMBARDMENT ROCKETS

FRANCE

◆ Storm/RAP-14

This Creusot-Loire system was announced in 1984. The launch platform, which carries two 160-mm (6.3-in) rocket pods, is computer-aimed. Pods can be reloaded by crane or reloaded

Storm. (Creusot-Loire)

semiautomatically. The launcher weighs about 2500 kg (5510 lbs). Storm resembles an earlier project, RAP-14, which was an adapted army launcher carrying a total of 20 single launchers (nine in each of two pods, two in between) for 360-mm (14-inch) rockets (2 m long, 18.5-kg warhead, range 15 km, speed 700 m/sec [78.7 in, 40.8 lbs, 16,400 yds, 2296 ft/sec]). Training speed was 20 deg/sec (25 deg/sec in elevation), and elevation limits were +90/−10 deg.

ITALY

◆ Breda 81-mm multiple launcher

This multiple rocket system carries 36 rounds; elevation limits are +55/−2 deg, and training/elevating speeds are 60/30 deg/sec. Weights: empty, 1270 kg (2799 lbs); loaded, about 1980 kg (4364 lbs), depending on rocket type. Trunnion height is 2.15 m, and working circle radius is 1.49 m (84.6 and 58.7 in).

The Oerlikon 81-mm SNORA folding-fin rocket fired by the Breda launcher weighs 19.7 kg and has a maximum range of about 10 km; maximum speed is 520 m/sec (43.4 lbs, 11,000 yds, 1706 ft/sec).

◆ NAROS

This multiple rocket system was announced in 1986 by SNIA/BPD; the name means Naval Rocket System. There are three versions: long-range (using the same rockets as the ground-based FIROS 25: 40 122-mm tubes, 25-km range), medium-range (30 81-mm tubes, 12-km range), and short-range (48 50-mm tubes for FIROS 6 rockets, 6-km range). The rockets are available with prefragmented, HE, spotting, and submunition (81-mm and 122-mm only) warheads. Maximum ranges: 50 mm, 6.5 km; 81 mm, 12 km; 122 mm, 25 km (7100, 13,100, and 27,300 yds).

USSR

◆ BM 14/17 and BM 14/18

BM 14/17 is a 17-barrel 140-mm (5.5-in) army-type rocket that entered service in 1954. The 70-lb rocket has a maximum range of 4.8 nm. The designation has been applied by NATO.

BM 14/18 is a 140-mm rocket launcher specially designed for naval service, on board all *Polnocny*-class amphibious ships. This launcher fires the same rocket as BM 14/17.

BM 14/18 rocket launchers forward on board a Polnocny-class landing ship. The radar is Drum Tilt, controlling a twin 30-mm gun at the after end of the superstructure. (U.S. Navy)

◆ BM 21

This 40-barrel 122-mm rocket launcher (101 lbs, range 8 nm) is found on board some amphibious ships. It is automatically re-loaded: the launcher carries two clusters of 20 tubes, empty sets being discarded and replaced from below. The rockets carry a 19.2-kg fragmentation warhead.

Shmel-class monitors can carry an eight-barreled 122-mm launcher.

Soviet 122-mm barrage rocket launcher, showing its two 20-rocket clusters.

UNITED STATES

◆ ABRS

For several years LTV has tried to interest the U.S. Navy in a naval version of its land-based multiple rocket launcher, which it calls ABRS (Assault Ballistic-Rocket System). Although the company has thus far been unsuccessful, ABRS would probably arm any new U.S. short-range fire-support ship, should congressional pressure result in the construction of such a vessel. It is the only U.S. bombardment rocket currently in production (for army and NATO use). For some years no such concept has survived analysis because, with the advent of air-cushion landing craft (and with the expected advent of the deep-strike Osprey), the U.S. Marine Corps has asked for support effective some considerable distance (such as 50 nm) inland from the coast. That support is extremely expensive; should the Corps reverse its position to favor coastline support, the marines could accept something much simpler.

The rocket is 8.94 in × 12.9 ft and weighs 678 lbs at launch (352-lb warhead); it normally carries 644 M 77 bomblets. The army and the NATO allies operating ABRS systems have developed a variety of mines and terminally-guided submunitions for the rocket to carry. Range is already considerably greater than that of the 5 in/54 and can be extended to about twice 5-in/54 range, i.e., to about 40,000 yds. Rockets are carried, and loaded, in six-round pod/containers (total loaded weight, 5004 lbs). The LTV proposal, which has not yet been accepted, is to mount two of the standard two-pod launchers on the super-structure of an LST, the hold of which could be converted to carry large numbers of pods.

AIRBORNE ECM

Airborne ECM systems divide into reconnaissance (ESM), stand-off or escort jamming, and self-protection (also called defensive ECM, DECM).

FRANCE

◆ ARAR-10B/ARAX-10B

Thomson-CSF's ESM system for Atlantic 1 and Nimrod patrol aircraft covers 2.3–11.1 GHz. The antennas are on top of the tail fin. This system gives data on pulse width, PRF, beam width, and scan rate. ARAX-10B is the associated frequency-measurement device.

◆ ARAR-13A

This ESM system for Atlantique Mk2 maritime-patrol aircraft is similar to the Thomson-CSF Dalia 500 and to the shipboard ARBR 17. The antennas are in wingtip pods, for high DF accuracy and reduced interference with (and from) other aircraft systems. Bandwidth is greater than that of the Atlantique Mk1 system.

The first preproduction units were delivered in November 1986.

◆ DR-2000/3000A/4000

These ESM systems are also used on board ships. Dahlia (DR-2000) is a manual frequency-measuring system operating in the D- through J-bands. Applications include the Embraer EMB-111 (with six D/F and one omnidirectional frequency-measuring antenna) and German Navy Sea Kings. DR-3000A is a heavier, fully automatic system, covering the D- through K-bands, for maritime-reconnaissance aircraft. DR-4000, which is also carried by frigates, is intended for large maritime-patrol aircraft.

United Kingdom

◆ Hermes

Hermes is the Marconi Defense Systems ESM system supplied for Indian Navy Sea King helicopters. It is derived from the ARI 18241/1 radar-homing-and-warning receiver fitted to RAF Tornado F.2 and F.3 fighters.

◆ Kestrel (Orange Reaper)

Racal's ESM system is made for the EH-101 helicopter and for small maritime-patrol aircraft. Orange Reaper uses the same six-port antenna as Orange Crop (MIR-2) but is described as an airborne equivalent of Cutlass. The processor and display match those of Sabre (see under shipboard radars and fire-control systems in the Antiaircraft Warfare section). The design emphasizes accurate frequency data (for radar identification) over high bearing accuracy, and there is a 2000-emitter threat library. Total weight is 47 kg. Frequency coverage is 0.6–40 GHz, bearing accuracy is better than 3.5 degrees, using pattern-correction techniques, and processing time is less than 1 second.

Orange Reaper is the Royal Navy version for the EH-101 helicopter. In this application it shares the helicopter's main display. Kestrel has been ordered for Royal Danish Navy Lynx helicopters. In these helicopters the ESM display is a 20 × 7.5 cm color CRT.

◆ MIR-2 (Orange Crop)

Racal's ESM system for helicopters covers the C- through J-bands. Orange Crop was designed for the Lynx helicopter but was extended to Sea Kings during the Falklands War. The system uses six antennas, each covering a 60-degree arc. The display shows frequency band (the 0.6–18 GHz range is divided into four), bearing (the scale is divided into 10-degree steps), and amplitude. Strobes are used to select signals by band and bearing for pulse analysis and accurate bearing measurement. For pulse analysis, the PRF is displayed digitally; bearing is displayed on a 30-degree display calibrated in 2-degree steps. Bearing accuracy is 4.5 degrees. Signal limits: pulse width 0.1–10 microsec, PRF 50–10,000 pps. Total weight without antennas is 30.7 kg. This system was originally designed to intercept and locate submarine burst transmissions.

Although originally developed for helicopters, MIR-2 was later extended to surface craft. The ship-based version is described in the Antiaircraft Warfare section. Racal has discussed license production in France.

◆ Yellow Veil

The Whittaker Electronics (U.S.) jammer for Lynx helicopters operating in the Persian Gulf is designed to protect British warships against Iranian antiship missiles. Based on the U.S. Navy ALQ-167(V), Yellow Veil can be carried either internally or as a pod, in the latter case replacing two Sea Skua missiles. Yellow Veil is also based in part on Falklands experience. The system protects a Lynx attacking with Sea Skua from hostile antiaircraft sensors; the helicopter is limited in maneuverability because it must keep the surface target illuminated. Yellow Veil is also carried by some Sea King HAS.5 helicopters.

◆ Prophet

Prophet is a Racal radar-warning receiver designed for export, particularly on board Hawk trainer/attack aircraft. However, Royal Navy Sea King helicopters operating in the Persian Gulf have been fitted with this system, an installation completed in two weeks. Prophet reduces its false-alarm rate by measuring the frequency of an intercepted signal, an unusual feature in so simple a system (most measure only PRF within a broad band, and may, therefore, easily confuse signals). Total weight, including a four-port antenna and an LED display, is 9 kg. Coverage is either 2–18 GHz or 6–18 GHz, and the threat library can store signatures of more than 100 emitters. Designed response time is less than one second.

UNITED STATES

In 1979–80 the U.S. Navy bought automobile radar-detectors ("fuzz-busters") for its tactical aircraft, attaching them with velcro strips to the instrument panels of some A-6s, A-7s, and F-14s. Police radars operate in K-band, and presumably existing radar-warning receivers did not cover those very high frequencies. No standard designations seem to have been assigned, and the commercial detectors were replaced by APR-43 and ALR-67 from 1987 onwards (replacement was scheduled for completion by late 1989).

◆ AAR-37

Hughes's IR warning system is made for P-3 aircraft.

◆ AAR-47

Honeywell's IR warning sensor is designed to detect incoming IR-guided missiles that cannot register on radar-warning receivers. AAR-47 has four sensors so that it can indicate from which quadrant the missile is approaching.

◆ ALE-29

The Tracor chaff-cartridge dispenser accommodates up to 30 RR-129 or RR-144 cartridges or Mk 46/47 IR flares. Aircraft normally carry two ALE-29s.

◆ ALE-39

The Goodyear/Tracor chaff-cartridge dispenser is standard on U.S. Navy aircraft. It is a square container typically attached to the side of an underwing hard-point pylon. Normal capacity is 60 cartridges, but it can be expanded to 300.

◆ ALE-43

The Lundy chaff dispenser cuts chaff from eight spools of aluminized glass fiber. The resulting chaff can counter radars from VHF up to millimeter-wave. In pod form (640 lbs), ALE-43 carries 320 lbs of chaff. This dispenser can also be housed internally, as in the EA-6B (total weight 420 lbs). Chaff is carried in up to nine packages, each feeding a roller and cutter.

This type of bulk pod is generally used to lay a chaff corridor.

◆ ALQ-39

CHAFFBUOY is a delayed-deployment chaff cartridge intended to counter surveillance systems. Aircraft are used to deploy ALQ-39 so as to bring it far enough from the fleet. The distances involved permit delays of an hour or more in deployment, and the counter-surveillance decoys need not be as large as those used to decoy missiles away from large ships. See also ALQ-190.

◆ ALQ-41

The Sanders track-breaker is part of the EA-6B suite.

◆ ALQ-78

Magnavox's ESM system for P-3 aircraft was replaced by ALR-66 in U.S. service. ALQ-78 uses a high-speed rotating antenna in the belly of the aircraft. Production began in the mid-1970s.

◆ ALQ-81

Sanders's jamming pod for A-7B and -7E light bombers was produced 1971–74.

◆ ALQ-86

The Bunker-Ramo ESM system was used originally in EA-6A (with the Loral ALQ-53 electronic reconnaissance system) and then in EA-6B ADVCAP.

◆ ALQ-91

Magnavox's communications jammer (to defeat the command links of surface-to-air missiles) for A-4Ms and F-14s was first ordered 1971.

◆ ALQ-92

The Sanders communications jammer for the EA-6B uses an antenna below the forward fuselage. ALQ-92 is being replaced by ALQ-149. See the discussion of ALQ-99 for notes on system integration.

◆ ALQ-99

ALQ-99 is the tactical support jamming system of the EA-6B Prowler, the standard U.S. Navy ECM airplane. The EA-6B derives its flexibility from the use of pod-mounted jammers, analogous to the underwing stores of the A-6 attack bomber, that are controlled by an inboard computer and sensors (just as the A-6 attack is controlled by a computer and the APQ-148/156 radar). The pods were conceived in connection with a 1960 Grumman proposal for an EA-6 to be built around the new ALQ-53 (Giraffe) and to carry noise jammers (ALT-13, -15, and -16), track-breakers (ALQ-41 and -51), and a VHF jammer (QRC-1022 AL). The standard A-6 APQ-92 radar was simplified (as APQ-103) and moved slightly forward to create a bay for the ALQ-53. A radome was built on the vertical fin aft to accommodate most of the sensor antennas. The advantage of the radome's position was its 360-degree field of view. Other antennas were located in the canopy.

The logic of the podded jammer was a combination of flexibility (pods could be changed to match the threat) and the need for sheer jammer power: an internal jammer probably could not match what could be carried underwing, powered by a ram-air turbine. The proposed pod, designated ALQ-31, had a trainable, elevatable antenna so that the jamming airplane could track an enemy radar while maneuvering in an almost unrestricted manner. Moreover, because the jamming airplane probably would not face the full spectrum of enemy radars during any one mission, the aircraft could carry only the jammers it needed, using the remaining hard points for additional fuel or (now) for antiradar weapons. ALQ-31 carried two complete jamming systems (noise, communications/navigation, or multitarget repeaters). The first pod to become operational, ALQ-76, carried four, so that an airplane with five hard points could, at least in theory, jam up to twenty individual radars. The airplane itself was designed with the potential to add four more hard points, for a total of nine. Alternatively, each hard point could carry a 300- or 450-gallon drop tank.

The first ECM version of the A-6, the EA-6A (which is still flown by reserve squadrons), carried an ALQ-86 receiver and display/control system instead of the ALQ-53 initially planned, and ALQ-76 pods. There was provision for the ALQ-54 noise-jammer pod and for chaff-dispenser pods (ALE-32, -41, and -42), so that the EA-6A could lay chaff corridors. EA-6As carried

An EA-6B Prowler displays the leading features of its ALQ-99 system: the tail radome (for all-around view) and the underwing jammer pods. All other U.S. Navy aircraft use internal jammers with antennas on the surface of the airplane skin, hence cannot really be illustrated meaningfully. (U.S. Navy)

ALQ-55 communications jammers, to disrupt ground-controlled interception. The EA-6A also carried defensive systems to protect itself: an onboard chaff dispenser and a self-protection jammer (ALQ-100).

This system was limited because its different elements had been conceived and developed separately and could be integrated only through the skills of the single ECM operator. He in turn could easily be overcome by the sheer complexity of a dense electromagnetic environment. He had substantial electronic firepower, but he lacked the means to acquire and identify his targets rapidly, particularly because the computer intended for ALQ-53 was not available in time. The operator, therefore, had to watch the system scan mechanically through its frequency range every two seconds, listening for the tone of an enemy radar. Worse, at this time the Soviets were introducing tunable radars, to overcome spot jamming. To be effective against such radars, a jammer must periodically shut down ("look through") to check whether its target is still emitting on the same frequency: the target has to be tracked both in position and in frequency (and, for that matter, in operating pattern).

Navy work on an integrated ECM airplane began in 1963, and Grumman conducted its own in-house study of an EA-6A at about the same time. The EA-6B, which is almost synonymous with the ALQ-99 system, was the result. The new idea was to develop the ECM system as an integrated whole instead of as a federated set of separate systems. The development contract was awarded in August 1966.

The key requirement was automatic radar identification and tracking in a very dense environment. Without accurate identification, jamming power could be wasted on low-priority radars such as IFF systems and airport landing systems. Very quick reaction was essential in the face of modern missile-control systems. Moreover, an operator would be presented with radars in very fast succession. Grumman estimated that in one case an airplane flying at 20,000 feet at 400 knots would encounter about ten distinct emitters per second, a rate which would double at 40,000 feet (because of the longer lines of sight). The solution was a combination of computer identification and of correlation of target bearing with emitter characteristics (radar function on land is generally associated with particular geographic positions). That solution, in turn, would require a computer memory.

The new system, ALQ-99, consisted of a series of antennas and signal processors feeding a central computer and integrated displays and jammer controls, which in turn fed self-contained pods with their own automatic frequency-and-direction tracking. The airplane itself had a doppler radar feeding a dead-reckoning navigator, which assisted in signal processing and jammer pointing, and defensive ECM for protection against counterattack. Even though ALQ-99 was much more automated than earlier ECM systems, it required three operators (ECM officers, or ECMOs). The standard A-6, then, had to be stretched to accommodate two more side-by-side seats.

Pods were designed for specific frequency bands, and aircraft were launched with a prebriefed set. Each consisted of an exciter flanked by two transmitters, with trainable antennas underneath. The typical load was three pods (centerline and outer store stations) and two drop tanks.

Thus the EA-6B began as a strike-support weapon, to jam acquisition and targeting radars. In the face of SAMs, for example, neutralizing the acquisition radar prevents hand-off to the missile-control system. Neutralizing the tracking radar of the missile system in turn prevents successful missile firing. Both tactics were often used in Vietnam. Early Prowler tactics called for the airplane to fly near a strike target, but outside the strike pattern proper. For example, an EA-6B on the strike axis could jam the radar net toward which the strike aircraft were flying. The next step was to jam defensive communications. The Soviets tend to rely very heavily on ground-controlled interceptors, and even if the directing radars work, the airplanes are helpless without their communications. It was natural, then, for the Prowler to be upgraded to deal with voice communications. The next step for the Soviets is to use a digital data link, which is more difficult to jam; and the next step for the Prowler is to neutralize that link as well.

A second mission, fleet defense, was added during the late 1960s. Prowlers could jam airborne targeting radars (which, in many cases, were needed to fire the surface-launched as well as the air-launched weapons) and, to a lesser extent, the missiles themselves. The EA-6Bs could also use their receivers for surface surveillance, providing passive early-warning of the approach of enemy forces without disclosing the presence of the carrier group.

About 1985 the requirement to be able to physically destroy enemy radars, by firing HARM missiles, was added. By this time HARM was valued, not only as a means of neutralizing ground defenses, but also as a means of rendering enemy warships vulnerable to salvos of antiship weapons. The rationales are quite different. A HARM may put a land-based radar out of action for a few hours or for a few days, when a particular target (among many) is hit. At sea, even temporary dislocation due to a HARM should open a ship to fatal damage.

These upgrades have been applied to virtually all EA-6Bs, which are periodically returned to Grumman for remanufacture (as of 1987, some had been rebuilt as many as three times). The major series are XCAP, ICAP-1, ICAP-2, "Block '86," and, in the near future, ADVCAP (Block '91). The flexibility inherent in the podded concept is very important here.

The original EA-6B, which entered service in 1972, was limited to four countermeasures bands, together accounting for 96–98 percent of the electronic threat in Vietnam: Band 1, 64–150 MHz (VHF communications); Band 2, 150–270 MHz (some P-band radars); Band 4, 0.5–1 GHz; and Band 7, 2.5–3.5 GHz. XCAP (expanded capability) added bands 5, 6, 8, and 9 to deal with newer high-frequency fire-control radars that were important outside Vietnam. XCAP, entering service in 1973, also incorporated a digital recorder (for electronics intelligence). Computer memory was doubled, and new computer-operated modes allowed simultaneous automatic coverage of several enemy radars. Jamming was driven by a new exciter.

XCAP and earlier aircraft can be distinguished by a pair of spear antennas protruding from the outboard pylons. The right-hand antenna transmits, the left-hand receives. The antennas initially served the ALQ-41 and ALQ-100 self-defensive (track-breaking) systems.

In the XCAP version, ECMO 1 (in the front seat) and ECMO 2 operated the main jammer, with ECMO 3 (who was not always needed) assigned to the ALQ-92 communications jammer. ECMO 1 also served as navigator. He, therefore, had a disproportionate work load.

ICAP-1 (1977) added digital receivers, which fed a computer display system, and an automatic carrier landing system (ACLS). Major changes in displays and cockpit layout considerably reduced the workload of the crewmen. The entire track/jam function was moved to the after pair of seats. ECMO 1 became communications jammer (ALQ-92), navigator, and radar operator. ICAP Prowlers can be distinguished externally by the two antennas of their ALQ-126 defensive (and deceptive) ECM system, which replace the two spears of the earlier aircraft: a receiving antenna on the refueling probe at the nose, and the "tin can" receiving antenna on the after edge of the fin radome.

The airplane still had to carry mission-oriented pods suited to particular frequency bands. In ICAP-2 (1984), this limitation was finally removed, with the provision of a universal exciter developed by AIL. Now any pod could cover all nine frequency bands. In effect, the universal exciter multiplied capability by a factor of five, since all five pods can now cover any radar. This version can also jam communications on a limited basis. ICAP-2 has an automatic signal processor and a mission planner, as well as the current carrier aircraft inertial navigation system (CAINS).

As the threat becomes denser, the operator cannot initiate action quickly enough, and the computer becomes the initiator, the human operator the monitor. The original ALQ-99 was semiautomatic, partly because it appeared before computers had become particularly reliable. Problems with operator speed were first noticed in ICAP-1 aircraft, and ICAP-2 introduces full automation, with a faster (AYK-14) computer.

The next version (Block '86, 1988) adds encrypted HF communications, enhanced signal processing and recording, and VHF/UHF communications. Like ICAP-2, Block '86 can fire HARM missiles.

Block '86 will be the last version to incorporate the ALQ-99 that marked the entire series. In 1991 advanced capacity (ADVCAP) Prowlers will begin to appear, built around an entirely new system, currently described only as the RPG (receiver-processor group). The RPG system will respond to considerable improvements in threat radars, such as more complex (coded) pulses, to overcome spot jamming, and pulse-to-pulse frequency agility. Successful jamming now requires an ability to analyze pulse and pulse-train patterns so that they can be mimicked. Moreover, radars can now tune over wider bands, so that jammers limited to specific narrow frequency-ranges may no longer be effective. Hence the vital interest in a "universal exciter" and in faster scanning of the spectrum. Increasing civilian use of the electromagnetic spectrum increases signal density and also makes it easier for a jammer to be seduced into action against a nontarget signal.

The RPG has been in full-scale development since 1983 and will be combined with the ALQ-149 system for command-control-communications countermeasures, which replaces the earlier ALQ-92. The RPG will substitute a disk recorder in place of the current digital tape, for greater information density and higher speed. ADVCAP aircraft will probably also have a new radar, which cannot be the multifunction type now specified for the A-6F. A third display (for the front cockpit) will be added to the two displays currently in the two rear seats. The forward operator currently is under-utilized, and as the electronics environment becomes more complex, he will become vital to the two men in the rear.

◆ ALQ-108

Magnavox's IFF deception set, for E-2C, EP-3E, and S-3A aircraft, originated in the early 1970s.

◆ ALQ-123

The Loral pod-mounted IR jammer jams by modulating an IR source. IR seekers are designed to deal with steady sources, so the modulation can penetrate their control wiring and cause missiles to pitch off-course. The choice of modulation frequency depends on the design of the target missile; in 1986 ALQ-123 was reportedly being modified to provide additional pulse rates to defeat newer Soviet missiles.

◆ ALQ-126/164

The defensive ECM (DECM) system of the F/A-18 Hornet is manufactured by Sanders Federal Systems Group. ALQ-126B, the current version, is the first U.S. Navy/Marine Corps reprogrammable DECM system. This system is also used on foreign-sales F/A-18s. It operates either autonomously or in concert with the ALR-45F/APR-43 or ALR-67 radar-warning receiver, the ALQ-162 CW jammer, and the HARM missile.

In an F/A-18, the system incorporates forward high-band antennas just aft of the radome (above and below the fuselage), an aft high-band antenna atop the port fin, forward mid-band antennas above and below the fuselage just forward of the air intakes (starboard above, port below), aft mid-band antennas just forward of the vertical fins (above and below), and low-band antennas (positioned with the mid-band antennas, but on the other side of the airplane).

Total weight is 190 lbs (two units, upper and lower deck, connected by blind-mate connectors), and the maximum power requirement is 3 kVA.

ALQ-164 is the podded version of ALQ-126B, for the Marine Corps AV-8B Harrier. ALQ-126 replaced the Sanders ALQ-100, which had been the standard navy self-defense jammer from the early 1960s on. ALQ-126 was initially referred to as ALQ-100X. The pod weighs 350 lbs (16 in × 85 in).

◆ ALQ-130

The AIL communications jammer on EA-6Bs is an updated ALQ-92. ALQ-130 attacks missile-command links, using broadband noise. This jammer is internally mounted on board EA-6Bs.

◆ ALQ-140

Sanders's CAIR II (countermeasure, airborne, IR) for F-4 installation consists of a heated ceramic block (presumably with modulator) that replaces the tail parachute doors.

◆ ALQ-142

Raytheon's ESM system for LAMPS Mk III helicopters is a repackaged version of SLQ-32(V)1/2 (ESM without jamming). See the Antiaircraft Warfare section for SLQ-32 details.

◆ ALQ-146

The Sanders IR countermeasure to protect CH-46D helicopters was tested in 1976 and first ordered in 1977. Each CH-46D carries two ALQ-146s, one above the cockpit and one above the tail doors. The crew selects the modulating frequency.

◆ ALQ-149

The new EA-6B tactical communications jammer, by Sanders Associates, is compatible with the existing ALQ-99 and uses cooperative jam/look-through cycles to allow simultaneous operation of both systems. ALQ-149 is also intended to detect, identify, evaluate, and jam enemy long-range early-warning radars. Presumably, those abilities mean that it operates at somewhat lower frequencies than ALQ-99, e.g., against shipboard P-band radars.

In 1988 it was reported that this program had been delayed because of a combination of severe technical problems and legal disputes between the original joint venture partners, Sanders and ITT. The current partners are Sanders and Lockheed Electronics. Reportedly, part of the problem was over-ambitious specification in frequency range; that problem has now been remedied. As of the fall of 1988, Sanders had delivered six of the seven engineering-development models on order. Because the Vietnam-era ALQ-92 was removed some years ago, EA-6Bs are limited in their capabilities. ALQ-149 was planned as part of the ICAP-2 EA-6B upgrade, but delays have made it part of ADVCAP instead (FY91 and beyond). ASQ-191 was purchased as an interim solution (see entry).

◆ ALQ-156(V)

In October 1988, Sanders Associates received an FSED contract for the ALQ-156 Missile Detector, Integrated Defense Avionics Program (IDAP) for use on various navy tactical aircraft. ALQ-156 consists of a receiver/transmitter, buffer box, and antennas. The receiver/transmitter is a pulse doppler radar, first developed by Sanders in 1976 for the army, that separates and detects threats based on their speed and radar cross section. To date, ALQ-156(V) has been used primarily to protect helicopters and slow aircraft. Now it is to be used on board fast attack jets. The new buffer box connects the system to other aircraft avionics. The FSED contract calls for the design and production of 12 sets of equipment; the contract is to be completed by September 1990.

◆ ALQ-157

ALQ-157 is the Loral IR jammer for large helicopters. Two emitters are mounted, one on either side of the vertical tail of the helicopter, and the pilot can choose one of five jamming modes. Production began in 1983, for CH-53 and CH-46E helicopters.

◆ ALQ-162 (Shadowbox)

Northrop's CW DECM system is a receiver-jammer and, thus, does not require any separate radar-warning receiver. However, Shadowbox is compatible with any radar-warning receiver, pulse jammer, or expendable countermeasure. Total weight is 40 lbs plus two 0.5-lb antennas and a 1-pound remote control unit; demonstrated MTBF is 335 hours (260 specified). ALQ-162 uses two vertically polarized antennas, covering 60 degrees to either side in azimuth and 30 degrees up or down in elevation; the system can also interface with other ECM antennas as required. In two NATO air forces, the system is actually installed in the underwing pylons of F/A-18s.

ALQ-162 has been under test since 1981 and is planned for (or installed on board) A-7E, F-4S, AV-8C, and NATO F/A-18 aircraft.

◆ ALQ-165

ITT/Westinghouse joint-services Airborne Self-Protection Jammer (ASPJ) is made for upgraded F-14s, F/A-18s, and A-6s. Work on this system began in the early 1970s, a specification being issued in 1976. The ITT/Westinghouse team was chosen in 1981, but work was delayed because of the severe weight constraints imposed by the F/A-18. The final (12th) prototype was delivered, two years late, early in 1986. At that time the navy was comparing ASPJ to a combination of two existing jammers: the Sanders ALQ-126B and the new Northrop ALQ-162, which are less expensive and simpler. ASPJ survived this comparison, and initial production contracts, for 96 systems from each consortium partner, were let in September 1987 (for delivery in 1989). The total requirement is about 2500 systems for both navy and air force.

ASPJ is to be carried internally, and the original navy requirement called for very dense packaging. As of 1984, the required frequency coverage was 0.7–18 GHz, with a system response time of 0.1–0.25 seconds; these capabilities were to fit within less than 2.4 cubic feet. Required resolution was 5 MHz, with an instantaneous bandwidth of 1.44 GHz and a minimum receivable pulse width of 0.1 microsec (false alarm rate 5 per hour or less). The associated jammer was to be capable of dealing with 16 to 32 emitters (noise and deception jamming), with an accuracy of plus or minus 0.5–20 MHz.

The ASPJ is a navy-led program, derived from the ALQ-129 of 1972–77 and from the ALQ-136 (for helicopters) of 1977–80. The latter actually entered production.

◆ ALQ-190

AIRBOC (Air-Launched Rapid-Blooming Chaff) is a fleet counter-surveillance decoy deployed from aircraft. Unlike

CHAFFBUOY (ALQ-39), AIRBOC deploys immediately upon being launched.

♦ ALR-45/ALR-68

The standard navy threat-warning receiver by Litton supersedes the earlier APR-25, from which ALR-45 was developed. It operates over a wider frequency range (2–14 GHz) and incorporates a fast digital threat-processor. The antennas are four planar cavity-backed spirals, covering 360 degrees around the airplane; and the display is a strobe on the aircraft's PPI. This system has been in production since the mid-1970s, and it has been adopted by several NATO countries. The current version is ALR-56F.

The original APR-25 was conceived in the early 1960s and purchased on a crash basis beginning in November 1965 after the first two U.S. aircraft, an F-4 and an RA-5C, were shot down by North Vietnamese SA-2s. APR-25 employed four antennas, and crystal video detectors concentrated in the threat bands. The direction of the threat signal was obtained by vector resolution of the four signals from the antennas, and the device was, therefore, initially called Vector IV. The related APR-26 was a launch-warning receiver, first employed in 1966. Both devices were developed by Applied Technology, Inc., a firm that had previously specialized in strategic reconnaissance and intelligence.

ALR-45 was a navy development based in part on the newly perceived Soviet naval surface threat in the Mediterranean. Introduced to the fleet in 1970, ALR-45 was a digital system employing early hybrid microcircuits. By this time it was essential that even a radar-warning receiver sort and prioritize hostile signals on a semiautomatic basis, in view of the sheer number of hostile or potentially hostile radars both in Vietnam and in the Mediterranean.

In mid-1972 Applied Technologies decided to modify ALR-45 by substituting a digital computer for a projected circuit board change; the result was Vector V. Given the programmable computer (called a variable programmer-alarmer), the device could analyze the received probability distributions of frequency, pulse repetition interval, PRF, pulse width, pulse coding, and other radar parameters. All of these data were probabilistic because the receiver could never be sure of whether it was sorting out signals entirely correctly. Even so, it could guess radar identifications based on pairs of frequency and pulse repetition interval (the inverse of PRF). The next step was for Applied Technologies to develop its own computer, the first intended specifically for electronic warfare. The desired characteristics were a volume of 100 cubic inches, a power consumption of 80 watts, and a throughput of 250k words/sec. The machine, the Applied Technology Advanced Computer (ATAC), appeared in July 1973, with a volume of 96 cubic inches, a power requirement of 45 watts, and a throughput of 1.25M words/sec. The computer was made part of Vector V, and this system in turn became the ALR-68 of the West German F-4 force and also the basis for the Enhanced Radar Warning Equipment of German Tornadoes.

In U.S. service, ALR-45 is being superseded by ALR-67.

♦ ALR-47/76

IBM manufactures these ESM systems. ALR-47 is on the S-3A; ALR-76 is an improved version for the S-3B. Each system uses an array of four cavity-backed spiral antennas in each wingtip. The aerials are directed to achieve monopulse direction-finding. The system feeds into two narrow-band tuning receivers. ALR-47 is also installed on board the Canadian CP-140 Aurora.

A target-acquisition console Mk 105, developed from ALR-47, was built for the *Asheville*-class gunboats, and an upgraded Mod 1 version was installed on board the *Pegasus*-class hydrofoils and on board some frigates and missile destroyers. These Mk 105s are programmable passive fire-control systems.

♦ ALR-50

Magnavox's threat-warning receiver, developed from APR-27, is being replaced (in U.S. service) by ALR-67. Production began in

the early 1970s, and very large numbers were ordered (e.g., 800 sets, for $22 million, in 1972). Platforms included the EA-6A and EA-6B, the A-7, and the F-14.

♦ ALR-52

The airborne version of WLR-11 (see the Antiaircraft Warfare section), by ARGOSystems, covers 0.5–18 GHz and uses separate octave modules. ALR-52 is carried by P-3s.

♦ ALR-54

The LAMPS I ESM system is being replaced by ALR-79.

♦ ALR-59/73

The passive detection system (PDS) for the E-2C Hawkeye uses four antennas: one at the nose, one at the tail, and one at the tip of each horizontal tailplane. PDS can process signals from any two of its four bands simultaneously, and it increases its dwell time on any part of the spectrum that shows increased activity. The system measures direction of arrival, frequency (presumably by superheterodyne rather than IFM), pulse width, amplitude, and scan rate. Emitter data are presented at the edges of the PPI displaying the main radar picture and also on a separate tabular display. Emitter position can be obtained either by correlation between two E-2Cs or by triangulation as the E-2C moves. Production began in 1980.

ALR-59 was offered as a major enhancement to NATO AWACS (E-3A) aircraft.

ALR-73 is an improved version of ALR-59. ALR-73 employs four groups of antennas, 52 in all, to cover four bands (500 MHz to 18 GHz). Each antenna has its own IFM, and pulse trains are separated and analyzed by a central computer. Direction-finding is by phase interferometry. Frequency-scanning is automatic, and each band is separately and simultaneously processed. This system will also be installed (in modified form) in the EA-6B ADVCAP.

♦ ALR-66/79/606

General Instruments manufactures these threat-warning systems. ALR-66(V)1 is used on board navy helicopters, (V)2 on board P-3B, and (V)3 on board P-3C. ALR-80 is an improved version for fighters. All of these warning receivers are entirely computer-controlled. ALR-66(V)3 was bought in 1984 specifically to provide P-3Cs with an over-the-horizon surveillance-and-targeting capability. ALR-66 replaced the earlier Magnavox ALQ-78.

In its export version, ALR-66 (VE) replaces earlier radar-warning receivers on a box-for-box basis. Crystal-video receivers cover the E–J bands, and coverage can be extended down to the C–D bands. Direction-finding accuracy is better than 15 degrees, and the associated threat library contains 1000 radar modes. ALR-66 (VE) can be reprogrammed on the flight line in 90 seconds. Total weight (in the (V)1 version) is 59.4 lbs.

The display shows up to three symbols per emitter: wide/narrow pulse, PRF (on a scale of 0 to 9), and band (E, G, I, or J).

ALR-79 is an upgraded ALR-66(V)1 for the SH-2F LAMPS I (modernized), with a frequency set unit and an interface for jammer control. The antennas are in the nose and tail of the helicopter; total weight is 102.75 lbs.

ALR-606 is an export system derived from ALR-66.

♦ ALR-67

Itek's radar-warning receiver is made for A-6E/G, AV-8B, F-14D, and F/A-18A aircraft. In June 1987 the navy issued an RFP for an advanced special receiver to upgrade ALR-67; this new device was also expected to be the basis for a common navy-wide radar-warning receiver. Coverage of the existing device is 1–16 GHz; it uses four spiral antennas.

Applied Technology, by that time a division of Itek, won the ALR-67 competition in 1975. The company became a division of Litton in 1983.

◆ ALR-77

Eaton AIL's ESM system for the P-3C was ordered in 1986 to replace the existing interim ALR-66(V)2. ALR-77 is used for passive surveillance, antiship-missile targeting (by detecting enemy ships' radar emissions), and threat warning (including warning of the approach of hostile aircraft).

This system uses new interferometer antennas, eighteen of which are mounted at each wingtip (36 per system, nine per quadrant). Each set of nine consists of three sets of three antennas each, the spectrum being divided into three bands. Bearing accuracy is reported as about 1 degree. A multiband converter at each wingtip converts all intercepted signals to a common base-band frequency for analysis. The converters also perform fine DF quadrant selection. Inside the airplane are an IFM/encoder, a preprocessor that summarizes signals and detects new contacts (and provides back-up threat warning), and a processor using an AYK-14 computer. There is an extensive threat library, and the processor can distinguish signals in a dense environment.

◆ APR-43

Loral's radar-warning detector is installed in aircraft such as the A-7E.

◆ APR-44

AEL's CW radar-warning receiver is used by both army and navy and is adapted from the earlier APR-42. The antenna, mounted on a horizontal surface, provides coverage of a 50-degree arc to the rear of the aircraft. The receiver triggers an audio signal, a lamp, and a flashing light. Bandwidth is selectable.

◆ ASQ-191

Rockwell/Collins communications jammer was developed originally by Collins to test its own communications system. The jammer was first purchased by the Fleet Electronic Warfare Support Group (FEWSG) to equip aggressor aircraft for fleet training. ASQ-191 was adopted for operational use on the recommendation of CDR James Powell, Readiness Officer for Medium Attack Tactical Electronics Warfare Wing, Pacific Fleet; he had encountered this jammer when he was a student at the Naval Postgraduate School. FEWSG lent three ASQ-191s to the Pacific Fleet VAQ organization, and VAQ-135 was the first squadron to deploy with the jammer. They used it during the Persian Gulf battle of 18 April 1988, helping to neutralize the Iranian Silkworm threat to U.S. warships in the Gulf. When VAQ-135 rotated home from the carrier *Enterprise*, the squadron left its ASQ-191s on board for the next EA-6B squadron to use. Ultimately the navy hopes to buy forty ASQ-191s for use until the more sophisticated ALQ-149 is ready.

ASQ-191 is small enough to fit easily into the EA-6B equipment bay, betraying its nonstandard origins in its requirement for a special control console (in front of the right front seat of the airplane). The jammer's reported unit cost is about $200,000.

◆ ULQ-16

ULQ-16 is the pulse analyzer for ESM in ASW aircraft.

◆ INEWS

Integrated Electronic Warfare System is the planned next-generation joint-service defensive ECM suite. The joint-venture team is Sanders/GE, augmented by Motorola and HRB-Singer. INEWS incorporates VHSIC technology. This program is led by the air force, and the planned applications are the next-generation tactical aircraft (ATF, ATA, and possibly ATB).

INEWS will differ from existing systems in that it will be an extension of the planned ICNIA (Integrated Communications/Navigation/Identification) suite that is to replace separate dedicated systems in future U.S. tactical aircraft, and that will be the most radical systems integration to date. Twenty separate systems, which together occupy about 8 cubic feet (600 lbs),

will be repackaged into a single box (4 cubic feet, 230 lbs). Promised improvements in reliability will stem partly from a drastic reduction in connectors and plugs between boxes. ICNIA was scheduled for flight-testing in 1988. Integration of INEWS with ICNIA suggests that both systems will share common antennas and, indeed, that the total number of antennas on board the aircraft will be drastically reduced. That reduction should be possible partly through the increased use of electronically scanned arrays, e.g., in the aircraft skin ("smart skin").

Because INEWS will share antennas with ICNIA, the former will be able to detect and jam communications links, e.g., between fighters and airborne control aircraft. In theory, INEWS will cover the entire frequency range from HF up through infrared and laser.

EXPENDABLES

In 1986 the U.S. Navy was experimenting with semiexpendables, small radar repeaters towed on cables. Compared to full expendables, these repeaters could provide long-term coverage (whereas the launch of an expendable must be accurately timed).

◆ AAED

The next-generation active expendable is under development by Naval Research Laboratory. There are two versions. One is a forward-fired version, based on the 2.75-in rocket, that is intended to use an autopilot to fly relatively slowly ahead of the airplane. The other version is towed on a cable, probably powered by the airplane. Naval Air Systems Command is developing a 600-lb pod (based on the current 2.75-in pod) to carry both AAED (forward-fired) and chaff/flare decoys.

◆ GEN-X

Texas Instruments's generic expendable jammer is to be carried in existing chaff/flare dispensers. In 1986 the design objective was a unit price of $3000. The standard expendable size is 1.63-in diameter × 5.8 in (note that the air force cannot use navy expendables because the air force's chaff chutes are rectangular in section). Compared to POET, GEN-X can operate over several frequency bands. Thus an airplane need not carry many different types of active expendables and can devote valuable chute space to chaff and flares.

In September 1987 the Naval Air Development Center awarded Texas Instruments a contract for 288 of these decoys,

GEN-X expendable jammer in combat. (Texas Instruments)

to be delivered by September 1989 ($19 million). The navy has an option for up to 30,000 such jammers. As of September 1987, Texas Instruments had already delivered 25 test decoys, as part of the competition leading up to the 288-decoy award.

Raytheon was selected as second-source in May 1988.

◆ POET

Sanders's Primed Oscillator Expendable Transponder (AN/AM-6988/A) is a small active system. POET was developed in the late 1970s in response to a suggestion by the Defense Science Review Board that the navy take the lead in developing expendable microwave decoys; POET was one of the first active expendables. It is launched via the standard chaff/flare dispenser. POET has a single antenna and is limited in frequency coverage. As of 1986, POET was the only expendable jammer in the U.S. inventory and was being manufactured at the rate of 2300 per month.

POET is to be replaced by GEN-X.

◆ Samson

Samson is the expendable decoy developed by Brunswick and produced by Israel Military Industries (IMI). Samson's success in the Bekaa Valley in 1982 prompted the U.S. Navy to buy 100 for operational evaluation. The decoy is a glider, carried on a standard aircraft hard-point, that dispenses chaff or generates false targets as the plane flies toward the target. This decoy was the outcome of a series of studies and prototypes for the U.S. Air Force; when U.S. support ended, the Israeli Defense Ministry took over.

Brunswick developed the Model 150 Maxi Decoy (tested 1973) for carriage, with folded wings, in the external-stores rack of a strike aircraft. Three Maxis could be carried in each of a Phantom's Sparrow-missile positions, and two could be carried on a 750-lb hard point. Maxi was a high-subsonic glider, but Model 290P (1974) was self-propelled, with a circular rather than square-section fuselage. That model in turn led to the design of the cylindrical-fuselage unpowered Samson 1, manufactured under license by IAI. The U.S. Navy bought 100 Samsons in 1985, for further operational evaluation, and in 1987 bought another 1000, plus 1500 of the improved TALD.

◆ TALD

The Tactical Air-Launched Decoy was developed from Samson and shown for the first time in 1986. TALD carries emitters, mimicking fighter radars and ECM systems, in its nose and dispenses chaff from its belly. The navy ordered its first batch of 500 TALDs from Brunswick in December 1985. In November 1987, the navy ordered another 600, with an option for 1000 more, production to be split between IMI and Brunswick. TALD reflects Brunswick experience in decoy design under the air force Maxi program (1973). Brunswick was also involved in an air force powered-decoy program in the late 1970s.

Both TALD and Samson are carried like 500-lb Mk-82 bombs, their swept wings folded back; over 20 can be carried in the multiple ejectors of a typical attack bomber or fighter. The decoy carries an autopilot, which can be programmed with launch altitude and flight profile (and, presumably, deception program) before take-off; no special on-board control equipment is required.

Compared to Samson, TALD has a square (rather than round) cross-section for greater chaff capacity, a better active emitter, better chaff dispenser, and a wider carriage-and-release envelope. Presumably, the next step would be a power plant, for a wider flight envelope; TALD could then also have an antiradar warhead (like Tacit Rainbow, which is listed as an air-to-surface missile).

The SAMSON decoy, predecessor of TALD. (Brunswick)

SAMSON being launched. (Brunswick)

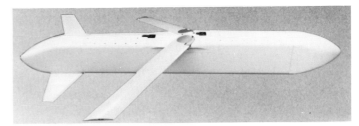

The Brunswick TALD decoy. (Brunswick)

TALD decoys carried on a triple ejector rack under the wing of an F-4 Phantom. (Brunswick)

ANTIAIRCRAFT WARFARE

Naval air defense is directed both against missiles fired at warships and against enemy aircraft. The same systems that can deny an enemy access to a fleet can also help cordon off an area some distance away in which friendly aircraft may be operating, e.g., while they attack shore or surface targets or pursue submarines. In peacetime or cold war, naval air-defense systems may be naval air-control systems, supporting surveillance or examining potentially unfriendly aircraft. Thus U.S. naval air defense, in the form of F-14s controlled by airborne radars (on board E-2C Hawkeyes), was able to identify and then to force down the Egyptian airliner carrying the hijackers of the *Achille Lauro* in 1985. The same air defense was able to isolate strike zones in Libya, in 1986, so that A-6 Intruders could attack without fear of Libyan air attack. In Vietnam, naval surface-to-air missiles offshore actually shot down enemy fighters attempting to engage U.S. strike aircraft.

Because modern aircraft are so expensive, they cannot be produced in vast numbers, and naval air-defense systems can help to achieve air superiority by the destruction of enemy aircraft. Such air superiority would result, for example, if the air defenses of American carrier battle groups destroyed a significant fraction of attacking Soviet bombers. In this case, defense would be transformed into an offensive means of gaining sea control (maritime air superiority). On the other hand, shorter-range missile systems almost certainly would not be positioned well enough to engage the bombers but would find themselves defending the carrier and her consorts from whatever missiles the Soviet bombers managed to fire.

Modern naval air-defense systems divide naturally into long (area)-, short (point)-, and very short- (close-in) ranges, with systems straddling each of these divides. Really long ranges become more difficult to achieve as incoming targets approach at higher speeds, since the fundamental limits of all air-defense systems include reaction and, therefore, detection times. At very long range, moreover, air defense can turn into an attack on the platforms from which the original attack is launched, be they aircraft (missile-carrying bombers), ships, or shore launchers. Only in the case of the bombers is this end of the air-defense spectrum included in classical antiair warfare measures.

Thus, the longest-range antiaircraft weapons are the long-range missiles carried by naval-defense fighters. For the purposes of this book, these defenders are carrier-based fighters, which are operated by only a very few navies. Land-based fighters, generally not under naval control, can, of course, contest the passage of antiship bombers. However, the historical record strongly suggests that such fighters often cannot appear in time to engage passing bombers, especially if the bombers can evade over enormous sea areas. The advantage of the carrier-based fighters is that their bases are in the bombers' target areas, so the bombers must necessarily fly toward them.

All long- and medium-range weapons are necessarily terminally guided. At shorter ranges, however, unguided gunfire can be effective, particularly if produced in sufficient volume. Missiles are generally limited not only in maximum but also in minimum range, as they require time to accelerate to a speed at which sufficient air is flowing over their fins for effective guidance. By way of contrast, guns can be aimed down to zero range. Their maximum range is determined by the predictability of their trajectories; as the range increases and the trajectory becomes more steeply curved, smaller and smaller errors in fire control can make them ineffective.

For all air-defense systems, there is a minimum acceptable kill range, since even a badly damaged missile may well follow a ballistic trajectory into a targeted ship, and since the fragments of a severely damaged missile will continue along its original path. Weapon lethality is, therefore, a very important issue. Proponents of very small caliber weapons, such as Phalanx, rely heavily for the physical destruction of an incoming missile on the fuzing of its warhead as a result of penetration by one or more projectiles. If the warhead is not fuzed, the missile may well continue into the ship. For example, in one 1986 U.S. Navy incident, a self-propelled Chukar target was hit by USS *Antrim* and scored as killed. It flew into the water but glanced off and continued into the ship, killing a man and severely damaging the ship's unarmored combat information center. Proponents of larger-caliber weapons (such as the Bofors 40- and 57-mm guns) claim that, although shots are much fewer, each is far more lethal, as its fragments can fatally damage a missile.

Thus, even if an air-defense system defeats all the missiles attacking it, those missiles may still do some damage. The lesson would seem to be, not that active defense is pointless, but rather that it must generally be combined with some form of passive defense: ships will be damaged, but they must remain afloat and at least partly effective. Most passive-defense issues are outside the scope of this book, but one is very important: the rise of distributed rather than centralized combat systems. To the extent that a combat system (and its power supply) can be spread over the length of a ship, the system cannot be eliminated by a single concentrated hit. Here the key technologies are probably data busing (so that several widely distributed computers can maintain the same current combat data base) and relatively inexpensive high-density electronics (so that there is no need to concentrate the combat system in a single central computer, either to provide enough computing power or to provide that power at a reasonable price). If a ship and her combat system can survive several hits, an increased burden will fall on the attacker, who must launch more weapons (of individually greater power) and who, thus, may find it difficult to deal with as many separate ships. Survivability may make decoying more effective or may force the attacker to concentrate his attack (e.g., to fly several aircraft together) in a manner increasing his own vulnerability and reducing saturation.

Lethality issues also apply to missiles. Very few missiles can be expected to actually hit small incoming targets. Rather, most will employ proximity fuzes to convert a near miss into a hit. The proximity fuze is triggered by the nose of the missile, and defending and attacking missiles may well be passing each other at or above Mach 4. There is a finite time lag while the proximity impulse activates the missile's fuze. Then there is also a finite interval while the explosive effect of the defending missile propagates to its target. Mach 4 is approximately 4000 ft/sec, and this speed leaves very little time to destroy a missile less than 10 ft (i.e., less than 1/400 of a second) long.

This problem explains the decision to abandon continuous-rod warheads in the U.S. and British navies. Continuous rods were adopted after World War II as a means of cutting through the airframes of large bombers and thus inflicting fatal damage; these warheads consist of rods joined together at alternating ends, wrapped around explosives. When the warhead detonates, the rods are forced apart into an expanding ring, which eventually breaks apart. The rods have considerable inertia and cannot move very fast. An alternative is pure blast-fragmentation, which may not chop up a bomber as effectively as a continuous rod but which propagates much faster. Presumably, the ultimate warhead would employ a shaped charge focused in one direction; the missile would roll toward its target before bursting.

The air-defense missiles described here vary considerably in guidance, ranging from self-guided (by infrared or active radar) to semiactive (homing on a signature imposed on the target) to command-guided (following decisions made externally). Each type of guidance has its own advantages. Self-guidance minimizes the load on the launch platform. In an airplane, self-guidance means fire-and-forget operation, allowing a fighter to engage multiple targets in quick succession. Similarly, in a ship, self-guidance helps counter saturation. However, because the intelligence that can be packed into a small missile is necessarily limited, the missile may be unable to overcome target countermeasures. In theory, the greater the intelligence that can be incorporated in a fighter or a ship, the greater that platform's abilities. However, pure command guidance necessarily becomes less accurate as range increases, since any particular angular error equates to a greater and greater miss distance (and ultimately to a miss distance beyond the lethal radius of the missile). Semiactive guidance is a compromise: the ship or airplane imposes a signature on the real target (and so limits the efficacy of countermeasures); but, homing on reflected energy, the missile, in theory, gains accuracy as it approaches the target. Semiactive guidance, however, requires that the weapons system dedicate a guidance illuminator to one target throughout the flight of the missile or missiles. For a ship, the number of such illuminators is limited by topside configuration. No airplane can afford more than a single illuminator. Thus, systems designed to defeat saturation are driven toward some mixture of command and self-homing. Command guidance has the additional advantage of extending a missile's range by flying the missile along an energy-efficient path. By way of contrast, semiactive guidance requires some type of pursuit path, which is inherently inefficient.

As in any other weapons system, the functioning of a naval air-defense system can be described as the sequence of detection, decision, and engagement. Initial detection is usually by radar at long range but may be by reception of enemy electronics emissions. Much depends on the speed and precision with which detection data can be converted into engagement commands. Simple radars feed into visual displays, such as PPIs (plan position indicators), which show the instantaneous situation. Weapons assignment (which includes fighter control), however, depends on target tracks, i.e., on the prediction of target position when weapons come into play.

In a simple radar system, then, weapons assignment is based on plots of successive radar data. Large numbers of incoming targets can saturate a manual plot (i.e., a manual CIC): hence the development of computer combat systems, such as NTDS, which make maintaining files easier. The next step is for the radar to incorporate a computer capable of distinguishing targets from the surrounding noise; this is automatic target detection (ATD). The following step is to use the computer to associate successive detections of each target: automatic detection and tracking (ADT). Moreover, the echoes received by the radar include doppler information from which target speed and direction (track) can be extracted, if the radar can maintain a coherent relationship between the pulse sent and the echo detected.

For the present, perhaps the single most important question is the extent to which shipboard systems can continue to provide area defense against faster and faster incoming attackers, i.e., in the face of shorter and shorter warning times. Without some form of area defense, each ship (and, ultimately, each merchant ship) needs its own point defense. On the other hand, if even modest area defense becomes sufficiently expensive, navies will be unable to field sufficient numbers of effective warships. One possibility is that missiles as they are currently understood will be superseded by lasers or other exotic directed-energy weapons, for which time of flight will no longer be a meaningful limitation.

This section includes a wide variety of shipboard missile countermeasures, both active (jammers) and passive (decoys). Often the two are associated, the jammers pulling an incoming missile off into the cloud of chaff. One problem with such systems is that the missile is unlikely to detonate in the chaff cloud. The missile may emerge from the cloud only to begin a target reacquisition routine; and the missile, if it still has sufficient fuel or energy on board, may then find the original target. That scenario would be most probable for missiles that hit their targets at very shallow angles, such as most sea-skimmers; missiles designed to make terminal dives may well dive through a chaff cloud into the sea. Thus, the best defense against a sea-skimmer may include some means of triggering the missile after it has been decoyed. One possibility would be to fire shells into the sea under the chaff cloud, to create a wall of splashes into which the missile would fly (or that would, at the least, trigger its fuze). No system integrating chaff and jammers and medium-caliber guns currently exists; but as combat systems become more fully integrated, such tactics would seem to be very easy to implement.

This section also includes submarine periscopes, with an emphasis on optronic devices. Because sonar may be limited in its ability to detect and track surface craft, periscopes are often the submarine's primary surface-search sensors and, thus, are in the same category as the submarine radars listed and described here. Moreover, the newer optronic (or photonic) periscopes share the technology of the optronic sensors and fire-control devices described in this section.

Periscopes are changing radically. Until the last decade, they were all optical, and most submarines had two types, a wide-angle search periscope and a narrow-angle attack scope, the latter intended to leave the narrowest possible wake so as not to reveal too easily the position of the submarine. A submarine commander would obtain his surface picture by making a quick sweep with his search periscope, the duration of the sweep determining both the quality of that picture and the extent to which he exposed himself to detection. Much of the submarine officer's training (for example, in the British "perishers'" course) was devoted to his ability to form a coherent surface picture after the briefest sweep.

As for the technology, very compact optics was developed to provide such facilities as alternative air and surface search in the same narrow tube, as well as stadimetric range finding. A stadimeter measures the angle between the horizontal and the observed height of an object; if the height (usually the masthead height) is known, the range can be calculated. From a submarine's point of view, the advantage of stadimetry is that the baseline is the object being measured, rather than the rangefinder (which must be quite small, so as to be unobtrusive). The horizontal equivalent of stadimetry, using the observed length of the target, is impractical because most targets will not be at right angles to the line of sight of the periscope.

There are also special night periscopes with greater light-gathering power. Some search periscopes are binocular, with duplicated windows at the top. At one time many search periscopes provided for air search, but now air warning is more usually the function of a radar-warning receiver found atop the search periscope.

Two major developments are associated with the post-1945 revolution in submarine design and performance, the combination of high underwater speed and indefinite submerged periods (snorkeling when required). The first development required search and radar periscopes that could be extended at relatively high speeds (the U.S. Navy called for periscopes that were extendable at 14 knots). High speed in turn induced severe vibration, and images had to be specially stabilized. The second development required sextants for taking navigational fixes to be incorporated in search periscopes. Conceivably, this requirement will lose its urgency with the rise of very accurate and universally available satellite navigational systems such as GPS, but surely the sextant will always be desirable as a backup against the destruction of the satellites.

Optronics is an outgrowth of television and thermal (IR) imaging technology. Periscopes were initially provided with these sensors, such as image intensifiers (low-light-level television, in effect), to extend the periscopes' usefulness to lower light levels. However, as with surface-ship and aircraft applications, the potential of converting the image into an electromagnetic signal is much greater since the image itself can be processed. In surface or air applications, the emphasis is usually on processing for tracking. In a periscope, the emphasis is more on processing the image to extract all of its information content and even to merge it with other relevant data.

The two applications of such cameras are quite different. A conventional or low-light-level television camera can be inserted in the bottom of the periscope, taking the same image as the periscope's eyepiece, on much the same principle as a single-lens reflex camera. However, an infrared sensor is best placed at the top of the periscope since thermal photons traveling all the way down the tube (e.g., to a camera at the base of the periscope) would suffer from added noise. Moreover, the optical components of the periscope will not focus or reflect infrared

radiation as they do light itself. Thus, a conventional periscope cannot be converted to infrared operation by simply installing a new crosshead, whereas that periscope can relatively easily be provided with an image intensifier.

Infrared operation requires installation of a thermal camera at the head of the periscope. The IR sensor must be cooled, and the coolant led up a very narrow periscope tube (or else a very compact refrigerator must be incorporated in the small periscope head).

Existing optronic periscopes employ a camera analogous to the window of a periscope, fixed rigidly to a tube that the observer rotates. However, there is no reason for the observer to memorize the scene as quickly as he can turn the periscope. In principle, the sensor can make a very quick scan (or even look simultaneously in several directions), and the image can be stored either digitally or in a video recorder, for display as desired on a CRT. The newer sensors can provide images of optical-periscope quality. That capability, in turn, opens up some very interesting possibilities.

The exposure associated with a periscope depends on two factors: the sheer size of the head and the time during which the head projects above water. Optronics probably always requires more space than simple optics, but optronics can also greatly reduce exposure time, since observation need not coincide with exposure. The submarine commander can view the resulting images for a protracted time, well after they have been created. Modern digital CRTs can display these images alongside other sensor data, such as ESM data collected at the same time by the same mast. The officer viewing such a windowed CRT can fuse the data from these various sources to form a much better tactical picture. In theory, the same CRT could also display relevant sound data, again adding to the overall tactical picture in a way impossible for a conventional optical system.

Perhaps at least as importantly, the commander of the submarine would no longer have to be the operator of the periscope sensor, just as he is not the operator, but rather the supervising user, of the various other acoustic and nonacoustic sensors on board a submarine. He could obtain his full tactical picture without having to concentrate all of his attention on the necessarily fleeting periscope image. Those manufacturers offering digital optronic or photonic periscopes, such as Dowty and Plessey, tend to suggest radically revised arrangements for submarine control rooms or operations rooms, in one case with the periscope image on a large screen on one bulkhead, surrounded by relevant data-base readouts (e.g., the characteristics of the ship shown on the screen, to the extent that the expert computer system connected to the data can identify the contact).

An optronic sensor unit might also be far lighter than conventional periscope-head optics and, thus, might be much easier to stabilize and even to control in an autotrack mode.

Moreover, there is no reason why an optronic or photonic sensor must be mounted on a mast penetrating into the control room of the submarine. In some submarines, such as the German IKL designs, all masts other than the periscope are already nonpenetrating; they telescope out of the sail of the submarine. Nonpenetration reduces structural stress in the submarine's hull and can simplify mast design, since the body of the mast no longer needs to be pressure tight. Instead, most of the mast can be free flooding. That design would allow the use of nonmetallic (i.e., non–radar-reflecting) materials. Moreover, there are considerable advantages (both in drag and in radar cross section) to be gained by using a noncylindrical mast (which is acceptable if the head, rather than the entire mast, rotates).

A control room or CIC served by an optical periscope must be directly under the sail, and that requirement complicates the arrangement of the submarine. For that matter, the central position of the optical periscope greatly complicates the internal arrangement of the control room or CIC; in theory, a much more efficient arrangement is possible. Presumably, the ultimate simplification would be to eliminate the mast altogether, placing the optronics and other sensors in a towed body that the submarine could launch and recover and that would use some inertial device (such as a ring-laser gyro) to locate itself relative to the hull of the submarine. In theory, such a development would greatly reduce the drag and noise of the submarine's hull, and the submarine could remain much farther below the surface at what would amount to periscope depth.

In practice, submariners have resisted total dependence on any form of electronics; an optical periscope will still work even if electrical problems have put computers and displays out of action. Attempts to eliminate the submarine's sail altogether have been quite frequent, at least in the U.S. Navy, but have generally failed because the sail is needed for some other quite essential purposes: for good depth keeping near the surface in relatively shallow water (but this requirement does not apply to a submarine with her foreplanes on her hull); for navigating on the surface, e.g., when entering port; and for supporting the snorkel.

It would be impractical to convert an existing optical periscope to optronic or photonic operation because considerable information is lost between the lens at the top and any sensor inserted at the bottom, particularly with infrared images. On the other hand, periscope photography, which is a sort of predecessor to optronics, has been common for many years.

SHIPBOARD RADARS AND FIRE-CONTROL SYSTEMS

CANADA

RADARS

◆ SPG-515

This new Norden radar replaces the U.S. SPG-48 on board Canadian destroyers (frigates); the modified fire-control system is designated Mk 60. The new fire-control system is said to show a 40-percent improvement in accuracy against moving, incoming targets. Mk 60 is a digital version of, and replaces, the U.S. GFCS Mk 69.

◆ SPS-501

This radar is essentially a Dutch LW-03 antenna combined with a U.S.-type SPS-12 transmitter. In 1984 a Canadian company, SPAR, marketed a new solid-state receiver for SPS-12 radars, presumably intended largely for the modernization of existing Canadian SPS-501 radars. The company also improved range

SPS-501 is the main radar on board the Canadian destroyer *Algonquin*, 1984. The array along the side of the barbette supporting the Signaal "egg" (WM-22) is a version of the U.S. ULQ-6. The small antenna visible on the platform above SPS-501 is an Italian-supplied SPQ-2D. (George G. Mortimore, RN)

resolution (to 200 m in wide-band/short-pulse mode, and to 800 m in narrow-band/long-pulse mode). Specified mean time between failure was over 10,000 hours. The modification kit was also much smaller than the original SPS-12 receiver.

◆ SPS-502

Cardion Electronics's solid-state surface-search radar, although using the SPS-10 antenna, has more than 95 percent of its parts compatible with the company's SPS-55.

◆ SPS-503

Band: S(2.7–3.2 GHz, i.e., frequency-agile over 500 MHz)
Beam: 1.5 × csc2 to 40 deg
Peak Power: 20 kW (average 800 W)   Gain: 30.75 dB
Pulse Width: 54 microsec (0.6 microsec subsidiary pulse)
PRF: 739 pps (stagger, plus or minus 12.5 percent)
Scan Rate: 10 or 20 rpm
Antenna Dimensions: 4.7-m width
Antenna Weight: total system weight 1300 kg (2865 lbs); antenna 490 kg (1080 lbs)

SPS-503 radar antenna at the Canadian Marconi plant, Kanata, Ontario. (Canadian Marconi)

This air/surface-search radar, by Canadian Marconi Radar (CMR), is made for the modernized frigates (DELEX program) and replaces the older U.S. SPS-12. An adapted Marconi S1821, SPS-503 is a pulse-compression radar using a coherent transmitter (providing digital MTI); it has both MTI and non-MTI channels. The SPS-503's antenna is that of the Plessey AWS-4. This radar can employ either linearly or circularly polarized radiation, the latter being useful in severe weather. There is an alternative 2.44-meter stabilized antenna in a radome, providing a beam of 2.8 × csc2 to 30 deg, with a total weight of 500 kg and a scan rate of 12 and 24 rpm. Gain is 28.5 dB. Signals are horizontally polarized. The basic radar using the alternative antenna is designated CMR-1 (a Canadian Marconi designation).

Canadian Marconi also offers a version using an unstabilized planar-array antenna (3.5-m aperture, 2.1 deg × csc2 to 40 deg beam, 29.8-dB gain, 10/20 or 15/30 rpm scan). Signals are vertically polarized.

SPS-503 uses two TWTs driven in parallel (with output phase matching) by a solid-state frequency synthesizer. Transmission modes: pulse-to-pulse frequency agility among sixteen frequencies (non-MTI), block-to-block (three pulse) frequency agility (MTI), and fixed-frequency (MTI). PRF can be staggered to protect against lock-on jamming, and a jamming-strobe indicator alerts the operator to the presence and azimuth of noise jammers. The transmitted pulse consists of a 54-microsecond chirp (which is pulse-compressed) and a short (0.6-microsecond) unmodulated pulse, the latter for short ranges, to reduce energy on target (and thus the reflected energy from nearby clutter). The receiver compression ratio is 207.7:1, and the range cell is

39 m (minimum range is 200 m). The first blind speed is 1700 m/sec (3300 kts). Rated ranges against 4, 1, and 0.1 square-meter targets: 152, 108, 61 km (126, 90, and 51 km, respectively, with the 2.4-m antenna). Instrumented range is 160 km. Accuracy: 2.5 m in range, 0.29 deg in azimuth. Resolution: 39 m, 1.5 deg. Rated reliability: 305 hours MTBF, 1.0 hours MTTR.

A related radar, CMR-4, uses the 2.4-m antenna also, but at C-band (5.4–5.9 GHz), with a single TWT, the same transmission modes as CMR-1, and peak power 14 kW (mean power 330 W, PRF 1600 pps). Rated ranges against 4, 1, and 0.1 square-meter targets are 74, 52, and 30 km, respectively.

◆ LN-66 (CMR-85, SPS-59)

Band: X (9375 MHz) **Beam:** 2.5 × 22 deg
Peak Power: 75 kW **Gain:** 30 dB
Pulse Width: 1.0 or 0.1 microsec
PRF: 500 or 2000 pps **Scan Rate:** 22 rpm
Antenna Dimensions: 36 in **Antenna Weight:** total weight 22.9 kg

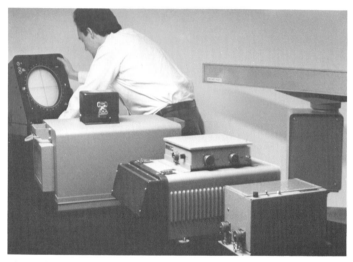

The 75-kW version of the LN-66 radar. A modified form is installed on board U.S. Navy LAMPS helicopters. (Canadian Marconi)

Data in this table refer to LN-66 HP, the search radar of the U.S. LAMPS I helicopter.

This surface-search radar, built by Canadian Marconi, has been very widely exported, both in its shipboard version and in a related helicopter version (on board U.S. LAMPS I helicopters). A related radar is used for submarine navigation (U.S. *Ohio*-class submarines), on board U.S. LCAC landing craft, and also on board U.S. small combatants such as the SEALs' Seafox. In the 75-kW version described above, range discrimination is 18.3 m. Range scales are 1, 2, 3, 12, 24, 48, and 72 nm.

The basic 10-kW version is designated SPS-59(V)1 in U.S. Army service. 59(V)1 uses a 5-foot slotted-waveguide antenna (AS-3146). A current solid-state version of the basic radar increases power to 12 kW. These radars can also be used with a 3-ft (radome-enclosed) or 8-ft slotted waveguide. This 3-ft antenna, not described above, produces a 2.7 × 26 deg beam (gain 26.5 dB). Pulse widths are 0.5 and 0.09 microsec (PRFs 800/1250 and 2500 pps, respectively). Minimum range is 20 yds, and range scales are 0.25–48 nm. There are also 5-ft (60-inch) and 8-ft (96-inch) slotted-array antennas used with the 75-kW transmitter described in the table. The 60-inch version has a 1.6 × 19 degree beam (gain 29 dB) and scans at 24 rpm. The 96-inch version has a 0.88 × 19 degree beam (gain 31 dB). A version with a dual-display is used as TPS-66 in the U.S. Navy AN/TSQ-108 Radar/Sonar Surveillance Center.

As of 1988, Canadian Marconi was offering a 90-kW version of the basic radar to replace the 75-kW version. The former has the same pulse widths and PRFs as the 75-kW version.

In addition, there is LN-66 SP, a 6-kW version for submarines and small craft, that uses either a 3-ft radome antenna or a 4-ft detachable slotted waveguide (1.9 × 26 deg beam, gain 28 dB). Pulse widths are 0.5 and 0.12 microseconds (PRFs 1200 and 3000 pps). Minimum detection range is 25 yds, and range scales are 0.5–32 nm. About 1988 the LN-66 SP was redesignated CMR-85. Despite the official AN/SPS-59 designation, LN-66s in U.S. naval service are almost invariably called LN-66.

◆ Sperry Mk 2

Band: X (9320–9430 MHz) **Beam:** 1 deg (horizontal width)
Peak Power: 35 kW **Pulse Width:** 0.25 microsec
PRF: 1000 pps **Scan Rate:** 15 rpm

For many years the Sperry Mk 2 was the standard surface-search radar of the Royal Canadian Navy.

OPTRONICS

◆ SAR-8

The Advanced Development Model of the SAR-8 IR search-and-tracking sensor. (SPAR Aerospace)

The General Electric/SPAR infrared-search and target-designation (IRST) system was a joint U.S.-Canadian project. SAR-8 was tested at sea in 1978 on board HMCS *Algonquin* and in 1979 on board USS *Kincaid*. Full-scale engineering development began in FY84.

SAR-8 is a cylindrical mechanism gimbal-mounted for stability, continuously scanning for a 2-second data rate (track-while-scan). This system can passively detect both air and surface targets, using a signal processor to detect small targets in heavy clutter. The surface display provides both a 360-degree panoramic view and an expanded display of any selected sector, for target identification. The published description suggests that SAR-8 is able to detect incoming air targets by the glint on their forward surfaces or by the aerodynamic heat generated on the targets' bodies. This type of system can also detect incoming missiles beyond the horizon by sensing their exhaust plumes. Although generally not precise enough for missile counterbattery fire, such detection can be used to trigger countermeasures under EMCON conditions.

Total weight is about 6500 lbs, of which 1350 lbs is above decks. The ship provides heading, speed, and altitude data, and SAR-8 scans at 0.5 revolutions per second. Power requirement is 25 kVA, and above-deck volume is about 150 cubic feet. The associated computer is the new standard UYK-44. A combination of filters (spatial and temporal) and tuned algorithms is applied to the scene as observed; each source is analyzed to determine whether it is either (i) an airplane or missile or (ii) clutter. Any source classified as (i) has its bearing, elevation angle, and track data transmitted directly and automatically to the combat system. This point-source processing is supplemented by a panoramic image of the surrounding ships and other surface features, which is provided to the operator.

SPAR Aerospace developed its first infrared search-and-track system in the early 1960s, and between 1962 and 1967 developed an infrared acquisition system for the abortive U.S. Mauler point-defense missile. In 1968–70 the company developed and tested an Infrared Electronic Warfare System (IREWS) for the U.S. Navy, and this system was further modified in 1971–73. In 1974–77 the Canadian Navy sponsored the development and test of a Shipboard Passive Surveillance-and-Detection System (SPSDS). That project in turn led in July 1976 to a U.S.-Canadian MoU and Joint Project Agreement to develop an advanced development model of the IR Search-and-Track System (IRST), which became SAR-8. The Joint Agreement for Engineering Development of SAR-8 was signed in January 1983, and SPAR was selected as prime contractor in August 1984.

The prototype SAR-8. (SPAR)

CHILE

The ASMAR national shipyard exhibited several radars at the 1984 Feria Internacional del Aire (FIDA) at Santiago. Foremost among them were a dual-band (S and X) shipboard fire-control radar (six of which had been produced) and a containerized S-band air-search radar.

CHINA (PRC)

SEARCH

◆ Bean Sticks/Pea Sticks

The two names indicate alternative antennas for the same P-band early-warning radar, in *Luda*-class destroyers. Bean Sticks consists of four bays, each with 8 yagis.

This *Luda*-class destroyer carries a Bean Sticks long-range air-search radar (4 × 4 array of yagis) just forward of her after funnel. The foremast radar is an Eye Shield (MX-902) short-range (target-indication) air-search set. The forward end of the platform carries a surface-search radar. The secondary battery consists of twin 37-mm and 25-mm machine cannon, and she carries two triple missile launchers. (U.S. Naval Institute)

This *Luda*-class destroyer carries a Pea Sticks long-range air-search radar. (U.S. Naval Institute)

◆ Eye Shield (MX-902)

An Egyptian *Jianghu*-class frigate shows, on her mast, an Eye Shield air-search radar at top and a Square Tie missile target-designator two levels down. One of the slotted waveguides is a Decca radar; the other is a Chinese Type 756. The director carries what appears to be a yagi array (like that of the old British Type 285) on its roof. The twin 37-mm guns are locally controlled. (U.S. Naval Institute)

A Chinese *Jianghu*-class frigate shows an Eye Shield radar at her mast-head, with a Type-756 navigational radar (the slotted waveguide) and Square Tie (missile fire control) below it. (U.S. Naval Institute)

Eye Shield is the air-search radar in *Jianghu*-class frigates. The antenna is a long, slim paraboloid, similar in overall shape to such Soviet radars as Slim Net and Head Net A, except that the Chinese antenna is of solid rather than lattice construction. (Slim Net is still in Chinese service on board four Riga-class frigates built in Chinese yards (with Soviet parts) in the late 1950s).

The Chinese designation for Eye Shield is MX-902.

This radar is also in service on board the Chinese frigates transferred to Egypt.

◆ ESR-1

> **Band:** S   **Beam:** 2 × 10 deg (dual-beam pattern)
> **Gain:** 33.5 dB   **Scan Rate:** 30 rpm
> **Antenna Weight:** 350 kg (770 lbs)

This low-altitude air-search radar was displayed at the ASIANDEX exhibition in Beijing in the fall of 1988. The antenna is roll-stabilized, and the 31-cm (12-inch) PPI is arranged for plot extraction by roller-ball. The scope can also display synthetic video, and the radar can extract moving targets. The MTI improvement factor is 22 dB. The manufacturer, the China Shipbuilding Trading Co., claims that ESR-1 can detect a 0.1 square-meter sea-skimming missile (flying at a height of 8 m) at a range greater than 12 km (about 13,000 yds.)

The data above are taken from the manufacturer's brochure. No power or pulse data were given.

◆ Rice Screen (Sea Eagle)

> **Band:** C (described as upper end of G-band)
> **Beam:** 2.7 × 1.4 deg   **Peak Power:** 150 kW
> **Pulse Width:** (i) 40 (ii) 20 microsec (compressed to 1 microsec)
> **PRF:** (i) 370 (ii) 730 (average power 2.2 kW) pps
> **Scan Rate:** 5 rpm

This planar-array three-dimensional pulse-compression radar entered service in the mid-1980s and was publicly displayed (with the data given above and below) at the ASIANDEX 1988 exhibition in Beijing. Rice Screen is marketed for export by the Nanjing Marine Institute.

There are two types, with larger and smaller antennas. The data above refer to a large antenna, much taller than it is wide. A smaller type is reportedly 2.3 × 3.0 m, which would not quite correspond to the beam figures above. However, the beam figures come from the claimed resolution performance, and the resolution in azimuth may be degraded somewhat as the beam sweeps up while the radar turns. The radar antenna shows a prominent fin on one side, presumably carrying a serpentine (frequency-scanning) waveguide. Phase shifters are presumably used to allow the radar to sweep in frequency (both for pulse compression and for frequency agility) without sweeping its beam up and down.

This radar can semiautomatically track ten targets simultaneously, using what the manufacturer calls an extraction PPI operating semiautomatically. Probably the operator designates

Rice Screen (top), Type 756, and Fog Lamp (bottom) on a *Jiangdong*-class frigate. (U.S. Naval Institute)

the targets to the associated computer. Two or more entries of the same target (on subsequent scans) provide the computer with a track. The operator then monitors later detections of the same target to see whether it remains on a constant course and speed. The target's altitude may be as high as 25,000 m (82,000 ft). There are two operating modes: low angle (up to 7.2 deg in elevation) to a maximum tracking range of 180 km (197,000 yds), and high angle (to 28.8 deg) out to a maximum range of 120 km (131,000 yds).

The transmitter is a TWT CFA chain, and reception is coherent, with an MTI improvement factor of 30 dB. Accuracy is 100 m in range and 0.8 degrees in azimuth and elevation. Resolution is 200 m in range. Operation is over a wide band (10 percent of frequency), with adaptive frequency selection on a pulse-to-pulse basis.

◆ Type 354

> **Band:** C   **Beam:** 1.2 × 5 deg
> **Peak Power:** 500 kW   **Pulse Width:** 2 microsec
> **PRF:** 400 or 800 pps   **Scan Rate:** 4–10 rpm

This low-altitude air-search radar is used for target acquisition on board missile frigates. The antenna is roll- and pitch-stabilized. Claimed range on a 10 square-meter target is over 50 nm, accuracy is 5 m in range and 5 mrad in bearing, and resolution is 300 m in range and 1.3 deg in bearing.

◆ Type 756

> **Band:** (a and b) X (c) S
> **Beam:** (a) 1.3 × 20 deg (b) 0.8 × 18 deg (c) 2 × 22 deg
> **Peak Power:** 50 kW   **Gain:** (a) 30 dB (b) 32 dB (c) 27 dB
> **Pulse Width:** (i) 0.08 microsec (ii) 0.5 microsec (iii) 1 microsec
> **PRF:** (i) 2000 (ii) 1000 (iii) 500 pps   **Scan Rate:** 18–22 rpm
> **Antenna Dimensions:** (a) 2 m (b) 3 m (c) 3.8 m

This navigational radar uses a slotted-waveguide antenna. Range scales are 0.5, 1.5, and 3 nm with short pulse; 6, 12, and 24 nm with 0.5 microsecond pulse; and 48 and 96 nm with long pulse. The complete system uses both X- and S-band antennas for all-weather performance. Minimum range is about 30 m (mast height 15 m), and range discrimination is 25 m. Accuracy is 1 percent of range or 0.02 nm (whichever is greater) and 1 degree.

FIRE CONTROL

◆ EFR-1

The China Shipbuilding Trading Co. displayed this new naval radar fire-control system at the ASIANDEX exhibition at Beijing in November 1988. EFR-1 is a radar fire-control system externally similar to the French Castor series (i.e., with a Cassegrain antenna), with a television camera and a laser alongside the radar. EFR-1 was described as operating in X-band, with MTI processing, and was credited with the ability to acquire targets with cross sections of less than 2 square meters at ranges beyond 30 km (and small sea-skimming missiles at 13 km).

EFR-1 is being offered as a feature of several new warship designs being offered for export; presumably this system is planned for a new generation of Chinese warships.

◆ Fog Lamp

This radar is the H/I-band SAM fire control for the HY-61 missile.

Top to bottom: Rice Lamp, Fog Lamp, and a twin HQ 61 missile launcher on a *Zhongdong*-class frigate. (U.S. Naval Institute)

◆ Rice Lamp

This radar is an X-band gunfire-control radar.

DENMARK

◆ Terma Skanter Mil Radars

Band: X (9 GHz) or S (3 GHz)
Beam: 1 deg (horizontal beamwidth) at X-band (2 deg for S-band version)
Peak Power: 20 kW   Pulse Width: (i) 0.06 (ii) 0.6 microsec
PRF: (i) 4400 (ii) 2200 pps
Gain: greater than 30 dB (X) or 28.5 dB (S-band)

Scan Rate: 24 or 48 rpm (60-Hz power; 20 or 40 rpm using 50-Hz power supply)
Antenna Dimensions: 2.1 m (X-band), 4 m (S-band)

Terma Elektronik AS, a Danish company, has developed several slotted-waveguide surface-search and navigational radars for the Danish and Swedish Navies. The Danish designations are NWS-1, -2, and -3; the standard Swedish unit is Skanter 009. The published data above refer to a radar whose development was completed in 1972. The transmitter is a magnetron, and the system as a whole can accommodate either S- or X-band operation, or a combination of the two (using different transmitters and antennas, feeding a common display). All displays are raster rather than rotating scan and are usable in daylight; they are adapted to show tactical system symbology and to operate with automatic tracking.

FRANCE

All French shipboard naval radars are products of Thomson-CSF. TRS numbers in parentheses are the commercial designations, where they apply. Many directors are produced by CSEE.

RADARS

◆ DRBC 32

DRBC 32E fire-control radar on board the corvette *d'Estienne d'Orves*. (U.S. Naval Institute)

DRBC 32 is an X-band monopulse radar designed specifically to control the 100-mm automatic gun; versions run from 32A through 32E. The beam is 1.5 degrees wide. Targets are automatically acquired, and all processing is digital. This radar is generally mounted on a director carrying an optical range-finder.

◆ DRBC 33 (Castor II: TRS 3203)

Band: X Beam: 2.45 × 2.3 deg
Peak Power: 30 kW, 120 W average   Gain: 36 dB
Pulse Width: 0.5 microsec
PRF: computer controlled between 4000 and 8000 pps
Antenna Dimensions: working circle 1.6 m; dish diameter 1.053 m
Antenna Weight: total director weight 620 kg

Data are for the Castor IIC version. The original Castor II may have used 4-microsecond, 80-kW pulses.

Reportedly capable of acquiring and tracking a 0.1 square-meter target at 8 nm, this radar is built both for the French Navy and for export.

Castor II is a monopulse tracker using a Cassegrain antenna. Tracking includes multigate doppler filtering (900 m) using an 8-point fast Fourier transform; the fully coherent transmitter is a TWT that can produce numerous computer-chosen frequencies over a 700-MHz bandwidth, somewhat less than 10 percent of base frequency. Tracking range is from 500 to 30,000 m, and the first blind speed is at or beyond Mach 2. Elevation limits are −25 and +85 degrees.

Acquisition is automatic, for very quick reaction, at ranges up to 25 km on a fighter and 15 km on an antiship missile. To ensure accurate tracking, the radar operates in short bursts (1.5 millisec) at constant frequency, associating frequency agility and doppler processing; the radar can also jump from frequency to frequency on a pulse-to-pulse basis. Castor II can also passively track a jammer using range information from a tracker linked to a search radar. When directing shellfire, this system can display the angular error between shell and target. The radar can also be used for autonomous surveillance, scanning at a fixed elevation.

Castor IIB (TRS 3200) is a somewhat less sophisticated radar using the same antenna as II, but with single-knob tuning within the 700-MHz band. Pulse width is set at 0.4 microsec and PRF at 3600 or 7200 pps (with staggering). MTI processing uses a 3-memory filter. Compared to Castor IIC, IIB's sea clutter rejection ratio is 30 rather than 40 dB, and the transmitter weighs 80 kg rather than 200 kg.

Castor IIC limits: tracking range 0.5–27 km, radial speed 1000 m/sec, maximum train (elevation) speeds 1 (1.5) rad/sec. The probability of automatic acquisition in free space, for a 2 square-meter target, is 80 percent at 25 km. Clutter cancellation ratio is 40 dB for ground clutter, 35 dB for sea clutter. The associated TV/IR camera (TRAKIR) can place extraction gates (2.2 × 1.7 or 4.4 × 3.4 mrad) around a target, for tracking. The camera has a 35 × 27 mrad field of view.

Castor IIJ is a J(Ku)-band radar/TV/IR director, designed as the basis of an all-weather antimissile system. This radar is specially designed to track in a cluttered and jammed environment, even at low altitude. Castor IIJ uses a Cassegrain antenna (gain 43 dB, beam 1.5 × 0.67 deg) and a TWT transmitter (pulses 7.5 microseconds). As in Castor IIC, there is an associated TRAKIR TV/IR tracker. Total height above deck is 2.422 m. The associated software uses a special low-altitude tracking algorithm that compensates for the image (multipath) effect of the sea's surface. In tests at Gavres in 1987 (see also the entry for the SATAN close-in weapon) the target, flying at an altitude of 7 m at 300 kts, was tracked with a standard deviation of 0.3 mrad (about 30 cm) at 1000 m range. Operational limits: tracking range 0.35 to 30 km, elevation +85/−25 deg, maximum speed 1000 m/sec. Acquisition time on an air target, with 90-degree bearing-slewing angle and 5-deg elevation search, is 2.8 sec; if identified as a sea-skimmer, 1.75 sec. The probability of automatic acquisition in free space (one false alarm/minute) is 90 percent at 18 km for 0.1 square meters and 90 percent at 30 km for 2 square meters: both figures are calculated for Swerling class 3.

Castor II is used with Vega fire-control systems in fast minor craft, including West German fast attack craft.

Castor IIC. (Thomson-CSF)

Castor IIJ. (Thomson-CSF)

♦ **DRBI 10**

Band: S　**Beam:** 2 × 2 deg
Peak Power: 1000–2000 kW　**Gain:** 37 dB
Pulse Width: 4 microsec　**PRF:** 500 pps
Scan Rate: 4 rpm (vertically: 800 scans/min)
Antenna Dimensions: 3.4 × 3.4 m

DRBI 10 is the height-finder on board the *Clemenceau*-class carriers. DRBI 10 uses a high-speed (Robinson) scanner. This radar is a naval version of the Picador (TRS 2200) ground system; the details above are all derived from the land-based version. Range on a fighter is said to be 100–140 nm.

The French carrier *Clemenceau*, 1972, shows typical radars: from top to bottom, they are: TACAN, IFF Mk 10, DRBV 22, DRBV 20 (large-ship version), DRBI 10 (both fore and aft of the funnel). (Giorgio Arra)

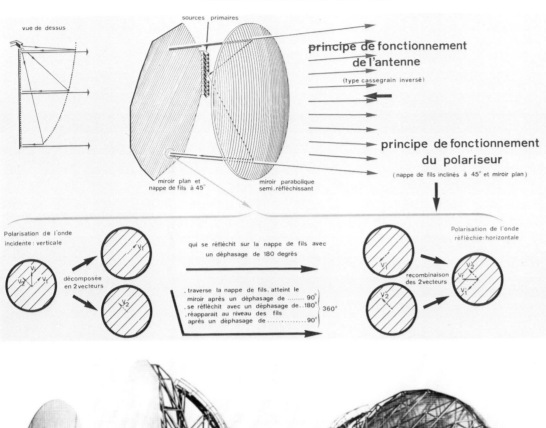

The antenna of the DRBI 23 radar, shown (*bottom*) without its radome. The array of stacked microwave horns produce the stacked beam used for monopulse height finding. (*top*) shows the principle of the antenna. The horns ("*sources primaires*") illuminate a semireflecting parabolic mirror. The mirror reflects onto a secondary reflector that twists the polarization of the beam so that it can pass through the first reflector. This type of folded optics makes it possible to achieve considerable focusing of the radar beam in limited dimensions, i.e., within a radome. Moreover, the elaborate feed does not block the main beam of the radar, an important consideration in any stacked-beam or monopulse system. This type of operation is typical of inverse-Cassegrain antennas, although most of them are not nearly as elaborate. (Thomson-CSF)

◆ DRBI 23

DRBI 23 is the large L-band radome-enclosed pulse-doppler antenna on board the missile frigates *Suffren* and *Duquesne*. The antenna is a big inverse Cassegrain reflector using stacked beams (monopulse height finding). A smaller version, DRBV 13, was formerly carried on board the destroyer *Aconit*.

◆ DRBJ 11

Band: S   **Scan Rate:** 15 rpm
Antenna Dimensions: diameter 3 m (dish)

DRBI 23 occupies the big radome of the French frigate *Suffren*. The two 100-mm guns are controlled by the DRBC 32A forward of the bridge, and the navigational radar is DRBN 32. The small radar on the foremast just above the big radome is DRBV 50. (Dr. Robert Scheina)

The Thomson-CSF electronically scanned radar uses a circular planar antenna covered by 1000–1500 phase shifters, which steer the beam in elevation (over a 60-degree angle) and in bearing. The antenna itself is inclined at a 15-degree angle and rotates inside a radome. Surveillance range is about 100 nm.

Development began in 1982. DRBJ 11 was not delivered because of ECCM problems. *Cassard*, therefore, had to be completed without the radar. The improved version, DRBJ 11B, is to appear on board the second C70AA ship, *Jean Bart*, which is scheduled for completion in March 1990.

♦ DRBN 32

Decca RM 1226 navigational radar (see the British section below) is being superseded by Decca 1229.

♦ DRBR 51

DRBR 51 is the Masurca missile's C-band monopulse guidance-radar, roughly equivalent to the U.S. SPG-55. The missile is built in both beam-riding and semiactive versions; each radar group consists of a pair of antennas, a large-diameter tracker (which can also measure the deviation of the missile from the line of sight) and a small-diameter command transmitter. A third antenna generates the initial gathering beam. CW power is injected into the main dish for semiactive operation. Missiles are tracked at a wavelength of 5 cm and command signals transmitted at a wavelength of 7 cm; the tracking channels are designated "blue" and "yellow."

♦ DRBV 15 (Sea Tiger: TRS 3001)

> **Band:** S **Beam:** 1.65 × 8 deg cos2 (to 45 deg)
> **Peak Power:** 60 kW (1 kW average) **Gain:** 29.5 dB
> **Pulse Width:** (i) 5.5 (ii) 12 microsec (compressed to 0.5) (In a later version, this radar produces two types of burst, each consisting of a 0.5-microsecond pulse and then a chirp, either 7.5 or 15.5 microsec long, compressed to 0.5 microsec in either case.)
> **PRF:** (i) 2200 (ii) 1100 pps
> **Scan Rate:** 12 or 24 rpm (also given as 15 or 30 rpm)
> **Antenna Dimensions:** 4.54 m **Antenna Weight:** 675 kg

Sea Tiger is a combined surveillance radar for medium and larger ships, its design emphasizing a low false-alarm rate to permit automatic tracking. The radar can carry out full air surveillance out to 170 km (55-deg elevation), surface surveillance to the horizon, and surveillance against sea-skimming missiles.

DRBV 15 (Sea Tiger). (Thomson-CSF)

The chief antijam and anticlutter measures are coherent transmission/reception (which allows doppler filtering of clutter), true frequency agility (either pulse-to-pulse on the nondoppler channel, or randomly in short bursts of ten pulses on the doppler channel), and use of two pulses at two different frequencies. The radar uses pulse compression and detects automatically using CFAR; and DRBV 15 can provide digital data to a weapons system. Doppler processing is by 4 or 8 point fast Fourier transform.

There are two operating modes, each using two pulses: one long pulse with compression followed by one short pulse for short-range surveillance, at a different frequency. PRF can be jittered ("wobbulated").

Free-space range on a 2 square-meter target (Swerling 3 case) is 110 km; on a 0.1 square-meter non-fluctuating target (probability of detection 0.9), 40 km. Actual performance depends upon the degree of surface clutter. Clutter-rejection ratios: 45 dB vs. ground clutter, 40 dB vs. rain and sea clutter.

Sea Tiger can be used as the search radar for a Vega fire-control system. Derived from the French Army Tiger air-search radar, Sea Tiger displaced the Saturne 2 naval air-search radar.

♦ DRBV 20

Radars on the mast of a French frigate: (1) DRBV 20 (small-ship version, now extinct); (2) DRBV 30 surface-search radar; (3) IFF Mk 10. (Thomson-CSF)

This large, high-powered (1-MW) P-band radar, with a flat mattress antenna (carrying three rows of dipoles), is found on board the cruiser *Colbert* and, formerly, on board the two French carriers. Pulse widths: 8 and 4 microseconds (PRF 100 and 200 pps).

♦ DRBV 22/23 (Jupiter: THD 1077)

> **Band:** L **Beam:** 2.5 × 50 deg (3.5 × 16 deg csc2)
> **Peak Power:** 2000 kW (600 kW) **Gain:** (26 dB)
> **Pulse Width:** 2.5 microsec (1.3 or 4 microsec)
> **PRF:** 450 pps (600 or 200 pps)
> **Scan Rate:** 7.5 and 15 rpm (6 or 12 rpm)
> **Antenna Dimensions:** 24.6 × 9.9 ft (DRBV 22: 5.18 × 2.13 m)

Jupiter is the export version of DRBV 23, and its characteristics are listed above (DRBV 22 data in parentheses). DRBV 22 resembled the U.S. SPS-6B externally; DRBV 22C introduced a new elliptical stabilized antenna, which in turn was combined with a new and much more powerful transmitter in DRBV 23. Development of this set began in 1961; its maximum range is about 160 nm. DRBV 22's range is about 70 nm.

Radars on board the French *D'Estrées*-class destroyer: (1) DRBV 22A (air search), (2) DRBV 50 (surface search), and (3) DRBC 32 (gunfire control). (Stefanio Cioglia)

♦ **DRBV 26 (Jupiter II: TRS 3010)/DRBV 26C (Jupiter IIS)/ Astral**

> **Band:** L (23 cm) **Beam:** 2.5 × 8.3 csc2 (to 50 deg)
> **Peak Power:** 2 MW (average 2 kW) **Gain:** 29 dB
> **Pulse Width:** 2.5 microsec
> **PRF:** 450 pps (fixed or staggered) **Scan Rate:** 7.5 or 15 rpm
> **Antenna Dimensions:** 7.535 × 3.05 m
> **Antenna Weight:** 1000 kg approx (total 1450 kg)

DRBV 26C (Jupiter III). (Thomson-CSF)

Work on an improved Jupiter, DRBV 26, began in 1972, for the new generation of missile ships. Range is said to be 150+ nm (on a 10 square-meter target). Protection against false alarms and clutter includes a low-sidelobe antenna, filters for protection against signals from nearby ships (high-frequency bands as well as the same band), multiple reception channels with wide dynamic-range receivers and anticlutter circuits, MTI for air surveillance, and a CFAR antijam receiver. The main improvement over Jupiter I may have been in reliability. Resolution is 400 m and 2 degrees.

Jupiter IIS has a pulse-compression transmitter (130 microsec, compressed to 0.8) and is frequency agile on a burst-to-burst or pulse-to-pulse basis. The tube transmitter of Jupiter II is replaced by a solid-state transmitter consisting of sixteen modules in parallel. Claimed reliability: MTBF for each module is 6060 hours, and for the entire transmitter, excluding the modules, 2180 hours. Mean time to repair (MTTR) is 15 minutes for the transmitter (excluding modules) and 4.5 minutes per module; modules can be replaced while transmitting. Free-space detection range on a 10 square-meter aircraft is 160+ nm and free-space range on a 2 square-meter target is 116+ nm. A plot extractor can be added for TWS operation.

Growth possibilities include provision of a three-beam antenna for "2.5-D" search capability, and an increase in transmitter power by a factor of two or four.

DRBV 27, which is presumably the improved DRBV 26, is scheduled for the carrier *Charles de Gaulle*, which will also have the Arabel missile-targeting radar (for the Syrinx system).

Astral is a new three-dimensional radar derived from DRBV 26C, but Astral uses a new antenna and scans one beam in elevation (as compared to two beams in DRBJ 11). Mean power will be twice that of the earlier radar (5 kW compared to 2.5 kW), and the radar will be offered as the long-range acquisition set of the FAMS missile system, turning targets over to the shorter-range multifunction radar (MFR). Coverage and other characteristics are compatible with those of Arabel, so that the two radars can work in tandem. Maximum range will be about 275 km.

♦ **DRBV 31**

This license-built Decca X-band navigational radar for destroyers and escorts survives on board a single ship.

♦ **DRBV 50**

The development of this low-flier/surface-search radar began in 1961. It equipped the *Jeanne d'Arc* and *Maille Breze* classes and was planned for the *Commandant Rivière* class (which is equipped with the DRBN 32 instead).

♦ **DRBV 51A**

The corvette *d'Estienne d'Orves* shows a DRBV 51A main search radar and a DRBC 32E fire-control radar atop her superstructure. The two light-colored circles in the after superstructure cover two torpedo-firing catapults. The small slotted waveguide immediately above the bridge is DRBN 32. (U.S. Naval Institute)

DRBV 51A is a low-altitude air-search and Exocet target-designation radar, a Triton with a higher-gain slotted-waveguide antenna (for longer range). DRBV 51A, most closely comparable to Triton II (see below), is the main radar of the *d'Estienne d'Orves*-class (A69 type) aviso.

DRBV 51 (top) and DRBV 26 (below) search radars on board the destroyer *Duguay-Trouin*. (L&L Van Ginderen)

◆ DRUA-32

DRUA-32 is a submarine surface-search radar.

◆ DRUA-33 (Calypso)

   Band: X   **Beam:** 3 × 8.5 deg
   Peak Power: 70 kW   **Gain:** less than 29 dB
   Pulse Width: (i) 0.15 (ii) 0.5 microsec
   PRF: (i) 1500–3000 (ii) 500–1000 pps
   Scan Rate: 12 or 24 rpm   **Antenna Dimensions:** 1 m × 48 cm
   Antenna Weight: 60 kg (total weight 450 kg)

Data are for Calypso III. Calypso II had a slightly greater gain and somewhat lower power.

The submarine surface-search radar, 1964, led to the Calypso export radar. Calypso III was developed in conjunction with the German IKL design organization, for Type-209 submarines.

Operating modes are continuous transmission, sector surveillance, short-time transmission (0.1 or 1 second only), and silent operation with a dummy load to permit testing. Scan modes are full 360 deg, sector (adjustable between 10 and 180 deg), short-time scan over 10 deg, or manual scan. Calypso II could detect a 10 square-meter airplane at 16 nm. The improved Calypso III can detect an ASW airplane (10 square meters) at 18 nm at 8000 ft.

In one version of Calypso, a separate range-only antenna is mounted on the attack periscope.

Calypso II has its antenna on a rotating mast that can be hoisted. Calypso III uses a non-rotating mast, with the scanning

mechanism at the masthead. Calypso III has the same transmitter, but with anticlutter processing for better range. Calypso IV has a telescopic mast that does not penetrate into the control room, as required for installation on board German Type-209 export submarines. Calypso V is of a modular design and has a much lower peak power (for lower counter-detectability); range on a low-flying 10 square-meter target is 20,000 m.

Calypso II is THD 1030; Calypso III is TRS 3100.

◆ Arabel

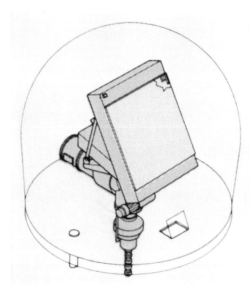

Arabel radar. (Aerospatiale)

Arabel radar. (Direction de Constructions Navales)

Arabel is the multifunction X-band radar for ASTER missile control. The planar antenna is inclined at 30 degrees inside a radome, rotating at 60 rpm. The beam is 2 degrees wide and can scan up to 70 degrees in elevation. The transmitter can hop frequencies over 10 percent of its frequency range. Thus, the radar is a much shorter-range, higher data-rate expression of much the same technology as is used in DRBJ 11. Production antennas will use a lens antenna (Radant) to steer the beam, reducing the overall number of phase shifters from several thousand to about 100, and drastically reducing both cost and energy consumption.

The first development contract was announced in April 1988, with completion of a naval prototype scheduled for the early 1990s, to meet the SAAM schedule (service entry 1999). SAAM is a short-range system, and Arabel is designed to match, with a stated range of about 50 km against 0.5 square-meter missiles and 100 km against larger targets. The associated computer is to be able to conduct simultaneous monopulse tracking of 50 targets, and to direct 10 simultaneous engagements. Trials are scheduled for 1988–89.

◆ **Calypso**

See DRUA-33, above.

Calypso radar on board the French submarine *Agosta* (atop the rightmost mast). The small sonar dome is probably for an underwater telephone. (U.S. Navy)

◆ **Canopus**

A Ka-band director for corvettes and similar craft, Canopus has a complementary television or IR tracker (see TRS 906 below). This system can acquire an attacking airplane at 11 km and a sea-skimming missile at 6.5 km. Tracking accuracy is 0.5 mrad and 10 m. This radar has a memory for TWS operation and can maintain 16 air or surface tracks. Beam dimensions are 1.2 × 22 degrees. There are two TWS modes, automatic and rate-aided tracking.

Canopus fire-control radar. (Thomson-CSF)

◆ **Castor I (TRS 3200)**

> **Band:** X **Beam:** 2.3 deg
> **Peak Power:** 175 kW **Gain:** 37 dB
> **Pulse Width:** 0.4 microsec
> **PRF:** 4000–8000 pps (stepped variation)
> **Antenna Weight:** 80 kg

Used with Vega fire-control systems in medium-sized ships, Castor I is a stabilized monopulse-MTI tracker. Maximum acquisition and tracking range is about 30 km. A 2 square-meter air target can be detected (PD 0.9) at 20 km; a 0.1 square-meter

missile can be detected (PD 0.9) at 15 km. Range accuracy is 15 m between 200 m and 15 km, and angular accuracy is 0.5 mrad. Tracking accuracy (18 km, 2 square-meter fluctuating target) is 15 m and 0.3 mrad.

Castor was conceived as a replacement for Pollux, to track fluctuating targets more accurately. Castor II, which entered French naval service, has a Cassegrain antenna with a multi-mode feed behind the reflector.

There is a colocated television camera.

This director replaced Pollux within the Vega II weapons system. Development began in 1969.

For later versions of Castor, see DRBC 33 above.

◆ **Jupiter**

See DRBV 26 above.

◆ **Pollux (THD 1280, TRS 3220)**

> **Band:** X **Beam:** 2 deg
> **Peak Power:** 200 kW (90 W average) **Gain:** 30 dB
> **Pulse Width:** 0.3 microsec **PRF:** 1500 pps
> **Antenna Dimensions:** diameter 1.1 m
> **Antenna Weight:** 450 kg

The Ecuadorian missile boat *Quito* has a Triton air/surface-search radar on her mast (with an ESM array above it), and a Pollux fire-control radar. The mast platform just aft of the Pollux dish carries a Decca 1229, barely visible because its antenna is end-on to the camera. (U.S. Naval Institute)

A Thomson-CSF export conical-scan fire-control radar, Pollux was capable of acquiring and tracking a small aircraft at 16 nm. Accuracy was 1 mrad in bearing and 20 m in range. Tracking accuracy was 0.5 mrad and 20 m in range at 18 km (2 square-meter air target). Acquisition range on a 2 square-meter air target was 30 km. Conscan requires several pulses to define a target's angular error, and conscan can, therefore, introduce errors if the target fluctuates. Hence the development of Castor.

Pollux was the tracker of the original Thomson-CSF Vega weapons-control system. Pollux was not accurate enough to control heavy (100-mm) guns, had limited ECCM capability, and was, therefore, replaced by Castor II (0.3-mrad tracking accuracy).

◆ **Ramses (THD 1022)**

> **Band:** X **Beam:** 1 deg
> **Peak Power:** 35 kW **PRF:** 1000 or 2000 pps
> **Scan Rate:** 20 rpm **Antenna Dimensions:** 250-cm span

Ramses is the small-ship radar developed for the French Navy in the early 1960s. The antenna is a rigid V-section girder forming a horn to shape the beam in elevation and is fed by a slotted waveguide at the base. Range scales are 1.5–60 nm.

♦ **Saturne (THD 1041 and TRS 3043)**

> **Band:** S   **Beam:** 1.7 deg × csc2
> **Peak Power:** 1 MW (average power 2kW)
> **Gain:** 28.5 dB   **Pulse Width:** 0.25 or 2 microsec
> **PRF:** 8000 or 1000 pps   **Scan Rate:** 10 or 20 rpm
> **Antenna Dimensions:** 5.7 × 4.5 m   **Antenna Weight:** 400 kg

Saturne was an air-search radar with a stabilized antenna. Introduced in 1969, this radar provided coverage out to 120 km. Saturne II (TRS 3043) equipped the Swedish *Visby*, for example. This radar was offered as an alternative to Sea Tiger within the Vega 2 weapons system; Saturne could detect a fighter (2 square meters) at 60 nm.

♦ **Sea Tiger**

See DRBV 15 above.

♦ **Triskel**

Triskel is a 3-D C-band medium-range planar-array radar, scanned one way in phase and the other in frequency, for use with antimissile defense systems. Triskel is intended for light corvettes and frigates. It was announced in 1984. As of 1989, Triskel has been abandoned. Its C-band niche in the FAMS program is considered filled by the Italian EMPAR, in which Thomson-CSF has a share (Arabel fills the alternative S-band niche). Triskel would, however, have been different from EMPAR and, presumably, could be revived if the multinational aspects of the FAMS program had to be abandoned.

♦ **Triton (TRS 3030, THD 1040)**

> **Band:** C (5.3 cm)   **Beam:** 2 × 22 deg
> **Peak Power:** 250 kW (200 kW in early units)
> **Gain:** 38 dB   **Pulse Width:** 0.2, 0.5, or 0.7 microsec
> **PRF:** variable over a wide range
> **Scan Rate:** 12 or 24 rpm   **Antenna Dimensions:** 2.5 × 0.4 m
> **Antenna Weight:** 170 kg (350 kg if stabilized)

This combined air/surface-surveillance and target-indication radar, for small- and medium-sized ships, was developed as part of the Vega system. Triton can shift both frequency and PRF as a counter-countermeasure. The antenna is not stabilized. Triton can detect a 2 square-meter air target at 30 to 45 km. Accuracy in range is 30 m. Work began in 1967, and the prototype appeared in 1968.

♦ **Triton II MTI (TRS 3035)**

> **Band:** C (5.3)   **Beam:** 2 × 22 deg
> **Peak Power:** 250 kW (average 200 W)   **Gain:** 28 dB
> **Pulse Width:** (i) 0.5 (ii) 1.0 microsec
> **PRF:** Non-MTI mode: adjustable PRF: (i) 1000–2000 pps (ii)
>   333–666 pps
>   MTI: three staggered PRFs around 1820 pps
> **Scan Rate:** 12 or 24 rpm
> **Antenna Dimensions:** 2.3 × 1.4 m (inlcudes pedestal)
> **Antenna Weight:** 180 kg

Triton II MTI is a combination air- and surface-search radar intended as the primary search and target indicator for small ships, and as the target indicator for ships equipped with a long-range air-search radar such as Jupiter (DRBV 26). Detection range on a 2 square-meter air target is over 30 km.

The main features are a lightweight low-sidelobe antenna; a tunable-frequency (and adjustable-PRF) transmitter; an antijam (STC, CFAR) receiver; and a linear digital MTI, useful at ranges of up to 56 km, for clutter rejection. The MTI uses a three-memory filter with a minimum blind speed of 340 m/sec (0.5-microsecond pulses). The CFAR channel uses 1.5-microsecond pulses. Clutter rejection ratio: ground, 30 dB; sea (3 m/sec), 25 dB.

♦ **Triton G (TRS 3050)**

> **Band:** C   **Beam:** 2.1 × 22 deg
> **Peak Power:** 8 kW   **Gain:** 27 dB
> **Pulse Width:** 6.5/12 microsec (compressed to 0.5 microsec) (A 0.5-
>   microsec uncompressed pulse can be included in the burst for
>   close-range surveillance.)   **Scan Rate:** 40 rpm
> **Antenna Dimensions:** 2.3 m wide   **Antenna Weight:** 180 kg total

Triton G. (Thomson-CSF)

This C- (now redesignated G-) band medium-range air- and surface-search radar has a lightweight antenna so that it can be mounted at a masthead. Triton G uses pulse compression and a frequency-agile coherent TWT transmitter (for MTI, for clutter rejection). Clutter improvement factor is 40 dB. Detection range on a 2 square-meter target is over 19 km. The lowest blind speed is 800 m/sec. Up to 32 air and/or surface targets can be tracked automatically. Air target tracks are automatically initiated (ATD).

The signal-processing hardware of this radar duplicates that of Sea Tiger (DRBV 15).

♦ **Triton S (TRS 3033)**

> **Band:** S   **Beam:** 3 × 22 deg
> **Peak Power:** 10 kW (average 250 w)   **Gain:** 25 dB
> **Pulse Width:** 2.7 microsec (doppler channel); 0.17 microsec as
>   pulse-compressed; compression ratio of 10
> **PRF:** 5380 pps (doppler channel); pulse compression: fractions of
>   5380 pps   **Scan Rate:** 24 rpm
> **Antenna Dimensions:** 3 m wide   **Antenna Weight:** 215 kg

Triton S (above Castor, on board a fast attack boat). (Thomson-CSF)

Triton S is a pulse-doppler development of the basic Triton. Triton S uses a crystal-controlled TWT and produces three frequencies for air search and six frequencies for surface search. Air-search frequency can be shifted on a scan-to-scan basis. Surface-search frequency can be shifted on a pulse-to-pulse basis.

Triton S is a combined air/surface-search radar, effective against sea-skimmers by virtue of its very high clutter-cancellation ratio (50 dB) and its high data rate (2.5 sec). Like several other recent Thomson-CSF radars, Triton S uses a coherent transmitter for doppler processing (16-point fast Fourier transform), both to get target speed and to reject clutter. Using pulse compression on the non-doppler channel, the radar is also frequency agile on a scan-to-scan basis. The lowest blind speed is Mach 1.

Performance of the pulse-doppler channel: 1 square-meter (Swerling III case) at 26 km; 10 square-meter target (Swerling III) at 44 km.

◆ Triton X (TRS 3040)

Band: X (300-MHz bandwidth)
Beam: 1.2 × deg **Peak Power:** 200 kW
Pulse Width: 0.3 microsec
PRF: 1500 pps **Scan Rate:** 24 rpm
Antenna Dimensions: 2.3 × 1.4 m **Antenna Weight:** 175 kg

Part of the Vega-Canopus small-ship weapons system, Triton X has a compact receiver-transmitter (80 kg compared to 470 kg for Triton, 700 kg for Triton II MTI, and 650 kg for Triton S). This radar was announced in 1979. Claimed detection range on a 2 square-meter airplane is 20 km.

◆ TRS 3405/3410

Band: X **Beam:** 0.24 × 25 deg (inverted csc2 to −25 deg)
Peak Power: 200 kW **Pulse Width:** 0.05 microsec
PRF: 1300–3000 pps

These coastal-surveillance radars are intended to sit atop cliff tops. TRS 3405 is fixed; TRS 3410, mobile. Sea clutter is reduced by frequency diversity, an adaptive detection-threshold, short pulses, and a very narrow beam. These radars can detect a wooden fishing boat (cross section 5 square meters) at 25 km.

TRS 3410 has a 5-m antenna producing a 0.5-degree beam.

◆ TRS 3501

This S-band long-range 3-D radar uses phase shifting in both directions. TRS 3501 is multifunction and multitarget and may be an alternative designation for DRBJ 11.

OPTRONIC SYSTEMS

◆ DIBV 10 (VAMPIR)

VAMPIR was announced in 1980. It was developed by SAT to meet a NATO requirement for an IR surveillance sensor, analogous to the Canadian SAR-8. Providing all-around low- and medium-altitude surveillance, VAMPIR can provide threat warning and target acquisition to a CIC. For example, this system can be used as acquisition sensor for both chaff launchers and point-defense weapons such as Mistral. VAMPIR can also designate targets to an optronic fire-control system such as Totem, or to a radar fire-control system such as DRBC 32. The sensor head weighs 250–275 kg and scans at 60 rpm. VAMPIR covers both IR windows (3–5 and 8–14 micrometers) with 20-degree fields of view. An approaching missile would probably be detected at a range of about 10 km, and target designation could be accurate to within 1 mrad (bearing and elevation). The display is divided into three horizontal strips, two for the two IR windows and one for processed video. Both windows are shown because the differences between the pictures seen through them can provide valuable information. In films shown at Bourget Navale in 1980, the processed-video strip displayed a missile marker before it was apparent in either window, suggesting the degree to which signal processing could enhance a target above the surrounding IR noise.

In 1980 it was reported that this sensor had detected a small helicopter at a range of 8 nm. In 1988, it was reported that VAMPIR had detected the heat plume of an Exocet before the missile came over the horizon.

VAMPIR (DIBV 10) equips the *Cassard*-class missile destroyers (C70AA type) and will equip the new nuclear carrier. DIBV 10 equips the three *Tourville*-class destroyers and will be installed on board other ships. VAMPIR means *Veille Air-Mer Panoramique Infra-rouge.*

In 1988 VAMPIR ML 11 was announced as a lighter and less expensive (one-third to one-half the price) of the existing VAMPIR. Operating in only one of the two IR windows used by VAMPIR, VAMPIR ML 11 is designed so that the operating wavelength can be changed relatively easily from one range to the other. The sensor is provided by SAT, the processor and turret by CSEE. Total weight is 80 kg, compared to 450 for VAMPIR, and scan rate is doubled to 120 rpm for better detection of sea-skimming antiship missiles. Elevation limits are +60/−10 deg, compared to a maximum elevation of 25 degrees for the original VAMPIR. Target designation accuracy is 3 mrad, compared to 1 mrad for the earlier system.

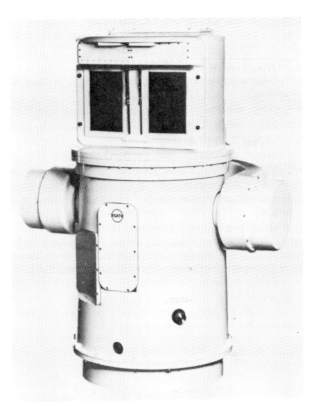

VAMPIR optronic sensor. In trials, VAMPIR reportedly detected sea-skimming missiles beyond the horizon by sensing the IR plumes rising out of the missiles' exhausts. (Société Anonyme de Télécommunications)

◆ Condor

An optronic night camera for laser target designation, Condor can also be used for tracking in conditions of radar failure or silence. The production version has two optical paths, one for daylight television and one for a low-light-level television. Condor is expected to equip all new French Navy destroyers and avisos. It is manufactured by Sintra.

◆ COTOL/COTROL

The self-contained lightweight optronic system by CSEE combines a laser range-finder (1.06 micron, 5 MW, 15 nanosec pulses), a TV camera (625-line, 25 frames/sec), and an IR camera (8–13 micron, 625-line, 25 frames/sec), and has an acquisition range of 7–10 km. Elevation limits are +85/−25 deg; maximum bearing and elevation rates are 90 deg/sec; time to slew 90 deg is less than 1.8 sec. Weight of the mounting is 220 kg. COTOL means *Conduite de Tir Optronique Légère* (Light Optronic Fire-Control System). COTROL replaces the laser with a Ka-band tracking radar (PEAB Sea Eagle).

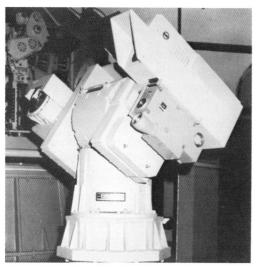

COTOL optronic fire-control system. (Compagnie de Signaux et d'Entreprises Electriques)

◆ IRDAR

This laser radar, announced in 1980, uses a 10.6-micrometer-wavelength pulsed CO_2 laser and a heterodyne receiver (a continuous-wave CO_2 laser serves as the local oscillator, to strip the laser frequency from the returning echo). The laser tracks in range, elevation, and bearing and also provides closing-speed data. As exhibited in 1980, the IRDAR mount carried a coaxial passive IR tracker, like that in Pirana. Because the laser radar covers so small an area, it requires target designation from a high-resolution optronic sensor, such as VAMPIR. In effect, IRDAR is the step beyond a pure laser range-finder of the type commonly included in optronic fire-control systems.

◆ NAJA/NAJIR

The manned optronic sight is used either as a primary director for a small ship or as a back-up to a radar director. NAJA can accept designations from other sensors (e.g., radar, ESM, or IR). It carries a pair of 2× binoculars and a standard or low-light television. The line of sight is biaxially stabilized.

Weight is about 500 kg (260 kg for the remote-control console) and elevation limits are −25 to +70 degrees.

In 1982 CSEE announced a private-venture version, NAJIR,

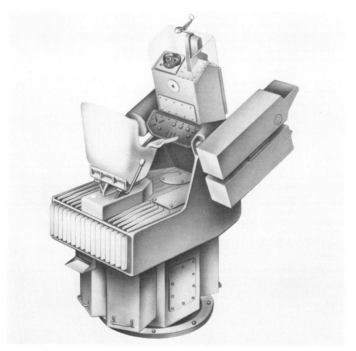

NAJIR director, with IR camera and laser range-finder alongside. (Compagnie de Signaux et d'Entreprises Électriques)

which adds an IR camera to the existing optical, television, and laser channels. The IR image can be observed either through the binoculars above deck, or on a below-decks monitor. Targets can be tracked automatically, by either television or IR; and the modernized system uses a digital computer in place of the analog unit of NAJA, for easy integration with any weapons system. The improvement was too substantial to be back-fitted to existing NAJAS. NAJIR was first shown publicly in 1986.

NAJA was developed from the earlier Panda power-driven optical director and by 1987 had replaced the latter in many Third World navies.

◆ PAON

The CSEE Lynx target designator is fitted with an image intensifier for day/night capability.

◆ Pirana

This passive two-color IR tracker is typically added to a radar or director. Field of view is about 17 mrad for acquisition, and Pirana can detect sea-skimming missiles at about 10 km. It is used as part of an optronic director such as Totem (see below) and is mounted, for example, on board the destroyer *Cassard*.

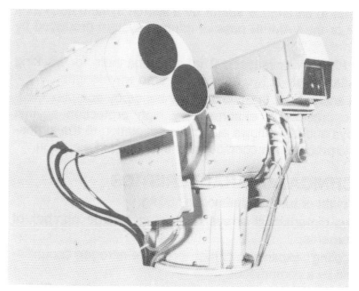

Pirana optronic tracker. (Société Anonyme de Télécommunications)

◆ Totem

Totem optronic fire-control system. (Compagnie de Signaux et d'Entreprises Électriques)

Totem is a fully automatic remote-controlled director intended specifically to deal with attacks by sea-skimming missiles. The director turret carries a television camera, laser range-finder, and IR sensor and is joystick controlled. There are four operating modes: search, search/acquisition, tracking, and weapons control. Designation is generally from another sensor, with automatic acquisition by the TV or IR sensor. Tracking is then automatic, and the laser range-finder is switched on. The director can measure range, bearing, speed, and target acceleration, and the operator can override the director and enter manual corrections (e.g., correcting a false lock-on). A Ka-band radar could be fitted as an option.

Elevation limits are −30 to +85 degrees.

As of 1980, the French Navy was evaluating Totem. This system was manufactured by CSEE.

♦ TRS 906

Thomson-CSF's remotely controlled optronic director was announced in 1978 as part of the Canopus system. TRS 906 uses a variety of sensors, including low-light-level TV, a laser range-finder, and IR. 906 can also accommodate an on-mount MMW radar, so that tracking can switch rapidly from radar to optronic mode. The maximum load is 40 kg on each side. TRS 906 is controlled in azimuth by a joystick. The angular tracking accuracy of the television is 2 mrad, and the director can continue to track by memory if the target is lost briefly. Elevation range is +85/−30 deg, and maximum speeds in bearing and elevation are 3 and 1 rad/sec, respectively (the director can slew through 180 deg in 1.8 secs).

When carrying only a television camera, the director weighs 120 kg (0.77 m high, 0.80 m in diameter), the associated servo box weighs 80 kg, and the control console weighs 300 kg.

For the radar's details, see Canopus above.

♦ Volcan

The IR surveillance sensor manufactured by SAGEM is intended as a lighter alternative to VAMPIR for small ships, or as a station-keeping and navigation sensor and back-up fire-control system for a large ship. Volcan is also the sensor for the SAMOS

The Volcan optronic director. (SAGEM)

point-defense weapon. Unlike most optronic devices, Volcan does not use a stabilized mounting for its sensors. Instead, all three sensors are fixed in the base and are fed by mirrors. Thus all sensors can share a common optical axis, using beam-splitting (dichroic) mirrors. The mirrors can be turned for stabilization and for accurate direction, the entire instrument turning for coarse direction settings. Stabilization and pointing (accuracy reportedly better than 25 microradians) are relatively easy because the mirrors are so much lighter than the sensor head as a whole. The ranger is a 5-MW laser pulsing 20 times per second. Acquisition range (on a sea-skimmer) is 4–8 km. Total weight is 80 kg, and the sensor typically scans at 15 rpm. Volcan was first tested in the early 1980s, and it was combined with the 30-mm gun in static tests in 1984.

SUBMARINE PERISCOPES

♦ PIVAIR

The SAGEM/SOPELEM PIVAIR is an optronic periscope incorporating a CTX thermal imager, usable under day and night conditions. The optical and infrared channels are both biaxially stabilized. The masthead carries an ESM antenna and the gyro-stabilized unit for both conventional optics and the IR camera. Besides the usual binocular optics, the base of the mast carries a sextant, a 35-mm camera, and the IR monitor. Optical magnification is by a factor of 1.5 or 6 (12 is optional), with corresponding fields of view of 26, 9, and 4.5 degrees. The angle of elevation of the field of view is +80 to −10 degrees. The IR camera operates in the 8–12-micron band, with a 3 × 6–degree field of view and the same sighting angle.

SAGEM offers a range of optronic periscopes employing thermal imagers. All can employ an IR surveillance mode (360-degree scan), and both optical and infrared channels are biaxially gyrostabilized so that high magnification can be employed usefully. These periscopes are insulated against vibration at high submerged speeds. The standard IR imager operates in the 8–12-micron band and is cooled by the Joule-Thomson effect; the images can be observed either by eyepiece or remotely. All periscopes incorporate both sextants and GPS receivers, the sextant data being automatically processed (using a built-in ephemeris). These periscopes can be connected so that target designation (elevation and true bearing) and range are automatically transmitted to the weapons-control system.

These periscopes still penetrate the submarine's hull. SAGEM also offers a new generation of nonpenetrating optronic masts, each carrying a thermal (IR) imager and a high-definition television, with slow automatic rotation. Both image channels are gyrostabilized, and magnification can be controlled. The mast is pressure-proofed.

♦ SOPELEM Periscopes

Optical attack and search periscopes are manufactured by SOPELEM. The standard search periscope can incorporate a gyrosextant, a range-only radar, and a radar-warning receiver. There is generally an integral 35-mm photographic camera (containing 250 frames in the case of PIVAIR, described below). Typical types are:

Attack periscopes:
ST3 for the *Daphne* class
ST5 for the *Agosta* class

Search periscopes:
M41 for the *Daphne* class
J for the *Agosta* class
K (incorporates an image intensifier)

SOPELEM designed a special integrated nonpenetrating periscope system for the projected CA-class low-manning export submarine. The system is interesting because, unlike all other existing periscopes, it is integrated with other sensors and mounted in the side of the control room rather than in the center. A single console carries a pair of airplane-type controls; the left-hand side carries a binocular eyepiece below a radar scope. Two television-type monitors occupy the right-hand side of the console, above the right-hand diving/steering control.

The submarine has three nonpenetrating masts: an optical periscope, an optronic periscope, and an ESM antenna; all are contained in a single watertight chamber outside the pressure hull, with the optronic and optical masts side by side. The hull is penetrated only by electrical cables, hydraulic piping (by means of which the masts are raised), and the optical path from the optical periscope. The latter is arranged so that it feeds a fixed binocular eyepiece, no matter in which direction it turns. The fixed eyepiece is part of a console, the other side of which carries two CRTs for the optronic mast. Each position carries a handwheel to power-turn the mast. The advantage of this arrangement is that the periscope observer can easily compare his image with those presented optronically. Moreover, he is located close enough to other instruments to be able to see the consoles and other displays used for navigation. However, because the optical image is viewed only through an eyepiece, such comparison and reference cannot be direct. Nor is there any provision for windowing, i.e., for presenting several different optronic (or other) displays simultaneously on the same CRT. That limitation probably means that the optronics is still analog rather than digital.

The optical periscope has two alternative magnifications, binocular viewing, a high resolution screen, and a capability for slow-search observation. The mast carries a radar-warning receiver. Optional improvements include a 3-magnification optical channel, a night-vision channel (second and third generation light intensification), a TV outlet, video recording, stabilized sight axis, a stadimeter, and a polaroid camera. The optronic mast carries an IR camera (with 2 alternative magnifications), a line-of-sight gyrostabilizer, power rotation for fast or slow scan, and a radar-warning receiver. Optional features are a sextant and a stadimeter. The radar mast carries Varan radar.

The CA submarine project was never sold, but its SOPELEM periscope console would seem to represent an interesting intermediate point between the current conventional optical periscope, which dominates control-room arrangement, and currently proposed pure-optronic arrangements. In the CA 3, the periscope console is still directly under the mast (which is, however, off the centerline of the boat), and the console still can be viewed only at very close range.

FIRE-CONTROL SYSTEMS

◆ Canopus (Tactical System)

Canopus was developed about 1976 as a small-ship alternative to Vega. Canopus consists of an X-band navigation/search radar (slotted-waveguide antenna), and X-band Pollux radar (with a television tracker for good weather), and a console including its computer (which is the same as that in Vega). Options include an optical sight and a navigational plotter. Weight is reduced partly by using very lightweight radars and partly by using a single radar transmitter-receiver for both the search and the fire-control radars.

The system is designed to engage two targets simultaneously, either with two guns or with one gun and two antiship missiles.

This tactical system is not the Canopus fire-control radar described above.

◆ Radop

CSEE's small-ship fire-control systems use Racal-Decca radars and CSEE optical/optronic directors. Radop 10 uses the Lynx optical director; Radop 20, Panda Mk 2; Radop 30, NAJA; Radop 40, NAJIR. These systems were conceived primarily for craft intended to enforce the new 200-mile exclusive economic zones.

Lynx is a simple optical pedestal sight weighing 195 kg, with 2.5× or 8× magnification. Panda is a power-driven optical director (480 kg) that can accommodate a television camera. NAJA and NAJIR are optronic directors (see above).

◆ Vega

The Thomson-CSF Vega is a small-ship fire-control system. Vega 1 consists of a search radar (Triton), a fire-control radar (Castor or Pollux), a computer, and several control consoles. Thomson-CSF chose a nonstabilized search antenna because it could be located higher in the ship, for a gain in range of about 4 km, equivalent to 3 minutes of earlier warning (40-kt target). Separate search and fire-control radars are used to reduce overall system vulnerability (the fire-control radar can be used as a back-up search radar, and Triton has TWS capability) and to improve ECCM, since the radars are dissimilar. Doppler filtering is used to reject clutter, and the system is partly digital.

The associated computer is a digital-analog hybrid; typical operating time is 2–5 microseconds (i.e., clock rate about 200–500 kHz). Thomson-CSF developed an associated combat information system, SATIN (*Système de Traitement Automatique de l'Information Navale*).

Development began in 1967, with first sea trials in 1971 (followed by Exocet trials in 1972). By 1973, over fifty systems were in production for five navies. The sensors were various combinations of Triton, Castor, and Pollux; Vega sometimes used only the Triton radar when controlling Exocet or Otomat missiles or torpedoes.

Vega 2 is a digital version of the basic Vega. The other main improvements are MTI for the Triton search radar, a new X-band monopulse tracker (Castor II), and a much more powerful computer, capable of handling 16 rather than 2 target tracks. The fire-control radar is fitted with a television, and the television screen is on the fire-control panel. Finally, Vega 2 can receive target data from a digital link. This link uses a format different from that of Link 11 but can be used for transmission to other Vega 2 or SENIT-equipped ships.

Vega 2 has sufficient computer power for larger ships but lacks the necessary long-range radars. Thomson offered three alternative longer-range radars: Triton with a higher-gain antenna (DRBV 51A in French naval service), Saturne 2, or Sea Tiger (DRBV 15). On larger ships, Vega can be connected to a long-range search radar (Jupiter), but then Vega has insufficient computer capacity and requires a SENIT tactical data system.

At least eight versions of Vega II were developed. Vega II 53 is intended for fast missile-armed antiship attack boats (Triton II MTI, Castor II); Vega II 73 is intended for fast patrol boats or ASW corvettes with antimissile weapons (Triton S, Castor II); Vega II 83 is intended for corvettes or multipurpose frigates (Sea Tiger with an integrated IFF, Castor II, and Canopus). Each has a tactical table. Vega II 53 has a single display console and one fire-control console, to operate guns and antiship missiles. Vega II 73 has two display consoles and one fire-control console; Vega II 83 has two tactical tables, three display consoles, and two fire-control consoles (two directors).

Canopus was developed as a smaller one-man fire-control system for fast attack craft of under 150 tons. The name Canopus was also later used for a dedicated fire-control radar.

GERMANY (WEST)

◆ TRS Series

AEG's family of C-band surveillance radars is derived from the land-based TRM series. Although a major radar supplier to the German Army, AEG is only now (1988) producing naval radars, and only the simplest of its radars has been purchased by the West German Navy. Presumably the navy considers TRS-C a test case for AEG's digital radar technology, and orders for the more elaborate three-dimensional radars (for example, for the new Type 123 interim frigate) may well follow.

The other major German manufacturer of land-based radars, Siemens, has not produced any naval sets, although its pulse-doppler missile-warning radar reportedly inspired the U.S. development of SPS-58/65 (see below).

The basic land-based model is TRM-S, a mobile planar-array three-dimensional radar employing phase-coded pulse compression; this model is capable of varying its PRF. The beam is steered in elevation by phase shifting, the large version of the antenna containing 4000 elements. Phase coding can be altered on a pulse-to-pulse basis, as can transmitting frequency. The receiver has two identical channels, one for sidelobe supression. Signal processing includes MTI and CFAR. Targets are automatically detected and correlated with targets detected by IFF, and the output is a combination of raw and processed video. AEG claims that TRM-S can detect a 1 square-meter target at 100 km (probability of detection is 90 percent). Scan rate varies from 4 to 20 rpm, and up to 4000 targets can be displayed simultaneously.

TRM-S is unusual in employing polarization agility (horizontal, vertical, and circular), and the radar can vary its vertical beamwidth by a factor of up to eight. Polarization agility is useful because circular polarization limits the effect of rain but imposes a sacrifice in target cross section. Each row of the array is fed by two sets of feeds, each set having its own ferrite phase shifters. Each shifter feeds a series of polarized elements, and adjustment of the phase between each pair of structures produces the desired polarization.

TRM-S was first installed in 1979.

TRM-L is a two-dimensional version using many TRM-S components but having a much less powerful transmitter (a 1 square-meter target can be detected at 46 km with 80-percent probability). TRM-L is the standard search radar for German Roland short-range air-defense missiles. TRM-L can change its PRF and frequency on a burst-to-burst basis, using doppler filtering to reject clutter, and using separate adaptive detection thresholds for each doppler channel (to defeat ground clutter, rain clutter, chaff, and noise jammers). As in the larger TRM-S, TRM-L automatically extracts radar targets (ATD). In addition, it uses doppler velocity data to calculate target velocity, thus improving overall tracking. Again, like the larger radar, TRM-L employs pulse compression to reduce the size of its resolution cell, uses sidelobe blanking, and has a jam detector. For TRM-L, the data rate is 2 or 4 seconds (15 or 30 rpm), and the maximum elevation coverage is 60 degrees (csc2 beam).

The naval versions are:

TRS-S, a navalized TRM-S, intended for larger vessels. The size, capability, and weight can be gauged from TRS-S's replacement of the current DA-08 two-dimensional radar on the German *Bremen*-class frigate.

TRS-MFR is a multifunction frigate or destroyer radar, currently under development, presumably for either Type 123 or the NATO frigate.

TRS-3D is a smaller three-dimensional radar adapted to fast patrol boats. It is presumably comparable in size to the Raytheon MBAR and to the Hughes TAS Mk 23, both of which

TRS-3D as it would appear on board a fast attack boat. (AEG)

have been considered for installation on board German attack boats.

TRS-C is a two-dimensional C-band radar for medium vessels, using either the S-band TWT of the others or a magnetron. TRS-C has recently (early 1989) been ordered by the German government for auxiliaries ("fleet service boats").

♦ OFLA-M

This optronic fire-control system is optimized to detect low fliers. A television tracker and laser range-finder are mounted on a pedestal above decks, the below-decks console showing range, elevation, and azimuth data. The television tracks automatically to provide a bearing rate for the ballistic computer. OFLA-M was designed specially for simplicity, and as a result the system initially lacked an IR sensor for night or bad-weather operation. However, when the contract was amended, an IR tracker and a laser range-finder were added, with a millimeter-wave radar available as an option.

The manufacturer was AEG-Telefunken, and the name means *Optronische Feuerleitanlage–Marine*. The German Navy awarded the first development contract in 1975, for delivery in 1978 for the hydrofoils then planned. The hydrofoil was canceled, and the contract amended to allow for all-weather operation.

OFLA-M was one of several optronic fire-control systems competing for the German 1985 minehunter contract, and later for the S143A fast patrol boat and the Type-122A frigate. The others included Canopus (Thomson-CSF), Totem (CSEE), LIOD (Signaal), and the Swedish 9LV100.

ISRAEL

RADARS

♦ AMDR

The Automatic Missile Detection Radar by Elta is associated with the Barak defensive system. Estimated range is 16 nm against a sea-skimming missile.

Operating in S-band, AMDR is a coherent doppler radar using DFT (discrete Fourier transform) and doppler filtering to reject slow-moving (less than Mach 0.2) targets and to measure a target's radial velocity from a single burst of pulses (i.e., during a single antenna scan). This mode of operation makes for track-while-scan capability. Threats are automatically evaluated and ranked, and threat data passed to the Barak weapons system, target azimuth and speed being extracted by a microprocessor.

TRS-S as it would appear on board a *Bremen*-class frigate. (AEG)

The display may be either a 16-inch PPI, a digital scan converter (colored TV), or an alphanumeric display (CRT). The data processor used for correlation and tracking is programmable.

The masthead weight is 220 kg.

♦ **EL/M-2207**

Band: S (3.1–3.3 GHz tunable)
Beam: 3.3 × 10 deg (csc2 to 30 deg)
Peak Power: 425 kW (average 425 W)
Gain: 28 dB   **Pulse Width:** (i) 1.4 (ii) 0.4 microsec
PRF: (i) 500–700 (ii) 1000–1500 pps   **Scan Rate:** 12 or 24 rpm
Antenna Dimensions: 2.4 × 1 m   **Antenna Weight:** 245 kg

An Israeli missile boat of the *Reshef* class, equipped with an ELTA air-search radar (either EL/M-2207 or -2208; both use the same antenna) and probably with an EL/M-2221 gunfire-control radar. The gun is an OTO-Melara 76 mm. Two single-barrel long-range chaff launchers are visible alongside the superstructure, under the bridge windows. Two box launchers (24 barrels each) for short-range chaff are visible, canted outboard, abaft and below the bridge. (U.S. Naval Institute)

Elta's air- and surface-search radar is part of the EL/M-2200 series of shore and naval radars, all of which use the same basic transceiver unit. The AT-101 antenna is stabilized, and the manufacturer, Elta Electronics, Ltd., (an IAI subsidiary) claims that its design is such as to require only 66 percent of the reflector area of a more conventional radar. Range is 30 nm against a 2 square-meter target. Resolution is better than 75 m for the short pulse, better than 230 m for the long pulse.

The AT-101 antenna is also used in the EL/M-2208 dual-band radar, and the antenna can be used in the L-band (7 × 20 deg beam) for IFF.

♦ **EL/M-2208**

Band:	S	X
	3.1–3.3 GHz tunable	9.345–9.405 GHz fixed
Beam:	3 × 10 deg	1 × 5 deg
Peak Power:	425 kW	25 kW
Gain:	28 dB	34 dB
Pulse width:	(i) 1.4 microsec (ii) 0.4 microsec	0.25 microsec
PRF:	(i) 500–750 pps (ii) 1000–1500 pps	1000–1500 pps
Antenna Dimensions:	2.4 × 1 m	
Antenna Weight:	245 kg	

EL/M-2208 is Elta's air- and surface-search radar. S- and X-band transmitters (and the L-band IFF) share the same fully stabilized masthead antenna, for reduced total weight. The long pulse and digital MTI give long range and air surveillance; the short pulse feature is useful for navigation. Estimated detection range of a jet fighter is 30+ nm, and surface targets can be detected out to the horizon. The PRF can be staggered for MTI without blind speeds.

Data above refer to the AT-101A antenna. In L-band, for IFF, this antenna produces a 7 × 20 degree beam (gain 17 dB). Scan rate is 12 or 24 rpm, and the antenna is stabilized. Antenna

elevation angle can be remotely controlled. The antenna weight listed is that of the basic unit; as fitted for X-band operation it weighs 200 kg, and as fitted for S-band, 270 kg. Resolution is 1 degree in azimuth and 50 m in range.

The EL/M-2200 radar series was introduced about 1980, to replace the French Neptunes that had previously equipped Israeli warships. These radars are described as suitable for ships of over 250 tons, i.e., the *Sa'ars.* Radar volume and weight were reduced by exploiting IAI's experience with airborne radars.

This radar was conceived as a dual-purpose unit for small warships, which could not accommodate separate air- and surface-search radars. Air search requires relatively long wavelengths to achieve long range (reduced transmission loss): hence the S-band feature. On the other hand, surface search requires a short wavelength (to reduce multipath effects), a narrow beam, and very short pulses (the last two to reduce clutter). IAI concluded further that the signal-to-clutter ratio is not a function of transmitted power, so the surface-search portion of the radar can operate at moderate power. The company argues that moderate power is an advantage to a ship operating in narrow waters such as estuaries (or just off shore), since under such conditions the radar may send and receive strong signals through its sidelobes, introducing ghosts and false targets. The choice, then, was S-band for air search (air alert), X-band for surface search, and L-band for the usual IFF. The same antenna is connected to three separate transceivers, and all data are collected in a single signal processor and then a single unified display.

The S-band beam is vertically polarized to reduce the effects of lobing, which creates holes in air coverage. On the other hand, the X-band beam is horizontally polarized to reduce the effects of sea clutter. In addition, the S-band beam can be circularly polarized to reduce weather clutter (circular polarization improves the signal-to-clutter ratio by 10 to 20 dB but reduces the target's radar cross section). The operator changes S-band polarization from vertical to circular by inserting a mechanical polarizer in front of the feeder connecting the radar transmitter to the mast waveguide.

To achieve high gain (to detect small surface targets), the designers selected a narrow pencil-beam shape. That choice in turn required stabilization, which was difficult to achieve within the 200-kg total antenna weight. The solution was to stabilize only the reflector rather than the complete antenna pedestal.

For air search, the choice was between a csc2 beam-form and helical scanning. The latter was rejected because the radar would require several scans to complete an air search up to a given elevation angle and, thus, would lose data rate (a key consideration for a radar designed to detect fast attackers). The radar has two alternative scan rates, fast (for high data rate) and slow (for longer range).

The X-band transmitter is a frequency-agile (for ECCM as well as to reduce STA problems, to eliminate target fading, and to decorrelate sea and rain clutter) TWT, for pulse compression. For short-range detection, short noncompressed pulses are interlaced between the compressed pulses. The operator can vary both pulse width and PRF, and he can synchronize PRF with the S-band transmitter (not necessarily in a 1:1 ratio). The system incorporates an adaptive (rather than manual) STC (sensitivity time control) to keep the threshold for displayed signals just above the sea clutter, taking into account the clutter's range and bearing. In at least some versions, the radar is not automatically frequency agile but instead can be tuned rapidly by hand knob, to use frequency-band diversity.

The S-band portion of the radar avoids clutter (such as chaff) by digital MTI, using a tunable magnetron capable of operating at multiple pulse widths and PRFs.

There is also a sidelobe blanker that uses a separate omnidirectional antenna and receiver.

Processing is by a combination of plot extraction and operator viewing of raw video. For example, in the surface picture a nearby land mass may appear to an automatic extractor (ATD) to be a mass of real targets (which will saturate the system's track memory), whereas the operator can ignore the land as irrelevant. Surface tracks are, therefore, manually initiated, although once they have been tagged, the system automatically tracks them (in TWS mode). On the other hand, air and sea-skimmer targets must be rapidly (hence automatically) detected and dealt with. The associated combat system, therefore, automatically detects and tracks air targets, conducts threat evaluation, and assigns weapons.

As of 1980, well over 50 EL/M-2200 series radars were delivered or on order, many of them for export to unspecified customers.

◆ EL/M-2221

Elta's X-band fire-control radar is associated with guns and Gabriel missiles. The monopulse antenna is housed in a trainable, elevating barrel-shaped radome. There is an autonomous search mode, although targets can be designated from other sensors. Diameter is 1 m, and overall weight is 150 kg.

◆ EL/M-2216

This coastal-surveillance radar is essentially an air-traffic-control radar with a different antenna, capable of detecting ships at a range of 20 nm.

OPTRONICS

◆ SPIRTAS (DS-35)

The details for this IR target-acquisition system by El-Op were first published in 1982. SPIRTAS is primarily a sea-skimmer detector, operating in the 3–5 micron band. The 120-kg mast-head sensor unit is 120 cm tall and 80 cm wide and houses a stabilized scanning head. The CRT in the CIC console can show three alternative displays: a low-resolution picture of the overall scene, an enlarged thermal display, and a special auxiliary display showing the intensity (i.e., heat) behavior of selected targets as well as the target data transmitted to other shipboard systems. Scanner elevation limits are $+20/-2$ degrees, and a full 360-degree scan takes 8 seconds (1.25 sec in the antimissile mode). The accuracy of target data is within 7 mrad. The detector is an InSb multi-element array, cooled to 77 degrees Kelvin.

ITALY

RADARS

RAN-2C, -7S, -13X, and -14X, which are all listed in many reference books, were experimental sets that did not enter production. In the past it has been reported that RAN-7S was designed for the Royal Danish Navy and developed from the land-based ATCR-3T about 1970. RAN-7S was described as using either a double-curvature antenna with added high-angle coverage (G6) or a modified csc2 antenna (G8); horizontal beamwidth was 1.4 deg, and pulse width was either 1 microsecond (air detection) or 0.5 microseconds (surface search). Stated range was over 100 km (PRF about 1000 pps). Reported peak power was 125 kW. RAN-7S may be the radar designated CWS-3 by the Danish Navy, on board the two *Peder Skrams* (with different antennas forward and aft).

◆ BPS-704

See 3RM Series below.

◆ SPN-703

See 3RM Series below.

◆ SPN-720

This combined carrier-landing radar was initially supplied to Argentina for the carrier *25 de Mayo*, and then to the Italian Navy for the carrier *Giuseppe Garibaldi*. SPN-720 was developed by linking the SPS-702 search radar with a new tracker. This radar, developed by SMA, was announced in 1984. The radar covers the 150–270 degree sector abaft the ship, and the glide path is adjustable between 2 and 21 degrees.

◆ SPN-728

SMA's X-band surface-search radar uses a high-gain double-curvature antenna with csc2 vertical cover; SPN-728 can be used for helicopter control.

◆ SPN-748

Gem Elettronica's X-band navigational radar for large ships uses a 10-in CRT. This radar is used on board the training ship *Amerigo Vespucci*, in two-antenna form.

◆ SPN-749

Gem Elettronica's navigation radar for the carrier *Giuseppe Garibaldi* consists of a master antenna at the bow and a slave antenna at the stern, for 360-degree coverage that does not interfere with the flight deck. Both antennas operate in X-band (9345–9405 MHz with peak power of 20 kW), and both antennas feed a single PPI.

◆ SPQ-2 (and MM/SPQ-701 and SPS-702)

> **Band:** X **Beam:** approx 0.6 deg wide
> **Peak Power:** 180 kW **Pulse Width:** (i) 0.15 (ii) 1.5 microsec
> **PRF:** (i) 2500–3000 (ii) 450–550 pps
> **Scan Rate:** fast rotation (40 rpm) available as option
> **Antenna Dimensions:** approx 3 m wide

Data listed is for SPQ-2.

This radar, produced by SMA, time-shares long and short pulses for both medium-range air and surface search and precise short-range navigational coverage. SPQ-2 is sometimes used for target designation. Users include the Italian, Canadian (SPQ-2D in the *Iroquois*-class frigates), and Venezuelan Navies. Options include fast antenna rotation (up to 40 rpm), MTI with an L-band system using the same antenna to detect low fliers, and a transponder. Both stabilized and nonstabilized versions exist. The current variant is SPQ-2F. This radar should not be confused with the U.S. SPQ-2, an obsolete (and extinct) missile-control set for the Regulus surface-attack missile.

SPQ-701 and SPS-702 are developments of the SPQ-2. SPQ-701 is the radar of the *Sparviero*-class hydrofoil; SPS-702 is for *Maestrale*-class frigates. The SPQ-701 antenna is a parabolic reflector with a narrow vertical dimension, for surface- and air-target detection. SPS-702 uses a broader antenna with a high-elevation component above the main reflector.

SPQ-3 is an S/X-band coastal-surveillance radar, the two units being mounted back to back; either can vary its angle of elevation from -5 to $+15$ degrees. Presumably SPQ-3 uses the same transmitter as SPQ-2.

◆ MM/SPQ-711

The radar of the Mariner (navalized Marte Mk 2, i.e., a renavalized Sea Killer adapted to small patrol craft) missile system is presumably an APQ-706 modified for use on a small patrol boat.

◆ SPS-768

See RAN-3L below.

◆ SPS-774

See RAN-10S below.

◆ MM/SPY-790 (EMPAR)

> **Band:** C (5.5 cm) **Beam:** 2.5 deg
> **Peak Power:** 120 kW **Scan Rate:** 60 rpm
> **Antenna Dimensions:** 2 m square
> **Antenna Weight:** 2500 kg (single-array version)

EMPAR (the European Multi-Purpose Array Radar), a candidate for installation on the NATO frigate, is to be used for target search, acquisition, and tracking. Under development by Selenia and Marconi, EMPAR consists of one or two (back-to-back) square arrays of phase shifters (about 1000 per face) fed by a TWT-driven transmitter. The array face is inclined at 30 degrees, and the beam scans over 45 degrees in azimuth in either direction, and from −25 to +95 degrees in elevation (including roll compensation).

EMPAR is designed to detect a 0.1 square-meter target at 50 km, a 2 square-meter target at 100 km, and a large aircraft (10 square meters) at 180 km. EMPAR is to be able to handle about 300 long-range targets and to track 50 of them well enough for missile engagement.

Selenia was awarded the development contract in 1986, for prototype completion in 1990, with sea trials in 1992. Marconi and Thomson-CSF joined the program. The Royal Navy is reportedly interested in an extended-range version for its Support Defence Missile System (see entry below under Surface-to-Air Missiles).

Italy has signed an MoU joining the French-led FAMS program, the missile of which is ASTER (SAAM). If Italy actually adopts FAMS and ASTER, the associated radar would be EMPAR rather than the French Arabel.

◆ RAN-3L (MM/SPS-768)

Band: L **Beam:** 2.15 × 9 deg plus csc2
Peak Power: 135 kW **Gain:** 30 dB
Pulse Width: 78.4 (compressed to 1.6) microsec
Scan Rate: 6 rpm
Antenna Dimensions: 7.56 × 3.65 m (24.9 × 11.8 ft)

RAN-3L (SPS-768). (Selenia)

The Selenia large-ship search radar was developed for the Italian Defense Science Technical Committee and the Italian Navy. RAN-3L is one of a range of such radars, the suffix indicating the frequency band. Rated maximum range is 150 nm (100+ nm on a fighter). Range accuracy is 70 m, and angular accuracy is 0.4 degrees. The transmitter is frequency agile, and the receiver uses doppler processing for MTI. The waveform is multipulse coded, as in RAN-10S (see below). Maximum range can be increased to 160 nm by using dual-frequency diversity (to overcome the problem of second-time-around echoes); range is slightly shorter with only one channel. The antenna is designated G12.

RAN-3L began in May 1966, following a navy proposal, as an Italian government research and development project (CTSD MM-9) for an early-warning radar with stringent anticlutter and ECCM requirements. Selenia was chosen on the basis of its work in ground radar. A contract was signed in 1968; the defense ministry R&D organization (CTSD) paid for the breadboard version and the first prototype, and the Italian Navy for four production prototypes, two of the bichannel and two of the monochannel versions. The project included Selenia's development of its own pulse-coding technique and also BITE. The breadboard model was completed in 1972, and three years later the prototype was tested on board the test ship *Quarto*. Operational tests were completed in November 1975, in the Gulf of Gaetta, against F-104S and T-33 aircraft.

This radar in its two versions replaces earlier U.S. types (SPS-12 and SPS-40) on board Italian cruisers and the *Audace*-class destroyers, and RAN-3L is the two-dimensional air-search set of the carrier *Giusseppe Garibaldi*. However, this radar was considered too heavy for small and medium ships. A new lighter radar, RAN-10S (MM/SPS-774) was, therefore, designed for the *Lupo*-class frigates, using substantially the same technology. RAN-10S is described below. Selenia also used some of the same technology in RAN-11L, which was intended for small warships and patrol craft.

◆ RAN-10S (MM/SPS-774)

Band: S **Beam:** 1.5 × 17 deg (coverage to 60-deg elevation)
Peak Power: 140 kW **Gain:** 28 dB
Pulse Width: 20.8 (compressed to 0.4) microsec
PRF: about 900 pps **Scan Rate:** 15 or 30 rpm
Antenna Dimensions: 4.3 × 0.7 m (14.1 × 2.3 ft)

This radar, derived from RAN-7S, was introduced in 1980 and is intended for frigates and corvettes. RAN-10S is installed on board *Lupo*-class frigates of the Italian, Peruvian, and Venezuelan Navies. Maximum unambiguous range is 90 nm; effective range, about 40 nm on a fighter. Range accuracy is 20 m, and angular accuracy is 0.35 degrees. The transmitter is frequency agile (sweep to sweep), and the receiver uses doppler processing for MTI. The processor includes CFAR.

RAN-10S was an early application of pulse coding, an operation in which bursts of related pulses are transmitted in place of the usual single pulses. Pulse coding was adopted to achieve a combination of sweep-to-sweep frequency agility (for antijam performance) and doppler filtering (for MTI and clutter rejection). The idea was to filter on a single-sweep basis, then shift the filter criteria for the different frequencies used on the next sweep. Matched filters tuned to different doppler frequencies can directly reject clutter on each sweep. The interval between bursts determines the maximum unambiguous range, just as the interval between pulses determines that range in a conventional pulsed radar. As with pulse compression, the use of a burst of pulses reduces peak power but maintains sufficient average power for the radar to achieve a reasonable chance of detecting a target at long range. Each pulse within the burst requires its own doppler filter, and it is, therefore, impractical to use too many pulses. However, the use of only a few pulses per burst also limits the effective pulse-compression ratio, and a high pulse-compression ratio (since it provides, in effect, shorter pulses) makes for better range accuracy and also for better clutter rejection. The solution in this case is to code each pulse within the burst, so that it is (in effect) a pulse-compression pulse.

The returning pulses are subject to Fourier analysis, to extract doppler shifts. The measured shifts cannot exceed the spacing between the different frequencies making up the pulses. For the

RAN-10S, four filters are provided, each with the maximum bandwidth (as determined by the pulse coding), and each shifted by that bandwidth so that they cover the whole bandwidth defined by the pulse spacing within the burst; this spacing (frequency) determines the range of frequencies within the pulses.

Scan-to-scan frequency agility is accompanied by scan-to-scan shifts in coding within the bursts, and that shifting in turn reduces clutter and makes deception jamming more difficult.

Each burst cannot be more than about 10 percent of the interval between bursts, to avoid excessive minimum range (dead time). RAN-10S uses four pulses, and the ambiguity speed is set at Mach 3 (1000 m/sec), corresponding to a pulse spacing of about 50 microseconds within the burst. Since that spacing implies a burst length of about 150 microseconds, the burst repetition interval is probably about 1.5 msec, corresponding to a burst repetition rate of about 670.

RAN-10S shares some of the design concepts (and parts) of RAN-3L. The roll-stabilized antenna is designated G10.

A new stabilized SMA-7104 antenna was exhibited at Genoa in June 1986 (beam 1.5 × 15 degrees, gain 28 dB, scan rate 15/30 rpm, and weight 960 kg).

The Danish frigate *Herluf Trolle* shows two different air-search antennas. They were manufactured by Selenia, designed for the abortive RAN-7S radar. In Danish service these radars are designated CWS-2 and -3. The fire-control radars are Signaal's M-46s. (U.S. Naval Institute)

RAN-10S. (Selenia)

RAN-10S. (Selenia)

◆ RAN-11 L/X and -12 L/X

Band: L and X (combined antenna)
Beam: (L) 6.6 × 16 deg, (X) 1.1 × 6 plus csc2 deg
Peak Power: (L) 0.3 kW, (X) 135 and 180 kW
Gain: (L) 22 dB, (X) 35 dB
Pulse Width: (L) 20 microsec (compressed to 2.9), (X) 1.5 and 0.15 microsec
PRF: (X) 450–550 pps   **Scan rate:** 15 or 30 rpm
Antenna Dimensions: 8 ft wide

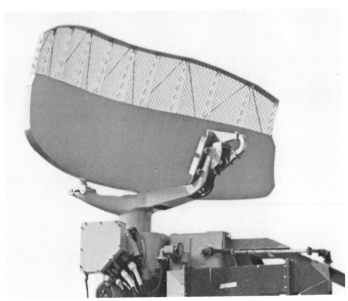

RAN-11 L/X. (Selenia)

Selenia/SMA's small-ship (hydrofoil) search radar operates simultaneously in L- and X-bands, using the X-band transmitter of the SPQ-2 and a new pulse-doppler L-band transmitter. The latter uses pulse compression. The antenna is cut horizontally, the upper portion reflecting in L- but not in X-band. Range accuracy is 160 m in L-band and 45 m in X-band; angular accuracy is 1.5 degrees in L-band and 0.2 degrees in X-band.

RAN-12 L/X is the same radar as the -11 modified with a higher-power (1.1 kW) L-band transmitter. Effective X-band range against a low flier is 20+ nm. At medium altitude, range (L-band) is 12+ nm for RAN-11, and 14+ nm for RAN-12. These figures are shorter than X-band ranges because the pulse-doppler L-band transmitter necessarily operates at a higher PRF.

Development of this system began in 1969.

◆ RAN-30X

The new (ca. 1987) Selenia shipboard air/surface-search radar for small- and medium-sized ships was derived from RTN-30X.

RAN-30X can use a single- or multibeam antenna. The multibeam antenna has three feeds that time-share power, to provide three stacked beams. The horn for the uppermost beam can be tilted, to vary its angle, by remote control. The transceiver is fully coherent, for MTI, and can also hop frequencies between pulses. Pulse compression is used to increase range. Range accuracy is 25 m, and angular accuracy is 0.4 degrees. The planar antenna is roll and pitch stabilized; it has a 3-meter swing circle and scans at 15 and 30 rpm. There are two operating modes: long-range with low scan rate and coverage of medium elevation angles, and medium/short-range with fast scan and coverage of high elevations. The manufacturer claims that a fighter can be detected beyond 20 nm.

It is possible to arrange RAN-30X and RTN-10X so that both operate from the same transmitter and receiver, with separate displays.

◆ RTN-10X/RTN-16X/RTN-20X/RTN-25X (Orion)

Band: X   **Peak Power:** 200 kW
Pulse Width: 1.5 microsec   **PRF:** 450–550 pps
Antenna Dimensions: 1.4-m diameter

RTN-10X trackers of an NA-21 fire-control system. (Selenia)

The first of the Selenia Orion fire-control radars (RTN-10X, -20X, -30X), the RTN-10X conical-scan set employs the same X-band transmitter as RAN-11 L/X. Orion was designed for one-man operation and particularly for integration into the Albatros fire-control system. Orion can scan in three modes: automatic blind-fire, operator-assisted blind-fire, and area. In the first mode the radar searches around a designated point, then locks on and tracks without further assistance. In the second, less accurate data are available, and the tracker searches a larger area. If the radar fails to lock onto a target, the operator can steer the radar to the target position shown on his display. Area search is a horizon or sector search at low elevation, or near a passive ESM bearing. A television camera is bore-sighted to the radar for use under heavy jamming. Targets can be acquired out to 35 km.

Development began in the early 1960s, and series production began in 1972. These radars were almost certainly derived from the 200-kW Orion 250 of the original NA-9 fire-control system. The 250 in turn was probably derived from the Nuova San Giorgio MLT-4 of about 1960, an improved version of the U.S. Mk 39 with a new open-work antenna. Mk 39 had a 30-inch dish with a nutating feed (3-degree beam) and a peak power of 35 kW (pulse width 0.5 microseconds, PRF 1800 pps).

RTN-16X, begun in 1969, is a private venture development of RTN-10X.

RTN-20X/25X are further derivatives of RTN-10X. Development began in 1973, and they were intended particularly for the Dardo close-in weapons system (for automatic target acquisition and for spotting rounds). RTN-20X is a digital coherent monopulse radar (TWT transmitter tube) with special ECCM features (antinodding and anticlutter). Image effects (because of reflections off the water) are reduced by comparing received signals in sequence, to select the direct-path signal. RTN-20X acquires its targets at 2–6 nm. This radar can acquire and track a target (e.g., an antiship missile) fired by the target being tracked. The antenna is a Cassegrain with twist polarization. There are two different (selectable) pulse widths, and the radar hops frequencies on a pulse-to-pulse or burst-to-burst basis; special signal processing is employed to avoid multipath effects when tracking low fliers.

RTN-25X is a higher-powered version of the same radar. The two operating modes are long pulse (coded waveform) and short pulse (single pulse). This radar is part of the NA-25 fire-control system.

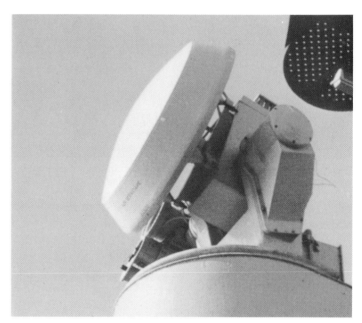

RTN-25X. (Selenia)

◆ RTN-30X

This automatic-target-acquisition and monopulse tracker was designed as part of the Albatros Mk 2 system. Range on low-level targets (such as sea-skimming missiles) in clutter is up to 8 nm. Features include MTI, frequency agility, a coded waveform (i.e., pulse compression), and jam alarm. As in the earlier Orions, there is special antinodding (i.e., antimultipath) signal processing. RTN-30X is the most powerful tracker of the RTN series and alone incorporates CW injection for missile guidance.

This radar is part of the NA-30 fire-control system (*Garibaldi, Maestrale* class, *Minerva*-class corvettes, etc.).

RTN-30X tracking radar of the NA-30 system. (Selenia)

♦ 3RM Series (BPS-704, SPN-703, etc.)

Band: X
Beam: 0.8–2.0 deg × 26 deg (shaped to 40 deg) (SPN-703: 1.2 × 25 deg; BPS-704: 2.2 × 11 deg)
Peak Power: (a) 7 (b) 20 kW   **Gain:** BPS-704: at least 27 dB
Pulse Width: (i) 0.05 (ii) 0.15 (iii) 0.5 (iv) 1.5 microsec
PRF: (i) 6000 (ii) 3000 (iii) 1500 (iv) 750 pps (SPN-703: 5200, 2600, 1300, 650, respectively)   **Scan Rate:** 25 rpm

SMA's surface-search radars have limited air-search capability. All use slotted-waveguide antennas, beamwidths depending upon dimensions. Two transmitters are available, as noted above.

The 3RM20-H version is the U.S. SPS-63 (see below) for the *Pegasus*-class hydrofoils; the Italian Navy uses the 3RM7-250 (with a second 250-kW transmitter, for air search) for its experimental hydrofoil *Sparviero*. 3RM20 is MM/BPS-704, in the *Sauro* class; her sisters all have SPQ-701. 3RM28-B is MM/SPN-703. Components of this radar are also used in the MM/APS-705 and -707 and in the MM/APQ-706 (see airborne radars).

In 1984 SMA announced a new radar, SPS-702, with a smaller antenna mounted back-to-back with the first and tilted at an angle of 45 degrees to the vertical. This antenna would provide something like the limited three-dimensional cover of the Soviet Head Net C.

MM/SPS-702 antenna. (Segnalamento Marittimo ed Aereo)

♦ HSS-1

SMA's X-band harbor-surveillance radar employs a single narrow-beam reflector. HSS-1 employs frequency and polarization decorrelation to distinguish targets in high density shipping lanes within highly reflective land areas, such as estuaries. The radar is semimobile.

♦ PLUTO

Selenia's coast-defense radar detects low fliers and surface craft. Its mast is self-erecting. Characteristics: S-band (TWT transmitter), peak power 135 kW (phase-coded pulses, fixed or randomly staggered PRF), beam 1.5 × 4 deg (super csc2 vertical coverage), tilt between +5/−2 deg, scan rate 12 or 15 rpm. The receiver includes an adaptive clutter attenuator. Signal processing techniques include an azimuth correlator (using a moving window and pattern recognition) and a jam strobe (to provide an unambiguous bearing on a jammer; but it is not clear how or whether signals entering through a sidelobe are eliminated). MTI is digital (first blind speed is faster than Mach 3). Plots can be extracted automatically in a form suited to narrow-band data link transmission, using a programmable message format.

IFF is integrated into the antenna (using a secondary feed in the main horn).

Pluto coastal-surveillance radar. (Selenia)

♦ RAT-33S/M

RAT-33 S/M coastal-surveillance radar. (Selenia)

RAT-33S/M is Selenia's medium-range coastal-surveillance (combined air and surface) radar. The radar operates in the S-band and has a dual-beam antenna (swing circle 5.5 m) and a scan rate of 15 rpm. Accuracy is 50 m in range and 0.35 deg in angle. Polarization can be linear, circular, or elliptical. The radar samples its clutter environment in the absence of targets and automatically adapts its operation accordingly, distinguishing, for example, between clear areas and ground (or sea) clutter. RAT-33S/M appears to employ ATD techniques (with CFAR), and signal processing includes doppler filters and an azimuth correlator (to reject false targets behaving nonphysically). PRF is staggered to avoid second-time-around echoes. RAT-33S/M is designed for remote operation via a narrow-band data link.

♦ SPQ-3

SMA's S- and X-band transportable coastal-surveillance (air and surface) radar is related to its SPQ-2 naval radar (see above). The SPQ-3B version has a special mine-watching feature to detect the splashes of mines dropped by air into coastal waters or harbors. This radar employs two separate antennas: back-to-back reflectors fed by slotted waveguides in X-band for spotting and tracking, and a more conventional horn-fed parabolic reflector in S-band. Typically the two antennas are mounted on a single pedestal, the X-band units below the S-band. Both elements are frequency agile, and PRF is variable. Data can be transmitted in either analog or digital (ATD) form.

OPTRONIC SYSTEMS

♦ LINCE

The OTO-Melara optronic director (Laser Improved Naval Combat Equipment, or Lynx in Italian) was first displayed in 1980, carrying a high-PRF laser range-finder beside a television or IR tracker in a horizontal cylindrical turret. LINCE can operate either fully automatically or in a back-up rate-aided mode, tracking in both bearing and range using either a joystick or a tracking ball. The associated hybrid computer is used either for air or surface fire, and in the latter mode the operator can insert spotting corrections. Range is 8+ km on air targets and 15+ km on surface targets, and elevation limits are +72/−15 deg. Training speed is greater than 60 deg/sec. The above-decks head weighs about 220 kg, with another 300 kg below decks.

♦ MEDUSA

This nonstabilized target-designation sight by Selenia/Elsag is used for remote control of light-caliber guns or as a building block for a more sophisticated system. MEDUSA carries either a twilight television camera or a low-light television camera, either feeding a 7-inch monitor. The pedestal carries a target designation button and an open-fire switch, and the console with the monitor carries a keyboard and a joystick, primarily to monitor the situation as viewed through the director.

♦ NA-12

The optronic back-up director in the private-venture fast patrol boat *Saettia* was built by Fincantieri as a technology demonstrator.

♦ NA-16

This optronic director for the *Minerva*-class frigates, for the 76-mm gun, is used in conjunction with the Dardo E fire-control system.

♦ NA-18

NA-18 is Selenia-Elsag's optronic director. See fire-control systems below.

♦ OG 30

The Officine Galileo optronic director, for *Maestrale*-class frigates, was introduced in 1980. The current version, OG 30A, is the electro-optical component of the NA-30 fire-control system but can also be combined with other systems or used alone. OG 30A carries a laser range-finder, an IR imaging camera, and a television camera on a stabilized pedestal. The system includes

a video converter, TV tracker (i.e., signal processor: it is designated P4700), and displays. With the tracker, the daylight and IR cameras can operate in either a surveillance or a tracking mode. The standard devices are: P4651 daylight television camera (1.8 × 2.4 degree field of view, 700 lines to CCIR standard), a Galileo IR television camera (8–14-micron wavelength, 3 × 6 degree field of view, 200 lines per frame, at a frame rate of 25 per second), and a P0700 laser range-finder (1.06-micron wavelength, peak power 20–25 MW, 15 bursts/sec, range 400 m to 15 km). The entire system can elevate at 2.2 rad/sec (about 126 deg/sec) within limits of −25/+85 degrees, and it slews at up to 1.5 rad/sec (about 86 deg/sec). It can turn continuously for surveillance or automatically track an air or surface target. Typically, the range on an air target is 16 km, and on a sea-skimmer, 6 km.

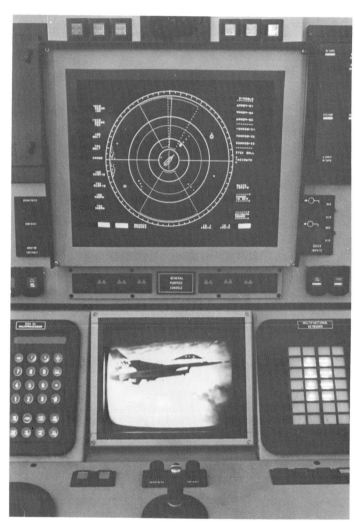

NA-18 optronic fire-control console, showing a combination of synthetic video on the upper screen and a television image below. (Selenia)

♦ OG.R7

The Officine Galileo manned optical director is essentially a telescope and open sight linked to a computer. Targets are tracked and the 76-mm guns controlled by means of a joystick. This director has been adopted by the West German Navy for secondary control in Type-143 fast attack craft. Total weight is 550 kg, and the current version is OG.R7/3.

♦ PEGASO

This optronic director by Selenia/Elsag, similar to NA-18, carries several sensors (e.g., IR camera, TV camera, laser range-finder), with a one-man below-decks console and a digital computer.

PEGASO optronic fire-control system director, showing television and infrared cameras. (Selenia)

◆ SIR-3

The Selenia thermal imaging surveillance system was announced in 1984.

FIRE-CONTROL SYSTEMS

◆ Albatros

Selenia-Elsag's medium-range surface-to-air missile system uses the semiactive Aspide missile. Albatros is designed to be added to an existing gunfire-control system so that no additional tracker/illuminators are required. Instead, Albatros uses one or two slaved illuminators (presumably CW injection in existing tracking radars).

The original Albatros Mk 1 fired the Sea Sparrow (RIM-7H) missile. Tested in 1973, Mk 1 never entered production. Mk 2 fires the Aspide. Mod 2 and Mod 5 employ Elsag (Elettronica San Giorgio) fire controls. Mod 8 uses the Ferranti WSA 400; Mod 9 uses a Signaal radar. Both the Elsag and the Ferranti versions use the Selenia Orion RTN-10X radar for fire control. Illumination is provided by a Selenia RTN-12X Sirio radar that uses the same antenna as the Orion. Total reaction time, from target designation to missile launch, is 8 seconds.

In some installations two radar channels are provided. The tracking radar can receive CW illumination reflected from the target and track that radiation, or the tracking radar can track conventionally. Both channels share the same antenna.

The system exists with both four- and eight-cell launchers, the latter duplicating the existing NATO Sea Sparrow launcher; however, in Albatros the eight-cell launcher is combined with an automatic reload magazine carrying up to 16 missiles; the missiles are carried in four-round trays, each of which duplicates one layer of the missile launcher. The magazine pivots up to mate with the rear of the launcher for reloading, and each missile is rammed into its launcher cell by a loading arm.

◆ Dardo

Selenia-Elsag's close-in weapons-control system was designed to deal with sea-skimming missiles. Dardo uses an Orion RTN-20X and a television camera to control a twin 40-mm/70 gun mount. The radar was developed specifically for the CIWS role, the television being used to monitor the engagement and also to control the gun in a jamming environment. Targets are detected by a separate search radar, and any target within a preset range can be engaged automatically. The system will shift automatically to deal with a sequence of targets.

Dardo is designed to engage targets between 900 and 3000 m. Its effectiveness derives from its very low dispersion, 2.5 mrad for the system as a whole (based on about 1 mrad for the 40-mm gun).

This system was first used on board *Lupo*-class frigates (the first of which was delivered in 1976). In July 1980 the frigate *Sagittario* used Dardo and the associated twin 40-mm to engage a series of six Rushton aerial targets (19-cm diameter, 2.8 m long) towed at high speed to simulate sea-skimmers. Four were shot down by the initial bursts, and two more were considered sufficiently damaged to count as kills at a range greater than 1000 m.

An extended Dardo E system was announced in 1984. It consists of the two separate systems of the carrier *Garibaldi*, a Dardo for close-in defense, and the line-of-sight NA-30 Mod B. The weapons might be a twin 40-mm gun, a 5 in/54, and an Aspide launcher, controlled by a search radar and a tracker.

◆ NA-9

This fire-control system by Nuova San Giorgio is based on the Orion 250 X-band radar and is derived from the earlier Italian Navy Argo system. The first of 23 ordered by the Italian and other navies entered service in 1964. Claimed performance: for a target approaching at up to 600 m/sec (angular velocity 6 deg/sec), average miss distance at 1000–4500 m is 8 m.

NA-9C simultaneously controls 40-mm and 5-inch guns.

NA-9D simultaneously controls guns and short-range antiaircraft missiles (two 5-inch and two launchers against one or two targets).

The system occupies a fixed cabin, with the radar dish on top and two periscopes flanking a cab in front. Each periscope operator has a director control panel.

◆ NA-10

These fire-control systems use the Orion 10X con-scan radar. Mod 2 is intended for frigates and larger ships, Mod 3 for fast attack craft. Note that Orion 10X was designed specifically for the Albatros system, so that NA-10 may be equated with the fire-control part of Albatros (see above). NA-10 is similar to NA-9 but incorporates further miniaturization and a closed-circuit television.

◆ NA-12

NA-12 is similar to NA-9/10 but is used for simultaneous control of guns and of missiles with blind-fire capability.

◆ NA-18

Selenia-Elsag's optronic fire-control system is used to control guns up to 3-inch caliber. The system consists of an optronic director (twilight TV camera, laser range-finder, IR camera) and

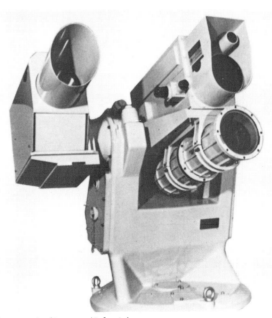

NA-18 optronic director. (Selenia)

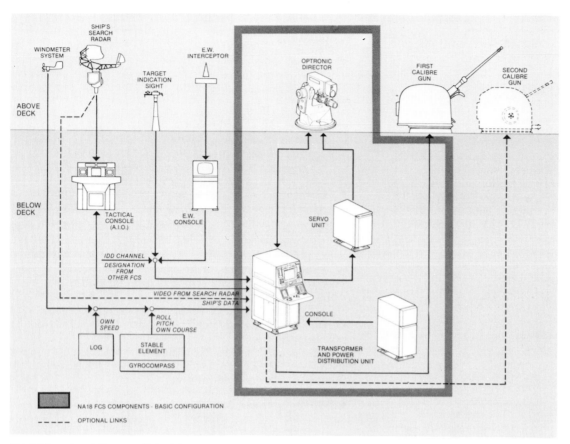

NA-18 functional diagram. (Selenia)

NA-18's display-and-control console, for one-man operation. (Selenia)

an operating console (raster displays for the images; a joystick for target acquisition and manual tracking; and processing, interface, and television automatic-tracker units). The console carries a 15-inch high-resolution monitor for synthetic video and a 9.5-inch monitor for television and IR images. As an option, the 15-inch monitor can carry the ship's search radar video. The system can then be used for navigation and command and control, becoming the SEN-100 small ships' combat system.

If the radar option is adopted, the 15-inch monitor can be arranged in either PPI (rastered) or B-scan (range × bearing rectangular format: 7.2 km × 60 degrees) form. The B-scan is particularly useful for splash spotting in a surface engagement. Radar targets are manually initialized, the system then performing rate-aided tracking on up to nine of them. They can be designated for fire control either with the trackball or by track number.

Targets can also be designated to the system from CIC or from shipboard ESM. To overcome difficulties in tracking fast targets by TV or IR, the 15-inch monitor uses a special display of four contiguous images corresponding to four adjacent director positions (either in elevation or in azimuth), all frozen, corresponding to a vertical or horizontal swath. This frame freezing eliminates blurring due to director motion and makes for easier acquisition by the operator. Laser echoes are presented as bars with range-gate limits superimposed.

The 9.5-inch monitor shows the cross hairs and the tracking window, the system status and warning messages, target data (coordinates, radial speed, angle of attack), main weapons status, and alarm messages. The 9.5-inch monitor is located under the large monitor, flanked by two keypads for quick inputs, with a trackball and joystick in front.

The NA-18 computer incorporates several alternative tracking models (algorithms), automatically selecting the one it supposes is appropriate to the target at hand. Targets are tracked in three dimensions (in range by the laser), and the computer filters this tracking data in all three dimensions. In the event the laser fails, the system can track in angle at a prefixed firing range (corresponding to a barrage-firing mode). The operator can always shift from automatic to manual (joystick) tracking, and he can aim using the cross hairs of the TV monitor.

The system can digitally control up to two guns of different caliber, and it can carry two independent sets of ballistics (for different ammunition) for each gun in the computer's memory. Control takes account of parallax and ship's motion, and guns are automatically triggered when the target comes within their precomputed effective range. In surface firing, spotting corrections are manually entered through quick-input devices at the console. In the antiaircraft mode, observed spotting errors are compensated for by joystick.

The standard TV camera uses a zoom lens (focal length 30–360 mm), with a 2.54–30.5-degree field of view; the camera operates at CCIR 625/50 scan standard. The IR camera operates in the 8–12-micron band, using a closed-cycle cooling system, with a 4 × 2.6 degree field of view. An alternative IR camera has two fields of view (6.9 × 3.45 and 2.3 × 1.15 degrees). The laser range-finder operates at 1.06 microns (Neodymium YAG3), with a 15-Hz PRF and a peak power of 18 MW; the range-finder can provide ranges between 400 m and 15 km. The associated computer is a 24-bit machine with a 250-nanosecond memory-access time (clock rate 4 MHz) with a combination of ROM, semiconductor memory, and tape memory.

The tracking platform servo's operating limits are as follows: elevation limits +84/−22 deg, training speed 126 deg/sec, elevating speed 86 deg/sec.

Elsag described NA-18 as the simplest of a series of modular weapons-control systems using common consoles and a data bus. NA-18 uses the simplest computer (which is also used by the SCLAR rocket launcher) and very nearly the simplest console. The more elaborate versions of the same system are NA-21 and NA-30.

◆ NA-21

Selenia-Elsag's radar gunfire-control system was announced in 1980. A digital version of the earlier NA-10, NA-21 is designed to control three guns of two different calibers plus a surface-to-air missile (typically Albatros), and can also designate targets to

a surface-to-surface missile. The associated fire-control radar is the Orion RTN-10X, with a television camera for visual control.

Like NA-18, NA-21 is a modular combat system using standard consoles, computers, and data busing.

◆ NA-25

This modular Selenia-Elsag radar and optronic fire-control system controls two guns of different calibers, using an Orion RTN-25X. An IR sensor and a neodymium YAG laser can be mounted on the radar director to provide an alternative range sensor, and a television camera is an alternative tracker. NA-25 can perform command-and-control as well as fire-control functions, using a multiprocessor (MARA 286) and a special console (MAGICS) incorporating two high-resolution color monitors. The system can be set for programmed autonomous search (360 degree or by sectors) or can be fed by video from the ship's search radar. NA-25 automatically evaluates the threat presented by various targets and engages them.

◆ NA-30

Selenia-Elsag's radar/optronic weapons-control system controls up to three guns of two different calibers, as well as antiaircraft missiles. The associated tracking radar is the Orion RTN-30X, combined with an electro-optical ranger (IR/laser) and a television tracker (as in NA-25). NA-30 is a modular combat system using a data bus and one or two control consoles.

NA-30 is designed to operate automatically (with operator veto) against a target designated by a search radar, by the system's own fire-control radar (in search mode), or by some other sensor, such as ESM. NA-30 is designed to control several weapons against a single target in coordinated firing mode: typically, an Aspide missile and up to three guns (with parallax corrections and two independent sets of ballistics with one fuze-setting computation). Automatic operation is intended to counter fast targets such as antiship missiles; there is also a manual mode for use against surface ships or slow air targets.

The main (supervising) console carries two monitors: a 19-inch raster-scan CRT to show radar PPI (search radar or fire-control radar, the operator choosing between them) or a B-scan

NA-30 functional diagram. (Selenia)

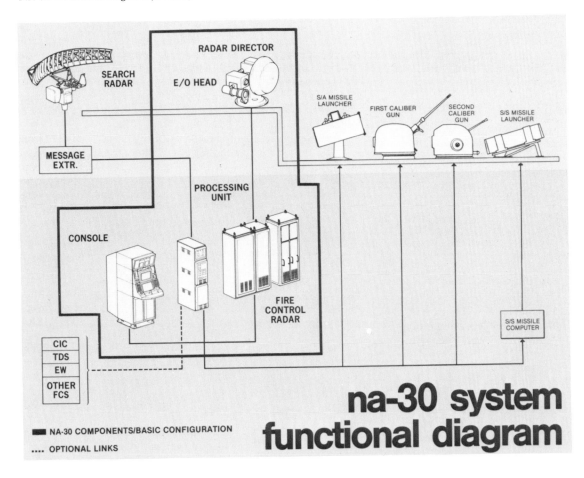

na-30 system functional diagram

■■ NA-30 COMPONENTS/BASIC CONFIGURATION

···· OPTIONAL LINKS

(azimuth/range) track presentation with track labels and other graphics; and a 15-inch raster-scan CRT for TV or IR images with superimposed alphanumerics (e.g., CIC orders, FCS and weapons status, and alarm messages). The operator interacts with the system mainly by means of a variable-function keyboard, a numeric keypad, a trackball, a joystick, and a range handwheel. There are also pedals for gunfire control and for "voluntary" tracking initialization.

The radar/optronic director has elevation limits of $+84/-22$ degrees; and the maximum training speed is 2.7 rad/sec (elevating 1.5 rad/sec), corresponding to 155 deg/sec (86 deg/sec). Like NA-18, NA-30 employs a 24-bit computer.

NA-30 was announced in 1982 and entered service in 1985. It is installed on board Italian *Maestrale*-class frigates and the carrier *Giuseppe Garibaldi*. When combined with the RAN-30X search radar, ESM, and CIC equipment, NA-30 forms the SEN 300 combat system for low- and medium-tonnage ships. In Italian naval service this system is called Dardo-E.

JAPAN

RADARS

♦ OPS-1

Designed about 1955, OPS-1 was a Japanese-produced version of the U.S. SPS-12. The structure of the antenna is more like that of SPS-6B/C (which was electronically much like SPS-6). Physically, the OPS-1 antenna showed features of both SPS-6B/C and SPS-12.

The Japanese destroyer *Akizuki* displays the OPS-1 air-search radar, with the antenna of an OPS-15 surface-search set visible above. Her main battery consists of three U.S.-supplied 5-in/54 Mk 39s. *(Ships of the World)*

♦ OPS-2

Reportedly OPS-2 was a Japanese-produced version of the U.S. SPS-6C. Peak power was given as 400 kW.

♦ OPS-4

This surface-search radar, with a solid antenna, still equips the former submarine-rescue ship *Chihaya* and once was common on board both combatants and auxiliaries. OPS-4 may be a Raytheon 1404 commercial set.

♦ OPS-9

This surface-search radar, with a very long slotted-waveguide antenna, operates in X- (I/J) band. OPS-9 equips the mine-countermeasures craft and some of the miscellaneous auxiliaries.

♦ OPS-10/13/19/22/29

These surface-search radars for small ships have slotted-waveguide antennas. OPS-13 is the search radar of the PT 11 class. OPS-29 equips the small patrol boats (PB type).

The Japanese torpedo boat PT 13 is equipped with an OPS-13 surface-search radar. *(Ships of the World)*

♦ OPS-11

OPS-11 is the first Japanese-designed air-search radar. The antenna is an 8×4 array of yagi antennas. Previous Japanese dependence on U.S. radar technology suggests that OPS-11 may be related to SPS-40, with a radically different antenna. Reports that OPS-11 is a UHF long-range pulse-compression radar would corroborate that relationship.

OPS-11B reportedly operates at about 300 MHz, its low frequency having been chosen for long range and for fewer fades. The antenna is an array of 24 yagis.

OPS-11 air-search radars at the mastheads of three *Iakatsuki*-class destroyers. (Jake Yamada)

OPS-11 on board an *Iakatsuki*-class destroyer, with OPS-17 surface-search radar above, and GFCS-1 atop the bridge. The big radomes are part of a jamming system called OLT-3; the small ones are probably DF radomes (NOLR-6). (Author)

♦ **OPS-12**

OPS-12 three-dimensional air-search radar on board the destroyer *Shirane*, with OPS-28 above it. The two gun directors above the bridge are GFCS-1A. (Japanese Maritime Self-Defense Force)

This planar-array air-search radar is probably similar in operation to SPS-52. Unlike SPS-52, OPS-12 lacks a serpentine feed running up one edge. However, an extension visible on the right side of the main antenna may contain the feed. This arrangement might make for a more symmetric array, easier to stabilize. OPS-12 equips only the *Kurama*-class helicopter-carrying destroyers.

NEC produces a land-based air-search radar, NPG-880, whose antenna is similar in appearance to that of OPS-12. NPG-880 is a frequency-scanning (serpentine feed) radar employing ferrite phase shifters between the serpentine feed and the radiating elements themselves. That arrangement makes it possible to use chirped (pulse-compressed) pulses at fixed elevation angles,

the ferrites canceling out the effect of frequency change within each chirp. The U.S. SPS-48E employs similar techniques. NPG-880 employs a TWT/CFA transmitter.

♦ **OPS-14**

OPS-14 is an L-band radar with a somewhat larger (higher gain) antenna than that of OPS-1/2. This radar is manufactured by Mitsubishi Electric. The first was fitted to the destroyers *Akizuki* and *Teruzuki*, and the radar is on board all destroyers and frigates after the *Murasame* and *Yudachi*. FY67 ships and later have OPS-14. FY73 and later have OPS-14B, with MTI. However, large warships are also being fitted with OPS-11. The peak power of OPS-14B is 400 kW (500 kW in OPS-14), and the beam dimensions are 5 deg × 30 deg csc2.

♦ **OPS-15/16/17/18/35/36/37**

These surface-search radars superficially resemble the U.S. SPS-5/10, with their openwork antennas. OPS-37, a Japanese version of the U.S. SPS-5B, has an antenna that is noticeably smaller than those of the others. OPS-18 is a 100-kW C-band set (5450–5825 MHz) with a 2 × 20 deg beam, manufactured by Nihon Musen. OPS-16, -17, -35, and -36 operate at somewhat higher frequency, closer to X-band. OPS-15 equips the training ship *Katori* and some of the ex-destroyers (now serving as auxiliaries). OPS-16 is the surface-search radar on board some older frigates. OPS-17 was the standard destroyer surface-search radar; it is now being replaced by OPS-28. OPS-18 equips the new *Towada*-class underway replenishment ships.

♦ **OPS-19**

A slotted-waveguide navigational radar, OPS-19 is sometimes used in combination with the much larger OPS-28 (e.g., in the destroyer *Kurama*, on the foremast, and in the *Yubari*-class frigates).

♦ **OPS-28**

OPS-28 is a large slotted-waveguide surface-search and short-range air-search radar. The current version, OPS-28C, is the functional successor to OPS-17, replacing it in the *Tachikaze*-class destroyer *Sawakaze*. OPS-28 is also replacing OPS-18.

OPS-28 is a specialized sea-skimmer detector, broadly comparable to the U.S. TAS Mk 23.

♦ **ZPS-4**

This search radar, installed in the *Uzushio*-class submarines, uses a fully enclosed antenna in a cylindrical radome.

The Japanese submarine *Makishio* shows a ZPS-4 radar. (*Ships of the World*)

♦ **ZPS-6**

ZPS-6 is a submarine search radar in the current *Yushio* class.

♦ **Furuno Radars**

These commercial navigational radars are used primarily by the U.S. Navy; they do not appear to be used by the Japanese Maritime Self-Defense Force. For details, see the U.S. entries below.

The new Japanese destroyer *Asagiri* shows both the OPS-14C air-search radar (forward) and the new FCS-2-12E missile (Sea Sparrow) fire-control radar (aft, under the big radome). The small surface-search radar on the platform atop the foremast is OPS-28, and the radomes on the main mast are part of an EW suit consisting of an OLR-9C passive system, an OLR-6C, and an OLT-3 jammer, plus SRBOC launchers. The gun director atop the bridge is FCS-2-21A. *(Sea Power)*

FIRE-CONTROL SYSTEMS

◆ GFCS Model 1 (GFCS-1)

Model 1A controls 5-in guns; Model 1B controls 3-in guns. This system is mounted from the *Natsugumo* and *Nagatsuki* on. Made by Mitsubishi Electric, GFCS-1 is also designated Type 72. An earlier Type-68 system is on board the *Harusame*. This radar-equipped director, similar to the U.S. Mk 56, is for 5-inch guns. In some ships it replaced a U.S. Mk 63.

◆ GFCS Model 2 (GFCS-2)

This Type-79 fire-control system exists in two versions. Model 2-12, enclosed in a radome, controls guns and Sea Sparrow mis-

siles from the *Ishikara* on. Model 2-21, on an open pedestal, controls guns only. Both are manufactured by Mitsubishi Electric.

Type 79 is a digital system replacing the earlier analog Type 72. Type 79 employs an unmanned director whose Cassegrain monopulse tracking antenna can be seen mounted on a pedestal. This arrangement is an improvement over the conscan tracker of Type 72, in which the on-mount operator is exposed to the elements. Reportedly the search antenna in the 2-12 system shares the same transmitter as the tracker, as in the Signaal "eggs."

NETHERLANDS

HSA (Hollandse Signaal Apparaten, often called Signaal) is the sole Dutch producer of naval radars and fire-control systems. It and Svensk Philips (Philips Electronics AB, or PEAB) are almost completely owned by Philips SA. The only other major owner is the Dutch government. The HSA and PEAB product lines are entirely different, but the two companies have noncompetitive agreements.

RADARS

◆ DA-01/02/04

DA-01. (Signaal)

Band: S (2.9–3.1 GHz)   **Beam:** 1.5 × csc2 (DA-02 1.7 deg)
Peak Power: 400 kW   **Gain:** 32 dB
Pulse Width: (i) 1.3 (ii) 0.5 microsec
PRF: (i) 500 (ii) 1000 pps   **Scan Rate:** 6 to 60 rpm
Antenna Dimensions: 15.3 ft wide   **Antenna Weight:** 4400 lbs

DA-01 was the first postwar Dutch target-designation (DA) radar, introduced in 1954 on board Dutch destroyers. The com-

FCS-2-21A. *(Sea Power)*

mercial (Signaal) designation was SGR-105. Claimed performance included detection of a 2 square-meter target at 50 nm and at 35,000 ft. DA-02 used a broader-beam (1.7-degree) antenna but greater power (500 kW, 40 nm at 30,000 ft) and was first exported to Argentina for the former U.S. light cruiser *Nueve de Julio*. There was no DA-03. DA-04 was the last of the series, a simplified version of DA-01 using an unstabilized antenna (1200 lbs).

DA-series antenna on board a Dutch frigate, 1978. The British UA-8/9 ESM antenna is on the pole mast above. For DA-05, see the photograph of the Indonesian *Malahayati* under the entry for the Bofors 4.7-in/46 gun. (U.S. Naval Institute)

◆ **DA-05**

DA-05/4 on board the Irish *Eithne*, 1986, with IFF interrogator above. (Author)

Band: S (6 preset frequencies between 2900 and 3100 MHz)
Beam: 1.5 × 8 deg (csc2 cover up to 40 deg)
Peak Power: 1200 kW   **Gain:** 32.2 dB
Pulse Width: (i) 1.3 (ii) 2.6 microsec
PRF: (i) 1000 (ii) 500 pps   **Scan Rate:** 10 or 20 rpm
Antenna Dimensions: 4.87 × 2.75 m (about 16 × 9 ft)
Antenna Weight: 725 kg

DA-05 was the first of a new series of DA radars, analogous to LW-04, using elliptical antennas and more powerful magnetrons. Like LW-04, DA-05 has digital MTI. Claimed performance includes detection of a 2 square-meter target at 72–84 nm and about 60,000 ft; minimum range is 1000 m. This radar can discriminate targets 1.5 deg apart in azimuth and 200–400 m apart in range. DA-05 is the primary air-search radar of the Belgian *Wielingen* class and is also used by the Dutch and Spanish Navies. DA-05/M is a land-based mobile version, and both DA-06 and -07 are land-based.

DA-05. (Signaal)

◆ **DA-08**

DA-08 on board a Turkish frigate. (Stefan Terzibaschitsch)

Band: S   **Beam:** 1.5 × csc squared to 40 deg
Peak Power: 145 kW (5.1 kW average)   **Gain:** 33 dB
Pulse Width: (i) 35 (ii) 69 microsec   **PRF:** (i) 1000 (ii) 500 pps
Scan Rate: 10 or 20 rpm (selectable)
Antenna Dimensions: 4.4 × 3.9 m; depth 6.5 m
Antenna Weight: 2500 kg

This coherent pulse-compression radar is derived from, and is analogous with, the larger LW-08. Claimed range on a 2 square-meter target is 78–92 nm. Minimum range is 0.8 nm. The antenna is stabilized. Each pulse consists of a one-microsecond nonmodulated pulse and a 34- or 68-microsecond frequency-swept (pulse-compression) pulse. Compressed pulse length is 0.6 microseconds. There are six fixed crystal-set fre-

DA-08. (Signaal)

LW-04. (Signaal)

quencies plus a jumping frequency. Resolution: 1.5 deg in azimuth, 120 m in range.

DA-08 is the primary air-search radar of German *Bremen*-class frigates and *Hamburg*-class destroyers.

◆ LW-02/03

> **Band:** L (1220–1350 MHz) **Beam:** 2.2 × csc2 (ratio 1:10) deg
> **Peak Power:** 500 kW **Gain:** 31 dB
> **Pulse Width:** (i) 2 (ii) 5 microsec **PRF:** (i) 500 (ii) 250 pps
> **Scan Rate:** 1–10 rpm (in some, 3/6 rpm)
> **Antenna Dimensions:** 7.8 × 4.25 m (25.6 × 13.9 ft)
> **Antenna Weight:** 2100 lbs

LW-02 was the first postwar Dutch destroyer radar; and it was exported to Australia, Colombia, Sweden, and West Germany under the commercial designation SGR-114/12. Claimed performance included detection of aircraft at 100 nm and 59,000 ft.

LW-03 was a similar radar with a scan rate of 5 or 10 rpm.

There is also LW-01, a much larger radar (antenna 11 × 4.88 m [36.1 × 16 ft], 3200 lbs, with a beam 1.8 degree × csc2 [ratio 1:12], gain 33 dB, scan rate 3 or 6 rpm or 1–6 rpm) using the same transmitter, for cruisers and aircraft carriers. The commercial designation was SGR-114/06, and the sole survivor is on board the Argentine aircraft carrier *25 de Mayo*.

◆ LW-04

> **Band:** L (6 preset frequencies between 1250 and 1350 MHz)
> **Beam:** 2.2 × 10 deg **Peak Power:** 1100 kW (LW-04/2 version)
> **Gain:** 30 dB **Pulse Width:** (i) 1.3 (ii) 2.6 microsec
> **PRF:** (i) 1000 (ii) 500 pps (staggered) **Scan Rate:** 7.5 or 15 rpm
> **Antenna Dimensions:** 7.35 × 4.8 m **Antenna Weight:** 1400 kg

LW-04 introduced the elliptical antenna characteristic of current Dutch air-search radars. No commercial (SGR) designation has been announced, but LW-04 first appeared on board the German destroyer *Hessen*. These radars have digital MTI and can operate on any one of six preset frequencies. Claimed range on a 2 square-meter target is 120 nm at 55,000 ft. Resolution is 2.2 degrees in azimuth, 200 or 400 m in range.

No LW-05 has been announced; LW-06 and -07 are land systems.

◆ LW-08

LW-08 on board a *van Heemskerck*–class missile frigate. This version has a double feed; there is also a single-feed version. (Signaal)

> **Band:** L (6 preset frequencies between 1250 and 1350 MHz)
> **Beam:** 2.2 × csc2 to 40 deg
> **Peak Power:** 150 kW pulse compressed; average power 5.2 kW
> **Gain:** 30 dB **Pulse Width:** (i) 35 (ii) 69 microsec
> **PRF:** (i) 1000 (ii) 500 pps **Scan Rate:** 7.5 or 15 rpm
> **Antenna Dimensions:** 8.8 × 7.525 m
> **Antenna Weight:** total 5000 kg (antenna 1500 kg)

The pulse-compression waveform includes a 1-microsecond pulse for short-range resolution, and then a long "chirp" for long-range performance. The high average power (5.2 kW) corresponds to 5100 kW applied to 1-microsecond pulses; that power gives some idea of range performance (a range of 145 nm at 85,000 ft is claimed for a 2 square-meter target). The short initial pulse is used for surface warning. Any of six preselected frequencies can be used, and there is provision for pulse-to-pulse frequency jumping through the entire band. Resolution is 2.2 deg in azimuth, 300 ft in range. Pulse-compressed pulses are equivalent to 0.6-microsecond pulses.

The antenna is stabilized.

The British Type 1022 marries an LW-08 transmitter to a Marconi narrow-beam (squintless) antenna.

LW-08 was first used on board the Dutch "standard" frigate *Kortenaer*.

◆ SPS-01

SPS-01 occupies the large radome of the Dutch destroyer *Tromp*. The small radome forward of the bridge is for a Signaal WM-25, and two SPG-51s aft control the Standard Missile. The two slotted-waveguide surface-search radars are Decca 1226s. (U.S. Naval Institute)

SPS-01 array. The serpentine waveguide feeding the diagonal slotted waveguides is visible between the two arrays. (Signaal)

Band: S
Beam: (search) 1.5 × 2 to 30 deg; (track) 1.5 × 1.5 deg (approx, depends on elevation)
Peak Power: 750 kW **Gain:** about 39 dB
Pulse Width: 40 microsec **PRF:** 460 and 540 pps, staggered
Scan Rate: 20 rpm

SPS-01 is the big multifunction radar of the Dutch missile-destroyers *Tromp* and *de Ruyter*. It combines a broad-beam search radar with a high-data-rate radar for tracking multiple targets. Five antennas are mounted to rotate together: two back-to-back paraboloids (with feed horns moving to generate any of five alternative beams, plus a sixth, fixed, low-angle beam); two

back-to-back frequency-scanned arrays at right angles to the paraboloids; and an IFF mounted below one of the two paraboloids. The low-angle search beam operates continuously to provide short-range warning (40 scans/minute using the back-to-back antennas). The other five search beams are used in sequence (one by one during subsequent rotations), so that for each the effective data rate is 8 scans/minute. This scheme is used, not for height finding, but rather to give solid vertical coverage. The search beam's dimensions vary with elevation, the vertical beamwidth being 2 degrees at an elevation of 2.5 degrees, but 30 degrees at an elevation of 21 degrees. Targets are automatically detected, and their two-dimensional (range and bearing) positions fed into the central computer, which instructs the two frequency-scanned radars to find the contacts in three dimensions for tracking. Each of the two frequency-scanned arrays is slanted to the vertical, the combination of the two oppositely slanted arrays making for full three-dimensional operation. The net data rate is 40 scans/minute, because of the back-to-back operation.

The entire radar is fed by a single time-shared power source.

Discussions with the Royal Netherlands Navy began in 1958, and a first working model was completed in February 1964. The two operational radars were completed in 1969. SPS-01 was originally known as MTTR, the Multi-Target Tracking Radar, and for a time was a joint project with the Royal Navy.

◆ VI-01 (SGR-109)

Band: S **Beam:** 3.5 × 1.2 degrees
Peak Power: 500 kW **Gain:** 39 dB
Pulse Width: (i) 1.5 (ii) 0.5 microsec **PRF:** (i) 500 (ii) 1000 pps
Scan Rate: (elevation) 50 scans/min (+8/−2 deg) or 20 scans/min (+50/−2 deg); the sector scanned varies automatically with range. scan in terms of bearing: 51 deg/sec

VI-01 is the nodding height-finder on board the Argentine carrier *25 de Mayo*. The transmitter is the same as that of the contemporary DA-01 series. Claimed performance for the very similar land-based radar is a range of 150 nm, coverage to 120,000 ft. Up to six randomly spread targets (over 360 degrees) can be handled per minute.

◆ ZW-01/3 (SGR-103)

Band: X (8.5–9.6 GHz) **Beam:** 1.0 × 3.5 deg
Peak Power: 180 kW **Gain:** 39 dB
Pulse Width: (i) 0.1 (ii) 0.3 microsec **PRF:** (i) 2000 (ii) 1000 pps
Scan Rate: 7.5 or 15 rpm **Antenna Dimensions:** width 2.56 m
Antenna Weight: 300 kg

ZW-01 appeared in 1954 and was widely used in the Dutch and German Navies. ZW-03 is an improved version, also widely used. These radars are described as surface and low-altitude air-search sets. The search antenna is stabilized on the horizon.

Typical performance: a jet fighter (1–3 square meters) can be detected at up to 30 nm, and a bomber (10–40 square meters) at up to 48 nm. Small vessels can be detected at about 18 nm, and periscopes at 4.5 nm. Minimum range is 50 meters.

◆ ZW-04 (SGR-116/08)

Band: X (8.5–9.6 GHz) **Beam:** 0.9 × 18 deg
Peak Power: 140 kW **Gain:** 32 dB
Pulse Width: (i) 0.1 (ii) 0.9 microsec **PRF:** (i) 2000 (ii) 1000 pps
Scan Rate: 24 rpm **Antenna Dimensions:** 2.76 m × 1.54 m (total)
Antenna Weight: 200 kg

This radar was originally designed specifically for Dutch coastal minesweepers. The antenna is not stabilized, the broad vertical beam having been chosen to provide a steady picture despite the rolling of the ship. Typical performance: jet fighters (1–3 square meters) can be detected at up to 18 nm; jet bombers (10–40 square meters) at 24–40 nm; height coverage is up to about 12,000 ft. Large vessels can be detected at 20–30 nm, small vessels at 15–20 nm, and reflector buoys (of sufficient height) at about 12 nm. Minimum range is less than 50 meters.

◆ ZW-06/07

Band: X (9.325–9.475 GHz) **Beam:** 0.9 × 19 deg
Peak Power: 60 kW **Gain:** 32 dB
Pulse Width: (i) 0.06 (ii) 0.6 microsec
PRF: (i) 4000 (ii) 2000 pps **Scan Rate:** 24 rpm
Antenna Dimensions: 2.9 × 1.2 m (about 9.5 × 3.9 ft)
Antenna Weight: 130 kg (287 lbs)

For ZW-06, range on a 10 square-meter target is about 14 nm, and an airplane at 20,000 ft can be detected at that range. The very short pulse was adopted for high resolution. The air coverage is necessary for helicopter control in ASW. The transmitter is coherent, for clutter and jamming rejection.

Applications include the Dutch *Kortenaer* class, the Brazilian *Niteroi*, the Spanish *Descubierta*, and the Indian *Leanders*.

ZW-07 is a submarine version of ZW-06, with a peak power of 50 or 60 kW (pulse width 1 microsec, PRF 1200 pps). There are also a short-pulse mode (0.1 microsec, 35 kW, 2400 pps) and a single-pulse mode (0.22 microsec, 100 kW, can be 2500 pps). Gain is 28 dB; dimensions of the half-cheese antenna are 1.0 × 0.250 meters. The beam is 2.4 × 16 degrees. Resolution is 2.4 deg in azimuth. Performance: range on a 10 square-meter target is about 16 nm (at 25,000 ft). In the single-pulse mode a ship (50 square meters) can be detected at 13.5 km, and a 10 square-meter target at 9 km.

ZW-06 surface-search radar. (Signaal)

ZW-07 surface-search radar for submarines. (Signaal)

◆ ZW-08

Band: X **Beam:** 1 deg
Peak Power: 150 kW (5 kW average) **Pulse Width:** 0.06 microsec

Although in principle a surface-search radar, ZW-08 has been designed for sea-skimmer detection, i.e., for AAW. ZW-08's transmitter is a synthesizer-driven TWT (for pulse-to-pulse coherence), and this radar has a pulse-compression receiver. ZW-08 can be set for low-level surveillance with a maximum elevation of 5, 10, or 30 degrees. Nominal resolution is 1.5 degrees or 30 m. Detection range against a jet fighter is 28 km at minimum elevation setting, 48 km at 10 degrees, and 73 km

(43 km against a missile) at 30 degrees. The antenna is stabilized, and the use of a narrower beam than that of earlier surface-search sets improves detection range on a surface or low-flying target. Maximum altitude is 10,000 ft.

◆ ZW-09

This surface-search and low-level air-search radar for small ships uses a stabilized antenna. ZW-09 is frequency agile and has digital MTI.

◆ ZW-12

Band: X **Beam:** (i) 0.9 × 19 deg (ii) 1.5 × 10 deg
Peak Power: 50 kW (100 W average)
Gain: (i) 31.2 dB (ii) 32.2 dB **Pulse Width:** 0.55 microsec
PRF: 4000 pps **Scan Rate:** (i) 24 rpm (ii) 60 rpm
Antenna Dimensions: (i) 2.65 × 1.2 × 1.78 m (ii) 1.5 × 1.2 × 0.85 m **Antenna Weight:** (i) 130 kg (ii) 175 kg

In the data above, (i) is the conventional parabolic antenna and (ii) the stabilized slotted waveguide (version 12S).

Despite the radar's surface-search designation, Signaal describes ZW-12 as a helicopter-control (using a special VESTA transponder) and limited air-warning radar. There are two antennas, a conventional mesh reflector and a stabilized cylindrical (slotted-waveguide) antenna (ZW-12S). There is provision for an optional track-while-scan unit, capable of tracking two surface targets simultaneously. ZW-12/1 has an unstabilized antenna, and ZW-12/2 is stabilized.

The control console has a 12-inch PPI and a 15-inch television for light-pen control.

◆ LIROD-8 GFCS4

See LIOD under optronic systems below.

◆ SMART/MW 08

SMART. (Signaal)

Band: S
Beam: 2 deg horizontal; each beam is about 9 deg wide
Peak Power: 150 KW
Gain: 23-dB transmitter; 31.5-dB receiver
Pulse Width: 0.6 microsec compressed **PRF:** 3800 pps
Scan Rate: 27 rpm **Antenna Dimensions:** 4.8 m × 2.05 m
Antenna Weight: 1200 kg (plus 385-kg drive)

SMART is the Signaal three-dimensional radar designed particularly to deal with antiship missiles, with radar cross sections as small as 0.1 square meter, and with speeds as high as Mach 3. SMART covers all threats from sea-skimmers up to divers approaching at a 60-degree angle. SMART can automatically detect and track (ADT) up to 160 air and 40 surface targets at medium and long range. Signaal chose S-band as the best balance between range, clutter rejection, and overall dimensions (for frigate installation). An X-band version was also designed.

MW 08. (Signaal)

Inside the antenna are a single horn transmitting antenna and a linear array of 16 strip-line receiving antennas. Received signals are preprocessed within the antenna itself: the output of the 16 receivers is fed into a digital beam former producing 12 independent elevation beams. The antenna rotates in bearing. In effect this operation is monopulse height finding by a novel form of stacked beams. The twelve beams cover the entire hemisphere (from 0 to 90 degrees of elevation. The combination of narrow beams (in bearing and elevation) and a high data rate makes it possible to designate targets directly to directors. Sidelobes are very small.

The transmitter is a TWT for pulse-to-pulse coherence and, therefore, MTI. MTI analysis (by fast Fourier transform) is applied only to areas affected by weather or sea clutter, to reduce the overall processing load. PRF is optimized to avoid second-time-around problems. The radar is arranged to react automatically to jamming by changing PRF, and the radar can vary PRF or frequency by burst. Target range and speed are compared on a burst-to-burst and scan-to-scan basis to avoid false targets (which can be discerned by their unnatural behavior).

Transmission modes are fixed frequency, frequency agility over scan, and burst-to-burst frequency jump.

The antenna is stabilized against roll and pitch.

SMART is to replace DA-08 in both *Van Heemskerck*-class missile frigates and in all eight *Karel Doorman*-class frigates (formerly the M class); the order was placed on 24 December 1986. SMART was an unsuccessful contender for the British Type-996 requirement.

MW 08 is a SMART development in G- (formerly C-) band for short- and medium-range cover, up to 70 degrees elevation. MW 08 can automatically detect and track up to 20 air and 10 surface targets, and it can control gunfire against two surface targets. The array is reduced to eight strip-lines (hence the reduced elevation coverage). Each of six pencil beams is 2 × 12 deg, and peak power is 50 kW (pulses are compressed to 0.6 microseconds). The antenna is 2.488 × 1.160 m (weight 430 kg plus 90-kg drive). Maximum free-space range (single scan, 80 percent probability of detection) on a 0.1 square-meter target is 17 km (45 km for SMART); on a 1 square-meter target, 27 km (65 km). The radar can handle target speeds of up to Mach 4 (Mach 5 for SMART).

MW 08 has been ordered for the three Portuguese MEKO frigates.

◆ STIR

Band: X and K **Beam:** 1.4 deg (0.3 deg K-band)
Peak Power: 220 kW (20 kW K-band)
Pulse Width: 0.29 (0.14) microsec
PRF: 1800 or 3600 (7200) pps
Antenna Dimensions: diameter 1.8 m
Antenna Weight: total weight 1700 kg

This Signaal Tracking-and-Illuminating Radar is the lineal successor of the postwar M 40 series dishes. Essentially the tracking radar of the WM 20 series, STIR is removed from the egg and weather-proofed. The original version used a magnetron transmitter. Then the TWT transmitter developed for Goalkeeper was combined with a larger antenna, primarily for missile fire control in the Dutch *van Heemskerck*-class frigates. The Canadian TRUMPs will use the TWT transmitter with the earlier 1.8-m antenna, as the larger antenna would add too much top weight.

STIR uses a Cassegrain monopulse antenna. There are two basic versions, STIR 180 (1.8-m antenna and magnetron transmitter) and STIR 240 (2.4-m antenna and TWT transmitter. STIR 180 can also be supplied with the TWT transmitter. The data above are for the STIR 180 magnetron. Instrumented range is 60 km, and total weight is 1800 kg. The TWT version uses pulse compression (0.3-microsecond pulses, PRF 3200 to 6400 pps). Average power is 5 kW (peak power 100 kW), compared to 230 watts (40 watts in K-band) in the magnetron-driven version. Instrumented range is 180 km. STIR 240 (TWT) provides a 1-degree beam and a target-acquisition range (not instrumented range) of over 140 km for a 1 square-meter target.

A version with a 1.2-m antenna is under development.

By the end of 1986, over 50 STIRs were operational, with over 30 more on order. The 100th STIR was ordered in 1988.

A version of STIR, VM40, was proposed (but rejected) as the British lightweight Sea Wolf director.

In 1987, Signaal announced STING, a modified STIR intended to control vertically launched Seawolf. The result is small enough (710 kg) to fit on board a fast patrol boat. A single unit time-shares the processing of all three signals produced by the radar: X- and Ka-band tracking, and a missile gathering beam (receiving a signal from the missile itself). Signaal credits the combination of X- and Ka-bands with image-free tracking virtually down to the sea surface. MTI (achieved through the use of a fast Fourier transform) is used for clutter rejection.

STIR (1.8-meter version). (Signaal)

STIR (2.4-meter version). (Signaal)

Both versions of STIR with ZW-06 (below) and DA-08 (above) on board the missile frigate *Jacob van Heemskerck*. (Signaal)

◆ Gemini

Band:	X	Ka
Beam:	1.5 × 30 deg	less than 1 deg
	(1.25 × 20 deg)	
Peak Power:	100 W avg	20 kW
	(200/4000 option)	
Pulse Width:	0.5 microsec	0.14 microsec
PRF:	3600 pps	14,400 pps
Scan Rate:	60 rpm	–
Antenna Dimensions:	1.5 m (1.8 m option)	diameter 0.6 m
Antenna Weight:	total 675 kg	
	(width 1.8 m,	
	height 2.25 m)	

There is also an optional X-band tracker, which can achieve a peak power of 50 kW (88 kW or 150 kW if search and track powers are combined), and which produces pulses of either 0.5, 0.58, or 0.6 microseconds (PRF 4000, or 2000/4000, or 10,800/ 12,000 pps).

Gemini is a lightweight modular director (Signaal calls it a weapons-control system) for ship self-defense, consisting of a two-axis stabilized X-band search antenna mounted coaxially with a Ka-band tracker. This combination is similar in spirit to that of the WM20 series, providing both antennas with unobstructed all-around coverage and making for very quick and very accurate designation from search to fire-control radar. X-band was chosen for reliable search, Ka-band for accurate tracking almost down to the surface of the sea, avoiding surface reflections (and multiple target images). The system can be operated from below decks by a single man.

The Ka-band tracker is that used in Goalkeeper, Flycatcher (land-based air defense), and LIROD-8.

Typical performance:

SEARCH RADAR'S RANGE[a]

	ANTENNA WIDTH	
	1.5 m	1.8 m
Transmitter Power		
100 W average	14 km	19 km
200 W	19 km	26 km
4000 W	33 km	45 km

TRACKING RADAR'S ACQUISITION[a]

	Antenna width 1.5 m
Transmitter Power	
K-band, 40 W average	12 km
X-band, 100 W average	21 km
X-band, 1000 W average	30 km

[a]On a 2 square-meter air target

These data were dated October 1981.

◆ Signaal Coastal Radar

This slotted-waveguide radar is in service in the Netherlands, Belgium, France, West Germany, and Saudi Arabia. Characteristics: X-band (8850–9150 MHz); beam 0.25, 0.4, or 0.5 deg × inverted csc2; pulse width 0.050 or 0.200 microsec; PRF, respectively, maximum of 4000 and 2000; peak power 40 kW.

◆ Reporter

Signaal's TWS coast-defense radar was announced in 1980. It can track up to eight targets automatically or four manually. The prototype was completed in 1979, using parts from the existing Flycatcher (Goalkeeper) radar.

OPTRONIC SYSTEMS

◆ LIOD/LIROD-8

LIOD is an unmanned optronic director carrying a television camera or IR sensor and a laser range-finder. LIOD can operate either autonomously or in conjunction with a larger fire-control system. Range on fast aerial targets is about 11,000 yds in good weather. By 1980 LIOD had already been sold to Indonesia, Morocco, Nigeria, and South Korea. LIOD is designed for simultaneous control of two dual-purpose guns (with identical ballistics).

LIROD is a smaller version in which a Ka-band or X-band tracking radar replaces the IR sensor. In LIROD-8, the radar is the Ka-band (35 GHz, beam 1 degree) set used in Goalkeeper and in the Gemini director. The director does carry a television camera, and LIROD-8 can be used as a tracking channel for a WM20 series fire-control system.

Estimated reaction time from target designation to open-fire was 5.5 seconds. The director could slew at 120 deg/sec and could elevate at 80 deg/sec (limits − 25 to + 85 deg). The director proper weighed 300 kg and had a width of 1.5 m.

LIOD is the basis of the Signaal/Bofors RBS 70-based small-ship defense systems; see the Swedish RBS 70 missile and the Signaal OPTICAT below.

FIRE-CONTROL SYSTEMS

Signaal does not distinguish between fire-control radars and the associated fire-control systems.

LIROD (foreground) and a WM20-series "egg." (Signaal)

◆ M1 (SGR 101)

Band: S (about 8 cm) **Beam:** 5 deg
Peak Power: 400 kW **Pulse Width:** 0.5 microsec
PRF: 1000 pps

M1 was the first postwar Dutch fire-control radar. Its commercial designation was SGR-101. M1, M2, and M3 can be recognized by their small circular dish antennas with waveguide feeds across them. The feed horns scan conically for tracking.

Versions: SGR-101/00 for cruiser main batteries (6-inch), SGR-101/01 for cruiser antiaircraft batteries (57-mm), SGR-101/02 for destroyer main dual-purpose batteries (120-mm). SGR-101/00 uses the paraboloid only for transmitting and a cheese for reception. SGR-101/01 and /02 use a stabilized paraboloid for both reception and transmission.

The display is an A-scope with a coarse range of 35,000 m and a fine range (expanded time base) of 3000 m; bearing and elevation are shown side by side for echo-matching. Splashes can be spotted out to 20,000 m (expanded time-base 2000 m).

◆ M2 (SGR 102)

Band: X **Beam:** 4.5 deg
Peak Power: 180 kW **Pulse Width:** 0.2 microsec
PRF: 2000 pps

M2 (SGR-107) was broadly similar to M1 but operated at a higher frequency to achieve greater precision, for 40-mm gun control. M3 was similar to M2. The A-scope showed range up to 24,000 m and could display any 1000-m range interval in expanded form.

◆ M4

Band: X **Pulse Width:** 0.5 microsec
PRF: 1600 pps

M4 (SGR-108) can be distinguished from earlier Dutch fire-control radars by its cut-parabola antenna with a central feed supported by heavy pylons. Examples of the M4 fire-control system include M4/1 for 40-mm guns (1957), M4/2 for 40-mm guns (1961), and M4/3 for 40-mm guns and Seacat missiles (West Germany, 1961).

◆ M40 Series

These X-band radars succeeded the M1 through M4; the M40 Series use enclosed-dish antennas with monopulse feeds. Examples are M44 for Seacat control and M45 for medium- and light-caliber gunfire control. Like the M1 through M4, the M40

Series are manned directors roughly equivalent to the U.S. Mk 56 and the British MRS 3.

◆ WM20 Series (Fire-control Systems)

These multichannel weapons-control systems can generally be recognized by their egg-shaped radomes. The weatherproof egg saves weight by eliminating the requirement to weatherproof antennas separately; dry air is pumped directly inside. Colocation of the search and track antennas eliminates parallax corrections. Because both antennas use the same transmitter, there is no need to shift range scales between them. The result is very rapid reaction. Similar colocation is used in Goalkeeper (though without a common radome), in the U.S. Phalanx, and in the Soviet Pop Group and Cross Sword fire-control systems. The chief disadvantages of colocation are a relatively low location for the search antenna and possible blind spots in a ship with several fire-control radars.

These systems are also sometimes referred to by M numbers, e.g., WM26 is also called M26. Type numbers indicate system capability:

—WM20 is designed to control torpedo and gunfire on board small attack boats. WM20 has one air and one (with an option for another) surface gun-control channel and two torpedo fire-control channels. The system can control two light or medium guns against one air and one surface target, or two torpedoes against two surface targets. WM20 can track one air and three surface targets simultaneously.

—WM22 is a simpler system for larger surface ships (such as frigates), tracking one air target. This system is intended for use with a long-range air-search radar and can control two guns against one air and one surface target simultaneously. A third gun channel can be added as an option. As an application, the WM22/41 mini combat system controls two gun channels. Performance, as of about 1980: air-search radar detection of a 1 square-meter target at up to 30.5 kyd (height, by helical scan, of up to 25,000 ft); surface surveillance up to the radar horizon; tracking of a 1 square-meter target at up to 29,000 yards, accommodating a target speed of up to 720 yd/sec. Maximum surface tracking speed was 100 kts in horizontal scan, or 60 kts in helical scan. System reaction time, from detection to firing, was about 6 seconds. These performance figures are typical of all dual-antenna (egg radome) systems as they were delivered about 1975.

—WM24 has one air and one surface gun-control channel (with an option for a third) plus an ASW-control channel; it is the only system in the series with an ASW capability.

—WM25 can control a semiactive surface-to-air missile (providing CWI for target illumination); this system also has two gun channels. It can simultaneously track one air, one surface, and one shore target; or one air and two surface targets. Air targets are tracked by the pulse-doppler dish and surface targets by the search antenna in TWS mode.

—WM26 is a simplified system for fire control and navigation, limited to two single-purpose guns. WM26 is the only version of the basic system that does not employ the double-antenna radome.

—WM27 has one antiaircraft gun channel, one surface gun channel, one surface-to-surface missile-control channel, and two torpedo-control channels. Besides WM20, WM27 is the only system in the series with torpedo-control capability.

—WM28 can track one air and one surface target simultaneously, plus one surface-to-air missile and two light or medium guns. This system is license-built (in modified form) in the United States as Mark 92. In its original form, WM28 has two gun channels and one surface-to-air channel.

—WM29 controls one command-guided surface-to-air missile (such as Seacat) and two gun channels (one surface only). WM29 is designed to include a Signaal lightweight optronic director (LIOD), which can be used as a secondary tracking channel.

In each case, one of the surface gunfire-control channels can be used for shore bombardment.

The series is modular; Signaal, the manufacturer, integrates it into a full combat information system, using a combination of vertical and horizontal displays, weapons-control consoles, target-designation sights, and optronic directors, plus the characteristic egg-shaped radome.

The egg-shaped radome (diameter 2.39 m, height 3.26 m, weight 780 kg) encloses a pair of antennas fed by a common radar transmitter and stabilized on a common platform. Generally there is a tracking dish above and a cut paraboloid search antenna below. In one case, M26, only the search antenna is used, and it is mounted above the platform. During search, all power is fed to the lower antenna, but once a target has been detected, some power is fed into the tracker. Signaal points out that mounting both antennas on a single platform eliminates errors in transferring a target from search to track. A small ship may, moreover, have only a single position suitable for antenna mounting. The search antenna can also be used to designate to a separate tracking antenna (STIR).

All versions operate in the X-band, and peak power is about 1000 kW. In 1973 it was claimed that the effect of cumulative improvements, including an enlarged search antenna, had been to double the effective range: 20 percent from the enlarged antenna, 20 percent from the use of a tunnel diode amplifier, and 50 percent from the power increase to 1000 kW by using a cross-field amplifier. At that time the claimed search range was about 25 nm on a 1 square-meter target.

As of 1979, Signaal was offering a fully coherent traveling-wave transmitter as an option in WM20-series radars, for clutter rejection and ECM resistance. Signaal also offered alternative frequencies for search and tracking, and doppler MTI for clutter rejection (fast Fourier transform analysis of returning signals to extract their frequency shifts). Fitted with this transmitter, the radar was expected to detect a 1 square-meter target at 60 km (search mode) or to track it at 50 km. Pulse compression was used for search, so the peak power may seem low. Transmitter characteristics were: peak power 150 kW; search pulse width 12.4 microseconds (compressed to 0.2) with PRF of 2000 pps; or 6.2 microseconds (compressed to 0.2) with PRF 4000 pps; or 0.2 microseconds with PRF 2000/4000 pps; tracking pulse width 0.6 microseconds with PRF 12,000 pps for pulse-doppler performance.

◆ OPTICAT

In May 1988 Signaal announced a new optronic/radar fire-control system for small combatants, to control guns and surface-to-surface missiles. OPTICAT combines a search radar with an all-optronic director (TV, IR, laser range-finder), and the mount can also accommodate a Ka-band tracker (in which case it would resemble the Gemini director of 1981). The combined sensor array is light enough to be mounted at a masthead.

As in Gemini and in the WM20 series, the combination of search and tracking sensors on a single platform solves the usual parallax problem.

The X-band search radar scans at 60 rpm and has a 40-degree vertical fan beam. The radar should be able to detect surface craft out to the horizon and fighters at about 13.5 nm. MTI simplifies identification and plotting and should help reject clutter. Because of its high scan rate, the radar can also be used for tracking while scanning (TWS). Generally the radar operator would hand over targets for optronic acquisition; that handover can be automatic. Optronic tracking is by contrast or centroid, and the TV camera is filtered to take account of variable light conditions. The colocated IIR camera (8–12-mm band) is intended for bad weather or night operations: the detector is cooled by a closed circuit based on the Stirling cycle. The associated laser range-finder operates at 1.06 mm.

The displays are a 16-inch PPI and a 15-inch television monitor, both for camera video and for simultaneous display of alphanumerics.

◆ Signaal 4-S (VM 4/61 -482NE)

4-S was announced in 1980 as a super lightweight antiaircraft system for mine-countermeasures craft, particularly the Tripartite Minehunter then under construction. 4-S was not adopted, but it represents a level of integration that remains interesting. Two Stinger or RBS 70 launchers were mounted alongside a K-band dish (60-cm diameter tracker), with a television tracker and a laser designator/ranger alongside. Below the tracker is an X-band search radar (160 × 30 cm slotted waveguide, producing a beam 3 × 15 degrees, gain 28 dB). The search radar scans at 60 rpm, and quick designation is ensured by colocating the search and tracking radars: transfer time is 0.35 seconds. The system can also control up to two small or medium guns, as well as surface-to-surface missiles.

X-band was selected for search because it has seven times less lobing than L-band, without excessive absorption. The system has digital MTI and staggers PRF to avoid blind speeds. The system can detect a one square-meter target at 14 km, and accuracy is 8 millirad at 1 km (altitude 200 ft).

SWEDEN

The primary electronics manufacturer is Philips (PEAB), which is part of an industrial group including Signaal (most of whose stock Philips owns) and MEL. There is an agreement between PEAB and Signaal for the former not to compete in areas in which Signaal is well established.

RADARS

◆ Eagle

PEAB's K-band (35 GHz) narrow-beam (0.8 deg wide) coherent pulse-doppler tracker, intended to work with the Trinity 40-mm gun, was announced in 1988. This radar employs pulse compression to reduce counterdetectability, and there is a special operating MTI mode allowing pulse-to-pulse frequency agility. Two nearby targets can be tracked simultaneously, and PEAB claims that the inherent multipath error at 10 km is less than 0.4 mrad. PEAB claims that antenna gain is so great (and sidelobes so small) as virtually to preclude any attempt at escort jamming. Peak power is 75 W, and PRF is 30–40 kHz. The radar head weighs 80 kg, and PEAB claims that a sea-skimming missile at an altitude of 5 m can be tracked at 5 km.

◆ Sea Giraffe 50/50HC/100/150/150HC (PS-75)

Band: C (5.4–5.9 GHz)
Beam: 2.1 deg (50), 1.7 deg in larger versions
Peak Power: 15 kW (50, 50HC, and 100); 60 kW (150, 150HC)
Gain: 29 dB (50); 30 dB (50HC and 150HC); 36 dB (100 and 150)
Pulse Width: 3.2 and 6.4 microsec, compressed to 0.3 microsec in surface-search mode. There is also a short pulse (0.2 microsec) for fire control.
PRF: 1000–7000 (depends on mode) **Scan Rate:** 30 or 60 rpm
Antenna Dimensions: 2.3 × 0.7 m (50); 2.4 × 0.8 m (50HC and 150HC); 2.4 × 1.8 m (100, 150HC)
Antenna Weight: 250 kg (50); 700 kg (100, 150HC)

Sea Giraffe, announced by Ericsson in 1982, is a family of five multipurpose (air- and surface-search, fire-control) naval radars, using three different fully stabilized antennas (one for Sea Giraffe 50, one for 50HC and 150HC, and one for 100 and 150) and two transmitters (one for Sea Giraffe 50, 50HC, and 100, and one for Sea Giraffe 150 and 150HC). Both transmitters operate in C-band and are fully coherent so that MTI can be used for clutter rejection (50–55 dB ratio). In the designations, HC denotes an optional high-elevation antenna to detect missiles diving at angles of 60–80 degrees.

These radars are all derived from the Ericsson Giraffe (PS-70R) land air-defense radar, so named because it is carried at the upper end of a tall tower. The main difference from Giraffe is

Sea Giraffe on board a *Spica-II*–class attack boat, at the masthead. The gun is a Bofors 57-mm/70 Mk 2. The box launchers aft carry RBS 15 missiles. (Ericsson)

the greatly improved range resolution (through pulse compression), so that the radar can distinguish small targets close together.

Waveform, PRF, and pulse width can all be varied to combine short- and long-range performance, e.g., for search out to 100 km or for high-accuracy search at 20–25 km. All versions are frequency agile both in MTI and in non-MTI modes, the frequency changing about four to ten times while the beam is on a target. Antennas have very low sidelobes to reject standoff jamming; all are of csc2 form, and all have integrated IFF via their antenna feeds. There are separate air- and surface-search modes. For air search, pulses are transmitted and received uncompressed, their nearly pure frequencies making for effective digital MTI performance. For surface search, the signal is modulated at the TWT by a linear FM signal (a chirp) produced in a surface acoustic wave (SAW) delay line.

Radar frequency was chosen partly on the basis of the requirement for clutter rejection through MTI. MTI performance varies with both the radar frequency and the character of clutter. Sea clutter has a typical velocity of 10 m/sec; and rain and chaff speeds depend on wind velocity: 25–30 m/sec are not unusual. The longer the wavelength (the lower the frequency), the higher the clutter velocity at which MTI begins to lose its efficacy. For X-band that velocity is about 10 m/sec, for C-band about 20 m/sec, for S-band about 35–40 m/sec, and for L-band about 70 m/sec. This characteristic limits selection to C-band and lower frequencies, Ericsson preferring the highest possible frequency to limit antenna dimensions and weight. On the other hand, the higher the frequency, the better the radar's resistance to jamming, and higher frequency produces less lobing loss against low-flying targets.

Ericsson chose a TWT rather than the more usual magnetron transmitter for its better MTI improvement factor (typically 50–55 dB rather than 25–30 dB in an incoherent magnetron, i.e., successful detection in clutter 100 times as strong); for its ability to suppress STA echoes (which become a serious problem for a radar operating at short instrumented range; the coherent radar remembers the phase of the transmitted pulse and so can reject any returning STA pulse because it will have the wrong phase); for its ability to combine MTI with frequency agility (the radar sends a burst of pulses with one frequency, then shifts to another); and for its flexibility in waveform (the TWT merely amplifies the incoming signal, whereas the magnetron both creates the signal and amplifies it). Sea Giraffe exploits this last quality of the magnetron by using both long uncompressed pulses (for air search) and compressed pulses of the same length (for surface search).

For air search, the signal processor uses MTI to eliminate clutter. The operator can avoid blind speeds by shifting or staggering PRF. MTI reduces sea clutter by 40 dB by using shifted PRF, or by 50 dB by using staggered PRF. The MTI can compensate for own-ship speeds of up to 45 kts. For surface search, the radar moves between four frequencies to avoid spot jamming. This mode employs pulse compression and instantaneous gain control (IAGC). The operator can select a combined mode, in which every two air-search scans are followed by a surface-search scan, and would choose to watch either air- or surface-search video. Finally, there is a fire-control mode employing a narrow pulse, in which the radar scans a narrow area around the target. The operator designates targets, and shell splashes can be spotted with an accuracy of 0.1 degrees and 20 meters.

Sea Giraffe 50 and 50HC were indeed for fast attack craft. Maximum range against a 0.1 square-meter target (single scan, 50 percent probability of detection) is about 18–19 km; a 4 square-meter target at low altitude can be detected at about 40 km by version 50 (45 km by 50HC). Accuracy is 0.3 deg in azimuth and 25 m in range; resolution is 1.7 deg in azimuth and 45 m in range.

Sea Giraffe 100 and 150 were intended for offshore-patrol vessels and fishery-patrol vessels. Sea Giraffe 150HC was intended for larger attack craft, corvettes, and frigates. Maximum range against a 0.1 square-meter sea-skimmer is about 27 km; against a 4 square-meter airplane, about 63 km. The HC suffix means high (angle) coverage.

Sea Giraffe 50, 50HC, and 100 are designed for minimum equipment below decks, all the radar units being mounted in a single cabinet.

The Swedish Navy ordered Sea Giraffe for its modernization of the Spica-II-class fast patrol boats, and the first boat completed her trials in September 1982. Sea Giraffe 150HC was ordered for the Canadian "City"-class frigates.

A modified system, embodying a new openwork antenna and a second (3-cm) transmitter, is to equip the new Swedish *Goteburg*-class corvettes. Philips supplies the 3-cm transmitter and the antenna; the rest of the system is the existing Sea Giraffe 5.5-cm transmitter. No designation has been released.

◆ 9GR600

Band: X (8700–9500 MHz, with 400–450 MHz bandwidth)
Beam: 1.1 × 7 (1 × 3) deg   **Peak Power:** 200 kW
Gain: 35.5 (38) dB
Pulse Width: (i) 1 microsec (ii) 0.25 microsec
PRF: (i) 1000 (ii) 3000 pps   **Scan Rate:** up to 60 rpm
Antenna Dimensions: 2.1 × 0.3 m (2.7 × 0.7 m)
Antenna Weight: 260 kg including turntable

Data refer to the radar with the 9GA209 antenna used in the 9LV200 fire-control system. This antenna is stabilized, and it can scan helically, elevating its beam to cover up to 40 degrees vertically (20 deg vertically as used in the 9LV200 Mk 2 system). Elevation and scan are independent, so the operator can trade off coverage against data rate. Data in parentheses refer to the 9GA218 antenna. This latter can also be used at L-band (1010–1110 MHz and 1250–1350 MHz), with a 6 × 20 or 8 × 25 deg beam (gain 20 or 17 dB, respectively).

The transmitter is a tunable magnetron, with a tuning rate of 1000 cycles/sec.

The same radar is used with a stabilized 9GA202 antenna in the TORCI torpedo fire-control system, with the 9GA205 in the Mareld coastal radar, and with the 9GA300 antenna in the Subfar submarine set. Characteristics of these antennas are:

	9GA202	9GA205	9GA300
Dimensions	2100 × 560 mm	4500 × 625 mm	1000 × 140 mm
Weight	135 kg	225 kg	85 kg
Beam	1.1 × 4 deg	0.6 × 4.5 deg	2.4 × 16 deg
Gain	37 dB	40 dB	26 dB
Scan	to 60 rpm	to 40 rpm	to 24 rpm

9GA202 can spiral-scan, up to 20 deg elevation (this optional feature adds 25 kg to the antenna's weight).

◆ 9LV200 Tracker

Band: Ku (bandwidth 670 MHz) **Beam:** 1.3 deg
Peak Power: 65 kW **Gain:** 40 dB
Pulse Width: 0.2 microsec **PRF:** about 2000 pps
Antenna Dimensions: diameter 1 m

The antenna is a stabilized monopulse Cassegrain, and television or IR trackers (including a laser range-finder) can be mounted alongside. Processing is MTI, and frequency can be shifted randomly on a pulse-to-pulse basis. The hydraulic drive can slew at 85 deg/sec.

The transmitter is a tunable magnetron, with a tuning rate of 1000 cycles/sec.

9LV200 Mk 3 employs a new coherent Ku-band (15.9–17.1 GHz) tracking radar, using a new TWT transmitter. Operating modes are pulse doppler, MTI, frequency agile, and fixed frequency. The antenna is still a monopulse Cassegrain. With the radar are mounted a television (field of view 42 × 31 mrad), an IR camera (8–12-micron band, field of view 52 × 35 or 157 × 105 mrad, with closed-cycle Stirling cooling), and a laser range-finder (Nd-Yag, 1.06-micron wavelength, peak power 4 MW, PRF 10 Hz). The associated TV/IR tracker can follow either a centroid or an edge, with an accuracy of better than 0.15 mrad. The radar of the 9LV200 Mk 3 system is designated 9GR400.

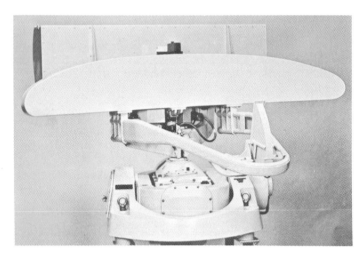

9LV200 search (top) and tracking (bottom) radars. (PEAB)

◆ ELSA

ELSA is a lightweight 3-D radar, under development by Ericsson and Marconi, for fast attack craft and frigates. This radar scans only in elevation (it rotates to scan in bearing), by phase shifting (by about 30 ferrites) rather than by the frequency scanning of current U.S. radars. Like Sea Giraffe, ELSA will operate at a wavelength of 5.5 cm and presumably will use a Sea Giraffe transmitter. Marconi is responsible for the antenna and beam-steering computer. The carbon-fiber antenna is electronically stabilized so that it weighs about one-third as much as a conventional 2-D stabilized antenna.

This approach is interesting because it suggests that the addition of a special antenna and a small beam-steering computer can convert an existing two-dimensional radar to three-dimensional operation.

ELSA is the new radar planned for the *Goteborg*-class missile/ASW corvettes, as part of their 9LV200 Mk 3 weapons system, superseding the Sea Giraffe of the earlier *Spica*s. The C-band antenna is surmounted by a slotted waveguide for X-band transmission, the whole being roll and pitch stabilized. The transmitter is a TWT, and frequency modes are fixed and slow/fast shift. Pulse compression is digital, and the receiver is fully coherent with MTI processing. The associated X-band transmitter, which is optional within the 9LV200 Mk 3 system, uses the PEAB spin-tuned magnetron. It can operate in either fixed or agile frequency mode and has associated MTI processing. Like Sea Giraffe, this radar scans at 30 or 60 rpm.

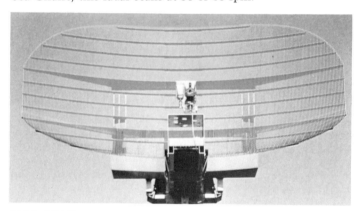

ELSA. (PEAB)

◆ PILOT

Band: X (9345–9405 MHz) **Beam:** 1.2 × 20 deg
Average Power: 1 W **Gain:** 30 dB
Frequency Sweep: 50, 25, 12.5, 6.25, 3.125, 1.5625 MHz
PRF: 1000 pps **Scan Rate:** 24/48 or 20/40 rpm
Antenna: single or dual 5-ft slotted-waveguide
Antenna Weight: 55 kg single antenna; 90 kg for dual antenna (121/198 lbs)

PILOT is a naval low-probability-of-intercept ("quiet") radar that uses frequency-modulated continuous-wave (FMCW) technology. Radar range is a function of average radar power, not of peak power. However, radar intercept receivers are triggered by the presence of a powerful peak signal; they do not sense the build-up of radar energy over time. The greater the pulse repetition rate, the closer the average power comes to peak power; conversely, the lower the peak power must be to provide useful amounts of average power. Ultimately, then, the least detectable way of providing sufficient average power would be a continuous radar transmission (CW). If continuous transmission occurred at a pure frequency, no information would be gained. In PILOT, the transmission frequency varies so that information can be recovered. This scheme seems analogous to the operation of an FM radio (as contrasted with normal radar, which is like an AM radio). It seems possible that FM transmissions are also easier to receive than standard AM transmissions (as most radio listeners have discovered), so that the average power level can be reduced, compared to that required by a conventional radar. PILOT uses 512 range-resolution cells; and at short range, resolution is typically about 3 m.

CW radars typically require separate transmitting and receiving antennas. However, a reflected-power canceler (RPC) makes it possible to use a single antenna. The RPC subtracts a sample of the transmitted signal from the received signal. In the data above, both antennas transmit and receive; the dual antenna adds about 25 percent more range.

PILOT is a joint venture of Signaal, Philips Electronics of Sweden, and the Philips Research Laboratories in the United Kingdom. PILOT was announced (in April 1988) at the British laboratory. The name means Philips Indetectable Low-Output Transceiver, and the radar is to be marketed jointly by Signaal and Philips of Sweden. It was announced in the fall of 1988 that PILOT would equip the new Swedish *Goteborg*-class corvettes, presumably as a stealthy navigational radar.

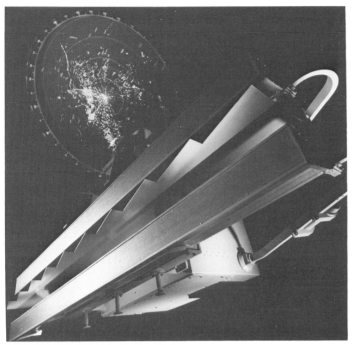

PILOT. (Signaal)

COAST DEFENSE

◆ 9KA100

PEAB's electro-optical coastal-artillery fire-control system consists of a sighting unit (Kobra) and a ballistic computer. Kobra incorporates a laser range-finder, and the pedestal can carry a low-light-level television or an infrared imager. This device is used to supplement the heavier 9KA400 and 9KA500 and also, as a stand-alone unit, to modernize older fixed or mobile coastal-defense batteries. At least twenty have been ordered, for use in Sweden and abroad.

◆ 9KA400 (Mareld/Kastell)

9KA400 are the current Swedish fixed coastal fire-control systems. The original Mareld entered service in the mid-1960s, and a digital version became operational in late 1976. A Mk 2 version is now in production. Sweden and at least four other countries, including Norway and Spain, ordered at least 70 Kastells, and Inisel produces the 9KA410 version under license. See 9KR400 for details of the radar. The digital computer is the same type as the one used in the 9LV200 Mk 2 naval fire-control system. 9KA400 is made by PEAB.

◆ 9KA500 (Kardinal)

PEAB's mobile coastal-artillery fire-control system is derived from the fixed 9KA400. There are two alternative versions, using two antennas: GA250/K (K-band, 15.9–17.1 GHz) and GA250/X (X-band, 8.5–9.6 GHz). Each is 2.3 × 0.55 m, the different frequencies making for different beams (respectively, 0.7 × 2.2 and 1.2 × 4 deg, gains 42 and 36 dB). Both are horn-fed reflectors, scanning in two alternative speeds (ratio 1:2, in the 6–60 rpm range). The K-band version gives the same precision as 9KR400 in a lightweight mobile form but has lower

peak power (65 kW rather than the 200 kW of the X-band version). On the other hand, the K-band version suffers less from multipath.

In fixed form, 9KA500 is designated 9KA400 Mk 3 Kastell; it has been sold to Norway.

◆ 9KR400

Band: X (8700–9500 MHz)   **Beam:** 0.6 × 4 deg
Peak Power: 200 kW   **Gain:** 40 dB
Pulse Width: 1 or 0.25 microsec
PRF: 1000 or 3000 pps, respectively   **Scan Rate:** up to 40 rpm
Antenna Dimensions: 4.5 × 0.625 m
Antenna Weight: 260 kg (including turntable)

The standard Swedish coastal-artillery radar, 9KR400 employs a 9GR600 X-band frequency-agile transmitter and a 9GA205 antenna. 9KR400 is the main sensor of the 9KA400 Mareld coastal-artillery fire-control system, which is also used by Spain, and of the 9CSI600 STINA naval command system. This radar is used by Spain and Yugoslavia, in the latter case integrated with 9LV200 fire-control systems on board fast attack craft.

OPTRONIC SYSTEMS

◆ TVT-300

The simple SAAB optronic director consists of a television camera on a gyro-stabilized platform, tracking electronics, and a display console. Targets are acquired either manually or from a search radar. The operator moves an electronic gate over the displayed target to initiate autotracking. The camera tracks the contrast between the target and its background (i.e., presumably the edge of the contrast rather than the centroid of the target).

TVT-300, a television sight. (Saab)

◆ EOS-400

SAAB's optronic director, announced in 1979, incorporates an automatic television tracker and a laser range-finder. The target is designated using coarse data from an associated radar, and a below-decks operator locks on the television tracker for autotracking. The operator can also manually track by joystick. The system can continue to project the position of a target by memory when visibility is poor or when the target is temporarily obscured, e.g., behind trees. The tracker locks onto the target again when it reappears. The tracker also has an optional surface-target search mode.

One or two weapons can be slaved to the director, ballistics being computed by an associated microcomputer. Elevation limits are +85/−30 deg, and slewing speed is 175 deg/sec.

EOS-400 was conceived as intermediate between TVT-300 and EOS-500.

EOS-400. (Saab)

◆ EOS-500

EOS-500 is a more sophisticated equivalent of EOS-400, usable either autonomously or as part of a larger fire-control system. On designation of a target the system is automatically turned onto the appropriate bearing, the operator scanning the sensor head vertically by joystick. He then manually tracks until the target is within a gate, when he can switch to autotrack. Like EOS-400, EOS-500 can memory-track in bad or obscured visibility.

The first example was built for the Swedish coast-defense artillery.

Fire-Control Systems

◆ 9LV100 Series

This lightweight optronic fire-control system for small patrol boats (75–100 tons) is manufactured by PEAB. The director carries a SAAB television camera and an LM Ericsson laser ranger (wavelength 1.06 microns, PRF 10 kHz) and is comparable to the Signaal LIOD. A Philips USFA thermal camera (8–13 micron range) is available as an optional extra. The optronic director is based on KALLE, a ground antiaircraft system (using the 40-mm/70 Bofors gun) in service with the Swedish Army. The associated surface-search radar is an unstabilized standard navigational type, operating in S-band for maximum aircraft detection range (15–20 km). The radar has both long and short pulses, for, respectively, search and navigation. In KALLE land tests, which should approximate the 9LV100's performance, a 40-mm/70 was able to place 80 percent of 300 rounds within lethal radius (5.5 m) of a target at 2000–3000 m, and average reaction time was about 5 seconds.

This system was announced in 1977 and thus was developed after 9LV200. The first was for the Finnish minelayer *Pohjanmaa*, and others were sold to Bahrein and to Malaysia.

LV indicates antiair warfare.

◆ 9LV200 Series

The 9LV200 is a fast patrol boat fire-control system, designed initially for the Swedish *Spica* class. The requirement, issued in 1968, emphasized defense against antiship missiles, using a new Bofors 57-mm/70 gun with special ammunition. The system also had to be very compact, given the small platform for which it was intended. PEAB won the competition in 1969, using its own broad-band pulse-to-pulse frequency-agile radar transmitter (a spin-tuned magnetron) as well as a new type of

motor and bearing promising very high tracking accuracy. Both were needed to detect, track, and engage small targets at relatively low altitude in a very cluttered environment. The pulse-to-pulse agility (frequency diversity) would seem to eliminate the second-time-around problem for longer-range targets.

The system employs a single X-band (200 kW) search antenna for both air and surface targets, plus a single air-target tracker carrying both a Ku-band (65 kW) monopulse radar (with Cassegrain antenna) and an automatic television tracker (as in the TVT-300 optronic director, see above). The search radar also tracks surface targets using track-while-scan techniques (scan rate 60 rpm). The stabilized search antenna scans helically, its feed rising as it rotates to tilt its beam upward.

Although the system was designed for very quick reaction, it appears to have been conceived too early to benefit from the automatic radar detection and tracking techniques embodied in, say, Phalanx or Goalkeeper. The operator designates a target on a 12-inch PPI, and then the tracker is activated. There is also an operator television display, taking the output from the camera mounted with the tracking radar.

Mk 1 is fitted to Spica-II–class boats, to the experimental *Jaegaren*, and to the Yugoslav *Rade Koncar* class. Mk 1 uses an analog computer.

The 9LV200 Mk 2 of 1977 was built around a digital computer, for the *Hugin* class; Mk 2 could control guns, surface-to-surface missiles, and torpedoes. It can track as many as 16 surface targets while scanning for more. The manufacturer estimates that a target can be detected at 9 km (with some margin), designated at about 7.5 km (5 seconds), with loss of tracking quality due to multipath at about 6 km (9 seconds). At that point tracking shifts to IR, the symbol being positioned at about 4.8 km (12 seconds) and IR lock-on achieved at a range of about 4.3 km (14 seconds). Fire begins at a range of about 3.7 km (15–16 seconds) and becomes effective at about 2.8 km (i.e., after about 19 seconds). These figures are for a 0.1 square-meter sea-skimming target (altitude 2–3 m, speed 333 m/sec.)

9LV200 Mk 3 (developed about 1986) has been adopted for the Swedish *Goteborg* class, the Danish Standard Flex 300, and the Finnish Helsinki-II. Mk 3 is based on a computer data bus (local area network) and multifunction consoles, a combination ensuring flexibility. That combination in turn makes it possible to reconfigure the Standard Flex very rapidly.

Mk 3 also differs from earlier versions of 9LV200 in using a coherent (TWT) radar transmitter. The design of the system emphasizes standardization of its consoles, its computers, its programming language (ADA), its local area network (Ethernet), and its interfaces. The basic system consists of a C-band search radar, a fire-control channel, a gun-control channel, an interface unit, a video distribution unit, a C3 processor (with data base), and control consoles; ECM and an X-band radar can be added. The system has sufficient capacity to add extra fire-control channels, a CIWS control channel, SAM and SSM control, ASW functions, helicopter control, and additional electronic-warfare capacities.

The standard console is a three-CRT (one 20-inch for color or random scan, two 12-inch to display video or tables) work station. There are two touch-input boards on which variable menus may be displayed (equivalent to variable action buttons), a standard keyboard, and one or two "joy-balls" (a mix between joysticks and trackballs). The associated single-board CPU is based on a Motorola 68020 processor; it carries 4 Mbytes of RAM (random access, i.e., working, memory) and 256 kbyte of EPROM holding permanent programs. There are three serial channel interfaces. Typically a ship will have a tactical console, a weapons console, and (optionally) an EW console. The consoles are tied together by a dual Ethernet bus, each of whose elements has a capacity of 10 Mbits/sec. The bus can accommodate up to 100 nodes per segment, far beyond the requirements of 9LV200.

As described by PEAB, 9LV200 Mk 3 is the combat system for the new corvettes; there is no separate tactical data system into which Mk 3 is embedded. It is fed directly by the search radar; on the tactical console, Mk 3 compiles the current situation picture into a single tactical plot, including track identification. Other automated functions include threat assessment of air targets (with consequent display of a threat priority table) and tactical navigation calculations (e.g., intercept and formation calculations). Presumably this last function includes recommendations for maneuvers during attack, such as maneuvers increasing the efficacy of chaff. The system is also designed to accept and process data link data, displaying such data on its tactical console.

Typically EW data and EW orders will be processed by a separate computer communicating with the main data bus. All other tactical functions, such as fire control, employ limited local processing, but most of the calculation is done by the fast computers in the two main consoles.

The system is generally designed to store its data base outside the consoles, providing data as required on demand. Thus the data bus feeds, and feeds from, this separate data base.

As planned for the new *Goteborg* class, 9LV200 Mk 3 is part of a larger 9LV450 system incorporating the ARTE-726E gun-control system, RCI-400 missile fire control, TORPE torpedo control, 9AU300 ASW control, and 9CM300 ECM control.

The Danish missile boat *Bille* is equipped with a 9LV200 fire-control system, including the 9GA208 search antenna (on the masthead platform). The slotted-waveguide is designated NWS-2 in the Danish Navy. (L&L Van Ginderen)

◆ 9LV300 Series

This weapons-control system for 250–400 ton vessels is manufactured by PEAB. 9LV300 consists of 9LV200 plus 9LV100. This system is on board Swedish *Spica*-III (*Stockholm*) –class fast attack boats.

◆ 9LV400 Series

This weapons-control system for frigates and corvettes up to 1450 tons, by PEAB, was announced in 1978. 9LV450 incorporates ASW as well as antiaircraft and antiship fire controls and is suited to a flotilla leader carrying an ASW helicopter. The 450 designation indicates a system with ASW capability added ("+50"); similarly, 9LV250 would be 9LV200 plus ASW.

SWITZERLAND

◆ Seaguard

Contraves's modular combat system is usually associated with a standard quadruple 25-mm gun (Sea Zenith 25). Seaguard includes a dedicated high-data-rate dual-beam C-band radar (the Plessey Dolphin/AWS-6) to detect both sea-skimmers and high divers (70-degree coverage, to 14 km altitude, and to 35 km range), and a 3-axis tracker (Ku-band radar, FLIR, and laser). The Siemens-Albis Ku-band radar (0.9-deg beam) incorporates a patented means of supressing mirror (multipath) effects, encountered in tracking very low flying targets, that result from reflections off the sea surface. Missiles flying at up to Mach 3 can be engaged.

The Ku-band tracking radar operates at 15.7–17.5 GHz, with a peak power of 85 kW, and 80 nanosec (0.08 microsecond) pulses; beam width is 19 mrad. This radar acquires missiles at

The Seaguard system is shown on board the new Turkish frigate *Yavuz*: a Dolphin radar at the foretop, a radar/optronic tracker atop the bridge, and a Sea Zenith 25-mm gun forward of the bridge. The big egg is the Signaal radar that controls her 5-inch gun and her Sea Sparrow. (U.S. Naval Institute)

0.25–10 km and aircraft at 0.25–16 km. Weights: above-decks 1350 kg, below-decks 1350 kg. The radar antenna's diameter is 1.23 m. The alternative X-band tracker (for SAM control, if desired) operates at 8.6–9.5 GHz (peak power 2 or 4 kW, with 0.4–4 microsec pulses and a 31 mrad beam). Tracking range is 0.3 to 45/70 km. Weights: above-decks 1200 kg, below-decks 1300 kg. CW illumination can be provided through this tracker. This radar's antenna diameter is 1.315 m.

The associated FLIR has a field of view of 3 × 2 deg (operating at 8–11.5 micron wavelength). It incorporates a centroid tracker. The laser operates at a wavelength of 1.06 microns, with a 25-Hz data rate, and a 13-nanosec pulse length. The television sensor has an 11 × 8 degree field of view.

The Ku-band module is designated TMK. It tracks with an angular speed of 3 rad/sec (172 deg/sec) in all three axes and weighs 1350 kg (2975 lbs). The three axes are alpha (train), beta (the offset radar turns around an axis at an angle to the horizon), and lambda (the radar antenna elevates through +120/−30 degrees relative to the canted beta axis). The alternative separate X-band module is designated TMX-CW.

An alternative X/Ka-band tracking and illumination module (TMX/KA-CW) employs a TWT transmitter and pulse compression; the module carries optional electro-optical sensors (TV or FLIR). The Ka-band radar operates at 34–34.45 GHz with a peak power of 75 W (pulse length 0.13/3.7 microsec: compressed/uncompressed lengths). Beamwidth is 8 mrad (0.5 deg), and tracking range is 0.3–20 km. The associated X-band radar, which shares the same antenna, has a peak power of 25 kW (pulse width 0.3/1.65 microsec) and a beamwidth of 30 mrad (1.7 deg). Tracking range is 0.3–70 km. Total above-decks weight is 1440 kg (3174 lbs); below-decks weight is 1390 kg (3064 lbs). Angular speed in all three axes is 3 rad/sec (172 deg/sec), and the radar dish's diameter is 1.4 m (55 inches).

X-band is used to achieve long enough range (70 km) for the system to engage air targets with a surface-to-air missile. The tracker can avoid multipath problems by using all of its sensors, and it can track targets all the way to the zenith, elevating up to 120 degrees. CWI can be injected into the X-band tracker waveguide. Contraves offers configurations controlling both conventionally mounted surface-to-air missiles and vertically launched missiles.

There is also an alternative electro-optical tracking module, TMEO, a pedestal carrying a FLIR or television on one side and a laser on the other; alternatively the pedestal can carry a light-weight W-band radar. The module is biaxially stabilized; the above-decks equipment weighs 230 kg, and the below-decks equipment weighs 490 kg. Elevation limits are +80/−20 deg, and train and elevation rates are both 1.3 rad/sec (74.5 deg/sec). The FLIR operates in the 7.5–11-micron band, with two alternative fields of view, 20 × 15 and 2.7 × 2.0 deg; resolution is 0.11 mrad. The alternative television camera has 31 × 23 and 3.1 × 2.3 degree fields of view. The laser range-finder, which is eye safe, operates at 1.57 microns and emits 1–3 pulses per second.

For data concerning the associated Dolphin C-band search radar, see the description of the British AWS-6 radar.

The gun consists of four independent Oerlikon KBB 25-mm cannon, with a combined rate of fire of 3400 rounds/min. The axis of the mount is canted to allow for very high angle engagement of diving targets even from a heavily rolling or pitching ship. Ammunition capacity in the standard system is 1600 rounds, sufficient for about 18 engagements without reloading (one 80-round burst per target), and the manufacturer claims that tests of the high energy AMDS (Antimissile Discarding Sabot) ammunition show that it can kill with a single hit. Contraves claims that the special 25-mm AMDS round is equivalent to a standard 30-mm round.

The original deck-penetrating module was designated GM25. Elevation limits are +127/−14 degrees, and angular speed (both for elevation and for train) is 2.5 rad/sec (143 deg/sec). Ammunition is carried in four 300-round drums, the hoists making up the rest of the total of 1660 rounds. The ammunition itself incorporates a 156-gram penetrator (total weight is 288 grams), and time of flight to 1000 m is 0.78 seconds (muzzle velocity is 1355 m/sec, or 4444 ft/sec). Total weight above decks is 4400 kg (2690 kg below decks), and swept radius is 2.591 m.

In 1989 Contraves announced a second gun module, Sea Shield (GM25-SS), to supplement the earlier Sea Zenith (GM25-SZ). Sea Shield is mounted entirely above decks (without any magazine below decks), and omits the very high elevation firing feature of the heavier Sea Zenith. Ammunition supply is limited to 1000 rounds in four 250-round magazines (11 engagements), and elevation limits are +80/−20 deg. Train rate is 2.0 rad/sec; elevation is at 2.5 rad/sec. Total weight above decks rises to 5450 kg, but below-decks weight is only 1590 kg. Swept radius is 2.6 m. Sea Shield cannot be reloaded while it fires; however, Contraves argues that there is enough ammunition on the mount to deal with a concentrated multiple missile and aircraft attack.

In both modules, burst length (and the number of cannons fired) can be controlled, e.g., when the gun is used in limited surface actions (e.g., in the naval policing role).

The manufacturer claims a reaction time from acquisition to open fire of 4 sec, compared to a reported 6 sec for Phalanx. The manufacturer also estimates that two to four scans by the search radar (i.e., 2–4 seconds) are required before the tracker can begin its own target search in azimuth.

The system is designed to permit expansion to control all ship's weapons, using additional trackers and a NAUTIS multiconsole combat system. All versions are linked together by data bus, the individual modules (tracker and gun) having their own microprocessors. The manufacturer claims that this architecture (as opposed to one incorporating a single central computer) makes for quicker reactions. Modules are: gun (CIWS-GM), tracker (CIWS-TM), general-purpose tracker (GPTM), electro-optical tracker (EOTM), electronic warfare (EWM), and command and control (CCM). GPTM can be used to control medium caliber guns and surface-to-air missiles, using a Contraves X-band pulse-doppler radar. The CCM is a horizontal two-man console that can be used both for command and control and for threat evaluation/weapons assignment, incorporating a 24-inch PPI screen.

Seaguard was adopted by the Turkish Navy for its *Yavuz*-class MEKO frigates. In these ships the system consists of one search module (SRM), two trackers (TMK), and three guns (GM25), each of the latter provided with sufficient ammunition for 15 engagements. A land-based version has been purchased for the Chinese Army (PLA).

Seaguard is a private-venture system; development began late in 1977. Contraves-Oerlikon collaborated with Plessey, with Siemens (both the German firm and its Swiss subsidiary), and with Elettronica of Italy. The project was announced at the beginning of 1980. By mid-1982 prototypes of all the modules had

been tested, and the Italian Navy had priority for deliveries for trials. However, Italy did not adopt Seaguard.

TAIWAN (GRC)

Taiwan currently manufactures a fire-control radar, designated SPG-24, which is used on board fast patrol boats armed with Hsiung Feng I missiles. Reportedly the U.S. contractor for the SPG-24 program was ABA. The main developmental problem was conversion of the radar from analog to digital processing.

Taiwan also manufactures a navigational radar using a small X-band slotted-waveguide antenna, designated UPS-60. The initial batch, to equip missile-firing boats, was 57 radars, and more have been ordered. UPS-600 is a larger (and presumably lower-frequency) surface-search set, possibly derived from the U.S. SPS-64. At least fifteen SPS-64s have been bought for coastal surveillance.

In July 1988 a model of a phased-array radar, externally similar to the U.S. SPY-1D (of the *Arleigh Burke* class), was exhibited. This radar is to be used on board the new Taiwanese version of the U.S. *Perry*-class frigate. Later in 1988 it was revealed that this radar had been developed with the assistance of the RCA Division of GE, which is responsible for SPY-1, but the radar does not incorporate Aegis technology. The system is intended for both land and naval use, the land version using a phased array larger than that of the U.S. SPY-1. The designation of this radar is Chang Bai (Long White).

The associated missile, for land use, is the CSIST (Chung Shun Institute of Science and Technology) Sky Bow 1 missile, similar in outline to the U.S. Patriot and currently using Improved Hawk fire controls. A naval version, to be fired from a vertical launcher, is being developed to equip the frigates. 170 SM-1 missiles, previously obtained by Taiwan, are intended to arm *Gearing*-class destroyers being modernized under the Taiwanese Weapons-Improvement Program 3. These missiles will be carried in box launchers, similar to those provided to Iran (see the discussion of SM-1 under U.S. missiles below).

The SPG-24 radar on board a Taiwanese (GRC) *Hai Ou*–class missile boat. The slotted waveguide above is UPS-60. There is a periscope in the foreground. (Fu S. Mei)

USSR

SEARCH RADARS

◆ Ball End/Ball Gun, High Sieve, Low Sieve

Band: S (2950–3020 MHz) **Beam:** 7 deg
Peak Power: 150 kW **Pulse Width:** 1 microsec
PRF: 427 pps **Scan Rate:** 6 rpm

These four radars (Ball Gun/Ball End, High Sieve, and Low Sieve) had the same transmitter/receiver but very different antennas. All were designated Ryf by the Soviets, the suffix number indicating the antenna type (High and Low Sieve are Ryf-1M and -2M, respectively, with slightly higher PRFs).

Ryf was conceived as a surface-target detector and fire-control radar, and it was developed, in parallel with Cross Bird and with Knife Edge, under the 1946–48 three-year radar plan. Ryf was tested with Cross Bird in 1948 on board the cruiser *Molotov*. Detection ranges: of a cruiser, 20–22 nm; destroyer, 14–16 nm; periscope (height 1.5 m), 1.0–1.5 nm. Accuracy on PPI is 15 m on 1 nm scale. Splashes could be detected at 2.5–10.0 nm.

Ball End and Ball Gun were first seen in 1950. The name Ball Gun was derived from the form of the radar feed, ending in a plastic ball. This radar replaced the earlier GYUIS-1M in Kronstadt-class submarine chasers.

High Sieve was a surface-search radar first seen in 1954, on board ships of the *Sverdlov* and *Skoryy* classes. Low Sieve was first seen in 1957, on board missile cruisers, cruisers, and the one Tallin-class destroyer (*Neustrashimyy*), since discarded.

◆ *Baku* Radar

The carrier *Baku*, the fourth of the *Kiev* class, emerged in mid-1988 with a new four-sided flat-faced array radar on her superstructure. The radar replaces the Top Pair of earlier ships of the class and presumably operates at a similar frequency (to achieve similar range performance). Top Steer is retained as a back-up. It is possible that the internal space required for the radar (and, presumably, for those maintaining it) precluded installation of any long-range surface-to-air missile system; the other ships of the class all have SA-N-3. *Baku* is limited to the SA-N-9 point-defense system.

The island of the new carrier *Baku* displays a new planar-array air-search radar. Above it is the sphere of a Big Ball satellite communications radar; another is abaft the cylindrical radome on the mast. The radar at the top of the island is Top Steer. Comparison with other units of the class suggests that the cylindrical radome houses the successor to Top Knot, an air navigation aid. This ship is unique among Soviet aircraft carriers in lacking an area-defense missile system. The Cross Sword SA-N-9 director is below the array antenna. This ship also introduced a new series of electronic warfare antennas. (Selçukemre)

◆ Band Stand

This radome is associated with the SS-N-9 missile on board Nanuchka-class missile corvettes and also with the SS-N-22 missile on board *Sovremennyy*-class destroyers and some Tarantul-class missile corvettes. Because these missiles have over-the-horizon range, Band Stand probably accommodates a targeting data link. However, Tarantuls also have a masthead antenna, Light Bulb, described as a probable missile data link. The combination of Band Stand and Light Bulb might be comparable to the combination used to target SS-N-3/12 missiles, the missile sending back its own radar picture for comparison with that provided by a targeting aircraft. Alternatively, Light Bulb may be the shipboard antenna for a Soviet equivalent of Link 11, as in the German AGIS system (in which missile boats are tied directly into a shore-based command-and-control system). Tarantul-II (the first production version) has Band Stand even though the ships are armed with SS-N-2C; in this case whatever

is inside the radome replaces Square Tie/Plank Shave (as in Nanuchkas built for export: see Square Tie below). These ships have Light Bulb, which thus far has not appeared on board any other Soviet warships.

Note that in export Nanuchkas, Band Stand covers a Square Tie antenna, apparently for cosmetic reasons.

◆ Big Net

> **Band:** L (about 850 MHz)   **Beam:** 5 deg
> **Pulse Width:** 3.5 or 2.0 microsec   **PRF:** 250 or 550 pps
> **Scan Rate:** 6.7–8.6 rpm   **Antenna Dimensions:** 25 ft wide

The large air-search radar, on Kresta-I- and some *Sverdlov*-class cruisers, and on some Kashins, Big Net can probably detect a large airplane at altitude at ranges of 100+ nm. Big Net is probably the cruiser/destroyer air-search radar developed in 1948–55 under the designation Fut-N, tested in the Baltic in 1955. The radar detected aircraft at a range of up to 150 km. This radar entered service about 1957 and is contemporary with Top Trough.

Big Net was the last major Soviet two-dimensional long-range air-search radar. About a decade after its introduction it was succeeded, in effect, by Top Sail.

Big Net is shown atop the mainmast of a Kashin-class destroyer; the foremast is topped by a Head Net C height-finder. (U.S. Naval Institute)

◆ Cross Bird (GUIS-2M)

> **Band:** P (210 MHz)   **Beam:** beam width 25–30 deg
> **Pulse Width:** 3–5 microsec   **PRF:** 400–445 pps

This P-band radar, still carried by some *Skoryy*-class destroyers, is effectively an improved (more powerful and more directional) derivative of the British World War II Type 291, with its yagi elements in a 4 × 2 arrangement. The Soviet designation means "Sea Gull."

The Cross Bird specification was issued in August 1946, and the radar was developed under the 1946–48 three-year plan for radar development. Cross Bird was tested on board the cruiser *Molotov* in 1948. There were two versions. The original GUIS-2 used a pair of yagis with a reflector; GUIS-2M used four paired dipoles, as in Type 291, and was the version used extensively at sea. In 1948 tests of the original GUIS-2, aircraft were detected at 14–29 nm, depending on altitude; a cruiser was detected at 11.5 nm, a destroyer at 8.5 nm, and a minesweeper at 4.5 nm. The dead zone for surface targets was no more than 0.4 nm, and for aircraft 1–2 nm. Resolution was at least 0.3 nm in range, 4 degrees in bearing.

◆ Don Series

> **Band:** X (9375 MHz)   **Beam:** 1.1 × 20 deg
> **Peak Power:** 80 kW   **Pulse Width:** (i) 1 (ii) 0.5 microsec
> **PRF:** (i) 800 (ii) 1600 pps   **Scan Rate:** 12 or 15 rpm

This series includes Don-2 and Don Kay. There was also a Donets-2, with a slotted waveguide (68.7 × 4.8 in, 1.4 × 20 degree beam, seen in 1960 on board a trawler). The data here are for Don itself.

A Koni-class corvette shows a Don-2 radar just above her yardarm. The air-search radar above is Strut Curve; the fire-control radar forward of the mast is Hawk Screech, and Drum Tilt is partly obscured aft. (U.S. Naval Institute)

◆ Egg Cup

An S-band range-only radar for 6-in and 3.9-in guns, Egg Cup is probably the radar called SHTAT-5 by the Soviets; it was developed under the 1946–48 three-year radar plan and tested on shore in the summer of 1948. Detection ranges: of a destroyer, 12 nm (tracking range 10 nm, median range error 15 m).

An early photograph of a *Sverdlov*-class cruiser shows an Egg Cup range-only radar atop a twin 3.9-inch mount. The radar just above the Long Ears 6-inch director is Top Bow. (U.S. Navy)

◆ Half Bow

Band: X   Beam: 0.8 deg

This radar entered service in 1951 and survives mainly on board *Skoryy*-class destroyers. Half Bow was the first Soviet blind-fire radar, sufficiently accurate in bearing for surface fire. Half Bow is probably the radar designated Zalp by the Soviets; the notes that follow apply to Zalp. It was developed in 1948–50 specifically to provide accurate bearing data, for blind firing. The antenna was stabilized. Peak power was 65–70 kW, and the radar could coordinate with Zarya (see Post Lamp below). This

set was tested in the Black Sea in September–November 1950 on board the destroyer *Bestrashnyy*. The second and third sets were tested on board the cruiser *Sverdlov* in 1951 in the Baltic. A modified version, Zalp-B, was developed for coast defense.

◆ Head Net A/B/C

This S-band small-ship radar is roughly contemporary with Slim Net. Range on a large high-altitude airplane is about 60–70 nm. Head Net A is a single antenna, about 22.5 × 5 ft. That size implies a fan beam somewhat less than 1 degree wide.

Head Net B had two antennas arranged back to back, providing a higher data rate. B is now extinct, having been installed only in *Desna*-class missile range ships (removed 1980, replaced by Head Net C). The back-to-back arrangement is widely used in Soviet naval radars (see Strut Curve, Strut Pair, Top Pair, Top Steer); presumably, both antennas typically share a common waveguide feed running up the mast between them. This arrangement reduces structural interference with radar emissions and increases the net data rate of the radar. In the case of a 2-D/3-D combination, the back-to-back arrangement probably greatly simplifies designation of a target from one radar to the other, since there is no parallax error, and also economizes on the mechanical stabilizers the Soviets seem to favor.

Head Net C, which is the height-finder used with the SA-N-1 missile (and is the secondary three-dimensional radar in Kresta-II- and Kara-class cruisers), has one of its two back-to-back antennas canted at 30 degrees to the horizontal. The two fan beams are, therefore, canted, and the relative apparent positions of the same target in the two beams measure its height (vee-beam height-finding). The operator finds his target with the conventional antenna, marks it, and sets range gates on the second beam to measure altitude. This vee-beam system was invented during World War II, and a U.S. vee-beam set, CPS-6, provided to the Soviets under Lend-Lease, was copied postwar. The system is simple, but it is not as satisfactory as a true three-dimensional radar. Head Net C entered service in 1963.

The Soviet designation for Head Net C is MR 310 (at least in the export version used by the Indian Navy).

It now appears that Head Net C has been superseded by Top Plate.

A Head Net C air-search radar occupies the top of the foremast of this Kashin-class destroyer (*Soobrazitelnyy*), photographed off Oran in 1982. The object at the base of the foremast is Tee Plinth, an optronic device. The two gun directors are Owl Screech; the two missile directors are Peel Group (SA-N-1 missiles). (U.S. Naval Institute)

◆ High Sieve

This radar is installed on some *Sverdlovs* and *Skoryys*. For waveform details, see the entry for Ball Gun, etc., above.

◆ Kivach 3

Kivach 3 is a current small-combatant (e.g., minecraft) navigational radar.

◆ Knife Rest/Spoon Rest

Band: P (75 MHz) **Beam:** 20 × 25 deg
Peak Power: 100 kW **Pulse Width:** 5 to 12 microsec
PRF: 50 pps

Knife Rest on the mainmast of a *Sverdlov*-class cruiser. The radar below it is Top Bow, and the small antennas at the mastheads are High Sieve. (U.S. Naval Institute)

Spoon Rest abaft the after funnel of a *Sverdlov*-class cruiser. The antenna below the High Sieve on the foremast is Square Head, the standard IFF interrogator. (U.S. Navy)

Data are for Knife Rest A.

This long-range low-frequency air-search radar consists of two vertical pairs of yagis, side by side. Knife Rest is a naval version of the land-based P-8, and it appeared in 1952 on *Sverdlovs* and some T-43 radar pickets. P-8 was conceived as a ground-based long-range early-warning radar. As such, it was included in the postwar three-year radar development plan (1946–48). Requirements were: aircraft detection range 150 km at 8000 m (while scanning); range resolution at least 2500 m, bearing resolution at least 24 degrees. Pulse power was 70–75 kW, and the entire installation weighed about 17 tons. There were both bearing and altitude indicators, the latter presumably based on vertical lobing. P-8 was tested in 1949–50. It was succeeded in ground service by P-10 (developed 1951–53), which had a similar antenna array and which incorporated an interrogator. The basic requirements of the new radar were: detection range 180–200 km, altitude up to 16,000 m; accuracy (resolution) 1000 (2500) meters, 3 (2.5) degrees; maximum altitude error was 2 percent of range. P-10 passed its acceptance tests in 1953.

Spoon Rest (P-12) was a third metric-frequency radar, using a frequency band distinct from (and higher than) that of P-8/P-10; this radar was capable of some rapid tuning within its band. Maximum range was 200 km (maximum altitude 18,000 m), and peak power was at least 180 kW. Maximum acceptable beamwidth was 7–9 degrees. The antenna was an array of six vertical pairs of yagis, and when Spoon Rest appeared at sea in 1965 it was credited with a 2.5 × 1 degree beam at 147–161 MHz, 350 kW, range about 150 nm.

Knife Rest A was primarily for *Sverdlov*-class cruisers, replacing Cross Bird. Some ships were later fitted with Spoon Rest, on their after superstructures (it was too large to fit on a mast), or with an enlarged Knife Rest B (presumably P-10).

The enlarged Knife Rest and Spoon Rest appeared on board cruisers well after Big Net and Top Trough. That may correspond to the U.S. process of shifting back and forth between relatively narrow-beam L-band radars such as SPS-6/12 and broader beam P-band sets (e.g., SPS-29/37/43 and SPS-40) that lost less of their performance when faced with highly streamlined aircraft. Incidentally, this phenomenon of radar performance loss would seem to foreshadow the effect of future stealthy aircraft, which presumably would owe some of their invisibility to shapes that reflect radar signals away from the searching radar. The longer the radar wavelength, the less the radar beam "sees" the details of target shape, and thus the less valuable antiradar shaping is likely to be. For the U.S., the broad-beam radars were eventually discarded (in favor of the narrower-beam SPS-49) because they could not effectively designate targets to antiaircraft missiles. The Soviet choice to adopt Top Sail (for SA-N-3) may have been analogous. SPS-49 and Top Sail operate in much the same part of the spectrum.

◆ Long Bow

Band: X **Peak Power:** 30 kW
Pulse Width: (i) 0.25 (ii) 0.75 microsec
PRF: (i) 3000–3300 (ii) 1650, 1100 pps

This blind-fire radar replaces Post Lamp. Long Bow was first observed in 1957, and it survives on board Kotlin-class destroyers.

◆ Neptune

Band: X (9430 MHz) **Beam:** 1.6 × 20 deg
Peak Power: 42 kW **Pulse Width:** (i) 0.25 (ii) 1.0 microsec
PRF: (i) 2700 (ii) 675 pps **Scan Rate:** 14 rpm

Neptune is a navigational radar of the 1950s. Production ended in 1960, but this radar remains in service.

◆ Palm Frond

This surface-search radar is the current standard, replacing Don 2 and Don Kay from the Krivak class on. In accord with previous Soviet policy on surface-search radars, the usual complement is three sets (Krivaks have only one, plus a Don Kay in Krivak-II; all Krivaks have two navigational radars).

◆ Peel Cone

This air/surface-search radar on Pauk and Stenka classes supersedes Pot Drum.

◆ Plank Shave

This search/missile-targeting antenna on Tarantul-class missile corvettes is the successor to Square Tie.

◆ Post Lamp

Band: X (9420–9430 MHz) **Beam:** 0.85 × 13 deg
Peak Power: 10 kW **Pulse Width:** 0.25 microsec
PRF: 3400–3900 (variable) pps
Scan Rate: 17 scans/sec (antenna scans 0.066 deg/sec to 3 deg/sec) (scan limited to plus or minus 4 degrees)

Post Lamp is a destroyer and cruiser torpedo fire-control radar, developed 1949–50 (tested on board the destroyer *Bestrashnyy* in the Black Sea, October–November 1950). Post Lamp was later modified as a gun-control set but then relegated again to torpedo control. The feed rotates to scan the antenna for better pointing accuracy. Range is 15 nm on a destroyer, somewhat more than 20 nm on a larger ship. Resolution in spotting is 50 yds in range and 1 mil in bearing.

The Soviet designation is Zarya. It was modified to control 3.9- to 6-inch coastal artillery.

A Matka-class hydrofoil shows her Plank Shave targeting radar at her masthead, with a Bass Tilt fire-control radar below, atop her bridge. (German Ministry of Defense)

◆ Pot Head/Pot Drum

> **Band:** (9275–9460 MHz)   **Beam:** approx 3 deg
> **Peak Power:** 100 kW   **Pulse Width:** 0.25–1.0 microsec
> **PRF:** 1600–1650, 3200–3300 pps
> **Scan Rate:** circular at 2.5–4 or 5–6 rpm; sector at 7–8

A Soviet Turya-class hydrofoil torpedo boat shows a Pot Drum radar forward (with Square Tie IFF interrogator below it) and Drum Tilt aft. Some units have a new Peel Cone radar with a large reflector instead. The guns are twin 30 mm (AK 230). (U.S. Navy)

Standard radar in SO.1-class submarine chasers and on many other patrol craft, Pot Head superseded Skin Head from about 1960 on. Pot Drum, which is externally very similar, entered service in 1958 and was carried by patrol craft such as Turya, Stenka, Shershen, and Pchela. It appears that Pot Drum had a peak power of 150 kW and a pulse width of 0.5–1.0 microsec, whereas Pot Head, which would have needed more resolution (e.g., for periscope detection) had a shorter pulse width (one source gives 0.3–0.5 microseconds). These radars were succeeded by Square Tie (which has a somewhat different role) in missile boats and by Peel Cone in recent patrol craft; Square Tie in turn gave way to the current Plank Shave. However, Square Tie is still in production for export craft.

◆ Skin Head

> **Band:** S (3000 MHz)   **Beam:** 17 deg
> **Peak Power:** 80 kW   **Pulse Width:** 1 microsec
> **PRF:** 400 pps   **Antenna Dimensions:** radome: 0.8 × 1 m

This patrol craft surface-search radar is reportedly derived from the U.S. SO series, now in PRC service. Skin Head was developed in 1946–48 and tested in the Black Sea in April–June 1948. Test results: destroyer detected at 7.5 nm; torpedo boat at 3.4 nm; aircraft at 100–300 m altitude detected at 9–17 nm.

Skin Head radar on a Soviet torpedo boat preserved as a memorial. Although the memorial is for World War II, the P-4 class boat and its equipment (including the twin 14.5-mm machine gun aft) are postwar. (U.S. Navy)

The Soviet name is Zarnitsa. This radar was manufactured in China during the 1960s.

◆ Slim Net

> **Band:** S (2840 MHz)   **Beam:** (est) 1 × 3 deg
> **Pulse Width:** 1–1.5 microsec   **PRF:** 420–425 pps
> **Antenna Dimensions:** 5.5 × 1.8 m

This early (ca. 1957) S-band radar on some cruisers, destroyers, and frigates can be used for both air and surface search, varying rotation rate (data rate) for the two functions (slow rotation for surface targets, fast for air targets). This radar appeared on board all Kotlins as built and was eventually mounted on all but one Riga. Slim Net was a slightly modified Hair Net (1950, now obsolete).

◆ Snoop Head

This submarine search radar has an ESM radome (Bald Head) on the same mast, above it. The reflector is slotted.

◆ Snoop Pair

This submarine surface-search radar has back-to-back antennas for increased data rate. The two feeds appear to be somewhat different, so it may be a dual-beam (dual elevation, not vee-beam) set. This radar is visible in photographs of the Sierra-class submarine, and Snoop Pair is also listed for the contemporary Akula and Typhoon (but not Oscar). The radar reflector is solid and resembles that of Snoop Slab (albeit with feed from above rather than from below, as in other Soviet radars; this type of feed is probably necessary since the waveguide runs up the mast between the reflectors). A circular ring of EW intercept antennas surrounds the base of the radar.

◆ Snoop Plate

> **Band:** X (around 9370 MHz)   **Peak Power:** 80 kW
> **Pulse Width:** 1–2 microsec   **PRF:** 1618 pps
> **Scan Rate:** 10 or 20 rpm (but rotation can be manual or sector scan, and minimum rate is 4 rpm)

The first Soviet postwar submarine search radar was seen in 1953; Snoop Plate was standard through early Foxtrot-class boats. Many components duplicate those of Neptune, Don, and Post Lamp. Range scales are 2, 5, 10, and 40 nm, but maximum range is about 10 nm in practice. Snoop Plate was replaced by Snoop Slab in Foxtrot-class and later submarines. Snoop Slab was later retrofitted to many earlier submarines, although Snoop Plate remains in service.

◆ Snoop Slab

This submarine surface-search radar replaced Snoop Plate from about 1957 on. Snoop Slab has a massive parabolic reflector and very noticeable motor housing.

◆ **Snoop Tray**

This submarine surface-search radar was introduced in 1962. It has a nearly flat and almost rectangular reflector, tipped over at an angle of about 25 degrees. This radar succeeded Snoop Slab in production (initially on board Tango, Golf, November, Hotel, Echo classes).

◆ **Spin Trough**

The surface-search radar in Krivaks and in auxiliaries, small craft, etc., is an alternative to Don 2.

A Soviet ocean minesweeper (T-58 class) shows typical slotted-wave-guide surface-search radars (Spin Trough and Don-2) and a Muff Cob fire-control radar for her twin 57-mm guns. The long cylindrical object on deck under the after gun mount is presumably an acoustic sweep. This Soviet ship is missing the clutter that is typical of Western mine-countermeasures craft. (U.S. Navy)

◆ **Square Tie/Type 331**

This X-band surface-search/targeting radar for SS-N-2 missiles is now being superseded by Plank Shave. Square Tie is enclosed in the Band Stand radomes of export Nanuchka-class missile corvettes, which are equipped with SS-N-2C rather than SS-N-9 missiles.

The PRC designation for this radar is Type 331.

Square Tie search and missile-targeting radars at the mastheads of Chinese Osa-type missile boats, center and left. (U.S. Naval Institute)

◆ **Strut Curve/Strut Pair**

This S-band small-ship air-search radar, contemporary with the Head Net series, is installed on Petya and Mirka frigates and Poti and Grisha corvettes. Strut Curve reportedly operates at the high end of the S-band and is unusual in lacking a balancing vane behind its reflector. That lack might indicate that the antenna was not stabilized, the vanes on other Soviet antennas being used to reduce the load on the stabilizer.

Strut Pair is two Strut Curve antennas arranged back to back (for high data rate), using pulse compression; Strut Pair is installed on two *Udaloy* class, one Mod Kildin, Grisha-V light frigates, and the carrier *Baku*.

Strut Curve air-search radar at the masthead of a Petya-class corvette. The ASW launchers aft are RBU-2500s. (U.S. Navy)

Strut Pair back-to-back pulse-compression radar on board the *Udaloy*-class destroyer *Vice Admiral Kulakov*. Three Palm Frond surface-search antennas surround the mast, and the Kite Screech radar director is to the left. (U.S. Naval Institute)

◆ **Top Bow**

This X-band fire-control radar, providing both range and accurate bearing, was first observed in 1952. Top Bow survives on board *Sverdlov*-class cruisers and on board some *Skoryy*-class destroyers. Presumably Top Bow is a modified version of Half Bow.

◆ **Top Plate**

Top Plate has back-to-back planar-array antennas (one shorter but apparently wider than the other) and is installed on the *Udaloy*-class destroyers *Marshal Vasilevskiy*, *Admiral Zakharov*, and later units. Top Plate probably operates in S-band, like Top Steer, and seems to be the successor to Head Net C. Both arrays are canted to the horizontal, at opposite (i.e., analogous) angles. The conclusion that the arrays are in fact frequency-scanned would seem to flow from the replacement of Top Steer by Top Steer/Top Plate; that replacement also suggests the likely frequency.

The effect of canting would be to run the beam diagonally across the sky as the radar elevated. If the beam is relatively narrow, and the time between pulse trains of different frequencies relatively long, it might be argued that such operation would compensate for the rotation of the antenna. The advantage of such a design would be that the radar could dwell longer at each elevation angle, achieving a better probability of detection. Back-to-back construction might make for a better net data rate, the shorter antenna producing a somewhat broader beam (in elevation) intermediate between the fan beam of a 2-D radar and the pencil beam of a true 3-D radar.

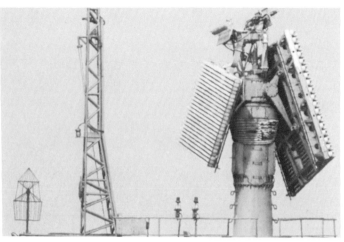

A Top Plate radar on board the *Udaloy*-class destroyer *Admiral Spiridov*. The folded waveguides at the side of each array confirm that the radar is a frequency-scanner like the U.S. SPS-39/52. The IFF interrogator is atop each of the two arrays. *(Sea Power)*

♦ **Top Sail/Top Pair**

Top Sail on board a Kresta-II–class cruiser. The long straight element in front of the reflector is the twisted feed, which performs the same function as the sinuous feed in a U.S. frequency-scanning radar. The extra feed at the top is presumably for IFF. (U.S. Navy)

The large frequency-scanning three-dimensional radar introduced in 1967 in the *Moskva* is the main search radar in all ships armed with SA-N-3 missiles. Top Sail probably operates at about the same frequency as Big Net, i.e., about 850 MHz, which is well below that used by the roughly analogous U.S. systems of a decade earlier (SPS-39/52 series). The typical U.S. flat serpentine waveguide is replaced by a waveguide twisted around a vertical pole in front of the reflector; very clear photographs show the twists, which are required to provide the greater length needed to operate at a longer waveguide. Presumably there are radiating slots on the pole where it faces the reflector. Antenna dimensions are about 6.1 × 7.5 m.

Top Sail is invariably combined with a Head Net C secondary or back-up three-dimensional radar.

Top Pair consists of Top Sail and Big Net antennas arranged back to back. Presumably that arrangement makes for better long-range coverage; the U.S. Navy has found that frequency-scanning radars do not dwell on any particular part of the sky long enough to provide the sort of detection probability achievable with a fan-beam (two-dimensional) radar. Top Pair first appeared in the *Kirov* and *Slava*. The usual back-up radar is Top Steer.

Top Pair radar on the mainmast of the cruiser *Slava*; the radar on the foremast is Top Steer. (HMS *Excellent*)

♦ **Top Steer**

This three-dimensional S-band radar consists of a frequency-scanned antenna arranged back to back with one Strut Pair antenna. There is no known example of the S-band frequency scanner alone (analogous to Top Sail). The two antennas share

Top Steer (left) and Top Sail (right) air-search radars on board the carrier *Minsk*. The radome atop the lattice mast is Top Knot, the Soviet equivalent of the U.S. TACAN. (U.S. Navy)

a common feed. Since Strut Pair is known to have been the first Soviet pulse-compression radar, it is difficult to avoid concluding that the Soviets use a single frequency-scanned pulse in the height-finder, rather than changing frequency pulse by pulse as in most Western frequency-scanned radars.

This radar actually preceded Top Pair into service, the *Kiev* carrying Top Sail (not Top Pair) and Top Steer. It appeared as the secondary three-dimensional radar of the *Kirov* and is the primary three-dimensional radar on the first three *Sovremennyy*-class destroyers.

Top Steer/Top Plate is an analogous antenna, in which the three-dimensional element of Top Steer is replaced by the planar array of Top Plate, canted to the vertical (as in other Top Plate installations), on the *Sovremennyy*-class destroyers *Osmotritel'nyy* and *Bezuprechnyy*.

Top Steer on the destroyer *Sovremmennyy*, with Palm Frond surface-search radars. (U.S. Naval Institute)

◆ Top Trough

The cruiser *Oktyabrskaya Revolutsia* shows a Top Trough radar at her maintop, plus a Knife Edge B air-search radar abaft her after 6-inch director, in these 1972 views. The foremast radars are Top Bow and, at the fore masthead, High Sieve. The navigational radar above Top Bow is unidentified. (U.S. Naval Institute)

This slotted-waveguide radar is like the British Type 983. Operating at about 850 MHz, Top Trough is installed on some *Sver-*

dlov-class cruisers and some destroyers. It presumably functions as a target indicator (short-range air-search radar) and probably uses the same radar transmitter as Big Net, with which Top Trough is roughly contemporary.

◆ *Kerch* Search Radar

A previously unknown planar-array air-search radar replaces Top Sail on board the Kara-class missile cruiser *Kerch*. This radar seems to have been fitted during a refit begun in April 1988 and completed about February 1989. The antenna consists of a series of slotted waveguides, the gaps between the arrays being quite visible. The serpentine feed characteristic of frequency-scanning is clearly visible on the right-hand side of the array, and the antenna is crowned by an IFF interrogator. Presumably, this new long-range three-dimensional air-search radar operates at a much higher frequency than Top Sail, presumably S-band.

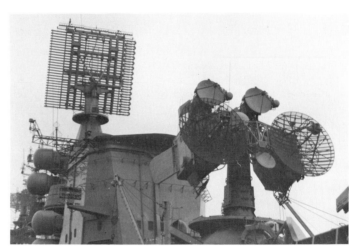

The new Soviet flat phased-array radar, seen on board the Soviet cruiser *Kerch*, early in 1989. The radar in the foreground is the Head Lights set used to control the ship's SA-N-3 missiles. The small flat array projected out from the uptakes is an IFF interrogator (Square Head). Although the ship retains her original series of ESM/ECM radomes, Rum Tub has been added (array visible just behind Square Head). (Eric Grove)

FIRE-CONTROL RADARS

◆ Bass Tilt

This radar operates in H-band and is used with the Soviet AK 630 Gatling gun. In Grisha-III, Bass Tilt also controls the twin 57-mm gun; and in Nanuchka-III, Matka, Grisha-III, Tarantul, and Pauk, Bass Tilt controls the 76.2-mm gun. As its name implies, this radar operates at a somewhat lower frequency than Drum Tilt, which it superficially resembles. Bass Tilt entered service about 1972.

A Tarantul-II–class missile corvette shows her Light Bulb data link antenna at the top of her mast, with a Bass Tilt gunfire-control antenna below. The small slotted waveguide atop the bridge serves a Kivach-3 navigational radar. The two objects right aft are standard chaff launchers. (*Ships of the World*)

◆ Cross Sword

Serving as the missile guidance for SA-N-9, which is the successor to SA-N-4, Cross Sword, like Pop Group, incorporates its own search antenna. Again there is a single large-target tracker, in this case apparently a monopulse dish (probably an inverse Cassegrain) with a big feed in front. There are two small enclosed antennas above the main tracker, and two further devices, probably electro-optical trackers, below it. The two radomes above the main tracker are of different sizes; presumably one houses a missile-tracking radar, the other a guidance-uplink transmitter. The larger of the two radomes resembles that of Front Dome (although Cross Sword's is considerably smaller) or that of one of the Drum-series gunfire-control radars.

The surveillance radar antenna consists of two paraboloids arranged back to back, for a high data rate. That arrangement might correspond to a new requirement to protect ships against very small antiship missiles appearing over the horizon at relatively short range. Such a requirement could also explain the choice of vertical launching, since a vertically launched missile can probably engage at extremely short range (because it is under positive control, through its thrust vanes, from the moment of launch, and because it picks up considerable speed while diving into the guidance beam).

It is possible that the small and presumably missile-related transmitter provides illumination for a short-range semiactive homing weapon, that SA-N-9 is not in fact command guided. In that case the director could control several missiles either simultaneously or in very close sequence. This capability in turn might help to explain the shift from a mechanically fed launcher in SA-N-4/Pop Group to vertical launchers in this system.

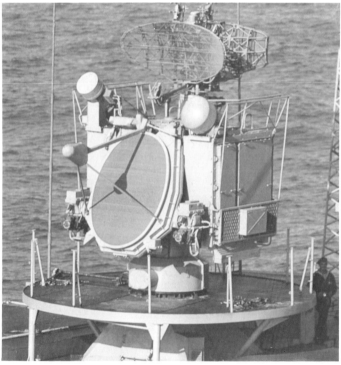

Cross Sword. Above are back-to-back air-search radars. *(Sea Power)*

◆ Drum Tilt

This radar operates in H- and I-bands; on Osa missile boats and others Drum Tilt controls twin 30-mm guns. Drum Tilt was the first of a new generation of drum-shaped fire-control antennas (1961). The housing is tipped up permanently at an angle of about 25 degrees, and approximate dimensions are 1.5 m in diameter and 1.7 m in length.

Drum Tilt radar on board an East German Koni-class frigate. (U.S. Naval Institute)

A Drum Tilt fire-control radar on board a Soviet torpedo boat, with the back-up optical director in the foreground. (TASS from SOVFOTO)

Drum Tilt 30-mm gunfire-control radar director, on board the Indian frigate *Ganga*. In Indian service the director is designated MR-104. *(Ships of the World)*

◆ Front Dome

The missile guidance for SA-N-7 is a tracker-illuminator. It resembles the Bass Tilt gunfire-control radar but is larger. In the *Sovremennyy* class, three such radars are associated with each SA-N-7 launcher.

Front Dome missile-guidance radar (for the SA-N-6 missile) atop the bridge of the cruiser *Kirov* (and pointed aft), photographed in November 1980. The big air-search radar is Top Pair, and the surface-search radar forward of Top Dome is Palm Frond. The big radomes just beneath Top Pair are Round House, the Soviet equivalent of TACAN. The objects just forward of the bridge structure are Tin Man optronic devices, and a Pop Group director is visible to one side of the bridge structure, just abaft the SA-N-4 launcher it controls. The radomes on the side of the mast are Side Globes (ECM). (U.S. Naval Institute)

◆ Hawk Screech

Band: X (9.2–9.5 GHz)   **Beam:** 0.6 deg
Peak Power: 150 kW   **Pulse Width:** 0.6 microsec
PRF: approx 1250 pps
Scan Rate: 30–31 cycles/sec linear scan (narrow sector)
Antenna Dimensions: diameter approx 1.7 m

Hawk Screech radar on board an East German Koni-class frigate. (U.S. Naval Institute)

Hawk Screech is the X-band fire control for 45-mm, 57-mm, and 76.2-mm dual-purpose guns (1954); it always has an optical back-up. Probably the radar conceived in 1949 and designated Yakor' by the Soviets, Hawk Screech introduced a new auto-track technique (lobing) that was used in several other radars. This radar was fully stabilized, for blind-fire and autotracking. Maximum range is probably about 6500 yards and 18,000 ft (altitude).

◆ Head Lights

The missile-control radar for SA-N-3 consists of two large (4-meter) and two small (1.8-meter) tracking dishes and a small dish for the command uplink. The large dishes track the target, the small dishes the missile. Soviet doctrine appears to be to fire two missiles (from one launcher) at the target, and in this system each missile apparently needs its own target tracker, the command signals presumably being generated by measurement of the expected miss distance between missile and target. There are several versions. Head Lights B added SS-N-14 control. All *Kievs* have Head Lights C, which presumably has additional power to control a longer-range version of SA-N-3. Head Lights C appeared in the Kara class. The early Kresta-IIs had Head Lights B forward and Head Lights A aft, but later ones had Head Lights B fore and aft.

Head Lights was probably one of the earliest Soviet applications of monopulse radar technology.

Head Lights fire-control radars on board the *Moskva*, with Side Globes radomes to the left and an SA-N-3 launcher to the right. (U.S. Naval Institute)

Head Lights on board the cruiser *Kerch*, 1989. (Eric Grove)

◆ Kite Screech

The X-band fire control for 100-mm and new 130-mm dual-purpose guns is similar in appearance to Hawk Screech but larger.

◆ **Muff Cob**

For 57-mm twin automatic guns, Muff Cob operates in H-band and has an attached TV camera. This system first appeared about 1962.

Muff Cob 57-mm gunfire-control radar director, on board the Indian frigate *Ganga*. In Indian service this director is designated MR-103. (*Ships of the World*)

Pop Group, the fire-control system of the SA-N-4 missile, on board a Koni-class frigate, 1981, just forward of the missile launcher. The gun aft is a twin 76.2 mm, controlled by the Drum Tilt just forward of the uptakes. The torpedo decoys are visible on the fantail. (U.S. Naval Institute)

◆ **Owl Screech**

This X-band fire control for 76.2-mm DP guns (about 1961) is an improved Hawk Screech. The reflector's diameter is about 2.3 m. Peak power is reportedly 250 kW. There is no associated back-up director/target designator.

◆ **Peel Group**

This missile-control radar for SA-N-1 consists of a command dish plus two groups of antennas: one to track the target, the other to track the two missiles normally fired in a salvo. Each group consists of two parabolic reflectors, one nodding vertically and one horizontally: hence the name (they resemble pieces of orange peel). Together, a horizontal and a vertical nodder equate roughly to a conical-scan dish, but the combination is likely to be less efficient. Presumably the command dish sends the missile separate signals for vertical and horizontal course correction. Reportedly the target is tracked in S-band, the missile in X-band. Maximum range is about 30–40 nm.

◆ **Pop Group**

Pop Group is the missile-guidance radar for SA-N-4, incorporating its own acquisition radar, atop the cab, with target and missile trackers in front (flat plate antennas). Presumably the acquisition radar is colocated with the trackers to reduce hand-over delays; in this sense Pop Group is analogous to the Signaal M20 series and to the U.S. Mk 92.

Although the missile launcher has two arms, there are only a single missile-tracker antenna and a single target-tracker antenna. Dual operation would still be possible using polarization diversity, two signals sharing a common antenna. That sharing might be the reason for the flat plate some distance ahead of the antenna proper.

The analogous land system (Land Roll) has one large and two small antennas plus a surveillance/acquisition antenna similar in appearance to that of Pop Group. In the land system, the search antenna operates at 6–8 GHz (slightly below Western C-band wavelength), with stacked feeds (probably for frequency diversity, possibly for integral IFF). Reportedly the big target tracker is a frequency-hopping monopulse antenna operating at 14.2–14.8 GHz (slightly above X-band as used in the West); reported maximum range is 25 km (effective range 20 km). The target tracker is almost certainly an inverse Cassegrain. The smaller antenna is a higher-frequency replica of the large one.

In the case of the land-based system, the two missile trackers can operate at different frequencies, to track two separate missiles engaging the same target.

Pop Group director for SA-N-4 missiles, on board the Indian frigate *Ganga*. (*Ships of the World*)

◆ Sun Visor

Band: X (9.3–9.44 GHz) **Beam:** 0.8 deg
Pulse Width: 0.2 microsec **PRF:** 2500, 3500 pps
Scan Rate: 40 scans/sec

Sun Visor radar is visible on the front of the Wasp Head director of this Chinese Riga-class frigate. The main air-search radar above is Slim Net. The dome alongside the mast is presumably one of the two elements of Jug Pair, which is probably a Chinese version of Watch Dog (ESM). (U.S. Naval Institute)

The secondary battery director of the *Sverdlov*-class cruiser *Dzerzhinskiy*, now discarded, shows its Sun Visor radar and its range-finder. The aerials in the background were part of the Fan Song radar controlling the SA-N-2 missile carried by this ship. In the foreground are standard twin 37-mm guns. (TASS via SOVFOTO)

This X-band fire control for 100-mm and 130-mm dual-purpose guns is mounted on a Round Top or Wasp Head director. Sun Visor appeared in 1953. The antenna feed is a dipole, and elevation limits are +90/−5 deg. Variations in the feed differentiate between Sun Visor A and B.

◆ Top Dome

The missile-guidance radar for SA-N-6 uses a 4-m diameter radome fixed in elevation but trainable. Three smaller radomes are mounted on the face of the mounting pedestal, and there is also a much smaller hemispheric radome below. The smaller radome may be the link transceiver for the track-via-missile system. The main tracking radar almost certainly operates in X-band, in analogy to the land-based Flap Lid engagement radar.

Each Top Dome is associated with six vertical launchers; on the basis of two missiles per target, presumably Top Dome can simultaneously control three intercepts against three targets. Since there is no separate target or missile tracker, the system must time-share between the target- and missile-tracking functions. Because Top Dome does not elevate, it must scan electronically (as, indeed, the land-based SA-10 fire-control radar does).

In the past, it has been Soviet practice to assign one launcher per director per target. However, it is possible that the Soviets consider the array of six SA-N-6 launchers as a single entity, and that doctrine now calls for more than two missiles per engagement.

OPTRONICS

◆ Squeeze Box

In *Sovremennyy*-class destroyers and in amphibious ships with 140-mm bombardment rockets, Squeeze Box probably combines infrared television with a laser range-finder. An "uncovered" version is carried by Pomornik-class ACVs. Squeeze Box is a fire-control device, not a remote-vision device like Tee Plinth or Tin Man.

◆ Tee Plinth

This television sensor was installed in the 1960s and 1970s and is now replaced in newer ships by Tin Man. Tee Plinth supplements the large optical periscopes that modern Soviet warships (from the Kynda class on) carry either atop or abeam their bridges. Both Tee Plinth and these periscopes presumably serve a below-decks command center. Such a center would be required if, as is said to be the case, the Soviets plan to fight their ships under fallout and chemical-attack conditions, using citadel protection (the center would be within the below-decks citadel). This type of arrangement would correspond to the much earlier and nearly universal practice, in the world's cruisers and battleships, of providing command facilities under armor, in a conning tower, served by periscopes projecting through the top of the tower. Presumably Tee Plinth replaces human lookouts, who could not survive in a nuclear- or chemical-warfare environment.

The presumed existence of a below-decks command center is suggested by the very minimal dimensions of the bridges of ships of the Kynda, Kashin, Kresta, Kara, and *Moskva* classes. Most are just not large enough to include adjacent missile and radar control spaces. These spaces must, therefore, generally be below the bridge, and they are probably the same spaces served by the periscopes. One would suspect, then, that the Soviets tend to combine the functions of a Western CIC and a Western ship-control space, using television and periscopes to provide the commanding officer, who is below decks during combat, with a reasonably complete picture of the outside world. The U.S. Navy will probably adopt a somewhat similar arrangement in its next-generation ships, to reduce the sheer size of its bridges and also to make collective protection (i.e., a citadel system) more practicable. For the U.S. Navy, a smaller bridge is attractive because it would reduce the ship's radar cross section. The Soviets presumably had to reduce bridge dimensions to provide more topside space for their large radars and weapons directors; the Kynda and later classes are very cluttered topside.

The bridge structure of the cruiser *Kerch*, 1989, showing the forward Head Lights director (which controls the SS-N-14 ASW missiles as well as the SA-N-3 battery) and an Owl Screech radar gun director further aft, above the enclosed bridge wing. The object visible above the Owl Screech is a periscope. The object just beneath the Head Lights radar is a Tee Plinth television camera. (Eric Grove)

Ironically, it appears that the Soviets had to adopt larger topside bridges, presumably for better ship-handling, in later designs, such as the Krivak, *Kiev*, and *Kirov*. This development would seem to parallel U.S. experience with conning towers (i.e., protected command centers) in battleships before World

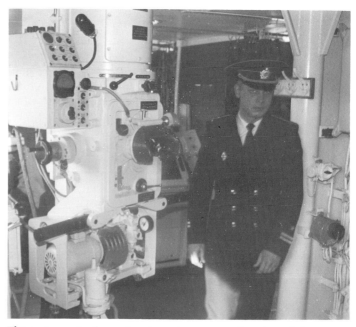

The periscope in the enclosed combat command station of the cruiser *Kerch*, on the same level as, and abaft, her bridge. This station does not contain radar fire-control equipment but does include radar directors like the one visible in the background, as well as a steering console. (Eric Grove)

War I. About 1910 the U.S. Navy sought to minimize open bridge space so that commanders would always operate from their protected conning towers. During World War I, when U.S. battleships operated with the British Grand Fleet, the American commanders found it difficult to conduct high-speed maneuvers from closed conning towers; substantial (unprotected) bridges were restored, though not on the same scale adopted by other navies. All major Soviet ships are still provided with the periscopes and electro-optical sensors (televisions) characteristic of their below-decks command spaces, i.e., of their citadel protection.

Tee Plinth and its successor (Tin Man) are trainable. The Soviets also use small fixed television cameras (Tilt Pot).

◆ Tin Man

Successor to Tee Plinth, Tin Man probably incorporates a laser range-finder, in newer ships.

FIRE-CONTROL SYSTEMS

Later radar fire-control systems (e.g., Hawk Screech) are designated by the associated radar. The systems listed here are early postwar optical/radar directors.

◆ Cylinder Head

An 85-mm dual-purpose gun director, Cylinder Head controlled 100-mm guns in the Kola-class frigates (now extinct). The associated radar was Fire Iron, now extinct, similar in form to the British 280-series of World War II. The director was not stabilized. Speed and tracking range limits were 300 kts and 45,000 yds.

◆ Four Eyes

Four Eyes was the single-purpose main-battery director in *Skoryy*-class destroyers. The associated radars were Top Bow, Long Bow, Sword Fish, Half Bow, or Post Lamp. Although the guns were usually described as dual purpose, this director did not incorporate dual ballistics; it was limited to surface fire. Speed and range limits were 40 kts and 60,000 yds.

The Four Eyes 130-mm director of an unmodified *Skoryy*-class destroyer, 1967. (Skyfotos)

♦ **Long Ears**

The main-battery fire-control director in *Sverdlov*-class cruisers is associated with the Long Bow surface fire-control radar. Maximum tracking speed is 40 kts, maximum tracking range 33,000 yds. This combination is suitable for surface blind-fire but not for antiaircraft fire. Each of the two range-finders is 8 m long.

♦ **Round Top**

The stabilized secondary-battery directors for the *Sverdlov* class descended from German designs. Each carries a 4-m stereo range-finder. The associated radars are Sun Visor and Egg Cup (range only); the tracking range limit is 81,000 yds. This system cannot autotrack.

♦ **Wasp Head**

This dual-purpose director is installed in Kotlin-class destroyers and Riga-class frigates. The associated radars are Sun Visor and Egg Cup (range only). The director is stabilized and is suited to blind-fire. Maximum tracking range is 81,000 yds, and maximum antiaircraft speed is reportedly 950 kts (70 kts for surface targets). This system is not capable of autotracking.

In the Riga class this system was called Sphaera 50.

UNITED KINGDOM

RADARS

♦ **Type 262**

Band: X   Beam: 5 deg
Peak Power: 30 kW   Pulse Width: (i) 20 (ii) 200 microsec
PRF: 1500 pps

This close-range armament blind-fire (CRBF) radar was formerly used to control both guns and Sea Cat missiles (GWS 21 system). Type 262 oscillates in both planes while searching for a target and then tracks by conical scanning, the antenna spinning. The associated fire-control system tracks by measuring apparent target angular rate (using a gyro).

Type 262 could autotrack at 5000 yds, acquiring its target at 7000 yds. Targets were acquired by scanning 30 deg/sec in azimuth (elevating 3 deg at the end of each horizontal sweep), at the same time searching for 750 yds on either side of the indicated range at 30 cycles/sec.

♦ **Type 275**

Band: S   Beam: 6 × 8.2 deg
Peak Power: 400 kW   Pulse Width: 0.25, 0.5, 0.75 microsec
PRF: 500 pps   Antenna Dimensions: diameter 4 ft (two dishes)

HMS *Puma*, a Type-41 antiaircraft frigate, shows her Mk-6 director with its Type-275 fire-control radar (just abaft her bridge). The gun mount forward is a 4.5-in Mk 6. Two sisters survive in the Bangladesh Navy. (HMS *Excellent*)

This dual-purpose fire-control radar was introduced at the end of World War II and is still in service in India and in Bangladesh. Type 275 was intended for the postwar Mk 6 director, and some were also fitted to U.S.-supplied Mk 37s. The antennas are 4-ft dishes that can elevate and that scan conically. Detection range is 36,000 yds (tracking range 30,000 yds).

♦ **Type 277/278**

Band: S   Beam: 4.5 × 2.2 deg
Peak Power: 500 kW   Pulse Width: (i) 0.7 (ii) 1.5 or 1.9 microsec
PRF: (ii) 500 pps   Scan Rate: 7.5 rpm
Antenna Dimensions: 8-ft spherical parabola with clipped sides

Data are for the postwar 277Q, with antenna outfit ANU.

This nodding height-finder is still in service on board "County"-class missile destroyers and one Bangladeshi frigate. In modernized form this system was designated Type 278. Type 277Q performance: aircraft between 5000 and 20,000 ft could be detected at 55 nm, and height-finding range on an airplane at 20,000 ft was 60 nm.

♦ **Type 293/993/994**

Band: S   Beam: 2 × 35 deg
Peak Power: 500 kW   Pulse Width: (i) 0.7 (ii) 1.5 or 1.9 microsec
PRF: (ii) 500 pps   Scan Rate: 5, 10, or 15 rpm
Antenna Dimensions: 12 ft

Data are for the 293Q version (antenna outfit ANS).

This short-range air/surface-search radar (target indicator in large ships) was succeeded by Type 993. The remaining examples are on board the Indian *Leopard*-class frigates. Estimated range was 30–35 nm.

Type 993 is Type 293 with a new "quarter cheese" antenna, outfit AKD. In this antenna the feed horn does not obscure the main radar beam, so that the beam is better defined, even over a broad tuning band.

Type 994 retains the same antenna but has a new transceiver based on that of the Plessey AWS-4 private-venture radar. Installation, e.g., on board frigates, began in 1978.

♦ **Type 901**

The missile-guidance radar for the Seaslug system survives only in the Chilean Navy. The gathering beam transmitter is on the right-hand side of the big radar nacelle.

◆ Type 903/904

> **Band:** X (8.5–9.05, or 9.05–9.6 GHz) **Beam:** 2 deg
> **PRF:** 3000 pps **Pulse Width:** 0.1 microsec

This X-band conscan fire-control radar, used in the MRS 3 system, was based on the U.S. Mk 35 (which is described below). Data given here apply to the Mod 1 version, as used in MRS 3. Scanning was spiral (to acquire targets) or conical (for tracking). Minimum range was 32.8 yds, and maximum lock-on range was 29,500 yds. Range accuracy was 10 yds, and targets could be resolved within 1½ degrees or 25 yds. Typical preset range rates in the MRS 3 system were 180 yds/sec (closing) in antiaircraft mode, or 22 yds/sec in the surface-fire mode. The director could turn 100 deg/sec when being run-in to a designated target.

Type 903's development began about 1946, and the radar entered service in 1958. Type 904 is a modified version for Sea Cat missile control, as part of the GWS 22 system.

Type-904 radar-equipped GWS 22 Sea Cat missile director, with Sea Cat being fired. The open hood contrasts with the enclosed hood of the very similar MRS 3/903 combination. (U.S. Naval Institute)

◆ Type 909

Type 909 is the tracking and illuminating radar for the Sea Dart missile system. The typical installation includes two radars. Type 909 is normally radome-enclosed but may be seen uncovered when ships are undergoing alignment trials. It is relatively heavy and, reportedly, unreliable, and it is being replaced by a lighter-weight radar, derived from the Marconi 805SD. Some existing Type 909 radars are being replaced by a more reliable derivative, Type 909I.

Type 909 dish diameter is 2.4 m.

◆ Type 910

Type 910 is the X-band pulse-doppler target-tracking radar for the Seawolf point-defense missile system. Electronic angle tracking is used to make small angular corrections to bore sight without moving the radar itself.

Type 910 tracks a 0.2 square-meter target at a range of about 10 km, and smaller targets at 5–6 km. The main dish is about 1.6 m in diameter (beamwidth about 1.5 deg). This radar also tracks the Seawolf missile, using signals from transmitters in two of the missile's wings (the other two wings carry command-link receivers). Command signals are calculated on the basis of the difference between the missile's and the target's positions (differential tracking). Two 80-cm dishes alongside the main antenna carry the microwave command links for two missiles, which can, therefore, be fired in salvo against a single target.

Multiplexing from a single dish was rejected as too complex. Command frequency is probably in the 10–15 GHz range. Between the main antenna and the two dishes is a gathering antenna consisting of a horn (for transmission) and four rectangular horns (for monopulse reception). The antenna also carries a television differential tracker, which uses a flare in the missile tail.

Type 910 is now being superseded by the lighter-weight Type 911. Two alternative replacements were considered. In Type 910M (about 1980), the television camera was replaced by a Blindfire Rapier DN181 mm-wave radar. There was also a Signaal VM40 radar director.

◆ Type 911 (805SW)

The lightweight Sea Wolf control radar, one of the Marconi 805 series, consists of two radars mounted side by side: A (left side of the array), a twist-Cassegrain narrow-beam reflector with a monopulse feed (and with an associated four-horn monopulse cluster gathering antenna); and B (right side of the array), a tracker (offset folded Cassegrain reflector with a steerable sub-reflector). The receiver of Radar A is coherent-on-receive, measuring target velocity by fast Fourier transform. The system measures the angle between the missile's and the target's paths. Both radars use filtered electronic angle tracking to overcome problems such as reflection from the sea surface.

Missile commands are transmitted through the antenna, initially via the wide angle beam cluster and then, after gathering, via the Radar B pencil beam.

Above-decks equipment weighs 1725 kg; between-decks equipment weighs another 2155 kg.

The Marconi 805SW was adopted in preference to the Signaal VM40.

Marconi 805SW, which is Type 911. (Marconi)

◆ Type 912

Type 912 is the British designation for the Italian Selenia Orion RTN-10X, used on board Type-21-(*Amazon*) class frigates (with a Ferranti WSA-4 processor).

HMS *Amazon*, a Type-21 frigate, shows a Type-912 fire-control radar abaft her funnel, just forward of her Sea Cat launcher. The two big radomes are SCOT satellite terminals. The two radars on the foremast are Types 992Q (above) and 1006 (below); below their platform are the direction-finding arrays of UAA-1 (Abbey Hill). The foremast also carries a pair of conical radomes, probably jammers. (U.S. Naval Institute)

♦ **Type 965/966**

Band: P (about 1.4 m) **Beam:** 12 × 40 deg
Peak Power: 450 kW **Gain:** 20 dB
Pulse Width: (i) 3.8 (ii) 10 microseconds **PRF:** (i) 400 (ii) 200 pps
Scan Rate: 8 or 10 rpm (depending on whether the power supply is 50 or 60 cycle)
Antenna Dimensions: 26 ft × 8 ft 11 in (or 16 ft 9 in) × 6 ft 1 in
Antenna Weight: 2425 or 5480 lbs

Type-965 radar (AKE-1 antenna, seen from behind). The "candlesticks" on the yardarms are UHF radio antennas, in this case either receiving or transmitting (the double candlestick carries both antennas). (Author)

Type 965 is the standard British long-range air-search radar of the 1960s, adopted in place of the roughly contemporary U.S. SPS-6. There are two alternative "bedstead"-type antennas (in effect, squintless horn arrays), AKE(1) and AKE(2), the latter in effect two AKE(1)s superimposed. Each of the 8 or 16 array elements is shaped as a reflector horn surrounding a loop dipole.

Reportedly this radar performed poorly in the Falklands because, without MTI, it was unable to detect Argentine aircraft approaching from overland. A modified version with crude MTI, 965M, has been reported. Type 966, which may be a private designation, is Type 965 with a modernized transmitter/receiver (but with the same antenna), which Marconi advertised in the mid-1980s.

Type 965 was first proposed in 1953 (and revived in 1955) to meet a staff requirement for a small-ship air-warning radar. Marconi proposed a modification of the existing Air Ministry Type 15 Mk 5, with a redesigned aerial (16 × 4 ft, 1500 lbs including the antenna-rotation motor) and a reduced radar office. The radar would scan at 6–10 rpm, with a 17-degree beam (190–215 MHz, 3.8-microsecond pulses, gapless vertical cover,

range 100+ nm on a 20 square-meter target). U.S. trials of 200 vs. 400 MHz radars (resulting in the adoption of the SPS-17 and then -28/29) were cited in support of this frequency choice; and the Dutch LW-02 was rejected because it would not meet the range requirement and because its high frequency would prevent detection of streamlined aircraft. In 1955, the aerial was expected to be 24 × 7 ft (beam 17 × 45 degrees); LW-02 used a 19.5 × 9.75 ft antenna (2300 vs. 1800 lbs, the latter figure including IFF). LW-02 would require a separate IFF antenna, special venting arrangements, and adaptation to British requirements (Anglicization).

A third alternative, the U.S. SPS-6C, was considered but rejected.

The two-array version was developed to meet a 1957 Staff Requirement for a radar-picket/missile-destroyer set, using the Type 965 transmitter and a new antenna. This version was to have been capable of detecting a Canberra bomber flying at 70,000 ft at 200 nm (150 could be accepted), with a 10 rpm data rate. The proposed antenna was about 24 × 20 ft (weight no more than 2 tons, probably 1–1.5 tons). If the aerial were not ready in time, the existing 965 (small-ship air-warning) could be used temporarily. The Staff was not happy with the Type 965 beam (17-degree beamwidth), wanting 2 degrees. DND wanted no more than 10 degrees.

It appears that the choice was to feed each of the two superimposed arrays in AKE(2) to a separate receiver (channel) and, in effect, to compare the two so that the result lay somewhere between the broad beam of the original 965 and the narrower beam achievable by two antennas side by side.

Type 965 is being superseded in British service by Type 1022.

♦ **Type 967/968**

Band: S **Beam:** 2 × 30 deg
Peak Power: 3 MW **Gain:** 30 dB
Pulse Width: 2 microsec **PRF:** 750 pps
Scan Rate: 30 rpm (max) **Antenna Dimensions:** 4 × 1 m

HMS *Andromeda* shows the combined antenna of Type-967/968 radars at her foremast head. The associated Type-910 Sea Wolf fire-control radar is above her bridge; the missile launcher is forward. (HMS *Osprey*)

Data are for 968.

The Seawolf search-and-acquisition radar consists of two units arranged back to back that designate to the Type 910 target tracker. Type 967 is an L-band pulse-doppler air-search radar; Type 968 is an S-band radar for low air cover and surface search. The Type 967 antenna contains the IFF interrogator. Signals from both radars are fed into a common Ferranti FM 1600B computer, which evaluates targets, decides to engage, and feeds target coordinates into the tracker.

The antenna mounting is fully stabilized, and detection and tracking are automatic.

In 1987, Type 967M was described as a special self-adaptive pulse-doppler radar for automatic detection of small targets.

These systems are manufactured by Marconi.

◆ Type 974

Band: X **Beam:** beamwidth 1.6 deg
Peak Power: 7 kW **Pulse Width:** 0.1 and 0.2 microsec
PRF: 1000 pps **Scan Rate:** 24 rpm

This high-definition surface-search radar was replaced in British service by Type 978. The aerial outfit was designated AKL or ATZ. Type 974 was based on the Decca 12, to which the above data also apply.

◆ Type 975

Band: X **Beam:** beamwidth 1 deg
Peak Power: 50 kW **Antenna Dimensions:** 6 or 10 ft

Kelvin-Hughes's surface-search and seaward-defense radar was replaced in British service by Type 1006. Minimum range is less than 35 yds. Type 975ZW is a minehunter radar with true motion display and with provision for marking sonar contacts on its PPI.

◆ Type 978/979

Band: X **Beam:** beamwidth 1.2 deg
Peak Power: 20 kW **Pulse Width:** (i) 0.1 (ii) 1.0 microsec
PRF: (i) 1000 (ii) 500 pps **Scan Rate:** 24 rpm

Obsolescent and being replaced, Type 978 uses a double cheese antenna (outfit ATZ), whose upper half transmits and lower half receives. This radar is based on the Decca 45, details of which are given above.

Type 979, first installed on board the survey ships *Echo* and *Vidal* in 1969, consisted of 978 plus an additional B-scope display.

◆ Type 982

Band: S **Beam:** 1 degree
Scan Rate: 0–7 rpm **Antenna Dimensions:** 26.5 × 3 ft

The sole surviving example of this long-range air-control radar is on board the Bangladeshi frigate *Umar Farooq*. Even so, this set makes an interesting comparison with Type 1022, which was intended to combine 982's sort of directional accuracy with long range. In British service, 982 often operated with a height-finder, Type 983, to provide a composite three-dimensional radar picture. The Soviet Top Trough radar is probably broadly similar in its operation, with a waveguide feeding a csc2 cylindrical reflector.

Altitude coverage is limited by the "squint" of the waveguide feed: the waveguide produces, not a narrow fan beam, but rather a cone, so that aircraft at different altitudes register at somewhat different bearings. Squint results from internal reflections within the waveguide.

Range scales are 40 nm and 80 nm (accuracies 250 and 500 yds).

◆ Type 992

Band: S **Beam:** 1.25 × 15 deg
Peak Power: 2 MW **Gain:** 30 dB
Pulse Width: 2.0 microsec **PRF:** 750 pps
Antenna Dimensions: 6.4 m **Antenna Weight:** 640 kg

Data are for 992Q. The improved Type 992R has a peak power of 3 MW.

This target-indicator radar is the last of a long series of high-precision short-range S-band air-search radars. All the earlier ones had cheese antennas; but the current version, 992Q, employs a slotted waveguide instead. 992 is the target designation radar in Type-42 destroyers (working with 965/1022) and is the principal air-search radar in Type-21 frigates. In larger ships, 992 can be synchronized with other radars in pulse and in rotation, for quick correlation with their targets. 992 is manufactured by Marconi. Effective range on an air target is about 80 or 90 nm; 992 is the primary source of radar data for the Action Information Organization, since the longer-range Type 965 has such poor definition.

Work on the original version began in 1948 and was completed in 1952. Type 992Q/R is now being replaced by Type 996.

Type-992 radar, HMS *Bristol*, 1979, with the direction-finding array of UAA-1 below its platform; the four sets of radomes, one tier per frequency band, are visible. (Author)

◆ Type 996/AWS-9

Type 996. (Plessey)

Type 996 is the three-dimensional S-band radar of the new Type-23 ("Duke"-class) frigate. 996 is replacing Type 992Q (target-indication radar) in Type-42 Sea Dart destroyers and on board the *Invincible*-class carriers. The staff requirement (Cardinal Points Specification) called for two versions, 996/1 and 996/2, the total likely order (as of 1982) being 19 Type 996/1 for retrofit and 24 Type 996/2 for new Type-23 frigates. Both were conceived as three-dimensional radars. Technical proposals for Type 996 were submitted in January 1983. The other contenders were a Marconi 1800-series dual-beam radar (reportedly using Martello height-finding technology), the Thorn X-band *Stix* pencil-beam radar with back-to-back phased-array antennas (based on Searchwater), and a version of the Signaal SMART.

Plessey won the design contest in 1983; 996 is based on the Plessey AWS-5, reportedly incorporating the 3-D signal-processing technology developed for the Plessey AR-320 radar. The commercial version, announced in 1985, is designated AWS-9. AR-320 uses an S-band FM pulse that scans in elevation (over a 30-degree range) by frequency-scanning. The radar determines target elevation by measuring the frequency of the reflected signal. Phase shifting is also used, so that the radar can alternate between frequency bands (the phase shifters are interposed between the serpentine feed and the antenna proper). The AR-320 transmitter operates at 125-kW peak power (average power 5 kW), and its pulses are of two types: 65 microsec (5 subpulses at differing frequencies) for low angles, 31.5 microsec (5 subpulses) for high angles, in each case with pseudorandom phase coding (31-bit at low angles, 15-bit at high angles). Pulses are sent at intervals of 550–3000 microsec (i.e., 0.55–3.0 millisec), depending on the elevation angle. The AR-320 array itself is much larger than that of Type 996 (5.1 × 4.3 m, tilted back at 10 deg, consisting of 76 slotted-waveguide arrays, and with a gain of 41 dB; beam dimensions are 1.4 × 1.5 degrees).

Type 996 seen from behind and below. (A. Wetback)

♦ **Types 1002/1003**

These types are the standard British submarine radars. Type 1002 is the X-band (9650 MHz) radar for *Porpoise*-class and later diesel-electric submarines. Type 1003 is the standard surface-search radar on board British nuclear submarines of the *Valiant, Swiftsure,* and *Resolution* classes. Compared to Type 1002, 1003 omits the periscope-attack (range only) and limited-air-search features. Recent British diesel-electric and nuclear submarines are equipped with the later Type 1006 (see below) or with the new Type 1007.

Type 1002 is descended from a series of experimental postwar British submarine radars, Types 973, 1000, and 1001. They were developed to replace the late wartime Type 267PW, which used two separate antennas, a P-band (214-MHz) air-search (airguard, in British parlance) antenna and a separate X-band (seaguard) unit. There was no periscope ranging radar. A postwar project

for an X-band periscope radar, initially modeled on the U.S. ST, led to the design of Type 973, tested in October 1951. This radar was rejected because the transmitter/receiver at the base of the periscope was unsatisfactory. The next stage was to integrate Type 973 with Type 267PW (using a common control panel, but different transmitters) as Type 1000, which was tested on board HMS *Thermopylae* in November 1952. The next step was to replace both the air- and sea-search antennas of 267PW with a new X-band antenna, so that the previous pair of radar masts could be replaced by a single mast. This new set, which was intended for the first postwar British diesel-electric submarines, was designated Type 1001. Type 1002 has better range accuracy, and uses a new display and ranging system.

Operational requirements, as stated in 1952, were: detection of a 15 square-meter air target at a range of 8 nm at 5000 ft (the requirement had been 15 nm at 10,000 ft); bearing accuracy of 0.25 degrees; range accuracy (for the periscope radar) of 25 yards at 6000 yards, with information transmitted directly to the torpedo's fire-control computer. The main antenna was not to exceed 4 ft in width, and it was to be stowable while the submarine proceeded at periscope depth at 12 kts. In 1952 it was expected that the 4 ft × 8 in cheese antenna, which would be tilted up at an angle of 3 degrees, would have a gain of 33 dB.

♦ **Type 1006**

Band: X (9445 MHz) **Beam:** (a) 1 × 18 deg (b) 0.75 × 18 deg
Peak Power: 25 kW **Gain:** (a) 31 dB (b) 34 dB
Pulse Width: (i) 0.8 or 0.25 (ii) 0.75 microsec
PRF: (i) 1600 (ii) 800 pps **Scan Rate:** 24 rpm
Antenna Dimensions: (a) 2.4 m (b) 3.1 m

A *Leander*-class frigate shows a Type-1006 surface-search radar (the slotted waveguide) below her Type-994 "quarter cheese" short-range air/surface-search antenna. The masthead array is UA-13, and below it are UA-8 and -9. The "sword" on the right just below Type 994 is a standard Anglo-American intercept antenna. This photograph was taken in 1986. (Author)

The navalized Kelvin-Hughes 19/9A replaces Type 975. Type 1006 was developed beginning in 1969, in response to an Admiralty request for a solid-state successor to vacuum-tube systems, with sea trials in 1970 on board HMS *Grenville* and *Otus*. Production began in 1971. This radar is now being replaced by Type 1007.

Both antennas, Outfits AZJ and AZK, are slotted waveguides, and there is also a submarine version. The PPI can also display helicopter transponder data, for ASW. Range scales are 0.5, 0.75, 1.5, 3, 6, 12, 24, 48, and 64 nm.

◆ Type 1007

Replacement for Type 1006, Type 1007 is a Kelvin-Hughes Series 1600 + Red Pac, a navigational radar with manual plot. Type 1007 was developed in 1971, adopted by the Royal Navy in 1984, and also bought for the Norwegian *Ula*-class submarines. This radar operates in X-band with a peak power of 25 kW.

◆ Type 1010

Type 1010 is a Cossor IFF interrogator (Mk X system). It can be mounted either independently or on the antenna of a radar, such as Type 965. A typical Cossor interrogator antenna, CS.381, is 3.35 m long. The combination of Types 1010 and 1011 supersedes the earlier interrogator-transponder combination, Types 944 and 954.

Some British warships carry an independent IFF interrogator, Type 1010. This slotted waveguide is visible atop the mainmast of a *Leander*-class frigate. The radome alongside contains a SCOT satellite antenna; below it is a Corvus chaff launcher. (Author)

◆ Type 1011

Type 1011 is an IFF transponder (Mk X system).

◆ Type 1013

Type 1013 is a lightweight, nonmagnetic IFF Mk X transponder, the Royal Navy version of the Cossor IFF 2720 airborne set. Type 1013 is carried by British minecraft.

◆ Type 1022

Type 1022 was described as a STIR, a combined Surveillance-and-Target-Indication Radar, to replace both 965 and 992Q. 1022 combines a new Marconi antenna with a Dutch LW-08 L-band radar transceiver. Type 1022 was first installed on board the carrier *Invincible* in 1979. An all-British STIR, Type 1030, was scheduled for operation in 1985, using a very similar antenna, but that STIR was canceled, with the associated Sea Dart Mk 2 (GWS.31), in the summer of 1980.

The Marconi antenna is probably Outfit AZV, with a squint-less feed (an array of forty feed horns) and a single-curvature reflector. Beamwidth is 2.3 degrees (the vertical beam is csc2). The feed is derived from that of the land-based S625 radar, although the reflector is different. Reportedly Type 1030 would have used two such antennas arranged back to back, and a single-sided Type 1031 was proposed. This antenna was first tested on board the frigate *Grenville* and was first installed on board the Type-42 destroyer *Exeter* (the first Batch-II ship) in 1978.

Type 1022 on board HMS *Ark Royal*, 1986, seen from below and behind. The squintless feed array of horns is visible. (Author)

Type 1022 from the front. (A. Wetback)

◆ MESAR

MESAR is an ARE (Admiralty Research Establishment)/Plessey single-array electronically scanned S-band radar. The designation means Multifunction Electronically Scanned Adaptive Radar. MESAR is an octagonal array of 1060 radiating elements, 918 of which can be elementary radiators rather than the usual phase shifters. The array is inclined at an angle of 15 degrees, and the beam (3.1 degrees on transmit, and 3.4 degrees on receive at broadside) scans through 45 degrees to each side in bearing and between -35 and $+37.5$ degrees in elevation; and the array can compensate for a 15-degree roll. Individual elements are $40 \times 95 \times 10$ mm (weight 135 g).

MESAR is a technology demonstrator rather than a prototype for an operational radar. Development began in 1982, and trials are scheduled for 1989. The key future technology, as reflected in the MESAR design, seems to be the active array. In theory each element of the antenna should be provided with its own receiver, for the fullest sort of monopulse operation. That provision is impractical; in MESAR, low-power microwave networks combine groups of array elements into the 16 subantennas actually used for adaptive beam-forming. Each such subarray has its own receiver controllable in both amplitude and phase, and monopulse patterns can be formed by comparing the outputs of the subarrays.

Beams are formed digitally; Plessey claims that MESAR will be unique in its ability to null (shut out) jamming signals, even in the main beam, and that MESAR can reject up to 15 jammers per face.

MESAR array. (Plessey)

◆ OTH Radar

The Admiralty Research Establishment has tested a shipboard OTH radar system on board the Royal Fleet Auxiliary *Grey Rover*, achieving ranges as great as 100 km. Reportedly that range was achieved by coupling special signal processors to the ship's high-frequency radio system. HF signals commonly propagate well beyond the horizon, and there is always some backscatter. Reportedly the trick is to set up an interference pattern between the outgoing and back-scattered waves. That interference might indicate the presence of a target, but apparently no ship is large enough to provide sufficiently accurate beams for much more than sheer warning.

Existing HF over-the-horizon radar arrays are far too large for ship installation; typically, too, the receive and transmit arrays have to be widely separated because wavelengths are so long that otherwise they interfere. Reportedly the British experiments are proceeding toward a bistatic mode in which reception and transmission would be on board separate ships.

Long-wavelength radar is now attractive because it is unlikely that any stealth technology can be effective at such wavelengths. It is not clear that OTH radar wavelengths are needed, although some years ago Australian scientists claimed that the Jindalee OTH radar could surely detect incoming stealthy aircraft. It is entirely possible that the longer (but still quite conventional) wavelengths from a system that can be practicably installed on the hull of an airship would suffice. That argument was made in 1988 in support of continuing the U.S. Navy's airship program.

The British program is not a ducting or surface-wave radar, which can detect targets at but not well above the sea surface. Stealthy aircraft and missiles might well approach at high, rather than low, altitude, to enjoy the aerodynamic fruits of their design. Many navies currently use ducting to target anti-ship missiles beyond the horizon, but that phenomenon is associated with short wavelengths such as X-band.

◆ AWS-1/AWS-2

Band: S (2880 and 3020 MHz) **Beam:** 1.5 × 40 deg
Peak Power: 750 kW **Gain:** 32 dB
Pulse Width: (i) 0.35 (ii) 1.5 microsec
PRF: (i) 1000 (ii) 400 pps **Scan Rate:** 10–12 or 20 rpm
Antenna Dimensions: 16 ft × 6 ft 6 in
Antenna Weight: 576 lbs

The Ghanaian corvette *Kromantse* uses AWS-1 as her air-search radar. The small slotted waveguide serves a Type-978 navigational set. This ship and her sister are armed with single 4-inch and 40-mm guns and with Squid. (U.S. Naval Institute)

These private-venture Plessey air-search radars are based on the land-based AR-1 and AR-15. The first prototype AWS-1 appeared in 1960. The very similar AWS-2 was begun in 1965, the prototype appearing in 1970; it is described as the first radar to go to sea with a digital MTI processor. Claimed range on a "small aircraft" is 60 nm.

AWS-2 is a frequency-diversity radar with modular signal processing, so that more sophisticated versions could be built up for larger ships. In the simplest form, AWS-2 had two transceivers feeding a single display. A more sophisticated version used a stabilized antenna. Either version could be fitted with a digital MTI signal analyzer, to compensate for ship motion and to help reject low-altitude (or overland) clutter. Plessey described the antenna coverage as gapless, from low altitude (vs. sea-skimmers) to relatively high altitudes (because of the shape of the fan beam).

◆ AWS-3

Band: S **Beam:** 1.45 × 40 deg
Peak Power: 1100 kW **Gain:** 32 dB
Pulse Width: 20 microsec (compressed to 0.1)
PRF: 380 pps **Scan Rate:** 10 or 20 rpm
Antenna Dimensions: 5.055 × 1.980 m
Antenna Weight: 4190 lbs

AWS-3 is a pulse-compression development of AWS-2, with increased transmitter power. Range limits are about 140 nm and 100,000 ft. The antenna is stabilized, and signal processing includes MTI. The radar is frequency agile.

In 1980, AWS-3 was described as a long-range, high-power development of AWS-5.

◆ AWS-4

Band: S **Beam:** 1.9 × 30 deg
Pulse Width: (i) 1 (ii) 0.3 microsec **PRF:** (i) 680 (ii) 1360 pps
Scan Rate: (i) 10 (ii) 20 rpm **Antenna Dimensions:** 3.8 × 0.8 m
Antenna Weight: 990 lbs (unstabilized version) or 2640 lbs (stabilized version)

AWS-4 is a further development of the AWS-1 series with a new antenna, a wide-band tunable magnetron transmitter, and pulse compression. There are two receivers, one matched to plot extractor requirements and one with various ECCM fixes. The radar can also be fitted with two parallel transmitters, for frequency diversity. AWS-4 was intended to provide AWS-2 performance at half the weight. Claimed detection range is 80–110 km on a 4 square-meter helicopter, using the long pulse (maximum range). Using the short pulse for best resolution, AWS-4 can detect the same target at 85 km (height 9000 rather than 12,000 m).

Combined with the Type 993 antenna, this radar forms Type 994; and combined with the World War II Type 293 antenna, AWS-4 forms the commercial Type 294. There is also a lightweight (450-kg) linear-array antenna for installation in fast patrol craft (as AWS-4B). Maximum range is 70 km (8200 m target altitude).

This radar is currently in service with the Royal Navy, the Royal New Zealand Navy, the Royal Norwegian Coast Guard, the Sultan of Oman's Navy, the Republic of Kenya Navy, and the Royal Canadian Navy. Canada uses the antenna in her SPS-503. Britain and New Zealand use Type 994.

◆ AWS-5

Band: S

Beam: High beam is 1.5 × 30 deg, directed upward at 45 degrees; low beam is 40 degrees wide in elevation, directed upward at 5 degrees. AWS-5B antenna: 1.5 × 32 deg (azimuth squint less than 1 deg over the operating range).

Peak Power: 58 kW (mean power 1.3 kW)

Pulse Width: (i) 0.4 (ii) 20 microsec (typically transmitted in sequence) **PRF:** 1100 pps

Scan Rate: 15 or 30 rpm **Antenna Weight:** 2640 lbs

AWS-5 at the foremasthead of the Danish frigate *Peter Tordenskjold,* with a NATO Sea Sparrow fire-control radar (Mk 91) aft. The two slotted waveguides are probably Decca TM 1229s (Skanter 009). (L&L Van Ginderen)

Transmitter data are estimated from those of the Watchman ground radar (see below).

AWS-5 incorporates a new dual-beam (high- and low-cover) stabilized antenna, essentially the AWS-4 double-curvature unit plus a squintless linear array canted back to provide cover above 60 degrees elevation. With the low beam, a 4 square-meter target can be detected at about 85 nm and 50,000 ft; a 0.1 square-meter target (such as an antiship missile) at about 40 nm and 25,000 ft. Like AWS-4, AWS-5 is a pulse-compression radar (for good range resolution). Pulses are coded for clutter and jamming resistance. AWS-5 has programmable frequency agility, and the IFF is integrated with the main antenna (IFF signals are fed directly into the antenna). The transmitter is coherent, so the radar can extract digital MTI information from returning pulses.

There are two pulse lengths: 0.4 microseconds for high resolution, and a longer 20-microsecond pulse that is compressed to 0.4 microseconds on reception. The two signals are separated by using a different frequency for each.

The TWT transmitter allows for considerable frequency diversity. One advantage of the dual-beam design is that the high beam is clutter-free: unlike a conventional fan beam, the high beam does not touch the sea. Processing features include skew correction for fast targets (i.e., correction of the error in bearing because of the motion of the antenna while the echo is returning).

The radar is available both in high power (HP) and medium power (MP) versions, the latter using the AWS-9 transmitter, the former the Watchman (coast-surveillance) transmitter.

AWS-5A was sold to the Danish and Nigerian Navies. A lightweight version, AWS-5B, employs a stabilized linear array antenna (1280 lbs, 1.5 × 32 degree beam). Claimed performance: detection of an aircraft at 40 nm at 100,000 ft. AWS-5C is a land-based version using a low-beam horn and reflector (range 60+ nm, because of the higher gain of the antenna, and elevation up to 40 deg). AWS-5D is a stabilized version of AWS-5C for ship installation, with two-speed scanning.

Development began in 1972, and design work in 1975, when the radar was announced. These radars have been installed on board Danish *Nils Juel*-class corvettes and one Nigerian frigate. The new British Type 996 (AWS-9) is partly based on this radar.

◆ AWS-6 (Dolphin)

Band: C **Beam:** beamwidth 1.5 deg (See below.)
Peak Power: 49 kW **Gain:** 29/26 dB (low/high beams)
Pulse Width: 0.1 and 4.3 microsec **Scan Rate:** 30 or 60 rpm
Antenna Dimensions: 2.6 m wide (102 in)
Antenna Weight: 520 kg, including mounting (1150 lbs)

AWS-6 (Dolphin). (Plessey)

Like AWS-5, AWS-6 is a dual-beam frequency-agile radar that uses a coherent (TWT) transmitter. Its beam is narrow enough for target indication, and the radar can be used for that purpose in conjunction with a very-long-range air-search set. The transmitter has a very broad band frequency agility. Radar contacts are automatically extracted, using CFAR processing. The pulses are frequency-coded and pulse-compressed; a high pulse-compression ratio was chosen for better target detection in chaff. The long pulse width listed above (4.3 microseconds) is a frequency-swept pulse for target indication; the short pulse is for navigation and splash spotting. There is also an optional long-range mode using a 10-microsecond pulse, in which the radar scans at 30 rpm. Pulse patterns include fixed frequency, scan-to-scan frequency agility, burst-to-burst agility, and pulse-to-pulse agility. There are four operating modes: two for anti-missile defense, and two for extended-range surveillance using the optional 30/60 rpm dual-rotation-rate version of the basic radar.

The main reflector is center-fed by a squintless linear array, as in Type 1022; a second squintless array provides a high beam. This combination provides much smaller sidelobes than a conventional horn-fed reflector because radiation at the antenna edges is better controlled. The manufacturer claims further that the use of independent beams makes jamming difficult, and that random frequency agility forces the jammer to spread out its power. The main beam of the radar covers all angles between 0 and 20 degrees, with csc2 shaping up to 40 degrees. The separate illuminator extends coverage to 70 degrees of elevation. The antenna as a whole is stabilized against roll (within 25 degrees) and pitch (within 10 degrees). Total weight of antenna and mounting is 520 kg; below-decks weight is another 1340 kg (2953 lbs). Average power input is 21.9 kVA.

Under the designation Dolphin, AWS-6 is part of the Plessey-Contraves Seaguard antiaircraft system (see the entry under Switzerland above). A larger-antenna version (in a radome) was supplied for Danish fishery-protection vessels, and there is also a single-beam target-indication version.

AWS-6 at the masthead of the Danish frigate *Ingolf*. (Gilbert)

◆ AWS-7

This Plessey S-band radar was announced in 1985 as the first fully solid-state radar (i.e., using neither magnetron nor TWS) in its frequency range. AWS-7 can be supplied with either a single- or a dual-beam antenna.

The power-amplifier stage consists of 40–70 identical modules operating in parallel, each supplying 20 kW, for a total peak power of about 800 kW to 1.4 MW. The modules are mounted in a carousel, and they can be replaced even while the radar is operating. They need no special high-voltage power supply, and no special liquid cooling (as in the case with a conventional single high-powered tube).

The AWS-7 designation was applied earlier to an AWS-2 with a higher-gain antenna.

◆ AWS-8

AWS-8 was described in 1980 as an AWS-5 with a special low-flier and surface-target detection antenna.

◆ AWS-9

See Type 996 above.

◆ AWS-10

AWS-10 is a projected radar based on MESAR.

◆ Decca TM 1226C/1229C/RM Series

> **Band:** X (3 cm: 9410 MHz)   **Beam:** 1.2 deg
> **Peak Power:** 25 kW   **Gain:** 30 dB
> **Pulse Width:** (i) 0.05 (ii) 0.25 (iii) 1.0 microsec
> **Scan Rate:** 28 rpm
> **Antenna Dimensions:** 72 in slotted waveguide (The same radar, with a 108-in antenna, is TM 1229C; beamwidth is then 0.8 deg.)

This Decca commercial pulse-compression radar is used as a small-ship search/target-indication set and as a secondary (surface-search) set on board larger ships. Decca's system is the basis of the Norwegian MSI-80S system. There is also an alternative S-band 30-kW version using a 12-foot antenna. In the designation, TM means true motion (display) and C means clearscan; 1226 means a 12-inch PPI and a 6-ft antenna. Similarly, AC1629C would be an anticollision radar with a 16-inch clearscan display and a 9-ft antenna. Clearscan itself is a form of clutter suppression. There are nine range scales: 0.25–48 nm, with short pulse on 0.25 nm, short or medium on the next three scales, medium or long pulse on the next three, and only long pulse on the last two. Resolution is 10 yds on the 0.5-nm scale with a 10 square-meter target. Bearing accuracy is better than 1 degree.

Radars designated RM (e.g., RM1226C) show relative rather than true motion and are, therefore, somewhat simpler and less expensive. Many warships combine a TM and an RM radar.

Users (for main radars on patrol boats) include the navies of Abu Dhabi, Argentina, Belgium, Brunei, Ecuador, Egypt, France, Iran, Indonesia, Libya, Malaysia, the Netherlands, Nigeria, Norway, Oman, Peru, Thailand, and Turkey. This series is one of the world's most widely used radars.

◆ Marconi 400 Series (and Sea Cobra)

Sea Cobra combines a Marconi 400-series radar with a Breda gun mount. (Marconi)

> **Band:** X (8–16 GHz)   **Beam:** 3.5 deg
> **Peak Power:** 2.5 kW   **Scan Rate:** 60 rpm in surveillance mode
> **Antenna Weight:** 168 kg (350 kg overall)

This new series of gunfire-control radars was announced in 1983. The antenna is an offset front-fed parabola that uses vertical polarization. A frequency-agile TWT transmitter provides MTI, and tracking is by monopulse. Marconi has employed a patented method for reducing angular errors due to multipath reflection off the sea surface; that method may be similar to that described by Thomson-CSF in connection with Crotale Navale (see entry under SAMs below).

The transmitter is unusual in that it covers a full octave in frequency, pulse-to-pulse frequency agility over this range being used to reduce multipath effects.

In the surveillance mode, the radar scans at 60 rpm. It tracks with an accuracy better than 1 mrad in angle (RMS) and 5 m in range (RMS). Elevation is −30 to +85 degrees.

Instrumented range: surveillance, 12 km; autotracking, 10 km. These ranges can be increased to 30 km if the radar is used to control medium-caliber guns.

The Breda-Marconi Sea Cobra integrates the Breda twin 30-mm gun with a Marconi 440 radar fire control.

◆ Marconi SNW-10

Band: P (1.5 m)   **Beam:** 19 deg
Peak Power: 450 kW   **Pulse Width:** 3.8 microsec
PRF: 250/500 pps   **Scan Rate:** 10 rpm
Antenna Dimensions: 14 × 7 ft   **Antenna Weight:** 336 lbs

The mattress antenna carries twelve dipoles (4 × 3) in front of a reflecting screen. SNW-10, developed in the 1950s, survives only on board the Chilean *Almirante Williams* class and the Pakistani destroyer *Badr*.

◆ Marconi SNW-20

This slotted-waveguide target-indication radar is installed only in the Chilean *Almirante Williams* class.

◆ Marconi SNG-20

This fire-control radar is found only in the Chilean *Almirante Williams* class.

◆ Marconi ST802

Band: X   **Beam:** 2.4 deg
Peak Power: 150 kW (100 kw at PRF 4400)   **Gain:** 36.5 dB
Pulse Width: (i) 0.33 microsec (ii) 0.67 microsec
PRF: (i) 4400 (MTI) (ii) 3000 (non-MTI) pps
Antenna Dimensions: aperture 1 m (1.4 m in ST858)
Antenna Weight: director 550 kg; double-bay cabinet 690 kg; weapons-control console 450 kg

ST802 is one of a series of Marconi radars (ST802, ST858 land mobile tracker, ST858 instrumentation radar, S810 and S820 shipboard surveillance radars). ST802 and S810 share a 200-kW X-band transmitter; S820 has a 400-kW S-band transmitter. All share a common digital MTI processor.

ST802 is the tracker associated with the S800-series surveillance radars (S810 and S820, below). ST802 is a fully automatic lightweight monopulse tracker; a television camera is mounted alongside. The antenna is a stabilized twist Cassegrain, and there is a second radar channel for shell spotting. Frequency is variable over 900 MHz (i.e., about 10 percent of the base frequency). Peak power is increased to 200 kW in one version.

In the search mode, the radar rotates at 20 rpm, stepping upward by a full beamwidth (2.4 degrees) under computer control to perform low, medium, and high scans. The radar can detect an aircraft at 10,000 ft at 20 km. If any target does appear on the target allocation panel, a button allows the radar to shift to tracking mode.

ST802 is carried, together with S1810, by Egyptian fast patrol boats. There is also a land-based equivalent, ST850, and an ST858 range instrumentation radar. ST801 is an alternative version designed for direct interface with a ship's weapons-system computer. See also the Sapphire fire-control system.

◆ Marconi 805 Series

This series of privately developed tracking radars are designed for a variety of weapons: 805SW, lightweight Seawolf (adopted by the Royal Navy as Type 911); 805SD, lightweight Sea Dart; 805AS, Aspide; and 805SS, Sea Sparrow. Each radar can also control medium- and small-caliber guns. 805SW is a dual-frequency tracker that includes a missile command link. 805SD is a tracker-illuminator incorporating Type 909 and S1800 series components. 805AS was developed in cooperation with Selenia and uses a Selenia illuminator; 805SS uses a Raytheon illuminating transmitter and can control either vertically or horizontally launched missiles.

◆ Marconi S810/S811

Band: X (8.6–9.5 GHz)
Beam: 2.2 × 25 deg (S810P: 2.2 × 4.7 deg; S810: 1.5 × 25 deg beam with alternative 1.8-m antenna)
Peak Power: 180 kW (MTI: 135 kW)
Gain: 29.5 dB (S810P: 33.5 dB)
Pulse Width: 0.67 or 0.33 microsec
PRF: 1500 (4400 for MTI) pps
Scan Rate: 24 rpm (S810P 40 rpm)
Antenna Dimensions: 1.2 m wide (radome diameter 1.7 m; 2.3 m with 1.8-m antenna)
Antenna Weight: 250 kg at masthead (plus 695 kg transmit/receiver)

An Egyptian 6 *October*–class missile boat (with her Otomat racks empty) shows an S810 search radar (in the big radome) and an ST802 fire-control radar (atop the superstructure). (L&L Van Ginderen)

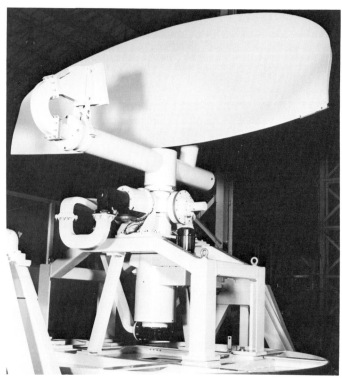

Marconi S810, without its radome. (Marconi)

This lightweight surveillance radar is used on board the Egyptian *October* class (Egyptian-built Komars) and as a secondary radar on board Egyptian *Ramadan*-class missile boats. The antenna is mounted inside a radome. There is an alternative 1.8-m radome (1.5-degree beam, masthead weight not including radome 300 kg rather than 180 kg).

MTI is by a double canceler using shift register storage, i.e., by pulse-to-pulse comparison. In this mode PRF is staggered around 4400 pps to eliminate blind speeds. Instrumented range is then either 10 or 20 km. The transmitter is a tunable magnetron, the operating frequency being motor controlled (i.e., the transmitter is not frequency agile but is adjustable).

S811 is a version without provision for MTI.

Estimated ranges against a 5-square-meter airplane: 28 m at 2000 m altitude (1.2m antenna), 20+ km at 6000 m; with a 1.8-m antenna, 32 km at 3000 m and 25+ km at 8000 m. S810P (for better low-altitude coverage) will detect a 0.1 square-meter target at 15 km.

These radars were announced about 1974.

◆ **Marconi S820**

Band: S tunable in three steps (2.7–3.3 GHz)
Beam: 3.3 × 30 deg   **Peak Power:** 600 kW
Pulse Width: 0.6/1.2 microsec   **PRF:** 1500/750 pps
Scan Rate: 20 or 40 rpm
Antenna Dimensions: 2.4 × 0.9 m (radome diameter 3.3 m)
Antenna Weight: 450 kg approx

The Egyptian patrol boat *El Yarmouk* shows Marconi S820 (forward) and S810 (aft) search radars, both in radomes. At her masthead she carries Cutlass and Matilda ESM; there is also a Cygnus jammer, and there are two Protean chaff mortars. (L&L Van Ginderen)

This radar was designed for large fast patrol boats, as a longer-wavelength alternative to S810/811. The antenna is entirely enclosed in a radome; range is up to 90 km. Optional MTI is available. The magnetron is manually tunable to operate over the 2.7–2.9, or 2.9–3.1, or 3.1–3.3 GHz bands.

Typical range: a 5 square-meter target will be detected at 90 km (5000 m altitude), and height coverage will extend up to 11,000 m.

◆ **Marconi ST1802**

Band: X (8.9–9.5 GHz)   **Beam:** 2.4 deg
Pulse Width: 0.67, 0.3, or 1.0 microsec
PRF: 3000 (non-MTI); 4400 (MTI) pps
Peak Power: 50 kW (average 150 W)   **Gain:** 37 dB
Antenna Dimensions: aperture 1 m
Antenna Weight: 550 kg (director weight)

ST1802 is the weapons-control radar for the S1800 series of small ship weapons systems. ST1802 employs a fully coherent (TWT) transmitter (for pulse-doppler MTI) and enjoys truly random frequency agility. MTI can be switched on and off; presumably that selectability means there are alternative high and low

ST1802 fire-control radar, with optronic back-up. (Marconi)

ST1802SW. (Marconi)

PRF modes, corresponding to the two rated tracking ranges given below.

Data above apply to the 1802AS radar, for Aspide missile control (part of the Albatros 10/0 system), which employs a twist-Cassegrain antenna and a side-mounted television tracker. The radar uses monopulse tracking, and the CW guidance beam is injected directly into its antenna. Maximum tracking range is 40 km (24 km if MTI is used), and maximum slewing rates are 120 deg/sec in train and 50 deg/sec in elevation. Continuous elevation rate (for target acquisition from a two-dimensional search radar) is 20 deg/sec. Elevation limits are −30 and +85 deg. Above-decks weight is 550 kg, plus a total of 1200 kg below decks (including a 650-kg transceiver and processor). These data were released in 1985.

ST1802SW is a Marconi commercial Sea Wolf director radar; at 1900 kg, it is about half the weight of the 805SW that became the Royal Navy's Type 911. Even so, ST1802SW's characteristics are a measure of the requirements imposed by the Sea Wolf system. The tracker uses a gregorian offset feed and is mechanically counterbalanced (for quick tracking) by an optronics head. The separate missile-command transmitter, in a drum-shaped radome, is on the antenna's left side. Antenna and transmitter characteristics match the figures above. Acquisition range is 32 km against a 3 square-meter target, and 13 km on a 0.1 square-meter target.

The associated thermal imager has a 3 × 2 degree field of view.

♦ Marconi ST1805SW Multifire

This advanced Sea Wolf tracker, conceived as a phased-array version of Type 911, was originally developed as part of the British GWS 27 program, now canceled. Multifire is now (1988) a Marconi private venture. ST1805SW operates at X-band (3 cm), using 5000 phase shifters to form an agile 1.5-degree beam scanning through 45 degrees. The stabilized antenna itself can elevate to scan from the zenith down to the horizon. This radar might be used either for low-altitude surveillance or as a multiple target illuminator for semiactive missiles. Total weight is 4500 kg (1500 kg above decks).

♦ Marconi S1810

Band: 3 cm (X-band: 8.6–9.5 GHz) **Beam:** 1.1 × cos2 5–30 deg
Peak Power: 50 kW **Gain:** 36 dB (midband)
Pulse Width: (i) 2 microsec compressed to 0.1 microsec (chirp); (ii) 1 microsec for air search; (iii) 0.2 microsec for surface search
PRF: (i) 2000 (ii and iii) 4000 pps
Scan Rate: 24 (standard, with radome) or 20/60 (lightweight, no radome) rpm
Antenna Dimensions: 2.44 × 0.84 or 1.2 × 0.42 m
Antenna Weight: 640 or 250 kg

S1810 is a small-ship frequency-agile surveillance radar intended for use as part of an S1800 series integrated weapons system. This radar can also be used for coastal surveillance. Typical detection ranges are: aircraft at 45 km (limited by the horizon) and small surface craft at 30 km; free space detection range is 60 km. Marconi claims that the radar can easily detect low-fliers and surface-skimming missiles well beyond engagement range. The light weight (GRP sprayed with a metallic coating) antenna is fully stabilized.

Beamwidth data refer to the larger antenna. The smaller antenna, referred to as a compact system, scans at 24 rpm. Both the standard and the compact radars are housed in spherical radomes. The TWT transmitter is capable of both pulse-burst agility and pulse-to-pulse agility; the transmitter can also be turned on and off easily, to permit radar silence without losing the ability to switch back on. Signal processing includes digital MTI, and the ship's motion (including velocity) is automatically compensated for.

ECCM features include low sidelobes, frequency agility, the ability to discriminate between signals of different PRF (as well as variable pulse length and PRF, and PRF stagger and jitter), sector transmission, a wide-dynamic-range receiver (with image rejection mixer), instantaneous automatic gain control, Dicke fix, and forward or reverse swept gain.

S1810 is the primary radar of the Egyptian *Ramadan* class and also of other fast patrol craft. The S1800 radar series was first publicly discussed in 1978.

♦ Marconi S1820/1821

This S-band search radar uses a TWT transmitter for coherence (digital MTI) and frequency agility. S1820 employs pulse compression (peak power 20 kW). The 2.4-m antenna is stabilized, and it has dual rotation rates. S1821, using the same transmitter and a 4-meter antenna (for greater range), is used by the Canadian Navy as SPS-503. Scan rate is 24 rpm, and csc2 coverage is up to 30 degrees.

♦ Marconi S1824/1825/1826

These combined S-band pulse-compressed air- and surface-search radars are differentiated by their antennas. S1824 uses a squintless linear-feed (5-m aperture, 34-degree vertical beam-width). S1825 uses a Cassegrain similar to that of S1821. S1826 is a dual-beam unit combining the two, the upper and lower beams being time- and frequency-shared.

♦ Marconi S1840

A new surveillance radar announced in 1983, S1840 was presumably the unsuccessful competitor for the Type 996 contract. S1840 operates in C-band (5 cm) and uses a squintless waveguide transmitter and a series of 16 strip-line planar arrays for reception. They are used to preform nine receiving beams. Each pulse consists of a long FM chirp plus a short pulse at an offset frequency. The latter detects at short range. Both MTI and non-MTI processing are available.

♦ Racal-Decca 2459 F/I

Band:	S (3.2 cm)	X (10 cm)
Beam:	2 × 30 deg	0.8 × 20 deg
Peak Power:	30 kW	25/75 kW
Gain:	26 dB	32 dB
Pulse Width:	(i) 1 microsec	(i) 1 microsec
	(ii) 0.25 microsec	(ii) 0.25 microsec
	(iii) 0.05 microsec	(iii) 0.05 microsec
PRF:	(i) 825 pps	(i) 825 pps
	(ii) 1650 pps	(ii) 1650 pps
	(iii) 3300 pps	(iii) 3300 pps
Antenna Dimensions:	12 ft	9-ft aperture

Racal-Decca 2459 F/I radar on board the Dutch replenishment ship *Poolster*. (Racal)

2459 F/I is a dual-band air/surface-search and navigational radar; the designation derives from the ECM band names (F and I). Returns on both bands appear together on the single display, and a master controller feeds the most appropriate combination of processed video to the weapons-control stations, which may include both surface and antiaircraft (and helicopter control). The use of a single rotating unit (X-band antenna atop S-band antenna) saves weight on top and makes for a clear arc for both frequencies. Note that timing and pulse length (and gain, swept gain/sea clutter, and rain differentiation) are provided by a frequency-independent unit, both antennas feeding into a single signal processor.

The S-band beam is centered on an elevation angle of 15 deg, the X-band beam pointed horizontally (for surface search). An alternative horizontal scanning S-band antenna can be provided.

Estimated range: 25 nm on a large airplane, 15 nm on a medium airplane.

♦ Racal-Decca 2490/2690 Series

Band:	X	S
Beam:	(i) 1.3 × 23 deg	–
	(ii) 0.8 × 23 deg	–
	–	(iii) 2 × 30 deg
Peak Power:	25 kW	30 kW
Pulse Width:	(a) 0.05 microsec	(a) 0.05 microsec
	(b) 0.25 microsec	(b) 0.25 microsec
	(c) 1.0 microsec	(c) 1.0 microsec

PRF:	(a) 1300 pps	(a) 1300 pps
	(b) 1300 pps	(b) 1300 pps
	(c) 650 pps	(c) 650 pps
Gain:	(i) 30 dB	(i) 30 dB
	(ii) 32 dB	(ii) 32 dB
	(iii) 26 dB	(iii) 26 dB
Scan Rate:	25 rpm	22–26 rpm
Antenna Width:	(i) 6 ft	(i) 6 ft
	(ii) 9 ft	(ii) 9 ft
	(iii) 12 ft	(iii) 12 ft
Antenna Weight:	(i) 34.3 kg	(i) 34.3 kg
	(ii) 44 kg	(ii) 44 kg
	(iii) 219 kg	(iii) 219 kg

These radars are the natural successors to the 1629 and similar Decca radars, which are so often used on board both fast patrol boats and larger vessels. These radars can be switched with the Master Series radars (see below). Alternative forms of signal processing include ARPA (automatic radar plotting aid) and AC (true motion, i.e., anticollision). The ARPA versions can carry up to 20 tracks, acquiring targets at ranges of 0.5–20 nm and tracking between 0.25 and 20 nm. Targets are continuously tracked after they are acquired and are retained on the display for 5 out of 10 consecutive scans. Plots are extracted by a limited-area analysis system (a preset window), the gain within the window being set according to expected target size (i.e., target strength) and the local measured noise level. The track table is assembled in true motion format.

The first two digits in the designation refer to the size (diagonally measured) of the rectangular raster-scan display. Like the Japanese Furuno radars described with the U.S. entries, this Racal-Decca series employ a multilevel display, providing synthetic graphics in combination with the rastered PPI. The 24-inch display is monochrome; the 26-inch display is in color. In both cases, the display is a standard high-resolution television type (819 lines, 64-Hz raster). The image is refreshed often enough to eliminate all apparent flicker. In place of the afterglow of conventional PPI tubes, these radars generate trails of specific duration to assist in picture interpretation. The operator selects true or relative motion, and this type of display does not "smear" when the operator changes mode, e.g., from "north up" to "ship's course up." Tracks are displayed as vectors.

Eight video maps are stored in the system's memory.

Minimum range is 30 m on a 10 square-meter target using the short pulse, with the antenna at a height of 4.5 m (14.75 ft). Range discrimination is 30 m on the 0.75-nm scale. Scales are 0.25, 0.5, 0.75, 1.5, 3.0, 6.0, 12.0, 24.0, 48.0, 96.0, and 192.0 (optional) nm.

◆ Racal-Decca Master Series (1290 and 1690 Series)

These X- and S-band radars preceded the 2490/2690 series. The first two digits indicate the diameter of the circular PPI. As in the 2490/2690, the X-band radar operates at a peak power of 25 kW and uses either a 6- or a 9-ft antenna. The S-band radar operates at 30 kW, with a 12-ft antenna. Prefixes indicate the display chosen: AC for anticollision (true motion), RM for relative motion, and ARPA for automatic plot extraction (surface ATD). The system can carry up to 20 target tracks, and up to nine markers can be positioned to monitor the bearing of a potential threat vessel. The markers are all short constant-bearing lines pointing back to own-ship: an echo that remains on the marker is closing at constant bearing and is on a collision course. The system also easily measures closest point of approach.

There are ten range scales, from 0.25 to 96 nm.

Racal-Decca offers a bright color PPI, the color being used to denote echo characteristics, e.g., orange for targets, black for tracks, white for ancillary data, and red for a guard zone. This display is raster scanned using digital scan conversion (DSC) and refreshing the picture 30 times a second, so fast that the eye detects no flicker. The color PPI is bright enough to be used in daylight.

◆ Watchman/Guardsman

Watchman and Guardsman are Plessey's coast-defense radars. Watchman has been selected by the British Ministry of Defense, and Guardsman has been exported. The S-band Watchman can detect a 1 square-meter target at 148 km (30 km at low altitude), and it can track over 100 targets simultaneously. The Watchman's transmitter is a high-powered TWT using pulse compression. Characteristics of the air-search version: peak power 58 kW; pulse pattern 0.4 microsec short pulse followed by 20 microsec long pulse (compressed to 0.4 microsec); average power 1.3 kW (implying a PRF of about 1100 pps; there is also an 840-pps mode); scan rate 12 or 15 rpm. Range on a 1 square-meter target is 100 or 110 nm. The air-search version uses a dual-beam antenna similar in form to early AWS-series naval radars. There are also a transportable air-search version and a coastal version with special signal processing for surface and low-flying targets.

The C-band Guardsman is based on the Plessey AWS-6, and in at least one form Guardsman uses much the same antenna as that in the Contraves Skyguard system. Scan rate, however, is 15, 30, or 60 rpm. Maximum range on a 3 square-meter target is 55 nm, and the beam is 1.5 degrees wide.

RADAR INTEGRATION

◆ British Radar Plot Extractors

Radar plot extractors are, in U.S. parlance, radar-video converters. Those in current service are the Ferranti LFX and LAX introduced in the early 1970s, associated with radars of Types 965, 992, and 1006. These systems are all semiautomatic: as in the U.S. NTDS, the associated combat system performs rate-aided tracking based on a series of initial plots, which the operator confirms. Further details of LAX can be found in the discussion of the British ADAWS combat system in the Surveillance and Control section of this book. These systems would be termed ATDs in the U.S. Navy.

The great drawback of the British systems is that the operator must still process large numbers of individual radar contacts, deciding which subsequent ones are properly associated with earlier ones to form tracks. That association can be difficult in a very cluttered environment: hence the need for automatic correlation of individual contacts to form tracks. The Royal Navy calls such systems radar automatic track extractors (RATEs), which are equivalent to the U.S. ADT.

The first experimental British RATE system was developed by Thorn-EMI and ARE (Admiralty Research Establishment) Portsdown in the late 1970s; that experiment led, in turn, to three production systems: LFA (for Type 996), LFB (for Type 1022, for which a contract has not yet been awarded), and LFC (for Types 1006/1007). These RATEs will appear on board ships now under construction and will also be retrofitted to ships already in service. At least in the case of LFC, the system combines radar plots with information from the radar transponder (Outfit RRB) used to track the ship's ASW helicopter.

There is currently no British IADT equivalent to the U.S. SYS-1 or -2.

OPTRONIC SYSTEMS

◆ EPO 409/010

Evershed Power Optics's Optical Fire Director is a lightweight remote-control director head for fast attack boats and smaller craft. It weighs less than 75 kg exclusive of the optronic sensors and the below-decks control console. Autotracking is available as an option.

◆ Evershed 429

Displayed at RNEE 1983, this system carries a Marconi day/low-light-level television camera and a thermal imager.

◆ ROD

Laurence Scott's Remote Optronic Director is a remote-controlled device stabilized in line of sight. Control is by joystick, or ROD can be slaved to another director for target acquisition. ROD incorporates memory tracking for use in bad or interrupted visibility. The stabilized platform can carry 150 kg (75 kg on either side of the training head) of sensors, typically an Ericsson laser range-finder, Ericsson IR camera, and Marconi TV tracker. Total weight exclusive of sensors is 155 kg, and elevation limits are −30 and +85 degrees.

ROD was first displayed in 1980.

A very lightweight development of the Laurence Scott ROD was announced in 1981. The director weighs 45 kg and carries a 45-kg optronic payload, typically an Ericsson laser range-finder and a Marconi low-light-level television. Height is 620 mm, and typical train and elevation rates are 45 deg/sec. Elevation limits are −30 and +85 degrees.

Like ROD, this director is joystick-controlled and can autotrack.

SUBMARINE PERISCOPES

Barr & Stroud is responsible for submarine optical periscopes.

◆ **CH84/85/86**

CH84 is the attack periscope of the *Trafalgar* and *Upholder* classes; the other two are related. Foreign sales include the new Australian submarines.

These periscopes often carry keypads on both sides of the binocular eyepiece so that the officer at the periscope can transmit periscope data to his fire-control system. The optics are arranged to reduce vibrations due to high-speed running (by splitting the optical path at the point at which the periscope enters the submarine's sail) and are quasi-binocular, to reduce eyestrain. The periscope can be fitted with an image intensifier, interposed between the head and the eyepiece, and also with a laser range-finder accurate to within 10 meters. The image intensifier, which uses an additional 110-mm (4.3-in) diameter window at the top of the main tube, provides a gain in luminosity equivalent to a factor of 30,000, the resulting scene resembling one seen in bright starlight. Alternatively, the periscope can carry an IR camera (thermal imager) displaying its image in the eyepiece at the bottom of the periscope tube.

A television camera can be fitted in the rear of the ocular box (i.e., opposite the eyepiece), transmitting the image as seen by the man at the periscope to a remote monitor, which may be connected to a video recorder (permitting the scene to be viewed at leisure). This arrangement is an approach to optronics, but only that, since the image is displayed in the eyepiece and only then picked up by an analog camera. In the case of a thermal imager, the image can be relayed directly to the remote monitor.

Relative bearing is taken from an optical encoder in the periscope crosshead, and the left eyepiece can display the corresponding true bearing. If the laser range-finder is fitted, its range data are displayed in the eyepiece. Otherwise, a stadimeter is used, and a target's range is computed automatically (given that the target's height is keyed in manually on a remote unit).

The main tube's diameter is 254 mm (10 inches), with a 70-mm upper tube (about 2.75 inches); total height is about 14 m (about 46 feet). Available magnifications are 1.5 and 6; corresponding fields of view are 32 and 6 degrees. The IR camera, when fitted, operates in the 8–13-micron band.

Existing earlier search periscopes are types CH74, 75, 77, and 81. Barr & Stroud offers an image intensifier, for night operations, suitable for such periscopes; the company also offers a laser range-finder. This modification was made in at least one case, that of the Canadian *Oberon*-class submarines. Their search-and-attack periscopes were fitted with television cameras and light intensifiers. The other likely candidates for such modification were the Australian and Chilean *Oberon*s.

◆ **CK34/35/36**

Barr & Stroud's current standard search periscope, CK34 is for the *Trafalgar* and *Upholder* classes; the others are modified versions. Operation is quasi-binocular with four magnifications (1.5, 3, 6, 12 power; corresponding fields of view are 24,

12, 6, and 3 degrees). The periscope carries a sextant, the new AHPS 4 (artificial horizon periscope sextant). This device automatically prints out the observed altitude, bearing, and time of observation. As in the case of the imager in the attack periscope (and in this one), this capability is one step away from full integration with other submarine systems: the sextant could, at least in theory, feed the submarine's digital navigation subsystem directly.

As in the case of the attack periscopes, the image in the eyepiece can be captured by a television camera for display on a remote monitor. Overall tube diameter is 254 mm (10 inches), and height is about 14 m (46 ft).

◆ **Optronic Masts**

Barr & Stroud has developed an optronic masthead carrying an imaging IR camera, a television camera, ESM, and communications. Diameter is about 340 mm (13.4 inches) but can be reduced to 220 mm (about 8.7 inches) if a reduced elevation (up to a 50-degree limit) is accepted. This masthead has been selected for the *Vanguard*-class Trident missile submarine.

Plessey now offers its own optronic periscope on a nonpenetrating mast originally developed for submarine communications.

FIRE-CONTROL SYSTEMS

◆ **GWS 20**

The optical Sea Cat director carries a pair of aimer's binoculars. The director is pushed around to the approximate target bearing (using a follow-the-pointer system) and then locked onto this bearing. The aimer inside can elevate and traverse his binoculars, and he has right- and left-hand pistol grips, one of which carries a joystick controlling the missile.

◆ **GWS 21**

This Sea Cat missile director uses the Type 262 close-range radar. GWS 21 is a missile equivalent of MRS 8. The director is an open-topped cylinder carrying an aimer and a director officer. There is a secondary optical sight.

GWS 21 was an interim system, placed in service while GWS 22, the full blind-fire type, was being developed. The radar is used to acquire and track the target automatically.

◆ **GWS 22**

MRS 3, with a modified (Type 904) radar, was adapted to Sea Cat control. The enclosed director-officer's blast hood of MRS 3 is replaced by an open platform carrying binoculars, and there is no director-aimer's position; the sole occupant of the director slews it into tracking position. GWS 22 entered service in 1962.

Sea Cat and two of its guidance systems: the launcher, with missiles, is at left; the GWS 22 director (Type-904 radar) is at the center of the photograph; and a Dutch M40-series director is at the right. This equipment was on board British and Dutch *Leander*-class frigates lying alongside at Portsmouth, 1979. The big radar at the left is Type 965, and that at right is the Dutch LW-02, which the Royal Navy considered buying instead of 965. (Author)

◆ **MRS 3**

This medium-caliber fire-control system was adapted from the U.S. Mk 56. The standard postwar British medium-gun control system, MRS 3 is distinguishable by the projection rising from its roof, the director-officer's blast hood. The window on the front of the director indicates the director-aimer's position, with the Type 903 antenna alongside. Development began in 1948, and MRS 3 entered service in 1958.

MRS 3 director, HMS *Diamond*, resembles the U.S. Mk 56. The radar is Type 903. (A. Wetback)

◆ **MRS 8**

This short-range antiaircraft fire-control system uses the Type 262 radar and evolved from the earlier CRBFD (close-range blind-fire director). MRS 8 could control 40-mm, 4-inch, or 4.5-inch guns. MRS 8 was essentially a CRBFD with its predictor replaced by a below-decks computer (single or dual ballistic unit, depending on which guns were being controlled). The dual ballistic unit also automatically opened fire when a target came within effective range.

As these directors became obsolete, they were converted into GWS 21s for Sea Cat control.

◆ **Sea Archer 1 (GSA 7)**

Sea Archer is the Sperry (UK) manned optronic weapons-control system. Sea Archer 1A adds below-decks controls. Sea Archer uses a modified Laurence Scott optical fire director (OFD). Applications include the Omani landing ship *Al Munassir*. As GSA 7, Sea Archer 1 controls the 76-mm gun of the British *Peacock*-class patrol vessels. A GEC V3800 thermal imager was added to their GSA 7s in 1986.

As supplied to the Royal Thai Navy in 1986, Sea Archer 1A had a low-light-level television (dual 12/3 degree field of view), a GEC V3807 thermal imager (LST version only), and a laser range-finder.

A Sea Archer 1B version, announced in 1983, has an unmanned director and autotrack.

The director is line-of-sight stabilized. The associated predictor turns the director into the direction of the target; the operator searches only in elevation to acquire the target. He tracks it by using a joystick with a pistol grip that contains controls for slew, for doubling the director rate. There is also a rate memory. Once the target has been acquired, the operator releases the

director from predictor control and triggers the range-finder. The latter may be either a range-only radar or a laser. Because the laser has so narrow a beam, the operator needs an indication that the beam has in fact pointed at the target; when the laser finds the target, the operator is given an audible click in his earphone. The operator's binoculars can be replaced by a trilite image intensifier or by a low-light-level television. It is also possible to replace the binoculars with a day/night scope, which allows the operator to view a scene either in natural light or in IR.

◆ **Sea Archer 2/Guardian**

The Sperry (UK) optronic weapons-control system was first displayed at Farnborough in 1978 and is based on Sea Archer 1. The fire director is an unmanned pedestal carrying a specially developed M-band (94-GHz) monopulse tracking radar on its left side (with a tracking TV camera beneath it), and on its right side a laser range-finder and a specially developed IR tracker. The radar was optional. The entire above-decks director is 48 inches high, with a 30-inch working circle. The director slews automatically to respond to target designation from an external sensor, and controls are located below decks. The stabilized director supports more than 150 kg of sensors; elevation limits are −30/+85 deg. Total above-decks weight is 305 kg; below-decks, 422 kg.

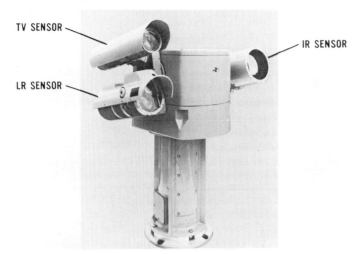

Sea Archer 2 director. (Sperry)

The lightweight IR imager/tracker operates in the 3.4–4.2 micron band, with a 48 × 25 mrad field of view, and scans at 30 frames/sec (120 lines/frame). A 7.75–11.75-micron IR imager using a Stirling-cycle cooler has recently been offered as an alternative. The television tracker operates in the 0.45–1.06 micron range, with a 40 × 30 mrad narrow field of view (resolution 0.1 × 0.1 mrad) and a 10:1 zoom lens ratio; the TV tracker operates at 30 or 25 frames/sec and 525 or 625 lines/frame. The associated laser range-finder operates at 1.06 microns, with a beamwidth of 1.2–1.5 mrad, a nominal pulse width of 20 nanosec (PRF 2–10 Hz), and an instrumented range of 0.28–20.475 km (resolution 5 m). Radar characteristics: peak power 1 kW, pulse width 0.5 microsec, PRF 10 kHz, beamwidth 0.5 deg, instrumented range 15 km. Target acquisition is automatic.

Sea Archer 2 is a joint development by Sperry (UK) and Sperry Gyroscope of the United States (now Unisys). The British firm ceased to offer this system in 1982, but it continued to be marketed by Sperry (U.S.) as Guardian (SA-2).

◆ **Sea Archer 30**

This optronic gunfire-control system was developed by Sperry (UK) and then taken over by British Aerospace. First displayed at RNEE 83, Sea Archer 30 was adopted in 1985 by the Royal Navy to control 4.5-in guns on board Type-22 and -23 frigates, under the designation GSA 8/GPEOD (Gun System Automation 8/General Purpose Electro-Optical Director). It is the first entirely autonomous digital Royal Navy gunfire-control system.

The director uses a television camera (CCD technology) with a variable field of view (3 × 2 to 17 × 11 degrees), a thermal imager (for night operations), and a laser range-finder (neodymium YAG). The director can accept data from such external sources as a command system (CIC), a tracking radar, or a target-designation sight. The fire-control system can be directed onto an urgent target by a special externally generated ALARM AA signal. The system can also be used for passive surveillance. The spherical shape is intended to reduce wind loading.

British Aerospace claims that Sea Archer 30 has quick enough reactions to deal with aircraft and antiship missiles; for the latter it has a special curved course-prediction mode.

The director proper weighs about 200 kg, with a swept radius of 448 mm. The internal power unit weighs another 45 kg, the gun control console 230 kg, and the predictor unit 110 kg. The predictor can incorporate ballistics for several different guns so that a ship's battery can be controlled by a single director.

GSA 8 demanded four director functions: naval gunfire support, antiship engagement, antiaircraft engagement, and chaff shell firing for both distraction and wind finding. The other competitor for the Royal Navy requirement was the Ferranti WSA 500 Modular Combat System.

With the failure of the U.S. Seafire program, British Aerospace proposed Sea Archer as an interim alternative. It does lack some of the features of the U.S. system, particularly the long-range laser designation capability (stability and beamwidth) required to control laser-guided 5-inch shells at maximum range; but Sea Archer is much lighter, and it does provide a valuable IR surveillance capability. Note that Sea Archer 30 was originally to have been marketed as Sea Archer 3.

◆ **Sapphire**

The Marconi/Sperry (U.K.) Sapphire radar fire-control system employs a Marconi ST802 or ST1802 radar, the predictor (the Sperry Digital Weapon Controller [DWC 100], consisting of a Sperry 1412 Computer and its interface and power supply) developed for the Sea Archer system, and a one-man control console. The system can function against air targets (in direct or coasting mode), against surface targets at relative speeds of up to 60 kts, and for naval gunfire support (including fuze computation for starshell and chaff). The AA coasting mode is extrapolation of target motion in the event that a target fades, e.g., passes behind terrain or chaff. Normally engaging targets designated from a search radar, Sapphire can also search autonomously, particularly against low-flying targets. In the horizon-search mode, a 0.1 square-meter sea-skimming missile can be detected at 12–15 km.

Typical system reaction time, including slewing to a designated target, is 7 seconds. The ST802 radar director accommodates a television camera, which automatically becomes the main tracker if the target drops below an elevation angle of 1.5 degrees, to eliminate multipath effects. Full radar tracking resumes automatically when the target passes above this angle. In a mass stream attack, the television can be used to acquire a second target while the first is being engaged, the radar being used to track the target being engaged.

The associated Sperry 1412A computer has a capacity of 16K words. It recalculates gun orders 64 times per second and provides new output 512 times per second.

Sapphire was evaluated for the Royal Navy in 1975 and announced in 1976 (and first sold that year); and an improved version was announced in 1985 (using the ST1802). The first Sapphire entered service about 1979. As of 1989, at least 18 systems had been sold for installation on board fast patrol boats.

UNITED STATES

RADARS

◆ **BPS-4**

    Band: S **Beam:** 5.3 × 60 deg
    Peak Power: 500 kW **Gain:** 23.5 dB
    Pulse Width: 1 microsec **PRF:** 400 pps
    Antenna Dimensions: 4 × 2 ft

Westinghouse's submarine air-search radar is no longer in U.S. service. Reliable range on a bomber was 15 nm, and accuracy was 200 yds plus or minus 3 percent of range, and 1 percent in bearing. Total installation weight was 2875 lbs.

◆ **BPS-5/12/14**

    Band: X **Beam:** 2.6 × 16 deg
    Peak Power: 75–110 kW **Gain:** 29 dB
    Pulse Width: 0.5 microsec **PRF:** 600 pps
    Scan Rate: 0–8 rpm **Antenna Dimensions:** 3 × 0.75 ft
    Antenna Weight: 300 lbs (total weight 2050 lbs)

Data apply to BPS-5.

Lockheed Electronics's submarine surface-search radar was originally designed for special target submarines (SSTs) but later installed on board *Permit*-class attack submarines. Reliable range on a destroyer was 12 nm, and accuracy up to 60,000 yds was 25 yds plus or minus 0.1 percent (to 120,000 yds, accuracy was 2 percent of range). Bearing accuracy was 0.25 deg. Range limits: 200 and 160,000 yds.

BPS-12 is a redesigned version, by Fairchild Camera and Instrument, using both a periscope antenna and a conventional one. Peak power is 75 kW and range limits are 400 and 80,000 yds. BPS-14 is very similar, except that its antenna drive is designed for use from within the submarine.

◆ **BPS-9**

    Band: X **Beam:** 2.6 × 16 deg
    Peak Power: 75–110 kW **Gain:** 36 dB
    Pulse Width: 0.5 microsec **PRF:** 600 pps
    Scan Rate: 0–8 rpm **Antenna Dimensions:** aperture 16 ft
    Antenna Weight: total installation weight 4000 lbs

This submarine surface-search radar is a modernized equivalent of the early postwar SS-2. BPS-9 was developed by Western Electric and first delivered in December 1958 (for SSBNs).

BPS-9A has a retractable antenna.

◆ **BPS-11**

    Band: X **Beam:** (i) 2.6 × 16 deg (ii) 30 × 10 deg
    Peak Power: 75–100 kW **Gain:** (i) 29 dB
    Pulse Width: 0.5 microsec **PRF:** 600 pps
    Antenna Dimensions: (i) parabolic (ii) periscope antenna

BPS-11 is a redesigned BPS-1/4 for the SSBN 616 class, similar to BPS-5 except for the antenna. BPS-11 uses a horn (parabolic in BPS-11A). Range limits are 200 and 160,000 yds.

◆ **BPS-15/16**

    Band: X **Beam:** 3 × 13 deg
    Peak Power: 35 kW **Gain:** 29 dB
    Pulse Width: (i) 0.1 (ii) 0.5 microsec **PRF:** (i) 1500 (ii) 750 pps
    Scan Rate: up to 9.5 rpm **Antenna Dimensions:** aperture 40 in
    Antenna Weight: 168 lbs

BPS-15 radar, USS *Hawkbill*. (*Ships of the World*)

Sperry's surface-search/navigational radar uses a horn-array antenna. Minimum range is 25 yds, and range resolution is 30 yds in the short-pulse and 100 yds in the long-pulse modes.

BPS-16 is the successor to BPS-15. Radar performance will be very similar, the main improvement being in the mechanical reliability of the mast. The two bidders were Norden and Sperry Marine, Norden being awarded the contract for what was then called BPS-( ) on 29 April 1987. The contract called for the development and production of 36 modular submarine radars. Sperry protested, and the contract was recompeted. Sperry ultimately received the contract, the radar now being designated BPS-16.

◆ SPS-5

Band: Xb (6400 MHz); C (5450–5825 MHz) in SPS-5C and -5D
Beam: 1.75 × 15 deg (csc2 to 22 deg)   **Peak Power:** 350 kW
Gain: 29 dB   **Pulse Width:** 0.5 microsec
PRF: 680 pps   **Scan Rate:** 17 rpm
Antenna Dimensions: 101 × 52.5 (including pedestal) × 101 (depth) in
Antenna Weight: 205 lbs including pedestal

Raytheon's small-ship surface-search radar was first delivered in 1952. Data above are for SPS-5C, introduced about 1960, which shifted from Xb- to C-band and used the AS-1002 antenna. Earlier versions used the AS-511 and -651 antennas.

USS *Bronstein* shows an SPS-5C surface-search radar, above her SPS-40 air-search set. Comparison with ships carrying SPS-10 will show how much smaller the -5C's antenna is. (U.S. Navy)

◆ SPS-6

Band: L (1250–1350 MHz)   **Beam:** 3.5 × 30 deg
Peak Power: 500 kW   **Gain:** 27 dB
Pulse Width: (i) 4 microsec (ii) 1 microsec
PRF: (i) 150 (ii) 600 pps   **Scan Rate:** 2.5–15 rpm
Antenna Dimensions: 204 × 95 7/8 in
Antenna Weight: 924 lbs (including pedestal)

SPS-6 was the first of the postwar generation of L-band air-search radars. These data apply to the SPS-6C version commonly installed on board destroyers and frigates. This radar could detect large high-altitude aircraft at 70–140 nm and fighters at 60–80 nm. SPS-6D omitted the integral IFF of SPS-6C, and -6E had a better receiver. Some sets may have had a peak power of 750 kW. The antenna was deliberately designed with a beam broad in its vertical dimension so that the radar could reliably detect high-altitude jets.

In U.S. service, SPS-6 remains on board only the *Thomaston*-class amphibious ships, but it is also in service on board destroyers, frigates, and similar vessels in foreign navies.

◆ SPS-10

Band: C (5450–5825 MHz)   **Beam:** 1.5 × 16 deg
Peak Power: 500 kW   **Gain:** 30 dB
Pulse Width: (i) 0.25 (ii) 1.3 microsec
PRF: 625–650 pps   **Scan Rate:** 15 rpm
Antenna Dimensions: 126 in × 76 in (with pedestal)
Antenna Weight: 442 lbs including pedestal

USS *Whipple* has an SPS-10 surface search radar and an SPS-40. The tall antenna above the SPS-10 is her LAMPS data link. (U.S. Navy)

Data are for SPS-10B (AS-936 antenna).

SPS-10 was the standard U.S. surface-search radar; it has been superseded, to a limited extent, by SPS-55 and is being replaced by SPS-67. In 1976 SPS-10 was considered the most reliable U.S. surface-search radar, with a mean time between failure of 150 hours (but with 5–6 hours mean time to repair because of the absence of automatic fault-finding equipment). The latest version is SPS-10G.

SPS-10 had a 285-kW transmitter; -10B introduced the current 500-kW type. SPS-10E introduced a new antenna (1.9 × 16 deg beam, 17 rpm), and -10F a new PRF (625–660 pps). The two pulse widths make for resolutions of, respectively, 41 and 213 yds. During trials in 1956, SPS-10 showed that it could detect a continuously exposed snorkel in sea-state 2 at an average of 9630 yards (maximum reliable range 12,100 yds) and could track a periscope (with 6 ft exposed) in sea-state 1 at 16,000 yds. Maximum reliable tracking range on a 3-ft attack periscope in sea-state 1 was 10,100 yds. These trials showed that the radar could reliably detect a submarine attack periscope intermittently exposed during an attack in sea-state 2 and below.

The associated IFF is integrated with the basic radar, and the IFF beam is 6 × 22 deg.

Note that some versions of this radar used the AS-1161 lightweight antenna, identical with the AS-1002 of SPS-5C. SPS-10 and -10A used AS-615; later versions use AS-936, which is essentially the same antenna with a 440-volt three-phase drive instead of the earlier 110-volt single-phase drive. AS-936B adds an extension to the bottom of the antenna and "blinders" on the sides of the feed horn, to reduce sidelobes and reduce minor interference with other ship antennas.

Deliveries began in October 1953. See also SPS-58, which sometimes uses the same antenna, and SPS-67.

♦ **SPS-12**

Band: L (1250–1350 MHz)   **Beam:** 30 × 3 deg
Peak Power: 500 kW   **Gain:** 25 dB
Pulse Width: (i) 4 microsec (ii) 1 microsec
PRF: (i) 300 (ii) 600 pps   **Scan Rate:** 2.5–15 rpm
Antenna Dimensions: 205 × 92 in
Antenna Weight: 990 lbs (with pedestal)

SPS-29 antenna, USS *Intrepid*. (A. Wetback)

A comparison among frigate air-search radars, 1968. HMS *Brighton*, at far left, has a Type-293 "cheese" short-range air-search (target-indicator) radar and a Type-277 height-finder. HMCS *Gatineau*, middle, has an SPS-12 air-search radar, with SPS-10 above it. The German frigate *Koln*, right, has a Dutch DA-02 air-search radar and an M-44 fire-control radar. The U.S. destroyer in the background has an SPS-40. All of these radars are still in use, although they are not as common as they were in 1968. (U.S. Naval Institute)

SPS-12 was, in effect, an improved SPS-6. Total weight was about 4600 lbs compared to 2550 for SPS-6B. Although peak power did not increase, long pulses could be emitted at a higher rate, for twice the average power of the earlier radar.

SPS-12 was first delivered in September 1953. This radar was also manufactured under license in Italy. The Canadian SPS-501 consists of a Dutch LW-03 antenna combined with an SPS-12 transmitter. The last U.S. set was removed from the training carrier *Lexington* in 1984.

♦ **SPS-21**

Band: C (5500–5600 MHz)   **Beam:** 2 × 15 deg
Peak Power: 10 kW   **Gain:** 28 dB
Pulse Width: 0.19 microsec   **PRF:** 1500 pps
Scan Rate: 17–20 rpm   **Antenna Dimensions:** 91.5 × 51 in

Versions of this small ship radar, developed in the early 1950s, run up through SPS-21D, using the AS-710 B and C antennas. Range scales are 2, 4, 16, 40, and 80 nm. SPS-21C has a variable range marker. Few if any of these radars survive in U.S. service, but some may serve foreign navies.

♦ **SPS-29**

Band: P (215–225 MHz)   **Beam:** 19 × 25.5 deg
Peak Power: 750 kW   **Gain:** 18 dB
Pulse Width: 10 microsec   **PRF:** 300 pps
Scan Rate: 7.5 or 15 rpm
Antenna Dimensions: 210 × 102 in (140 with pedestal)
Antenna Weight: 1275 lbs including pedestal (below-decks weight is 8700 lbs)

SPS-29D, the standard Coast Guard air-search antenna, on board the cutter *Barataria*, now discarded (mainmast). (U.S. Coast Guard)

Although extinct in the U.S. Navy, this P-band radar survives in some foreign ships. A version with a very different (corner reflector) antenna, SPS-29D, remains in U.S. Coast Guard service but is being replaced by SPS-40B. The usual mattress antenna, AS-943, is identical to that used in SPS-37/43 and consists of 28 folded dipoles spaced a half wavelength apart vertically and horizontally, and about a quarter wavelength in front of a flat reflector.

This radar was first delivered in 1958; in all, 89 were made.

A few ships had SPS-28, whose antenna was virtually indistinguishable from that of SPS-29. SPS-28 operated in the same frequency band, but peak power was only 300 kW, pulse length 4 microseconds, and PRF 120 pps; gross weight was 4440 lbs, compared to 7510 for the much more powerful SPS-29. The antenna was AS-839.

◆ **SPS-35**

Band: X (9335–9405 MHz) **Beam:** 2 × 15 deg
Peak Power: 7 kW **Gain:** 28 dB
Pulse Width: 0.2 microsec **PRF:** 1500 pps
Scan Rate: 20 rpm
Antenna Dimensions: 49 × 42 7/16 in (including pedestal)
Antenna Weight: 150 lbs (including pedestal)

The Raytheon 1500 Pathfinder was very widely fitted as a navigational radar during the Vietnam War. The transmitter/receiver is in the pedestal under the antenna, the only inboard unit being the radar display. The antenna is AS-923, a small horn-fed parabola.

This radar was first delivered in December 1957.

◆ **SPS-36**

Band: X (9350–9400 MHz) **Beam:** 2 × 28 deg
Peak Power: 10 kW **Gain:** 29 dB
Pulse Width: (i) 0.15 (ii) 0.5 microsec
PRF: 1000 pps **Scan Rate:** 17 rpm
Antenna Dimensions: 53 × 19 in (including pedestal)
Antenna Weight: 100 lbs

SPS-36 is a small-craft nonmagnetic navigational radar, primarily for minecraft. The radar transmitter is mounted on the back of the slotted-waveguide antenna (AS-925) and rotates with it. Minimum range is 25 yds; maximum is 16 nm.

This radar was first delivered in March 1958. It was made by Edo.

◆ **SPS-37/43**

Band: P (200 MHz) **Beam:** (i) 19 × 25.5 deg (ii) 7 × 20 deg
Peak Power: 180 kW (pulse compressed)
Gain: (i) 18 dB (ii) 23 dB
Pulse Width: 200 microsec (compressed to 6)
PRF: 230–250 pps **Scan Rate:** 7.5 or 15 rpm
Antenna Dimensions: (i) 210 × 102 in (ii) 495 × 121 in

Antenna Weight: (i) 1275 lbs (with pedestal) (below-decks weight 8300 lbs) (ii) 5720 lbs (with pedestal) (below-decks weight 8700 lbs)

This radar was built with two antennas, a simple mattress (i) and a much larger antenna consisting of two stacked corner reflectors (ii). The antennas are, respectively, AS-943 (broadbanded and redesignated AS-1091 in SPS-43) and AS-1092. In SPS-37, the shift from one to the other increased the effective detection range from 233 to 300 nm. The smaller antenna was used on board missile destroyers and cruisers, the larger one on board aircraft carriers. These radars have been replaced by SPS-49.

The transmitter is a tetrode.

SPS-37 was first delivered in September 1960, having been operationally evaluated the previous summer. Forty-six were built.

SPS-43 is an improved version with better resistance to countermeasures. For example, -43 has 20 rather than 10 channels (bandwidth is 20 MHz rather than 10 MHz). Below-decks weight is 9900 lbs. SPS-43 scans at 7.5 and 15 rpm, but -43A scans at 5 or 10 rpm. The first SPS-43 was delivered in March 1961, and 49 were built.

◆ **SPS-39/42/52**

Band: S (2910–3100.5 MHz)
Beam: 1.1 × 2.25 deg. (1.9 × 2.25 deg in SPA-64)
Peak Power: 1000 kW **Gain:** 39.5 dB (37 dB in SPA-64)
Pulse Width: (i) 2.5 (ii) 4.6 (iii) 10 microsec
PRF: (i) 1850 (ii) 925 (iii) (see notes below) pps
Scan Rate: (i) 15 (ii) 6 (iii) 6 rpm (SPS-39A: 5, 7.5, or 15 rpm)
Antenna Dimensions: 165 × 167 in (including pedestal) (SPA-64: 165 × 160 in including pedestal)
Antenna Weight: 3200 lbs (including pedestal) (SPA-64: 2950 lbs)

SPS-43A radar on board the carrier *Nimitz*. (U.S. Navy)

USS *Brooke* shows her three-dimensional radar (SPS-39 with planar-array antenna) at her masthead. SPS-39 and -52 arrays are physically indistinguishable; a wider array was manufactured for missile cruisers, which are no longer in service. The smaller antenna above the main array is an IFF interrogator; the array at the masthead is SPS-10. (U.S. Navy)

SPS-52C antenna. (Hughes)

An SPS-52C antenna, on board USS *Tattnall* (DDG 19), the first ship so fitted. The bar above is an IFF interrogator. (Hughes)

These three-dimensional radars are scanned electronically (frequency scanned) in elevation and mechanically in bearing. SPS-39 originally had a cylindrical-section antenna, but all ships now have the planar array, with a serpentine delay line on one side. Stabilization is achieved electronically. The antenna itself consists of a stack of 60 linear arrays. The early planar-array antenna (SPA-64) used 63 radiating slots per array; the later SPA-72 (for which most of the data above are given) uses 98. In each case, the antenna is tilted back at 25 degrees, and total vertical coverage is 42 degrees (41.6 degrees for SPS-52B).

These radars use klystron transmitters. All have low-power modes (peak power 16 kW; but 14.4 kW, with 900 kW maximum, in SPS-52B) and variable pulse rates. SPS-39 and -39A have only 2-microsecond (PRF 1850 pps) and 4-microsecond (PRF 925 pps) pulse widths. SPS-39A's PRF is 488 to 2000 pps. In the order given above, SPS-52A's PRFs are 1220–2000, 488–2000, and 329–1050 pps. Presumably the figures above are the usual values corresponding to the given pulse widths. Below-decks weights: SPS-52, 15,500; SPS-52B, 15,934 lbs; SPS-52C, 14,040 lbs.

The original SPS-39 was credited with a maximum range of 160 nm and a maximum altitude of 75,000 ft. The pulse data above refer to an improved (Series III) version introduced in 1963, with the planar-array antenna. The three modes were high-data-rate mode (i), with an instrumented range of 60 nm; high-angle mode (ii), 160 nm; and long-range mode (iii), 245 nm. Maximum elevation in the high-data-rate and high-angle modes was 42 degrees (with an alternative limited angle of 13 degrees in these modes and in the normal long-range modes), and there was an alternative limited long-range mode with a 4.5-degree maximum elevation. The improved SPS-52 is credited with a maximum range of 240 nm and a maximum altitude of 100,000 ft (maximum elevation 42 degrees).

SPS-42 was an SPS-39 modified to provide data directly to NTDS.

SPS-52 introduced the planar-array antenna now standard for both types, as well as a parametric amplifier and a wide-pulse feature for longer range. Stabilization is digital rather than analog. SPS-52B introduced clutter rejection. The current SPS-52C differs from the previous SPS-52B in reliability (because of increased use of solid-state components and de-rating of some components), in maintainability, and in compatibility with the SYS-1 Integrated Automatic Detection-and-Tracking (IADT) system.

In effect SPS-52C is an improved SPS-52B with a video extractor and control group (VECG) added to interface with SYS-1 via a UYK-20 computer. The VECG can store up to nine consecutive detections of the same object, find their centroid in three dimensions, and then pass that centroid location to the IADT as a single target report, thus reducing the IADT's workload and increasing the overall system's accuracy. SPS-52C is also more reliable than its predecessor, with a mean time between failure (as reported in 1979) of 216 hours, compared to a requirement for 170 hours: a 14-percent improvement over SPS-52B.

SPS-52C has four modes: high-angle (moderate range and data rate); long-range (high-energy pulse); high-data-rate (quick detection and rapid update of close-in targets); and MTI (clutter rejection). For medium range, the radar has a 6-second data rate (scan at 10 rpm); for long range and MTI, 8 seconds (7.5 rpm); and for short range, 4 seconds (15 rpm).

SPS-39 was first delivered in January 1960; it was the first operational U.S. frequency-scanning three-dimensional radar. -39 suffered from limited reliability (in 1960–62 MTBF was only 14.3 hours, although figures as great as 67.4 hours were achieved on board some ships). SPS-52's development began about 1963.

SPS-52C's design began in 1973, and it (with SYS-1) was tested on board USS *Towers* beginning in December 1977; approval for service use was granted in 1978.

For details of the associated IFF antennas, see the entry for SPS-48 below.

♦ **SPS-40**

> **Band UHF:** (400–450 MHz band) (10 channels)
> **Beam:** 11 × 19 deg **Peak Power:** 200 kW (pulse compressed)
> **Gain:** 21 dB **Pulse Width:** 60 microsec (compressed to 1.0)
> **PRF:** 300 pps (jittered)
> **Scan Rate:** 7.5 or 15 rpm (6 rpm in SPS-40 and -40A)
> **Antenna Dimensions:** 216.0 × 116.8 × 111.0 (deep) in
> **Antenna Weight:** 1425 lbs, including pedestal (1728 lbs for SPS-40B and later versions) (3200 lbs below decks; 3400 lbs for SPS-40A; 3474 lbs for later versions)

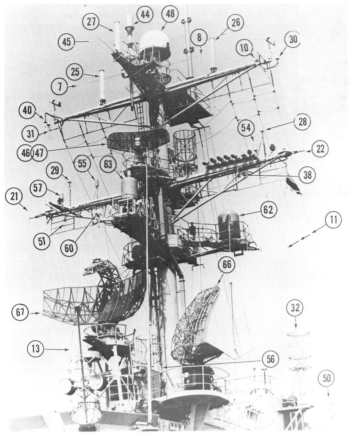

SPS-40 radar (67) on board USS *Tripoli*, 1976. SPS-10F is (47), and SPN-6, an air-traffic-control radar now superseded by SPN-43, is (66). A Sea Sparrow fire-control radar is visible below the number 13. Other important electronic devices visible in this picture are: TACAN (URN-20, number 48), broad-band radio antennas (AS-1018/SRC, numbers 25, 26, and 27), and ESM radomes: AS-571/SLR (62) and AS-899/SLR (63) (a third, AS-616A/SLR, is symmetrical with number 62, hidden by the mast). Numbers 54, 55, 56, and 57 are IFF transponders (AS-177/UPX). Although the photograph is over a decade old, most of the antennas shown are still in use. (U.S. Navy)

This radar and SPS-49 are the current standard U.S. two-dimensional sets. SPS-40 is in effect a compromise between very long range (achieved by using low frequency) and reasonable definition; 400 MHz is about the minimum acceptable frequency for a current set, because the next lower band, around 200 MHz, cannot provide enough information.

The original SPS-40 was manufactured by Lockheed Electronics. SPS-40A, an improved version by Sperry, introduced a broad-band transmitter and some solid state receiver changes. Peak power was increased to 255 kW. SPS-40B, by Norden, incorporated a new IFF (AIMS), for air control of friendly aircraft, a low-flyer-detection mode (LFDM), digital MTI (DMTI), and an automatic target detector (ATD) that allows the radar to feed into an automatic combat system (SYS series). DMTI provides clutter rejection over land. ATD employs a radar-video converter (RVC), which automatically detects targets and provides range and bearing data to the central combat-system computer. There are also ECCM improvements. SPS-40B and later versions have an alternative 3-microsecond (short) pulse and alternative PRFs of 278 and 300. SPS-40C is a modified SPS-40A (to -40B standards), incorporating LFDM and reliability improvements. SPS-40D is a modified SPS-40A corresponding to SPS-40C standards. An improved antenna is under development, and Norden has developed a frequency-agility (FA) module. It selects an unjammed frequency and shifts frequency on a pulse-to-pulse basis. Other possible improvements are main and sidelobe cancelers; at present the antenna has fairly fat sidelobes (27 dB horizontal, 10 dB vertical).

Data above apply to SPS-40B; some models may compress the 60-microsecond pulse to 0.6 microseconds. Minimum range is 0.25 nm. Current MTBF is 252 hours; MTTR is 45 minutes. The transmitter is a tetrode tube.

U.S. SPS-40s are currently being fitted with Westinghouse solid-state transmitters (SSTx) in place of the existing tube transmitters, for much-improved reliability. The SSTx can also power up very fast so that the ship can operate with her radar shut down when in EMCON without risking loss of radar capability when it is needed. In addition, the SSTx automatically protects itself from damage due to battle damage to the waveguide or antenna: it shuts down, then powers up to the level allowed by the other components. Westinghouse offers a less expensive lightweight (half-power) SSTx for coastal defense.

The prototype SPS-40 was delivered in June 1961. Deliveries of SPS-40A began in November 1971.

◆ **SPS-41**

> **Band:** X (9375 MHz) **Beam:** 2 × 20 deg
> **Peak Power:** 10 kW **Gain:** 27 dB
> **Pulse Width:** 0.5 microsec **PRF:** 1600 or 500 pps
> **Scan Rate:** 21 rpm
> **Antenna Dimensions:** 37 1/2 × 33 1/2 in (including pedestal)
> **Antenna Weight:** 119 lbs (including pedestal)

SPS-41 is a lightweight navigational radar for small ocean-going vessels. The transmitter-receiver is mounted in the pedestal above deck. Minimum range is 25 yds, maximum 32 nm. The antenna is AS-1004, a small horn-fed parabola.

The first SPS-41 was delivered in March 1959.

◆ **SPS-46**

> **Band:** X (9345–9405 MHz) **Beam:** 2.2 × 15 deg
> **Peak Power:** 7 kW **Gain:** 20 dB
> **Pulse Width:** 0.2 microsec **PRF:** 1500 pps
> **Scan Rate:** 15–21 rpm
> **Antenna Dimensions:** 48 1/2 × 27 3/4 in (including pedestal)
> **Antenna Weight:** 85 lbs (including pedestal)

SPS-46 is a navigational radar for seagoing ships; minimum range is 25 yds, maximum 32 nm. The antenna is a small parabolic section fed by a horn (AS-1066).

SPS-46 entered service in 1961.

◆ **SPS-48**

> **Band:** S (2900–3100 MHz) **Beam:** 1.5 × 1.6 deg
> **Peak Power:** 2200 kW **Gain:** 38.5 dB
> **Pulse Width:** 3 microsec (per beam: 27 total)
> **PRF:** 1250–2000 pps **Scan Rate:** 7.5 or 15 rpm
> **Antenna Dimensions:** 194 × 228 in (including pedestal)
> **Antenna Weight:** 4495 lbs (including pedestal) (below-deck weights: -48, 18,211 lbs; -48A, 19,651 lbs; -48C, 20,548 lbs) SPS-48E: 5684 lbs above-decks (24,018 lbs below-decks).

SPS-48 is the most sophisticated U.S. frequency-scanning radar, scanning multiple beams in elevation to combine long range with high data rate and multiple-pulse (i.e., high-probability) detection. Each stream of nine pulses generates nine beams, spread in frequency to give a total spread of 6 degrees for the group. Successive groups elevate from 0 to 45 degrees. In an alternative burn-through (antijam) mode, the entire 27 microseconds are transmitted at one elevation angle, and pulse-compressed (with a ratio of 9:1). There is also a 9-microsecond pulse. Instrumented range is 230 nm, and rated range is 220 nm, with a minimum ceiling of 100,000 ft. Vertical coverage is up to 45 degrees. The transmitter is an amplitron.

SPS-48C incorporates ADT.

SPS-48E (formerly SPS-48NTU), the current version, doubles the effective radiated power, reduces sidelobes (sidelobe level is -33 dB, compared to -23 dB for earlier versions of this radar), and increases the receiver's sensitivity. Maximum elevation angle is increased to 65 degrees. Because the antenna incorporates ferrite phase-shifters, SPS-48E can combine pulse compression (i.e., frequency-swept pulses) with vertical phase scanning in frequency. The ferrites are interposed between the serpentine feed and the slotted arrays, compensating for the frequency sweep within each pulse. Pulse width is 27 microsec (com-

SPS-48 radar on board USS *Mississippi*, with AS-3430 IFF antenna above. (Stefan Terzibaschitsch)

SPS-48. (U.S. Naval Institute)

pressed to 3 microseconds). Input power: -48, 65.8 kVA; -48A, 72 kVA; -48C, 74 kVA; -48E, 112 kVA.

Associated with the New Threat Upgrade (NTU: SYS-2) program, SPS-48E incorporates a new cross-field amplitron transmitter with twice the average output and greater reliability (it can continue to function despite some subcomponent failures, a technique called fail-soft), a digital receiver/frequency control, and a combined programmer/processor with half the equipment racks of previous versions. There is also a new single unified display group. The new transmitter permits snap-on/snap-off operation for simpler and more complete EMCON. All of these improvements have greatly increased the system's reliability. Predicted MTBF was 268 hours; but in a 146-day Sixth Fleet deployment, SPS-48E achieved an MTBF of 586 hours. The first ship to be fitted was USS *Biddle*.

Improved reliability is, in part, a result of a redesign that reduced radar part count by over 50 percent (280,000 to 126,000). The number of required adjustments has been reduced from 768 to 70, and the operator typically chooses only between four scan modes, with adjustments of four controls.

SPS-48E has three transmitter power modes (high, medium, and low power). Energy coverage modes are: equal angle coverage (EAC), maximum energy management (MEM), and adaptive energy management (AEM). In EAC mode, the highest power is concentrated at the lowest elevation angle, so that detection range is greatest at the elevation angle at which most targets are likely to appear. Cover is provided from the horizon to 45-degrees elevation, and out to 220 nm (instrumented range). MEM provides high power in the lowest four elevation groups and medium power in the upper four. AEM is automatically activated when SYS-2 generates a priority track gate or surveillance priority gate around a target or expected target area of particular interest. The radar adapts its power to the jamming environment and target's cross section. There are both 5-degree (in elevation) and 2-degree (chirp) modes. Both of these modes can be steered, whereas the other modes merely involve the preset elevation channels. The beam can also be scrambled to complicate countermeasures.

SPS-48D was the engineering development prototype for -48E and was tested on board USS *Mahan* in 1982–83, including operations off Lebanon.

Data refer to the AS-1686 antenna. The antenna, electronically stabilized against pitch and roll up to 20 degrees, consists of 76 linear horizontal arrays. The new SPS-48E antenna has 95 linear arrays, each 18 ft long, with a total height of 18 ft.

SPS-48 is manufactured by ITT-Gilfillan.

Several IFF antennas can be used with SPS-48: AS-1065, AS-1688, AS-2188, and AS-3430. AS-1688 is intended as an integral part of the SPS-48 antenna; the others can be mounted either independently or on the antenna. Beamwidths: 9 × 45 deg for AS-1688, 7 × 48 deg for AS-2188, and 7.5 × 50 deg for AS-3430. These antennas are also used for other major U.S. radars.

In 1985 ITT-Gilfillan displayed a new GaAs/fiber-optic technology (then in its early stages) for a future phased- (active) array radar. In such a radar, the waveform is created, and phases are shifted and then transmitted via optical fiber into the bank of GaAs RF transmitters in the antenna. That scheme greatly reduces the usual power losses in such a radar; in a conventional radar, the phase shifters themselves cost 1.5–2 dB (and faster phase shifting consumes more power), not to mention the DC power required to run the diode phase shifters (typically tens of kW). In the fiber-optic radar, phase shifting is done at very low power. The other alternative, phase shifting by frequency scanning (as in SPS-48), is limited by microwave frequency. For widebeam steering, the antenna must use time-delay beamforming; the beam must be many wavelengths across and very precisely made. By doing the beam-forming and beam-steering in the cabinet rather than in the antenna, the fiber-optic radar can use cut lengths of fiber and integrated optical switches to create the necessary time delays. In theory, then, an individual optical fiber would be used for each element; but wavelength multiplexing can give as many as ten elements/fiber, so that the apparent requirement for about 6000 can be reduced to 600. The result should be less expensive high-resolution beam-forming with adaptive weighting for better beam-shaping.

SPS-48 was designed because SPS-39 had insufficient range for the Talos missile system; development began in 1959. The first production set went to sea on board the cruiser *Worden* in March 1965.

◆ SPS-49

Band: L (851–942 MHz)   **Beam:** 3.3 × 9 deg
Peak Power: 280 kW
Pulse Width: 125 microsec, compressed (ratio 83:1); there is also a 2-microsec pulse for short ranges
PRF: 280 pps for long range, 800 or 1000 pps for short range
Gain: 29 dB   **Scan Rate:** 6 or 12 rpm
Antenna Dimensions: 288 × 171 in (including pedestal)
Antenna Weight: 3040 lbs (including pedestal)

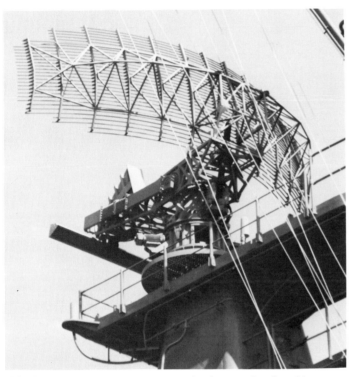

SPS-49 on USS *Mississippi*, June 1988. (Stefan Terzibaschitsch)

SPS-49, manufactured by Raytheon, is the best current U.S. two-dimensional air-search radar. It is currently replacing the SPS-37/43 series. Based on experience with the SPS-40, Westinghouse is currently (1988) conducting full-scale engineering development of a solid-state transmitter (SSTx) to replace the SPS-49's existing klystrom (vacuum-tube) transmitter.

The radar is mechanically stabilized in line of sight and is adapted to ADT. Total below-decks weight is 13,791 lbs.

Versions of SPS-49 are denoted by (V) numbers. (V)1 is the original version, e.g., on board *Perry*-class frigates. (V)2 was the version for New Threat Upgrade (NTU) modernization of cruisers. (V)3 is the Canadian version, with an embedded tracker (i.e., with ADT). (V)5 is the current ATD version, with a digital signal processor that requires its own cooling system. (V)7 is essentially the same radar without the cooling package, for ships such as Aegis, which provide cooling.

The (V)5 version employs digital pulse-doppler processing to reject clutter; the system has parallel coherent and incoherent processing channels, a mean-level digital CFAR processor, five finite-impulse-response (FIR) doppler filters, and amplitude clutter-map compensation in each channel. To reject jamming through the sidelobes, the system uses a four-loop coherent sidelobe canceler (CSLC), and jammers' bearings are automatically detected and reported digitally. The PPI shows a jammer–direction-finder (JDF) strobe. There is a special antichaff mode, in which PRF is increased to improve doppler processing.

At Yokosuka in October 1984, USS *Midway* shows her SPS-49 and SPN-43 radars; SPN-43 is the antenna mounted on the stub pole mast to the right. The smaller antenna above is SPS-10/58, and the antenna atop the bridge is a telemetry unit for weather balloons. (*Sea Power*)

The beam can be elevated (up-spotted) to help reject main-lobe jamming.

Peak power is increased to 360 kW (average power is 13 kW, compared to 10 kW for earlier versions described above), and the beam is 3.4 deg × 30 deg csc2; antenna gain is 28.5 dB. Range accuracy is 0.03 nm, and bearing accuracy is 0.5 degrees. Estimated MTBF is greater than 600 hours, and MTTR is less than half an hour. Total above-decks weight is 3165 lbs, and below-decks weight is 14,004 lbs; the power requirement is 86 kVA of 440 volt power and 10.1 kVA of 115 volt power. The internal space requirement is about 200 square feet.

For details of IFF antennas, see the entry for SPS-48 above.

SPS-49 was conceived as part of the same frequency-diversity program that produced SPS-40; the prototype was tested on board the destroyer *Gyatt* between July 1964 and June 1965. Although this radar figured in many U.S. warship designs of the late 1960s, it was not bought in numbers. However, it was revived in 1970 in much modified form and then evaluated on board the missile cruiser *Dale* in 1976. SPS-49 was first bought in quantity to equip U.S. *Perry*-class missile frigates. As a measure of improvement in reliability since the mid-1960s, the original prototype showed an MTBF of about 60 hours, a tenth of the current figure.

Work is currently proceeding on an IADT (i.e., SYS-type system) for *Perry*-class frigates, to tie their air- and surface-search radar pictures together. Operational evaluation is scheduled for FY89.

Several major SPS-49 improvements are being considered, some under a Naval Research Laboratory program, SENRAD. One is a solid-state transmitter (SSTx). The other may be an antenna upgrade, possibly a planar-array three-dimensional antenna. The two goals would be reduced sidelobes and an agile beam. Any future agile-beam antenna would probably employ phase shifting for beam steering since the transmitter would have to employ pulse compression and would probably be fre-

FASR antenna. (Westinghouse)

quency agile. Phase shifting might be done either at low power (before the signal passes through the amplifier) or at high power (in the antenna itself). Phase shifting at low power might be easier, but in that case the radar would have to pass multiple signals simultaneously through its rotary joint (otherwise the signals are multiplexed in the antenna, e.g., by stripping them from a serpentine waveguide that imposes phase differences). Westinghouse recently received contracts for both the SSTx and a 20-channel UHF rotary joint.

Westinghouse has been developing low-sidelobe UHF planar-array dipole antennas for some time. FASR (Fixed Array Surveillance Radar) is a $31 \times 12\frac{1}{2}$ ft array consisting of two rows of vertical strip-line elements (27 per row). It was developed under contract for NRL. Another dipole array antenna was developed for the SPS-65 radar (see that entry).

As of 1989, the navy is also considering an improved SPS-49 processor, to take advantage of the new antenna. All of these projects are still in the experimental stage, but the French Navy expects to replace its standard long-range two-dimensional radar, DRBV 26, which is broadly analogous to SPS-49, with a long-range three-dimensional radar. That process would seem to meet the threat of high-altitude, steeply diving missiles such as AS-4/6, which may pass over the coverage of long-range two-dimensional air-search radars.

◆ SPS-53/60

Band: X   **Beam:** (a) 1.6×20 deg (b) 1×20 deg
Peak Power: 40 kW   **Gain:** 30 dB average
Pulse Width: (i) 0.5 (ii) 0.1 microsec
PRF: (i) 750 (ii) 1500 pps   **Scan Rate:** 15 rpm
Antenna Dimensions: (a) 5 ft (b) 8 ft
  AS-1652: 59 7/8 × 22 3/8 in
  AS-2321: 59 7/8 × 21 1/4 in
  AS-2322: 96 1/4 × 21 1/4 in
  AS-2645: 96 × 22 3/8 in
Antenna Weight: (includes pedestal)
  AS-1652: 100 lbs
  AS-2321: 87 lbs
  AS-2322: 97 lbs
  AS-2645: 100 lbs

Sperry's high-resolution navigational radar is used by both the coast guard and the navy. The antenna is a slotted waveguide. In some ships it replaced SPS-5. Minimum range is 25 yds; maximum range is 32 nm. The current version is SPS-53M. Four antennas, all slotted waveguides, are used, two 5-foot and two 8-foot. AS-1652 (5 ft) is used with SPS-53, -53A, B, and H; AS-2321 (5 ft) with -53D, F, G, K, and M; AS-2322 (8 ft) with -53E and L; and AS-2645 (8 ft) with SPS-53J.

SPS-60 is a solid-state version of the vacuum-tube SPS-53E and uses a standardized 8-ft navy antenna. SPS-60 survives in U.S. service on board minesweepers and auxiliaries.

◆ SPS-55

Band: X (9.05–10.00 GHz)   **Beam:** 1.5×20 deg
Peak Power: 130 kW   **Gain:** 31 dB
Pulse Width: (i) 0.12 (ii) 1.0 microsec
PRF: (i) 2250 (ii) 750 pps   **Scan Rate:** 16 rpm
Antenna Dimensions: 80×28 in (including pedestal)
Antenna Weight: 195 lbs including pedestal

SPS-55 is the X-band successor to the C-band SPS-10; the frequency was chosen to avoid interference with C-band missile trackers. The antenna consists of two slotted waveguides arranged back to back, the operator choosing either circular or horizontal polarization. The former helped to overcome rain clutter, as the rain drops tend to reverse the circular polarization of the waves they reflect, and the radar can reject signals of opposite polarization. More complex targets do not reverse polarization in so systematic a way; and their echoes are, therefore, not entirely rejected (although some target echo is lost). Each antenna consists of an array of 80 narrow slots skewed in angle (with alternating skew angles for squintless feed). Minimum range (short-pulse mode) is 50 yds; it is 300 yds in the long-pulse mode. Resolution: 75 and 650 ft, respectively. Reliability: 500 hours MTBF were required, 1200 hours demonstrated.

SPS-55 was developed by Raytheon but produced by Cardion; the first contract was let in June 1971. This radar was first used in quantity on board the U.S. *Spruance* class.

SPS-55 antenna, showing its back-to-back construction. (Cardion)

◆ SPS-57

Band: X   **Beam:** 1.9×25 deg
Peak Power: 3 kW
Pulse Width: (i) 0.1 (ii) 0.2 microsec
PRF: (i) 2000 (ii) 1000 pps   **Scan Rate:** 25 rpm

SPS-57 is Ridge Electronics's small-craft surface-search radar for the coast guard. Minimum range is 25 yds (2-nm scale); maximum instrumented range is 16 nm.

◆ SPS-58/62/65

SPS-65(V)ER antenna. (Westinghouse)

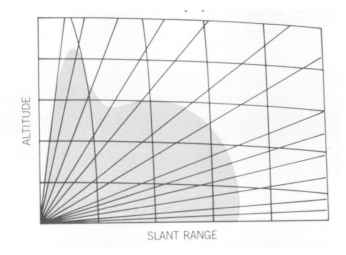

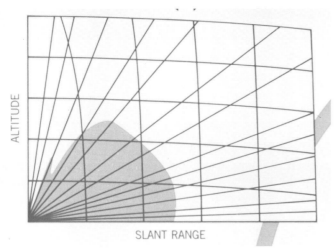

Comparative coverage of SPS-65(V)ER (top) and SPS-65(V)1 and 2 (bottom). (Westinghouse)

Band: L (1215–1365 MHz)
Beam: 6 × 16 deg (12 deg in SPS-58)   **Peak Power:** 12 kW
Gain: SPS-58A and -65: 23 dB, SPS-58: 26 dB
Pulse Width: 5 microsec (SPS-65: 7 microsec)
PRF: 2290 or 3050 pps (SPS-58A: 2285 or 3048 pps; SPS-65: 2315 or 3064 pps)
Scan Rate: 20 rpm (SPS-58A and -65: 15 rpm)
Antenna Dimensions: 126 × 76 in, with pedestal; SPS-58: 234 × 120 in
Antenna Weight: SPS-58A: 425 lbs, with pedestal; SPS-58: 1200 lbs; SPS-65: 439 lbs. Below-decks weight: SPS-58: 2100 lbs; SPS-58A: 1300 lbs; SPS-65: 1594 lbs

These short-range air-search radars, manufactured by Westinghouse, share the antenna of the standard SPS-10 surface-search set, the air- (actually horizon) search employing C- rather than L-band emissions. The transmitter is a three-stage coherent klystron, for fully coherent operation (e.g., for MTI).

Early SPS-58s (and SPS-58Bs) used a separate antenna (AS-1067), but SPS-58A, -58C, and the subsequent SPS-62 and SPS-65 used the SPS-10 antenna, the usual feed horn of the surface-search device being replaced by a dual-feed waveguide horn. Maximum range is about 25 nm. SPS-58B and -58D have no displays but feed directly into NTDS, to trigger missile firing.

In 1979, Honeywell advertised the H-930 combat system (see entry below), which incorporated an SPS-58 that automatically detected any target flying faster than an 80-kt MTI threshold. In this installation, the SPS-58 would have been mounted back-to-back with an SPS-55 surface-search radar. This SPS-58V radar had a 26-dB antenna (4 × 18 deg beam) and an instrumented range of 125 nm; scan rate was 15 rpm. Minimum range was given as 1 nm, and a 1 square-meter target could be detected at

66.4 nm. Azimuth accuracy was 0.5 deg, and range accuracy 1 percent. This version operated on any one of six selectable frequencies.

The Taiwanese Navy uses a stand-alone SPS-58, without any associated back-to-back antenna, as the missile detector for the Honeywell H930 fire-control system. This radar incorporates both MTI and ADT; the operator has only to press the firing switch. H930 Mod 1 has three channels, one Mk 35 optical system, and two CS/SPG-24 (similar to RCA HR-76) tracking radars. Reportedly the two SPG-24s are to be fitted with coaxial TV/IR trackers so that they can deal more effectively with sea-skimmers. These radars can also be used for low-level air search, to make up for the low data rate (19 rpm) of the SPS-58.

SPS-65 adds automatic target detection (to feed target data directly into a computer combat system), is more reliable, and has ECCM features. MTI is used to reject clutter.

Westinghouse currently offers three versions of SPS-65: (V)1 for self-defense, (V)2 for fire control, and (V)ER for long (extended) range. All can be fitted with the company's solid-state L-band transmitter (SSTx), and all can be provided with a special antijamming frequency-agile mode (the radar automatically changes frequency based on its detection of the least-jammed frequency). (V)1 and 2 have a 25-nm instrumented range mode. The ER version has three range modes: 25, 50, and 100 nm.

As in the original SPS-58, these transmitters and signal processors can use the SPS-10 antenna. However, Westinghouse offers two alternatives. One is a dual-beam antenna for missile guidance, to detect high- or low-flying targets; this antenna requires additional signal processing. Another is a dipole-array antenna. In addition to the normal scan rates (15 rpm) for the three range modes, both the dual-beam and the dipole-array can be provided with an alternative high-speed mode.

(V)1 is the direct successor to the version originally developed as an acquisition radar for the Basic Point-Defense Missile System (SPS-58). (V)2 adds a fire-control interface group (FCIG) to (V)1, for ADT, manually initiated autotracking, NTDS symbology, target centroids, track history, and outputs suitable for gun and missile control. The (V)ER version, formerly SPS-58(LR), was announced in 1987. It has a higher-power solid-state transmitter and an enhanced signal processor. (V)ER can operate in short-, medium-, or long-range modes, and these modes may be timed for alternate scans. In long-range mode the radar uses a pulse-coded stretched pulse (pulse-compressed on reception); full MTI is provided out to 100 nm. The short-range mode is optimized for sea-skimmer detection within 25 nm.

SPS-65(V)1 and 2 use a 12-kW transmitter (average power 260 W); the ER version uses a 25-kW transmitter (average power 1200 W). Detection ranges on a 1 square-meter (Swerling case 1) target are, respectively, 23 and 61 nm. The ER version has an instrumented range of 100 nm, and it is frequency agile on a burst-to-burst basis. It employs digital MTI for clutter rejection. Elevation coverage is up to 16 deg in the (V)1 and 2 versions and up to 30 deg in the ER version. Accuracy is 1500 ft and 0.5 deg in (V)1 and 2, 608 ft and 0.5 deg in (V)ER. Resolution is 3000 ft in both cases, but azimuth (beamwidth) is 5.8 deg in the (V)1 and 2 versions and 3.5 deg in (V)ER. In all cases, the MTI improvement factor is 60 dB. The ER version employs variable PRF (300 to 625 pps), and the antenna's rotation speed is 10 or 20 rpm. Horizontal beamwidth is 3 deg.

Current MTBF for SPS-65(V)1 is 350 hours, and MTTR is less than 2 hours.

The new L-band transmitter can use existing SPS-6, -12, and -58 antennas, as well as the modified dual-frequency SPS-10 antenna used for earlier SPS-65 radars.

Data apply to a modified SPS-10B antenna. SPS-62, described officially as an "alarm radar," shared many SPS-58 components but had a modified receiver-processor and a new planar-array antenna (114 in wide, beam 5.5 × 21 degrees, 12-kW pulses, 5 microseconds long, PRF 2280 or 3040 pps). Development was abandoned in 1973 in favor of advanced versions of SPS-58. The relatively long pulse was probably compressed, for increased average power.

These radars were developed at high priority following the sinking of the Israeli destroyer *Eilat* in 1967, and they were reportedly patterned on a German Siemens radar with excellent anticlutter capabilities, probably the MPDR-45, one of a series of mobile pulse-doppler radars.

In U.S. carriers, SPS-58s with special separate antennas are being replaced by TAS Mk 23s (see below for description).

◆ SPS-59

SPS-59 is the U.S. version of the Canadian LN-66.

◆ SPS-63

Band: X (9345–9405 MHz)   **Beam:** 1.2 × 20 deg
Peak Power: 7 or 20 kW   **Gain:** 28 dB
Scan Rate: 25 rpm
Antenna Dimensions: 74 × 29 1/2 in (including pedestal)
Antenna Weight: total weight 217 lbs (antenna 90.5 lbs)

A lightweight navigation and surface-search radar for the PHM missile hydrofoil, SPS-63 is a U.S. (Norden-built) version of the Italian 3RM-20N. Accuracy is equal to 2 percent of the range scale selected; resolution is 10 yds at 0.25 nm, 100 yds at 10 nm, and 400 yds at 40 nm (maximum instrumented range). The display can stabilize fixed targets against own-ship motion. Minimum range is 10 or 20 yds, maximum 40 nm.

The AS-4052 antenna is a slotted waveguide illuminating a parabolic cylinder reflector.

Only one was bought, and all the PHMs now use SPS-64.

◆ SPS-64

Band: X (9345–9405 MHz) or S (3025–3075 MHz)
Beam: four alternative X-band slotted-waveguide antennas: (i) 1.9 × 22 deg (ii) 1.25 × 22 deg (iii) 0.9 × 22 deg (iv) 0.7 × 22 deg   S-band slotted-waveguide antenna: (v) 2 × 25 deg
Peak Power: three alternative transmitters: (i) 20-kW fixed or tunable X-band, (ii) 50-kW X-band, (iii) 60-kW S-band
Gain: 28 dB   **Pulse Width:** (a) 0.06 (b) 0.5 (c) 1.0 microsec
PRF: (a) 3600 (b) 1800 (c) 900 pps   **Scan Rate:** 33 rpm
Antenna Dimensions: (i) 4 ft X-band only (ii) 6 ft (iii) 9 ft (iv) 12 ft (v) 6 ft   **Antenna Weight:** (ii) 140 lbs (iv) 332 lbs

SPS-64 on board the Coast Guard cutter *Bear*. The egg atop the bridge is a Mk-92 fire-control system for the 76-mm/62 gun forward. Also visible is the box containing an SLQ-32 ESM system, on a platform just aft of the bridge windows. The flat object atop the mast is a TACAN aircraft beacon. (U.S. Naval Institute)

Raytheon's navigational radar for the army, coast guard, and navy has three alternative transmitters and four alternative antennas (as shown above). SPS-64(V)1 has only a single 20-kW transmitter. SPS-64(V)2 and (V)3 have two X-band transmitters

each, and (V)4 has one X- and one S-band. (V)5 has a tunable 20-kW transmitter, and (V)6, for vessels over 270 ft long, has the 50-kW X-band transmitter.

The standard system uses the 6-foot AS-3194 antenna and a 20-kW transmitter. In the dual-band version, the 12-foot AS-3195 is added.

Range scales are 0.25–3, 6, 12, 48, and 64 nm.

◆ SPS-66A

Band: X (9345–9405 MHz)   **Beam:** 2 × 23 deg
Peak Power: 7 kW   **Gain:** 28 dB
Scan Rate: 30 rpm   **Antenna Dimensions:** 56 × 22 1/2 in
Antenna Weight: 100 lbs

SPS-66A is Raytheon's model CRP-3100 small-craft search and navigational radar. Range scales are 0.5, 2, 4, 8, 16, and 32 nm. The AS-4072 antenna is a slotted waveguide. There is an alternative 33 1/2-in antenna that rotates within a transparent radome, for coast guard patrol craft.

◆ SPS-67

This Norden solid-state radar is intended to replace SPS-10 on a one-for-one basis. SPS-67 uses the same antenna, the improvements being confined to the electronics of the transmitter, receiver, and display. The magnetron is the same as that of the SPS-55. SPS-67 is the first U.S. Navy radar built of standard electronic modules (SEMs) for commonality with future radars; Norden claims 92 percent SEM construction (including 46 types already approved, and only 29 new types), and 80 percent commonality to current navy sonars and to potential navy radars. Designed MTBF is 600 hours, and designed MTTR is 29 minutes, the short repair time being achieved partly by means of built-in test equipment.

The design provides for future addition of an automation module (digital MTI/automatic target detection) to feed data into a combat system (integrated automatic detection and tracking, IADT, as in SYS-1).

A new harbor-navigation mode (using a 0.1-microsecond pulse) allows clutter-free detection of targets (buoys and small craft) at shorter range than is common with SPS-10. Tests have shown that buoys and small obstructions can be detected at 75 yds.

SPS-67 currently exists in three versions. (V)1 is the original type, essentially duplicating SPS-10 with more modern technology. (V)1 has demonstrated an MTBF of considerably better than 1000 hours and an MTTR of only 29 minutes. (V)2 replaces the original SPS-10 antenna with a nuclear-survivable (and much more reliable and maintainable) linear-array antenna. (V)2 should perform much better under conditions of extreme roll and pitch (e.g., in northern waters), and bearing accuracy is improved. (V)3, now under development for the *Arleigh Burke* class, has a two/four-second data rate, digital MTI (DMTI), automatic target detection, and TWS. (V)3 is designed to provide digital data directly to fire-control, command-and-decision, and SYS systems. (V)3 shares the new (V)2 linear-array antenna.

◆ SPY-1/FARS

Band: S (3100–3500 MHz) (sustained coherent bandwidth 10 MHz, instantaneous 40 MHz)   **Beam:** 1.7 × 1.7 deg
Peak Power: 4–6 MW (average power 58 kW)   **Gain:** 42 dB
Pulse Width: 51, 25.4, 12.7, and 6.4 microsec (pulse-compression ratio 128:1)   **PRF:** variable
Scan Rate: 1 horizon scan/min, 12 scans/min above horizon
Antenna Dimensions: 12 ft hexagon
Antenna Weight: 13,030 lbs per face; below-decks weight 131,584 lbs

SPY-1A, manufactured by RCA (as of 1988, this RCA division had been taken over by General Electric), is the S-band phased-array radar of the Aegis weapons system. Each of four faces is a 12 × 12 ft (3.65 × 3.65 m) octagon containing 140 array modules, each containing 32 radiating elements and phase shifters (a total of 4480; actually, because some modules are empty, there are 4096 transmitting and 4352 receiving elements, plus 128 auxiliary elements) driven by eight transmitters. Array

GE's concept of a NATO frigate fitted with the NATO AAW Weapon System. The flat phased-array radar, which might be FARS (but might also be an alternative) is supplemented by a pair of illuminators similar in form to the Signaal STIR series, and also by an electro-optical sensor in between. The gun is Goalkeeper, which General Electric markets in the United States. This model was displayed at the U.S. Navy League show in March 1989. (General Electric)

Microwave "plumbing" in the back of an SPY-1 panel. See the illustration for SPG-62 (the associated target illuminator) for the outside of the radar. (U.S. Naval Institute)

modules are paired to form receiving subarrays, and two such arrays are paired to form a transmitting subarray. Finally, these subarrays are grouped to form 32 transmitting and 68 receiving arrays, with separate receiving and transmitting terminals. Operation is monopulse. Total weight per face is 13,030 lbs. The multiple beams are controlled by UYK-7 computers. The computer-controlled beam can update target positions several times per second, and over 200 contacts can be tracked simultaneously. The basic transmitter uses 32 crossed-field amplifiers, each with a peak power of 132 kW. Required power input is 490.9 kVA, compared to 64 kVA for the various versions of SPS-52, 65.8 kVA for SPS-48A and -48C, and 112 kVA for SPS-48E. For comparison, typical power inputs for two-dimensional air-search radars are: 94.4 kVA for SPS-49; 15 for SPS-29/29E; 45 for SPS-37/37A; 21 for SPS-40; 27 for SPS-40A; 33.5 for SPS-40B,C,D; 45 for SPS-43/43A; 7 for SPS-58 and -65; 8.5 for SPS-58A.

SPY-1B (the first of which is on board CG 59) uses lighter-weight phase shifters, and the total weight per face is reduced to 3600 kg (7900 lbs), compared to 7700 kg (16,970 lbs) for SPY-1 and 5450 kg (12,000 lbs) for SPY-1A. SPY-1D uses SPY-1B electronics but occupies only a single deckhouse, with a single radar transmitter. As shown in 1983, SPY-1B was expected to have 15 dB lower sidelobes and a better signal processor. Its transmitter tube was redesigned for a double duty cycle (with the same peak power) so that SPY-1B could transmit longer pulses or more energy at higher elevation angles, to counter diving missiles (such as AS-4/6) and jamming. The low sidelobes should reduce the effects of standoff jamming. VLSI electronics saves considerable weight and reduces the number of electronic cabinets from 11 to 5. Better software should also improve ECM resistance against threats such as self-screening jammers and sophisticated repeaters.

The effect of electronic steering in both azimuth and elevation is to produce a very narrow pencil beam that can be steered randomly across the entire hemisphere. The radar can, therefore, search steadily, taking time out to track targets of interest by going back to dwell on the area around their last appearance.

SPY-1 reportedly scans a hemisphere of 175-nm radius while using a single beam to search the horizon out to 45 nm for sea-skimmers.

Development began in 1965, and the system was first tested at sea in 1974. SPY-1A is the current production version, and SPY-1B is improved and simplified for later-production Aegis cruisers (from *Princeton*, CG 59, onward). SPY-1C was a proposed version for aircraft carriers. SPY-1D is the lighter-weight version for Aegis destroyers (*Arleigh Burke*, DDG 51, class).

The associated IFF interrogator is also electronically scanned. It is the Lockheed AIMS (AS-3134/UPX), which consists of 64 elements in a 12.5-ft ring (16 in high). The interrogator can operate in continuous, sector-scan, or jump-scan modes, shifting from one beam to another in 50 microseconds. Beamwidth is 7 × 44 deg in any one of 1024 directions (so that a signal can be localized much more accurately than the beamwidth alone might indicate). The associated system is UPX-24(V), a central IFF (by Litton) that can integrate the outputs of as many as four unrelated radars.

FARS (Frigate Array Radar System) is an RCA proposal for an S-band system based on SPY-1, but with arrays only a quarter as large and a two- rather than four-channel signal processor. The transmitter will be driven by a TWT instead of the crossed-field amplifier of SPY-1, since less power is required. FARS was originally proposed for the projected German 4500-ton missile destroyer (which has presumably become Type 123); the company (now a division of GE) claims that FARS can fit ships as small as 3100 tons. FARS has also been proposed for the various NATO AAW programs. This system is compatible with both vertically launched Sea Sparrow and SM-2, and in 1987 RCA suggested that a mix of the two (4 Sea Sparrows per cell) was ideal for the Baltic. The SM-2s would keep most intruders out, and the Sea Sparrows were numerous enough to deal with leakers and with pop-up attackers. GE describes FARS's range as about 54% of SPY-1 (literally, the same number of units of range, but km rather than nm).

See also the Aegis system and the SM-2 missile entries below.

◆ **UPS-3**

> **Band:** S   **Beam:** 8 × 17 deg
> **Peak Power:** 230 W   **Gain:** 22 dB
> **Scan Rate:** 60 or 90 deg/sec
> **Antenna Weight:** 56 lbs (plus 45.2 lbs pedestal and 25 lb quadrupod)

This lightweight radar, by Lear Astronics, was developed to alert Stinger operators assigned to provide forward-area air-defense for the U.S. Army's Light Divisions. UPS-3 is included here because it has been supplied to the navy to support Stinger missile operators on board ships. UPS-3 is designated TDAR (Tactical Defense Alert Radar) and can be set up by two men in less than 10 minutes. Maximum range is 20 km, and maximum target altitude 10,000 ft. Solid-state electronics makes for very high reliability (MTBF is 2180 hours). The antenna is a slotted waveguide. The LED display identifies a target as either a fixed or rotary wing aircraft, presumably on the basis of a moving target indicator (MTI).

This radar was based on the Israeli EL/M-2106 point-defense alert radar.

◆ **FAST**

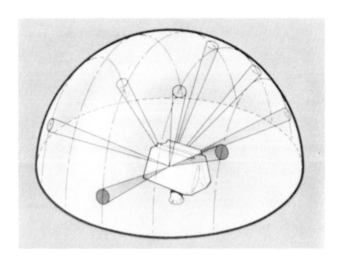

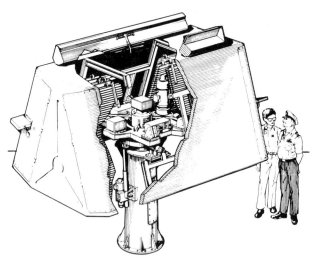

FAST radar. (General Electric)

Band: C (5.4–5.9 GHz) (There is also an S-band version, operating at 3.1–3.5 GHz.)
Beam: 1.4 × 2.0 degrees (8 beams)
Peak Power: 1 MW (average 10 kW) in C-band; 2 MW in S-band (average 20 kW)
Pulse Width: 0.6–200 microsec (pulse compressed)
PRF: 50–13,000 pps
Scan Rate: 15 (S-band) or 30 (C-band) rpm
Antenna Dimensions: 10 × 6 ft (S-band: 15 × 9 ft)
Antenna Weight: 3500 lbs (total weight 11,550 lbs) (S-band: 7000/20,300 lbs)

This C-band surveillance and missile-guidance radar was announced by General Electric in 1983 (the prototype was completed in mid-1982 as a private venture). The name means Flanking-beam Array Switching Technique. FAST is one possible approach to future multiple-target engagement radars and may be typical of the systems proposed for the NATO frigate. FAST uses two back-to-back rotating arrays, each capable of generating four independent pencil beams, using 5376 elements per face. The beams are phase-scanned only in elevation, and this design greatly reduces the total number of phase shifters required per face (to 224). They are fixed in bearing relative to the face of the radar, each being 1.4 × 2.0 degrees in size. As the radar turns at 30 rpm, a target may be painted eight times per rotation, for a high (4-Hz) data rate.

GE built only one face. Estimated performance of the C-band version included target detection at 143 nm (246 nm in the S-band version) in search mode (at up to 100,000 ft), with a 12-second frame rate; horizon search with a 1-second frame rate (i.e., data-renewal rate); track initiation in less than 2 seconds, based on a sequence of detections; track maintenance with 0.5–4 updates/sec; and automatic tracking of over 100 (200 in the S-band version) targets simultaneously. The radar was fitted for MTI to reject clutter (apparently it had a coherent transmitter, since MTI was by fast Fourier transform). FAST was an automatic detector/tracker.

◆ **FLEXAR**

Hughes's track-while-scan multiple-engagement radar (the name means Flexible Adaptive Radar), for both search and fire control, is based on AWG-9 technology. The antenna is a 40-inch dish rotating mechanically at 60 rpm while scanning a pencil beam electronically in both train and elevation. Coverage extends from the horizon to nearly the zenith. Targets can be accepted from other radars, or Flexar can automatically detect and track by itself. The adaptive feature applies to the automatic selection of waveforms to reject clutter and to resolve complex targets, a feature made possible by using a powerful general-purpose computer rather than a hard-wired transmitter. FLEXAR can track and illuminate simultaneously by stealing 10 out of 100 milliseconds for search or target-position update while illuminating. When the antenna stops, the radar has a 120-degree field of view (90 degrees in the prototype); and FLEXAR can switch the beam within that field in 20 microseconds. The radar can generate up to four steerable beams simultaneously, then go back to one beam for higher power. A track is typically established in 4 seconds based on 13 independent observations of target position.

FLEXAR has been proposed to the U.S. Navy as a multiple-target tracker/illuminator and was one of several radars funded by the NAVSEA prototyping office under small-ship AAW programs. This radar has also been proposed as a new I-Hawk control radar (multifunction radar, MFR). Navy tests consisted of search/track experiments at Point Mugu, followed by SM-2 control experiments at China Lake. Proof-of-principle tests were completed in 1981, and intermediate weapons-control tests in 1982. FLEXAR successfully controlled Hawk and Standard missiles in 1983.

◆ **MBAR**

Band: C (5.4–5.9 GHz)
Beam: 1.75 × 5 deg low angle; 8 deg high angle
Pulse Width: 1.8 microsec (average)
Peak Power: 70 kW (average 2.1 kW) (see notes)
Gain: 32 dB peak reception; transmission gain is 26 dB (fan beam)
PRF: 17,200 pps average (four 32- or 16-pulse groups, of differing PRFs, per look) (see notes)
Scan Rate: 40 rpm (less for long-range mode)
Antenna Dimensions: 8.5 × 3 ft
Antenna Weight: 1500 lb at masthead, 4500 lb below decks

Raytheon's private-venture Multi-Beam Acquisition Radar is a small-ship 3D air-search set designed to cover both very high and very low angles. Like the Signaal SMART, MBAR transmits a fan beam and uses a multibeam receiver (with a beam-forming lens rather than strip-lines) to resolve elevation. There are 17 beams (16 active, 1 reserved for electronic stabilization) formed by a lens. The 16 receiving beams are multiplexed into 8 processors. MBAR is a pulse-doppler radar (using a TWT transmitter), so it can obtain a target's range, bearing, altitude, and range rate in a single scan (1.5 seconds). Raytheon, therefore, called MBAR a 4-D radar (position plus speed). MBAR can maintain track on 100 targets simultaneously. Maximum time from first detection to designation is 3 seconds.

Besides the primary local-area (self-defense) operating mode, there were two others: surface-search for navigation and surface-gun control (40-rpm data rate, noncoherent 4-kHz PRF, pulse compression to achieve a range accuracy of 10 meters, a beam-splitting processor to achieve a bearing accuracy of 0.17

MBAR. (Raytheon)

deg, and an instrumented range of 37 rather than 80 km); and long-range (extended acquisition, elevation limited to 40 degrees of elevation by scanning with only the lower nine beams; data rate 7.5 rpm; and instrumented range increased to 185 km [100 nm]).

Effective range is 30 nm on a 1 square-meter target (20 nm on a 0.2 square-meter target at altitude, about 6 nm on such a target at an altitude of about 10 ft). In the long-range mode, a 1 square-meter target can be detected at about 55 nm. Target speeds of up to 3900 ft/sec incoming and 1200 ft/sec retiring can be accepted. Accuracy: better than 0.4 degrees in bearing, 1 degree in elevation (0.6 degrees for the high beams, 1.0 deg for the lowest beam), 200 ft in range, 23 ft/sec in range rate, 0.15 deg in bearing in surface gun-control mode. Resolution: 900 ft in range, one beamwidth in elevation.

Raytheon also proposed more powerful versions, with peak powers of 165 kW (average power 5 kW) or 350 kW (average power 10.5 kW). The 165-kW version was expected to detect a small aircraft (1 square meter, cumulative probability of detection 0.9) at 37 nm. For a sea-skimmer (0.1 square meter at 8 meters in altitude), calculated detection range was 10 nm (the range at which single-scan probability of detection would be 0.9). At 350 kW, aircraft detection range was expected to increase to 42.2 nm at Mach 1 (allowing for 2 or 3 radar hits before detection). Raytheon credited the larger versions with the capability of tracking 200 targets simultaneously, in three dimensions.

In this version, the angular resolution is calculated as 10 deg in elevation and 3.5 deg in azimuth; range resolution is 350 m (1150 ft); single scan accuracies are better than 0.4 deg in azimuth and 0.7 deg in elevation (1.2 deg at low angles), 100 ft (30 m) in range, and 7 m/sec (23 ft/sec) in range rate.

In 1981 Raytheon claimed that MBAR could function in an ECM environment ten times worse than the next decade's predicted standoff jammer threat (100-nm range), and that MBAR was ten times less vulnerable to jamming than any earlier radar of its type, thanks to extremely low sidelobes (-50 dB), frequency agility, high average power, and narrow beamwidth.

MBAR uses the same missile-guidance transmitter as the land-based Patriot missile system; Raytheon also used the same transmitter in its C-LAS (C-band Lightweight Acquisition System), which the company hoped to use with vertically launched Sea Sparrow missiles, and which ran trials on board the Norwegian frigate Narvik in 1977 (this test demonstrated the new clutter-rejecting waveform, low-angle detection at C-band, track-while-scan operation, and weapons-system integration). C-LAS proved unsuccessful, and Raytheon modified that system to carry out horizon and medium-altitude sweeps on alter-

nate scans (rather than selecting a single mode). MBAR was a much more capable multibeam radar developed from C-LAS.

The MBAR prototype was tested on board USS Stump (DD 978) in 1984 off Virginia Capes (as a demonstration of low-angle detection and weapons-system integration) and then on board the German test ship Hans Burkner in 1985, in the Baltic, in the Bay of Biscay, and off the Norwegian Coast. These latter tests were intended to demonstrate Exocet detection; clutter and chaff rejection; low sidelobes; 3-D detection and measurement; and hemispheric coverage. For example, in the Bay of Biscay on 13 May 1985, MBAR detected two Exocets, at 14.2 and 15.6 km (predicted range 15 km) and tracked them in to self-destruct range (4 km). By 1987, the German Navy planned to begin installation of MBAR on board its fast attack craft in 1989. However, when the U.S. Navy failed to adopt the new radar, the Germans were unwilling to become its sole users, and they purchased the Hughes TAS Mk 23 instead.

◆ Furuno Radars

The U.S. Navy now uses Japanese commercial (Furuno) navigational radars, as in the past it typically used Pathfinder 1500s. Furuno radars are now very common in commercial service (e.g., on board fishing boats). The great advantage of using standard commercial radars on board combatant ships is that ESM surveillance systems cannot distinguish ships navigating with such radars from noncombatants. It seems likely that the Furuno was the Japanese radar planned for the abortive SWCM, the special warfare craft, medium.

U.S. aircraft carriers use the Furuno 904. Some coast guard cutters have Furuno 1510s. These radars are on board at least the submarine Sunfish (SSN 649), the destroyer Hewitt, the submarine tender Emory S. Land, and the tanker Monongahela. Some of the smaller Furunos are used on board coastal (special warfare) craft, such as 65-foot patrol boats and 36-foot Sea Foxes. These standard commercial sets have not been assigned AN/SPS designations.

Radar characteristics are listed here because, although the radars are of Japanese origin, their main military user is the U.S. Navy.

Model:	8050D	904
Band:	X	X
Beam:	(i) 1.8 × 25 deg	2.4 × 25 deg
	(ii) 1.23 × 25 deg	
	(iii) 0.95 × 20 deg	
Peak Power:	5 kW	3 kW
Pulse Width:	(a) 0.08/0.3 microsec	(a) 0.08 microsec
	(b) 0.3/0.6 microsec	(b) 0.5 microsec
	(c) 0.6/1.2 microsec	
	(d) 1.2 microsec	
PRF:	(a) 2100 pps	(a) 2500 pps
	(b) 2100/1200 pps	(b) 840 pps
	(c) 1200/600 pps	
	(d) 600 or 500 pps	
Scan Rate:	24 rpm	24 rpm
Antenna Width:	(i) 4 ft	3 ft 5 in
	(ii) 6.5 ft	
	(iii) 8 ft	

In this list, 8050D is taken as typical of small-ship Furuno radars. There are three alternative slotted-waveguide antennas, denoted (i) through (iii). Some models have higher-powered (10- and 25-kW) transmitters. The 1500 series matches 8050 series characteristics.

These radars use raster-scan (TV-like) displays rather than the previous standard PPIs. They are digitized, with sufficient memory to store the radar picture and display it in flicker-free form. Echoes are sufficiently persistent to show target tracks, and the radar controls are typically provided in touch-pad form. Display options in the 1510 include an off-centered display, a zoom display (the area of interest can be doubled without changing radar range (i.e., PRF), and echo trail (as much as one minute of target history can be displayed). Echoes are sorted into eight brightness categories; the manufacturer claims that this feature prevents targets from fading in and out, as in radars with a single displayed brightness level. Signal processing includes echo stretching and echo averaging, plus a radar interference rejector.

The 8000 series has a 12-inch diagonal CRT, equivalent to a 180-mm (7.1-in diameter) PPI. The 904 has a 10-in diagonal three-color CRT. The 1500 series has a 15-in diagonal CRT, equivalent to a 10-in diameter PPI.

◆ Pathfinder 1500

This Raytheon commercial radar was very widely installed on board U.S. warships during and after the Vietnam War, supplementing standard naval surface-search sets for navigational purposes. At the time Pathfinder was also an extremely popular civilian radar, and its use may have been intended to confuse some hostile ESM operators.

Typical characteristics (1500B): X-band, 7 kW, pulse width 0.14 microsec, PRF 750 or 1500 pps, 48-in slotted-waveguide, 2 × 20 deg beam.

Raytheon also produced a radome-enclosed 1900, which was installed on board many lesser craft. Typical characteristics: X-band, peak power 5 kW, pulse width 0.16 microsec, PRF 2000 pps, scan rate 20 rpm, reflector 33 in wide, beam 3 × 27 deg.

◆ Falcon

Falcon is ITT-Gilfillan's C-band pulse-compression (two alternative compression ratios) coastal-surveillance radar. Development began in 1981, and by 1988 nearly 50 copies were on order (or had been delivered) for five countries. This radar was designed specifically for coast defense, the main desiderata being clutter rejection (against both rain and the sea surface) and reliability. High frequency and relatively short pulses make for high resolution so that the volume around the radar can be split into small resolution cells, to be processed individually. The manufacturer claims that relatively inexpensive solid-state electronics makes such processing economical. Dual feed horns (one 4 degrees higher than the other) produce high and low beams simultaneously, for air and surface coverage. The high beam improves detection at short ranges and high elevation, where the target would otherwise be in a low-gain part of the beam. Polarization can be chosen (horizontal or circular) to limit rain clutter, and doppler processing (biased toward low-velocity echoes) separates moving targets from background clutter. Targets are detected and tracked automatically out to 100 km (an optional extension to 160 km is available), and from sea level to 10,000 ft.

Falcon is frequency-agile over a 500-MHz band (48 channels). When doppler processing is being used, the radar hops in four-pulse bursts. Radar characteristics: beam 1.25 × csc2 to 25 deg; peak power 60 kW (average 1.5 kW); instrumented range 100 or 160 km (corresponding to PRFs of 1500 and 9375 pps, respectively). The system can maintain 100 target tracks simultaneously.

FIRE-CONTROL RADARS

◆ Mk 13

Band: X   **Beam:** 0.9 × 3.5 deg
Peak Power: 50 kW   **Pulse Width:** 0.3 microsec
PRF: 1800 pps   **Antenna Dimensions:** 8 × 2 ft

The fire-control radar of the *Iowa*-class battleships is mounted atop their main-battery directors. Mk 13 is also installed on board the two reserve cruisers armed with 8-inch guns. The antenna rocks back and forth inside its radome to scan in bearing over a 5.75-degree sector to either side (to achieve the two-dimensional equivalent of conical scanning). Tracking range is 50,000 yds; range accuracy is 15 yds plus or minus 0.1 percent of range.

◆ Mk 25

Band: X   **Beam:** 1.6 deg
Pulse Width: 0.25 microsec   **Peak Power:** 250 kW
Gain: 39 dB   **PRF:** 1320 pps
Antenna Dimensions: diameter 60 in   **Antenna Weight:** 625 lbs

Mk 25, the dish antenna radar associated with the World War II Mk 37 gunfire-control system, employs spiral scanning (over a 12-deg cone) to acquire the target and conical scanning (over a 2.6-deg cone) to remain on target. Accuracy in bearing is 0.1 degrees. For spotting, it has a 10-deg field of view. Angular resolution is 1.3 deg, and range accuracy is 15 yds plus or minus 0.1 percent of range. Maximum tracking range is 100,000 yds. The antenna, but not the feed system, was also used in the later SPG-53.

Tests were completed in 1947, and over 400 of these radars were built. The only examples in current U.S. service are on board the four *Iowa*-class battleships, but Mk 25 equips many former U.S. destroyers in foreign service.

◆ Mk 26

Band: S (about 3000 MHz)   **Beam:** 10 deg
Peak Power: 50 kW   **Gain:** 26 dB
Pulse Width: 0.5 microsec   **PRF:** 540–660 pps
Antenna Dimensions: 36 in (truncated paraboloid)

Mk 26 is the range-only radar of the Mk 52 fire-control system, which survives on board some former U.S. destroyer escorts. Range on a bomber at 10,000 ft is 15,000 yds; range on a fighter at 1000 ft, 700–12,000 yds; range on a ship, 400–25,000 yds. Maximum tracking range is 27,500 yds. Range resolution is 200 yds (accuracy is 100 yds).

◆ Mk 34 (SPG-34)

Band: X (8740–8890 MHz)   **Beam:** 3.0 deg
Peak Power: 25–35 kW   **Gain:** 30 dB
Pulse Width: 0.3 microsec   **PRF:** 1800 pps
Antenna Dimensions: diameter 40 in
Antenna Weight: 130 lbs

Mk 34 is the radar of the World War II Mk 57 and 63 fire-control systems and is sometimes designated SPG-34. Targets are acquired using a nodding scan (over a 4.5 × 34.5 deg field of view). Tracking is by conical scan (4.5-deg cone). Range resolution is 200 yds (accuracy is 15 yds plus or minus 0.1 percent of range).

◆ Mk 35 (SPG-35)/SPG-48

Band: X (8.5–9.6 GHz)   **Beam:** 2 deg
Peak Power: 50 kW   **Pulse Width:** 0.1–0.15 microsec
PRF: 3000 pps   **Gain:** 37.5 dB
Antenna Dimensions: diameter 48 in   **Antenna Weight:** 265 lbs

Mk 35 is the radar associated with the Mk 56 fire-control system. Accuracy is 20 yds plus 2.5 percent of range. Resolution is 35 yds and 1.5 degs. Limits: tracking 100 deg/sec in train, 35 deg/sec in elevation. In acquisition mode, the radar spiral scans over a 12-deg cone; conical tracking is within a 3-deg cone.

SPG-48, the radar for the Mk 69 gunfire-control system and GUNAR, is a repackaged Mk 35, designed for reduced space and weight, and uses the 250-kW transmitter and the reflector of Mk 25. Maximum target range is 40,000 yds, and acquisition range is 25,000 yds.

◆ SPG-50

Band: X (8.5–9.6 GHz)   **Beam:** 2.5 deg
Peak Power: 50 kW   **Gain:** 36 dB
Pulse Width: 0.25 microsec   **PRF:** 2000 pps
Antenna Dimensions: diameter 40 in
Antenna Weight: 130 lbs (total weight 1460 lbs)

SPG-50 is an alternative radar for the late World War II Mk 63 fire-control system. Accuracy is 50 yds. Resolution is 200 yds and 3 deg. Scan is spiral (for acquisition) at 2 Hz or conical (for tracking) at 29 Hz.

◆ SPG-51

Band: C and X
Beam: (C-band) 1.6 × 1.6 deg (X-band) 0.9 × 0.9 deg
Peak Power: (C-band) 30 kW
Gain: (C-band) 39.5 dB (X-band) 45.0 dB
Antenna Dimensions: diameter 91 in   **Antenna Weight:** 550 lbs

SPG-51 Standard MR directors, USS *Mississippi*, June 1988. (Stefan Terzibaschitsch)

Data apply to SPG-51C (antenna AS-2649). This radar combines a C-band pulse-doppler tracker, to remain on target, with an X-band continuous-wave illuminator for missile guidance. Both radars share a common reflector structure but employ individual feeds and reflector surfaces (a horizontally polarized solid C-band reflector and a vertically polarized X-band wire-grid reflector embedded in dielectric material on its face). The radar tracks in C-band by monopulse, using a four-horn cluster feed. SPG-51 reportedly differs from other high-PRF systems in using multiple medium PRFs to permit conventional range tracking and doppler clutter rejection.

SPG-51C introduced automatic acquisition and tracking, improved ECCM features, clutter rejection, and multiple target resolution as well as greater reliability. The current SPG-51D is described as dual channel, presumably so that, using adjacent radars, a ship can control two different missiles fired at two different targets. SPG-51E, which was not built in quantity, was intended as a "universal fire-control radar," to control Talos as well as Tartar (now Standard) missiles.

SPG-51 radars are manufactured by Raytheon.

◆ SPG-52

Band: Ku (16.3–16.5 GHz) **Beam:** 5 deg
Peak Power: 50 kW **Gain:** 30 dB
Pulse Width: 0.5 microsec **PRF:** 1500 pps (modulation 400 Hz)
Antenna Dimensions: diameter 12 in **Antenna Weight:** 2 lbs

SPG-52 is the radar associated with the Mk 70 gunfire-control system. Manufactured by Lockheed Electronics, SPG-52 must have been one of the earliest practical applications of Ku-band technology. SPG-52 was a range-only radar, with no means of tracking, functionally equivalent to Mk 26, above. Maximum range was 10,000 yds. Total weight was 1177 lbs, compared with 890 lbs for Mk 26.

◆ SPG-53

Band: X **Beam:** 1.6 deg (spiral or conical scan)
Peak Power: 250 kW **Gain:** 39 dB
Pulse Width: 0.25 microsec **PRF:** 1000 pps
Antenna Dimensions: diameter 60 in
Antenna Weight: 163 lbs (antenna only); total 5000 lbs

SPG-53 is associated with the Mk 68 gunfire-control system found on board many U.S. frigates, destroyers, and cruisers. Later ships (such as the *Spruances*) have Mk 86 systems, incorporating SPG-60 radars. The original SPG-53 had a maximum tracking range of 50,000 yds, but this figure was doubled in SPG-53As intended for missile ships (*Mahan* class and later). SPG-53A's accuracy is 10 yds plus or minus .025 percent of range. Resolution is 80 yds and 1.3 deg. Tracking limits are

50 deg/sec in train and 30 deg/sec in elevation. The radar spiral scans to acquire targets (within a 12-deg cone) and tracks by conical scanning (within a 2.6-deg cone).

SPG-53B and -53C incorporate X-band continuous-wave illuminators (CWI) and can, therefore, control semiactive missiles. Associated with GFCS Mk 68 Mods 9 and 10, these latter versions employ an AS-1868 antenna rather than the AS-515A of earlier SPG-53s. The radar's diameter is 64 in (318 lbs for the antenna alone). Like SPG-51, SPG-53 employs vertical wires to reflect the CW illumination. Gain is 38 dB for the main (tracking) radar and 41.6 dB for the main CW illuminator. These radars are used on board some missile ships to provide an additional missile-control channel.

The original SPG-53 used spiral (12 deg, for acquisition) and conical (3 deg, for tracking) scans and had a maximum instrumented range of 120,000 yards. There was also a 4000-yard precision sweep. Since SPG-53E (or earlier), these radars have used monopulse tracking. The -53E model also has low-elevation-angle tracking that uses clutter cancelation, and has surface splash-spotting and a missile-launch alarm for quick reaction. At least -53E and the current -53F incorporate simulated ECM for training.

These radars are manufactured by Western Electric.

◆ SPG-55

A pair of SPG-55 fire-control radars, with Harpoon canisters visible in the foreground. (U.S. Navy)

Band: C and X
Beam: 1.6 × 1.6 degrees (C-band tracker) 0.8 × 0.8 degrees (X-band illuminator)
Peak Power: 1000 kW (C-band) average power 5 kW (X-band illuminator)
Gain: 39 dB
Pulse Width: 12 (compressed to 0.1) and 13 (compressed to 1) microsec (C-band)
PRF: 427 pps
Antenna Dimensions: 175 × 281 in (total); dish 96 in
Antenna Weight: 12,970 lbs (total radar assembly)

SPG-55 is the radar associated with the Terrier and the SM-1(ER) missiles found on board U.S. missile destroyers (*Mahan* class) and cruisers. In modified form, SPG-55 can control SM-2(ER) missiles. SPG-55B employs a C-band pulse tracking radar and an X-band illuminator.

This system was originally designed to control beam-riding missiles, the last of which were nuclear-armed Terriers (BT(N) version). In beam-riding operation, the wide-beam capture antenna conically scans by means of a nutating feed. The system gains control of the missile within about 4 seconds and steers it into the main beam, which nutates at about 30 cycles per second. In semiactive operation, the radar produces two X-band beams: a narrow illuminator and a wider reference beam, against which the missile can compare the doppler-shifted reflected energy.

There is also an auxiliary short-range mode for antiship missile defense, using a Custer horn (beam 12 × 3 degrees) to illuminate short-range low-altitude targets and, at the same time, provide a rear reference beam. The Custer horn is used in sector-scan-engagement and continuous-boat-track modes.

The radar tracks by using either pulses (from the main antenna) or CW doppler, and there is also a special low-elevation tracking mode. Alternatively, in heavy jamming, the radar can track a jammer (passive-angle-track mode) and can accept external range data, e.g., from NTDS. Alternatively, the operator can manually track the target using a range rate control (local-range-track mode), the computer maintaining the range rate at the value last entered. There is also a "coast" mode in which tracking is abandoned, but values of range and range rate are estimated using prejamming figures.

◆ SPG-60

Band: X **Beam:** 1.2 × 1.2 deg
Peak Power: 5.5 kW **Pulse Width:** 0.27, 1, or 6 microsec
PRF: 25,000–35,000 pps **Gain:** 41.5 dB
Antenna Dimensions: diameter 160 in
Antenna Weight: 4015 lbs total

SPG-60 is the pulse-doppler tracking-and-illuminating radar associated with the Mk 86 fire-control system; SPG-60 operates in conjunction with the SPQ-9 track-while-scan search radar. The radar tracks using a four-horn monopulse assembly, the CWI feed being mounted on front of the horns.

Typically SPG-60 acquires targets designated either by SPQ-9 or by a search radar, searching the designated area and then tracking at ranges of up to 50 nm. SPG-60 can illuminate targets for both Sea Sparrow and Standard missiles. An associated computer is used to vary pulse width and PRF, to resolve the range ambiguities inherent in pulse-doppler operation.

This radar is made by Lockheed Electronics.

◆ SPG-62

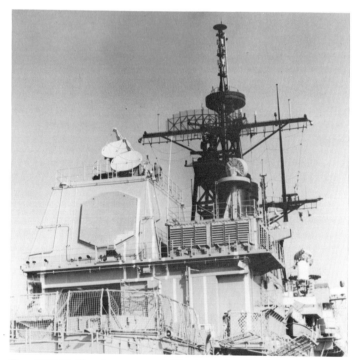

Two SPG-62 illuminators are visible above the after face of the SPY-1 radar on board USS *Ticonderoga*, 1983. The large circular structure is the IFF associated with the Aegis system; above it are the TACAN (the flat radome at the masthead) and the LAMPS data link. (Department of Defense)

Band: X **Average Power:** 10 kW
Antenna Dimensions: diameter 90 in

SPG-62 is the illuminator associated with the SPY-1 (Aegis) radar and its Mk 99 missile-fire-control system. Unlike SPG-51, which SPG-62 resembles, it does not track its targets. The Aegis system points the illuminator at targets detected and tracked by the main radar, during the last few seconds of missile flight, to provide terminal guidance for the SM-2 missile.

SPG-63 was the alternative tracker-illuminator, using the same antenna, with C-band (42.5 kW, PRF 10,400–10,800 pps) tracking. SPG-63, however, was unnecessary: SPY-1 provided sufficiently accurate track data that SPG-62 could be slaved to it, with no tracking feedback.

◆ SPQ-9

Band: X **Beam:** 1.35 × 3 deg
Peak Power: 1.2 kW **Gain:** 37 dB
Pulse Width: 0.3–16 microsec
PRF: 3000 pps **Scan Rate:** 60 rpm
Antenna Dimensions: 54.5 × 70.825 in (radome 120 × 96 in)
Antenna Weight: 1185 lbs (including radome)

SPQ-9 is the surface-search and target-acquisition radar of gunfire-control system Mk 86; this radar can also acquire and track low-flying aircraft. SPQ-9 is a track-while-scan pulse-compression radar; the entire Mk 86 system reportedly can handle 120 tracks simultaneously. SPQ-9 was one of the earliest applications of optical pulse compression.

Maximum range is 20 nm, minimum 150 yards. There are two versions: one for surface search and very limited (2000 ft) air search, one for air search (with integral IFF) up to an elevation of 25 degrees. Only the pure surface-search version is dome-enclosed. The operator can choose among five operating frequency ranges, using pulse-to-pulse frequency agility to defeat ECM. SPQ-9 is a digital radar, with digital MTI. The antenna is stabilized against roll and pitch.

The alternative version, for combined air- and surface-search, had a 25-degree (elevation) fan beam and an IFF antenna and was generally mounted on deck. No production versions of this antenna appear to have entered service.

Current work is concentrated on an MTI/low-noise front end (LNFE). MTI should counteract chaff and heavy weather; LNFE should reduce the minimum radar cross section of a target to a quarter of the present value.

SPQ-9 radar without its radome. See also the illustration for the Mk-86 fire-control system. (Lockheed Electronics)

◆ STIR

Separate Target Illumination Radar was designed for the Mk 92 fire-control system of the *Perry*-class frigates. STIR has no separate AN-series designation. Thanks to its greater diameter (i.e., higher gain), the STIR antenna can be used to track targets at ranges beyond those of the Mk 92 with which STIR operates. It also has a CWI to guide SM-1 (Medium Range) missiles. Tracking is by monopulse, and in the CWI mode the antenna functions as a Cassegrain, the illumination being reflected off a subreflector at the monopulse cluster, and focused by the main dish. A CW fill-in horn is mounted in front of the monopulse cluster. The dish is pierced for two aligning telescopes and also for a coaxial television tracker (which, however, has not been fitted). Diameter is 100 in (turning radius 78 in), and height, including pedestal, is 138 in. This antenna is designated UD 417. UD 417 is substantially smaller than the Mk 39 antenna of SPG-60 (diameter 160 in), which is also a monopulse tracker with CWI and which is very similar in appearance.

◆ TAS (Target Acquisition System) Mk 23

Band: L   **Beam:** 3.3 × 75 deg
Peak Power: 200 kW   **Gain:** 21 dB
PRF: See below
Scan Rate: 15 or 30 rpm
Antenna Dimensions: 231 × 129 in (including pedestal)
Antenna Weight: 1950 lbs topside; 10,000 lbs total

The Hughes Target Acquisition System Mk 23 is the search radar and associated combat-control system with the Improved Point-Defense Missile System (NATO Sea Sparrow Missile System) in U.S. Navy service. The designation parallels that of Aegis, except that there is no separate designation for the search radar (analogous to SPY-1). The TAS radar is a range-gated pulse-doppler type, mounted back to back with an IFF antenna, and is intended to locate, acquire, track, classify, and designate missiles diving or popping up 30–60 seconds before impact. The broad (vertical) fan beam covers missiles diving at steep angles, and the doppler processor can separate moving low-level targets from the surrounding clutter of the sea return. The beam is shaped so that most of its energy is transmitted at low elevation angles.

The waveform is ramped FM.

The radar automatically detects and tracks, feeding data into an associated combat-system computer. TAS is broadly equivalent to the British Type 967/968 associated with the Seawolf point-defense missile system. Mk 23 can track up to 54 targets simultaneously. The manufacturer claims that it can reject over 50 dB of clutter around a moving-target return. ECCM features include the ability to switch rapidly on and off (for EMCON, without risk of being unable to switch back on); and doppler processing helps TAS overcome jammers, both on and off axis. Range-gating makes it possible for a ship to concentrate on targets without accidentally tracking nearby friendly aircraft or surface ships (when, for example, an ASW ship is stationed between a carrier and a suspected-submarine contact). The operator selects a controlled-reaction zone (CRZ), in which the radar picks up targets either automatically or semiautomatically, the latter method allowing the operator to override friendly or neutral tracks and so to prevent the system from engaging them.

The two primary operating modes are normal (automatic point defense, 20-nm scale) and medium-range (surveillance and air control beyond 90 nm). They can be mixed for combined point defense and air surveillance. PRFs corresponding to the two modes would be, respectively, about 4000 and about 900 pps. A PRF of 4000 corresponds to a first blind speed of about 1900 kts.

The radar antenna consists of 26 flared feed horns, plus one for sidelobe blanking and one for sidelobe cancellation. Total weight is 10,000 lbs (2,000 lbs topside). TAS radars are connected to general-purpose standard navy computers (UYK-20), which determine whether targets are threats (using IFF), rank them, and then designate weapons to engage. The computer can maintain more than 50 target tracks, each of which requires 20 words of the 60K memory. Reaction time is typically 60–80 seconds, but the minimum is less than 30 seconds. The operator uses a standard NTDS console (UYA-4).

Originally Mks 20 to 24 were developed, sophistication increasing with Mark number. Mk 24 incorporated an infrared sensor. Mk 23 was tested at sea on board the destroyer *Downes* in 1975. Mod 0 was the engineering development model. Mod 1 is integrated with NTDS, for the *Spruance* class; Mod 2, for major auxiliaries, is a stand-alone model, with its own NTDS-type UYA-4 console.

In 1984 TAS was modified so that it could be connected directly to the SLQ-32 ESM warning system. TAS is currently being updated with UYK-44 computers, the associated memory being increased from 60K to 512K. The UYA-4 console is replaced by the new standard UYQ-21.

Hughes announced an updated version, MTAS (multimission TAS) in 1985, and a prototype has been in operation since 1986. The antenna consists of a 26 × 6 dipole array controlled by diode phase shifters. It can produce either the sort of fat fan beam used by a conventional TAS or a fat elevating lobe beam as in a conventional electronically scanned antenna (such as SPS-52). However, because the array is phase-phase controlled, the beam can be moved electronically in both elevation and in azimuth. Normally a target would be detected in the two-dimensional fan-beam mode. At shorter range the radar would shift to three-dimensional operation to obtain target elevation. The elevating beam is fat because it is essential to obtain full coverage at short range and at very steep angles; pencil beams do not provide enough "paints" of the target to give a high probability of detection at short range. Phase-phase steering is necessary to allow the radar to return very quickly to a target detected in two-dimensional mode, before the antenna has turned completely away.

The combination of normal two-dimensional operation with three-dimensional operation only as required explains Hughes's description of the radar as "2½D." Hughes also calls MTAS a "4-D target designation radar" (bearing, range, elevation angle, and range rate).

As of early 1989, the conversion of a TAS system to improved TAS is a U.S. Navy–approved ORDALT, which can be carried out at pierside in ten days. Conversion entails installation of the new antenna, reprogramming of the displays, and insertion of some new electronic cards in the equipment cabinets. No such conversions have, however, been carried out. When MTAS was first announced in the spring of 1985, Hughes expected its incorporation in the sixtieth TAS to be delivered (1987).

Hughes has offered a version of the improved TAS radar as the MFR of the NAAWS program. Instead of elevating the entire beam, this version would maintain a fixed lower lobe pointed at the horizon, the same radar antenna simultaneously conducting horizon and hemisphere searches.

Hughes also offers a small-ship version of TAS, with a smaller transmitter and antenna, at a total weight of 6000 lbs (compared to 10,000 for the basic TAS).

The FY86 program included a new requirement to integrate the SAR-8 IR search-and-track device (IRSTD) with Mk 23 and SLQ-32 via the Mk 23 computer. IR-to-radar and IR-to-ESM track associations will be used to complement the radar-to-ESM association already being developed. The Mk 23 integration will permit a demonstration of IR designation to NATO Sea Sparrow in support of SAR-8 tests. The NATO Sea Sparrow office is currently trying to fit the fully integrated TAS/SLQ-32/SAR-8 system into Sea Sparrow ships; this system can also designate targets to the RAM missile. The result is a relatively inexpensive system with impressive track-handling capability, which some in the office have called "Polish Aegis." The system includes a Hughes-designed TEWA (threat evaluation and weapons assignment) component, which decides whether a given threat should be engaged by hard- or soft-kill systems, and, if hard-kill, by RAM or Sea Sparrow.

As of early 1989, the NATO Sea Sparrow office had just given permission to integrate a Hughes FLIR and a Ball Aerospace low-light-level television (LLLTV) into the overall system. The FLIR, originally developed for the Abrams tank, is the nonradar tracker of the system. The Ball LLLTV is installed atop the Mk 91 director. One problem in this installation was that director slew was too coarse for the LLLTV, with its very narrow field of view; Ball had to dampen director motion to keep the LLLTV on target. These electro-optical sensors will both be integrated with the TAS, to increase detection range, particularly when long radar range operation is precluded. SAR-8 is likely to be a future feature of this system.

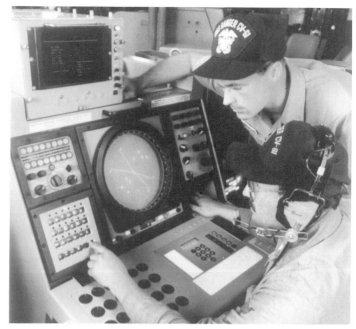

UYA-4 display of the TAS Mk 23 system, on board the carrier *Ranger*, July 1986. The display consists entirely of processed rather than raw video. (Hughes)

TAS Mk 23 antenna. (Hughes)

◆ R76/HR76

Band: X (12 preselected frequencies over 800 MHz)
Beam: 2.7 deg   **Peak Power:** 250 kW
Gain: 32 dB   **Pulse Width:** 0.25, 0.5, or 1 microsec
PRF: 1000–3000 pps   **Antenna Dimensions:** 1 m
Antenna Weight: 205 kg (1200 kg total; 360 kg including TV)

RCA's small-ship fire-control radar is gyro-stabilized for horizon search. The antenna is a parabolic reflector with a four-horn Cassegrain feed for monopulse tracking. The mount also carries an electro-optical contrast tracker (television or infrared), and a separate electro-optical director carries a tracker with a laser range-finder and a remote-control zoom lens (with a field of view variable from 30 to 1.5 degrees). Under the designation HR76, this radar is part of the Honeywell H-930 series of naval fire-control systems. Acquisition range on a 1 square-meter target is 40 km, and accuracy at 20 km is 10 m in range and 1 mrad in bearing/elevation. Search-scan period is 4 sec (15 rpm), and reaction time from designation to tracking averages 3.5 seconds.

If a target is very close to the horizon (less than half a beamwidth in elevation), the antenna is held at a fixed elevation, and the target is tracked off-axis.

R76 could be adapted to track an airplane or helicopter while receiving down-linked data from a coded beacon, for over-the-horizon missile targeting.

RCA offered a variety of versions: the basic R76, R76C for large patrol boats and destroyers, R76M for guided-missile ships, R76D to control drones and RPVs, R76LB for land-based guns for coast defense, and R76P for small patrol craft. At least in some versions, R76C uses a radome-enclosed antenna and has a higher-power transmitter. R76M uses the same components but has a two-operator console, the second position for missile control. Missiles are guided by modulating the tracking beam, the missile being tracked by the second channel of the two-channel monopulse receiver. R76D has a two-operator console (one operator for drone control), and the two-channel receiver and coding capability of the transmitter are used for drone operation. Maximum instrumented range is 160 km, to track a beacon-equipped drone or RPV. R76LB has an instrumented range of 80 km, to take advantage of the greater horizon range of a cliff-mounted radar.

The R76C5 version was bought for modernization of the Royal New Zealand Navy's frigate *Wellington*. This radar is also installed in Taiwanese destroyers, as part of the Honeywell

TAS Mk 23 on board the carrier *Ranger*, July 1986. It is the bar antenna on the mast, above the large flat plate of SPS-48C. The radar on the after side of the mast, just below it, is SPN-43, a short-range air-search set for carrier air control. (Hughes)

H930 weapons-control system (which uses two R76C5s). Some examples of this version have also been installed in coastal defenses.

HR76 was derived from RCA range-instrumentation radars and airborne satellite-tracking antennas.

◆ W-120/W-1200

Westinghouse's private-venture shipboard fire-control radar is based on the APQ-120 of the F-4J. Target acquisition is by automatic search either around an externally provided target position or around the last known target position (if track is broken). Typically a 4000-yard acquisition window is placed around the designated range. The radar acquires a target in 20 milliseconds after designation. If automatic track is lost, the radar attempts to reacquire the target. There is also a mode for detecting low fliers. Peak power is 165 kW (pulse widths 0.4 and 2.0 microseconds, PRFs 1000 and 500 pps). Westinghouse claims that W-120 can detect a 1 square-meter target at 30 nm; that range accuracy is 0.01 percent to 2.5 nm, then 2 percent at greater ranges; and that angular accuracy is better than 2 mrad. The antenna is a radome-enclosed 32-inch paraboloid (gain 34.5 dB) that can elevate/depress to +90/−30 degrees. Beamwidth is 2.8 degrees. Search patterns are 10-deg azimuth × 30-deg elevation scan; 10 × 15 deg scan; spotlight or fixed beam position. Reliability: 300 hours MTBF. The antenna/pedestal assembly weighs 860 lbs, and the display/controls 100 lbs.

Westinghouse offered several optional features: CW guidance for Sea Sparrow; 250-kW peak power; MTI/MTT (moving-target track) noncoherent mode (which was particularly useful against low fliers and could be entered automatically whenever the space-stabilized elevation angle fell below a preset angle of about 2.5 deg; this mode improved signal-to-clutter ratio by about 20 dB); and a new slotted planar-array antenna (lower sidelobes).

W-1200 is a series of fire-control systems employing the W-120 radar, higher numbers (W-1200 up through -1240) indicating greater complexity. W-1200 and -1210, for fast attack and patrol boats of up to 100 tons, require one operator; the others require two each. W-1200 employs only a navigation/surface-search radar and an optical director. In W-1210, a W-120 fire-control radar replaces the optical director; in W-1220 (for craft of 100–180 tons), the radar is supplemented by the optical director, permitting divided fire. W-1230 (for craft of more than 180 tons) adds a stand-alone SPS-58 air-search radar, for quick detection and engagement of sea-skimming or pop-up targets. W-1240, the most complex of the series, adds ESM and ECM equipment, to be able to engage targets without switching on the radars.

In 1982 Westinghouse replaced W-120 with the W-160 pulse-doppler radar. As of 1988, the company claims that all components of the overall W-1200 system are currently in service on board fast patrol boats abroad.

◆ W-160

Westinghouse's private-venture shipboard fire-control radar is based on the APG-66 fire-control radar of the F-16 fighter. The X-band pulse-doppler radar, using a 42-inch reflector (effective aperture 36 inches; gain 36 db) has a range of 25 nm on a 1 square-meter target, claimed mean time between failure being 600 hours (mean time to repair 30 minutes). Tracking is by monopulse (six-, rather than the usual four-, horn feed for greater countermeasures resistance). Tracking accuracy is better than 1 mrad in angle and 15 m in range. An alternative 6-foot antenna (42-db gain) extends range to 46 nm. A digital computer takes angular data from the radar and computes a target's position in three dimensions. The computer controls the antenna both for search and for tracking and is powerful enough to calculate gun ballistics, making the system self-contained. The radar is compatible with guns of up to 5-inch caliber and with NATO Sea Sparrow and SM-1 missiles.

Radar characteristics: peak power is 16 kW; pulse width is 1 or 10 microseconds; PRF can be one of eight between 1000 and 14,200 pps; beamwidth is 2.5 degrees (1.25 degrees with 6-foot antenna). The transmitter is coherent, so it is suited to moving-target indication (MTI), using a fast Fourier transform to extract the frequency characteristics of the returned echo. That ability is important both for tracking and for clutter/jamming rejection. The radar can operate in either a search mode (low elevation, 360 degrees at 15 rpm) or in its primary tracking mode. At low elevation angles, off–bore sight tracking is used to avoid multipath propagation (mirror images off the sea).

The associated computer has 16K RAM and 48K ultraviolet Erasable Programmable Read-Only Memory (EPROM), using 16-bit words.

As of 1987 at least one sale of W-160 had been reported.

RADAR INTEGRATION

◆ Aegis

Aegis is the overall weapons system (Weapons System Mk 7) that uses a SPY-1 radar to control SM-2 antiaircraft missiles. Mod 2 was planned for the abortive U.S. strike cruiser (CSGN). Mod 3 equips *Ticonderoga*-class missile cruisers. Baselines: (1) *Ticonderoga*; (2) CG 52–58, with the vertical launching system, Tomahawk, and ASW upgrades; (3) CG 59–64, with SPY-1B and UYQ-21 consoles; (4) CG 65–73, with UYK-43/44 computers and increased battle-group capacity in the Aegis display system. The *Arleigh Burke* (DDG 51) combat system is a combination of (2) and (3); baseline 4 builds on DDG 51 and introduces the UYK-43/44 computers. The baseline-2 program was demonstrated at the Aegis land test site in FY86, and the ASW upgrade was added to the program in September 1986. Tomahawk was integrated into baseline 2 in FY87. Baseline 3 was demonstrated in June 1987. Baseline-4 integration and demonstration were scheduled for March 1988 through February 1989 (as of January 1987).

Aegis replaces the NTDS/WDS combination of earlier U.S. missile cruisers. Aegis is built around Command and Decision System Mk 1, Aegis Display System Mk 1, and Weapons Control System Mk 1, the first and last replacing, respectively, NTDS and a WDS (the original Aegis test ship, USS *Norton Sound*, had WDS Mk 12). All of these systems are built around UYK-7 computers. In the Mod 3 version, Aegis employs sixteen UYK-7, eleven UYK-20 minicomputers, and one UYK-19 computer.

The display system has four very large (42 × 42 inch) paired screens and is entirely new. In principle, one pair of screens is for the ship's captain and one for the embarked group commander. Each pair of large screens is supported by two command-display consoles, a data-input console, and five automated status boards (ASTABs). In addition, two ASTABs are on the bridge.

The large screens display processed, rather than raw, radar video as tracks, NTDS symbols, and Aegis symbols, in white on a blue background. Each screen can operate individually, at its own range scale; and controls allow for irrelevant tracks to be suppressed, for tracks to be tagged (track numbers or alphanumeric labels of up to 24 characters in three lines), and for offsets from a display centered on the ship. Additional information is supplied on the associated command-display consoles and the ASTABs above the large screens. In principle, the commanding officer and TAO sit at the two command-display consoles, with a data-input assistant at the adjacent input console.

Because the two displays of either group can show the same situation at radically different scales (calling up the same computer data base), operators can position their ball tabs on either large-scale display (LSD), and operators working to different scales or in different warfare areas can share the same target data without changing screens or even manually pointing (as in standard NTDS systems). Important tracks and symbols can be highlighted without being tagged.

The display system can also store up to 40 patterns, such as formation diagrams, anchorages, and amphibious boat lanes. It can automatically initiate up to 16 simultaneous track histories

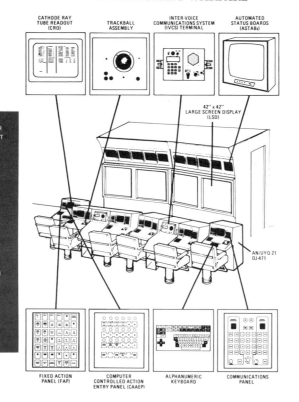

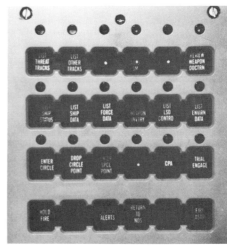

The Aegis display system. (RCA)

Aegis large-screen decision displays. (RCA)

Aegis large-screen displays on board the cruiser *Vincennes*. They are paired: one set for the embarked group commander, one for the ship's commanding officer or tactical action officer. In this case the pair of screens show the same scene (the southwestern coast of the United States) in two different scales. The *Arleigh Burke*–class destroyer, which is not designed to carry an embarked group commander, has only one pair of screens. (Hughes)

until ordered to stop doing so. It can also provide digital maps of the area in which the ship is operating, refreshing own-ship position every 2 1/2 seconds.

Aegis as a whole is credited with the ability to handle 128 tracks. The SPY-1 radar can actually handle more, the extra capacity being used to avoid overflow. The most important limit on track capacity is the interface with the track file in the associated command/control system. The margin in the radar prevents overflow when numerous long-range tracks of little immediate interest are present.

The Aegis display system is to be the basis of a future battle-group antiair-warfare display group, which will allow an embarked battle-group AAW commander to control his force.

◆ BGAAWC

Battle-Group AAW Coordination is a program to tie together all the ships of a battle group. Aegis data will ultimately be disseminated throughout the group so that non-Aegis ships will be able to use that information for firing. That dissemination requires both more efficient use of existing sensors and better gridlock within a force, since without good gridlock ships can-

not use one another's data. By 1986 an SPS-48 detection data converter had been tested and deployed. A surface-gridlock system was installed on board the *Ticonderoga* class, solving a twenty-year-old problem. An airborne-gridlock system was under test on board an E-2C. Air gridlock was demonstrated in the *Vinson* battle group, and Aegis autogridlock technology was transferred to non-Aegis ships. These efforts together constituted Phase I of the BGAAWC program.

Phase II concerns force-control items to place weapons on target, e.g., improved gridlock using the GPS satellites and improved Aegis displays.

Phase III initiates cooperative engagement capability, in which CDS (Aegis command) fire-control quality data is exchanged, and missiles are remotely fired. This capability has already been demonstrated by an Aegis ship and a Terrier ship; the next stage is the remote firing of an SM-2 Block II missile on board a vertical launcher ship, by another Aegis ship, against a real target.

The effect of BGAAWC is to increase the efficacy of fleet air defense substantially, since non-Aegis (even non-AAW) ships can become, in effect, spare magazines for Aegis ships, which can order launches and control the missiles in terminal engagements. That capability in turn is possible because SM-2 is fired into a preset basket and only intermittently command-guided.

Aegis's use for remote missile operation is of two types: remote track launch on search (RTLOS) and, at a more primitive level, transmission of Aegis data by Link 11 to designate a target to a fire-control radar. In RTLOS, a missile is launched by a ship that is not emitting at all, the Aegis ship carrying out the entire fire-control function. The firing ship, then, can be (in effect) in ambush, since an oncoming airplane may well be unaware that it is within attack range. In theory, RTLOS could be extended to include control (or at least designation) from an airborne platform.

◆ New Threat Upgrade (NTU)

NTU is an AAW upgrade for U.S. missile cruisers and *Kidd*-class destroyers. Existing air-search radars are replaced by SPS-48E and SPS-49(V)2, and a new SYS-2 IADT feeds NTDS, which in turn feeds a new WDS Mk 14. The existing SM-1 missile system is replaced by the autopilot-controlled SM-2 Block II. That replacement makes for greater range because of the option of flying missiles along the most efficient possible paths. Another reason is that each missile can home on a more distant target. SM-1 must receive substantial illumination energy virtually at the time of launch; indeed, missiles are designed to self-destruct if they do not receive the reflected illumination within a few seconds of take-off. Because reflected energy at the launcher falls off as the fourth power of range, every increase in range is extremely expensive. If, however, the missile can approach close to its target before having to pick up much reflected energy, then effective range depends on the level of energy at the target, not at the launcher, and that energy falls off only as the square of the range. Finally, because the SM-2 autopilot can be programmed in flight, missiles can be guided into appropriate homing baskets even near maneuvering targets. The result is not quite Aegis—without SPY-1 accuracy the SM-2s cannot be guided very close to their targets before requiring illumination—but is far better than earlier SM-1 systems, in increasing range and allowing multiple engagements. Because SM-2(ER) is the longest range SM-2, NTU is particularly valuable when applied to extended-range ships (formerly Terrier ships). SM-2(ER) will become less important only when the boosted version of SM-2 Block IV enters service.

In Tartar ships, NTU uses CW acquisition and tracking to improve performance against high altitude, supersonic, steeply diving missiles.

As of March 1987 the U.S. Navy planned to upgrade 31 ships (9 nuclear cruisers, 9 *Belknap* class, 9 *Leahy* class, and 4 *Kidd* class) in FY85–93. However, this program may be reduced because of budgetary problems.

◆ RVP/SIDS

Radar-video processors are used to provide existing radars with an automatic detection-and-tracking capability. One such system, the Hughes CV-2834/UYA-4(V), was applied to the DDG-2 combat system about 1972 at the NTDS Development and Evaluation Site, Mare Island, as part of a projected DDG-2 class NTDS installation. This sytem was not applied to U.S. *Adams*-class destroyers, but it was installed on board the three Australian ships of this class. Trials were conducted between June and July 1975 on board HMAS *Perth*. The system was extended to the SPS-52 three-dimensional radar, and fully auto-

matic control and surface tracking was added in 1976. In this system, radar-video processing could be applied to one radar (SPS-10, -40, or -52) at a time.

Initially (1974–75) the main mode of operation was manual track initiation, followed by automatic tracking; and there was no surface tracking mode. The Royal Australian Navy asked for fully automatic tracking, the CV-2834 program being modified for automatic target detection (with manual override). After these modifications, the radar operator's task was reduced to choosing a radar, setting optimum video level, and then turning on the RVP autocontrol; he would then monitor RVP performance. By 1981, the Australians typically operated their RVP in automatic control 90 percent of the time, finding that tracking was much better than earlier manual methods, with excellent target resolution at long range, and (because the system does not lose alertness as its operator tires) with a seven-fold improvement in probability of detection for a given opportunity. Reaction time is dramatically reduced: the estimated range at which a Mach-2 target must be detected to provide enough reaction time so that the target can be killed before passing inside minimum missile range is about half that required by the original system in totally manual mode.

In the *Perth* system, ADT data are checked by a tracking program, to see whether they correspond to realistic target motion, and those that are evaluated as real are retained in a target track file. In exercises about 1980, HMAS *Perth* was able to exercise primary tracking responsibility for a force whose other members were all non-ADT NTDS ships. One result of the success of the *Perth* system was that the Australian Navy specified RVP/ADT for its *Perry*-class frigates. The German *Adams*-class (*Lutjens*-class) missile destroyers have been fitted with SYS-1, as have three U.S. *Adams*-class destroyers.

SYS-1 and -2 differ from the *Perth* system by fusing data from all the shipboard radars; there is no operator selection of which radar to use.

The Sensor Interface Data System (SIDS) uses a CV-2834 and a computer to provide an existing radar with automatic detection and tracking, providing track data to the shipboard command-and-control system as would a manual operator. It is driven by a UYK-20 computer fed by raw data from an SPS-49 or -55; it services command/control either directly (as in FFG 7) or through a sensor synthesizer called SIDS (CGN-9 and CG-26 class). The RVP/UYK-20 combination is also incorporated in the Hughes TAS Mk 23.

◆ SYS-1/2

The Integrated Automatic Detection-and-Tracking (IADT) System is intended to integrate the disparate radars on board a missile destroyer into a single system. Video inputs (contacts) from the individual radars (SPS-65, SPS-40, SPS-52C) are correlated to form unduplicated tracks, the computer tracking the apparent centroid of an array of blips associated with a single target.

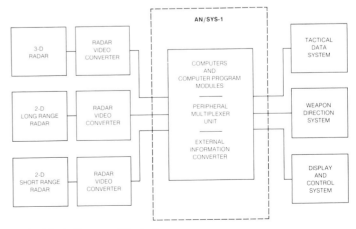

SYS-1 block diagram. (Norden)

Each radar is fitted with a radar-video converter (RVC). The raw radar video is passed through a video processor consisting of an integrator, an automatic detector, and a data extractor. The integrator sums echoes from a single target. The automatic detector estimates background clutter and noise and compares them with this sum, deciding that a target is present when a set threshold ratio (intended to hold the false-alarm rate to a preset value) is exceeded. That comparison suppresses much of the surrounding clutter. The associated data extractor computes the associated target's range and bearing and puts this data into a form appropriate to the track-while-scan computer, which correlates this data with existing tracks.

This technique can be used to refine the target's position on a beam-to-beam basis, in three dimensions. The SPS-52C radar carries out this refinement internally, in its video extractor and control group. Conversely, false targets can be rejected when they fail to reappear on a beam-to-beam basis. The system can also adjust its detection criterion depending on circumstances; for example, the system can increase detection probability in a high-threat area by accepting a higher rate of false alarms.

SYS-1, which uses two UYK-20 computers, supports two NTDS-type (OJ-194(V)3/UYA-4) consoles, whose operators include the radar-control (RC) and detector-tracker-monitor (DTM) operator. Track symbols and vectors are shown on the PPI together with a track-history display (THD) on tracks requested by the operator. The THD is a time-compressed display of about one minute of track history. There is also a digital display of track data, radar environment parameters, and program status. Both consoles are driven by one of the SYS-1 computers, the other serving as a backup.

The single-target tracks are transmitted directly to the tactical data system (TDS), a specialized destroyer system in missile destroyers upgraded with SYS-1, and NTDS in the case of cruisers fitted with SYS-2. The TDS operators decide which tracks the system supplies to the WDS, which in turn assigns guns and missiles to the targets. There is an alternative quick-reaction mode in which the SYS system passes its data directly to the WDS, to respond quickly to short-range and pop-up attackers. In the late 1970s it was claimed that SYS-1 more than halved reaction time.

SYS-1 may function either as an ADT or as an IADT system. In a *C. F. Adams*–class destroyer, SYS-1 integrates data from SPS-52C and SPS-40C/D; SYS-1 has provision for later integration with SPS-67 with AM. The integrated tracks flow into the DDG-TDS command-and-control system, which also receives IFF and sonar data. SLQ-32(V)2 data is entered by keyset, and the system also receives data links (Link 11 and Link 14). The system, in turn, provides data to the weapons systems and their specialized computers.

SYS-1 was designed specifically for DDG 2–class missile destroyers, using SPS-40 and SPS-52C radars as its primary sensors. Land tests began in October 1977, and these systems were then tested successfully on board the missile destroyer *Towers* in December 1977–September 1978. This program was part of the *Adams*-class modernization. Only three ships were fitted: *Tatnall*, *Goldsborough*, and *Benjamin Stoddert*, the first at Philadelphia (August 1981–November 1982), and the other two at Pearl Harbor (April 1983–July 1984 and April 1984–August 1985).

SYS-2 is an IADT designed for CG/CGN/DDG 993. It integrates the SPS-48E and SPS-49(V)5 radars instead of SPS-52C and SPS-40, and interfaces with an NTDS computer instead of with DDG-TDS, and with WDS Mk 14 rather than Mk 13. SYS-2 incorporates a Kalman tracker and is being installed as part of the New Threat Upgrade (see above).

SYS systems are currently in service in the U.S., Australian, Italian, and German Navies. Norden is currently developing a next-generation system, IRDIS (Integrated Radar Detection and Identification), for an unnamed foreign customer's corvettes (presumably the new Israeli *Sa'ar-V* class now being built in the United States). IRDIS will automatically integrate nonradar data, such as ESM data, with the radar-generated track files.

IRDIS-type systems should become increasingly important as ships operate more frequently under conditions of radar silence.

AIR-TRAFFIC-CONTROL RADARS

◆ SPN-35

> **Band:** X (9000–9160 MHz)
> **Beam:** (e) 3 × 1.15 (scans in 10- or 35-deg sectors) (a) 1.1 × 3.5 (tilted −1 to +25 deg)
> **Peak Power:** 175 kW   **Gain:** (e) 34 dB (a) 36.5 dB
> **Pulse Width:** 0.2 or 0.8 microsec   **PRF:** 1200 pps
> **Antenna Dimensions:** (e) 30 × 152 in (a) 78 × 159 in
> **Antenna Weight:** 3500 lbs (total for radar, including radome)

Although not strictly an air-defense radar, SPN-35 is included in this section because, as a blind-approach radar, it helps make all-weather carrier air operations possible. SPN-35 is typically enclosed in a radome and consists of separate antennas to measure the elevation (AS-1669) and azimuth (AS-1292) angles of an incoming airplane. In the table above, these antennas are distinguished as (e) and (a), respectively.

SPN-35 is a shipboard version of the land-based TPN-8 blind-approach control radar, mounted on a stable platform. First evaluated at sea in 1963, SPN-35 was designed to enable its operator to direct a pilot along a predetermined glide path to a point a mile from a ship, after which he could land visually. SPN-35 was installed on board virtually all U.S. carriers, including amphibious ships, but it is being removed from full-deck carriers as part of the SLEP modernization program; the standard combination of carrier landing radars is SPN-41, SPN-42 (or -46), SPN-43A, and SPN-44. SPN-35 is manufactured by ITT-Gilfillan.

◆ SPN-43

> **Band:** S (3590–3700 MHz)   **Beam:** 1.5 × 45 deg
> **Peak Power:** 850 kW   **Gain:** 32 dB
> **Pulse Width:** 0.6 or 0.25 microsec   **PRF:** 1125 pps
> **Scan Rate:** 15 rpm   **Antenna Dimensions:** 120 × 150 in
> **Antenna Weight:** 3400 lbs (including pedestal)

SPN-43, manufactured by ITT-Gilfillan, is the marshal or air-search component of the carrier-controlled landing system. SPN-43 can also function as a secondary or back-up air-search radar. Maximum range in clear weather is 50 nm (35 nm in rain), and minimum range 250 yards. The antenna can be tilted from 2.5 to 6.0 degrees.

◆ SPN-46

This planned low-probability-of-intercept (LPI) air-traffic-control radar is to replace SPN-42. Two SPN-46s were authorized in FY86, with engineering demonstration due in FY89. SPN-46 uses an existing radar antenna and standard navy computers. LPI will be achieved by frequency agility, which should also increase the effective echoing area of incoming aircraft and thus eliminate the need for radar augmentation in the form of the corner reflector currently used. LPI is essential because the air-traffic-control radar is the only system specific to the carriers; all other carrier radars are common to other ships. Thus the carriers can be identified passively only through their air-traffic-control emissions.

SPN-42, of which SPN-46 is an LPI equivalent, is a dual-channel automatic-aircraft-landing system, each channel of which can handle one airplane at a time. Each channel employs a pair of antennas, a Ka-band dish (AS-1347/SPN-42) and a smaller X-band beacon receiver (AS-2407/SPN-42) rigidly mounted to the dish. The main dish tracks by conical scanning, using a 0.57-degree beam scanning at 6000 rpm. SPN-42 tracks the incoming airplane and transmits track data to NTDS; the system transmits course corrections back to the incoming airplane. There are three alternative operating modes: automatic, in which commands are sent directly to the autopilot of the airplane; semiautomatic, in which the pilot responds to corrections sent via a pointer in his cockpit; and a manual (talk-down) mode.

OPTRONIC SYSTEMS

◆ Mk 35 Optical Director

This Kollmorgen periscope system was designed for the U.S. post-Vietnam small-combatant program of the early 1970s. Mk 35 has been incorporated in the Korean *Paek Ku* class. The periscope carries day/night stabilized optics plus a television. The operator can estimate range by stadimeter (i.e., by an angular measurement of a known distance on the target), or the director can track in bearing while radar is used for ranging.

Although this director is primarily optical, and primarily driven by the operator's joystick, Mk 35 has provision for automatic tracking using the television camera. Elevation field-of-view limits are +80 and −30 deg, the field of view itself being 8 × 32 deg. The director can slew at 80 deg/sec (e.g., when accepting designation from another source). Resolution is 0.2 m at 3000 m, or 0.9 m at 15,000 m in daylight; corresponding night figures (clear with quarter moon) are 1.5 and 7.5 m.

◆ CWDD (AN/KAS-1)

Texas Instruments's Chemical-Warning Directional Detector is a modified Army TAS-6, mounted on a ship's railing or TDT pedestal. CWDD is a binocular direct-view FLIR that can also be used for intelligence collection and gunlaying. Production began in 1982.

◆ Seafire (EX-121)

This abortive electro-optical gunfire-control system, carrying a laser range-finder/designator, was intended for the *Arleigh Burke* (DDG 51) class. Seafire was canceled because of cost escalation, reportedly due to the combination of stabilization and laser power required to designate targets at the substantial range of the 5-in/54 laser-guided projectile, Deadeye. The Seafire turret above decks was stabilized in gimbals; from left to right (looking toward the turret), the system carried a daylight television, a laser range-finder/designator, and a thermal imager. Data fed into a dedicated Seafire processor and UYK-20 computer and into the Mk 86 gunfire-control system weapons-control console.

Seafire could be integrated with Mk 86/68/92 or used independently. It tracked targets in three dimensions (using its laser range-finder), provided gun orders, and illuminated targets. Total weight (estimated) was 3200 lbs.

The initial contract was awarded in July 1979 and canceled in March 1983. Congress pressed for an optronic system in DDG 51, and development was ordered to start again, on a competitive basis, on 25 February 1983. Three competitors were chosen on 26 September 1983, and Texas Instruments was chosen in November of that year. The contract was again canceled in FY86, leaving the DDG-51 class with only the Aegis radar system to control their 5-in/54 guns.

◆ SIRIS

The Ship-based IR Imaging System was developed by Texas Instruments for a Mediterranean intelligence mission in 1970 and used for surveillance by USS *Turner*, *Huntsville*, and *Belknap*. The imager was stabilized in elevation and in azimuth, and images were both recorded and viewed in real time.

◆ Sea Serpent

Kollmorgen's small-combatant optronic fire-control system, announced in 1980, comprises a Model 975 optronic director (a low-light-level television with automatic target tracking, an IR target pointer [which can be replaced by a FLIR], and a laser range-finder), plus a Raytheon Pathfinder radar and a Rolm fire-control computer. The Pathfinder can automatically track up to 20 air targets simultaneously; they are designated to the fire-control system by joystick and then tracked optronically, the laser providing the range. The computer can handle up to two directors, three guns, and one missile launcher.

As in the Mark 35, the director is in the form of a periscope.

◆ Sea Tiger

Texas Instruments's optronic fire-control system was tested by the South Korean Navy in 1985. The stabilized cylindrical body, on trunnions, carries a laser range-finder/designator next to a day television camera, above a larger-diameter thermal imager (as used in Night Chaparral). There is an automatic video tracker, which can use either the television or the infrared image. The one-man console is below decks. Sea Tiger was originally designed to control guns and surface-to-surface missiles, but it can also control SAMs, since it can elevate to 70 degrees. Frigates can be acquired and tracked at up to 14 km. The pedestal-mounted director weighs 270 kg and has a working circle (radius) of 60 cm.

See also electro-optical enhancements to the Mk 68 gunfire-control system below.

SUBMARINE PERISCOPES

Attack (left) and search (right) periscopes, USS *Batfish*. The big hydrodynamic fairings are typical of U.S. practice. (*Ships of the World*)

The U.S. submarines *Pogy* (foreground) and *Michigan* (background) display standard U.S. masts and the BPS-15 radar (foreground). The attack periscope is on the right, the search periscope on the left, and the snorkel intake at the extreme left. The big hydrodynamic fairings are typical of U.S. periscope practice. Four countermeasures launchers are visible just under the sail of the *Michigan*; they are now standard in U.S. ballistic-missile submarines. (G. Arra via *Ships of the World*)

All existing operational periscopes are optical, manufactured by Kollmorgen. Attack submarines carry one attack and one search periscope. The current standard attack scope is Type 2F, replacing 2D. The corresponding search (navigation, in U.S. parlance) periscope was Type 4, which was succeeded by Type 8, then by Type 8B, and then by Type 15; the current search periscope is Type 18B. Type 15 introduced ESM receivers integral with the periscope. There was also an experimental Type 6 sit-down periscope, used in only a few cases (possibly only one). *Permit-*, *Sturgeon-*, and early *Los Angeles*–class submarines are equipped with Type 15D search periscopes. More recent attack submarines use Type 18 or 18B. *Ohio*-class ballistic-missile submarines are unusual in carrying two general-purpose periscopes, Type 8L and 15L.

Like the Royal Navy, the U.S. Navy required a postwar periscope capable of use at high speed. The two navies followed different paths. Barr & Stroud accepted a larger-diameter tube to increase stiffness. The U.S. approach was to build a hydrodynamic fairing around the outside of the periscope, retaining the small diameter of earlier tubes (compare the figures for the commercial Kollmorgen periscopes with those for the Barr & Stroud periscopes). This choice would have been a major advantage in the large U.S. post-1945 submarine modernization (Guppy) program.

◆ Type 2

The original Type 2 was introduced in 1942. It had a long slim neck, 1.4 in in diameter, and a very small head to make optical detection difficult. During the war, a range-only radar, ST, was added. Later, in the 1950s, optical design and optical coating technologies both advanced enough to justify a new design, Type 2D (1959). It is the basis of current U.S. attack periscopes.

Type 2D contains a tilting head prism (elevation limits +74/−10 deg) and is bifocal, for both high (6-power) and low (1.5-power) power observation. Corresponding fields of view are 8 and 32 deg. The stadimeter in the periscope head can be used at both powers, and the head window and eyepiece are electrically heated to avoid fogging and ice formation. A camera adapter can be fitted. Overall length is 45 ft 2.875 in (optical length 43 ft 3 in), and the outer tube diameter is 7.5 in.

◆ Type 8L Mod (T) and Type 15L Mod (T)

This combination equips the *Ohio*-class ballistic-missile submarines, Type 8L being mounted to starboard and Type 15L to port. Both periscopes support antennas, 8L for the ST range-only periscope radar, and 15L for tactical ESM. Both are general-purpose (search) periscopes, the *Ohio* class being unique in lacking a specialized attack periscope. Elevation limits are +60/−10 deg, and magnifications are 1.5 and 6 power (corresponding fields of view are 32 and 8 deg, respectively). Periscope length is 46 ft in both cases. Television camera and still photographic camera attachments are available.

◆ Type 18

Type 18 is the current U.S. submarine search periscope, for the *Sturgeon* and *Los Angeles* classes. It carries ESM intercept antennas above its gyrostabilized optics and can provide image intensification and LLLTV for low-light-level operation. Train is power assisted. There are two models. Type 18B has an overall length (to top of radome) of 36 ft 10 in and an optical length of 36 ft from the center of the eyepiece to the zero-elevation line of sight at the prism in the head. Type 18D has an overall length of 42 ft (optical length 41 ft 4 in). Magnifications (powers) are 1.5×, 6×, 12×, and 24× (corresponding fields of view are 32, 8, 4, and 2 deg). Elevation limits are +60/−10 deg. The LLLTV scans in a 525-line format interlaced 2:1, 30 frames/sec, using a minimum of 16 gray scales; the sensor is a silicon intensified target vidicon. Periscope functional modes are day, night, visual, TV/visual, IMC (image-motion compensated) camera, and gyro.

◆ Model 76

Kollmorgen's export periscope is produced in both search and attack versions; in both cases it carries a binocular eyepiece with split optics. Magnification is 1.5 and 6 power (corresponding fields of view are 32 and 8 deg), and elevation limits are +74/−10 deg in the attack version and +60/−10 deg in the search version. Optics are line-of-sight stabilized. The overall barrel diameter is 7.5 in.

The attack version carries a broad-band radar-warning receiver, with a display on the control unit of the periscope. The head carries a stadimeter. Optional features include a 12-power telescope, line-of-sight stabilization, power rotation, a television camera feeding a remote control unit carrying a 9-in television monitor, an image intensifier, an IR camera, and video, laser, or radar range-finders. The optics can be focused down to a minimum range of 50 m.

The search version has the same powers of magnification as the attack version. Higher magnification in the form of a 2× Galilean telescope (mounted in the inner structure of the mast) is available as an option. Like the attack version, the search version incorporates a stadimeter transmitting range electronically to a submarine fire-control system. The search version can carry a sextant, LF communications antennas, a satellite navigation antenna, and an ESM early-warning antenna, as well as laser and radar ranging, thermal imaging, and image intensification.

The image intensifier is mounted in the mast. In the night mode, the cube containing it is rotated 90 deg, placing the intensifier in the main optical path of the periscope and feeding the eyepiece. Typical performance, based on a ship with a vertical dimension of 10 m (a corvette), with target reflectivity of 17 percent is (85 percent probability)

Illumination	Detection	Recognition	Identification
Starlight	1.5 km	0.7 km	0.5 km
Quarter Moon	2.5 km	1.3 km	1.0 km
Full Moon	4.5 km	2.4 km	1.7 km

A thermal imaging camera can be mounted between the periscope's optical head and the ESM antenna. Kollmorgen offers a camera operating in the 8–12-micron band, with a 12/4 deg variable field of view (instantaneous field of view, in effect beamwidth, 0.2 mrad). The detector is a SPRITE, and it is serially scanned. It is cooled by a split Stirling/closed-cycle refrigerator, and Kollmorgen claims that a target can be detected at 15 km, recognized at 5 km, and identified at 1.9 km.

Kollmorgen offers a television video range-finder ("stad monitor") as a complement to its television video monitor, performing split-field ranging. When the operator presses the INIT button, the image doubles vertically; the operator moves the upper image to place the mast of the lower image on the waterline of the upper one. He dials in the masthead height of the target, and the range is automatically computed. Without this special option the periscope observer sees an image split by lenses at the top of the periscope, and the range is automatically computed and presented in his eyepiece.

The radar range-finder uses a slotted-waveguide antenna below the optical window of the periscope. Kollmorgen claims that the radar can be used to track surface ships. The laser range-finder is mounted in the base of the periscope, opposite the viewing optics, with a swinging mirror (as in a single-lens reflex camera) to bring its beam into the main optical path.

Kollmorgen offers a broad-band antenna with a crystal video receiver integrated into the top of the attack periscope head, with omnidirectional coverage (2–18 GHz, sensitivity 35 dBm). Indication is by LED (band, CW, or pulse) and audio alarm, the indicators being mounted on the periscope crosshead. Alternatively, a more elaborate (and more massive) ESM/DF antenna can be mounted in the head of the periscope, covering the same frequency range but providing either quadrant or 10-deg directional accuracy. This system can connect to other submarine systems.

The sextant uses the periscope synchro to read off its line of elevation from the deck plane, the target-bearing transmitter to measure the target's direction relative to the submarine, and a built-in vertical reference to determine tilt and cross tilt angles so that the sextant can measure star altitudes relative to the true horizon. The corrected altitude angle, bearing angle, and time are displayed and printed.

The basic periscope can also be fitted with a microphone,

allowing the user to communicate with other parts of the submarine while making observations.

Applications of Type 76 (S76) include the Brazilian Type 1400 submarines, the Indian Type 1500 (*Shishumar* class), the Italian *Pelosi*-class submarines (models 322 and 323, one including a laser range-finder), and the Swedish *Nacken* class.

♦ Optronic Periscopes

The U.S. Navy does not currently use any optronic periscopes. However, in recent years there has been considerable interest in the subject. A research and development (technical demonstration) optronic scope project, Dark Eyes, was begun about 1979 and was tested at sea but never entered production, and by about 1984 Dark Eyes had been retired. Dark Eyes suffered because it was a special-purpose system (limited to the 8–12-micron infrared band) and because installation in the sail of a submarine proved extremely expensive. It did employ a nonpenetrating mast.

The broader-spectrum optronic ("photonic") concept is now being pursued. An experimental electro-optical periscope image-storage system is operational at NUSC New London. About 1985 the U.S. SSN 21 (*Seawolf*) project office became interested in a nonpenetrating photonic mast. A research program, began in 1986 under navy auspices, was soon taken over by DARPA, the latter issuing Kollmorgen a $3.5 million prototype contract early in 1989. This prototype nonpenetrating mast is to be installed on board a *Los Angeles*–class submarine early in 1990.

Late in February 1989 Kollmorgen announced a joint effort, with Riva Calzoni of Italy, to develop a new generation of nonpenetrating mast and sensor systems for future submarines. Riva Calzoni has supplied numerous nonpenetrating masts, both to the Italian Navy and to other NATO and non-NATO navies, since 1967. Earlier the same month, Dowty (of the UK) had announced a collaborative venture with Kollmorgen to develop optronic systems to replace existing optical periscopes, initially for the Royal Navy, but later for other potential customers. Dowty described the new joint venture as a combination of the electro-optical skills of Kollmorgen and its own command, control, and display expertise. In this case the mast would also be nonpenetrating, its head carrying both optical and IR cameras. Images would be transmitted into the hull by fiber-optic cable.

The DARPA, Riva Calzoni, and Dowty projects are all separate. DARPA and the Dowty projects are concentrated on the requirements of, respectively, the U.S. and Royal Navies, whereas the Riva Calzoni project is for wider commercial application. Prior to these announcements, Kollmorgen had advocated optronic nonpenetrating periscopes for some considerable time, publicly at least since 1986.

GUN AND MISSILE FIRE-CONTROL SYSTEMS

The new *Arleigh Burke* (DDG 51) is the first U.S. surface combatant without any independent gunfire-control system as such. The SPY-1D radar is sufficiently precise to track targets and shells, for improved accuracy and reaction time. A gun-mount processor and display provides an alternative method of gun computing and a back-up mode. The gun weapons system as a whole is designated Mk 34, consisting of the Mk 45 gun (5 in/54) plus a Mk 160 computer (which does the ballistic computation).

♦ Mk 37 (GFCS)

The standard U.S. dual-purpose fire-control system of World War II was designed primarily to control 5-inch gunfire. In the U.S. Navy, Mk 37 survives only on board the four battleships and the two reserve cruisers (*Des Moines* class). It also survives on board many ex-U.S. destroyers in foreign navies. All existing versions employ the Mk 25 fire-control radar. These directors carry 15-ft stereo range-finders. Mk 37 was the first U.S. anti-aircraft fire-control system to employ a below-decks computer (Mk 1A), separate from the above-decks optics and, later, the

radar. Mk 37 is a linear-rate system, most effective at relatively long range.

Mk 37 was superseded by Mk 67 and then by the very similar Mk 68. For a typical version, Mod 62, operating limits were a lead angle of 30 degrees and a range rate of plus or minus 450 yds/sec. Detection and tracking ranges were 100,000 yds, and maximum computed range was about 20,000 yds. Total weight was 40,150 lbs including the below-decks computer, and the working circle radius was 100 in. Elevation limits: +110/−25 deg.

♦ Mk 38 (GFCS)

The battleship *Iowa* shows a Mk-38 director (carrying a Mk-13 radar) atop her fire-control tower. The structure below it carries SLQ-32 ECM arrays. Atop the bridge is a Mk-37 (5-inch fire-control) system, carrying a Mk-25 radar. (Author)

The *Iowa* class's 16-inch gunfire-control system was the first U.S. application of amplidyne drive. Mk 38 incorporates a stable vertical (Director Mk 41) and a long-base (26 ft 6 in) stereo range-finder, as well as a ranging/spotting radar (Mk 13). The main functions of the aloft director are to obtain target range and bearing, and level angle and cross-level (which are also supplied by the below-decks stable vertical). Weight is 50,450 lbs above decks and 10,305 lbs below decks, with 12 men above and 20 men below decks (2 plotting rooms). The associated computer is Range Keeper Mk 8. The director operates in primary control (observed target bearing transmitted directly to Range Keeper in plot). The director can be manually driven (by hand wheels) or power driven.

Because the computer is electromechanical, it requires a special cam for each combination of projectile and velocity. Cams exist for the 2700-lb AP shell (2500, 2300, and 1800 ft/sec) and for the 1900-lb HC shell (2690, 2525, and 2075 ft/sec). The latter shell did not enter service until late 1942, and ships did not receive the necessary cams until late in the war or postwar. Calculating limits are 45 kts (target speed) and 50,000 yds.

Ships were completed with a Mk 40 standby director in their conning towers, connected to a small radar. In addition, the turrets (Nos 2 and 3) have their own long-base (46-ft) stereo range-finders and Mk 3 analog fire-control computers.

A Mk 48 shore-bombardment computer was added to the forward plotting room in the 1950s; a second unit was added aft upon modernization (in USS *New Jersey*, for service in Vietnam). In addition, upon modernization two HP-85 digital computers were added, one to estimate initial velocity for each shell on the basis of erosion, powder temperature, and previous shell velocities from that gun; the second, to correct for trunnion height, target height, earth curvature/rotation, and temperature. In addition, the system can correct for errors in the cams of the Mk 8 Range Keeper.

The system as a whole is less than satisfactory because it still relies on a few precut cams to deal with a wide variety of current and new shells and ballistic conditions. The ships will, therefore, be modernized with new Mk 160 computers (as in the new *Arleigh Burke* class) tied to the existing 16-inch fire-control systems.

◆ Mk 51/52/63/70 (GFCS)

Mk 51, essentially a remote lead-computing gunsight, was the most successful World War II light director. Mk 52 was a modified Mk 51 carrying a Mk 26 range-only radar, primarily for destroyer escorts. The typical weight of Mk 51 was 710 lbs above decks. Mk 52 weighed 1710 lbs above decks and 1320 lbs below decks. Mk 52 incorporated Computer Mk 6 for surface fire. Operating limits for Mk 52: lead angle 20 degrees, target speed 350 kts, range for surface fire 12,000 yds, for AA fire 7000 yds.

Mks 51 and 52 survive in some foreign navies.

Mk 63 is essentially a Mk 51 with a tracking radar (Mk 34 or SPG-50) on the gun mount itself. Typical weights: Mod 23, 3900 lbs; Mod 24, 4000 lbs; Mod 28, 5300 lbs; Mod 29, 5400 lbs. Operating limits: detection range about 37,000 yds; tracking range about 35,000 yds; computing range about 7000 yds. Maximum lead angle 20 deg, maximum range rate +350 kts, -800 kts. Range limits are 800 and 7000 yds. The above-decks director pedestal (carrying a Mk-29 sight) weighs 1300 lbs.

Mk 70 was a modified Mk 63 in which radar range was introduced automatically, rather than manually, into the lead-computing gunsight. Mk 70 was installed on board the helicopter carrier *Iwo Jima*, to control twin 3-in/50 guns Mk 33. The other ships of the class had Mk 63 directors. Mk 70 had an SPG-52 radar, and maximum target speed was 650 kts.

Mk-52 gunfire-control system with Mk-26 range-only radar, on board a destroyer escort. (Naval Historical Center)

◆ Mk 56 (GFCS)

This standard U.S. postwar 3-in/50 blind-fire director also incorporated 5-in/38 or 5-in/54 ballistics. Unlike Mk 37, Mk 56 is a relative rate, i.e., a medium-range, system. In such a system the overall fire-control problem is approximated by concentrating on the motion of the target relative to the firing ship at any

given moment; the faster the targets, the less the effect of omitting the motion (other than roll and pitch) of the firing ship. The firing solution is generated within 2 seconds of beginning tracking a target. Mk 56 carries a Mk 35 (SPG-35) radar and employs a Mk 30 below-decks computer. Mk 56 was the first U.S. blind-fire director without an optical range-finder. Operating limits: lead angle 30 deg, range rate plus or minus 260 yds/sec. Maximum detection-and-tracking ranges are 30,000 yds, and maximum computing range is 15,000 yds. Elevation limits: +82/-23 deg. Total weight: 17,000–26,000 lbs, with a 51-inch (radius) working circle. Above-decks weight is 9809 lbs.

An abortive Mk 75 fire-control system, based on Mk 56 but without dual ballistics, was intended as a replacement for Mks 63 and 70.

Mk-56 gunfire-control system, in this case controlling 5-in/38 guns on board a U.S. *Essex*-class carrier, now discarded. (U.S. Naval Institute)

◆ Mk 57 (GFCS)

Extinct in the U.S. Navy, this system survives only in two auxiliaries (ex-destroyers) in the Japanese Maritime Self-Defense Force. Mk 57 is similar in configuration to Mk 51/52/63 but different in principle, having been intended from the first for radar control. The line of sight is fixed (rather than "disturbed," as in the others), the precessions of gyros tracking the target being detected by electrical pick-offs and transmitted to a below-decks computer (Mk 16). Because the line of sight is fixed, the director can accommodate a heavy radar, Mk 34.

The chief drawback of the system is the absence of a radar target-acquisition mode, so that Mk 57 cannot be used for blind-fire.

◆ Mk 68 (GFCS)

Mk 68 is a 5-inch linear-rate gunfire-control system, found on board many U.S. cruisers, missile destroyers, and frigates. It employs the SPG-53 radar and was succeeded by Mk 86. Mk 68 carries an 11-ft stereo range-finder and uses two below-decks computers, Mk 47 and Mk 116. Mk 47 was an electronic/electromechanical analog replacement for the electromechanical Mk 1 of the Mk 37 fire-control system; and Mk 47 provided faster, smoother solutions. It was first employed in the postwar Mk 67 director. Mk 68 was essentially a Mk 67 modified to handle supersonic targets. Limits: detection range about 90,000 yds, tracking range about 100,000 yds, computing range about 18,000 yds. Maximum lead angle 50 deg, maximum range rates plus or minus 1125 yds/sec. Elevation limits +85/-20 deg. Above-decks weight is 15,300 lbs (working-circle radius 80 in). Total installed weight: 26,600–28,000 lbs.

Texas Instruments produced two electro-optical adjuncts to Mk 68. In 1972, under the Quick Reaction (QRC) program, over a dozen Mk 68s were modified to include a FLIR, laser range-finder, displays, and the necessary control electronics. The system could then operate at night or in low visibility without emitting radar signals. Ships so modified were used extensively during the closing stage of the Vietnam War; because existing equipment was used, the first installation was completed eight weeks after contract award.

In 1973, based on the QRC work, Texas Instruments was awarded a contract for a Mk 68 Electro-Optical Sensor System (EOSS), as part of the Navy Gun Improvement Program. The Mk 68 optical range-finder was replaced by a high-performance FLIR plus a laser designator/range-finder; and an automatic video tracker was installed. The tracker pointed the laser, which could track to better than 0.2 mrad independent of the director. The EOSS could receive designation from other ship sensors or could acquire targets independently during conditions of radar silence. The system was installed on board the missile destroyer *C. F. Adams* and was used for three years. EOSS could be recognized by the installation of the laser and television camera alongside the director turret, on its left-hand side.

There were several major modifications to the basic Mk 68: Mods 9 and 10 added CW injection for missile control (i.e., an additional missile control channel) for, respectively, DDG 31 and 32 and DDG 33 and 34, all of which no longer exist. Mod 15, for the *Adams* class, had improved optical imaging of the target, with electro-optical and laser tracking. Mod 16 was for the *Belknap* and *Adams* classes and presumably added CW injection (CWI).

Mk-68 director, with its SPG-53 radar (USS *Pharris*). (U.S. Navy)

◆ Mk 69/60

GUNAR fire-control system is extinct in the U.S. Navy but still in use in the Royal Canadian Navy. Mk 69 could handle supersonic targets. Tracking range was 40,000 yds (computing range 10,400 yds); maximum target speed was 1250 kts; and maximum lead angle was 30 deg. The director was intended for use against air targets only, controlling guns firing proximity-fuzed ammunition. Typical topside weight was 5000 lbs, with another 8400 lbs below decks, and working-circle radius was 36 in. Personnel: 2 in the director and 2 below decks. Mk 60 is the Canadian designation for the solid-state version now being substituted for the original U.S. Mk 69 (with the SPG-515 radar).

◆ Mk 71/72/73 (MFCS)

The Terrier fire-control systems are now obsolete. Mk 71 was for *Boston*-class cruisers. Mk 72 was for the destroyer *Gyatt*. Mk 73 was used on board early *Farragut*-class missile destroyers and converted *Cleveland*-class cruisers, using the SPQ-5 radar. Mk 73 has been superseded by Mk 76, using the SPG-55 radar (Mods 3, 7, and 8).

◆ Mk 74 (MFCS)

Mk 74 is the Tartar and SM-1(MR) guided-missile fire-control system, in U.S. and foreign service. Mk 74 uses the SPG-51 tracker/illuminator radar. As upgraded with NTDS, this system became Mk 74 Mod 6 (WDS [Weapons-Direction System] Mk 13). *California*-class missile cruisers have Mod 4 (WDS Mk 11, SPG-51D, the Tartar D digital system); *Virginia*s, with ASW capability in their Mk-26 launchers, have Mod 5 (WDS Mk 13). The FFG-1 class have Mod 2 or 6 with WDS Mk 4.

In 1982, Raytheon announced a new phased-array antenna, which could replace SPG-51 and which could provide two tracking or illuminating beams, particularly for the terminal engagement. Trials were scheduled for 1983.

About 1975, the Tartar fire-control system was credited with a tracking capability between 2000 and 200,000 yds; targets were acquired at 120,000 yds (the associated 3-D radar could detect targets at 160–240 nm, and the associated 2-D radar could detect them at 20–285 nm, depending on the radar).

◆ Mk 76 (MFCS)

Mk 76 is the Terrier and SM-1(ER) guided-missile fire-control system in U.S. service. In the *Farragut* class Mk 76 incorporates WDS (Weapons-Direction System) Mk 3; in the *Leahy* class, WDS Mk 7 (on refit, with NTDS, WDS Mk 11). The associated fire-control radar is SPG-55. Mk 76 Mod 7 combines the digital computer and CW Acquisition and Tracking (CWAT) module in SPG-55B to provide an additional tracking channel in a different band for better ECCM. Mod 7 is the baseline for the CG/SM-2(ER) system (Mod 9).

◆ Mk 77/79/83 (MFCS)

The Talos missile-control system is obsolete. Mk 79 and Mk 83 were abortive replacements.

◆ Mk 78 (MFCS)

This abortive Tartar missile-control system appeared in 1957.

◆ Mk 80/84/85 (MFCS)

The Polaris fire-control system is obsolete in the U.S. Navy.

Mk 84 is the Polaris A-3 missile-control system for *Lafayette*-class missile submarines, replaced by Poseidon fire control (Mk 88). Presumably one system or the other remains on board British Polaris submarines.

Mk 85 was an abortive Polaris fire-control system for cruisers.

◆ Mk 81/82 (MFCS)

The abortive Typhon fire-control systems led to the current Aegis.

◆ Mk 86 (GMFCS)

The Lockheed Mk 86 gun-and-missile fire-control system employs the SPQ-9 track-while-scan radar, the SPG-60 tracker-illuminator, and an electro-optical sensor (closed circuit television or low-light-level television). A laser range-finder can be mounted on the stabilized television camera platform or on the SPG-60 antenna, and bore-sighted to the television tracker. An IR sensor can be mounted over the television and laser range-finder to track multiple targets, detect gun flashes, and provide a passive image of the area around the ship. The two radars operate independently and are linked only by the computer. SPQ-9 provides surface search and low-altitude air coverage. SPG-60 automatically scans to acquire a target but can also provide horizon search. The system can accept data from other

The two radars of the Mk-86 gunfire-control system on board USS *Mississippi*, June 1988: radome-enclosed SPQ-9A above, SPG-60 below. The hole in the SPG-60 antenna is for the television tracker. (Stefan Terzibaschitsch)

standard U.S. systems such as NTDS or ITAWDS (for amphibious fire support) or the Mk 74 missile-fire-control system, and Mk 86 can accept data from other shipboard sensors and from one of four target-data transmitters (TDTs).

VERSIONS

	Mod 3	Mod 4	Mod 5	Mod 8	Mod 9	Mod 10
Surface/low-fliers tracked	4	4	4	4	4	4
Air targets tracked	1	1	1	1	2	1
Simultaneous surface/low-flier engagements	2	3	2	2	2	2
Simultaneous air-target engagements	1	1	1	1	2	1
Semiactive illumination	No	No	Yes	Yes	No	No
Visual trackers	2	3	2	1	1	2

Mod 9, for Aegis ships, has no SPG-60 radar, using Aegis data for gunfire control against air targets. Mod 10, replacing the Mk 152 computer of Mod 3 with the newer and more powerful UYK-7, was developed to replace existing Mod 3s.

Mod 10 was conceived partly as an adaptation of the Mk 86 to fire laser-guided shells (Deadeye; see the discussion under the Mk 42 5-in/54 gun, below). The standard gun-control console was replaced by a Mk 113 weapons-control console, providing an interface between fuze-setting and function-setting, selecting ammunition, calculating ballistics for the guided shell, and designating a suitable laser (Seafire).

Mod 1 was for the *California* class; Mod 2 was for the test ship *Norton Sound*.

The prototype was delivered in March 1970. Mk 86 is fitted to *Spruance* (Mod 3), *Kidd* (Mod 5), *Ticonderoga* (Mod 9), *Virginia* (Mod 5), and *California* (Mod 3) classes and to *Tarawa*-class assault ships (Mod 4). Mk 86 was also to have been installed on board *Charles F. Adams*-class missile destroyers (Mod 8), but modernization plans for the class were canceled before the first three ships had been completed. Mk 86 did replace the earlier Mk 68 system on board the three West German *Adams*-class destroyers, and a similar modernization is being applied to the three Australian ships of this class.

Conversion of Mk 86 systems on board U.S. cruisers to the UYK-43 computer began in FY88.

◆ Mk 87

The U.S. version of the Dutch Signaal M22 fire-control system is for the *Asheville*-class fast gunboats. The antenna is designated Mk 35, and in some ships CWI is provided to control Standard Missiles against surface targets.

◆ Mk 88/89

Mk 88 is the Poseidon C-3 strategic-missile fire-control system. Mk 89 is the corresponding land test-facility fire-control system. Mk 88 correlates ballistic data (submarine position and motion, sea motion, earth rotation) and continuously computes missile trajectories in its Digital Geoballistic Computer (DGBC), feeding this information continuously to the missiles. The positions of a large number of potential targets are stored on a magnetic disk file. The computer has two channels, either of which can be used to target all sixteen missiles.

◆ Mk 90

Mk 90 is the self-contained fire-control system of the Phalanx close-in weapon.

◆ Mk 91

NATO Sea Sparrow on board the Norwegian frigate *Narvik*, March 1985, showing the radar of the Mk-91 fire-control system atop the raised platform at the left, and the eight-cell box launcher below and abaft it. The gun is an enclosed version of the standard U.S. twin 3 in/50, and the containers hold Penguin antiship missiles. (L&L Van Ginderen)

Band: X   **Peak Power:** 2 kW (average, CW)
Antenna Dimensions: 100 × 96 in
Antenna Weight: 3315 lbs

Mark 91 is the U.S. fire-control system associated with the NATO Sea Sparrow Missile System (NSSMS). Mk 91 succeeded BPDMS (Mk 115) and, like the earlier system, uses separate transmitting and receiving CW antennas. Targets are automatically designated from either SPS-58/65 or TAS Mk 23 radars, the Mk-95 radar of the Mk-91 fire-control system tracking the target automatically and illuminating it. Unlike BPDMS, NSSMS incorporates a wide-beam antenna to provide the missile with a reference beam. That reference in turn makes it possible for the missile to use proportional navigation, which is more efficient than a direct pursuit path.

Both transmit and receive antennas are 39 inches in diameter; the transmitter is a parabolic dish, the receiver a Cassegrain twist reflector.

Mod 0 is the single version, Mod 1 the dual version as used by the Danish, Norwegian, Italian, Japanese, and U.S. Navies. There is also a special "Netherlands" configuration used by the Belgian, West German, Dutch, and Spanish Navies employing the Dutch M25 fire-control system.

NATO Sea Sparrow launchers and Mk-91 illuminators (radar Mk 95) on board the carrier USS *Ranger*, July 1986. An electro-optical tracker is located between the two radomes of the radar illuminator-tracker. (Hughes)

◆ **Mk 92 and Mk 94**

Band: X
Antenna Dimensions: (search) (track) 96-inch diameter
Antenna Weight: 6300 lbs (topside weight)

Mk 92 is a U.S. version (produced by Sperry) of the Dutch Signaal M 28 fire-control system. The associated track-while-scan radar, which employs two antennas (the combined antenna system (CAS), UD 401) inside an egg-shaped radome, has no separate designation and is, therefore, described here. As installed on board *Perry*-class missile frigates, Mk 92 controls both the designator in the egg and a separate tracker/illuminator, the STIR (UD 417). Mk 92 controls both Standard Missiles (SM-1) and a 76-mm gun. As installed on board *Pegasus*-class missile hydrofoils, the Mk 92 is limited to the CAS and controls only a 76-mm gun.

The single console (weapons-control console Mk 106) provides a PPI for tactical display and two track displays (A- and B-scopes). Tracks are designated by means of a ball on the console, an acquisition gate being placed around the target blip on an A-scope. Once the target is being tracked, the A-scope displays engagement limits around the target blip so that the operator can gauge when to engage. The time-shared B-scope indicates designation or track error by the position of the target blip relative to the scope's center. Maximum instrumented range on the PPI is 128 nm (on the A-scope, 64 nm).

Versions:
- Mod 0: one air-engagement channel, two TWS surface channels, missile and gun control; 1905 lbs topside/9086 lbs below decks.
- Mod 1: one air-engagement channel, two TWS surface channels, guns only; 1905/5637 lbs. Mod 5 (Saudi PCC/PCG) is similar.
- Mod 2: two air-engagement channels (i.e., one STIR), two TWS surface channels, missile and gun control; 6318/15,848 lbs. This version is installed in the *Perry* class and requires a separate Mk 107 console, incorporating a PPI, for STIR control.

The two CAS antennas, a search antenna below and a tracker above, share a common feed and time-share their power. The search antenna scans at 60 rpm, a rate rapid enough to allow

for TWS tracking of up to two surface targets. The search antenna provides a measure of height-finding, by spiraling the beam up in three revolutions (four beamwidths), then down again in half a revolution, for interlaced coverage.

The parabolic dish at the top of the egg is used for three-dimensional (i.e., air) target acquisition and monopulse track. Like the search antenna below, the parabolic dish can track up to two air targets while searching for more. This array is designated Mk 53.

The 100-inch-diameter STIR antenna tracks targets out to greater ranges. It employs a modified Mk-39 antenna, with a monopulse cluster and CWI fill-in horns, on an SPG-60 pedestal. The STIR antenna is designated Mk 54.

Mod 1 is the version on board the hydrofoils, controlling only a 3-inch gun. Mod 2 is on board *Perry*-class frigates. Mod 5 is mounted on board Saudi PCG- and PCC-class gunboats built in the United States.

Mk 94 was the functional prototype, an imported HSA system.

Several improved versions of the basic Mk 92 have been proposed. Phase I is a near-term get-well program, and it is being carried out. Phase II adds a new coherent receive/transmit (CORT) transceiver to counter heavy jamming, clutter, and second-time-around clutter (i.e., targets just beyond instrumented range that are so large that their second-time-around echoes swamp echoes from small nearby targets). CORT is, unfortunately, quite massive, and it is not likely to be very widely applied. As of 1988, the U.S. Navy planned to buy six sets of CORT electronics. *Ingraham* (FFG 61), the last of the *Perry* class, has a unique combat system combining CORT with an IADT. Phase III, proposed by Sperry (now Unisys), is a much more ambitious program, adding a new high-elevation array. Phase III is intended to counter high-altitude targets in a heavy jamming environment. The navy has argued that Phase III is too expensive and too massive for ships that are already almost overloaded. Congress kept the program alive, but as of 1988 it had been canceled.

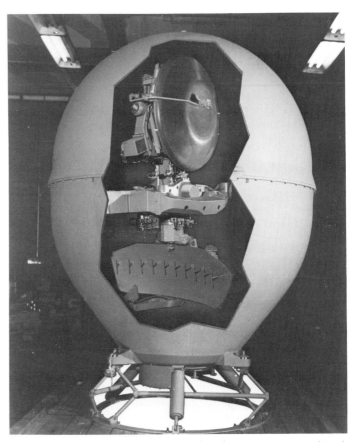

The antennas inside the Mk 92 Combined Antenna System (CAS). (Sperry)

The frigate *Robert E. Bradley* shows her Mk-92 "egg" (atop her bridge), as well as two SLQ-32 boxes, an SPS-49 air-search radar, and two satellite communications dishes. The egg provides both a fire-control channel and a secondary air-search radar, hence insurance against the destruction of the big SPS-49. The bar at the front end of SPS-49 is the associated IFF interrogator. (Giorgio Arra)

◆ Mk 93 (GFCS)

The gunfire-control system of the CPIC-prototype export coastal-attack boat is associated with the EX-74 (Emerlec-30) gun and uses the Mk 35 periscope director. This system appears in modified form on board other small combatants built for foreign navies, armed with the Emerlec-30 and using the periscope director. The radar is a Litton LN-66HP, a lightweight computer permitting two-target TWS operation. The optical director can provide two more target tracks. The lightweight (1100-lb) computer can handle ballistics for 20-mm through 76-mm calibers.

◆ Mk 98 (MFCS)

Mk 98 is the Trident fire-control system for *Ohio*-class submarines.

◆ Mk 99 (MFCS)

Mk 99 is the Aegis AAW fire-control system. The Aegis system as a whole is designated Weapons System Mk 7.

◆ Mks 100–114

Mks 100–114 are ASW fire-control systems.

◆ Mk 115

> **Band:** X
> **Antenna Dimensions:** total 79 × 84 in (including pedestal)
> **Antenna Weight:** 1800 lbs

Mark 115 is the fire-control system associated with the Basic Point-Defense Missile System (Sea Sparrow); at this writing BPDMS installations are being replaced by Phalanx close-in defensive guns and also by NATO Sea Sparrow missile systems. Because the associated radars have no separate designations, they are described here.

Sea Sparrow Basic Point-Defense Missile System handlebar director (Mk 115), with its missile launching. (U.S. Navy)

Fire is controlled from the CIC, where a fire-control panel monitors the system. The operator there turns on launcher and radar and selects and fires the missiles. Interception range is described as 4+ nm.

The missile homes on continuous-wave energy, so the radar cannot employ a single antenna to receive and to transmit. The Mk-33 transmitter is a 2-foot parabolic dish. The Mk-19 receiving antenna is a 2-foot planar array using 52 slotted waveguides in four sections, and is electronically conically scanned to track a target.

Tracking is manual: errors detected by comparison of transmitted and received signals are displayed in a gunsight atop the modified director pedestal, and the operator moves his "handlebars" to keep the error signal centered in his optical display. Manual pointing was adopted because the targets were expected to have high closing velocities but little angular motion relative to the ship being attacked. Even so, the man in the loop makes for a relatively long reaction time.

Work on this system began in 1963, and production began in 1967. The Mark number is higher than that of the later NATO

Sea Sparrow System (Mk 91) because this quick-development system was inserted into the series numbered Mk 100 and above that is otherwise restricted to underwater fire-control systems.

♦ **Mks 116–119**

Mks 116–119 are ASW fire-control systems.

♦ **Mk 121**

See optronics above (Seafire, EX-121).

♦ **Weapons Direction Systems (WDS)/Target Designation Systems (TDS)**

Weapons Direction Systems mediate between CIC and the missile fire-control system. They are all outgrowths of post–World War II work on automatic and semiautomatic Threat Evaluation and Weapon Assignment (TEWA) systems; the TEWA was needed to decide, very rapidly, whether a given target could be or should be engaged, i.e., to take into account the effective engagement capabilities of the weapons on board the ship. A ship's actual target-handling capacity depends on the capacity of her WDS, since directors are cued, not directly from CIC, but rather from the series of tracks held by the WDS, itself fed by the same radars feeding CIC. Only with the advent of NTDS is the WDS fed directly from the automated track file in CIC, since in earlier nonautomated ships the grease-pencil track data in CIC are not accurate enough for such assignment. Thus, the difference in target capacity between an NTDS ship and a non-NTDS ship is enormous, the pre-NTDS ship being limited to perhaps four or eight targets. This limitation is entirely separate from the limitation imposed by the number of missile directors, i.e., of fire-control channels. Once a particular fire-control channel has completed its engagement with a particular target, it obtains its next target, not directly from CIC, but rather from the WDS.

Non-NTDS ships with computer-driven combat systems, such as the *Perry*-class FFG, are equivalent to NTDS ships in this sense: they can maintain very large numbers of tracks ready for designation to fire control. Precomputer ships must generally assign a tracking console to each target, and the number of such consoles is very limited. As in NTDS, tracking on each console is rate aided; but the consoles do not communicate, and each carries only a single track. The pre-NTDS missile systems in current U.S. service are on board *C. F. Adams*–class missile destroyers.

Typically a WDS is included within a larger group of Weapons Direction Equipment (WDE). In the Japanese Maritime Self-Defense Force the progression has been from Designation Equipment directly to Tactical Data Systems (see above).

All of the WDS systems are outgrowths of a series of automated target-designation systems conceived by Bell Laboratories in 1945–47 under a Bureau of Ordnance project, FCS Mk 65, intended to deal with future fast jet aircraft. The reader may sense a certain convergence between Mk 65 and NTDS; the latter, however, was a Bureau of Ships project. One might see Aegis as the final merger between NTDS and WDS. Bell's major contribution was to see that some form of TEWA and some form of accurate tracking was needed to mediate between search and fire-control radars. The original concept, then, was to provide a highly accurate short-range air-search radar (SPS-3) for mediation, together with an ATEWA. In fact SPS-3 failed, but SPS-39 was conceived as the replacement.

The earliest Bell-type system, Target Designation System (TDS) Mk 3, was installed on board the command cruiser *Northampton*. The TDS series also included a much simpler category of equipment, intended to permit a CIC to designate directly from search radar to gun directors. These TDSs were the electronic equivalents of optical target data transmitters (TDTs) used by an officer to assign a target he could see to a director. Until the end of the Korean War, targets were typically designated from CIC by sound-powered phone, the radar in the director finding its target by searching around the location reported by CIC. However, as aircraft speeds increased, this

system no longer sufficed, and more direct means of transferring data directly from CIC to director were required.

The chief systems in service by the mid-1950s, some of which probably survive on board ex-U.S. warships in foreign navies, were TDS Mks 5, 6, and 7. Mk 5 was designed for destroyers, Mk 6 for carriers, and Mk 7 for missile cruisers. Mk 5 employs a horizontal PPI with four joysticks, for a supervisor and three designators. The PPI is a PPI repeater (actually a television), and the joysticks move four designating hooks (semicircles on the screen). They transmit designations to the directors, which provide repeat-back hooks to show the directors' own positions. The horizontal display can also be used for grease-pencil marking (e.g., to enter nonradar data, such as lookouts' reports). The designator who hooks a target tracks it manually (with the joystick) until it is picked up by the director.

The PPI is, in effect, an integrated tactical display (albeit of only one search radar), and in this case threat evaluation is entirely manual. In such systems, maximum displayed range is generally 30 nm (60 kyds). Although the system as such does not impose any limit on target velocity, clearly it cannot easily serve as a link to the directors if the targets are very fast, as in that case they cannot easily be manually tracked, no matter how good the joystick operator.

There was also a rather more ambitious TDS Mk 1 on board the frigates (actually large destroyers) of the *Norfolk* and *Mitscher* classes, and on board contemporary destroyers converted for ASW (*Basilone* and converted *Fletcher* classes). These TDSs were essentially manual target-designation switchboards, capable of tracking two to three targets simultaneously and of controlling two to eight directors. Mk 1 could not assign weapons to targets.

TDS Mk 3 was the first U.S. automatic target tracker, handling twice as many targets as directors, automatically tracking all of them (in an early application of TWS), and automatically evaluating the threat each target presented. Directors and guns were assigned automatically. The entire system weighed 23,905 lbs in its four-director installation on board USS *Northampton*. Mk 3 included an integrated target display and could deal with target ranges as great as 30 nm (60 kyds). TDS Mk 3 is worth describing here because it was the basis for subsequent forms of WDS. An evolved version, TDS Mk 7, was installed on board the first two U.S. missile ships, the cruisers *Boston* and *Canberra*.

It turned out that the automatic threat evaluator and weapon assigner incorporated in TDS Mk 3 was impractical. The later WDSs descended from Mk 3 all used manual threat evaluation, which generally meant the operator would decide which target would enter engagement range first. Only when the WDS was integrated with the powerful computer of the NTDS system could threats be evaluated automatically.

The WDS was associated with long-range missile fire, by Talos (now extinct) and by Terrier (which was later replaced by SM-1 Extended Range). The third missile of this generation, Tartar, was conceived as a one-for-one replacement for the existing 5-in gun and was initially provided with a simpler WDE (Weapons Designation Equipment). As Tartar matured into SM-1, its range increased greatly, and it, too, required a WDS.

WDS Mk 1 was intended for the first U.S. missile ships. It added a long-range radar (SPS-2) with manual tracking (2 targets, for ranges of 60–120 kyds) to the shorter-range hemispheric-scan SPS-3 (16 TWS channels, maximum range 60 kyds). Missile directors were manually assigned; gun directors (which would have to come into action at very short range, i.e., at very short notice) were automatically controlled. Total weight was 51,470 lbs, and the system required a total of 1335 square feet. WDS Mk 1 eventually equipped the cruisers *Boston* and *Canberra*, albeit without the massive SPS-2 radar (GMFCS Mk 71).

WDS Mk 2 was a manual tracking system actually employed on board early U.S. missile ships, capable of displaying targets at ranges as great as 240 nm and of designating at 300 kyds (150 nm); it could handle 6 targets simultaneously. There was no integrated tactical display. Total weight was 11,300 lbs, and floor area was 665 square feet. This system was carried by *Cleveland*-class cruisers converted to fire the long-range Talos missile and by *Mahan*-class missile destroyers.

WDS Mk 3 could handle 6 targets; but maximum displayed range was 60 nm, and maximum designation range was 120 kyds. Tracking was rate aided, and 3 or 5 tracks could be designated simultaneously. Threat evaluation was automatic. Weight was 10,924 lbs (floor area 380 square feet). This system equipped the converted *Cleveland*-class Terrier cruisers and also the *Mahan*s (Mk 73 fire-control system). *Cleveland*-class cruisers had two WDSs, destroyers one.

WDS Mks 4 and 5 had similar limitations (6 targets tracked simultaneously) and similar dimensions. Mk 7 was slightly more massive, capable of handling 8 targets simultaneously. WDS Mk 4 was the Tartar system in *C. F. Adams*–class missile destroyers (GMFCS Mk 74). It also equips *Brooke*-class missile frigates.

WDS Mk 6 was a long-range system, with maximum displayed range of 256 nm and maximum designation range of 395 kyds (198 nm). Mk 6 could track 24 targets simultaneously, each target being tracked (using rate-aided techniques) on a separate PPI console. Target-elevation data had to be manually updated, and directors and launchers were assigned manually. This system was designed for *Albany*-class cruisers, which were armed with a combination of Talos and Tartar missiles. On board the cruiser *Long Beach*, WDS Mk 6 was integrated with an early NTDS, which could maintain 128 tracks and could pass twelve targets to her WDS.

WDS Mk 7 equipped *Leahy*-class cruisers (which received Mk 11 when fitted with NTDS).

WDS Mk 8 was a later Terrier/SM-1 system, roughly equivalent to Mks 3 and 4.

WDS Mk 9 was planned for the abortive Typhon program; Mk 9 was part of Weapons Control System Mk 1.

WDS Mk 11 is a typical WDS designed for integration with NTDS in a missile cruiser carrying the SM-1(ER) missile. Typically a target is detected by a detector/tracker in NTDS, who enters the track into the computer. A separate identification operator decides that the track is hostile, and it is then passed to a track supervisor, who makes sure that the rate-aided tracker stays on the blip. The ship's weapons coordinator (SWC) decides that fleet aircraft cannot intercept and, thus, that the target must be handled by the ship's missile system. He alerts the ship's fire-control system and at the same time passes the target to a special tracker, who refines target position by using an expanded (4-nm) scale on his PPI. He in turn passes the target to a fire-control system coordinator, who assigns it to a particular fire-control system. At this stage the target is passed to the fire-control system, and a missile and launcher are selected. The fire-control system and launcher feed back to the FCS coordinator and the associated engagement controller. WDS Mk 11 is also on board several *California*-class cruisers.

Mk 13 is the WDS in a Tartar ship provided with NTDS (GMFCS Mk 74 Mod 6). This system equips *Virginia*-class cruisers.

Mk 14 is the system associated with the NTU modification to USS *Mahan* (1979).

◆ Honeywell H-930

This modular air-defense fire-control system uses HR-76 tracking radars and is fed by SPS-55 and SPS-58 search radars. H-930 can also incorporate the Kollmorgen Mk 35 optical director originally developed for the CPIC small-coastal-craft program of the 1970s. This system was sold to Korea (for the *Paek Ku* class) and to Taiwan (for modernized destroyers).

Each module consists of a sensor, served by a distributed computing unit (DCU), and a weapon, similarly served. The modules feed into a data bus serving another DCU, which in turn serves a weapons-control console. For example, two modules (a tracker and a missile launcher plus two DCUs, and a surface-search radar and a gun plus two DCUs) can feed into a common control console. In a more elaborate system, a surface-search radar, a Mk-35 optical director, and a hull-mounted sonar might all feed one control console, which in turn might use their data to control antiship guns, torpedo tubes, and an antiship missile. Such a network would, in turn, feed into a command-and-control console, which would be used for battle command. That console might simultaneously control another network, consisting of an air-search radar, a weapons-assignment console, and an antiaircraft gun and antiaircraft missile. One HR-76 tracker/illuminator would be connected to each network. In principle, because all of the sensors feed data into all of the control consoles, any weapon can engage any target detected by any sensor. In theory, too, because much of the data generated by any sensor is processed at that sensor (by a DCU), reaction time should be very short.

Throughout, Honeywell's design philosophy was that its system should exploit the falling cost of computing, going from centralized to distributed architecture.

Because SPS-58 can be set to detect targets automatically, the system can continuously evaluate air targets, processing highly threatening ones automatically. Given one target track, the computer typically takes 4 seconds to evaluate a second report. If the second is more threatening, the computer takes 10–18 seconds to slew onto that new target.

Typically operators initiate tracking by marking the blip to be tracked on their PPIs; they can also initiate tracking by entering a target's coordinates, range, and speed (to enter a target visible only from some other platform). The tactical coordinator at the command console then assigns weapons. Four weapons-control positions are available: one at the optical director, two at the ASW/ASU console, and one at the AAW console. All of the guns may be controlled from either console, since commands can be transmitted back via the link between the command console and the two weapons consoles.

Against a low-flying target, with the HR-76 director initially centered in a 60-degree sector, reaction time from the arrival of the antenna at the designated position (0.75–2 secs after SPS-58 detection) is 6–12.5 secs (10 sec average).

Work on H-930 began in 1972 with Honeywell's development of a Honeywell Experimental Distributed Processing system (HXDP). Communications protocols and the data-bus hardware were developed at this stage. H-930 itself was produced in four versions. Mod 0 was a patrol-boat system, on board five boats, using one air-search radar, one surface-search radar, one track radar, and one Mk 35; and employing two operators to control one 76-mm gun, two 30-mm guns, and SSMs. Mod 0 employed two minicomputers and five microprocessors. It first became operational in November 1978. The boats in question were probably PSMM Mk-5 patrol craft of the South Korean Navy.

Mod 1 (January 1981) was installed on board ten destroyers and employed one air-search and one surface-search radar, two tracking radars, and one optical director. Mod 1 employed six operators to control two 5-in/38 gun mounts, two 40-mm mounts, one 76-mm gun, and SAM and SSM missiles. Mod 1 included ESM inputs. Support was provided by five minicomputers and 23 microprocessors. This system probably applies to ex-U.S. *Sumner*- and *Fletcher*-class destroyers of the Taiwan Navy.

Mod 2 (November 1980) was another patrol boat system, on board two boats. It employed one air- and one surface-search radar, one tracking radar, and one optical director. Six operators controlled one 76-mm and one 40-mm gun and SSMs. Unlike Mod 0, Mod 2 employed ESM inputs. Mod 2 employed four minicomputers and 19 microprocessors. This system probably applied to the two Taiwanese *Lung Chiang* (PSMM Mk-5) patrol boats.

Finally, Mod 3 was a land-based system. Five were delivered, beginning in March 1980, to control SSMs. Mod 3 employed one surface-search radar, one tracking radar, and one optical director. Three operators used two minicomputers and 11 microprocessors.

Further versions were installed on board other Taiwanese destroyers, including at least four of fourteen ex-FRAM *Gearing*s.

H-930 or a similar system is presumably part of the Taiwanese Weapons Improvement Program Mk 3 now being applied to all of these ships.

Honeywell conducted a series of related tests of combat systems at U.S. naval bases and on board USS *Moosebrugger* (DD 980).

♦ **Sharpshooter**

Lockheed Electronics's on-mount digital-radar fire-control system for 20–40-mm guns was announced in 1974 and incorporated in the Spanish Meroka close-in weapons system. Sharpshooter embodies some Mk-86 fire-control system technology. This system was offered in four versions: Mk 1 (on-mount, as in Meroka), Mk 2 (off-mount, with stabilized optical sight), Mk 3 Mod 0 (off-mount, with television tracker but without an optical sight, and with dedicated tracking radar), and Mk 3 Mod 1 (off-mount, with television tracker combined with its stabilized optical sight, but without a dedicated tracking radar).

The X-band pulse-doppler monopulse radar is a developed version of the range-only radar used in the U.S. Army Vulcan system, but with greatly improved clutter rejection (and with tracking capability). There is also a stabilized optical sight with zoom magnification, slaved to the radar; and the control panel has two handgrips (one for mode control—local/remote track, the other with the firing trigger and joystick). The gunner uses his optics and joystick to acquire the target and monitors the track. Maximum target lock-on range is 7000 m, and accuracy is 1.5 mrad and 30 ft in range. Maximum radial target speed is Mach 1.8. The director's angular rate in both axes is 2 rad/sec. Elevation limits: +90/−25 deg.

Total weight of Mk 1 is 1323 lbs; of Mk 3 Mod 0, 1778 lbs; of Mk 3 Mod 1, 350.7 lbs.

AIRBORNE RADARS AND FIRE-CONTROL SYSTEMS

FRANCE

♦ **Vigil**

Vigil is Thomson-CSF's project for an airborne early-warning radar to be carried by aircraft flying from the new nuclear carrier. Reportedly Vigil will operate at K-band, using a new high-powered transmitter recently developed by Thomson-CSF. The company claims that computers are now sufficiently powerful (in small enough dimensions) to permit operation at very high PRF while at the same time resolving most or all of the associated range ambiguities.

Existing French radars for maritime-patrol aircraft all have some air-to-air capability, to provide surface ships with limited support.

UNITED KINGDOM

♦ **Blue Fox**

See the Strike/Surface Warfare section.

♦ **Blue Vixen**

See the Strike/Surface Warfare section.

♦ **Searchwater**

See the Strike/Surface Warfare section.

UNITED STATES

♦ **APG-65**

The Hornet (F/A-18) dual-purpose fire-control radar (air-to-air and air-to-surface) was developed by Hughes. It is now in service in the U.S. Navy and also in Canada, Australia, and Spain. This radar has also been adopted by West Germany for the F-4F improved-combat-efficiency (ICE) upgrade program.

The most important new feature is a high-speed (7.2-megaflop) software-programmable signal processor (PSP), which makes the radar flexible. Doppler-filter and range-gate configurations are defined by software, whereas in previous fighter radars these configurations were hard-wired.

The antenna is a low-sidelobe planar array with direct electric drive rather than the hydraulic drive of earlier airborne radars.

Air-to-air modes are velocity-search, range-while-scan, track-while-scan, single-target-track, raid-assessment (expanded coverage of a target to resolve a raid into individual aircraft), air-combat-maneuvering, and gun-director. There are also a narrow-beam vertical-scan mode and a bore-sight-acquisition mode in which the pilot points his airplane at a target. In the acquisition mode, the radar searches the entire volume equivalent to the heads-up display (HUD) and locks onto the first target detected. The gun-director mode uses pulse-to-pulse frequency agility to reduce target scintillation, for highly precise tracking. As in AWG-9, the longest range is achieved in velocity search (high PRF giving only velocity and bearing data). The range-while-scan mode uses a combination of interleaved high and medium PRF waveforms, the high-PRF waveform giving some range data and the medium-PRF waveform permitting the use of range-gate processing. Track-while-scan gives the shortest ranges. Single-target-tracking uses monopulse angle logic and can extrapolate the target's position while the target fades out of view during violent maneuvers; this mode employs a special high-PRF waveform for Sparrow guidance.

Air-to-surface modes are real-beam-ground-mapping, doppler-beam-sharpening (sector or patch), synthetic-aperture, fixed-target-track, sea-surface-track, terrain-avoidance, precision-velocity-update, and air-to-surface-ranging. Doppler-beam-sharpening achieves a 19:1 improvement in sector scan and a 67:1 improvement in patch mode.

The claimed mean time between failure is more than 100 hours. The entire system weighs 340 lbs (exclusive of rack) and occupies less than 4.5 cubic feet. By way of comparison, the APG-63 of the F-15 weighs 483 lbs and occupies just less than 9 cubic feet, exclusive of the antenna. Digital operation greatly reduces field adjustments; Hughes claims that built-in test equipment can detect 98 percent of all faults.

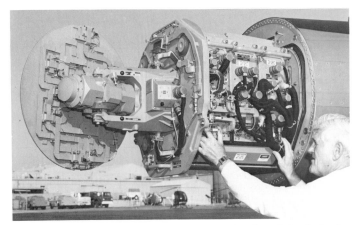

APG-65 prototype, showing the microwave plumbing behind the flat slotted-array antenna. (Hughes)

♦ **APG-71**

This replacement for the AWG-9 in the F-14D upgraded Tomcat incorporates some APG-70 (F-15C/D/E) technology but retains features of the original AWG-9. The first production unit is scheduled for delivery in September 1989. The signal processors of the APG-70 and -71 are 86 percent common.

Because AWG-9 is still the most powerful airborne fighter radar, APG-71 will retain its transmitter, power supply, and aft-cockpit display. The new features include a digital signal processor, a frequency synthesizer, a new low-sidelobe antenna array with a revised antenna scan control, a digital display, and a multichannel receiver.

The improvements provide better overland performance (which will be improved further by a future medium PRF mode),

GROUND TRUTH

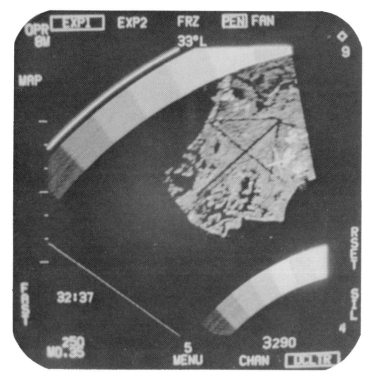

DOPPLER BEAM SHARPENING PATCH (short range)

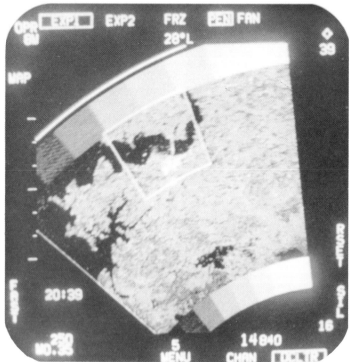

DOPPLER BEAM SHARPENING SECTOR

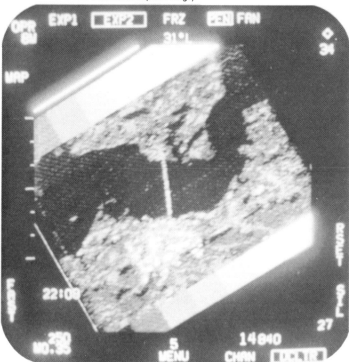

DOPPLER BEAM SHARPENING PATCH (long range)

Effect of Doppler beam sharpening in an APG-65 ground-mapping display. (Hughes)

broader velocity search coverage (eliminating the need for separate settings depending on whether the target was approaching or flying away from the radar), a more flexible target-engagement zone, a new long-range passive-identification mode, a raid-assessment mode (to count closely bunched aircraft), and programmable ECCM and clutter control.

One consequence of the new antenna control is that the radar is no longer constrained to fixed two- and four-bar patterns, which in the past had prevented it from detecting some targets that were widely separated vertically. In bar scanning, the radar sweeps across a bar before shifting to the next bar below. In the new mode, the scan can be interrupted to track a target (even if it is outside the normal pattern), then return to scanning.

Presumably APG-71 incorporates the new radar waveform projected for the APG-70: range-gated high PRF. In the past, the choice has always been between low PRF for long-range and high PRF for good doppler performance but short unambiguous range. Moreover, high PRF is best for an airplane approaching at high speed, whereas medium PRF is best for a tail chase. Typical fighter radars interleave the two PRFs in a "four bar" search, leaving some gaps in coverage. APG-70 uses a combination of range gates and doppler filters (20,000 filters, 500 per range gate); the PRF is 200,000. The new technique should also make raid assessment much more accurate.

The new signal processor has four units compared to three in the F-15 and operates at 40 million complex operations/sec (40 MCOPS). The associated digital data processor operates at 3.2 MIPS (million instructions/sec).

APG-71 flight tests, on board a converted TA-3B, began in July 1987.

♦ APQ-104

Band: X **Beam:** 4.5 deg
Peak Power: 160 kW **Gain:** 31 dB
Pulse Width: 0.7 microsec **PRF:** 1200 pps
Scan Rate: 71 deg/sec horizontal, 30 scans/min vertical
Antenna Dimensions: diameter 20 in
Antenna Weight: total weight 537 lbs

The radar for the U.S.-built French F-8E(FN) replaces the APQ-94 of earlier U.S. versions of this airplane, for compatibility with the French R.550 missile. APQ-94 was presumably similar; its characteristics are listed above. APQ-94 used a magnetron transmitter and hence was not a pulse-doppler radar. Presumably the modification represented by APQ-104 was a CW injection mode.

APQ-94 was built by Magnavox.

♦ APS-120/125/138/139/145

Band: UHF (400–450 MHz) **Beam:** 7 × 20 deg
Peak Power: 1 MW **Gain:** 21.5 dB
Pulse Width: 13 microsec (compressed to 0.2 microsec)
PRF: 300 pps **Scan Rate:** 6 rpm
Antenna Dimensions: 2.5 × 24 ft (in rotodome)
Antenna Weight: 1700 lbs

Data are for APS-96, the predecessor to the current APS-120/125/138/139, to give some idea of overall characteristics. APS-96 is no longer in service. These characteristics are quite comparable to those of the UHF shipboard radar, SPS-40.

The standard U.S. naval airborne early-warning radar, installed on the Grumman E-2C Hawkeye, the General Electric APS-125 is now also in service in Egypt, Israel, and Japan. Lockheed is marketing an alternative installation on board converted P-3 airframes for land-based naval air surveillance, perhaps by Australia and Norway; this look-down P-3 is now entering service with the U.S. Customs Service. Although APS-125 and its relatives are primarily intended for air search, they have a very significant surface search capability, and aircraft equipped with these radars can control antiship attacks. The functional predecessor radar, APS-20, is now used exclusively for surface search. (See the Strike/Surface Warfare section for details.)

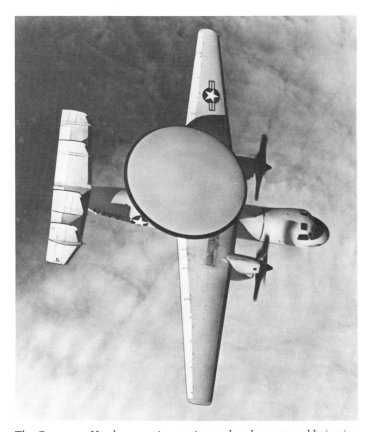

The Grumman Hawkeye carries an air-search radar comparable in size to that found on board a major surface ship. (Grumman)

Since 1986, Grumman has been testing a conformal (active phased-array) radar to replace the rotodome of the current E-2C. Arrays occupy leading edges of the wings, and others could be installed in the leading edge of the tail. The test rig, which includes a rotodome, is shown. Grumman expects to have a flying system by 1992 or 1993, for service introduction in the late 1990s. The array has to adapt its beam form as the wing flexes, and Grumman achieves this adaptation by means of rapid feed-back calculations at each of the thousands of antenna elements. The system has been tested by running a propeller just ahead of the wing. The company points out that, quite apart from the advantage of reducing airframe drag, a conformal array is not limited to a steady scanning rate. Instead, the array can concentrate on areas of particular interest. Such operation might help separate a stealthy target from its background; reportedly the ability to dwell on areas of interest may, by itself, add 20 to 30 percent to the effective detection range. Reportedly, too, the new conformal array uses instantaneous radial-velocity measurement (presumably by fast Fourier transform applied to returning echoes) to separate targets of interest from sea clutter. (Grumman)

UHF frequency was chosen for maximum ability to detect small targets at long range (based partly on available transmitter power) and for sea-clutter rejection (transmitter stability, pulse compression for high resolution, and single-delay analog AMTI). The selection of UHF paralleled the shift to such UHF shipboard radars as SPS-17 (which led to SPS-37/43). The first such U.S. AEW radar, APS-70 (425 MHz, 2 MW), was designed for airship use, and in tests it achieved 40 percent greater range than comparable earlier S-band sets. The E-2 radars were conceived about 1957 as the carrier-based equivalents of the big airship radar. The earlier airborne early-warning radars (APS-20 and -82) operated at S-band and, although they had considerable transmitted power (e.g., 1 MW in APS-82), they also suffered greater transmission losses. Thus APS-96 was credited with somewhat greater range than APS-82 at the same transmitted power. Maximum range, as limited by PRF, was over 200 nm, about twice the nominal range of APS-82.

The antenna is an array of twelve yagis in a rotodome (a rotating radome) 24 ft in diameter. It produces a vertical fan beam, narrow in azimuth. The radar measures target altitude by comparing pulses reflected directly by the target to pulses that have reflected off the surface as well as the target (either coming or going or both). This technique is probably effective mainly at sea, where the surface is highly reflective. By way of contrast, it appears that the APY-1 radar of the Boeing E-3 AWACS produces a beam narrow in both azimuth and elevation, sweeping the beam vertically for height-finding. That scheme reflects that radar's primary function, which is air search over land.

APS-96 did not incorporate the AMTI initially specified (primarily to detect small low fliers at long range). The method employed, comparison of echoes on a pulse-to-pulse basis (the differences being detected as beat frequencies in filter banks) required very stable transmitter frequency. Existing klystrons were too massive for airborne use, so a special tetrode amplifier tube was developed. The experimental APS-111 (1963) introduced AMTI into this radar series. This AMTI was ineffective in eliminating land clutter, and further measures were necessary. AMTI processing is now digital, and the radar is sometimes described as pseudo–pulse Doppler (perhaps using spacing within the compressed pulse).

APS-125 is a modified successor to APS-96, the original E-2 radar, via the experimental APS-111 of the E-2B and the APS-120 of early E-2Cs. APS-111 had improved clutter rejection for overland operation, including special circuits to cancel out the clutter that was frequency shifted by aircraft operation and that would have interfered with both moving target indication and pulse compression. There were also new techniques for sidelobe suppression. APS-111 was tested in 1964–68, and APS-120 incorporated these improvements plus an automatic radar detector, linking the radar to the tracking-and-intercept computer (airborne ADT). The computer seeks a constant false-alarm rate (CFAR) and sorts radar returns before presenting them to the intercept operators. APS-120 also had a more stable (and more reliable) radar transmitter.

APS-125, the version that entered production in 1976, incorporates ARPS (Advanced Radar-Processing Subsystem), with digital rather than analog MTI, as well as better clutter rejection and false-alarm control, for fully automatic overland operation; ARPS also has lower sidelobes (suppression of sidelobe jamming). ARPS tests began in December 1972, and an APS-120 retrofit program began in 1977. APS-125 is said to be able to track 300 targets simultaneously, out to a maximum range of 250 nm. This capability is the ATD modification to the basic radar. After tests, the operational-test-and-evaluation force recommended that the sysem be modified to alert the operator if performance was degraded for any reason. Such degradation (e.g., through jamming) must be a major worry in automatic detection systems. It was also suggested that some rapid means be provided to clear the detector processor of alerts without shutting it down (i.e., as a means of clearing saturation that results from false targets).

The next improvement was APS-138, which has a new low-sidelobe antenna (total radiation aperture control antenna, TRAC-A). The first was delivered to Grumman in December 1982. All 84 existing APS-125s are being brought up to -138 standards. APS-138 can reportedly track a cruise missile at a range of 150 nm. Goodyear (Loral) claimed that, equipped with an array processor, an E-2C equipped with TRAC-A can track over 600 targets simultaneously, and can direct more than 40 simultaneous interceptions. However, TRAC-A was initially unsuccessful, the operational-test-and-evaluation force calling for broad-band TRAC-A in all ten radar channels and improvement to match ARPS performance levels. The system passed an operational test in June 1983 but still suffered from excessive weight.

APS-139 is a further improvement with better ECCM and better surface-search performance. Scheduled to enter service in 1988, this radar can reportedly maintain over 2400 tracks simultaneously. It will be introduced in aircraft number 122.

APS-145 further rejects overland clutter, using environmental processing, in which radar sensitivity is adjusted cell by cell (range interval × beamwidth) on the basis of the clutter and traffic in that cell. PRF is being reduced to permit detections at ranges as great as 350 nm, and the scan rate is being reduced from 6 to 5 rpm. PRF may be varied during operation to eliminate target blind speeds. APS-145 was under test in 1988 and is scheduled to enter service in 1990. APS-125 and its successors all transmit on ten channels. In early versions, channel selection was manual. However, in APS-145 channels are monitored and automatically selected, to avoid jamming signals; channels are selected on a scan-to-scan basis (every 12 seconds). Grumman and GE tested a 100-channel version for the U.S. Navy, but that version was not deemed necessary. Automatic channel selection was important for the 1986 GE bid for the British airborne early-warning (Nimrod 2) contract; APS-125 was initially rejected because it would have interfered with some other NATO signals. GE argued that the new automatic selection system would avoid such interference. Similar problems had already been overcome in Japan (where there was fear of interference with the taxi-radio band).

These radars initially fed their data into a magnetic-drum computer, which was replaced by a Litton L-304 digital computer in the late 1960s; and in 1972 the Litton OL-77/ASQ was introduced. It was initially built around two L-304s with eight 8k memory units. As of 1982, about 50 percent more capacity had been added.

The new airship is initially to carry a modified APS-138 or -139 with a 40 × 10 ft antenna, for operational testing. However, advocates of the airship for fleet air defense have proposed a longer-wavelength (for antistealth operation) antenna wrapped around the airship envelope.

All of these radars are manufactured by General Electric.

For some years Grumman and General Electric have been working on a next-generation conformal-array airborne early-warning radar. A passive receiver in a wing structure passed ground tests during the summer of 1984.

See also ATDS, the airborne tactical data system fed by the E-2C's radar (described with NTDS in the Surveillance and Control section).

◆ AWG-9

The F-14 Tomcat's radar is built by Hughes. It weighs about 1300 lbs, and volume is about 28 cubic feet. The antenna is a 36-inch slotted-plate planar array, with 12 (6 × 2) IFF dipoles on its face. AWG-9 uses a variety of raster scan patterns, designated by their horizontal sweep width and by their vertical extent in "bars"; they range from 8 bars and 65 degrees (to either side of the airplane every 13 seconds) down to 1 bar and 10 degrees every quarter-second. Other azimuth limits are 20 and 40 degrees; search in elevation can cover 1, 2, 4, or 8 bars. There is also a vertical-scan lock-on (VLS) mode in which the radar sweeps a 4.8-degree-wide beam up and down over a 40-degree vertical sector, which can extend from −15 to +25 degrees, up to +15 to +55 degrees.

There are six pulse-doppler modes: pulse-doppler search (PDS, giving only range rate and bearing: 5 square-meter target detected at 115 nm); range-while-search (RWS, to 90 nm, giving range, range rate, and bearing); track-while-scan (to 90 nm, forming a complete track file, and limited to 2 bars/40 deg or 4 bars/20 deg to achieve sufficient data rate); pulse-doppler single-target-track (PDSTT, including both velocity tracking and jam-angle tracking, JAT). There is also an associated slaved mode for use with an IR tracker, permitting illumination of a selected IR target. Pure pulse modes are pulse search (PS, out to 63 nm) and pulse single-target-track (PSTT, out to 49 nm). There is also a slaved pulse mode. Finally, there are three mixed modes: pilot-rapid-location (PRL, a lock-on using a 2.3-degree beam centered on the pilot's line of sight), vertical-scan lock-on, and manual rapid lock-on. Each is effective out to 5 nm, presumably using the spacing of the doppler pulses. The TWS mode is used only for Phoenix missile launch, the radar achieving a 2-second data rate.

Reportedly AWG-9 achieves 2.5 times the range of the AWG-10 installed at about the same time in F-4J Phantoms. AWG-9 can track 24 targets simultaneously. A measure of its radiated power is its ability to guide an AIM-7F Sparrow at a range of 38 nm, compared to 24 nm for earlier radars.

AWG-9 is being replaced by APG-71 in the F-14D upgraded Tomcat.

◆ BGPHES

The Battle-Group Passive Horizon-Extension System is a passive detection system (ESM) to be carried by ES-3 aircraft and to be controlled from the carrier. BGPHES supplements land-based EP-3s. The surface-ship terminal for this system is SLQ-50.

◆ IRSTS

General Electric's infrared search and tracking device is for use in the F-14D fighter. The production decision will be made in the fall of 1989. IRSTS is conceived as complementary to the AWG-9 or APG-71 radar, allowing the F-14 to passively detect and track aircraft at long range. IRSTS flight tests began on board an air force F-15 in the summer of 1988 and continued on a modified F-14A.

Compared to a search radar, an IRSTS has a wider field of view and a narrower effective beamwidth, although IRSTS cannot determine a target's range. The narrow beam makes it possible to distinguish aircraft within a distant raid, and current systems can track multiple targets simultaneously, on a TWS basis. In theory, an IRSTS could be used to set up a missile fire-control solution, the firing aircraft using its radar (or a laser range-finder) only for a one-time check on the target's range. Such practice would be analogous to the submariners' technique of passive tracking plus single-ping ranging and would greatly reduce the warning provided by an enemy's radar receiver. On the other hand, infrared radiation does not pass through clouds and other weather, so a pure infrared sensor system is unlikely to be satisfactory.

The current IRSTS operates in the mid-infrared (3–5-micron band) and uses a linear focal plane array of 256 indium-antimonide detectors. The focusing IR optics scan this array, in effect, over the scene outside the fighter to form an image. Compared to staring FLIRs, this system scans a very narrow beam over its array, providing greater range. Software is used to reject clutter and such hot spots as solar reflections off clouds. Future detectors may use 4 × 256 or 8 × 256 arrays. Both General Electric and Martin-Marietta have also experimented with longer-wave (8–12-micron band) mercury-cadmium-telluride arrays; one is to fly on board an F-14A at Point Mugu in May 1989. The longer-wave system is expected to provide longer range, as well as better performance against targets with reduced IR signatures, such as slow aircraft and cruise missiles. As of early 1989, it will probably be the one chosen for production.

As currently designed, the IRSTS gimballed infrared optics weigh 85 lbs and have a diameter of 9 in. The system consists of two weapon replaceable assemblies (WRAs), the sensor head and the processor.

IRSTS appears as navy fighters move from the current analog cockpit arrangement to a new "glass cockpit," in which all of the single-purpose dials are replaced by multipurpose digital CRTs. In such a cockpit, the pilot can use the same CRT to view radar or IRSTS (or TCS—see below) images. In theory, the CRT could also be arranged to superimpose or compare such images, to simplify the pilot's task of interpretation. Simplified interpretation has certainly been the effect of analogous developments in surface ships' systems.

The IRSTS chin pod was originally designed to be interchangeable with the television chin pod (TCS), but it has been decided that F-14Ds will all have dual pods.

Airborne infrared sensors have had a long history in U.S. fighters. In the mid- to late 1960s, many IR sensors were carried by North American Air Defense Command aircraft such as F-106s, and the F-14 originally incorporated such a sensor. These devices were abandoned because their range was very limited, because they provided very limited data, and because their false-alarm rates were high. F-14As were initially produced carrying a chin-mounted ALR-23 infrared detector, whose seeker head could slew independently of the fighter's radar. ALR-23 was not an imaging device. It operated in the 3–5-micron band and used an indium-antimonide detector cooled by a closed-cycle Stirling refrigerator. Reportedly ALR-23 was provided largely to detect the Soviet MiG-25 Foxbat, which would have presented a very hot target image against a cold sky. The sensor proved ineffective and was soon deleted from the F-14. Many aircraft were completed without any chin pods, but the pod originally designed for the ALR-23 was used instead for a television, the TCS.

By the late 1970s a new generation of IR technology was available. A new air force IRSTS program was begun in 1981, and the U.S. Navy joined in 1984. Official justifications for IRSTS include the claim that the sensor may help to detect aircraft with low (i.e., stealthy) radar cross sections.

The new-generation IRSTS was first flight-tested in 1985, but the air force reduced its participation in the program in February 1986. Reportedly the air force considered the sensor less effective than expected in a look-down situation. The navy, planning to use the sensor in the outer air battle (where the targets would generally be at considerable altitude, against a cool sky), remained in the program and approved full-scale development in 1986. Recent improvements in IRSTS have satisfied most air force concerns, although there are still no plans to place the sensor on F-15s.

General Electric is prime contractor; Martin-Marietta was selected as second-source contractor in June 1987. As of early 1989, production was expected to begin in FY90. In January 1989 the U.S. Navy requested industry proposals for an integrated long-wave IRSTS/laser range-finder, for large aircraft such as P-3s, capable of tracking multiple targets at ranges beyond 100 km. Such a system might also be applicable to the E-2 or to a future unmanned fleet early-warning airplane.

IRSTS infrared sensor under the nose of an F-14A for tests. The operational version will be one of two identical under-nose pods, side by side, the other containing the television camera sight (TCS). The protrusion under the chin pod is an ALQ-100 jammer. (GE Aerospace)

◆ TCS (AXX-1)

Northrop's television camera sight for the F-14A incorporates a stabilized long-range telescope in a chin pod. The TCS was introduced to provide fighters with a means of positively identifying targets even at very long range, so that the planes could use their long-range air-to-air missiles effectively. Prior to the advent of the TCS, typical rules of engagement required the fighter virtually to fly alongside its target before firing. That handicap was unacceptable when enemy aircraft carried long-range air-to-air missiles.

The optics have to be stabilized to keep the very distant object in view as the F-14A moves. TCS can be used independently, e.g., in an automatic search and target-acquisition mode (in analogy to shipboard optronics), or it can be slaved to the AWG-9 radar for target identification. The TCS image is captured by a video recorder on board the fighter. The telescope has a magnification of 10 and can scan over a 30-deg field of view. The instantaneous field of view is selectable as either narrow (0.44 deg) or wide (1.42 deg); the black-and-white image is presented on the pilot's vertical display indicator and on the radar officer's tactical information display.

The television pictures of the battle between navy F-14s and Libyan MiG-23s in January 1989 were taken by TCS. TCS production began in 1981, and as of 1988 all F-14As were equipped with this pod.

TCS is descended from the U.S. Air Force TISEO, target identification system, electro-optical (ASX-1), which was developed in the early 1970s as part of the Rivet Haste and Combat Tree programs. TISEO's camera and stabilized telescope are mounted in the left wing's leading edge on some air force F-4E fighters, with the video processor and power supply in the body of the airplane; and the video image is shared with the back-seat radar display. Over 500 TISEOs were delivered during the 1970s. They allowed a pilot to identify potential targets well beyond normal visual range and, thus, permitted him to use his long-range air-to-air missiles (Sparrows) even under stringent rules of engagement, solving one of the major problems of air combat in Vietnam.

Navy tests of an adapted version, TVSU, the television sight unit, began in 1977. Typical effective range was 9 nm, compared to 2 or 3 for the unaided eye; reportedly observers could even decide what sort of stores the observed aircraft were carrying. That was certainly the case for the TCS-equipped F-14s in the 1989 Libyan incident. TVSU was tested at sea, on board the carriers *Kennedy* and *Constellation*, in the summer of 1978, proving particularly successful in reconnaissance. An airplane detecting a ship on radar could slave TVSU to the radar image and obtain a usable ship image at a range as great as 50 miles. TCS is a fully navalized version of TVSU.

SURFACE-TO-AIR MISSILES

BRAZIL

◆ Avibras SSA-N-1

Dimensions: 15 cm × 2.72 m (5.9 × 107 in)
Weight: 85 kg (187 lbs) **Warhead:** 12 kg (26.4 lbs)
Propulsion: Rocket **Speed:** Mach 2.0+
Range: max 6 km (6600 yds)

Data apply to the air-to-air Piranha missile (MAA-1).

SSA-N-1 is a ship-launched version of the Piranha (MAA-1) air-to-air missile, which is replacing Sidewinders in Brazilian service. SSA-N-1 is manufactured by the Centro Tecnico Aeroespacial (CTA) of Brazil. Concept studies were conducted in 1975, and development began in March 1976. However, the army and navy withdrew from the program late in 1977, returning only in mid-1982. The first trials were completed in mid-1984, and the air-to-air weapon entered service in 1987. Reportedly there were initially some problems with motors, and at least six French-built motors were provided for the prototypes.

The naval version was to have armed later-production Brazilian patrol frigates, which will be built during the 1990s. Since the missile itself broadly resembles Sidewinder, presumably the surface-to-air version would have been comparable to Chaparral. However, this system was canceled in 1987 when the Brazilian military budget was cut by 20 percent. Given the erratic history of the program, it may be revived later.

CHINA (PRC)

◆ HQ-61

Dimensions: 28.6 cm × 3.99 m; span 1.166 m (11.3 × 157 × 45.9 in) **Weight:** 300 kg (661 lbs)
Warhead: continuous-rod warhead
Propulsion: single-stage rocket (boost-glide) **Speed:** Mach 3
Range: 10 km against a low-flying target; maximum altitude is 8 km; maximum range at that altitude, about 5.5 km (10,900; 8700; 6000 yds)

HQ 61. (U.S. Naval Institute)

HQ-61 is a ship- and ground-launched short-range surface-to-air missile. Guidance is semiactive, using a tracker-illuminator and a rear reference beam for proportional navigation.

The missile's configuration broadly matches that of the U.S. Sparrow, although HQ-61 is a much larger weapon. It is unique among rail-launched surface-to-air missiles in lying atop, rather than being suspended from, the (twin) launching rail.

HQ-61 was first exhibited in 1986 although it has not yet been offered for export. The missile is made by CPMIEC, the China Precision Machinery Import and Export Corporation, the commercial arm of the Ministry of Space Industry. Development seems to have been protracted; only two ships carrying this weapon have been built, and they were completed in the early 1970s.

FRANCE

◆ Crotale Naval

Dimensions: 15 cm × 2.89 m; span 54 cm (5.9 × 113.7 × 21.3 in)
Weight: 80 kg (176 lbs) **Warhead:** 15 kg (33 lbs)
Propulsion: boost-glide rocket (SNPE Lens III motor; burn time 2.3 secs) **Speed:** Mach 2.3 (800 m/sec; 2624 ft/sec)
Range: 8.5–13 km (6.5 km vs. a sea-skimmer; 700 m minimum). Effective range is 10+ km against an airplane and 13+ km against a helicopter. Altitude: 150–12,000 ft (9300–14,200 yds; minimum 765 yds): see below for anti–sea-skimmer modification.

Crotale is now the standard French point-defense missile system, installed on board the two carriers and ten escorts (three F67- and seven C70-class frigates); it is also carried by the four French-built Saudi *Al Madinah*–class frigates. The typical installation is an eight-round launcher and sixteen reloads, manually reloaded. Reload time for the entire launcher is about 5 minutes. There is also a lightweight four-round launcher, tested on board a French aviso about 1986; it replaced the ship's 100-mm gun.

The system is fired from CIC. In large ships the fire direction radar (with associated TV camera and IR telescope) is mounted on the launcher, the missile tubes being grouped to either side. In a smaller ship, the director can be off the mount, the electronics in a deckhouse underneath. The version for small ships is modular; a larger ship uses the compact version, in which

Crotale Naval launcher and magazine (below the launcher) on board the destroyer *Duguay-Trouin*, 1982. There are rows of blow-out patches in the magazine, one per missile; missiles are stowed in three groups of eight each. (L&L Van Ginderen)

Crotale Naval launcher with colocated fire-control radar. The IR tracker is to the left of the radar dish. (Thomson-CSF)

the electronics are carried in a deckhouse under the launcher/ director. Thomson-CSF claims that the modular launcher is about the same size and weight as a single 40-mm gun.

Compared to the land-based version, Crotale Naval has larger-diameter tubes for launching missiles, to keep the missile's fins from striking the sides of the tube when launching in rough weather, and lighter caps.

Guidance is command to line of sight, using a radar tracking the transponder on the missile. Upon firing, the missile is gathered into the radar's line of sight by an IR tracker (field of view 5 degrees). Steering is by measurement of the error angle between missile and target, using a fin-mounted transponder on the missile and a Ku-band digital data link. The monopulse doppler tracking radar has a range of 20,000 m. A second IR tracker can be used to fire a missile at a second target in anticipation that the main command channel will become free when the first target is destroyed. This anticipation-firing mode makes for quicker engagement of multiple targets, even when they are not very close together.

Reaction time is 4.5 seconds from reception of the target-designation signal. Because the missile is command-guided, the system can deal with only one target at a time. However, Thomson-CSF points out that a really fast missile with a high single-shot kill probability can destroy several targets in rapid succession (almost certainly with the important caveat that the targets are approaching as a stream attack). For example, Mach 0.9 sea-skimmers can be intercepted successively at 8500, 4500, and 1900 m. The manufacturer claims that anticipation firing increases the engagement rate, so that five targets can be engaged and killed in quick succession, before they pass within the minimum engagement range.

Designed to counter missiles flying at 50-m altitude or above, Crotale originally did not have an anti–sea-skimming capability. At very low angles of elevation the tracker beam can suffer from reflections off the surface of the water (image effect). The solution was an infrared tracking/guidance system (SEID, Système d'Ecartométrie Infra-rouge Différentielle), which can help Crotale engage a sea-skimmer at up to 8500 m (depending on atmospheric conditions). The system using SEID is termed EDIR, Ecartométrie Différentielle Infra-rouge.

Fitted with SEID, Crotale is considered effective against Mach-2.0 targets at altitudes as low as 4 m. Because tracking is by IR, the missile must be fired offset from the target so that the missile's own IR signature does not blank out the target's. Typically Crotale is made to dive at the target at a 1-degree angle. Evaluation gates around the target are used to counter

possible IR countermeasures, and the manufacturer claims that interception accuracy is 0.1 mrad in a 20 × 30 mrad lobe. The system evaluates the quality of the different tracking sensors available to it, choosing automatically the one most suited to the engagement.

Moreover, an improved version of the radar tracker, using special filtering, can track a missile by comparing the direct- and reflected-image (off the sea surface) radar signals, out to 3000 m. This mode is important because under some weather conditions the infrared tracker would be ineffective.

Very low level operation also required modifying the missile's proximity fuze to reject sea clutter. Thomson-CSF claims that the combination of a proximity fuze and a directed-blast warhead (into a plane perpendicular to the missile's axis) makes for very high kill probabilities: 0.82 for an airplane at a range of 10,000 m and 0.90 for an antiship missile at a range of 8500 m. These figures are probably conditional on successful target acquisition and missile guidance.

The current motor accelerates the missile to Mach 2.3 in 2.3 seconds, and the missile reaches 5 km in 10 secs and 8 km in 20 secs, by which time it is subsonic; it takes another 26 secs to get to 13 km. Matra is developing a new motor, which will enable the missile to reach 15 km in 25 secs; only beyond that range will Crotale be subsonic.

This missile was originally called Murene and was designed to engage targets at ranges between 1500 and 9000 yds. Development of the basic land missile, Crotale, was largely (85%) financed by South Africa, beginning in 1964, the British government having refused a South African order for Bloodhound missiles. The first unguided round was fired in 1965 (the first guided round was fired in September 1967). Development of the naval version began in 1972, the French Navy ordering ten systems in May 1974. The first sea-based test was in November 1978, the target, a CT20 drone, being hit at 6-km range. Trials were completed in October 1979, and series production began in January 1980. On board the carriers, two Crotale Naval launchers replaced the original 3.9-inch battery in 1986/87, the navy having expressed concern about possible sea-skimming missile attacks when the ships were deployed off the Lebanese coast.

◆ **Masurca**

> **Dimensions:** 406 mm × 5408 mm; span 1277 mm; booster length 3222 mm and tail span 1500 mm. The missile penetrates 114 mm into the booster, so total length is 8516 mm. (16 × 212.9 × 50.2 in; 126.9 × 59.0 in; total length 335.2 in)
> **Weight:** 840 kg; booster 1858 kg (1850/4095 lbs)
> **Warhead:** 120 kg (264 lbs)
> **Propulsion:** booster (burn time 4.5 sec) plus sustainer (burn time 30 sec); booster thrust about 35 tons, sustainer thrust 2300 kg (5070-lbs thrust)   **Speed:** 900 m/sec max (2952 ft/sec)
> **Range:** 40,000 m; kinematic range 62,000 m (43,700/67,800 yds)

The destroyer *Suffren* displays the Masurca system: the twin launcher with two DRBR 51 guidance radars, and the big DRBI 23 three-dimensional acquisition-and-tracking radar under its radome forward. When this photograph was taken in 1966, the ship had not yet received her DUBA 43 variable-depth sonar, so the cut in her stern was still empty. (U.S. Naval Institute)

Masurca on board the cruiser *Colbert*. (ECP Armées)

Masurca missiles on board the cruiser *Colbert*. (*Ships of the World*)

control, 31.5 tons for the launcher itself, 202.0 tons for the loading system, and 105.0 tons of missiles, 450 metric tons in all.

The three remaining systems, on board the two *Suffren*-class destroyers and the cruiser *Colbert*, were modernized 1983–85 to maintain the system until the end of its scheduled life in 1998–2000.

Masurca was one of five French naval missiles whose development began in the first postwar decade: three antiaircraft missiles (Masurca, Maruca, and Masalca), one ASW missile (Malafon), and one antiship missile (Malaface). Each designation indicated the role and manufacturer: MA for *marine* (navy), then the manufacturer (SUR, for Supersonique RUELLE), then the mission (CA, for *contre-avion*, antiaircraft). For Malafon, the only other survivor of the program, LA indicated Latecoere, and FON indicated underwater (FACE was *surface*). The program was drastically reduced about 1958, as finances tightened: Masurca had the highest priority, and Malaface was killed on the theory that the carrier's strike aircraft had made the missile unnecessary. Masalca, developed by Latecoere, was a longer-range (95-km) antiaircraft missile intended for a cruiser, a French equivalent of the U.S. Talos. Presumably the related cruiser project was dropped about 1960.

◆ **Mistral (Sadral and Simbad Systems)**

Masurca is an area-defense weapon broadly comparable to the U.S. Terrier/SM-1(ER). The configuration is similar, but the French missile is larger and heavier. There were both semiactive and beam-riding (Mk 2 Mod 2) versions; currently only the semiactive Mk 2 Mod 3 remains in service. Fire control is by a DRBC 51 tracker-illuminator. The design requirement was to intercept two 1 square-meter targets at altitudes of up to 18,000 m and at ranges of 25,000 m (beam-rider) or 35,000–40,000 m (semiactive).

Like Terrier or SM-1(ER), Masurca is stowed horizontally, on a revolving drum, without the long booster fins, which are fitted by hand before firing. The rate of fire is one two-missile salvo every 30 seconds. The launcher carries a total of 46 missiles (18 per drum plus 10 missiles in reserve, broken down with missile and booster separate). Total system weight: 111.5 tons for fire

DRBR 51 directors for the French Masurca missile. (*Ships of the World*)

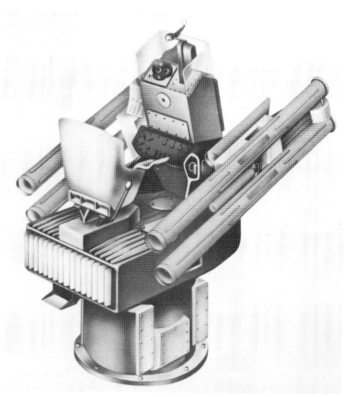

LAMA (*Lance-Missiles d'Autodéfense*) director/launcher for Mistral missiles. (Compagnie de Signeaux et d'Entreprise Électriques)

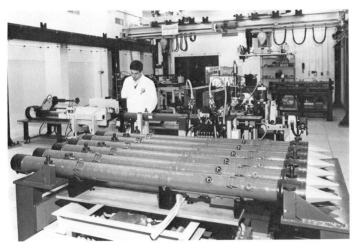

Mistral missiles in the factory. (Matra)

Dimensions: 90 cm × 1.81 m (3.5 × 71.3 in)
Weight: 17 kg (37.5 lbs)
Warhead: 3 kg (1800 tungsten balls) (6.6 lbs)
Propulsion: boost-sustain rocket (The booster burns only inside the launch tube, accelerating the missile to 40 m/sec [131 ft/sec], and the sustainer ignites 15 m away; the motor is based on that of the Super 530 air-to-air missile.) **Speed:** Mach 2.6
Range: 6 km against aircraft; 4 km against helicopters; 6 sec to 4000 m. Minimum range: 500 m (6600/4400 yds; minimum 550 yds)

The Matra Mistral is a short-range defensive missile used in several naval systems. Matra describes the weapon as the first shoulder-fired Mach-2.5 defensive missile. It uses an all-aspect infrared seeker and a laser proximity fuze, and the manufacturer claims that Mistral can attack helicopters with reduced IR signatures.

Sadral (*Système d'auto-défense raprochée anti-aérien légère*) is a close-in six-round defensive system for second-line ships, using Mistral. There is also a lightweight two-round launcher,

Simbad two-missile shipboard launcher for Mistral. (Matra)

Simbad (*Système integré de Mistral bimunition pour l'auto-défense*). Simbad is a modified 20-mm pedestal mount (a configuration that in itself explains the function of this and analogous weapons) carrying a simple optical sight.

The Sadral launcher is stabilized, elevating and training. It carries a television camera and an IR camera for night firing. The missile is locked onto the target before firing, presumably to limit the amount of background visible to the seeker, thus improving the effective signal-to-noise ratio. An audio signal indicates that the missile has locked on before it is launched. A more elaborate version of the basic Sadral mount, Lama, carries four or six missiles and an optical target designator that can act as a secondary director for other shipboard weapons.

Tests of the basic Mistral missile were completed in March 1988, with firings against low-flying CT20 drones. One firing resulted in a head-on hit at 5 km.

Sadral is in service on board French antiaircraft frigates (C70 AA type) in a version called SATCP (*surface-air, à très courte portée*), using a CSEE automatic director and a six-missile rapid-reload mount. Mistral is also combined with a close-in defensive gun in the proposed Samos/SAGEM close-in weapons system. An air-to-air version, A/HATCP, is planned for French Air Force helicopters; Santal is used by ground forces, and the basic man-portable infantry version is SATCP.

This program began with feasibility studies in 1978, Matra being selected as prime contractor in August 1980. The naval version was announced in October 1980, and tests began early in 1985. Deliveries of Mistral began in June 1988. As of 1988, the estimated cost per missile, including the kevlar launch tube, was $60–100 thousand.

◆ SAAM/ASTER

Dimensions: caliber 180 mm (7.1 in)
Weight: 250–300 kg (550–660 lbs)
Warhead: 15–20 kg (proximity fuze) (33–44 lbs)
Propulsion: ramjet (SA-90) or rocket (SAN-90) **Speed:** Mach 3.0
Range: 5–15 km (see below); 20–30 km for SA-90 (5500–16,400 yds)

This French advanced point-defense (antimissile) system is under development by Thomson-CSF and Aerospatiale and is a candidate for the NATO frigate's AAW system. The overall system is called SAAM (*Système de défense surface-air antimis-*

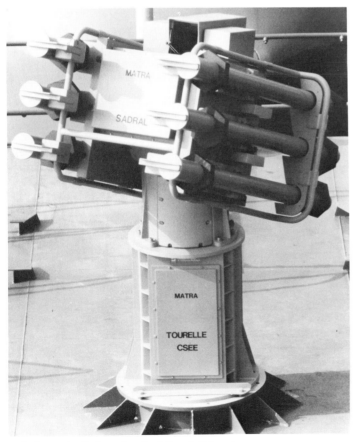

Sadral six-missile launcher for Mistral. (Matra)

sile), and the missile is ASTER. The potential targets are Mach-2.5 (15-Gs) sea-skimmers, diving antiradar missiles, and fighter aircraft. Claimed performance is a range of about 10 km against supersonic and maneuvering missiles, or 15–17 km against high-altitude aircraft and subsonic missiles. The same upper-stage missile is to be developed for land service as SAMP (*Sol-Air Moyenne Portée*). The land-based SA-90 (ASTER 30) is to be ramjet-powered; the sea-based SAN-90 (ASTER 15), rocket-powered. Otherwise, these versions have most systems in common, requiring radar acquisition ranges of, respectively, 25 and 10 km (27,300 and 10,900 yds).

Key design requirements are very short reaction time, multiple engagement capability, great agility, and a very short guidance time constant. Quick reaction is ensured by a combination of vertical launching (from the canister tube in which the weapon is shipped) and highly automated operation. As in the U.S. Aegis system, a flat-face phased-array radar (in this case a single rotating face), the Thomson-CSF Arabel, tracks both missile and target. The missile is sent into a terminal "basket" by a command up-link programming the autopilot. The system is designed to handle ten targets simultaneously. Unlike the U.S. Standard Missile, however, ASTER will use active terminal guidance, requiring no dedicated illuminators. Presumably ASTER has that capability because the missile is intended to engage its targets at short range: there would not be enough time to share a few illuminators.

The designers expect that violent missile maneuverability (up to 50 Gs) will allow the weapon to approach within 2 meters of its target. At that range the missile can achieve catastrophic structural damage even with a relatively light warhead. A light warhead in turn makes it possible to package high maneuverability within a reasonable volume.

The missile itself consists of a separate booster and a guided vehicle incorporating a sustainer motor. By separating booster and sustainer, the designers again reduce terminal homing weight. They achieve maneuverability by a combination of aerodynamic forces and direct-force control (i.e., rockets firing perpendicular to the axis of the missile), a system they call PIF-PAF. Direct-force control has previously been used only in antiballistic-missile weapons. For ASTER, the claimed virtues of direct-force control are that it can operate even at very high altitude and, at any altitude, can permit violent maneuvers even at low angles of attack.

As in the U.S. SM-2 Aegis (ER), the booster employs thrust-vector control to tip the missile into the appropriate trajectory. ASTER, however, is finned. The booster's size controls the missile's range. The naval version of the system is designated ASTER 15 (15 km); the land version, with a larger booster, is ASTER 30. At the end of acceleration, ASTER 15 should have a velocity of 1000 m/sec; ASTER 30 will be somewhat faster. The naval version will be fired from a vertical launcher employing 8-weapon cells.

Reportedly the French credit current systems with a reaction time of 15–20 seconds; using the Arabel radar, ASTER is to have a 5-second reaction time.

The RFP for a collaborative European missile (the French government is seeking partners for SAAM/SAMP development) was issued in 1980/81, with a 31 December 1981 deadline; the Aerospatiale–Thomson-CSF development contract was announced in August 1983. The SAN-90 design was frozen in 1984 (and a model displayed at Le Bourget in October 1985). ASTER was selected over the Matra SAMAT (which is, however, being continued as a back-up) early in 1986.

As of 1988, ASTER was due to enter French Navy service by 1996, on board the new carrier *Charles de Gaulle,* and SAMP was due to enter French Army service in 1998. The first missile test, which demonstrated PIF-PAF maneuvering, was at the French CEL test range, 17 June 1987. About 1987 the estimated unit price of an ASTER was $400,000–$700,000.

The overall ASTER weapons system is designated Syrinx (*Système Rapide Interarmées à base d'Engins et Fonctionnant en Bande X*).

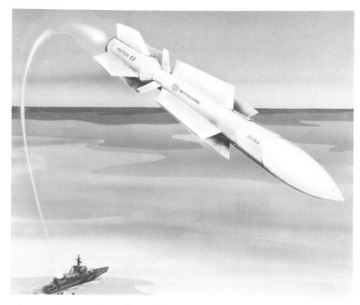

The ASTER missile will arm future French aircraft carriers. (Aerospatiale)

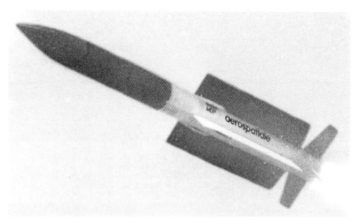

The ASTER missile in flight. (Aerospatiale)

♦ **SAMAT**

> **Dimensions:** length 3.1 m (SAMAT 3, 3.5 m) (122 and 138 in)
> **Weight:** 110 kg (SAMAT 3, 300 kg) (242 and 661 lbs)
> **Speed:** SAMAT 3, Mach 2.5
> **Range:** 6–10 km (SAMAT 2, 12–20 km; SAMAT 3, 15–35 km) (6600–10,900 yds; 13,100–21,800 yds; 16,400–38,300 yds)

SAMAT is Matra's alternative to the ASTER series. Although not selected by the French government, SAMAT remains as an alternative in the event of some failure of the ASTER program. SAMAT 1 uses IR guidance; SAMAT 2 and 3 use a combination of inertial (programmed autopilot) and active radar.

These weapons were developed along the lines of the future MICA air-to-air missile; all use narrow-chord wings and thrust-vector control (accelerations up to 45 Gs have been reported). SAMAT 1 is the MICA airframe adapted to surface launching, with an IR seeker. It competes with Mistral. Several such missiles can fit one Crotale tube (just as several RAMs can fit a single Sea Sparrow tube). SAMAT 2 uses the same airframe but has an all-weather radar seeker and is vertically launched; 2 is a potential Crotale replacement. SAMAT 3 has higher power for longer range and is currently intended only for land use; 3 has the same radar seeker as SAMAT 2. SAMAT 3 has been proposed for naval use as an alternative to ASTER.

Because the two naval missiles use the existing MICA airframe, they were relatively easy to develop. The system was announced in September 1982, and a technical demonstrator was fired that October. A SAMAT vertical-launch system was displayed at Le Bourget in October 1986, but the French government chose ASTER early in 1987. As of 1988, estimated unit price was $400–750 thousand.

INTERNATIONAL

◆ FAMS

FAMS stands for Family of Antiair Missile Systems. The partners are France, Italy, Spain, and the United Kingdom. The system is conceived as a series of modules that could serve as an extended point-defense missile for France and Italy and as a longer-range LAMS for Britain and Spain, and that could then be extended to a medium-range area-defense missile for France, to replace the current Standard. As of mid-1988, contracts for an 18-month preliminary study were imminent, the contractors being Thomson-CSF, Aerospatiale, Selenia, Ibermisil (Spain), Marconi, and British Aerospace. Presumably, then, the missiles will be ASTER derivatives. France and Italy have already signed an MoU for an astern extended-point-defense system, controlled by either the French Arabel or the EMPAR (for the Italian version). EMPAR is led by Selenia, but the other contractors are Marconi and (apparently to a limited extent) Thomson-CSF.

◆ LAMS (Local-Area Missile System)

LAMS is the generic name for the self-defense missile system of the projected NATO frigate (NFR-90); LAMS would be controlled by a multifunction radar. The name is derived from the perception that it is impossible to provide true area defense (over tens of miles) against very fast sea-skimming weapons or against very fast pop-up missiles. Instead, it may be much wiser to limit missile ranges to a few miles, with very rapid reaction and very high one-round kill probability.

LAMS formally originated in an NIAG study (PG 33, Sub-Group 17) begun in 1985 and completed in the fall of 1986, although the idea of local-area defense dates at least to 1982–83. The U.S. NATO AAW Missile System (NAAWS) is one of several alternatives. Another is the Family of Antiair Missile Systems (FAMS), based on the French ASTER, in which France, Britain, and Spain are collaborating. In each case, the missile is associated with a multifunction radar (MFR) such as EMPAR or the RCA FARS (mini–SPY-1).

◆ NATO 6S

The program to develop a NATO small-ship self-defense missile was begun in the late 1970s, and the missile was intended for service in the 1990s. Feasibility studies were completed early in 1980; British Aerospace was the prime contractor. The French and German partners were Thomson-CSF and AEG-Delefunken, and there was some Danish participation. The object was to keep the total weight of the launcher equal to that of an OTO-Melara 76-mm gun; a sketch showed two deck modules, for a total of eight two-missile cells, replacing a single gun. Targets would be acquired by a stacked-beam three-dimensional radar and also by an independent IR sensor, the data being computer-correlated; and as of 1980 the preferred guidance method was semiactive mid-course with terminal active radar. Projected range was 10–15 km.

Although this particular project died soon after its first public announcement in 1980, 6S is interesting as an indication of the sort of system NATO has been seeking in such programs as LAMS. The basis for this system's rejection was skepticism that area defense was really possible against future Mach-3 antiship missiles. The British Aerospace role suggests that NATO 6S would have used a vertically launched version of the basic Sea Wolf airframe.

◆ NATO AAW Missile System

The NATO AAW Missile System is a U.S.-led project to replace the existing Sea Sparrow and to arm the NATO frigate. The primary requirements are quick reaction and multitarget handling, to deal with salvos of very fast low-altitude weapons like SS-N-22. The system must also be able to counter steep divers. In theory, that requirement might demand something like Aegis controlling a new, very high energy missile. However, like Sea Sparrow, NATO AAW is conceived as a secondary system for ships intended primarily for other purposes, such as ASW.

Therefore, NATO AAW has to be relatively small and, it is hoped, inexpensive. The U.S. Navy has proposed that NATO AAW run in parallel with LAMS, but the main difference is the time scale: NATO AAW is being pressed more urgently because of fears that Sea Sparrow is becoming obsolete in the face of SS-N-22 and similar weapons. Thus, the contractors are required to have test systems running in 1989, and this requirement in turn ties them to existing hardware, at least on an interim basis.

The key elements of the NAAWS requirement are the ability to deal with fast surface-skimmers and the ability to handle saturation attacks. The typical building blocks of the system, then, are a horizon-search radar (to pick up surface-skimmers with a very high probability, albeit at relatively short range), a hemisphere-search radar sufficiently accurate for fire control (generally termed an MFR, or multifunction radar), one or more electro-optic or infrared sensors integrated with the radars, a combat system core, and a vertically launched missile (for very quick reaction, even at very short range). All the competing consortia include radar and missile builders on both sides of the Atlantic. The consensus seems to be that the most successful (i.e., saleable) NAAWS will have to be adaptable to several quite different radar/missile suites, even though the U.S. Navy is pushing for definite selections. In turn, the most innovative and important element of NAAWS should be a highly adaptable, modular computer combat system, programmed in the software equivalent of the hardware of the German MEKO frigate. Such flexibility has been most publicly identified with the Ferranti WS500 series (see the Surveillance and Control section), but all of the NAAWS competitors have probably adopted something roughly comparable.

This need for flexibility probably explains the reticence of two of the three current NAAWS competitors, who have steadfastly avoided mentioning specific sensors or weapons in advertising. The sole exception is Raytheon, which has suggested a developed version of its Sea Sparrow. Reportedly Raytheon was initially dropped from the NAAWS competition because the company's proposed system was insufficiently advanced over existing ones (i.e., because it was too specific). The company's rejoinder is that anything much less specific cannot possibly meet the NAAWS deadlines (delivery of operational systems by 1998) and that, moreover, full development of a completely new set of systems will break any realistic NAAWS budget.

It is also possible that some developments financed under NAAWS will be applicable to existing ships and systems. For example, Raytheon's new developed Sea Sparrow, with a new motor and multimode guidance, was intended for launching from the existing vertical launcher; the company argued that up to 64 missiles could be fired from a standard 16-cell vertical launcher (Mk 41). FMC demonstrated "four-pack" Sea Sparrow launching (four Sparrows in one VLS cell) for the first time in June 1988. The company described this success as its contribution to NAAWS (at the U.S. Navy League show, March 1989). In the past, in connection with proposed German ships (presumably Type 123), RCA (now GE) has commented that the ideal weapons suite would be a combination of Standard Missiles and Sea Sparrows in a common vertical launcher.

Several alternative NAAWS configurations have been published. At the U.S. Navy League show in March 1989, GE (which absorbed the RCA division that manufactured SPY-1) showed a possible NATO-frigate design employing a four-face fixed phased-array radar, with two illuminators (similar in shape to the Dutch STIR or STING), and an electro-optical sensor between them. Presumably the fixed radar would carry out both the horizon- and hemisphere-search roles (as SPY-1 does in Aegis ships), and the illuminators would be slaved (as in Aegis). GE would probably use the improved Sea Sparrow as its interim missile, choosing later between new U.S. and European weapons.

Raytheon has published a sketch showing two radars, a relatively low frequency rotating unit to detect and track long-range targets (the company's sketch seems to show stacked waveguides), and a higher frequency fixed array to deal with shorter-range targets.

Hughes has suggested the improved version of its TAS Mk 23 as a potential MFR.

The usual published sketch of the NATO frigate shows only one MFR, a rotating back-to-back pair of flat-faced arrays atop the ship's tower foremast. That MFR presumably represents Arabel or EMPAR.

The original competing consortia were:

—GE (RCA), with British Aerospace, CSC (which developed the Aegis tactical software), FMC, General Dynamics, Inisel (Spain), Marconi, Siemens, Signaal, and Thomson-CSF.

—Martin-Marietta, with Hughes, ITT, Lockheed Electronics, Magnavox, Norden, HSA (Signaal), Bazan, Litton of Canada, AEG, Krupp Atlas, and Plessey.

—Raytheon, with AEG, Fokker, Plessey Radar, Bristol Aerospace, Martin-Marietta, ERIA (combat direction software), and MBB.

—Westinghouse, with Hughes Aircraft, LTV, Martin-Marietta, McDonnell-Douglas, MCR, ORI (analysts), Vitro, Canadian Marconi, MEL, Oerlikon (of Canada), SPAR, AEG, BGT (the German missile manufacturer), Contraves, Dornier, Philips (ELCOMA, of the Netherlands), Bazan, Ceselsa (Spanish radar systems house), Babcock Power (UK), Ferranti, Short Brothers, and Thorn-EMI. This group is called UNISAMS.

By September 1988, the Martin-Marietta and Raytheon proposals had been dropped. However, Raytheon protested, and by early 1989 it had been reinstated in the NAAWS program.

◆ NATO Sea Sparrow

See Sparrow (U.S. air-to-air missile) below.

◆ RAM (RIM-116A)

See RAM under U.S. below.

ISRAEL

◆ Barak I

Dimensions: 170 mm × 2.175 m; span 0.68 m (6.7 × 85.6 × 26.8 in) **Weight:** 86 kg (189.5 lbs)
Warhead: 22 kg (48.5 lbs)
Propulsion: triple-thrust (boost/sustain/terminal engagement) rocket **Speed:** 580 m/sec (1900 ft/sec)
Range: 0.5–10 km (550–10,900 yds)

Israel Aircraft Industries's point-defense missile for small fast attack craft is designed to achieve very short reaction time (time to maximum range less than 30 seconds). Barak is vertically launched, and guidance is by automatic command to line of sight. There is also a back-up optical command–to–line-of-sight tracker using a laser range-finder. Engagement is fully automatic (with operator veto).

Control immediately after launch is by thrust vanes (which flip the missile over in 0.6 seconds, at 25 Gs, i.e., 10 rad/sec), which are jettisoned once the missile has accelerated sufficiently for aerodynamic control. Total angular coverage is from −25 to +85 degrees (and 360 degrees in bearing). In 1987 Barak was successfully tested against a TOW missile representing a low-cross-section sea-skimmer.

The rocket motor has three thrust levels, presumably initial boost (to avoid damaging the launching ship), then high-energy boost, then sustain. There is no conventional proximity fuze because the weapon may often have to engage sea-skimmers; instead, it uses a special Rafael adaptive proximity fuze with an integrated altimeter to control the sensitivity of the downward part of the fuze envelope.

The weapon is carried in 8-missile cells, and one control system can accommodate up to 32 missiles. Each vertical launch unit can be split into pairs of 2 to 8 missiles, either in above- or below-deck launchers. The radar and fire control weigh 1300 kg, and one 8-cell unit weighs 1300 kg. Barak was conceived for the *Reshef* class, which has a total armament weight of 40 tons. A more conventional self-defense weapon would have consumed a quarter of that weight.

Barak was announced at the June 1981 Paris Air Show, and a model displayed in 1983; tests began in May 1984. Development was reportedly accelerated because of the experience of the Falklands War. The development contract reportedly requires delivery to the Israeli Navy from the end of 1988, with the system operational during 1989. However, as of 1988 sea trials were expected only that year, with the system becoming operational in 1990. An export customer (not named) was announced early in 1988. Reported unit price is $200,000 (1987).

A land-based version of this missile is called Adams. It is described as having a limited ATBM capability, presumably against short-range tactical weapons (such as the FROGs that the Soviets have supplied to many client states).

Barak. (IAI)

ITALY

◆ Aspide

Aspide in flight. (Selenia)

Dimensions: 20.3 cm × 3.7 m × 80 cm (100 cm in the air-to-air version) (8 in × 12 ft 2 in × 2 ft 7.5 in/3 ft 3.4 in)
Weight: 200 kg (485 lbs) **Warhead:** 35 kg (77.2 lbs)
Propulsion: single-stage solid-fuel rocket
Speed: Mach 4.0 (AAM role) **Range:** 15+ km (16,400 yds)

Aspide is an Italian-designed alternative to the current Sparrow and Sea Sparrow. The airframe is derived from that of AIM/RIM-7H, but the internal systems are new, including an X-band monopulse seeker for snap-up/snap-down firing and for better countermeasures and clutter resistance. The missile enjoys better endurance than Sparrow, using closed-loop rather than open-loop hydraulics. It also has a new SNIA motor with higher thrust and specific impulse, for greater velocity and range. There is a home-on-jam guidance mode.

This missile is widely used as a naval point-defense weapon, and there is also a tactical ground-defense version, Spada. In the naval version, the associated overall system is Albatros, developed by Selenia. Albatros can also accommodate the Sparrow missile and predates the appearance of the navalized Aspide. Aspide's box launcher is much like that of NATO Sea Sparrow, and the substitution of one missile for the other involves only a change in circuit boards and programming, which can even be done at sea. However, unlike Sea Sparrow installations, Albatros/Aspide can accommodate a semiautomatic reloader (and a 16-missile below-decks automatic reloader is under development). There is also a lightweight quadruple launcher for small ships of less than 300 tons (4000 rather than 9000 kg for the launcher, and 1600 kg for the fire-control system); this launcher has been ordered by Ecuador.

The associated radars are usually the Selenia RTN-10X tracker and the Sirio RTN-12X illuminator (but Albatros Mod/10/0, using a Marconi 1802AS, has been developed by Marconi and Selenia-Elsag).

Development of the air-to-air version began in 1969, with trials in 1974–75. Albatros was developed in parallel (initially using the Sea Sparrow missile), with sea tests in 1973. Aspide's production began in 1977, and the first Albatros/Aspide system was exported to Peru in October 1978. The first Italian Navy firing of the Aspide missile (from a modified NATO Sea Sparrow launcher) was in July 1979. In 1986, unit price was about $250,000. By that time over 2000 were on order worldwide, and about 1000 had been delivered.

In 1984 Selenia announced that it was developing a vertically launched derivative of Aspide with an active radar seeker. This derivative was announced as the new Idra missile in April 1985.

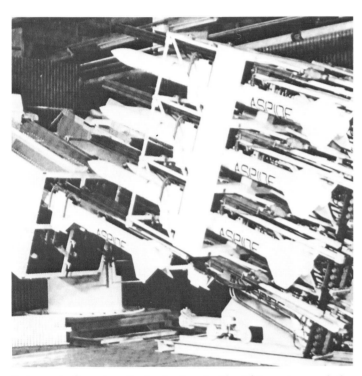

Sixteen-missile automatic loader for Aspide. This system and the Canadian Tribal-class Sea Sparrow are the only Western point-defense missile systems not reloaded by hand. (Selenia)

Four-cell Aspide launcher for corvettes. The Orion tracker-illuminator is visible above the launcher. (Selenia)

◆ Idra

Dimensions: 21.2 cm × 3.65 m (4.63 m with booster); span 64.4 cm (control-fin span 68 cm) (8.3 × 143.7/183.1 × 25.4/26.8 in)
Weight: 210–220 kg (460–480 lbs)
Propulsion: dual-boost low-smoke rocket with optional booster
Speed: Mach 2.5+ **Range:** 2–20 km (220–22,000 yds)

Idra is intended as replacement for Aspide and also as an alternative to the U.S.-developed AMRAAM. Like Aspide, Idra will be available in air-, ground-, and sea-launched versions. In 1985 Selenia announced that Idra would be available from 1994 onward.

Idra is intended to be compatible with the existing Aspide logistics. The missile's airframe is very similar in form to Aspide, but Idra is inertially guided with a programmable autopilot (using an antijam data link) and an active J-band pulse-doppler seeker. There is also a home-on-jam mode. Although Aspide, like Sparrow, is steered by the wings, Idra is to be tail-steered. Presumably the associated naval radar is the new Selenia MM/SPY-790.

Thrust-vector control (for vertical launching) will be provided by Martin-Marietta. The dual boost motor can be switched on and off, to provide extra power for terminal maneuvers. Typically an initial 3-sec burn would boost the missile to maximum speed, and the missile would glide toward the target until the on-board computer started up the motor for a final 1–1.5 sec burn. At short range the glide would be omitted, the missile achieving a peak velocity of more than 900 m/sec.

Selenia began work on this missile in 1983. An Idra model was exhibited in June 1987, and at that time a captive seeker flight was scheduled for late 1988. However, Italian official support has not been forthcoming in recent years, and the decision to participate in the French ASTER program may imply that no support will be forthcoming in the future. On the other hand, Idra would seem to have a guaranteed market among Aspide's current users, who will presumably be unwilling to invest in an entirely new system for their ships.

NETHERLANDS

◆ Sweeper

In April 1988 Signaal and Bofors jointly announced what they describe as a new naval surface-to-air missile system, Sweeper. It appears to be a further development of the four-missile system jointly announced in 1986 (see RBS 70 below), using the longer-range RBS 70 Mk 2 and the Signaal LIOD electro-optical director. Operation is entirely automatic, no above-deck operator being required.

SWEDEN

◆ RBS 70 (Rayrider)

Dimensions: 10.6 cm × 1.32 m; span 32 cm (4.2 × 52.0 × 12.6 in) **Weight:** 15 kg (33 lbs) (system weight 250 kg [551 lbs])
Warhead: 1-kg prefragmented (with tungsten pellets) using impact and laser proximity fuzes (2.2 lbs)
Propulsion: boost-sustain rocket (booster burns only in launch tube; sustainer ignites at a safe distance)
Speed: Mach 1.0+
Range: 5,000 m (5500 yds); 6000 m in the Mk-2 version. Height coverage is 3000 m (9480 ft).

Rayrider is the naval version of the Bofors laser-guided infantry weapon; RBS 70 is currently used on board Swedish *Landsort*-class minesweepers and Finnish *Helsinki-II*–class fast attack craft. The missile is a laser beam-rider; Bofors claims that the missile is unjammable because it receives its information from the launcher, not the target. Laser beam-riding automatically confers forward-aspect capability. By way of contrast, most short range SAMs, which home on a target's infrared radiation, typically fly toward a target's tail. Thus they cannot hit an approaching attacker. Only very sophisticated infrared weapons, such as Stinger, can match RBS 70's forward-hemisphere per-

Bofors RBS 70 Rayrider being launched from shipboard. (U.S. Naval Institute)

formance. The laser transmitter/tracker is already gyro-stabilized for use as a hand-held infantry weapon and is, therefore, automatically adaptable to a moving ship. The current standard installation is a single missile-launcher tube on a pedestal, which also carries the operator's seat. Reaction time is 4–5 seconds.

The current RBS 70+ (Mk-2) version has a greater range and a better laser receiver, increasing the defended area by 30–50 percent. Mk 2 uses digital guidance (which takes up less volume than the earlier analog electronics and, thus, leaves more space for a warhead), a 50-percent larger warhead (shaped charge plus fragmentation pellets), and a larger sustainer. Finally, Bofors describes Mk 2 as armor-piercing and, therefore, capable of dealing with armored missiles and aircraft such as helicopters (and, presumably, thin-skinned armored vehicles). Mk 2 is fully in-

terchangeable with Mk 1. Early in August 1988, Bofors tested a Mk 2 against a sea-skimmer approaching at an altitude of 5 m (about 16 ft). The target was destroyed at a range of 1800 m. The target's dimensions were 40 cm (16 in) in diameter and 4.5 m in length. Mk 2 entered production during the winter of 1988–89.

In 1986 Bofors and Signaal (HSA) announced a more elaborate system, combining a quadruple RBS 70 launcher with the pedestal, processor, and console of the Signaal LIOD director. Targets would be designated by one or two optronic designators, each carrying a coarse sight and a 7 × 50 binocular. Targets would be tracked by the Signaal LIOD in the launcher itself, using a daylight television with a 3-degree field of view, with an effective tracking range of 11,000 yds (and effective up to a target speed of 875 yds/sec). The two-pod quadruple launcher weighs 425 kg, plus 85 kg for each target designator and 375 kg for the control console.

A new version, RBS 90 (formerly RBS 70M Nightrider), combines the Mk-2 missile with a new remotely controlled twin launcher with a laser transmitter and TV and IR cameras on board. Although RBS 90 is intended for land use, it has obvious naval application.

Work on the basic missile began in 1967, and Bofors received a development contract in 1969 and a production contract in June 1975. The naval version was tested in February 1984, and a vertically launched version was demonstrated on 9 September 1986 (tests completed November 1986). In 1988, the estimated cost per missile was $90–100 thousand.

Sweeper launcher. (Bofors)

USSR

◆ SA-N-1 Goa

Dimensions: 37 cm × 6.1 m; span 1.2 m; booster diameter 55 cm and span (folding fins) 2.3 m (14.6 × 240 × 47 in; 21.6/90.6 in)
Weight: 950 kg (2090 lbs) **Warhead:** 60 kg (132 lbs)
Propulsion: separate booster (burn time 3 seconds) and sustainer (19 seconds); boost-glide flight
Speed: maximum Mach 3.5
Range: 18.3 km, minimum 2.4 km; altitude limits 45 m to 18.3 km (2600–20,000 yds; 150–60,000 ft)

RBS 70 Missile Mk 2. (Bofors)

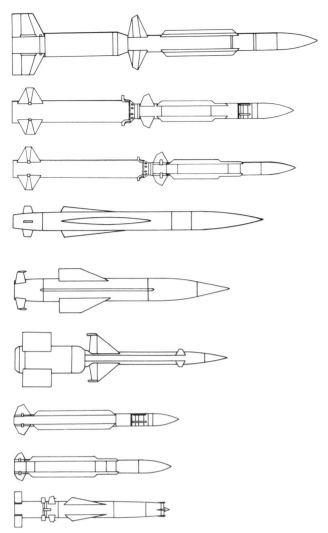

Typical area-defense missiles. Top to bottom: Masurca, Terrier, SM-2(ER), SA-N-6, SA-N-3, SA-N-1, Tartar, SM-1(MR), Sea Dart. (*Ships of the World*)

Data are for the land-based SA-3.

A navalized version of the land-based SA-3, SA-N-1 was the first Soviet naval surface-to-air missile to enter widespread service. The land-based SA-3 is known as Neva (S-125) in Soviet service and was developed by the Lavochkin design bureau. SA-3 was conceived as a low-altitude complement to the SA-2, which had been designed primarily to attack bombers at high altitude. SA-3 was the first Soviet surface-to-air missile to use solid fuel for both stages, a consideration that would have made the missile much more attractive than the massive SA-2 for naval use. Prototype testing of SA-1 began at Sary Shagan in 1959, and that missile became operational in 1961.

The naval missile, SA-N-1, is designated M1 Volga-M in Soviet service; the Soviets may use the name Volga for the missile itself within the land-based Neva system. The first test platform was the Kotlin-class destroyer *Bravyy*, which ran trials in June 1962. This system arms Kashin-class destroyers and Kynda- and Kresta-I–class cruisers. The roughly contemporary SA-N-2, a navalized SA-2, was employed only on board one now-discarded ship and seems to have been an unsuccessful experiment.

SA-N-1 is command-guided, with one double Peel Group director per twin-armed launcher. The director can, therefore, engage only one target at a time; the doctrine is presumably to fire two weapons per target. The system presumably operates as command to line of sight, measuring an error between the line of sight to the missile and to the target, and sending correction signals. That scheme is probably also characteristic of SA-N-3, -4, and -9.

The missile has a canard configuration, with relatively large fixed wings, and there is a short booster, whose fins fold out as the missile leaves its launcher.

Standard magazine capacity per launcher is 16, the missiles being carried in two 8-missile race-tracks.

An SA-N-1 missile on its dual launcher. (TASS from SOVFOTO)

◆ **SA-N-3 Goblet**

> **Dimensions:** 60 cm × 6.1 m; span 1.4 m (23.6 × 240 × 55.1 in)
> **Weight:** 545 kg (1200 lbs) **Warhead:** 80 kg (176 lbs)
> **Propulsion:** boost-sustain rocket motor **Speed:** Mach 2.5
> **Range:** 32,800 yds (improved version, in *Kiev*, 60,100 yds) (altitude 300–80,000 ft)

SA-N-3 on board the *Moskva*, with SUW-N-1 to the left. (French Navy, 1969)

SA-N-3 missile being launched, with another on the launcher. (*Ships of the World*)

SA-N-3 is unique among Soviet naval surface-to-air missiles in having no army equivalent; reports that Goblet was related to the semiactive SA-6 proved erroneous. SA-N-3 is command-guided (Head Lights is the radar director), with one director per twin launcher. The missile has shallow delta wings, perhaps adopted for lengthened surface-to-surface range, for something approaching dual-purpose performance. The rear fins carry fixed antennas that probably carry the command link.

Reportedly SA-N-3, like SA-N-1, was developed by the Lav-ochkin/Grushin design bureau, and a proposal for this weapon was prepared for Khrushchev in 1961.

Missile capacity per launcher is 36 (it may be 22 in some ships).

◆ SA-N-4

Dimensions: 21 cm × 3.2 m; span 64 cm (8.2 × 126 × 25.2 in)
Weight: 168 kg (370 lbs) **Warhead:** 18 kg (40 lbs)
Propulsion: boost-sustain rocket (burn times 2 and 15 sec)
Speed: Mach 2+
Range: 13 km (minimum 1.6–3 km) (14,200 yds; minimum 1750–3300 yds); altitude limits 30–20,000 ft

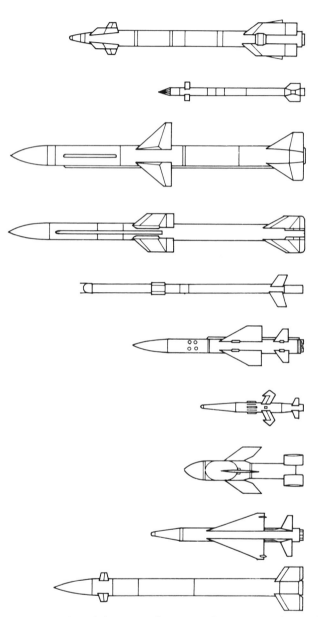

Short-range naval air-defense missiles. Top to bottom: Crotale Naval, Mistral, Sparrow, Aspide, RAM, Barak, RBS 70, Sea Cat, Sea Wolf, SA-N-4. (*Ships of the World*)

The Soviet designation of this point-defense missile system is Osa-M; the Soviet launcher designation is ZIF-122. SA-N-4 is a naval equivalent of the land-mobile SA-8 (Gecko). Apparently the naval version entered service first. SA-N-4 is broadly comparable to the U.S. Sea Sparrow or to Crotale Naval. Missiles are housed nose-down in the protective silo. The twin-arm launcher is normally housed; it emerges before firing and retracts to pick up reloads. Missile capacity per standard 4.2-m diameter silo is 20, on four revolving drums, each carrying five rounds. The nose-down position reduces the distance missiles must be lifted into firing position and may be required for fuzing

before firing. This arrangement would also simplify protection against a cook-off, since all that would be required would be to open the door to vent.

SA-N-4 is command-guided (by the Pop Group radar) and can be used against surface targets.

The missile details above refer to the land-based equivalent, SA-8.

SA-N-9 is the replacement for this system.

SA-N-4 missiles on their twin-arm launcher.

◆ SA-N-5 Grail

Dimensions: 70 mm × 1.34 m (2.76 × 52.8 in)
Weight: 9.2 kg (20.3 lbs)
Warhead: 1.1 kg (370 g RDX/AP) (2.4/0.82 lbs)
Propulsion: boost-sustain rocket
Speed: 385 m/sec (Mach 1.13) (1260 ft/sec)
Range: 3.6 km; min 800 m; altitude limits 50–3500 m (875–3900 yds; 165–11,500 ft)

SA-N-5 is a naval version of the ubiquitous SA-7 shoulder-launched surface-to-air missile. Grail is either hand-held or fired from a special quadruple launcher. SA-N-5 is widely distributed on board Soviet patrol and amphibious craft, much as the U.S. 20-mm gun once appeared wherever space was available. Many Soviet submarines reportedly carry one or more in the sail, for self-defense when surfaced. Compared to the U.S. Stinger, SA-N-5 is reportedly less effective against anything but a hot tailpipe and is easier to counter.

The basic missile is called Strela or 9M32 in Soviet service; development was reportedly inspired by the revelation of the U.S. Redeye in 1959. The naval version is called Strela 2M in Soviet service.

◆ SA-N-6 Grumble

Dimensions: 45 cm × 7 m (17.7 × 276 in)
Weight: 1500 kg (3300 lbs) **Warhead:** 90 kg (198 lbs)
Propulsion: rocket **Speed:** Mach 6
Range: 100 km; max altitude 30.4 km, min altitude 300 m (about 109,000 yds; 984–99,700 ft)

SA-N-6 is a naval version of the land-based SA-10 area-defense missile. The land-based weapon was reportedly designed in the late 1960s or early 1970s to deal with a new generation of high-speed threats, presumably including the new U.S. SRAM short-range ballistic stand-off bomber missile. In naval service, SA-N-6 supersedes the SA-N-3 area-defense missile and provides (in theory) the ability to counter much faster threats and, probably, pop-up threats (thanks to the vertical launcher). However, because Grumble almost certainly cannot engage incoming threats around a 360-degree arc, SA-N-6 is not a true anti-saturation system like the Aegis system.

Reportedly the missile is extremely energetic.

The land-based system was developed by the Grushin design bureau, and tests began in 1972. In land service, the missile is associated with a large S-band surveillance-and-tracking radar (Big Bird), a pulse-doppler target tracker, and a flat-plate X-band control radar. It seems likely that the naval Top Dome radar combines the tracking and missile-control functions in a single device, and that the Big Bird surveillance/acquisition function is carried out by Top Sail or a similar three-dimensional search set.

The naval test ship, the cruiser *Azov*, appeared in 1977. This weapon is the primary antiaircraft armament of *Kirov*- and *Slava*-class cruisers. Missiles are carried in eight-round vertical revolver mounts, with one Top Dome guidance radar for every six mounts. Based on past Soviet practice (two weapons per target), each Top Dome, which probably covers something less than a full 180-degree arc, can control three simultaneous engagements. Guidance is reportedly by track-via-missile, as in the U.S. Army Patriot. Top Dome is apparently electronically scanned.

Ships differ substantially in their launching arrangements. *Kirov* and *Frunze* have revolvers, with one opening per group of eight missiles. *Slava*, however, has eight doors per launching group. They are still circularly disposed around a central position, but there is probably no gas disposal problem. One might conclude that the original system, in the *Kirovs*, employed cold launching (otherwise hot gas would flood each revolver), in which case the failure of a rocket motor would allow the missile to fall back onto the ship. In the *Slava* system, as in the U.S. VLS, each missile can presumably fire in its launch cell.

◆ SA-N-7 Gadfly

Dimensions: 40 cm × 5.6 m; span 1.2 m (15.9 × 220 × 47.2 in)
Weight: 650 kg (1433 lbs) **Warhead:** 80 kg (176 lbs)
Propulsion: solid rocket **Speed:** Mach 3
Range: 30 km; min 3 km (3300–33,000 yds); altitude limits 100–46,000 ft

An SA-N-7 missile on its launching rail on board a *Sovremennyy*-class destroyer. The resemblance to the U.S. Standard Missile is apparent. (German Ministry of Defense)

SA-N-7, a navalized SA-11, is the first Soviet naval semiactive missile. SA-11 was itself derived from SA-6, a semiactive weapon inspired by the U.S. Hawk. SA-N-7 uses a single-arm fast-firing launcher (as in the U.S. Standard series); but instead of a single tracker-illuminator dish, each launcher is provided with three Front Dome illuminators, each of which appears to

cover a limited field of view. However, standard practice in SA-N-6 firing is to salvo up to three weapons at once: it is possible that the illuminators are arranged so that three can point simultaneously at a target on any one bearing, the missiles being assigned different frequencies. The trials ship, *Provornyy*, had eight illuminators, but she also had provisions for up to three launchers (two forward, which were not fitted), so this number of illuminators may be confusing.

The land-based SA-11 appeared about 1979, the naval test installation (on board the destroyer *Provornyy*) appearing in 1981. The missile itself is similar in external configuration to the U.S. Tartar-Standard (MR) series. Only one ship per year is being built to accommodate this missile.

The standard magazine holds twenty missiles.

◆ SA-N-8 Gremlin

Dimensions: 75 mm × 1.4 m (2.9 × 55.1 in)
Weight: 10.5 kg (23.1 lbs) **Warhead:** 2 kg (4.4 lbs)
Propulsion: boost-sustain rocket **Speed:** 600 m/sec (1970 ft/sec)
Range: 6 km, min 600 m; altitude limits 10 m and 5500 m (660–6600 yds; 33–18,000 ft)

A follow-on to SA-N-5, SA-N-8 uses the next-generation Soviet hand-held weapon, SA-14. Reportedly SA-14 introduces a more sensitive IR detector but still lacks full forward-aspect capability and, thus, does not quite compare with the U.S. Stinger. The next type, SA-16, reportedly can attack an approaching target and is probably also in naval service.

This weapon apparently entered service about 1980.

◆ SA-N-9

Dimensions: 20 cm × 3.5 m (7.9 × 103 in)
Weight: 200 kg (441 lbs) **Warhead:** 20 kg (44 lbs)
Propulsion: boost-sustain rocket **Speed:** Mach 3
Range: 15 km; maximum altitude 12 km (16,400 yds; 39,000 ft altitude)

This vertically launched missile is the successor to SA-N-4. SA-N-9 first appeared in the destroyer *Udaloy* and is to be fitted in the cruiser *Frunze*, the carrier *Novorossisk*, and presumably in other future construction. SA-N-9 is found on board the carrier *Baku*. Reportedly SA-N-9 is a naval version of the land-based SA-15, which has superseded SA-8 in Soviet ground forces. Data above describe SA-15.

The associated radar director is Cross Sword.

UNITED KINGDOM

◆ Blowpipe/Javelin/Starstreak

Dimensions: 3 in × 53.1 in; span 10.8 in **Weight:** 24 lbs
Warhead: 4-lbs blast/shaped-charge (capacitance proximity or impact fuze)
Speed: Mach 1.5 maximum **Range:** 3500 yds (minimum 300 yds)

Javelin on shipboard. (Short Bros.)

Data above apply to Blowpipe.

Blowpipe and its successor, Javelin, are hand-held antiaircraft rockets comparable in role to the U.S. Stinger, the Soviet SA-7, and the Swedish RBS 70. Blowpipe and Javelin can be used for small ship's self-defense, either hand-held or on the lightweight multiple mountings that the manufacturer, Short Brothers, has promoted for some years.

Blowpipe began in 1966 as a private venture, with final British Army trials following in April 1970 and production beginning in mid-1971. In July 1978 Blowpipe began to replace the Bofors 40 mm L70 in the British Territorial Army (reserves). An improved version with better guidance, Javelin, was announced in July 1979; and the British Ministry of Defense let a development contract in June 1980.

Short Brothers marketed a variety of Blowpipe mounts for ship installation from 1973 onward: two- or ten-missile launchers for surface ships; and SLAM, carrying six missiles, for submarines. None appears to have been adopted.

The Royal Navy used the Short Brothers Blowpipe as an emergency point-defense weapon during the Falklands War and may currently deploy Blowpipe on board some ships in the Middle East. Blowpipe was offered as a submarine self-defense antiaircraft missile in the abortive SLAM system, in a six-round launcher.

Javelin is now the standard British very short range ships' self-defense missile, replacing Blowpipe. First purchases were made in June 1984, trials following on board HMS *Phoebe.* A five-round mount is being developed. Sea Javelin was formally announced in September 1985, and in November 1986 it was reported that British minesweepers in the Persian Gulf had been armed with Javelin for self-protection. No GWS designation has been announced.

The missile is command-guided to line of sight, the aimer using a sight and thumb controls to maintain the apparent coincidence between missile and target. The missile is automatically gathered into his field of view by an infrared sensor, and that process reduces minimum range to 300 yds. Time of flight to full range is 14 seconds. Javelin uses semiautomatic command–to–line-of-sight control, the operator merely keeping the target in his aiming sight, and the missile being tracked automatically. This scheme increases accuracy and reduces minimum intercept range. Javelin also has a higher impulse motor for greater range (5.5 km [6000 yds]), and a blast-fragmentation rather than a shaped-charge warhead (2.72 vice 2.2 kg). Dimensions match those of Blowpipe, except that the missile is slightly heavier, and the total system, including the clip-on aimer, weighs 24.1 rather than 20.25 kg.

As of 1988, estimated costs per missile were $8000 for Blowpipe and $12,000 for Javelin. Blowpipe was sold to at least 14 countries, and production probably amounted to about 36,500 rounds, with one clip-on aiming unit for every 5–10 rounds.

The successor missile is Starstreak, which uses a boost-sustain rocket to attain Mach 4.0 and has a range of 7 km (7700 yds). Unlike any previous British antiaircraft missile, Starstreak fires three separate warheads (darts), which are described as both explosive and kinetic-energy penetrators. The darts are not themselves powered, but reportedly they are laser-guided to the target after the motor burns out. Since the motor is Javelin-derived, it would appear that the very high speed is achieved by using very light darts, perhaps analogous to the use of sabots in conventional guns.

Competitive contracts for a follow-on hand-held antiaircraft weapon were let to Shorts and British Aerospace on 25 January 1985, the latter proposing Thunderbolt (which used a nonexplosive kinetic-energy warhead). Final proposals were submitted 14 January 1986, and Starstreak was recommended in April and formally selected in June 1986.

In 1986 Short Brothers received a prefeasibility contract from the Royal Navy to study the application of Starstreak to point defense, under the VSRAD 2000 program.

♦ **Sea Cat (GWS 20, 21, 22, 24)**
   Dimensions: 7.5 × 58.3 in; span 25.6 in   **Weight:** 138 lbs
   Warhead: 45 lbs (38-lbs HE) in Mod 1; Mod 0 is a 31-lb continuous-rod warhead (5-lbs HE); both mods have both impact and IR proximity fuzes.   **Propulsion:** boost-glide
   Speed: Mach 0.6 (average at the end of boost)
   Range: 5000 yds, minimum 1500 yds; max altitude 3300 ft

Quadruple Sea Cat launcher (with two missiles on board) on a British *Leander*-class frigate, 1979. The eight-barrel chaff launcher below and to the left is Corvus. (Author)

Sea Cat firing, during trials of a new low-altitude height-keeping capability. (Short Bros.)

A Sea Cat being launched from its quadruple launcher on board HMS *Intrepid.* The radome visible at the right (actually in the middle of the launcher) transmits the command signal. (Royal Navy)

Sea Cat was the first point-defense missile to enter naval service. Sea Cat was conceived (by Short Brothers and Harland) as a one-for-one replacement for the existing twin 40-mm Bofors gun and was based on the Malkara antitank missile. Sea Cat is command-guided by an operator using a joystick (Mk 20 Visual Guided Weapon Director); he first captures the missile after launch using sighting binoculars, then tracks it to the target. GWS 20 can also be integrated with the Contraves Sea Hunter, the Elsag NA 9, or the Signaal M40/44 fire-control systems.

GWS 21 is controlled by the Type-262 radar originally developed for 40-mm gun control.

GWS 22 employs a modified radar director originally designed for medium gunfire control, MRS 3 (the British equivalent of the U.S. Mk 56), with Type-904 radar and a Type-323-series closed-circuit television. In this MEASL system, ordered by the Royal Navy in 1972, the television, which is slaved to the target-tracking radar, tracks the missile automatically.

GWS 24 employs the WSA-4 fire-control system with Type-912 radar (Amazon-class frigates).

Sea Cat was modified in 1977 with a special altimeter, for the antiship-missile-defense role; Sea Cat carried out sea-skimming trials late in 1980 and was ordered (as a target) in September 1980.

The standard launcher carries four missiles, with the command-guidance antenna in the center. The launcher weighs about 6600 lbs. A lightweight (2800 lbs) three-missile launcher was adopted by the Iranian and Nigerian Navies. It is controlled by a set of binoculars atop a single manually operated pedestal director.

The Swedish Navy adopted Sea Cat as RB 07, using an HSA M4 director, on board now-discarded destroyers. Altogether, the weapon is or has been in service in seventeen navies.

Because of its low speed and short range, Sea Cat cannot engage supersonic targets. Development of a proposed Sea Cat 2 was dropped in favor of Sea Wolf; the much greater sophistication of the latter system testifies to the complexity of the supersonic sea-skimming–missile problem.

◆ Sea Dart (GWS 30; CF 299)

Dimensions: 16.5 × 172 in, including booster; span 36 in
Weight: 1200 lbs   **Warhead:** 50-lb HE/continuous rod
Propulsion: ramjet with rocket boost   **Speed:** Mach 2.5–3.0
Range: 25–30 nm (altitude 100–60,000 ft)

Sea Dart. (*Sea Power*)

Sea Dart is the standard British area-defense missile, a semi-actively homing ramjet. Like the defunct U.S. Talos, Sea Dart uses four interferometer aerials (polyrods) for guidance, rather than a dish. They provide monopulse tracking; the missile has a reference antenna pointing back and flies a proportional-navigation path. Guidance is provided by two Type-909 tracker-illuminators. This radar is cued by a Type-992Q high-definition

(target-indication) radar, which in turn is cued by a Type-965 or Type-1022 broad-beam search radar; only the illuminator searches in elevation.

Because it employs vacuum-tube technology, this system is reportedly not entirely reliable. A Sea Dart 2 program, announced in November 1977, reportedly amounted to a British equivalent of the U.S. 3-T "Get-Well" program of the 1960s. However, Mark 2 would also have had thrust-vector control (and a more powerful booster), new wings and fins to allow the missile to engage higher-altitude targets, more fuel tankage, and a higher proportion of solid-state circuits. Presumably solid-state circuitry would also have applied to the guidance radars, which had the most serious reliability problems. Moreover, using the separate search and target-indication radars in combination increased the system's response time. Marconi proposed, then, to replace the obsolescent 965/992 combination with a single search/target-indication radar, STIR. By 1980 the Sea Dart 2 program had been reduced to ECCM improvements, including the new radars. However, the program (including the new Type 909M and STIR radars) was killed in 1981 as part of the Nott Defense Review. This program seems to have been revived following the Falklands War, without the Mk 2 designation. Modernization will include replacement of existing Type-992Q radars with the new Type 996 for better targeting.

A new blast warhead (GMk 39A1) was delivered beginning in 1987. Presumably this warhead is a response to the problem of intercepting fast passing targets.

Missiles are loaded in two stages. Stowed vertically in a magazine below the water line, missiles are then carried up (by chain hoist) into an intermediate position, warmed up (for 30–60 seconds), hoisted into an upper-deck position, and only then rammed hydraulically onto the launcher: this process is analogous to the two-stage hoists used by many heavy naval guns. This practice should increase safety (the Royal Navy has been extremely conscious of safety requirements for magazines since World War I) but may also reduce the rate of fire. Reportedly at least one Sea Dart ship found in the Falklands War that her blast or flash (outer hoist) doors did not close properly at times. Typically two missiles are held in readiness below the launcher, with another two in the intermediate position. The intermediate position is probably required to fin the booster, just as in Terrier/SM-1 and Masurca. The cumbersome magazine arrangement may explain proposals for box-launched Sea Dart. However, reportedly HMS *Invincible* was able to fire six Sea Darts in two minutes on one occasion, or one salvo (2 missiles) every 40 seconds. HMS *Bristol* is equipped with a heavy Mk-30 (i.e., GWS 30) Mod-0 electrically-driven launcher, whereas later ships have the lighter-weight Mod 1. Missile capacity: HMS *Bristol*, 40 missiles; Type-42 Batches I and II, 24 missiles; Batch III, 42 missiles; *Invincible* class, 24 missiles. The 24- and 42-missile figures are often rendered 20 and 40, and the difference may be test missiles.

Development began in August 1962, with full development approved in May 1963, tests in 1965, and production announced in November 1967. The 500th missile was fired by HMS *Bristol* in November 1986. Using Sea Dart, HMS *Invincible* shot down a Petrel target drone on the Hebrides missile range in November 1985.

Argentina was the only export customer, for her two Type-42 destroyers. As of 1986 estimated production was 1600 (plus 60 for Argentina), and estimated unit price was $300,000. A new production contract, reportedly for 100 missiles with the new warhead, was let in August 1986.

Sea Dart was the major British naval area-defense missile used in the Falklands War and is credited with having shot down seven Argentine aircraft. Unfortunately several other firing opportunities were lost because of the system's unreliability, e.g., because magazine doors did not always allow missiles to be loaded promptly. The system was also degraded by its surveillance and acquisition radars, which reportedly lacked the MTI required to detect and track Argentine aircraft popping up over the nearby shore.

A box-launched Lightweight Sea Dart system was announced in 1978, using the Marconi ST805 tracker-illuminator (ranges are reportedly 60 km on an airplane and 14 km on a missile, the former increasing to 80 km with a larger dish). The missile has also been promoted as a surface-to-surface weapon with a range of 25–30 km, climbing steeply after launch, then diving at 30 degrees to build up momentum for deep penetration of a target. Thus far none has been sold. A land-based version, Guardian, for defense of the Falklands, was offered in September 1982 but was not purchased.

◆ **Sea Slug (GWS 1)**

> **Dimensions:** 16.1 in × 20 ft (19 ft 8 in for Mk 1); span 56.6 in
> **Weight:** approx 4400 lbs total (1980 lbs without boosters)
> **Warhead:** approx 200 lbs
> **Propulsion:** strap-on boosters with sustainer rocket
> **Speed:** Mach 1.8
> **Range:** Reported range for Mk 2 is 24.3 nm.

HMS *Devonshire* fires a Sea Slug. The cylindrical radar just forward of the helicopter platform is Type 901; forward of the after funnel are the Type-278 height-finder and the Type-965 (AKE-1 antenna) search radar. (U.S. Naval Institute)

Sea Slug is obsolete; it is the survivor of the initial postwar generation of Western command-guided (beam-riding) surface-to-air naval missiles. The U.S. equivalent, now extinct, was the beam-riding version of Terrier. The original requirement, defining Sea Slug Mk 1, was that the missile be able to engage a high-altitude 650-knot bomber at 30,000 yards (15 nm), i.e., at about 50 percent greater range than the contemporary U.S. Terrier. Sea Slug Mk 2, then, might be considered equivalent to later (but still early) versions of Terrier. These weapons were intended to deal with high-altitude subsonic (and nonmaneuvering) bombers, and they had little capability against anything more agile.

Two ships, *Antrim* and *Glamorgan,* carried Sea Slug into the Falklands War, and the missile was fired at least once against aircraft. *Antrim* fired hers ballistically against Port Stanley airport.

This missile was carried only by British "County"-class destroyers. All of these ships have now been sold to Chile and Pakistan; only the Chileans retained Sea Slug and bought all the remaining spare parts and spare missiles in 1986. Probably they intend to use Sea Slug primarily as a surface-to-surface missile. However, in the spring of 1988 it was reported that the Chilean shipyard, ASMAR, had removed Sea Slug from one "County"-class destroyer, *Blanco Encalada,* using the former Sea Slug magazine for helicopter support. The hangar was enlarged to take two AS.332F Super Puma helicopters. The yard reported that it expected a second conversion contract, most likely for *Almirante Latorre.* Chile would then have two Sea Slug ships.

Sea Slug is unique in having its four strap-on boosters attached around its nose rather than its tail. The wings and control surfaces are attached at 45-degree angles. The missile was designed to be stowed horizontally, rather than vertically (as in the first U.S. Terrier launchers); and in "County"-class destroyers the centerline magazine takes up much of the total length of the ship, resembling the hangar of a small carrier.

◆ **Sea Wolf (GWS 25, 26)**

> **Dimensions:** 18 cm × 2 m; span 56 cm (7.1 × 75 × 22 in)
> **Weight:** 82 kg (180 lbs)   **Warhead:** approx 14 kg (31 lbs)
> **Propulsion:** boost-glide; burn time 2–3 sec
> **Speed:** Mach 2   **Range:** approx 5 km (5500 yds)

Sea Wolf being loaded. (British Ministry of Defence)

Sea Wolf vertical launch (with booster). (British Aerospace)

Sea Wolf is a point-defense missile, normally carried in a six-round trainable launcher. Guidance is by command to line of sight, using either a radar or a television tracker. The missile is gathered into the tracking beam and command-guided up the beam until intercepting the target. A ship carries one radar per missile launcher, so that (for example) a Type-22 frigate has two engagement channels. The tracker operates in I-band, the command link in J-band; individual trackers operate in different frequencies, so that a ship can guide two missiles independently toward the same (or alternative) targets simultaneously. Missile launch is entirely automatic (subject to operator veto), the weapons system ranking and engaging threats in turn. During the Falklands War, this system (on board Type-22 frigates) was used for the close-in defense of the British aircraft carriers. It was discovered that the automatic threat-ranker tended not to deal with crossing targets, and new software had to be provided on the spot. This experience shows both the inherent flexibility of software-based digital systems, and also the effect of the assumptions (in this case, that the system was purely for self-defense) written into that software.

Targets are acquired and tracked by back-to-back Type-967/968 radars, and the associated guidance radar is Type 910. The search/track radars are two-dimensional, the target being located in elevation by the Type-910 tracker itself.

A lightweight version (GWS 25 Mod 2) is being developed for the *Invincible*-class carriers and Type-42 Batch-III destroyers, using a four-barrel launcher and a lightweight tracker (Type 911, the Marconi 805SW); the contract award was announced 1 February 1988. The Type-911 tracker had already been tested on board HMS *Brave*, in November 1986. All subsequent Type 22s are so fitted. This system is GWS 25 Mod 3. Besides Type 911, Mod 3 employs upgraded Type-967/968 radars. The lightweight Mod 2 system uses a launcher based on that developed for Sea Cat; Mod 2 fires containerized missiles. Total weight is 2.5 tonnes, compared to 7.5 tonnes for the earlier six-barrel launcher. Each containerized missile weighs 170 kg.

A vertical-launch system (GWS 26) is being developed for the new Type-23 ("Duke"-class) frigates, a Sea Wolf with a booster already having been launched from an obsolete frigate (September 1982). It appears that British Aerospace was interested in vertical launch at a much earlier date, since seven Sea Wolf–type missiles were launched and turned over to normal flight mode in 1978 in Project SINNER. The first British official development contract was let in the fall of 1983. Vertical-launch Sea Wolf installations will use a new Type-911(2) tracking radar, an improved version of the Type 911(1) now being installed. In the vertical-launching system, the missile itself is provided with a long, finned booster with thrust-vector control. The booster reportedly adds about 50 percent to the range of the missile, for a maximum of about 8 km.

A development contract for a more sophisticated version of the system, GWS 27, was let in 1986. It was later canceled. GWS 27 would have used an active seeker and a phased-array tracker, the Marconi S1805SW Multifire. Reportedly one goal of the GWS 27 program was to more than double the range of the missile, to beyond 10 km. Missiles would have been command-guided into a terminal homing basket, or else fired with preprogrammed inertial mid-course guidance autopilots. The Marconi seeker intended for GWS 27 was displayed at RNEE 1985.

British Aerospace has also marketed a lightweight Sea Wolf using the Signaal VM40 tracking radar.

Sea Wolf was initially conceived as a faster follow-on to Sea Cat, to engage supersonic targets. In June 1967 a contract for what was then designated PX430 (CONFESSOR) was let to British Aircraft Corporation. The initial production contract followed in July 1968, and the first missile was fired in 1973. A Sea Wolf hit a Mach-2 Petrel target in 1974 and a 4.5-inch shell in June 1977. This missile proved quite successful during the Falklands War. On one occasion, four Argentine aircraft attacked a frigate. Two were shot down, and a third crashed trying to evade a Sea Wolf. Only the fourth escaped. In all, Sea Wolf was credited with having shot down five aircraft during the war.

This system was ordered by Kuwait, but in March 1988 the British Ministry of Defence blocked the sale on the grounds that the technology involved might be transferred further.

In 1988 British Aerospace offered a modified vertical-launch Sea Wolf, named Wolverine, as a near-term land-based anti-tactical-ballistic-missile weapon. The initial Wolverine pro-

posal was a boosted missile with an elongated nose carrying flechettes and an active radar seeker, which was derived from the seeker originally proposed for an active version of the Sky Flash air-to-air missile. With the disappearance of the Soviet SS-20 (because of the INF Treaty), the remaining threat was considerably less demanding, and BAe was able to discard active guidance. The current proposal employs MRCLOS (Missile Reference Command to Line of Sight). MRCLOS uses an inertial reference unit in the missile, reducing the number of updates required by a pure command to line of sight (CLOS) system. That reduction, in turn, permits a single fire-control unit to guide several missiles on a time-shared basis. BAe currently claims that MRCLOS would suffice against weapons such as the upgraded Soviet SS-23 and SCUD B, although an active missile seeker will still be needed to deal with future weapons. Presumably MRCLOS would have a potential naval application.

◆ SDMS

Support Defence Missile System is similar in concept to the NATO LAMS. A missile ship would defend the adjacent two or three ships, as the Type-22 frigates defended the carriers in the Falklands. As of 1988 no contracts had, apparently, been let; but Marconi hoped that an extended version of the EMPAR radar (see above under Italian AAW radars) would be suitable, and the company was investing its own funds in the project. Marconi's missile partner is British Aerospace; some years ago it was reported that the missile would be a Sea Wolf with a booster. The canceled GWS 27 envisaged Sea Wolf with an active seeker (and with command mid-course guidance), much the sort of system required to fulfill the SDMS mission.

◆ VSRAD-2000

This British program for Very Short Range Air Defense uses a high-velocity missile. Short has offered its new Skystreak (the planned replacement of Javelin). Marconi is the competitor. Short Brothers received a VSRAD study contract on 29 June 1987, for completion in November 1987.

◆ Racal CIWS

At the RNEE exhibition in the fall of 1987, Racal displayed a mock-up of a new private-venture close-in weapons (missile) system the company is developing, for introduction about 1995. The system consists of a box launcher on a stabilized platform, with a nonelevating radome on top. The box (about 1.7 m wide, 1.8 m long, and 0.7 m high) carries three missiles on each side, stacked vertically, with electronics and hydraulics between and with windows for two optronic sensors in the front. The radome carries a K-band CW search radar, scanning at high speed, and covering an 80-degree arc in elevation. Presumably the radar detects targets by their doppler. Threats are automatically evaluated and passed to an M-band tracking radar using an array antenna (to form both a wide beam for missile gathering and a narrow beam for command to line of sight). Very fast missiles are to be used, so that even though engagement range will be short there will be time for at least one re-engagement should the first fail. Maximum delay from detection to interception will be 3 seconds. Total system weight is to be no more than 1.5 metric tons. Reportedly the missile will be an adaptation of the British Aerospace Thunderbolt, the unsuccessful competitor with Starstreak for a British Army contract.

The Racal system is interesting because it suggests a movement away from current gun-based CIWS systems back toward missiles, which should have a high unit-kill probability, but which are often ineffective inside a substantial minimum range. Although the system was described as a private venture, the Racal proposal may reflect the requirements of VSRAAD 2000.

UNITED STATES

◆ Aegis

See radar integration under AAW radars above.

◆ RAM (RIM-116A)

Dimensions: 5 × 111 in; span 17.25 in   **Weight:** 162 lbs
Warhead: 5 lbs   **Propulsion:** solid-fuel rocket
Speed: Mach 2.0+   **Range:** 5 nm

RAM (RIM-116A) firing. (General Dynamics)

The Rolling Airframe Missile (RAM) is a new point-defense weapon developed as a joint U.S. (General Dynamics)–West German (RAM GmBH)–Danish (Per Udsen) program.

Unlike Sea Sparrow, RAM is a fire-and-forget weapon, homing either on the infrared signature (forward-aspect glint) or the emissions of the homing radar of the incoming weapon. RAM uses a Sidewinder motor, warhead, and fuze, a Stinger infrared seeker, and a new two-antenna RF seeker. The missile spins as it flies, so that two canard control fins (and two RF antennas) do the work that four of each do in a nonspinning missile. Four tail fins keep the missile spinning.

In theory, the missile is fired in response to radar (or passive electronic intercept or passive electro-optical) warning, launched on a selected bearing and elevation. RAM flies toward its target on the basis of RF mid-course guidance. The missile shifts to infrared terminal guidance but can continue on RF if weather conditions (e.g., too little sun to provide too little glint) provide too little IR signature. In theory, this fire-and-forget operation should make it possible for even a small combatant to deal with multiple attackers.

There are three alternative launchers: a standard 21-round EX-31 for patrol boats up to large amphibious ships (using the same base and turning mass as a Phalanx mount), a modified NATO Sea Sparrow launcher (two cells occupied by a total of ten RAMs), and a special RAM Alternate Launching System (RALS) carrying ten rounds in two arms. RALS has been designed specifically for small craft, and it has been proposed to the Royal Danish Navy for installation on board Standard Flex-300 and *Niels Juel*–class ships.

Planned U.S. EX-31 installations: 2 LCC, 5 LHA, 7 LPH. The Sea Sparrow change will go into aircraft carriers, LHDs, AORs, and the *Spruance* class.

LAUNCHER CHARACTERISTICS

	Standard	*RALS*
Above-Decks	11,424 lbs	7200 lbs
Below-Decks	2,105 lbs	
Working Circle	129 in	
Elevation	−25/+80 deg	−25/+85 deg
Capacity	21	10

RAM production was suspended because of test and cost problems, which have delayed the system about five years in all. However, on 30 March 1987 U.S. Secretary of Defense Caspar Weinberger certified that the missile had passed its tests and would, therefore, enter production. At that time it was expected that the first 500 would cost $145,000 (FY86) each, cost averaging $100,000 for the remaining 4500 planned U.S. weapons.

A Memorandum of Understanding for U.S.-German production was signed in August 1987, at which time the United States planned to buy 30 launchers, and Germany planned 58 launchers (1923 missiles). The German producer will be RAM GmBH, and it and General Dynamics are to compete for up to 70 percent of the annual binational purchase.

The first 117 U.S. production missiles were authorized under FY86; FY88, 240; FY89, 260 (U.S. production only). The January 1989 U.S. budget request showed 580 RAMs in FY90 and 540 in FY91.

Drawings of the new Japanese 1900-ton frigate show RAM; presumably the Japanese plan to manufacture the missile under license.

◆ Sea Chaparral

See Sidewinder (U.S. air-to-air missile below).

◆ Sea Sparrow

See Sparrow (U.S. air-to-air missile below).

◆ Standard Missile-1 (Medium Range) (RIM-66A and -66B)

Dimensions: 13.5 × 176 in; span 42.5 in
Weight: 1240 lbs (1390 lbs for RIM-66B)
Warhead: 137-lb continuous rod
Propulsion: boost-sustain rocket   **Speed:** Mach 1.25–3.5
Range: 35,000 yds, minimum 3000 yds for air targets; maximum intercept altitude 65,000 ft (maximum intercept range 50,000 yds, maximum altitude 80,000 ft for RIM-66B)

Data are for RIM-66A except as noted.

The Standard Missile replaced the earlier Tartar and Terrier, using as many parts in common as possible for, respectively, the medium-range (MR) weapon with a boost-sustain motor and

Standard Missile (Medium Range) being fired from a Mk-26 launcher. The SM-1, SM-2, and Tartar missiles are virtually identical in appearance, though quite different in capability. (U.S. Navy)

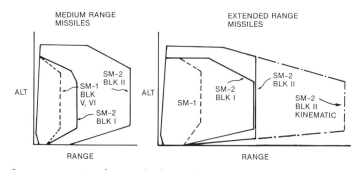

Improvements in the Standard Missile's intercept envelopes resulted from the change from semiactive to command guidance. (General Dynamics)

the extended-range (ER) weapon with a separate booster and sustainer. The design was adapted from that of the TRIP (Tartar Reliability Improvement Program) weapon, which had also been specified for the abortive Typhon program. Reliability improvements included all-electric design (hydraulic power for control surfaces was eliminated) and solid-state electronics with the first battery power in a U.S. missile (which drastically reduced warm-up time, from 26 seconds to 1/15 second). Those improvements in turn eliminated the requirement for shipboard checkout, missiles being shipped as "wooden rounds" good for a three-year no-test cycle. The Standard Missile also incorporated a single-sideband receiver (for improved ECCM and clutter rejection) and "doppler offset" to improve discrimination among multiple targets. An increase from 12 to 19 guidance channels reduced ship-to-ship interference. While RIM-66A was an interim weapon that used the existing Tartar motor, RIM-66B introduced a new Mk-56 dual-thrust rocket motor, to achieve 45 percent greater intercept range, 33 percent greater peak velocity, 25 percent greater peak velocity, 25 percent greater intercept altitude, and greater terminal maneuverability. RIM-66C is SM-2(MR) (see below).

Other weapons in the series were designed for specific antisurface applications: RGM-66D was Standard ARM (ship-to-ship, homing on the target's radar emissions); RGM-66E was a Standard ARM adapted for firing from an ASROC launcher; RGM-66F was a Standard Active antiship missile. AGM-78, Standard ARM (see Strike/Surface Warfare section), is an air-launched antiradar version, now being replaced by HARM, AGM-88A (see Strike/Surface Warfare section). In the surface-to-surface mode, Standard ARM follows an up-and-over trajectory and thus achieves a range of 35–40 nm (minimum range 7000 yds) carrying a 219-lb warhead (102-lbs high explosive). Standard ARM (shipborne) was fitted to two U.S. patrol gunboats; it is carried by the Korean *Paek Ku 51* (ex-USS *Benicia*) and *Paek Ku 52–55* of the PSMM-5 class. Standard was fitted to the Iranian destroyers *Babr* and *Palang*, in box launchers (four per ship, with four reloads) as a surface-to-air missile, not Standard ARM (and so is limited to horizon range for surface-to-surface fire).

The West German Navy reportedly bought Standard (at that time, Tartar) for German missile destroyers because the weapon promised a useful surface-to-surface capability. For a time General Dynamics was developing a version of the missile armed with a Bullpup warhead, specifically for the antiship role, to be carried on board German fast attack craft. This weapon was tested, but the Germans chose Exocet instead.

Developments of the basic RIM-66B are incremental and are denoted by block changes. Acceptance trials for Block VI were completed in March 1983, and Block VI began to replace Block V in procurement in FY80. Block VI adds the SM-2's monopulse seeker, for better resistance to countermeasures, a new proximity fuze (target detection device Mk 45 Mod 4); but the guidance section is interchangeable with that of Block V. Block VI, as well as SM-2(MR) Block II, is 10 in longer than earlier Standard Missiles, to accommodate RIM-66B's new dual-thrust motor, as described above. RIM-66B Block VI also has a new dual-initiated warhead for greater fragment velocity and density, to deal with targets closing at higher speed.

Development of the Standard Missile began in FY63, with tests in FY65–67, and procurement from FY67 onward. Procurement of SM-1(MR) ended in FY85 (700 in FY84, 600 in FY85). Consequently, in the future ships firing off their SM-1 missiles will have to use SM-2(MR) with its programmable autopilot disabled; that use should lengthen the SM-2's production run and cut that missile's unit cost. Total SM-1(MR) production was reportedly 12,000.

The termination of SM-1 production has had two important consequences. First, to the extent that the current effort at battle-group AAW coordination is successful, SM-1 ships carrying SM-2 missiles can act as spare magazines for Aegis ships, contributing to the overall firepower of the battle group. Second, since the United States is not yet willing to export SM-2 technology, she is unable to provide further missiles to those NATO allies currently operating SM-1. The U.S. decision reportedly contributed, in part, to the French choice not to build the planned second group of SM-1–armed missile destroyers (*Cassard* class).

♦ **Standard Missile-1 (Extended Range) (RIM-67A)**

This successor to Terrier (RIM-2) incorporates many components in common with RIM-66 SM-1(MR), but with a different rocket motor capable of greater range. Performance is much like that of Terrier HT-3 (see below). Procurement of the SM-1 Block II (ER) version ended after 1983 (1095 ordered FY82, 375 FY83). Compared to Block I, Block II has a more energetic motor (for higher intercept altitude), a more lethal warhead, and better resistance to countermeasures.

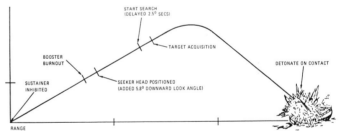

SM-1(ER) being launched; Terrier is externally virtually identical to this missile. (U.S. Naval Institute)

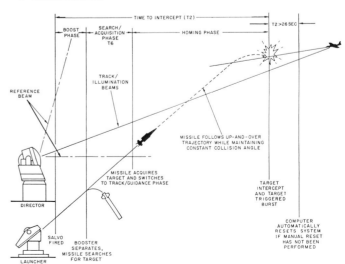

Standard Missiles' flight paths.

♦ Standard Missile-2 (RIM-66C and RIM-67B)

SM-2 adds a programmable autopilot to the basic SM-1 missile, so that SM-2 can be command-guided into a homing "basket" near the projected position of the target. SM-2 was the first tactical missile to incorporate inertial navigation, to guide the missile from the launching ship up into the designated homing "basket." Semiactive illumination is needed only toward the end of the missile's flight. SM-2 is the basis of the Aegis system, which counters saturation by time-sharing illuminators. SM-2, in both (MR) and (ER) versions, is also part of the New Threat Upgrade (NTU) to existing missile systems. NTU ships do not enjoy the tracking precision of the SPY-1 phased-array radar, so illumination must be provided for a longer period, but even so they can engage more targets per unit time.

Like SM-1, SM-2 exists in two versions: a single-stage Medium Range (MR) weapon (RIM-66C), and a two-stage Extended Range (ER) version (RIM-67B). Both share the same programmable autopilot. Aegis ships fire only the (MR) version because their rapid-fire launchers cannot accommodate the manual finning required by the (ER) weapon. The big boosters of these missiles require large fins; the smaller tail fins of the (MR) missiles fold during stowage. Missile cruisers with Mk-10 launchers can fire the (ER) version after undergoing NTU modernization.

The addition of command guidance increases a missile's range in two ways. A conventional semiactive missile homes all the way to its target: the illuminator must, therefore, provide enough energy for a sufficient amount to be reflected all the way back to the missile on its launcher. By way of contrast, a command-guided SM-2 requires illumination only near its target. The illuminator must still provide sufficient energy to reach one way, but only a fraction of the way back. The combination of command and semiactive is preferable to pure command because tracking (both of missile and of target) is unlikely to be precise enough to bring the missile within lethal range at many tens of miles, while the target maneuvers violently.

The missile also gains range because it can fly a more energy-efficient path than the direct chase of a semiactive weapon. When SM-2 replaced SM-1 (without any change in rocket motor), effective range approximately doubled (the stated improvement in the (MR) version was 60 percent). SM-1(MR)'s range was probably about 25 nm, so this improvement probably brought the range of SM-2(MR) to about 40 nm. In the case of SM-2(ER), the improvement was 50 percent or more. Altitude performance also improved. Published diagrams of SM-2(ER) Block I/II's range suggest a maximum range of 90 or even 100 nm. Maximum missile range against a given target is ultimately determined by terminal energy, as the missile glides after its sustainer engine burns out.

SM-2 Block I introduced a monopulse seeker, which counters self-screening jamming.

SM-2 Block II had an improved rocket motor, to deal with faster and more maneuverable targets. This motor doubled the effective range of the (MR) missile, probably bringing it up to the limit imposed by illuminator power. The (ER) Block II missile could fly much farther (i.e., enjoyed a much greater kinematic range), but its effective (illuminator-limited) range is presumably about the same as that of (MR) Block II (which in turn is about the same as that of (ER) Block I). In this case the advantage of the new motor was increased maneuverability against more difficult targets.

Block II also adds digital signal processing and a high-velocity fragmentation warhead (to kill targets passing at very high speeds). Block II was developed in response to a 1975 directive by the secretary of defense, who called for a faster, i.e., more energetic, weapon (in both (MR) and (ER) versions). In March 1981, an SM-2 with the new Mk-70 booster set an altitude record for the interception of a drone.

Missiles procured from FY88 on are Block III, with an improved low-altitude fuze. Development of another new motor, the dual-thrust Mk 104, was announced in the FY86 budget.

Mk 104 is presumably intended for an SM-2(MR) Block V, an unboosted equivalent to Block IV.

SM-2(ER) required a data link back to the launching ship. The link was first tested on board the destroyer *Mahan* in FY79, and installation of the link is associated with the New Threat Upgrade (NTU) program (see the entry under shipboard AAW radars above).

SM-2 Block I procurement ended in FY83. Block II (ER) was approved for service use in May 1983, and the (MR) version in December 1983.

In December 1985 it was estimated that 13,560 SM-2 missiles would be required; another estimate shows 8119 (MR) and 7270 (ER) missiles. The difference may reflect estimates of test and practice firing. Unit costs, as of FY82, were $513,333 for (MR), $572,333 for (ER). Total Standard Missile procurement (all versions): FY84, 1190; FY85, 1380; FY86, 1316. SM-2(MR) procurement began with 30 in FY80; then FY83, 150; FY86, 846; FY87, 844; FY88, 1310; FY89, 1310; as of January 1989 the U.S. budget request was 590 for FY90 and 900 in FY91. SM-2(ER): FY80, 55; FY86, 470; FY87, 350; none in FY88 or FY89.

The Navy's proposal for a nuclear version, denoted SM-2(N), using a W81 warhead, was rejected in the FY80 budget but reinstated in FY81 (for procurement of test rounds). However, (N) was deleted from the FY86 budget by the congressional conference committee in favor of a nonnuclear solution. The chief argument in favor of SM-2(N) was the threat of steeply diving nuclear-armed air-to-surface missiles such as the Soviet AS-4/6. If a weapon could intercept such a missile only as it dove, a conventional weapon might tear off wings without destroying an armored nuclear bomb; and the Soviet weapon, tumbling, might still destroy its target by a near miss. The nonnuclear alternative was presumably a higher-energy missile (Block II or even Block IV), which could attack the incoming weapon further out, before it began to dive, and bring it down outside any damaging range.

♦ SM-2 Aegis (ER) (SM-2 Block IV)

Dimensions: 13.5 × 256 in (booster: 21 × 72 in)
Weight: 3076 lbs (total)

SM-2 Aegis (ER). (Raytheon)

SM-2 Aegis (ER) is a boosted version of SM-2(MR) designed specifically for Aegis ships equipped with Mk-26 or Mk-41 launchers, to deal with very fast or very high altitude targets. Added energy should make the weapon more agile, particularly at the edges of its flight envelope. The missile should also achieve greater range. Aegis ships could not use the regular SM-2(ER) configuration because their launchers are automatic (for high rates of fire) and, therefore, cannot accommodate the manual finning of the usual Mk 10 (SM-2(ER)) system. In 1987 the contract for SM-2 Block IV development was given to Raytheon; General Dynamics Pomona had been responsible for all SM-1/2 development up to that time.

Block IV is designed specifically for vertical launching, so the new missile's short (finless) booster uses thrust-vector control. Modifications to the missile itself include a slip-cast silica radome, a modified antenna with a new signal processor, an improved autopilot, and modified dorsal and tail fins (the latter with new actuators and a new clamp). Raytheon claims that the new aerodynamic surfaces will give considerable improvements in lift and control.

Block IV is to enter service in 1989, the first series of 280 divided between Raytheon (220) and General Dynamics (60).

♦ **Stinger (FIM-92)**

> **Dimensions:** 2.75 × 60 in   **Weight:** 34.5 lbs
> **Warhead:** 6.6 lb (proximity fuze)   **Propulsion:** two-pulse rocket
> **Speed:** Mach 2.0   **Range:** about 5500 yds

This surface-to-air missile was intended for use on land (e.g., by the marines), but since 1984 Stinger has been issued to many U.S. warships for point defense, particularly in Middle Eastern waters. For example, movies of the missile cruiser USS *Vincennes* showed a Stinger operator on deck. Target acquisition was initially entirely visual (via head phones), but the navy is now buying UPS-3 battlefield radars for this purpose. Compared to other hand-held infrared missiles, Stinger is said to have a greater capacity to home on the forward aspect of an incoming target. SA-7, for example, seems to be more limited to tail-aspect attacks and is more likely to be vulnerable to relatively simple infrared countermeasures.

Special features include a dual-color (IR and ultraviolet) seeker (for resistance to countermeasures) and a rosette-scan seeker (in Advanced Stinger) for target discrimination, e.g., between an airplane and a flare.

Recent procurements: FY84, 1205 navy; FY85, 2360 navy; FY86, 3439 navy; FY87, 536 navy; FY88, 425 navy, 3067 marines; FY89 request, none for navy, 3115 for marines. It was reported in April 1988 that purchases of Stinger by the navy had ended, with about 150 fewer than the 685 originally planned. Because it was designed for use on land, Stinger incorporated no shielding against the electromagnetic radiation typically present on shipboard. This problem is typical of land-warfare weapons placed on ships without special adaptation. In addition, the missile's launch blast could damage the ship's structure.

Stinger has been extremely successful in Afghanistan, against Soviet helicopters and ground-attack aircraft. In 1988 it was reported that some missiles had been transferred to Iran, and that the Iranians planned to use Stingers to defend their small attack craft against U.S. air attack. As of early 1989 this threat had not yet materialized.

♦ **Tartar (RIM-24B)**

> **Dimensions:** 13.5 × 186 in (wingspan 24 in, fin span 42.3 in)
> **Weight:** 1310 lbs   **Warhead:** 130 lbs
> **Propulsion:** boost-sustain rocket (dual-thrust motor)
> **Speed:** Mach 1.8–2.2
> **Range:** 17.5 nm (35,000 yds; minimum 2000 yds); altitude limits 50 to 70,000 ft

Although Tartar is no longer in U.S. service, the missile may survive in two ships in the French Navy, the destroyers *du Chayla* and *Dupetit Thouars*. Data here are presented for comparison with the Standard Missile (RIM-66), which is essentially

a redesigned Tartar. Details given here are for the Improved Tartar version; the original Tartar had a nominal range of only 7.5 nm.

The overall Tartar system includes not only the missile but also the fire control. Several U.S. warships (*Kidd*-class guided-missile destroyers and *Virginia*- and *California*-class cruisers) are fitted with a Tartar-D, i.e., a digital Tartar, fire-control system developed during the 1960s. These ships are now receiving NTU updates.

Tartar was originally conceived as a point-defense missile replacing 5-inch guns on a one-for-one basis, effective between 2000 and 15,000 yards at altitudes up to 50,000 ft; as early as May 1957 a requirement for an Improved Tartar (25,000-yards range and 65,000-ft altitude) was issued. In 1959 work began on a Tartar Reliability Improvement Program (TRIP), which sought a 25-nm missile (i.e., with greater range than the contemporary two-stage Terrier) with a maximum effective altitude of 80,000 ft. TRIP became the Standard Missile (Medium Range). Presumably TRIP was motivated by advances in solid-state electronics as well as by early Terrier experience. Tartar itself did not begin technical evaluation until 1961. It encountered severe maintenance problems, particularly in the fire-control system. Improved Tartar was tested in 1962–63, incorporating the semiactive seeker of the HT-3 (Terrier) missile, as well as an improved motor.

Tartar (as well as its successors) has a significant surface-to-surface capability. The destroyers *Henry B. Wilson* and *Lynde McCormick* each fired four at the ex-carrier *Makassar Strait* in October 1961 and January 1962, scoring two hits at 15–20 thousand yards. The weapons were production Tartars with slight modifications to their speed gates. The West German Navy bought Tartar-armed destroyers in the 1960s partly because it wanted this supersonic surface-to-surface capability. Because the missile homes semiactively, it is effective only against targets at relatively short (horizon) ranges. At least one SM-1 (Tartar successor) was used in this mode during the surface engagements in the Persian Gulf in April 1988.

♦ **Terrier (RIM-2)**

> **Dimensions:** 13.5 × 162 in (wing span 24 in, fin span 42.3 in) plus 18 in × 310 in booster (fins 63 in)
> **Weight:** 1180 lbs plus 1820-lb booster
> **Warhead:** 218 lbs in earliest versions of Terrier
> **Propulsion:** sustainer-rocket with separate booster
> **Speed:** Mach 3.0
> **Range:** 40 nm (minimum 7000 yds; altitude limits sea level to 100,000 ft for BT(N); 50 to 80,000 ft for HE warheads)

Data refer to the HT-3B version after the Performance Extension Program of 1964 (RIM-2F, the final production version). The BT (beam-riding/tail-control) version of the missile was credited with a range of 7,000–40,000 yds, HT achieving much greater range by using a more efficient trajectory and a longer-burning sustainer. It is not clear whether surviving BT(N) missiles use the later sustainer.

Terrier was the first U.S. naval surface-to-air missile to enter service. Although virtually all Terriers have been replaced by SM-1(ER) or SM-2(ER) (RIM-67) missiles, the U.S. Navy retains small numbers (reportedly about 250) of the beam-riding nuclear-armed version of Terrier, the nuclear version of SM-2 having been canceled. Beam-riding is necessary so that this nuclear weapon can be command-guided to engage massed aircraft. One of the nuclear version's main virtues is that its threat can force an enemy to spread out his formations, thus making him more vulnerable to conventional antiaircraft weapons. BT(N)'s other major virtue has been the ability to destroy incoming nuclear-armed missiles, particularly Soviet air-launched steep divers. Conventionally armed surface-to-air weapons tend to destroy the airframe of an incoming weapon, perhaps leaving an armored nuclear warhead intact. Such a warhead might be quite devastating, even if it fell some miles from the intended target. This threat is associated with steep divers because any other missile, shorn of its airframe, would fall into the sea, whereas the diver, if caught high in its dive, will tumble down. The ultimate solution is probably a weapon with sufficient range and energy to catch the fast steep-diver before it begins its dive, and this requirement is presumably met by later versions of SM-2.

As the last U.S. beam-rider, Terrier BT-3A(N) requires guidance by the existing SPG-55 radar. Although SPG-55 is used to illuminate targets for SM-1 and -2 (ER) missiles, in theory that task could be accomplished by a simpler and lighter tracker-illuminator, such as SPG-51.

The figures given above describe Terrier HT-3B, a late semiactive model, and they may not apply to the BT-3A(N) version. Using a new end-burning sustainer, HT-3B achieved a range of 40 nm. Since command guidance should make for energy efficiency, the BT-2(N) version may enjoy a somewhat greater range, more like that ascribed to SM-2(ER), assuming that BT-2(N) uses the newer sustainer. However, the original beamriders rode a beam pointing directly at the target, and so flew a less efficient flight profile than a proportional-navigation semiactive homer. To achieve greater missile range, the SPG-55 would have to be able to sweep its beam without directly tracking the target, relying on data from the search radar for initial positioning. That way of operating would be much the way Talos, now extinct, worked.

◆ ASAT

The antisatellite weapon is a new U.S. Navy program to begin in FY90, with a proposed budget of $218.9 million for the first two years. The United States has had active antisatellite programs through the Reagan Administration, but in the past they have been an air force responsibility. The navy has argued that the satellites of most immediate tactical significance are relatively low flying Soviet naval reconnaissance craft, and that their prompt destruction may be essential in battle group operations. For example, destruction of a radar satellite just prior to launch can disrupt an Oscar's SS-N-19 missile attack by denying the submarine vital last-minute information. This tactical move is precisely analogous to destroying a Bear-D radar airplane to disrupt an SS-N-3 attack.

This type of attack is quite distinguishable from an attack on an early-warning (or, probably, signals intelligence) satellite in a higher orbit. It seems at least arguable that the Soviets cannot afford to place their tactical radar satellites in very high orbits, particularly if the U.S. Navy uses decoys and cross section–reduction techniques to make radar tracking of its ships more difficult. There will, then, generally be a very clear distinction between attacks on naval-related tactical satellites and attacks on satellites that might be considered more strategic in character. That distinction in turn should help differentiate naval ASAT, as a tactical operation, from strategic-warning ASAT, which some might consider destabilizing.

Reportedly the decision to allow the navy to develop a seabased ASAT reflects OSD agreement, late in 1988, that space should not be controlled by a single (i.e., air force) manager, but rather that at least some space defense tasks should be considered natural outgrowths of air defense at lower altitudes.

Reportedly, too, the navy's program is a response to rejection of the air force's ASAT program, which many in Congress considered strategically destabilizing. The air force's weapon was a miniature homing vehicle, carried aloft by an F-15 and then fired into orbit atop a rocket. The same weapon could be carried by an F-14; in each case, the fighter must fly a precisely defined high-energy trajectory, acting as the first stage of the interceptor rocket. A navy ASAT might also be fired out of a shipboard vertical launcher. As of the late spring of 1989, it appeared that tactical ASAT, which had been carried in budget documents as a joint army-navy program, would be developed by the army, presumably by ABMDA, the old Army Ballistic-Missile Defense Agency, at Huntsville, Alabama. The joint nature of the program would presumably be reflected in a requirement that the missile fit the standard navy vertical-launcher cell. Any possibility that the weapon would be carried aloft by a navy fighter

thus seems to be ruled out. It may be that limitations on the size of the tactical ASAT missile will be reflected in inherent performance limitations sufficient to convince potential Congressional critics that the weapon cannot be used against strategic warning satellites.

◆ Outer Air Battle Missile(s)

Since the 1970s the U.S. Navy has sought a longer-range, higher-energy replacement for the SM-2 series. Ideally, this replacement would be able to engage Soviet bombers before they could launch their antiship missiles, during what is now called the Outer Air Battle.

For a surface-launched weapon, the problem is twofold. First, some means of guiding a missile, perhaps beyond the fleet's horizon, is needed. Second, the missile requires sustained high power. The second problem is more easily solved, since very long range hypersonic weapons already exist. In the 1970s it seems to have been assumed that the solution would be an integral rocket-ramjet, and the new Mark-26 launcher developed for Aegis ships was deliberately designed to fire future larger weapons with this type of propulsion. Because the current Vertical Launching System (Mk 41) is designed to accommodate Tomahawk cruise missiles, it can also accommodate a future long-range surface-to-air weapon.

Guidance is a much more serious problem. The most obvious solution is active homing rather than the semiactive homing of SM-2, but a small missile-borne active radar is unlikely to be able to overcome terminal countermeasures, as the targets will enjoy much greater power resources. It might be possible to use a combination of active radar and infrared "glint." One alternative is to limit the missile to a specific mission, the destruction of the escort jammers that generally accompany Soviet antiship air strikes. The missile could then home on the jamming emissions; the threat of the missile might force the Soviets to shut down their jammers, thus opening the platforms to shorter-range weapons. Another alternative is to use a platform closer to the target to provide guidance, a technique once called Forward Pass. One version is the Surface-Launched Air-Targeted (SLAT) missile, for which ships carry the heavy missiles and air platforms the relevant radars. In 1984 Martin-Marietta proposed that over-the-horizon guidance be furnished by a dedicated radar satellite, but this idea was apparently too radical (and probably far too expensive).

Several extremely long range surface-to-air missiles were proposed through the 1970s, usually using rocket-ramjet power to achieve a combination of range and terminal maneuverability. The usual choices for guidance were concentration on Soviet escort jammers (home-on-jam) and Forward Pass (SLAT). LORAINE (see below) represents yet another, and quite different, alternative. A very long range home-on-jammer project, SOJS (Stand-Off Jammer Suppression), was canceled in 1981 with the announcement that, as important as this threat was, some new technical approach was needed.

At about this time there was also official reference to a ramjet-powered Long-Range Dual-Mission Missile (LRDMM), which could attack surface targets (at Mach 2.5) as well as very distant air targets (at Mach 4.5). As of 1978, the navy hoped that LRDMM could enter engineering development in April 1983. LRDMM would extend Aegis's range and might rely on E-2Cs for over-the-horizon engagement of targets such as Backfires and stand-off jammers. There was some interest, at the time, in commonality with the air force ASALM ramjet cruise missile, and some hope that the army would join in a triservice program. The ramjet missile Martin-Marietta proposed for ASALM later surfaced as a possible Outer Air Battle alternative, and then became the SLAT supersonic target (and a Harpoon follow-on candidate—see Harpoon II in the Strike/Surface Warfare section).

Another project of the late 1970s was Thor, an abortive Martin-Marietta project using a Sprint (ABM)-like very high acceleration missile. The Thor concept seems to have been applied both to very long and to very short range projects of this type, since the very high acceleration could boost a weapon to considerable range, or allow the missile to engage short-range targets that were maneuvering very violently.

A series of Outer Air Battle studies was carried out in the early 1980s, the objective being a pair of missiles, one for surface ships (to replace SM-2) and one for aircraft (to replace Phoenix). Ideally, both would use many of the same components.

A unitary Outer Air Battle Missile program began under the FY81 program, under the designation SM-3. Research efforts included improvements in IR guidance to supplement semiactive homing; more maneuverable aerodynamic design; the development of a linear autopilot (superior for high altitudes); and a directional, aimable warhead (for greater lethal radius and better effect against hardened targets). The Outer Air Battle study, which was completed on 15 June 1983, set development milestones (a breadboard design in FY84, with wind tunnel tests and design review, followed by an FY85 concept definition competition). An RFP issued on 4 February 1985 included such guidance concepts as Forward Pass (see above) and called for commonality between the advanced air-to-air missile (AAAM) and the surface-to-air missile (ASAM). Reportedly ASAM was conceived as an 800-nm, Mach-4.5 ramjet.

Concept contracts were awarded on 31 May 1985 to Hughes, Martin-Marietta, McDonnell-Douglas, and Raytheon; study contracts were also awarded to General Dynamics and Grumman. Submissions were due in the first quarter of FY86. A navy program review during the summer of 1986 concluded that it was impossible to develop a satisfactory unitary missile and, moreover, that it was unwise to develop a totally new very long range surface-launched surface-to-air weapon. Instead, effort would be concentrated on a new long-range air-to-air missile (AAAM) and on an evolutionary improvement of SM-2, which became SM-2 Aegis (ER). AAAM was separated from ASAM.

◆ LORAINE

LORAINE is an experimental program sponsored by the Defense Advanced Research Projects Agency: the letters mean Long-Range Aircraft Interceptor Experiment. LORAINE is intended to attack targets at very long range with nonnuclear weapons and, therefore, is a candidate technology for the navy's Outer Air Battle project. There are also possible air force applications, for example, as part of the Air Defense Initiative (ADI, the air-breathing complement to SDI). In common with other DARPA projects, LORAINE is a technically risky attempt to achieve a dramatic improvement in overall performance.

From the sketchy information available, it appears that LORAINE is a ballistic weapon sized to fit the standard launching cell of a Mark-41 vertical launcher. LORAINE boosts its reentry vehicle (the "boost-glide vehicle") above the atmosphere. As the vehicle falls back to earth, the active conformal-array radar searches over a wide area matched by its kinematic footprint. The missile has sufficient energy to connect with any conventional air-breathing craft; speeds of Mach 8–10 have been mentioned. The homing footprint might be so wide that the weapon could use target-designation data from a sensor as crude as an over-the-horizon radar. Reportedly the reentry vehicle might use a multimode seeker (e.g., active radar, antiradar, and home-on-jam). One technical problem would be to distinguish the target from the surrounding ground clutter; this problem would be for LORAINE a worse version of the usual look-down/shoot-down question.

Because the missile is relatively small (limited by vertical cell dimensions to roughly Tomahawk size), it is potentially quite mobile and can be carried by aircraft (Tomahawk was considered as an alternative air-launched cruise missile). Given the missile's mobility and flexibility of basing, DARPA saw LORAINE as a means of rapidly improving national air defenses in a crisis.

The program began formally in FY86 ($2.5 million) as a continuation of earlier exploratory work (the SWERVE III experiment). The SWERVE III vehicle was apparently assembled at the Sandia National Laboratory (which normally concentrates

on nuclear weapons and which would, therefore, be familiar with the problems of ballistic reentry vehicles); and under the FY85 program a SWERVE III test vehicle flew 600 nm to Johnston Island (20 April 1985) to verify electrical, mechanical, and thermal performance. This project was tentatively killed off in DARPA cuts for the FY86 budget, but the money was restored when another project, Teal Ruby, had to be delayed.

In FY87, $20 million was provided, and the request for FY88–90 is $52 million ($18 million for FY88, $22 million for FY89, and $12 million for FY90) to bring the weapon to full-scale development stage. A test flight against a drone is planned for 1991. The key technology is a radar array capable of operating at very high temperature and at high speed. In the FY87 budget congress rejected a navy request for $16.3 million for a study of a hypersonic wide-area-defense missile on the grounds that the LORAINE technology would be superior.

◆ TASD

Rockwell's target-acquisition ship-defense system was first displayed at the U.S. Navy League show in March 1989. A sketch showed a box missile launcher surmounted by a radar dome containing a pair of radars, operating in Ku- and W-bands. Rockwell argues that guns cannot expect to destroy incoming missiles at sufficient range to avoid damage from their fragments. The next best alternative is command-to-line of sight–guided missiles. Rockwell's proposal shows two radar dishes side by side on a single pedestal, the two frequencies being used together to solve multipath and glint problems. Both dishes would transmit simultaneously, and the associated control system would also use data from other ship sensors, such as ESM and electro-optical devices. Rockwell has already tested the radar concept; the company's stand showed a photograph of the dual dishes (which are the same size) side by side on a test pedestal.

Further data were not available; it is not clear whether Rockwell has a specific command-guided point-defense missile in mind.

◆ MIRACL

Although not currently a satisfactory weapon, the Mid-Infrared Chemical Laser has shot down drones in tests, and presumably it is intended as the forerunner of future U.S. naval laser weapons. In 1985 Congress rejected a navy request that MIRACL be developed as the basis for a future naval tactical directed-energy system; the laser project was left alive largely by its connection with the Strategic Defense Initiative (SDI) program. In current form, MIRACL reportedly occupies several acres.

The first successful test was on 18 September 1987, against a target drone flying at 500 kts and at an altitude of 1500 ft. On 2 November MIRACL shot down a BQM-34S drone at twice that first range: figures were not disclosed.

On 23 February 1989 MIRACL, using a Sea Lite beam director, destroyed a supersonic drone (later identified as a Vandal, a converted Talos ramjet missile) at what was described as a realistic tactical range. MIRACL had destroyed subsonic targets in the fall of 1987 but never a supersonic one. The press release issued at the time stated that the laser lethality demonstrated in the test had been predicted and tested against static missile parts but never against a real high-speed target. The 1989 test was the culmination of a two-year program. MIRACL itself is much too massive to use at sea, and Sea Lite is also quite massive, but the successful test, conducted at White Sands Missile Range, may provide motivation for a usable tactical system.

The tactical problem is quite different from the strategic or space-based laser problem. A missile warhead damaged in space may well burn up as it reenters the atmosphere, so relatively low damage levels may suffice. On the other hand, that damage must be imposed at very great ranges, on the order of thousands of miles. In contrast, a tactical laser hits its target at relatively short range, but the lethality must be very great, since a pinhole fatal in space may have no effect whatever on a large aerodynamic missile. The destruction of the Vandal is particularly impressive because it is so large and robust a missile. The precise damage mechanism involved is still of interest. For example, if the laser destroyed the Vandal by igniting its fuel tanks, then the result may not be generally applicable. If, however, the laser literally melted large areas of the missile's surface, the result is much more significant. The possibility of countermeasures such as defensive types of missile construction remains open in either case, however.

Proponents of a naval air-defense laser can point to the massive power supply available on board ship and to a ship's great reserves of space and weight. For example, much of the weight of the laser might be carried well below decks, with only the optical path of the beam emerging into a beam director above decks. Compared to a conventional missile, the laser promises lethality down to zero range. Compared to a small-caliber gun, the laser greatly simplifies the fire-control problem, presumably destroying the target so thoroughly that there is no danger of fragments traveling on to damage the ship. The three great technical issues are probably propagation through the water vapor–laden air near the sea's surface (e.g., shooting down sea-skimmers); the rate of fire (i.e., providing enough energy for quick multiple engagements); and the sheer mass of the beam director.

The MIRACL laser was developed by TRW and uses a Texas Instruments beam director.

◆ U.S. Missile Launching Systems

The principal current types are Mks 10, 11, 13, 26, 29, 41, and 43. All types, including obsolete launchers, are listed below for completeness.

Mk 1 test launcher, USS *Mississippi*, obsolete.

Mk 2/3 land-based Terriers for the Marine Corps, obsolete.

Mk 4 first operational Terrier system, in the *Boston* class (vertically stowed missiles, two two-arm launchers), obsolete.

Mk 5 Talos prototype launcher, obsolete.

Mk 7 Talos launcher for *Cleveland*-class cruisers, obsolete.

Mk 8 Terrier launcher for *Gyatt* (missile destroyer), obsolete.

Mk 9 Terrier for *Cleveland*-class cruisers, obsolete.

Mk 10 standard DDG and CG Terrier launching system, for SM(ER) (originally Terrier) missiles. The missiles are stowed horizontally without their booster fins, in 20-missile rotating rings. They are raised onto parallel monorails for ramming onto the launcher (through armored doors), and the boosters are finned manually. Rate of fire: four rounds per minute (one missile every 30 seconds per rail); typical weight, including missiles and fluids, 400,347 lbs (275,875 lbs without missiles). Mod 1

A missile in a Mk-10 launcher, waiting to be finned before being rammed out onto the rails. Below it can be seen the blast doors leading to the rotary magazine; the stations at either side are for the men who ram the fins onto the missile booster. The fins are too large to fold for stowage, and the operation of finning slows the firing rate of the launcher. (U.S. Navy)

has two rings; Mod 2, the superfiring launcher in the cruiser *Long Beach*, has four (80 missiles: 695,329/450,857 lbs); Mods 3 and 4 were for the carriers *Kitty Hawk* and *Constellation* (now removed); Mods 5 and 6 (two rings, 40 missiles) are on board *Leahy*-class cruisers. Mods 7 and 8 (*Belknap*-class cruisers) have three rings (60 missiles) and fire both surface-to-air missiles and ASROC (twenty ASROC can be interspersed with the missiles on the two upper rings). This system was called ASTER. Weight: 546,734/361,994 lbs. Complement: 16. Dimensions, for a two-ring installation: 360 × 395 inches (magazine, not counting launcher). Train rate: 30 deg/sec (elevation rate 20 deg/sec; limits +90/−10 deg).

Mk 11 twin-arm SM(MR) (originally Tartar) launcher, virtually automatic because the missiles did not have to be finned. Mk 11 was, however, considered unreliable, and it was superseded by Mk 13. The 42 missiles are stowed vertically in a 196-in diameter (209-in high) magazine. Total weight: 201,370 lbs loaded, 148,450 lbs empty. Crew was 3, and rate of fire one 2-missile salvo every 18 seconds. This launcher can also fire Harpoon missiles.

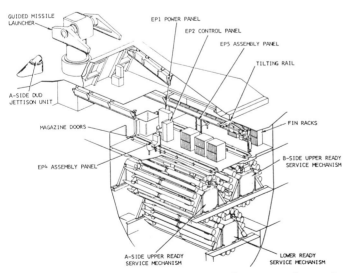

Mk-10 missile launcher. The ready service mechanisms are the rotating rings carrying the missiles. Other versions of the Mk-10 launcher employ two or four rings.

Mk-11 missile launcher. (U.S. Navy)

Mk 12 Talos system, obsolete (*Albany*- and *Long Beach*-class cruisers).

Mk 13 current standard SM(MR) launcher, with a single arm, first installed in late *Adams*-class missile destroyers. Mk 13 fires one missile every ten seconds (continuous salvo rate is one missile every 7.47–7.82 secs in the Mod 4 in the *Perry* class). The 40 missiles are stowed vertically, in two concentric rings (Mk 22, below, is in effect the inner ring of a Mk 13). Both the rings and the launcher rotate; the blast door is fixed. Train rate: 90 deg/sec (elevation rate 45 deg/sec); elevation limits are +95/−15 deg (+93/−15 for Mod 4). Diameter: 203 in. Weight (Mod 4): 134,704 lbs empty. Mod 4 was designed specifically to fire Standard Missiles, which require no warm-up, and, therefore, lacks the warm-up connectors of earlier versions. This launcher can fire Harpoon missiles.

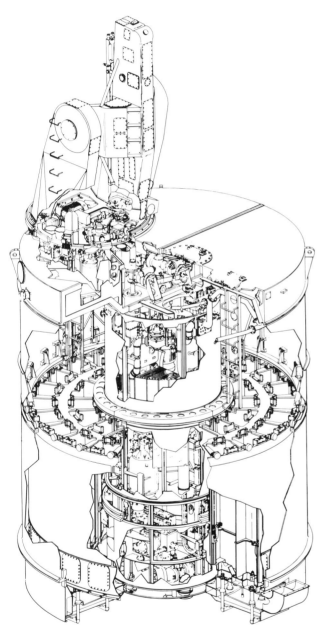

Mk-13 Mod-1 missile launcher. The missiles are carried in the two concentric rings surrounding the central column. (FMC)

Mk 14 Mk 13 modified to fire Typhon missiles, some with nuclear warheads; Mk 14 was not built.

Mk 15 Polaris launcher.

Mk 16 ASROC "pepperbox," carrying eight missiles in two-missile cells elevating separately. Maximum rate of fire is 3 missiles/minute. Elevation limits: +85/−3 deg. This light-weight launcher is often criticized for its vulnerability to weather damage. Most versions are reloadable; in *Knox*-class frigates the magazine is under the bridge, abaft the launcher,

and the missiles are stowed horizontally. In *Spruance*-class destroyers, the magazine is under the launcher, the missiles are stowed vertically, and the launcher elevates to 90 degrees to reload. The *Spruance* version was designed specifically so that it could later be replaced by Mk 26 Mod 0. Instead, these ships are being fitted with 61-cell vertical launchers to hold 45 Tomahawks and 16 Vertical-Launch ASROCs.

Mk 17–21 Polaris launchers.

Mk 22 lightweight single-arm SM(MR) launcher, for *Brooke*-class frigates and for the Spanish *Baleares* class, carrying 16

Mk-22 missile launcher, similar to Mk 13 but with a single ring (between the outer and inner walls). (FMC)

missiles in one fixed vertical storage ring (the blast door revolves). Rate of fire: 7/minute. Train rate: 85 deg/sec (elevation 45 deg/sec); elevation limits: +85/−10 deg. Magazine diameter is 146 in. Weight (empty): 94,003 lbs.

Mk 23 Typhon twin-rail launcher (modified Mk 10) for White Sands Missile Range.

Mk 24 Poseidon C-3 launching system.

Mk 25 BPDMS (initial Sea Sparrow) launching system, consisting of ASROC boxes on a former 3-in/50 twin mount (two outboard, two between the vertical arms of the mount), all elevating and training as a unit, carrying 8 Sea Sparrows and firing them at a minimum interval of 2 seconds (all in 16 seconds). There is no means of automatically reloading. Training rate: 30 deg/sec (elevation rate: 24 deg/sec); elevation limits +65/−15 deg). Total weight: 31,500 lbs. Mod 1 has frangible doors.

Mk 26 twin-arm dual-purpose (SM and ASROC) launcher, used in place of Mk 13 on *Virginia* and *Ticonderoga* classes. Missile length limit is 200 inches (diameter 14.75 in, weight 2200 lbs, compared to 13.5 × 186.45 and 1500 lbs for Mk 13). Missiles are stowed vertically, in two parallel chains running fore and aft under the launcher. Rate of fire per arm reportedly approximates that of Mk 13 (in theory a Mk 26 can fire two missiles every 10 seconds). Train rate: 90 deg/sec (elevation: 50 deg/sec). Three versions: Mod 0, 24 missiles (193,022 lbs/162,302 lbs empty, largely for ASROC); Mod 1, 44 missiles (264,897/208,577 lbs); and Mod 2, 64 missiles (337,031/255,111 lbs).

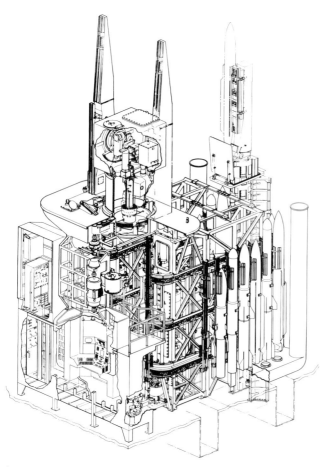

Mk-26 Mod-1 missile launcher, showing a variety of weapons (Standard, two kinds of ASROC, and Harpoon) and the strike-down hatch at the right, with a Standard Missile being loaded. The missiles are carried on a pair of vertical conveyors, one for each launcher arm. (FMC)

Mk 27/28 chaff launchers using Zuni rockets in aircraft-type 4-rocket pods, now obsolete.

Mk 29 NATO Sea Sparrow launcher, more compact than Mk 25 and considerably lighter (12,768 lbs), firing one round

A standard Mk-25 launcher for the Basic Point Defense Missile System, on board the helicopter carrier *Tripoli*, July, 1984. The girder in the background carries a ULQ-6 jammer. (Zeitlhofer)

every 2 seconds. Train rate: 40 deg/sec (elevation 65 deg/sec), elevation limits +85/−5 deg.

Mk 30 40-mm antiambush grenade launcher, firing a 14-round pattern at 130–170-m range, averaging 40 m wide. Mk 30 carried 4 × 14 6-inch barrels and could fire 200–1000 rounds/min. The main adjustment was in elevation angle. This designation was assigned in March 1970, but Mk 30 was never operational.

Mk 31 twenty-round flare launcher for Decoy Mk 48 (launcher Mk 133). Mk 31 used a revolver arrangement, pneumatically indexed and manually trained (elevation was preset). This designation was assigned in 1971, and Mk 31 was not operational.

Mk 32 Standard Missile box launcher, for *Asheville*-class gunboats (Mods 0 and 1) and for the Iranian destroyers *Babr, Palang,* and *Damavand* (Mod 2). Mk 32 is fixed in train and elevates to an angle of 25 degrees for firing, with a maximum rate of fire of 2 rounds/min (two rounds per launcher, in a magazine forward of the launcher proper). Total weight: 22,420 lbs. The launcher is 205 in long, with a 203-in magazine, and the launcher itself is designated Mk 134.

Mk 33 RBOC decoy mortar, firing three 112-mm (10-lb) cartridges (*Knox*-class and other frigates, and the first ten *Spruance*-class destroyers). The standard installation is two or four triple launchers.

Mk 34 two-barrel RBOC mortar for *Pegasus*-class PHMs. The launcher itself is Mk 135.

Mk 35 Trident C-4 launcher for strategic submarines.

Mk 36 SRBOC chaff launcher, replacing Mk 33 (130-mm, 40-lb cartridge). The launcher itself is Mk 137.

Mk 37/38/39 launchers for CAPTOR mines from, respectively, surface ships, P-3 aircraft, and submarines.

Mk 41 Vertical Launching System (VLS), conceived in 1976, and first installed operationally on board the cruiser *Bunker Hill* (CG 52). The system was originally designed to fire only Standard Missiles, using a 228-inch canister (which allowed for future expansion). However, it was decided that all VLS would also be able to launch Tomahawk missiles, so the standard canister slot was enlarged, to a length of 264 in. Standard Missiles are, therefore, loaded in short canisters with a 37.5-inch adapter; all canisters are 25 inches square in cross section. There is also a short canister, 144 inches long, e.g., for Vertically Launched Sea Sparrow (four missiles per canister space). This canister has not yet been used but has been proposed for the NATO frigate. Maximum missile size is 22 × 220 in (2500 lbs).

Launchers are assembled from modules (eight cells each, in two rows of four; but each group also includes one five-cell

Vertical-launcher cells ready for installation.

module with a three-cell strike-down crane). The usual combinations, then, carry either 29 or 61 missiles. Each module carries its own launch sequencer, motor control panel, and gas exhaust system. When a missile is fired, it exhausts through the canister blowout cover into the plenum and then up through the deck between the two rows of cells. The plenum can withstand seven firings per cell plus a restrained firing from any other cell. The Mk 41 is said to cost half as much as a Mk 26 (cost per missile) and to require fewer men (8 guided-missile mates on *Bunker Hill*, 11 on an earlier Aegis cruiser).

Rate of fire is reportedly 1 missile/sec.

Mk 43 box launcher for 21 RAM (RIM-116) point-defense missiles on a Phalanx chassis, part of ASMD Weapons System EX-31 (the system is often described as EX-31).

Mk 44 Tomahawk armored box launcher (for Tomahawk Weapons System Mk 32). Mod 1 was the ground-launched system (GLCM), now obsolete, and Mod 2 is the shipboard launcher.

Mk 45 Tomahawk vertical launching system for submarines.

Mk 48 Sea Sparrow vertical launching system (using the Mk-164 launcher). Mod 0 is in the Canadian "City"-class frigates; Mod 1 is in the Dutch M-class frigate; and Mod 2 is in the Greek MEKO-200 frigate. Mk 48 has now (1989) been chosen for LHD 5, planned for the FY91 program. Mod 0 consists of two individual cells with exhaust uptakes between them. Mod 1 has paired cells with uptakes alongside. Mod 2 is 16 cells concentrated in four rows, with paired uptakes between the first and second and the third and fourth rows. The Mod 0 and Mod 1 installations are designed to be placed along a ship's side; Mod 2 is a centerline installation. Mod 0 dimensions: total height 190 inches, total width 89 inches, depth 52 inches. These figures

include the dual manifold between the two cells. The total weight of a 16-missile system is 34,393 lbs. For the basic two-cell launcher, 2 canisters weigh 1450 lbs, two missiles 1100 lbs, exhaust control 725 lbs, shipboard mounting interface 800 lbs; the total for two cells 4075 lbs. The system as a whole requires one missile-launch controller (825 lbs) and one electrical interface (242 lbs). The total is 34,393 lbs. Each controller can accommodate 2 fire-control systems, 16 missiles, and 8 electrical interface units.

AIR-TO-AIR MISSILES

FRANCE

◆ Super R 530

> **Dimensions:** 26 cm × 3.54 m; span 90 cm (530D: 26 cm × 3.8 m × 87.5 cm) (10.2 × 139.4 × 35.4 in [10.2 × 149.6 × 34.4 in])
> **Weight:** 250 (265) kg (551 [584] lbs)   **Warhead:** 30+ kg (66+ lbs)
> **Propulsion:** dual-thrust rocket (2-second boost, 4-second sustain)
> **Speed:** Mach 4.5 (5.0)
> **Range:** 35 (45) km; ceiling 21,350 (24,400) m (38,300 [49,200] yds; 70,000 [80,000] ft)

Data refer to 530F, with 530D data in parentheses as shown.

R 530 is the standard French heavy air-to-air missile, currently carried by Crusader carrier-based interceptors. R 530 is broadly equivalent to the U.S. Sparrow. The 530F version is semiactive and is carried by the Mirage F-1 fighter with its Cyrano IV X-band monopulse radar. The 530D is carried by the Mirage 2000, which has an RDM multimode radar (for export) or an RDI radar (for the French Air Force).

The Super 530 missile can maneuver at up to 20 Gs (at 17 to 18,000 m in altitude) or 6 Gs (27,000-m altitude). The 530F version can snap-up (rising 9000 m to 27,000 m). The 530D can also snap-down.

Work began in 1958, and the original R 530 was in service in 1963. Design of the improved Super 530 began in 1968; development began in January 1971, and trials of the AD 26 seeker in September 1972. The first guided firing was in 1975, and production began in 1980. The first Super 530D with RDM pulse-doppler radar was delivered in May 1983, and the missile became operational (on board Mirage 2000 fighters) in mid-1986.

◆ Magic (R 550)

> **Dimensions:** 16.4 cm × 274.8 cm; span 66 cm (6.4 × 108.2 × 26.0 in)
> **Weight:** 89 kg (Magic 2: 90.7 kg) (196.2 [199.9] lbs)
> **Warhead:** 12.5 kg (including 6-kg HE) (27.6 [13.2] lbs)
> **Propulsion:** single-thrust rocket, 1.9-second burn
> **Speed:** Mach 2+
> **Range:** 10 km (minimum range 300 m) (range 1000–11,000 yds)

Magic is France's current, standard IR-guided missile, carried by Super-Étendard strike fighters and by Crusaders. It can be launched at airspeeds of up to 700 kts and is credited with a maximum maneuverability of 30 Gs. The IR seeker is nitrogen-cooled. Typical range is 2.5 km (2750 yds) at medium altitude, or 10 km at high altitude.

The improved Magic 2 entered production in September 1984. It has a better detector (80–100 times as sensitive) and can be slaved to the aircraft's fire-control system. The maneuverability limit is increased to 50 Gs.

Magic was conceived as a private-venture replacement for Sidewinder. Concept and feasibility studies were carried out in 1966–68, and the French government let a development contract in 1969. The first guided launch was in January 1972. The 1000th missile was delivered in December 1976, the 2000th in November 1977, the 3300th in March 1979, the 4500th in August 1980. More than 8000 have been manufactured for at least 18 countries; 75 percent of total production is for exports. Magic was first used in combat, in the Persian Gulf War, in August 1980. There, Magic is carried by French naval aircraft and Indian Sea Harriers.

In 1988, estimated cost per missile was $175,000 ($200,000–$250,000 for Magic 2).

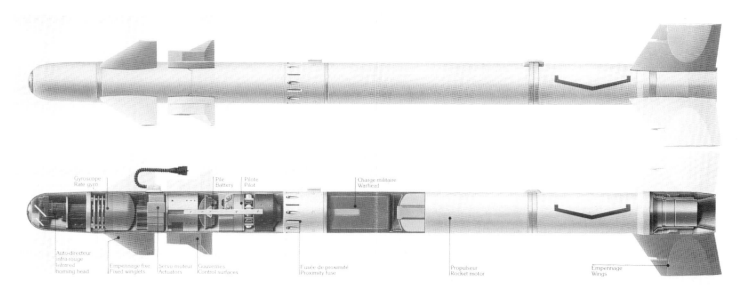

Magic 2 (R 550) missile. (Matra)

INTERNATIONAL

◆ ASRAAM (AIM-132A)

ASRAAM or Advanced Short-Range Air-to-Air Missile is the projected Sidewinder replacement. Under an August 1980 Memorandum of Understanding, the United States was to develop the Sparrow replacement (which became AMRAAM, Advanced Medium-Range Air-to-Air Missile) but would adopt a Sidewinder replacement developed by Britain and Germany. Britain, the lead developer, selected British Aerospace; the German partner is BGT (Bodenseewerk Geratetechnik), the license manufacturer of the existing Sidewinder missile. By this time British Aerospace had already carried out considerable development of projected Sidewinder replacements for the Royal Air Force and Royal Navy, under the SRAAM (Short-Range Air-to-Air Missile) program.

SRAAM used thrust-vector control and had a dual-mode (radar and IR) seeker. Published photographs of the ASRAAM model show fin control. Reportedly the missile will use a triaxially stabilized IR seeker capable of all-aspect acquisition and tracking, and of discrimination between multiple targets. The missile will be slaved either to the aircraft's search radar, or perhaps to the pilot's helmet, and will probably be locked on before launch. There may also be a lock-on-after-launch mode, the missile being fired outside its field of view. The missile's seeker may also be used as an alerting IR sensor while searching from its launch rail, e.g., for an airplane not equipped with a search radar (or not using its radar, for electronic silence). Photographs show a wingless missile, presumably using body lift in flight; and the motor will probably be a boost-sustain type to provide sufficient energy for terminal maneuvers.

ASRAAM is to have an IIR head, but it has not yet been decided whether it will be strap-down or gimballed. Current British seekers provide a picture consisting of 64 × 64 pixels; Hughes has demonstrated a 256 × 256 pixel array. This level of imaging makes jamming difficult, and also makes it easier to provide off-boresight capability. As of mid-1988, reported performance includes: 20–50-degree off-boresight capability, speed about Mach 2.5, 10-G maximum maneuverability. Reportedly this performance may be within the capability of an updated Sidewinder.

The U.S. Defense Department has complained about the slow pace of ASRAAM development. DoD also wanted ASRAAM and AMRAAM to be interchangeable on an airplane's pylons. That requirement ruled out the Missile Support Unit (MSU) planned for ASRAAM (the MSU contained interface electronics and cooling pack). The U.S. DoD argued that at the least an MSU would have to be tested after firing an ASRAAM, because it could be damaged by the hot gases of the launch. BAe has, therefore, had to integrate the MSU with the missile, and that integration, in turn, has protracted development. As of mid-1988, completion of development was scheduled for 1989.

During 1988 the national armaments directors of the UK and West Germany decided to transfer prime responsibility from Germany to Britain (BAe dynamics division). This decision does not affect work shares, but it is now more clearly a leader/ follower program. In return, Euraam, the company set up to produce AMRAAM in Europe, will move from Britain to Germany. The partners in Euraam are MBB, AEG, BAe, and Marconi Defence Systems.

France has observer status in the ASRAAM consortium, and the government of Norway joined in 1986; in 1987 it was reported that Canada might join.

In March 1988 it was reported that the United States might be developing an alternative "black" (code-word) missile that might even be ready for service before ASRAAM, which is unlikely to be available before 1995 at the earliest (despite an initial schedule requiring production in 1983 or 1984). According to these reports, the black Sidewinder-replacement program has been proceeding for some years, and there are even test airframes. ASRAAM was described as too heavy and as requiring too many modifications to the aircraft intended to carry it. Reportedly the U.S. alternative program is classified partly because the U.S. services do not want other multinational programs, such as the Modular Stand-Off Weapon, jeopardized.

ASRAAM mock-up on a British Sea Harrier. The United States is trying to avoid using the launch rail adapter. (British Aerospace)

USSR

◆ AA-8 Aphid (R-60)

Dimensions: 13 cm × 2.0 m; span 52 cm (5.1 × 78.7 × 20.5 in)
Weight: 55 kg (121 lbs) **Warhead:** 6-kg HE (13.2-lbs)
Propulsion: solid-fuel rocket **Speed:** Mach 3.0
Range: 7 km (7650 yds)

AA-8 is the Soviet equivalent of the modern versions of
Sidewinder, replacing the earlier AA-2 Atoll. Although Aphid
exists in both IR and radar-guided versions, only the IR version
is probably carried by Forger carrier-based VTOL fighters.

UNITED STATES

◆ AAAM

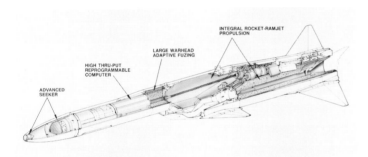

The General Dynamics version of AAAM, being fired by an F-14. (General Dynamics)

The Hughes version of AAAM, an integral rocket-ramjet. (Hughes)

The Advanced Air-to-Air Missile is intended to replace Phoenix
(see below) with a Sparrow-sized weapon. Two competitors have
emerged: a General Dynamics–Westinghouse team and a
Hughes–Raytheon–McDonnell-Douglas team. Proposals were
submitted in May 1987, and both contractors received demon-
stration/validation contracts for FY88–90, the winning team to
receive its contract in FY91. Funding may make it impossible
to carry both teams all the way through to flight tests.

Reportedly the navy wanted an AAAM with a diameter of
less than 9 inches and a weight of less than 650 lbs, with a unit
cost of less than $750,000, to attack crossing and violently ma-
neuvering targets at ranges of 100 nm. The hope was that an
F-14, which can fly with six Phoenix and land with four, could
land with at least eight AAAM on board. The navy has specified
a maximum AAAM-system weight of 5303 lbs for the F-14D,
on the basis of acceptable carrier-landing weights.

The General Dynamics project dates to the mid-1970s and
began as a private venture. The company proposes a combination of a small long-range two-stage rocket missile (380 lbs; 5.5
× 144 in) and an external multifunction airborne track-illu-
minator or ATI (16 × 142 in, 750 lbs), the two communicating
through the standard internal digital data bus already used for
pods such as laser-trackers. The ATI would have a limited
search capability, although usually targets would be designated
to it by the aircraft's main search radar or main IR search/

tracker. The ATI would have front and back antennas, so that
it could continue to track while the airplane maneuvered freely.
Once the target(s) had been designated, the ATI would track
them and compute engagement envelopes. The aircrew would
select and fire missiles, which would fly out using mid-course
inertial guidance. The missile's autopilot would be updated via
a signal time-shared between the missiles. Missiles would transition to semiactive terminal guidance (interrupted continuous
wave), and in at least some cases missiles might home by infrared (perhaps millimeter-wave) using a common-aperture
dual-mode seeker. Missiles homing semiactively would time-
share a common illuminator, just as Phoenix does.

The General Dynamics missile is so small that the company
estimates that an F-14 can carry as many as 15 AAAMS, normally 6 to 9. The missiles themselves would be stowed in universal launch tubes, with their fins and wings folded. The motors would have selectable burn, i.e., they would be able to
reserve fuel for terminal maneuvering. The missiles would use
a combination of aerodynamic and thrust-vector control for violent maneuvering. General Dynamics claims that this approach
and the ATI's ability to function as a (limited) acquisition radar
make it possible to provide almost any airplane with an advanced very long range air-to-air capability.

The alternative Hughes-Raytheon missile is powered by an
integral rocket-ramjet, for a high-power output throughout the
flight. Hughes's missile would use a combination of infrared
imaging and active-radar homing. Like Phoenix, the missile
uses semiactive mid-course guidance. No dimensions (other
than a length of 12 ft) are given, but Hughes describes the missile as Sparrow-sized with Phoenix or better performance
("stand-off ranges that are up to 4 times greater than current
systems'"). Engagement modes include launch-and-leave and
silent- (pure-passive) engagement.

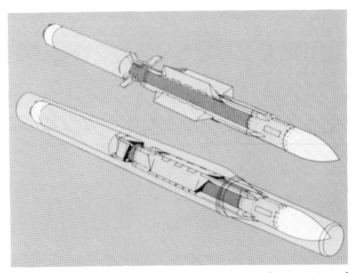

The General Dynamics/Westinghouse AAAM, stowed in its universal
launch tube and deployed. The ogival radome is radar transparent and
would be discarded if the missile went into IR-homing mode (there is
an internal hemispherical dome over the IR seeker). (General Dynamics)

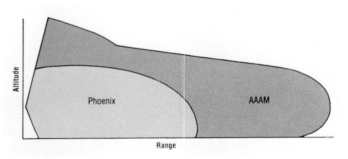

AAAM envelope compared to that for Phoenix. (General Dynamics)

◆ AMRAAM (AIM-120A)

Dimensions: 7 × 144 in (wing span 21 in, tail span 25 in)
Weight: 335 lbs   **Warhead:** 50-lb class
Propulsion: solid-fuel rocket   **Speed:** reported approx Mach 4.0
Range: reported 60,000–80,000 yds

AMRAAM (AIM-120A) with Phoenix and Maverick in the background. (Hughes)

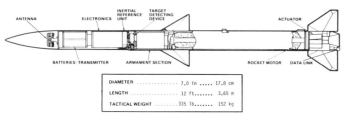

DIAMETER	7.0 in	17.8 cm
LENGTH	12 ft	3.65 m
TACTICAL WEIGHT	335 lb	152 kg

AMRAAM's inboard profile. (Hughes)

The Hughes Advanced Medium-Range Air-to-Air Missile is intended to replace Sparrow. Much lighter than Sparrow, AMRAAM may be carried in greater numbers. More importantly, it is a fire-and-forget weapon, providing a fighter with a capacity to engage multiple targets. The missile is sent into a homing basket on the basis of data fed in before firing, supplemented by data-link data supplied by the launching fighter. Approaching the target, AMRAAM switches on its X-band pulse-doppler seeker. Long range and good maneuverability are assured by a boost-sustain motor, which replaces the boost-glide motor of the Sparrow.

In 1982 Raytheon was chosen as a second-source supplier. Although an air force project, the missile has several vital naval applications. It provides F/A-18s with the capability to engage multiple targets, and AMRAAM will probably provide late-production A-6 Intruders (A-6G and later) with a self-defense or even fleet radar-picket capability. In addition, AMRAAM has been chosen as the armament of the modernized Royal Navy Sea Harrier fighter.

AMRAAM has always suffered from very high unit cost. Hughes, the prime contractor, has suggested from time to time that the missile is the natural successor to Sea Sparrow as well as to Sparrow itself. Raytheon has suggested that the missile can never be made inexpensive enough to supplant Sparrow entirely, and that a developed Sparrow will be the basis of the next-generation NATO naval air-defense system.

The first production AMRAAM missile was delivered on 26 October 1988. The initial production lot (for navy and air force) is 180 missiles, 105 from Hughes and 75 from Raytheon. The U.S. Navy FY89 program included 26 AMRAAMs, and the January 1989 budget proposal showed 150 in FY90 and 800 in FY91. The current AMRAAM export price is $475,000. There is some question as to whether these missiles will be manufactured in Europe by the Euraam consortium because the U.S. manufacturers, Hughes and Raytheon, are asking a 13-percent licensing fee. Euraam may, therefore, be unable to offer a competitive price.

The only current foreign naval customer is the Royal Navy, which plans to carry AMRAAMs on board its Sea Harrier FRS.2 fighters, and which cannot substitute any existing medium-range semiactive radar missile. The reported current British requirement is at least 330 missiles. Very large numbers of AMRAAMs are required to replace Sparrows in current service with European air forces.

Concurrent with initial AMRAAM production, there is an AMRAAM product-improvement program. Replacement of the current electronics by custom VLSI chips should drastically reduce the number of circuit boards, and heat production is to be reduced by 90 percent. The current mechanical gyro is to be replaced by laser ring gyros.

Early in 1989 the Norwegian government signed a study contract with Hughes and with Norsk Forsvarsteknologi (NFT) to develop a mobile land-based surface-to-air missile system using AMRAAM, to be called NASAMS (Norwegian Advanced Surface-to-Air Missile System). Each battery will consist of 3 radars, 3 fire-control centers, and 9 six-missile launchers, the controlling radars being based on the current Hughes TPQ-36. Should NASAMS proceed to production, the modified AMRAAM developed for it would presumably become available for naval service.

◆ Phoenix (AIM-54)

Dimensions: 15 in × 13 ft (span 36 in)
Weight: 1008 lbs (985 lbs for AIM-54A)   **Warhead:** 133 lbs
Propulsion: solid-fuel rocket (single-pulse)
Speed: Mach 5.0 (Mach 4.3 for AIM-54A)
Range: 80 nm (minimum 2.0 nm) (AIM-54A: maximum 72.5 nm, minimum 2.1 nm)
Launch Altitude: 60,000 ft maximum (-54A: 48,800 ft)
Missile Max Altitude: 100,000 ft (-54A: 81,400 ft)

Phoenix missiles carried by an F-14A fighter. (U.S. Navy)

Data apply to AIM-54C version.

Phoenix, manufactured by Hughes, is the longest-range air-to-air missile in operation; stated maximum range is 86 + nm. Phoenix is carried only by F-14 Tomcats and is guided by their AWG-9 radar. The missile incorporates a programmed autopilot to fly into a basket near the target; Phoenix then picks up semiactive illumination from the launching airplane. Not needing that illumination at launch time, Phoenix can fly a more energy-efficient (up-and-over) trajectory. Moreover, not needing to pick up reflected energy at very long range, the missile can make use of an illuminating radar of reasonable power (the missile is closer to the target when illumination is needed). Illumination is intermittent, and the missile uses its X-band active seeker for terminal guidance. The combination of precomputed/data-linked initial trajectory and terminal active homing makes it possible for several missiles to time-share a single tracker-illuminator; an F-14 can engage six targets simultaneously.

AIM-54A was manufactured from 1972 through 1980. The only foreign customer was Iran, and it seems likely that the missile was compromised during or after the fall of the Shah. No reliable reports of Phoenix engagements during the Iran-Iraq War have come to light, but it has been reported that the Iranians have used their F-14s as airborne radar-control platforms.

AIM-54C was the second production version, incorporating five major improvements: digital rather than analog circuitry so that the missile can be programmed for target discrimination in stream raids, improved beam (crossing-target) capability, and improved capabilities to engage an opening target from its rear quarter; better resistance to ECM; greater range and altitude; greater maneuverability; and a fuze (target-detecting device) better adapted to detonating on small targets or very low altitude targets found in clutter such as chaff. Deliveries began in 1981, and the last of 330 were delivered in September 1986. Deliveries of AIM-54C Plus began in March 1986. This last version incorporates internal heaters.

Although designed primarily as an outer-air-battle weapon, to attack bombers rather than their missiles, Phoenix can shoot down antiship missiles. In June 1983 it was reported that in a test Phoenixes had shot down eleven of eleven Harpoons.

Current U.S. Navy policy is to maintain two competing suppliers of all major weapons; Raytheon was chosen as the second source, making initial deliveries early in 1988.

Like SM-2, Phoenix is designed to deal with saturation attacks. During the early 1970s, Hughes proposed a sea-based version, which some saw as a less expensive alternative to Aegis. This version was also substantially less capable, and it did not progress very far. Phoenix is ultimately to be replaced by AAAM, which is Sparrow-sized.

The basic concept of a very long range air-to-air missile was developed in 1960, and Hughes was selected in August 1962. The first guided flight (from an A-3) was in May 1966. AIM-54C's engineering development began in October 1976, with first deliveries of development missiles in August 1979. Production began late in 1982, and AIM-54C was operational in January 1984. Approximate unit costs: AIM-54A, $750,000; AIM-54C in FY83, $796,000, but in FY84, $681,000. Reported inventory objectives are: 2932 AIM-54A, 7249 AIM-54C (including 45 for RTD&E). The 1000th AIM-54C was delivered 27 October 1988; this figure includes more than 600 AIM-54C+. The FY89 program included 450 Phoenix missiles; and in January 1989 the U.S. budget proposal showed 420 in each of FY90 and FY91. Current plans call for completion of Phoenix procurement in FY93, although there is some question as to whether that will make second-source production (by Raytheon) uneconomical.

Four engagements give some idea of AIM-54/AWG-9 capability. In one case, an F-14 (at Mach 0.7, 31,500 ft) intercepted five targets simultaneously. Four missiles were launched from 30-nm range at four of the five, flying (at Mach 0.6 at 20,000–25,000 ft) in a wave-front formation 20 nm wide. One target was hit directly, and the other three missiles passed within lethal range.

In a second exercise, an F-14 began to track a BQM-34E drone that was using ECM (Mach 1.5 at 50,000 ft). The missile was launched into an up-and-over trajectory at a range of 110 nm, reaching a peak altitude of 103,500 ft, and flying 72.5 nm to intercept the target. The drone had been augmented to present the radar cross section of a bomber.

A third exercise simulated an engagement with a MiG-25 Foxbat (simulated by an AQM-37A at Mach 2.2 at 82,000 ft). The F-14 fired from a range of 35 nm, the missile climbing about 36,000 ft to destroy the drone.

Finally, the F-14 engaged a BQM-34A simulating a cruise missile that was flying at 50 ft. The fighter flew at 10,000 ft, and its radar operated in TWS mode; it killed the missile at a 22-nm launch range.

◆ Sidewinder (AIM-9)/Sea Chaparral

Dimensions: 5 × 112.2 in (canard span 15 in, wing span 24.8 in)
Weight: 188 lbs **Warhead:** 25 lbs
Propulsion: boost-sustain **Speed:** Mach 2.5
Range: 10,000–20,000 yds

Data apply to AIM-9L version.

The Sidewinder is virtually the Free World's standard short-range air-to-air missile. It has also been copied by the Soviets

Sidewinder (AIM-9L). (U.S. Navy)

Sea Chaparral on board a Taiwanese destroyer. (Republic of China Navy)

and by the Chinese. Several other countries have developed externally similar weapons. The current version, used by the U.S. and Royal Navies, is AIM-9L/M, to which the figures above apply. Because Sidewinder (and its brethren) need very little support by the airplane carrying them, they are the natural missile armament for attack aircraft and for fighters without long-range radars, such as current Sea Harriers.

Guidance is passive infrared, with proximity and contact fuzing (the early version had only a contact fuze). There was also a semiactive-radar–guided version, AIM-9C. Stocks of this weapon have been converted to Sidearm short-range antiradar missiles (see the Strike/Surface Warfare section). AIM-9L introduced full-aspect homing, using the heat generated by high-speed flight and also the forward-aspect "glint" of sunlight on an airplane. The basis of current versions, AIM-9L is the version that proved so successful in the Falklands War, when the missile was carried by British Sea Harriers defending the fleet against Argentine air attacks.

Major versions:

AIM-9B (Sidewinder IA) was the first production version. Over 40,000 were manufactured in the United States, with others overseas by BGT. AIM-9B had a 25-lb blast-fragmentation warhead (lethal to 30-ft range) and a proximity fuze. Maximum range at high altitude was about 2.6 nm, using a 4000-lb–thrust motor burning for about 2 seconds; maximum speed was Mach 1.7. The seeker's field of view was about 4 deg, and range decreased to 4000 ft at low altitudes.

AIM-9C (Sidewinder IB) was the radar semiactive-homing version, many of which were converted to Sidearm antiradar missiles. This missile shared a common airframe and motor with AIM-9D.

AIM-9D (Sidewinder IC) had a new 60-second (vice 20-second) motor, which increased range to 11.5 nm, and a continuous-rod warhead. A new seeker improved streamlining of the missile's nose. The liquid-nitrogen seeker had a smaller field of view (2.5 deg), to reduce background noise, and a higher tracking rate (12 deg/sec). Compared to -9B, -9D could be used at greater angles to the target's tail. The missile was also more maneuverable than -9B. About 1000 were made for the U.S. Navy.

AIM-9E was a modified -9B for the air force, modifications including a new seeker and revised electronics and wiring. The seeker was thermoelectrically cooled, and tracking was faster (16.5 deg/sec). About 5000 missiles were converted to this type, about 1967.

AIM-9G was the U.S. Navy's equivalent to -9E, developed under the SEAM (Sidewinder Expanded Acquisition Mode) program. The seeker was slaved to the fighter's radar as it scanned.

AIM-9H replaced -9G, and about 3000 were made. This version is credited with limited all-weather capability, i.e., with the ability to continue to track a target through haze and light cloud cover. The seeker is forward biased, to hit an airplane near its cockpit, where the target is most vulnerable. This version introduced solid-state electronics, and it has a faster-tracking seeker and double-delta wings, for better maneuverability. AIM-9H was the last purely naval version of the Sidewinder missile. This program dates from about 1972.

AIM-9J was a -9B or -9E rebuilt for the air force, with partially solid-state electronics and double-delta wings, plus a longer-burning gas generator (for flights lasting up to 40 seconds). About 6700 were delivered by Ford Aerospace, about 1970.

AIM-9L was a joint-service weapon based on -9H but effective at all aspects, capable of engaging violently maneuvering targets, and effective against fast aircraft even at medium range. AIM-9L has a new active-laser proximity fuze and a new annular blast-fragmentation warhead, using preformed fragments. An indium antimonide seeker replaces the earlier lead sulfide and is sometimes described as a two-color (i.e., two-wavelength) seeker. In 1980 it was reported that a combination of modified signal processing and a new seeker reticule would improve background discrimination by a factor of three, and that new tracking software would greatly improve performance against glinting targets, i.e., targets visible only by the reflection of sunlight on their surfaces. This program began in 1977.

AIM-9M is the current U.S production version, with improved resistance to countermeasures. Production began in 1981.

AIM-9N is a rebuilt -9J1 (three major circuit boards redesigned), about 7000 of which were manufactured. It was formerly designated AIM-9JI.

AIM-9R is a product-improved -9M; Ford was awarded the contract in April 1987, and the missile is to enter service in 1992. -9R has an uncooled IR detector (charge-coupled device rather than conventional IR) for longer acquisition range and easier support. This detector is the imaging infrared (IIR) seeker in a Sidewinder. The U.S. Air Force is testing a new control system developed by Elbit (of Israel) to provide off-boresight capability. This control system slaves the seeker head to the aircraft's radar or to a helmet sight. Tests were completed in March 1988. Work on this version, originally called AIM-9M (PIP), began in 1986. Current navy plans call for conversion of 5000 AIM-9M to -9R standards.

AIM-9P is an export version, either a rebuilt AIM-9B/E/J or new production. AIM-9P1 introduced a laser proximity fuze in place of the earlier IR influence fuze. -9P2 has a reduced smoke motor. -9P3 has an IR fuze, a reduced-smoke motor, and a stronger warhead and guidance/control section; this version employs a new explosive that is less sensitive to high temperatures. -9P4 has increased IR acquisition and guidance capability, and an optimized fuze.

The current versions use a magnesium fluoride IR seeker and have a 20.8-lb annular blast-fragmentation warhead (WDU-17/B) with an active optical (i.e., laser) fuze (DSU-21).

In FY85, flyaway unit cost was $55,000. Recent procurement by the navy: FY84, 350; FY85, 1000; FY86, 2120; FY87, 627; FY88, 288; none in FY89. Total production run, approximately: AIM-9B (-9A was the prototype), 80,000; -9C, 2000; -9D, 12,000;

-9E, 5000; -9G, 2120; -9H, 7700; -9J, 10,000; -9L/M about 14,950. Reportedly it would take about four months and $18 million to triple the current production rate under mobilization conditions.

AIM-9L is manufactured in an improved form by a European consortium (West Germany, Norway, Italy, and Great Britain) headed by BGT, which made earlier forms of the missile; in addition, Mitsubishi has been manufacturing AIM-9L under license since 1981. Reportedly the West German Army plans to use AIM-9L (with a modified microchip) as a short-range surface-to-air missile, and five test firings were conducted in August 1986. Although no naval application was reported, such a missile might serve as an emergency alternative to RAM.

In the United States Navy, Sidewinder is used only in an air-to-air version. However, the army uses a land-based version, Chapparal, with four missiles on an optically trained launcher. A navalized version, Sea Chapparal, was used on board several destroyers during the Vietnam War and in 1980 was exported to Taiwan, for use on board five classes of destroyer.

Sea Chapparal is fired from a four-round turret, with eight more missiles stored for ready use. The operator uses an optical sight to lock onto the target, and the system can be improved by adding a FLIR; targets can also be designated by other ship's sensors. Range is about 2.2 nm. The land version of Chapparal, which is presumably the missile exported to Taiwan, is designated MIM-72F.

Sidewinder is to be succeeded by a British-developed ASRAAM (AIM-132). However, ASRAAM development has been protracted. Hence the decision to place AIM-9R in production in 1990, as an interim weapon.

◆ Sparrow and Sea Sparrow (AIM-7/RIM-7)

Dimensions: 8.03 × 141.5 in (wing 24.65 in folded, 40.6 in open; tail span 24.3 in) **Weight:** 500 lbs
Warhead: 67-lbs continuous-rod (17.9-lbs DATB explosive) in 7E version; 86-lbs continuous-rod WEU-3/B in AIM-7M
Propulsion: rocket boost-glide **Speed:** Mach 4.0
Range: depends on guidance radar (24–28 nm air-to-air for AIM-7M). Sea Sparrow's range (7E version) was 12,000 yds (1500 minimum); maximum altitude was 18,000 ft. Maximum speed was 1600–1800 ft/sec, and warm-up/reaction time was 8 sec/ 9–16 sec. These data are now obsolete, but they give some idea of the system's performance. The current NATO Sea Sparrow range is reported to be 8–14 nm (16,000–28,000 yds).

Data apply to RIM-7M; AIM-7M has longer wings.

Sparrow (AIM-7) is the current standard U.S. radar-guided air-to-air missile, supplemented by Phoenix (AIM-54) only on F-14 fighters. Sparrow arms F/A-18 Hornets. Because it is semiactively guided, Sparrow requires a large illuminating radar on the fighter, and the firing airplane must illuminate the target all the way from launch to kill. For these reasons Sparrow cannot be carried by lighter naval aircraft such as the Harrier/Sea Harrier and the A-6 Intruder; Sparrow also cannot be used effectively against saturation raids. In theory, AMRAAM (AIM-120) solves both problems, by combining a data link and an active seeker. However, AMRAAM is quite expensive; and Raytheon, which manufactures Sparrow, believes that AMRAAM will continue in development for some time.

Sparrows and a Sidewinder carried under an F-14. (U.S. Navy)

Sea Sparrow being loaded into one cell of its launcher. Only the Canadian version of Sea Sparrow (on board Tribal-class destroyers) is power-loaded; the NATO version and the earlier Basic Point-Defense Missile System both use hand-loaded eight-cell launchers. (U.S. Navy)

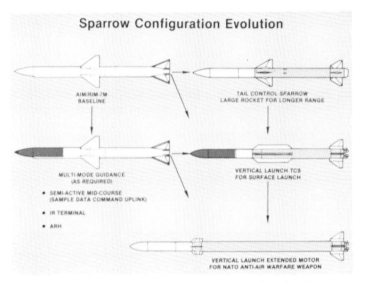

Sparrow Configuration Evolution

AIM/RIM-7M
BASELINE

TAIL CONTROL SPARROW
LARGE ROCKET FOR LONGER RANGE

MULTI-MODE GUIDANCE
(AS REQUIRED)

VERTICAL LAUNCH TCS
FOR SURFACE LAUNCH

• SEMI-ACTIVE MID-COURSE
(SAMPLE DATA COMMAND UPLINK)

• IR TERMINAL

• ARH

VERTICAL LAUNCH EXTENDED MOTOR
FOR NATO ANTI-AIR WARFARE WEAPON

Raytheon's proposals for advanced Sparrows, 1988. (Raytheon)

Sea Sparrow launcher on board HMCS Algonquin. The launcher is loaded inside the deckhouse, and emerges only to fire. The pop-out blast panels protect against fire and explosion. (Stefan Terzibaschitsch)

The original version, AIM-7A, was a radar beam-rider (Sparrow I). Sparrow II (AIM-7B) was an abortive active-radar version. Sparrow III is the semiactively radar-guided form of the basic missile, which has developed through several versions. Production of AIM-7E, which had begun in 1963, ended in June 1973. AIM-7E was the missile used in Vietnam, and hampered there because its maneuverability was limited by low terminal energy. The AIM-7E rocket motor was a pure sustainer that was considerably more energetic than the boost-glide engines of its predecessors and that added about 75 percent to the range. AIM-7E2 (and the related RIM-7H, the first Sea Sparrow) was a modified and more reliable version introduced in 1968. It had a "dog fight" guidance mode and an improved fuze and could fly at higher altitudes.

The next Sparrow, AIM-7F, introduced yet another new motor, this one a more powerful boost-sustain type, for a combination of high speed and terminal energy. The variations in range in the data above correspond to variations in the energy of the illuminator; the AWG-9 of the F-14 is credited with providing sufficient energy to realize a range of 38 nm. Presumably the F/A-18 cannot do nearly as well (the 24-nm figure applies to F-4s). AIM-7F also receives the target's initial range at launch time, computing course to intercept by calculating the target's velocity (doppler); target speed is used to calculate the target's current range and so to set a range gate for countermeasures resistance. AIM-7F was approved for production on 1 October 1974, the first production award (to Raytheon) following on 31 October 1975; the projected requirement was 6864 for the navy and 5415 for the air force.

AIM-7G had a new seeker but was only a prototype (1970). The -7H designation was reserved for Sea Sparrow (see below), and there appear to have been no -7J, -7K, or -7L versions.

Instead, the next version was designated AIM-7M, the M standing for an inverse monopulse seeker, the principal improvement in the new missile (for better resistance to countermeasures). This version also has an active (presumably laser, rather than radar) fuze, a missile-borne digital computer, and an autopilot. The effect of the autopilot is to allow the missile to fly a considerable distance without requiring illumination. Thus missiles can be fired at several different targets in sequence, illumination being used only for mid-course and terminal homing. The autopilot permits the missiles to fly an energy-efficient trajectory. The combination of proportional navigation with a preset autopilot flies the missile in such a way that it almost never points directly at the target. The antenna points to one side. In theory, therefore, there is space alongside for an IR seeker, an option not incorporated in -7M missiles, but tested recently. Although in theory the autopilot allows for intermittent command guidance, there is no provision for a data link. Full-scale production of AIM-7M was approved on 12 December 1982, the first missile having been test-fired in April 1980.

In 1985 the U.S Navy reportedly proposed a next-generation Sparrow, AIM-7X, as an alternative to AMRAAM (AIM-120A). In 1987 Raytheon won a $19.6 million contract for this product-improved version, now redesignated AIM-7P. The new version incorporates current low-altitude fuzing modifications and has new guidance electronics (using VHSIC technology) capable of accepting mid-course guidance commands (with software modifications).

Production: AIM-7A, about 2000; -7B, 100; -7C, 2000; -7D, 7500; -7E, 25,000; -7F, 5000. In March 1987 the reported requirement for these missiles was 7988 for the navy and 6321 for the air force. Recent navy procurement: FY84, 695; FY85, 1671; FY86, 1948; FY87, 1716. None were requested for FY88, but congress directed that the navy buy 600 because of delays in the designated successor program, AMRAAM. The navy's FY89 program included 450 Sparrows. The navy also plans to upgrade 4000 AIM-7F to -7M standards. It was reported in 1987 that the maximum production rate from two sources is 250 missiles per month. Unit cost (FY83) was $198,209.

Sparrow has been very widely exported, and it is license-built by Selenia and by Mitsubishi. The Selenia Aspide (see above under SAMs) uses much the same airframe but with different internal components, both for air-to-air and for surface-to-air use. The British Sky Flash, which has also been adopted by Sweden, is a modified Sparrow.

RIM-7, Sea Sparrow, is a ship-launched self-defense variant, the current version being RIM-7M. It is used in three major systems: the Basic Point-Defense Missile System (BPDMS), which uses the Mk 115 fire-control system and is being replaced by Phalanx guns (replacement of all 72 was announced 1981, to be completed by the end of FY88, but this target has not been met); the NATO Sea Sparrow System (Mk 91 director); and some examples of the Italian Albatros system (though most such systems fire the Italian Aspide missile). BPDMS was developed from 1963 on to fire a folding-fin version of AIM-7E designated RIM-7H; it was first tested in May and June 1965. An alternative RIM-7F was derived from the AIM-7F air-to-air missile. Modifications consisted of rapid run-up, folding wings, and clipped tail fins. All versions of BPDMS were considered deficient against low-flying attackers.

NATO Sea Sparrow (the Improved Point-Defense Missile System) uses the same missile but a very different overall combat system. The director is automatically trained, on command from CIC. The NATO Sea Sparrow program was reportedly inspired by the sinking of the Israeli destroyer *Eilat* (the first combat casualty caused by a surface-to-surface guided missile) in 1967. Later that year a NATO Project Group prepared a Memorandum of Understanding (MoU); it was signed by Denmark, Italy, Norway, and the United States. Belgium and the Netherlands joined the consortium in 1970, West Germany in 1977, and Canada and Greece in 1982. Raytheon was awarded the prime contract in September 1969. A production contract followed in August 1973.

An eight-cell box launcher (Mk 29) with frangible panels at the ends of each cell, was developed; it replaces the modified ASROC launcher of the U.S. BPDMS system. Raytheon, which manufactured the air-to-air weapon, was awarded the prime development contract in September 1969. The other development firms were Terma Electronisk of Denmark (microwave receiver), Selenia of Italy (firing officer's console/display module), and Kongsberg Vapenfabrikk of Norway (director controller, director pedestal, and computer). The system was first tested on board the frigate *Downes*, a second model going on board the Norwegian frigate *Bergen*; and all evaluation was completed by the end of April 1973. The first production systems were delivered in 1975. A full NATO Sea Sparrow system employs one or two Mk 91 directors. Typically the eight-cell launcher is manually reloaded. At this writing (1988) a standard modification is in train to fill two of the eight cells with RAM point-defense missiles.

NATO Sea Sparrow Block I uses the RIM-7H-5 missile (modified AIM-7E). Operational evaluation was completed in February 1974. Development and operational testing of the full Block I system was completed in December 1977, with full-scale development following from June 1978. Block II uses the RIM-7M monopulse missile, which was introduced into the system in 1978. The U.S. Navy plans to introduce the RIM-7P in 1990.

Total system weight, including eight RIM-7M missiles, is 28,648 lbs (13,676 lbs for the loaded launcher, 3431 for the director and its television camera).

The Sea Sparrow system is triggered by a main search radar, such as the U.S. TAS Mk 23 or SPS-65. The radar designates a target to the Mk-91 director. The director then scans and acquires the target, modulating emissions for ranging and angle tracking. If the target fades during track, the director coasts in range, bearing, and elevation until it reacquires. During the target-tracking process, the Sparrow's time of flight to the target is computed; and the operator is alerted if the target is engageable. Shortly before the target comes within range the launcher is automatically assigned to the appropriate radar director and aimed at the predicted intercept point. In automatic mode, a salvo is fired when the target becomes engageable. In semiautomatic mode, the operator issues a firing command. Typically the U.S. Navy operates its Sea Sparrows in semiautomatic mode. European navies tend to use the automatic mode. This distinction reflects a difference in operating conditions. Except in wartime, when they would face submarine-launched missiles anywhere at sea, U.S. ships probably would not face air attack unless they approached hostile shores. European warships are almost always within range of potentially hostile air or missile attack.

RIM-7M differs from AIM-7M only in that the former's wings are folded and tail fins clipped, for launcher stowage. Wingspan is 40 in (25 in folded) and tail span is 24 in. In addition, the rocket motor is remotely armed. The warhead is a WAU-17/B blast-fragmentation type, chosen over the earlier continuous rods (WAU-10/B) to destroy a nearby target passing at very high speed.

The current (1988) Sea Sparrow is RIM-7M, which is adapted for vertical launching. This version has improved surface-to-surface capability, improved surface look-up capability, and improved performance and reliability. Vertical- and box-launched missiles are identical, apart from the additional jet-vane control (JVC) unit bolted onto the tail of the vertically launched weapon. Both have a new active fuze, which incorporates a target-range gate and a sea-range gate, the latter to keep the missile from detonating against the sea at low altitude. The jet-vane control unit incorporates an inertial strapdown navigation computer; it pitches the missile over onto a course toward the target. Missiles fired from vertical launchers begin to tip over 0.7 seconds after launch and do not rise above 200 ft when fired against low altitude targets. The missiles are fully tipped over by the time they are 250 ft from the ship.

Compared to the standard trainable-launcher version, the VLS version provides more ready missiles (against saturation attack), quick launch after target detection, reduced topside space and weight, and quick engagement of fast sea-skimmer or pop-up missiles.

Like AIM-7M, RIM-7M incorporates an autopilot and, thus, has the potential for multiple engagements if that autopilot is set at launch time. Since the missile can fly for a considerable time before needing to detect energy reflected from the target, Raytheon has proposed engaging multiple targets by floodlighting: using a broad-beam radar (e.g., 45-degree beam) to illuminate several incoming targets simultaneously, and using an engagement radar to compute autopilot settings. The floodlight would illuminate each target only weakly, but weak illumination might be enough if the missile does not need to pick up radiation until fairly close to the target. In this way a single search radar and a very simple floodlight might bridge the gap between the current single-target Sea Sparrow system and a much more sophisticated system meeting the NATO AAW requirements. This floodlighting system has not been tested, and presumably it was the one rejected when Raytheon was dropped from the NATO AAW System program. However, the company argues that any substantially more complex solution will be prohibitively expensive. The Raytheon illuminator has eight apertures, each producing a 45 × 75 degree beam, plus a zenith horn (60 × 60 degree beam). The system transmits through one selected illuminator at a time, power being 2 kW average (gain 10 dB). The beams are so wide that no mechanical stabilization is needed. The full pattern covers the entire hemisphere, down to 15 degrees below the horizon (to allow for rolling motion).

A version of Sea Sparrow using a Signaal fire-control system was developed independently for the Canadian *Iroquois*-class destroyers; that version employs launching rails that deploy from the sides of the ship.

A vertically launched Sea Sparrow prototype was tested at sea in 1981, and a formal NATO Sea Sparrow ORDALT issued in 1981. Canada decided to purchase the vertical-launch system for her "City"-class frigate in 1983, Raytheon receiving the contract the following year. The vertically launched RIM-7M was successfully tested at White Sands in 1985. Test launches included shots at simulated low-altitude targets, at mid-range and off-axis, the missiles avoiding the simulated ship's superstructure; there were also low-altitude short-range shots. The Royal Netherlands Navy bought this system for its M-class frigates in 1985, and Greece chose it for the new MEKO-200 frigate in 1988. Delivery of six-launcher ship sets for Canada was completed in 1987, and production deliveries of 155 Canadian was completed in 1988. A total of 256 missiles are on order for the Netherlands Navy, as of 1988.

In 1988, the expected total production run of RIM-7M was 2950 missiles, and unit cost in FY85 was $214,000.

In 1988, Raytheon announced a program for further Sparrow evolution, using the RIM-7M as a baseline. For improved aerodynamics against violently maneuvering targets, the missile is redesigned for tail control. With this modification, the missile can carry a larger rocket motor with increased thrust and can maintain its current vertical-launch capability. The missile's existing reprogrammable computer is adaptable to multimode guidance (semiactive mid-course, IR terminal, and antiradar homing). This wingless Evolved Sea Sparrow (ESS) offers twice the maneuvering power of the winged missile. ESS would have a new autopilot, rocket motor, and tail controls. The forepart would match the existing Sparrow, but the after part would be necked out to 9-in diameter; total weight would be 245.1 kg (540 lbs), and length would be 145.7 inches (3.7 m). Evolved Sea Sparrow could be in service by 1994. Raytheon claims that ESS will have two to four times the energy of the existing Sparrow and that ESS can easily be back-fitted on board ships now equipped with NATO Sea Sparrow.

A further stretched version, the Long Ship-Defense Missile (LSDM), which Raytheon claims could be in service by 1998, would offer Mach-3 speed and twice the current range. ESS and LSDM would share common control and tail-fin (jet-vane) systems. The missile would receive mid-course guidance through the illuminator, whose signal would be modulated.

Raytheon proposes a 4-missile canister launcher for these weapons, each cell of which would be about 11 inches across (total width 25 inches).

The ESS/LSDM combination was Raytheon's candidate for its unsuccessful proposal for the NATO Antiaircraft Warfare missile system. The company still argues that this system may well be adopted when the alternative, more sophisticated, systems that remain in the U.S. Navy's program prove too expensive.

SHIPBOARD GUNS AND GUN SYSTEMS

The terms gun and mount are often used nearly interchangeably in this section. In a few cases, the same gun (barrel and breech mechanism) is used in different gun mountings, and the distinction is worthwhile. In most cases, however, a particular combination of gun tube and breech and loading mechanism is always associated with the same mounting, and no distinction is worth making. The term "mount" (or mounting) is generally taken to include the guns it carries, so that one describes a weapon as, say, a twin 40-mm mounting or a twin 40-mm gun.

CHINA

◆ 100 mm

A twin auto-loading 100-mm gun has supplanted the single 100 mm/56 in Chinese production. 100 mm arms Jianghu-II– and -III– and Jiangdong-class frigates and has been offered for export on board a projected frigate designated EF30. There has been some speculation that the Chinese would manufacture the French 100-mm Compact gun or a derivative, having bought two from France.

FRANCE

◆ 100 mm

> **Caliber:** 3.9 in/55 (13.5-kg projectile)
> **Rate of Fire:** 90 or 40 or 10 (selectable) rnds/min

> **Muzzle Velocity:** 870 m/sec (2850 ft/sec)
> **Maximum Range:** 17,500 m; maximum effective range 12,000 m for surface fire, 6,000 m for antiaircraft fire (19,100/13,100/6600 yds)
> **Training Rate:** 50 deg/sec (elevation 32 deg/sec)
> **Elevation/Depression:** +80/−15
> **Ammunition Capacity:** 66 or 114 (ready-use)
> **Weight:** 13,500 kg (29,750 lbs)

The 100 mm is the standard French dual-purpose gun mount; the larger 127-mm (5-in) gun formerly mounted on board cruisers and destroyers is no longer in service. In effect the 100 mm replaced both the 127 mm and the contemporary twin 57-mm antiaircraft gun (see below for details of the surviving mounts) with a single weapon. This 100-mm gun fires a shell heavy enough for shore bombardment but light enough for the gun to

Two 100-mm gun mounts on board the destroyer *Duguay-Trouin*, 1982. (L&L Van Ginderen)

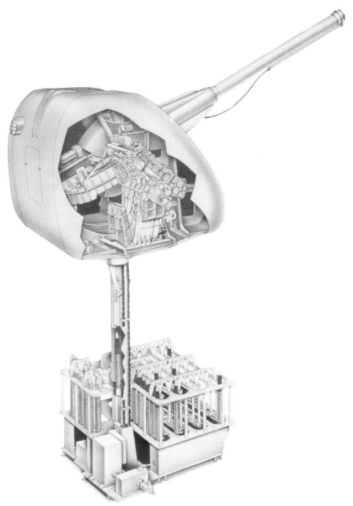

The 100-mm Compact mount, showing the ammunition fan feed up the side of the mount and the conveyer that elevates with the gun. (Creusot-Loire)

achieve a rate of fire high enough for useful antiaircraft work. 100 mm was the first French-designed fully automatic medium-caliber gun and follows an earlier (Model 1945) twin 100-mm weapon (mounted on the battleship *Jean Bart*). Development of the 100-mm gun superseded work on a projected 105-mm/60 twin triaxially stabilized mount, which would have used surviving stocks of German ammunition.

Data refer to the export (Compact) version, used in the Portuguese, Saudi Arabian, and Malaysian Navies; two copies were sold to China (PRC). Most have a 42-round magazine; those for Malaysia had 90-round magazines. In addition, 18 rounds are carried in an intermediate magazine next to the gun (see below for an explanation of these figures).

The Compact mount is a lighter-weight (7.5 tons saved) version of the standard French 100-mm Model 1953 or 1968, Model 1968 being a somewhat lighter version of Model 1953. Model 1968 weighs 22 tons, and its training rate is 40 deg/sec (elevation 25 deg/sec). The rate of fire is 78 rounds/min in recent weapons (60 in older ones). Claimed maximum effective range is 15,000 m against surface targets and 8,000 m against air targets, presumably reflecting better steadiness in the older mount. The 1968 version has a 35-round ready-use magazine.

The 100-mm Compact can fire preselected 1-, 2-, 3-, or 6-round bursts. Ammunition feed is arranged so that rounds can be passed back down into the magazine when others are selected. The ammunition supply consists of a main magazine below the gun, with a 12-round secondary magazine (but Creusot-Loire offered 36 rounds to the Canadians, for the "City"-class frigate). Both magazines are modular, in 24-round palletized units. Rounds are carried up horizontally, by a fixed hoist (duct), into an intermediate 18-round magazine that elevates with the gun. From this magazine they are transferred down and around (in a horizontal fan) so that they can be rammed into the breech. Typically the intermediate magazine carries 12 rounds (so that it and the secondary magazine carry a total of 24, explaining the figures above). Shells are paired, with an empty space between each pair. The intermediate magazine, which is more typical of smaller-caliber guns, brings the gun into action more quickly and makes for rapid access to alternative types of ammunition.

All of these guns are water-cooled (barrel life 3000 rounds), and all have a fuze-setter that allows for adjustments just before a round is loaded into the breech.

Model 1953 (*Jeanne d'Arc*, *Suffren* class, *La Gallissonnière*, *Surcouf* T47 ASW destroyers, and Commandant Rivière class) uses an analog fire-control system with electro-mechanical computer. Model 1968 (*Colbert*, *Tourville* class, *Georges Leygues* class, *Aconit*, *Duperré*, A-69 class) uses a digital fire-control system. At least in the Compact version, the mount is fully automatic, requiring no on-mount personnel.

In 1980 DTCN announced developmental work on an IR-homing round for this weapon, using a staring IR sensor. DTCN did not expect the IR sensor (which drove fins at the base of the shell) to be sensitive enough to ensure a hit on an approaching sea-skimming missile. Instead, the shell was provided with a proximity fuze and a relatively large warhead.

◆ 57 mm M1951

Caliber: 57 mm/60 (5.73-lb projectile)
Rate of Fire: 120 rnds/min per barrel
Muzzle Velocity: 865 m/sec (2840 ft/sec) (originally 3018 ft/sec)
Maximum Range: 13,000 m (5,000 m effective antiaircraft) (14,200/5500 yds)   **Elevation/Depression:** +94/−10 degrees
Ammunition Capacity: 80/rnds/barrel   **Weight:** 16 tons

The gun is the postwar Bofors 57 mm/60, a scaled-up version of the wartime 40 mm/60. The mount is of French design but retains Bofors's fan-feed system for supplying ammunition. The fan feed is joined at the trunnion axis by an inverted-U feeder-hoist extending down to an automatic-feed ready-service box on the deck of the mount; the total of 80 rounds per gun includes box, feeder hoist, and fan feed. The ready-service box in turn is refilled by hand (at 40 rounds/min) from a hoist turning with

the mount, extending down to a handling room below. Bofors produced its own mounting, described in the Swedish section. This once common gun survives on board the French cruiser *Colbert* and the missile destroyers *du Chayla* and *Dupetit Thouars*, having been superseded in French service by the single automatic 100-mm gun (which is not much heavier).

A French 57-mm/60 twin gun mount on board the missile destroyer *Dupetit Thouars*, 1964. The radars are U.S.-supplied SPG-51s, to control the Tartar missile shown on its launcher. (U.S. Naval Institute)

◆ 30 mm (CAS 62 mounting)

Caliber: 30 mm/70 (0.42-kg projectile)
Rate of Fire: 650 rnds/min
Muzzle Velocity: 1000 m/sec (3280 ft/sec)
Effective Range: 2800 m (3000 yds; maximum range 9300 yds)
Training Rate: 50 deg/sec (elevation 40 deg/sec)
Elevation/Depression: +83/−18 deg
Ammunition Capacity: 215 rounds
Weight: 3620 kg (3920 kg including ammunition) (7980/8640 lbs)

A 30-mm CAS 62 gun is visible amidships, abeam the uptakes, on board the French frigate *Commandante Riviere*. The gunfire-control system aft carries a DRBC 32C radar. The short torpedo tubes under the gun were originally provided to fire K-2 unguided ASW torpedoes. Some ships in this class were completed instead with 40-mm Bofors guns. (U.S. Naval Institute)

This power-operated mount, carrying the HS 831A gun, is found only in the frigates *Balny*, *E. de V. Henry*, *Protet*, and *Victor Schoelcher*. These data may refer to a modified version of the mounting in the Commandant Rivière class, since these ships originally had an ammunition capacity of 300 rounds per gun, loaded hydraulically. Other ships in this class are armed with single 40-mm guns.

◆ SAMOS

SAGEM's close-in weapons system (SAGEM Anti-Missile Optronic System) uses the General Electric 30-mm GAU-8/A Gatling gun, the same weapon as in the Dutch Goalkeeper (see entry below for details). SAMOS competes with Satan for the French Navy CIWS requirement, and was announced in 1986. There is no associated radar; the gun relies entirely on electro-optical tracking by a Volcan fire-control system. That tracking avoids multipath reflections from the sea but is presumably

SAMOS test-firing. (SAGEM)

subject to limitations of weather and daylight. The Volcan weighs about 150 kg, containing a biaxially stabilized optical sight for tracking, plus fixed television, IR, and laser sensors. Gun elevation/depression is limited to +83/−19 degrees.

The 30-mm gun can be supplemented by four Sadral missiles atop the gun mount, to extend maximum range from 2–3 km out to 6 km.

SAMOS was demonstrated at the French Navy Gavres range in October 1987, against a Rushton target. The target was engaged at 1100 m, and the first hit was made at 850 m, in the area of the IR flare at the rear of the target. The acoustic miss-distance indicator was destroyed on the 28th round, and the system made at least three hits before the target disappeared.

♦ Satan

Thomson-CSF's close-in weapons system uses the General Electric GAU-8/A 30-mm Gatling gun, the same weapon used by

Satan on trial (director at right, gun at left). (Thomson-CSF)

Satan on display, November 1986, with both a radar and a Volcan optronic director, and with three launch tubes for the Mistral missile atop the 30-mm gun mount. (Thomson-CSF)

the Dutch Goalkeeper system (see entry below for details). Satan competes with SAMOS (see above) for the French Navy CIWS role and was announced in 1986. The associated radar is an off-mount Castor IIJ.

Satan was demonstrated at the French Navy Gavres range in October 1987, against a Rushton target. The target was engaged at 1200 m and destroyed at 943 m. An acoustic miss-distance indicator inside the target showed six rounds within 0.5 m and five between 0.5 m and 1 m from the target, before the indicator was destroyed after 44 rounds had been fired. They were part of a burst of 200 rounds, presumably the standard burst, the last 100 of which were fired after the target had been destroyed (in less than two seconds).

♦ GIAT 20 mm

Caliber: 20 mm **Rate of Fire:** 650–720 rnds/min
Muzzle Velocity: 1050 or 1250 m/sec (3440/4100 ft/sec)
Maximum Range: 10,020 or 6,770 m depending on ammunition (10,960/7400 yds); effective range 2000 or 1200 m (2200 or 1300 yds)
Training Rate: manual
Elevation/Depression: +60/−15 **Ammunition Capacity:** 300
Weight: 336 kg (741 lbs) empty

The DCAN gun mount for the new GIAT-CN-MIT-20F2 gun has two 150-round magazines. This weapon arms the Tripartite minesweepers, and there are also army and air versions.

At Farnborough in 1988 GIAT displayed a naval version of its M621 20-mm low-recoil gun, which had previously been shown only on land and air mountings. It is typically carried by helicopters and small aircraft. Muzzle velocity is 980–1030 m/sec (3215–3380 ft/sec), depending on the type of ammunition, and cyclic rate is 750 rounds per minute (an alternate rate, 300 rounds/min, is available in the aircraft version). The naval mounting is similar to a land mounting (Army 15A) already shown and carries 160 rounds (total weight, presumably without ammunition, is 184 kg [406 lbs]), with elevation limits of +45/−15 degrees). A collimator sight is provided. Recoil is minimized by a muzzle brake and a shock-absorbing mount. Total gun length is 2.207 m (86.9 inches), and without the mount the gun weighs 47 kg (104 lbs) in its aircraft version.

DCN-GIAT 20-mm gun (20F2). (Direction des Constructions Navales)

GERMANY (WEST)

◆ Mauser 27 mm

Caliber: 27 mm **Rate of Fire:** 1000 or 1700 rnds/min/gun
Muzzle Velocity: 1025 m/sec (3363 ft/sec)

Mauser is developing a quadruple naval version of its 27-mm aircraft cannon for close-in defense. Details above are for the aircraft weapon.

◆ Rhinemetall 20 mm Mk 20 Rh202

Caliber: 20 mm **Rate of Fire:** 1000 rnds/min
Muzzle Velocity: 1050 m/sec (HEI-T, TP-T ammunition) or 1100 m/sec (API-T ammunition) or 1150 m/sec (APDS-T) (3440/ 3770 ft/sec)
Maximum Range: 2000 m effective range (2200 yds)
Elevation/Depression: +55/−10 deg
Ammunition Capacity: 200 rnds, linked, in two boxes
Weight: 408 kg total; 74 kg ammunition (899/163 lbs)
Working Circle: approx 2.45 m (96.5 in) radius

20-mm Rhinemetall gun on board the Irish *Eithne*, 1986. (Author)

This pintle-mounted 20-mm gun was announced in 1973. The gun is also used on land and in the Marder APC. The gun is designed to minimize recoil forces and for long barrel life. As offered in 1973, the only sight was a speed ring, but a lead computing sight was offered as an option.

Norway uses the same low-recoil gun in a different mounting designated KV-SK/20 (derived from the FK20-2 field-gun mounting). Elevation limits are +70/−15 deg, and the working circle is 1730 mm. Total weight is 400 kg without ammunition. This gun is manufactured by Kongsberg (now renamed Norsk Forsvarsteknologie).

ISRAEL

◆ TCM-30G

Caliber: 30 mm/70 **Rate of Fire:** 650 rnds/min/gun
Muzzle Velocity: 1080 m/sec (3540 ft/sec)
Maximum Range: approx 9000 yds
Training Rate: 1.5 rad/sec (elevation 1.5 rad/sec) (85.9 deg/sec)
Elevation/Depression: +85/−15
Ammunition Capacity: 150 rnds/gun
Working Circle: 2600 mm radius (102.3 in)

The twin 30-mm (Hispano Suiza 831) mount was developed by the MBT Division of IAI. The distinctive feature is a heavy support between the two barrels, supporting the muzzles; it is intended to limit dispersion drastically (to less than 2 mrad). The gun is remotely controlled, and its barrels fire in bursts of 5, 10, 15, or 20 rounds. It can track targets at 250–300 m/sec (820–980 ft/sec, i.e., 485–580 kts).

The weapon is controlled by the Elta EL/M-2221 X-band monopulse radar used to control Gabriel. None of the guns has been purchased to date.

ITALY

◆ OTO-Melara 127 mm/54 LW

Caliber: 5 in/54 **Rate of Fire:** 45 rnds/min
Muzzle Velocity: 807 m/sec (2650 ft/sec)
Effective Range: 15,000 m surface; 7,000 m antiair (16,400/7660 yds); maximum range 23,680 yds
Training Rate: 40 deg/sec (elevation 30 deg/sec)
Elevation/Depression: +83/−15 deg
Ammunition Capacity: 66 rounds (3 drums) **Weight:** 37.5 tons
Working Circle: 6.108 m (240.5 in)

HMCS *Iroquois* is armed with an OTO-Melara 5-in/54 (127-mm/54) lightweight gun, forward. It is now being replaced by a vertical missile launcher. (Canadian Forces Photo)

This gun is a lightweight equivalent of the U.S. Mk 45, enjoying a higher rate of fire and capable of higher elevation for antiaircraft use. The light weight is achieved by using light alloys and a fiberglass shield. The gun is fitted with a muzzle brake. 127 mm/54 loads from two drums, a third being loadable while the gun fires. Each drum can, therefore, be loaded with a separate type of ammunition. The type of ammunition (surface, air, pyrotechnic, or chaff) can be selected during firing. Two oscillating arms (which include fuze-setters) strip rounds from the vertical hoist and place them on loading trays. Mounting reaction time is 5 seconds. The ammunition is the standard U.S. semifixed type, the ammunition being brought together only at the bottom of the two fixed-structure hoists.

This weapon has been exported to Argentina, Canada, and Nigeria, and is to arm the new Japanese Aegis destroyers.

◆ 4.7 in

Caliber: 120 mm/45 **Muzzle Velocity:** 850 m/sec (2790 ft/sec)
Maximum Rate of Fire: 7 rnds/min **Training Rate:** manual
Elevation/Depression: +33/−10 deg
Maximum Range: 14,500 m (15,900 yds)
Working Circle: 3.96 m radius (155.9 in)
Weight: 16,900 kg (37,250 lbs)

This pre–World War II weapon survives only on board Paraguayan *Paraguay*-class gunboats built by Odero in 1931. Presumably the 4.7 in is the 1924 twin destroyer mount carrying the Vickers-Terni gun, data for which are given here.

◆ OTO-Melara 76 mm/62 Compact Mounting

Caliber: 3 in/62 **Rate of Fire:** 85 rnds/min
Muzzle Velocity: 925 m/sec (3034 ft/sec)
Maximum Range: 8000 m surface; 4000–5000 m antiair (8700/ 4400–5500 yds)
Training Rate: 60 deg/sec (elevation 35 deg/sec)
Elevation/Depression: +85/−15 deg
Ammunition Capacity: 80 ready-service (drum magazine)
Weight: 7.35 tons **Working Circle:** 208 in (radius)

The OTO-Melara 76/62 Compact, on a fast attack boat. (L&L Van Ginderen)

76 mm/62 is one of the most successful recent medium-caliber weapons, widely exported. This gun is manufactured under license in Spain and in the United States (as the Mk 75). The single feed drum, holding 70 rounds, surrounds the screw feeder hoist (6 rounds) leading up to a station below the left trunnion. Two arms alternately pick up rounds and place them on a loading drum (4 rounds) at the breech. The drum feeds rounds into a loading tray, which receives the spent cartridge case as the gun recoils. As the gun runs out after recoiling, the tray feeds in the next round. The drum around the base of the hoist can be reloaded while the gun fires. Light overall weight is achieved by using light alloys and a fiberglass shield. Recoil forces are reduced by a small muzzle brake.

The lastest version, "Super Rapid," weighs 7.5 tons and carries 85 rounds on the mount (selectable 1, 10, or 120 rounds/min). This version fires faster because its ramming sequence is much quicker: the gun does not move as far in recoil, and ramming is not part of the sequence in which the spent cartridge is ejected. In addition, because the magazine is independent of the turret, the feed can be interrupted to insert different types of ammunition. Because the feed in the Super Rapid is quite different from that of the earlier Compact, the earlier guns cannot be converted to the later standard. However, there is a retrofit kit that converts the earlier gun to 100 rounds/min; kits have been supplied for evaluation to the Italian, German, and U.S. Navies. The Royal Netherlands Navy has bought two kits and has purchased the Super Rapid gun for its M-class frigates. Super Rapid has also been purchased to arm Danish Standard Flex 300s, to arm Singaporean 62-meter fast attack craft, and to be the main gun armament of the rebuilt Canadian "Tribal"-class destroyers.

The Italian Navy considers the Super Rapid an effective antimissile weapon. Thus, each of the new Italian *Animoso*-class destroyers will be armed with three Super Rapids, and there will be no smaller-caliber close-in weapon (earlier ships had the Breda twin fast 40 mm with Dardo fire control).

There is also an older 76 mm/62 (from which the Compact mount was developed), with a muzzle velocity of 850 m/sec, which fires 60 rounds/min. The older gun is recognizable by its more angular gunhouse. This weapon is currently in service only in its single version; a twin mount, with barrels stacked vertically, was the predecessor.

In 1985 British Aerospace and OTO-Melara announced a new course-corrected guided 76/62 round, using ten small booster rockets; four fins deployed from the base of the shell reduce the spin rate so that the rockets can be effective. This round can be mixed with conventional unguided rounds. Guidance (for a one-shot correction of up to 10 degrees) is by radio command. The projectiles are not tracked; rather, their course is predicted by the ship's ballistic computer based on known conditions. First tests were conducted in 1987. The cost target for the smart round is 15–20 times less than that of a point-defense missile

such as Mistral. An extended-range round is also under development, and there is a new base detonating delayed-action fuze.

OTO Melara also offers a dual-purpose (antiship and antiaircraft) MOM (Multirole OTO Melara) round. It has a proximity fuze and contains tungsten cubes embedded in the casing.

◆ Breda 40 mm

> **Caliber:** 40 mm/70   **Maximum Recoil Length:** 100 m (3.94 in)
> **Muzzle Velocity:** 1025 m/sec (HE) (3362 ft/sec) 1350 m/sec (APFSDS) (4428 ft/sec)
> **Maximum Horizontal Range (HE):** 12,500 m (13,700 yds)
> **Maximum Altitude:** (HE) 8700 m (28,500 ft)
> **Rate of Fire:** 900 rnds/min/mount
> **Maximum Elevation/Depression:** +85/−13 deg
> **Working Circle:** 2.902 m (114.3 in)

This Israeli *Saar-II*–class missile boat shows single Breda 40-mm guns with prominent autoloaders extending up from the gun platforms. This photograph seems to show the original radars, the French Neptune and the Italian Orion. (U.S. Naval Institute)

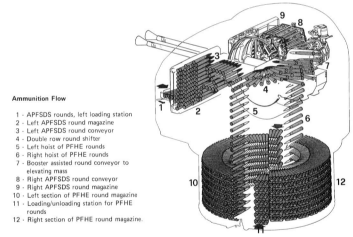

Ammunition Flow

1 - APFSDS rounds, left loading station
2 - Left APFSDS round magazine
3 - Left APFSDS round conveyor
4 - Double row round shifter
5 - Left hoist of PFHE rounds
6 - Right hoist of PFHE rounds
7 - Booster assisted round conveyor to elevating mass
8 - Right APFSDS round conveyor
9 - Right APFSDS round magazine
10 - Left section of PFHE round magazine
11 - Loading/unloading station for PFHE rounds
12 - Right section of PFHE round magazine.

Ammunition flow in the Breda twin Fast Forty (40-mm) gun. (Breda)

Data are for the Twin Fast Forty.

Breda produced two versions of the twin 40 mm/70 (see Bofors, below). One was a compact twin mount. It in turn was succeeded by the Twin Fast Forty. The main features of the new mount are a new recoiling mass, a dual-feed system, and digital servo control. The new recoiling mass reduces the recoil stroke by better than half to speed the firing cycle. The dual-feed system employs a lower magazine, under the mount platform, plus an upper magazine split between the two guns. Both upper and lower magazines feed into each gun.

The Fast Forty exists in two magazine versions, Type A (736 HE rounds in seven horizontal layers) and Type B (444 rounds in four horizontal layers). In each case, the upper magazine contains 200 APFSDS (Armor-Piercing Fin-Stabilized Discarding Sabot) rounds.

The Compact version has a similar ammunition capacity and is rated at about 600 rounds/min (300 per gun). Total weight without ammunition is 5500 kg for Type A, 5300 kg for Type B (7300 kg in Type A, 6300 kg Type B, with ammunition). Training and elevation rates are 90 and 60 deg/sec. Breda claims that this weapon shows a much shorter reaction time than the earlier Bofors gun and saves considerable manpower. However, at least when the Compact version is used in the antimissile role, the most important improvement is much greater accuracy. In June 1976 official Italian Navy trials showed a mean dispersion of 1 mrad, compared to the manufacturer's estimate of 1.8 mrad. Breda/Bofors calculated that, given an error rate of 3 mrad (which is very conservative), and missile accelerations of 2.8 Gs in the vertical and 4.7 Gs in the horizontal, the gun should have a 30-percent probability of destroying an incoming air target outside 900 m (i.e., outside the range at which ballistic fragments would be a problem).

In Italian service the usual fire-control system is Dardo, with an Orion RTN-20X radar (see above under shipboard radars and fire-control systems).

Breda also manufactures conventional open-topped 40-mm mountings carrying air-cooled guns. Type 106 is a twin 40 mm/70; Type 107 is the corresponding single mount. Each gun carries a 32-round Breda autofeeder that elevates with the gun, or it can be loaded with the usual four-round clip. Train and elevation speeds are both 95 deg/sec. Type 106 serves in the West German Navy (e.g., in the *Hamburg* class).

Type 64 is a twin mount, each gun carrying a 100-round automatic magazine. Total weight without ammunition is 7900 kg, and training and elevation rates are 85 and 95 deg/sec.

Type 564 is a single 40 mm/70 carrying a Model 1971 144-round automatic magazine. This weapon is also marketed as the Breda-Bofors 350P. Total weight without ammunition is 3300 kg. Training and elevation rates are 80 and 45 deg/sec.

For defense against sea-skimming missiles, these guns use ammunition with a special Fratelli Borletti proximity fuze that adjusts its fuzing range to the altitude, to avoid premature bursts. At 40 m above the sea, the burst range is 4.5 m; at 20 m, about 3 m; and at 5 m, about 1 m.

Breda twin 40-mm/70 compact naval guns. (Breda)

♦ **Oerlikon/OTO 35 mm**

Caliber: 35 mm/90 (1.56-kg round, including 550-g shell) (3.43/1.21 lbs)
Rate of Fire: 1100 rnds/min (550 rnds/min/barrel)
Muzzle Velocity: 1175 m/sec (3850 ft/sec)
Maximum Range: 6000 m (5000 m air target) (6600/5500 yds)
Training Rate: 120 deg/sec (elevation 70 deg/sec)
Elevation/Depression: +85/−15 deg
Ammunition Capacity: 800 (400/barrel)
Weight: 6400 or 6600 kg with ammunition (through- or above-deck version) (14,100/14,500 lbs)
Working Circle: 3500 mm (137.8 in)

This Oerlikon type GDM-C can be compared to the Oerlikon-Buhrle GCM-A01 manufactured under license in Britain (see British guns below). 35 mm was produced as a private venture, and its design emphasizes light weight. Unlike the Swiss mount, the OTO Melara mount carries its two guns on either side of a central mass. A special dual feed allows a choice, for each gun, between the main ammunition container and a separate container holding 20 rounds of special ammunition. The two guns are KDAs, slightly lighter than the clip-fed KDCs of the Swiss mount.

To reduce weight, OTO Melara used aluminum extensively in the mount and also used a watertight fiberglass shield. The unit as a whole is interchangeable with the OTO Melara 76/62 Compact gun. The design emphasizes quick reaction, and time from off to fire is 2.6 seconds. High muzzle velocity and low drag make for short time of flight, e.g., 6 seconds to 4400 yds.

This gun was very nearly selected as the main armament of the U.S. *Perry*-class frigate; but the OTO Melara 76/62 (U.S. Mk 75) was chosen instead. Similarly, 35 mm was nearly selected for the *Pegasus*-class hydrofoil. The U.S. Navy bought one mount for evaluation, but no trials were conducted.

♦ **Breda 30 mm**

Caliber: 30 mm/82 (369-g projectile) (0.813 lbs)
Rate of Fire: 800 rnds/min
Muzzle Velocity: 1040 m/sec (HE) (3410 ft/sec) 1220 m/sec (APDS) (4000 ft/sec)
Maximum Range: effective range 3000 m (time of flight 5.36 sec with HE round) (3300 yds)
Training Rate: 140 deg/sec (elevation 80 deg/sec)
Elevation/Depression: +85/−13 deg
Ammunition Capacity: 160 rnds
Weight: 1200 kg empty/1330 kg loaded (2640/2930 lbs)
Working Circle: 2.72 m (107.1 in)

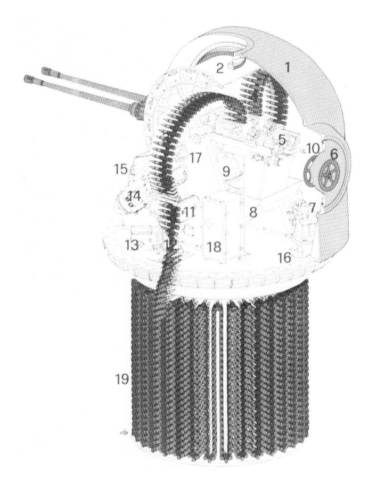

1 - Gunhouse of reinforced fibreglass. 2 - Mantlet plate. 3 - Left feed belt. 4 - Right feed belt. 5 - Mauser elevating mass. 6 - Access door. 7 - Training power drive. 8 - Spent case and link deflector chutes. 9 - Elevation toothed sector. 10 - Firing mechanism. 11 - Booster. 12 - Guide. 13 - Firing limiting device. 14 - Elevation power drive. 15 - Spent case and link evacuation tubes. 16 - Training lock. 17 - Elevation lock. 18 - Auxiliary junction box. 19 - Magazine.

Breda twin 30-mm compact mounting. (Breda)

Breda single compact 30-mm mounting. (Breda)

This Breda single mounting for the German Mauser MK 30-mm Model F gun uses a dual feed and standard NATO ammunition (as in the U.S. GAU-8). In effect 30 mm is a scaled-down version of the Breda twin 40-mm gun. The 30-mm gun was announced in 1984. A new locally controlled version was announced in 1986. It is gyro-stabilized and joystick controlled using optics that are line-of-sight stabilized. Aim-off is automatically calculated while the target is kept in sight. Breda claims that the new version should be effective against surface targets at up to 3000 m.

There is also a twin compact version, announced in 1980, carrying 1100 (Type B) or 2000 (Type A) rounds. Training and elevation rates are 130 and 75 deg/sec. Elevation limits are +80/−13 deg, and the working circle has a radius of 2.523 m. Marconi and Breda jointly proposed a close-in version of the twin 30-mm mount using a colocated Marconi 440-series radar mounted atop the shield, under the designation Sea Cobra. This weapon was tested in England (on the Fraser Gunnery Range) in the early summer of 1988, against Rushton targets. The first operational installations were made in 1987, for the Italian Customs Service.

◆ Breda-Oerlikon 25-mm KBA

Caliber: 25 mm/80　**Rate of Fire:** up to 600 rnds/min
Muzzle Velocity: 1100–1360 m/sec (3600–4460 ft/sec)
Maximum Range: see below
Training Rate: manual (power-assisted)
Elevation/Depression: +50/−15 deg
Ammunition Capacity: 200 rnds
Weight: 660 kg without ammunition (1455 lbs)
Working Circle: radius 2.31 m (90.9 in)

This weapon, announced in 1988, is the first result of a new collaboration between Breda and Oerlikon Italiana. KBA is intended as a direct replacement for the earlier manual 20-mm gun. Firing much more powerful ammunition, it is too heavy to handle entirely manually, particularly on board a lively ship. The mounting, therefore, provides hydraulic power assistance, not at all times, but only when power is needed. Power assistance is triggered by the amount of inertia resisting the gun's movement. In effect, the power assistance cancels out the unpredictable inertial forces due to ship motion, so that the gunner always applies only the degree of force he would need if the ship were not moving at all. The gunsight, which is ranged out to 2000 m, is fixed to a parallelogram system: the gunner can remain standing at any gun elevation, instead of having to crouch uncomfortably as in earlier manually operated guns. Light alloy construction is used to hold down the total weight of the

mounting. This weapon retains the dual-feed system of the earlier land-based KBA gun, permitting the mounting to be reloaded while it is still available to fire.

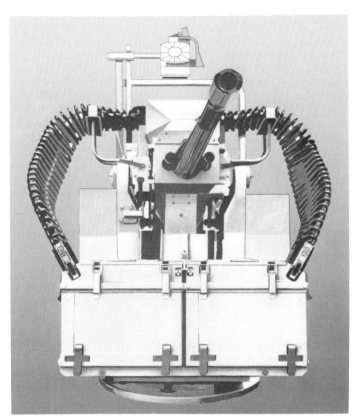

The Breda-Oerlikon single 25-mm naval gun (using the KBA weapon) announced in 1988. (Breda)

◆ Myriad

Selenia's new close-in defensive gun was first displayed at Mostra Navale in Genoa in 1989. Myriad is a joint venture of Selenia, Elsag, Contraves, and Breda, to deal with next-generation violently maneuvering missiles, at ranges within 3000 meters. Like some current close-in weapons, Myriad will use kinetic-energy ammunition (discarding-sabot small-diameter hittiles) with an exceptionally high rate of fire (over 10,000 rounds per minute). The gun is a twin Gatling. The director carries a pair of radars, a Ka-band set for acquisition, and a W-band set that takes over at short ranges. With a much narrower beam, the W-band radar suffers less from multipath (reflected in radar nodding).

NETHERLANDS

◆ Goalkeeper (SGE-30)

Caliber: 30 mm　**Rate of Fire:** 4200 rnds/min
Muzzle Velocity: 3318 ft/sec (3900 ft/sec firing discarding sabot ammunition, MPDS)
Maximum Range: Engagement range about 2000 m (2200 yds)
Training Rate: 100 deg/sec (elevation rate 80 deg/sec)
Elevation/Depression: +85/−25 deg
Ammunition Capacity: 1200 rnds
Weight: 14,018 lbs loaded plus 7766 lbs off-mount
Working Circle: 100 in

This close-in weapon developed by Signaal and General Electric uses the latter's 30-mm 7-barrel GAU-8/A Gatling gun. A linear-array X-band search radar on the mount (1.5 × 30/60 degree beam, scanning at 60 rpm) relays the target's range and bearing to the dual-frequency (X- and Ka-band) tracking radar (which uses a Cassegrain dish) on the gun mount. The beam-width of the X-band tracker, 2.4 degrees, is larger than that of the acquisition radar, to assure very rapid acquisition without search. Once the X-band tracker has acquired the target, the 0.6-degree beam of the Ka-band tracker takes over. In automatic operation, the radar limits itself to targets in a 2–7 km range bracket, and with radial speeds of over 150 m/sec. Total reaction time against a Mach 2 sea-skimmer, including automatic detection, IFF interrogation, 90-degree tracker slew, tracker elevation, X-band lock-on, and computer run-in, is about 5.5 sec, the engagement beginning at 1.5 km with maximum kill probability at 300 m. The radar is derived from the Signaal Flycatcher ground AA unit.

The system, using data from its radars, automatically and continuously evaluates and prioritizes targets. Signaal claims that the use of Ka-band (8-mm wavelength) provides a very narrow beam that avoids reflections off the sea (even against sea-skimmers) and, thus, produces no deceptive mirror images. The broader X-band tracker radar captures the designated target, and the signal/noise ratios of the X- and Ka-band tracker radars are continuously and automatically compared to reject clutter and jamming. Both radars have standard anticlutter and ECCM features, such as pulse compression, pulse-to-pulse coherence (for doppler-MTI tracking), frequency diversity, and flexible waveforms (adaptive transmission). Tracking is by monopulse in both frequency bands.

This system employs closed-loop spotting of the type used in Phalanx.

The 30-mm Gatling gun in its EX-83 mount is also the basis of the French close-in weapons, SAMOS and Satan. Signaal chose the GE Gatling gun in preference to the Mauser 30-mm gun, for which Goalkeeper was originally designed, because the quadruple Mauser (SEM-30) could not meet a Dutch Navy requirement for 1.7-mrad dispersion; SGE-30 demonstrated 1.2-mrad dispersion in a 6-second burst (420 rounds).

Signaal demonstrated the GAU-8/Flycatcher combination in November 1979, against targets at a range of about 1000 m; Goalkeeper is the result, the Dutch Navy choosing the GE gun over the Mauser gun in mid-1980.

In 1983 the Royal Navy chose Goalkeeper rather than the VSEL Sea Dragon, a similar EX-83 gun controlled by a masthead Sea Giraffe 150HC and an on-mount tracker derived from the DN181 millimeter-wave radar of the Rapier blind-fire system. Reportedly this choice was based more on political and economic than on technical factors.

Goalkeeper. (Signaal)

SPAIN

◆ Meroka

Caliber: 20 mm/120 (round weight 320 g, including 102-g projectile) (0.71/0.225 lbs)
Rate of Fire: 2 bursts/sec (9000 rnds/min during burst that lasts 0.080 sec)
Ready-use Ammunition: 720 rnds (60/barrel) (2160 in future version)
Muzzle Velocity: 1300 m/sec (4260 ft/sec)

Maximum Elevation/Depression: +85/−15
Weight: 4500 kg on mount; plus 421 kg off mount (9920/928 lbs)

A close-in weapons system developed by the Spanish manufacturer Bazan, Meroka is mounted instead of the U.S. Phalanx on board Spanish equivalents of U.S. warships (*Perry* class and the Sea-Control Ship *Principe de Asturias*). Meroka is designed to operate on the basis of target detection (by an associated search radar) at 15,000 m, using its own I-band tracking radar to acquire targets at 5000 m, and achieving first impact at 1500 m and target destruction at 500 m (16,400/5500/1640/550 yds).

Targets are tracked by monopulse, using an on-mount Lockheed Electronics PVS-2 Sharpshooter. In current Spanish installations, targets are designated via an Orion RTN-12L/X search radar via a Selenia PDS-10 tactical-data console. There is no closed-loop spotting. An optronic system is provided for back-up in a jamming environment, and there is an off–bore sight tracker to deal with extremely low targets.

Bazan claims that the ammunition is a special hard-core type, for maximum penetration of missile bodies.

The twelve 20-mm barrels are arranged in two horizontal rows, very close together.

Meroka. (Bazan)

SWEDEN

◆ Bofors 6 in DP

Caliber: 152 mm/50 (101-lb shell, 71.8-lb cartridge)
Rate of Fire: 12–15 rnds/min/gun   **Muzzle Velocity:** 2950 ft/sec
Maximum Range: 28,400 yds
Elevation/Depression: +60/−10 deg
Weight: 113 tons (no ammunition)

This dual-purpose cruiser gun was designed beginning in 1937, primarily for the Dutch Navy. When the Netherlands was overrun, twin and triple mounts were diverted to the Swedish *Tre Kronor*–class cruisers. These ships have now been discarded, but twin mounts remain on board the two former Dutch *de Zeven Provincien*–class cruisers in the Peruvian Navy. Those mounts represent one generation of technology beyond the Soviet's triple 6-inch mount (*Sverdlov* class) and are roughly com-

The Dutch cruiser *de Ruyter* (now Peruvian) shows both the Bofors twin 6-in and twin 57-mm/60 (superfiring above the 6-inch turrets) guns. (U.S. Naval Institute)

parable to U.S. wartime automatic heavy guns (6 in/47, now discarded, and 8 in/55, in the *Des Moines* class).

This weapon is unusual in that the shell and cartridge case are stowed separately (for ease of handling) but are rammed together into a single round on a cartridge carrier before hoisting to the gun; the weapon, therefore, enjoys the advantages of fixed-round loading. The breech is a vertical sliding wedge, and the loading tray elevates with the gun for all-elevation loading. The design was criticized by British observers on the grounds that the ramming together of shell and cartridge case demanded extraordinarily close production tolerances.

Armor: 4.9-in face and rear, 2-in roof, 1.2-in sides.

◆ Bofors 4.7 in/50 (120 mm)

Caliber: 120 mm/50 (21-kg HE shell; 40-kg complete round) (46.3/88.2 lbs)
Rate of Fire: 45 rnds/min/barrel
Muzzle Velocity: 850 m/sec (2790 ft/sec)
Maximum Range: 13,000 m surface fire; 7,000 m antiaircraft (14,200/7700 yds)
Training Rate: 25 deg/sec (elevation 40 deg/sec)
Elevation/Depression: +85/−10 deg
Ammunition Capacity: 104 rnds (52/gun)
Weight: 55 tons (67 including rotating platform and ammunition)

Bofors 4.7 in/50 on board the Dutch destroyer *Friesland,* now discarded (however, sisters are retained in the Peruvian Navy). The surface-search radar is the Signaal ZW-01 (now replaced by ZW-06 in the surviving ships); the radar on the foremast is DA-01, and the big air-search antenna aft belongs to LW-02. The fire-control radar is M 1. The foremast carries the standard British DF antennas: FH 4 at the foretop and UA-2 below, for HF and UHF, respectively. (U.S. Naval Institute)

Data refer to the twin destroyer mount, which was manufactured for the Swedish, Dutch, and Colombian Navies. This gun survives in the two Dutch *Tromp*-class destroyers and in several ex-Dutch destroyers transferred to the Peruvian Navy. The Swedish and Colombian ships have been discarded.

The twin 4.7-in gun was developed by Bofors (beginning in 1944) as an intermediate weapon between the 6 in/50 and the 57 mm/60. Bofors developed three types of loader, a horizontal fan (which was used in the 57-mm mount), a vertical fan, and a pendulum swinging up from the vertical ammunition hoist to the breech. In each case, the loader had to be able to accept rounds at any elevation and then shift them to the elevation of the breech. The pendulum was chosen for this mount. Its arm is pivoted at the trunnion, and it swings between the top of the hoist and a loading position behind the breech; rounds are rammed from the top position directly into the breech. After ramming, the round debullets, i.e., the shell separates from the cartridge case and seats. Bofors claims that this process decreases barrel wear and also retains the cartridge case more firmly in the chamber until the breechblock has closed sufficiently.

Each of the two hoists has two 26-round hoppers at its bottom, so that both surface and AA ammunition can be carried. It takes 5–15 seconds to switch ammunition by turning the hoppers to line up the unused one.

This mount was considered extremely advanced when it appeared in 1950, and about 1953 the Royal Navy considered adoption. The mount was rejected: it was too heavy, too noisy, and not flash- or gas-tight. Reportedly the Dutch Navy found the mount rather too heavy (and vibrations too violent during rapid firing) for the 2700-ton destroyers.

Bofors also developed a single automatic mount of this caliber, designated TAK 120L/50-93, for destroyers or frigates. In Swedish service, this mount would have replaced the twin 120/50 in a later-generation destroyer, but that project died when Swedish naval policy shifted to an emphasis on small coastal craft and submarines. Rate of fire was 70 rounds/min (with a water-cooled barrel), using twin-drum magazines below the mount; range was 21,000+ m (time to 10,000 m was 19.2 seconds). Elevation limits were +78/−10 degrees. Training speed was 40 deg/sec (elevating speed 30 deg/sec). Total mount weight was 57 tons, including the foundation (with control room) and 300 rounds, and the gunhouse was built of 10-mm steel. Each round weighed 40 kg. The entire mount could be laid by one man, and the gun was liquid-cooled so that it could sustain a high rate of fire. The turret had an unusually low profile. Ammunition feed was by a dual swinging arm (as in the twin 4.7-in gun). The crew was limited to three. Work began about 1956, the goal being a single self-contained unit including on-mount fire control (as in the contemporary U.S. GUNAR), firing 60 rounds/min. This weapon is interesting as an example of what might be possible if the Swedish Navy continues toward larger craft, as it now seems to be doing.

◆ Bofors 4.7 in/46

Caliber: 120 mm (21-kg HE shell; complete round is 35 kg) (46.3/77.1 lbs)
Rate of Fire: 80 rnds/min
Muzzle Velocity: 800 m/sec (2620 ft/sec)
Maximum Range: 18,500 m (20,200 yds)
Training Rate: 40 deg/sec **Elevation/Depression:** +80/−10 deg
Ammunition Capacity: 52 rnds ready use (plus 16 in mount)
Weight: 28.5 tonnes (without ammunition or flare launchers)
Working Circle: 6.33 m (249.2 in)

The Indonesian *Malahayati* is armed with the Bofors 4.7-in/46 gun, controlled by a Signaal WM-28 in the egg-shaped radome. The radar aft is a Signaal DA-05/2. (R. Gillett)

This dual-purpose enclosed gun, for large fast attack craft displacing 600 tons or more, is currently in service only on board two Finnish corvettes of the *Turunmaa* class, the minelayer *Pohjanmaa*, and the Indonesian *Fatahillah* class. The barrel is water-cooled, and the gun has a vertical sliding breechblock. There are two magazines, one fixed to each side of the breech. Each magazine has five ammunition channels (five rounds each), and the gun feeds alternately from each magazine into the ammunition chamber of the autoloader. The dual-magazine arrangement permits loading with two kinds of ammunition, so that the type can be switched instantly without interrupting the loading cycle. The enclosure is 4–6-mm steel for splinter protection.

Development (on a private venture basis) began in 1963, and the first prototype was tested in 1967. This weapon is an adapted antiaircraft field gun. The Bofors designation is TAK 120.

◆ Bofors 76 mm

Caliber: 3 in/50 (5.9-kg [13-lbs] Mk-27 ammunition)
Rate of Fire: 30 rnds/min
Muzzle Velocity: 823 m/sec (2700 ft/sec)
Maximum Range: 12,600 m at 30 deg elev (13,800 yds)
Training Rate: 25 deg/sec (elevation: 25 deg/sec)
Elevation/Depression: +30/−10 deg
Ammunition Capacity: 16 ready-use rounds on the sides of the hoist frame **Weight:** 6.5 tonnes empty

This fully-automatic single gun is intended primarily to deal with surface targets. It is controlled by an external director and is unmanned, for a low silhouette. The gunhouse is 6 mm thick. This gun is used only on board Norwegian *Storm*-class fast attack craft and on board Singaporean 110-ft "Type B" patrol boats. In both cases the associated fire-control system is the Signaal WM-26, a "half-egg" incorporating a single track-while-scan radar.

Bofors 76-mm gun on board the Norwegian patrol boat *Hvass*. The radome conceals a Signaal WM-26 fire-control radar, and the search radar above it is a Decca TM 1226. The missiles aft are Penguins, and the gun aft is a Bofors 40-mm L70. (G. Koop)

◆ Bofors 57 mm/60

Caliber: 57 mm/60 (5.73-lb shell, 6.27-lb cartridge)
Rate of Fire: 130 rnds/min/gun   **Muzzle Velocity:** 3018 ft/sec
Maximum Range: 15,880 yds
Training Rate: 30 deg/sec (elevation 30 deg/sec)
Elevation/Depression: +90/−10 deg
Weight: 68,300 lbs (no ammunition)

Bofors developed the 57-mm gun during and after World War II as the natural successor to the 40 mm/70 then under development; the 57 mm/60 is a scaled-up version. The French Model 1951 uses a Bofors-manufactured gun in a French mounting. This gun was also adopted, in a Bofors-designed mounting, by the Dutch and Swedish Navies, as a secondary-battery weapon, in an enclosed twin automatic mount. The 57 mm/60 survives on board one ex-Dutch Peruvian cruiser.

With this weapon, Bofors abandoned the four-round clip of the 40-mm gun, theorizing that fire could not be fast enough, and that clips would be far too heavy. Instead, loaders drop rounds into ammunition boxes, which in turn feed two fans (quadrant-shaped hoppers). The fans are mounted at the gun trunnions, so that the position of the gravity feed is always constant (horizontal, perpendicular to the gun's axis). The fan itself elevates with the gun, and rounds move along the fan from the perpendicular position to a position directly over the breech. Similar fan feeds can be seen in other postwar Bofors and Breda-Bofors weapons.

◆ Bofors 57 mm/70 Mk 2

Caliber: 57 mm/70 (6.1-kg [13.1-lbs] round)
Rate of Fire: 225 rnds/min
Muzzle Velocity: 1025 m/sec (PFHE; 950 m/sec for HCER) (3360/3120 ft/sec)
Maximum Range: 17,000 m (18,600 yds)
Training Rate: 55 deg/sec (elevation 40 deg/sec)
Elevation/Depression: +75/−10 deg
Ammunition Capacity: 120 rnds in cupola, 40 rnds ready to fire
Weight: 6500 kg without ammunition (14,300 lbs)
Working Circle: 4.325 m (170.3 in)

Bofors claims that this gun is truly dual-purpose: that it is accurate and agile enough to destroy sea-skimmers (by using proximity-fuzed ammunition and by attempting to set off their warheads); and that, with penetrating (delayed action) HE rounds (HCER, or high-capacity extended-range), it puts more explosives into a surface target in the first 30 seconds than any other gun of up to 100-mm caliber. The company claims that 57 mm/70 should be an effective shore bombardment weapon because it can pepper an area with shell fire before the targets can move or take cover. The delayed-action fuze should permit penetration of 20 mm of steel before the round bursts about 2 m inside the target. Bofors claims, too, that using better steel allows reduced shell thickness, so that the shell carries 40 percent more explosive than its predecessors.

The loader and the gun mount are two-sided, so that two types of ammunition can be handled simultaneously. Ammunition comes up from the magazine into two 20-round cassettes, mounted on a rail behind the gun. When filled, they move into position above, and discharge their ammunition down into, the ready-use magazines. There are also two intermediate cassettes,

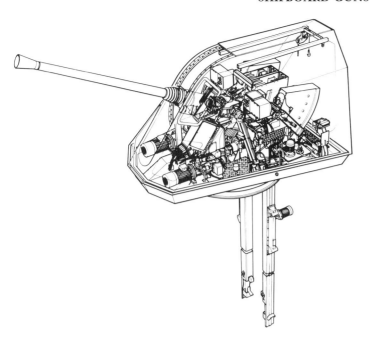

Bofors 57-mm/70 Mk 2.

each holding 20 rounds, so that the cupola (turret) carries 60 rounds (two cassettes and the ready-use magazine above the gun itself) on each side, the total of 120 being sufficient for 15 or 20 engagements.

Bofors particularly emphasizes a new servo system that greatly reduces aiming errors and damping time, for greater accuracy when engaging air targets. Compared to the earlier Mk 1 (see below), Mk 2 uses a special monobloc steel barrel that does not require water cooling, and the turret of Mk 2 has a reduced radar cross section (10–20 percent lower than that of the earlier mount).

This weapon is used on board Swedish corvettes (*Spica-III* class) and has been selected for the Canadian "City"-class frigates.

Mk 1 is a less sophisticated version, for offshore patrol vessels, coast guard vessels, etc. In Swedish service Mk 1 arms *Hugin*-class missile boats and *Spica-* and *Spica-II*–class missile boats. Mk 1 is also used by the Malaysian and Yugoslav Navies. The rate of fire is 200 rnds/min, and elevation limits are +78/ −10 degrees (training rate 55 deg/sec, elevation 20 deg/sec). Ammunition capacity is 128 rounds plus 40 ready-use rounds in the dual hoists.

Work on the 57/70 began in 1972, based largely on experience with the earlier 57/60. The major improvements were a higher rate of fire (200 vs. 130 rnds/min), the use of new ammunition with proximity and/or impact fuzes, an improved water-cooling system for the gun tubes, reduced weight (by using light alloys

more extensively), and a new electro-hydraulic system for rapid slewing and elevation.

Reviewing this weapon, the U.S. Navy's Foreign Ordnance Review Team considered the 57/70 Mk 2 heavy compared to the OTO-Melara 35-mm and 76-mm weapons.

♦ Bofors 40 mm L70/Trinity

Caliber: 40 mm/70   **Rate of Fire:** 300 or 330 rnds/min
Muzzle Velocity: 1005–1025 m/sec (3300–3360 ft/sec)
Effective Range: 4000 m (4400 yds)
Training Rate: 85 deg/sec (elevation 45 deg/sec)
Elevation/Depression: +90/−10 deg
Weight: 2.8, 3, or 3.3 tons without ammunition

Bofors 40-mm L70 on board a Yugoslav Type-80 fast patrol boat. The launchers forward of the gun are for chaff/illumination. (U.S. Naval Institute)

Bofors Trinity 40-mm/70 gun. (U.S. Naval Institute)

Bofors 40 mm/70 fitted with a new Trinity 99-round magazine, as in West German service. (Bofors)

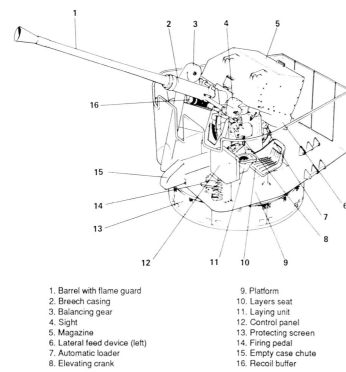

1. Barrel with flame guard
2. Breech casing
3. Balancing gear
4. Sight
5. Magazine
6. Lateral feed device (left)
7. Automatic loader
8. Elevating crank
9. Platform
10. Layers seat
11. Laying unit
12. Control panel
13. Protecting screen
14. Firing pedal
15. Empty case chute
16. Recoil buffer

The Bofors 40 mm/70 with a Trinity 99-round magazine. (Bofors)

This weapon was conceived by Bofors to replace the World War II L60 gun. In various forms the 40 mm/70 has been in production since the late 1940s. All current production versions are single air-cooled guns. The current versions are SAK 40L/70-315, which is hand-operated; SAK 40L/70-350, which is power (electro-hydraulic) operated, gyro-stabilized, and remotely controlled; and SAK 40L/70-600, which employs the Trinity 99-round magazine (2 more rounds are in the intermediate feed position and in the ramming position). All three versions employ open-topped shields (for which GRP weather covers are available), the -600 version (Trinity) being recognizable by its special magazine. All of the Bofors-built 40-mm guns, then, use gravity-feed magazines directly descended from those of the earlier World War II Bofors 40 mm/60.

In August 1986 the West German Navy awarded Bofors a contract to upgrade the existing German 40-mm/70 guns, using the new high-capacity magazine and elevating mass that had been developed for the Trinity (-600) version of the gun. The modernized guns have a higher rate of fire. Ships involved include the Type-343 minesweeper and the Type-148 missile attack boat.

The Royal Navy planned single-, twin-, and six-barreled versions of the 40 mm/70, but all were canceled in 1957 in favor of the Sea Cat missile; the gun was used by the British Army.

Projected British naval designations were Marks 10, 11, and 12, respectively.

Breda has produced the Bofors 40 mm/70 under license since 1969. The company has specialized in automatic loading mechanisms, which are described under the entry for the Breda Twin Fast Forty, above. The Breda 144-round automatic feed system

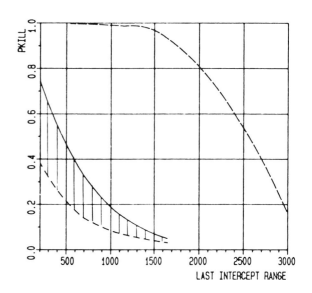

EFFECT AGAINST SEASKIMMING MISSILE.
KILL PROBABILITY AS A FUNCTION OF LAST INTERCEPT RANGE (M).
MISSILE ALTITUDE=5M. MISSILE SPEED 300 M/S. ACCELERATION=0.1G.
TIME FOR TARGET MOVE RELATIVE TO THE FIRING
OF FIRST ROUND=0. (MOST DIFFICULT CASE.)
TRINITY FIRING WITH OPTIMIZED BURST PATTERN.
TIME OF FIRE 2 SEC.

——— 30 MM APDS CIWS ————— 40 MM TRINITY
———— 20 MM APDS CIWS

Bofors' argument in favor of proximity-fuzed antimissile ammunition. This is the company's estimate of missile kill probability as a function of last intercept range, in meters, assuming a missile altitude of 5 m and a speed of 300 m/sec. It is assumed that the gun fires a 2-sec burst. The closer the kill, the more likely it is that fragments of the missile hit the ship. The dashed line on the right is for Trinity; the full line is for a 30-mm CIWS like Goalkeeper, and that below it is for a 20-mm CIWS such as Phalanx. (Bofors)

Trinity test-firing on board the Swedish minehunter *Landsort*. The small objects to either side of the gun mount are Elma ASW launchers. (Bofors)

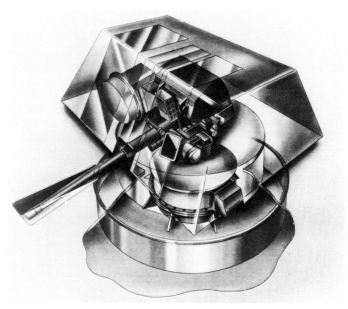

Trinity in a "stealth" mounting. (Bofors)

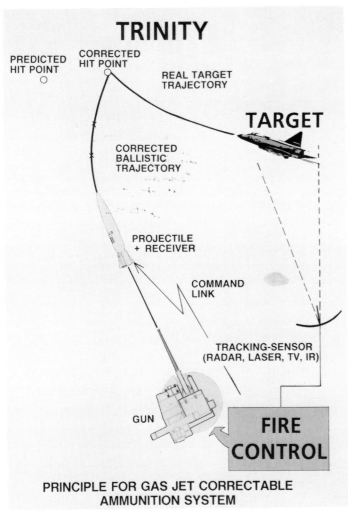

TRINITY

PREDICTED HIT POINT

CORRECTED HIT POINT

REAL TARGET TRAJECTORY

TARGET

CORRECTED BALLISTIC TRAJECTORY

PROJECTILE + RECEIVER

COMMAND LINK

TRACKING-SENSOR (RADAR, LASER, TV, IR)

GUN

FIRE CONTROL

PRINCIPLE FOR GAS JET CORRECTABLE AMMUNITION SYSTEM

Proposed 40-mm course-corrected shell. (Bofors)

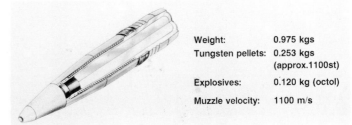

Weight:	0.975 kgs
Tungsten pellets:	0.253 kgs (approx.1100st)
Explosives:	0.120 kg (octol)
Muzzle velocity:	1100 m/s

Trinity 3P shell. (Bofors)

is also manufactured under license by Empresa Nacional Bazan of Spain, for the Spanish Navy.

Bofors has developed a variety of ammunition. The 40 mm/70 originally fired either armor piercing (AP) or high-explosive with tracer (HE-T). Bofors developed the first production proximity fuze for a 40-mm shell, for the L70 gun, beginning large-scale production in 1975 (40-mm proximity fuzes are also manufactured by Borletti in Italy and by Thomson-CSF in France). Bofors has recently developed a similar fuze for the older 40 mm/60, many of which are still in service. In 1982 the company announced a proximity-fuzed prefragmented HE (PFHE) shell to deal specifically with low-flying aircraft and sea-skimming missiles. The shell contains 650 carbide tungsten pellets,

each of which can penetrate 14 mm of duraluminum. They surround the core of octol (HMX/TNT) explosive and are projected outward when it bursts. The steel body of the shell itself produces another 2400 fragments. The shell body is boat-tailed for optimum splinter spread. Lethal radius is 6.5 m against aircraft and 4.5 m against missiles. Bofors argues that such a shell is more effective than a penetrator such as that used by the Phalanx or Goalkeeper systems, because the PFHE shell has a better chance of destroying an incoming missile. Although the overall rate of fire of the 40 mm/70 is much lower than that of a Gatling gun, Bofors argues that one of its shells is broadly equivalent to a burst fired by the Gatling.

The PFHE shell uses a doppler proximity fuze with special ECCM features; the shell can also explode on impact. Bofors claims that a ten-round PFHE burst is as effective as 50–75 rounds of HE-T. In theory, the doppler feature prevents the shell from bursting prematurely when it nears the sea surface.

There is also a high-capacity HE round (HCHE) using a point delay fuze, which allows the shell to penetrate a target for 0.3 milliseconds (equivalent to 20 mm of armor) before bursting. Bofors claims that the large charge inside its HCHE shell provides blast effects equivalent to those of a conventional 57-mm shell.

An Italian firm, SNIA BFD, has developed an armor-piercing fin-stabilized discarding sabot (APFSDS) 40-mm shell, and this company has also developed a preformed fragmentation (PFF) round.

Bofors is currently developing a course-corrected 40-mm shell, which the company is convinced will be needed to deal with next-generation targets. The shell would carry enough propellant to allow several corrections in sequence, on the basis of command signals. Such a shell would have to be somewhat heavier (hence slower) than the Trinity 3P shell (see below), but Bofors argues that course correction would make up for any reduction in initial accuracy caused by lengthier time of flight. The command link might also be used to set the 3P fuze in flight, e.g., to penetrate if the shell seemed likely to hit the target instead of passing nearby (in which case a proximity burst would be best).

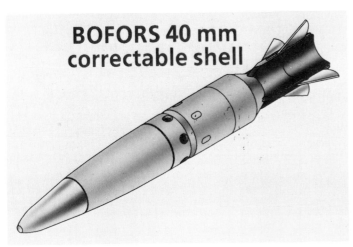

BOFORS 40 mm correctable shell

Bofors's projected 40-mm course-corrected shell. (Bofors).

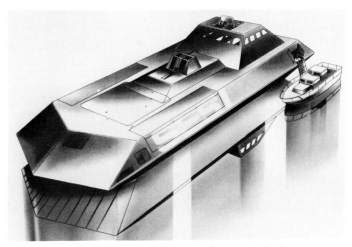

The projected Swedish "stealth" SES attack craft. (Bofors)

Trinity is a modernized 40-mm/70 gun, conceived primarily as a close-in antimissile weapon, competing with systems such as Phalanx. As with Phalanx, the fire-control radar is mounted directly with the gun. The Bofors view was that, rather than rely on bursts of small-caliber projectiles, it would be better to use smaller numbers of larger-caliber ones, which would have predictable trajectories, and each of which would have much greater lethal effect. The company also determined that any future close-in gun would have to achieve much greater range than existing weapons. Work began about 1982, and Trinity was announced at Farnborough in 1984. Initial tests were conducted in 1985–86.

The name Trinity is derived from the synergistic combination of ammunition, weapon, and fire control.

Bofors argues that 40 mm is very nearly the ideal caliber for such a weapon, since that size makes for a larger and hence much more lethal shell than the 20–35-mm weapons in use elsewhere; yet 40 mm can be fired much faster than the next natural size, 57 mm. Trinity's development began with an improvement in the ammunition. Higher-energy propellant was used to slightly increase muzzle velocity while increasing projectile weight by 25 percent. The new 3P shell weighs 1.1 kg (compared to 0.88 kg for the earlier PFHE and 0.96 kg for the old HE-T) and is slightly longer, for better aerodynamics. Explosive content is about 25 percent greater than that of the PFHE; upon bursting, the 3P produces more than 3000 fragments, including 1000 tungsten alloy pellets. The weight of a complete round is 2.8 kg, compared to 2.4–2.5 kg for older 40-mm/70 rounds. Because the new shell is much more energetic than the older ones, the gun must absorb greater recoil forces; it uses a muzzle brake.

The fuze is programmable: it can be set, as it enters the breech, for proximity or point detonation. The burst pattern can also be preset: for example, a circular pattern to attack a high-altitude airplane or a fan pattern against a sea-skimming missile. The fire-control system is designed to position a ten-round burst around a missile, the pattern measuring 15–20 m across, with each fuze programmed individually during firing so that the pattern can be arranged to keep the lower rounds from triggering off the sea. Trinity can also fire a new AP shell.

There is a new high-capacity (99-round) magazine, holding 45 rounds to the left and 54 to the right of the gun, in eleven vertical rows. This division allows the gun to carry two kinds of ammunition at the same time. Only one side is used at a time, its outer row being emptied first. Typically, the gun carries 101 rounds, 99 in the magazine and two in the gun. Bofors assumes that the gun will typically fire 5–15 rounds per engagement. The gun is rated at 330 rounds per minute, and claimed dispersion is 0.7 mrad.

The mounting as a whole is largely nonmagnetic since Swedish minesweepers are a major likely application. Elevation limits are +80/−20 degrees, and the working circle radius is 2.974 m (117 inches). Total weight is 3700 kg (8155 lbs).

The Trinity mount incorporates a specially built Bofors microprocessor, a radar, a laser range-finder, a gyro-stabilized reflex sight, and an image intensifier for night operation. The computer determines the number of rounds to be fired, the fuze setting, the programmed burst pattern, and the actual moment of firing for greatest effect.

Claimed effective range is 2000–3000 m against a low-flying fast attack airplane, or 2500 m against a sea-skimming missile.

A remotely controlled version, Trinity Spartan, has also been designed; it incorporates the same ammunition and weapon, but the fire control is off-mount. Bofors conceived Trinity as an integrated system using its own sensors. However, the company has also offered to combine Trinity with existing fire-control radar systems, such as that employed in the Dutch Goalkeeper.

Trinity was tested on board the Swedish minesweeper *Landsort* in the winter of 1988. Trinity was to be integrated with a new Ericsson Eagle coherent-doppler tracking radar.

Trinity was first demonstrated in public in September 1988. Sea Trinity was shown engaging a helicopter hovering behind a curtain of trees at 2600-m range, then firing bursts against a simulated maneuvering target, then firing against armored containers. The gun then fired a burst of eight rounds, each set for a different mode (to demonstrate the programmability of the 3P round); and then the gun fired 100 rounds against a target container at 1100-m range.

In 1988 the Swedish Defense Procurement Administration commissioned Bofors to study a "stealth" version of Trinity, for use on board a future warship. Trinity is already shaped to reduce its overall radar cross section and incorporates radar absorbing material to cover openings and cavities. The gun also has a low magnetic signature, and Bofors claims that the basic design allows for further signature reduction by computer-controlled active compensation. A sketch released at the time shows the basic Trinity enclosed within a cupola with flat sides angled inward to reduce radar reflections.

♦ **Bofors 40 mm (old types)**

Caliber: 40 mm/60 (barrel length is actually 56 calibers) (0.9-kg (1.98-lb) shell)   **Rate of Fire:** 120 rnds/min
Muzzle Velocity: 800–880 m/sec (2620–2890 ft/sec)
Maximum Range: 10,000 m; effective range 3000 m (10,900/3300 yds)
Elevation/Depression: +90/−5 deg
Ammunition Capacity: 4-round clip

The Bofors 40 mm/60 was the standard Allied heavy automatic antiaircraft gun of World War II, remaining in service in some numbers, both in single and in twin mounts. See the British and U.S. sections, below, for details of their 40-mm mounts. Postwar, Bofors developed a higher-velocity 70-caliber gun, which was adopted by many navies. Breda developed a series of automatically fed 40 mm/70s (see Italian entries above).

The original Bofors guns all used four-round clips that were gravity-fed into the gun from above. All subsequent Bofors 40-mm and 57-mm guns continue to use the same basic gun mechanism, which is fed from above. Land-based (and some single naval) versions were air-cooled; naval twins were all water-cooled.

Borfors currently offers a variety of modernization options for the 40 mm/60. Although generally described in connection with land-based guns, these options are applicable to surviving naval units. Bofors claims that the effect of modernizing the three main components of the weapon—the gun itself, its sight, and its ammunition—improves kill probability against a typical fighter-bomber by 50–80 percent (e.g., kill probability at 1 km rises from about 18 to nearly 100 percent), based on a nine-round burst. The gun's rate of fire is increased by about 50 percent, from 120 to 180 rounds per minute; the hopper at the top of the gun is enlarged to hold 20 rounds (so that two to three targets can be engaged between reloadings; the rounds are still carried in clips of four, for easy handling); and power laying is introduced (for guns on land; naval mountings are generally already power operated).

The earlier point-detonating ammunition is replaced by PFHE proximity rounds similar to those developed for the L70 gun (see above). Bofors claims that the effect of the proximity fuze is to increase the effective bursting area of the target (i.e., the probability that a shell will burst) by a factor of 50–300. Maximum bursting range is 5.5 m (reducible by automatic sensitivity control to 1–2 m for use against missiles flying at low altitude). Muzzle velocity is 860 m/sec (2820 ft/sec), and total shell weight is 980 g (2.16 lbs), including 90 g of octol explosive. The gun is fitted with a proximity fuze disconnector, so that the shells can still function in the point detonating mode if required. The disconnector is attached to the front of the ammunition hopper atop the gun. The gun can also fire HET (high-explosive tracer; in this case HE means greater penetrating power rather than a high-explosive filling), PT, and APHC-T (armor-piercing high-capacity tracer) ammunition. The APHC-T shell is unusual in carrying a heavy armor-piercing slug within an aluminum shell body; Bofors claims that APHC-T penetrates 30 percent deeper than earlier armor-piercing capped tracer

(APC-T) rounds. As a side benefit, the aluminum body should have an incendiary effect on the target.

A new gun-mounted "U-sight" system is added, incorporating a laser range-finder.

As modernized, the land version of the gun trains at 85 deg/sec and elevates at 50 deg/sec; dispersion is less than 4 mrad.

For other versions of the 40 mm/60, see the U.K. and U.S. guns below.

SWITZERLAND

◆ Oerlikon 35 mm (Type GDM-A)

Caliber: 35 mm/90   **Rate of Fire:** 1100 rnds/min
Muzzle Velocity: 1175 m/sec (3850 ft/sec)
Effective Range: (air/surface) Radar Control: 5000/8000 m (5500/8700 yds) Optical Control: 2500/5000 m (2700/5500 yds) Local Sight: 3000/5000 m (3300/5500 yds)
Training Rate: 120 deg/sec (elevation 130 deg/sec)
Elevation/Depression: +85/−15
Ammunition Capacity: 336 rnds
Weight: 10,500 lbs without ammunition
Working Circle: 4716 mm (185.7 in)

The Oerlikon twin 35-mm gun (GDM-A). (Oerlikon)

The Oerlikon twin 35-mm gun (GDM-C), developed in collaboration with OTO-Melara. (Oerlikon)

Unlike the British BMARC/Oerlikon GCM, this weapon is clip-fed, with 112 rounds of ready-use ammunition and another 224 rounds carried within the mount. The guns can be reloaded

while they fire. GDM-A is electrically controlled and biaxially stabilized, and the gun has a stabilized sight and joystick for local control. The gun can also be manually controlled in an emergency.

The GDM-C version was developed jointly with OTO-Melara, using the same Type-KDC gun. A U.S. Navy Foreign Ordnance Review Team concluded about 1971 that the OTO-Melara version, described as an updated GDM-A, was better suited to U.S. requirements. The users are Iran (one mount aft on the single Mk-7 frigate) and Greece (two each on four missile boats).

◆ Oerlikon 30 mm

See United Kingdom BMARC-Oerlikon 30 mm below.

◆ Sea Zenith (Type GBM-B1Z)

Caliber: 25 mm/92   **Rate of Fire:** 850 rnds/sec
Muzzle Velocity: 1335 m/sec (4380 ft/sec)
Training Rate: 2.5 rad/sec (elevation of 2.5 rad/sec) (143.2 deg/sec)
Elevation/Depression: +127/−14 deg
Ammunition Capacity: 415 rnds/gun
Weight: 4600 kg plus 2150-kg ammunition feed system (10,140/4740 lbs)

The Oerlikon 30-mm twin manned antiaircraft gun (GCM-A03-1). The A03-2 version has provision for local control (the sidecar lacks a windshield) but can also be remotely controlled. A03-3 is entirely remotely controlled. (Oerlikon)

Sea Zenith is the four-gun weapon associated with the Swiss Contraves Seaguard system (see above under shipboard radars and fire-control systems). The guns are designated KBB-R03/L03. The ammunition supply is sufficient for 18 engagements, and the guns can be reloaded while they fire.

The unusual elevation arc makes it easier for the gun to engage very high targets; that arc is achieved by having the gun train in a plane canted at a 35-degree angle.

◆ Oerlikon 25 mm (Type GBM Diane Navale and GBM-A01)

Caliber: 25 mm/80   **Rate of Fire:** 600 rnds/min/gun
Muzzle Velocity: 1100–1360 m/sec (3600–4460 ft/sec)
Training Rate: 1.4 rad/sec (elevation of 0.85 rad/sec) (80.2 and 48.7 deg/sec)
Elevation/Depression: +80/−20 deg
Ammunition Capacity: 500 rounds
Weight: 2300 kg (1900 kg without ammunition) (5070/4190 lbs)

This naval version of the towed twin 25-mm gun was announced at Mostra Navale 1984. The mount can carry either the KBA gun (data given) or the more powerful KBB of the Sea Zenith. In a low-recoil version, KBA can also be used as a helicopter gun.

The KBA gun can also be carried in a GBM-A01 single manual mount; Oerlikon describes GBM-A01 as the most powerful available manually operated gun mount. Ammunition capacity is 140 rounds (two 70-round boxes), and elevation limits are +55/−10 deg. Cyclic rate is reduced to 570 rounds/min. Total weight, including ammunition, is 600 kg (1320 lbs). The boxes can be enlarged to carry 100 rounds each. This mount is no longer in production.

◆ Oerlikon 20 mm (Type GAD-A0A)

Caliber: 20 mm/85 **Rate of Fire:** 1000 rnds/min
Muzzle Velocity: 1100–1200 m/sec (3600–3940 ft/sec)
Elevation/Depression: +70/−12 deg
Ammunition Capacity: 100 rnds
Weight: 1055 kg including ammunition (2325 lbs)
Working Circle: radius 2755 mm (108.5 in)

This turreted belt-fed 20-mm one-man cannon (Type KAA, formerly known as 204GK) was designed for patrol craft, e.g., the Austrian Danube gunboat. GAD-A0A was manufactured under license by BMARC, reportedly for a Commonwealth customer. The mount probably dates from the late 1960s, BMARC announcing its version in 1977.

◆ Oerlikon 20 mm (Type GAM-B01)

Caliber: 20 mm/85 **Rate of Fire:** 1000 rnds/min
Muzzle Velocity: 1050 m/sec (3440 ft/sec)
Maximum Range: 2000 m (2200 yds)
Elevation/Depression: +55/−10 deg
Ammunition Capacity: 200 rnds
Weight: 92 kg without ammunition (90 kg of ammunition) (203/198 lbs)

Oerlikon 20-mm single mount as selected by the Royal Navy (GAM-B01). (Oerlikon)

This manual mount carries a KAA cannon. Arming many fast attack craft, the 20-mm cannon is mounted on board most British warships as a result of the Falklands emergency. This cannon is manufactured in Britain by BMARC under the designation A41/820. The Royal Navy uses the GAM-B01 designation.

This cannon is essentially equivalent to the World War II Oerlikon 20-mm gun, with a higher muzzle velocity.

◆ Oerlikon 20 mm (Type GAM-C01)

Caliber: 20 mm/95 **Rate of Fire:** 900 rnds/min
Muzzle Velocity: 1050–1150 m/sec (3440–3770 ft/sec)
Elevation/Depression: +55/−10 deg
Ammunition Capacity: 200 rnds

This weapon is very similar to GAM-B01 but is a Hispano-Suiza 820 (now designated KAD-B13-3 by Oerlikon). Like the other mount, GAM-C01 was manufactured by BMARC as well as by Oerlikon itself.

◆ Oerlikon 20 mm (Type A41A)

Caliber: 20 mm **Rate of Fire:** 800 rnds/min
Muzzle Velocity: 835 m/sec (2740 ft/sec)
Elevation/Depression: +50/−10 deg
Ammunition Capacity: 58 rnds
Weight: 225 kg (496 lbs)
Working Circle: 1.7 m (66.9 inches)

Type A41A, with its ammunition drum, is the closest current equivalent to the World War II Oerlikon. The other current Oerlikons are belt-fed from a rectangular box on the front of the mount.

The gun is the Hispano-Suiza HS804, originally designed for aircraft use and having, therefore, a very low recoil force. A41A was dropped from the Oerlikon line but revived about 1980 because some customers liked its simplicity, ease of handling, and reliability.

This weapon has been manufactured both by Oerlikon and by BMARC.

◆ Oerlikon (Old Type)

See the U.S. entries below for details of typical World War II Oerlikon 20-mm cannon, which are still used by many navies.

USSR

◆ 6 in (B-38)

Caliber: 6 in/57 (50-kg shell)
Muzzle Velocity: 915 m/sec (3000 ft/sec)
Maximum Rate of Fire: 4–5 rnds/min/barrel
Elevation/Depression: +50/−5 deg
Maximum Range: 27,000 m (effective to 18,000 m) (29,500/19,700 yds)
Weight: approx 180 tons

B-38 is the triple-mounted gun on board *Sverdlov*-class cruisers and is a pre–World War II design. The barrels can be elevated and fired separately, and the weapon is credited with limited antiaircraft capability in barrage fire. However, B-38 is more properly a dedicated surface-to-surface weapon. Control is by optical Long Ears director (carrying two 8-mm [26.2-ft] rangefinders) with an associated Top Bow radar. Each superfiring turret was originally fitted with an Egg Cup range-only radar for local control, although many of these radars have since been removed. This gun is often credited with the ability to fire a nuclear shell.

The Soviet designation, B-38, reflects the prewar origin of the weapon.

◆ 130 mm/70

Muzzle Velocity: 1000 m/sec
Maximum Rate of Fire: 65 rnds/min/mount
Maximum Range: about 28,000 m
Elevation/Depression: +85/−15 deg

This fully automatic dual-purpose weapon was introduced in the *Sovremmennyy* class and is also mounted on board *Slava*-class cruisers and the *Frunze*. 130/70 may be triaxially stabilized. The barrels are liquid-cooled.

The associated fire-control radar is Kite Screech.

130/70 twin mount on board a *Sovremennyy*-class destroyer. (*Sea Power*)

◆ 130 mm/58

Caliber: 5.1 in/58 (33.5-kg shell with 20-kg cartridge)
Rate of Fire: 15 rnds/min/barrel (max)
Muzzle Velocity: 945 m/sec (3100 ft/sec)
Maximum Range: 28,000 m (surface); 16–18 thousand (effective) (30,600/17,500–19,700 yds)
Elevation/Depression: +85/−5 deg **Weight:** approx 60 tons

Twin 130/58 mount on board a Chinese Luda-class destroyer. (U.S. Naval Institute)

This standard postwar dual-purpose semiautomatic gun is installed on Kotlin-class destroyers. Triaxially stabilized, the gun is probably identical to the M-46 coast-defense weapon, which was later used for antiaircraft fire (M-55) and as a field gun (M-54). The naval gun is designated 56-SM, and the mount may have been derived from the wartime German 128-mm fully stabilized antiaircraft weapon. This gun and mount are currently manufactured in China (PRC), the Chinese version differing from the Soviet by lacking mechanical cross-level stabilization; the edges of the Chinese gunhouse are rounded, and the gun lacks the range-only radar of Soviet mounts.

The associated fire-control radars are Sun Visor and Post Lamp or Half Bow (Wasp Head director). All mounts originally incorporated Egg Cup range-only radars, but they have gradually been discarded.

◆ 130 mm/50

Caliber: 5.1 in (33.4-kg [73.6-lbs] shell)
Rate of Fire: 6–8 rnds/min/barrel
Muzzle Velocity: 870 m/sec (2854 ft/sec)
Maximum Range: 24,000 m (effective to 14–15 thousand) (26,300/15,300–16,400 yds)
Elevation/Depression: +40/−5
Weight: 35 tons without ammunition (single mounting: 12 tons)

Twin 130/50 gun mount on board a *Skoryy*-class destroyer. The masthead radars are Top Bow and, above it, High Sieve. (Skyfotos)

This obsolescent pre–World War II, semiautomatic twin-mount design survives on board *Skoryy*-class destroyers. Fire control is by Four Eyes optical director and Top Bow, Half Bow, or Post Lamp radar. Reportedly the gun was derived from the Vickers semiautomatic 5.1-in/55 VSM Mk "B" delivered before World War I for Russian cruisers and destroyers. In the 50-caliber version, as introduced about 1936, the gun had a loose liner and a horizontally sliding breech block.

The Soviet designation for the mount is B13-2C. It has 10-mm (0.4-in) protection to the gunhouse.

A single-barrel open-mount version of this gun survives on board four Chinese *Gordy*-class destroyers transferred by the Soviet Union in 1954–55. The PRC mounts are controlled by Cylinder Head directors without radars. Elevation limits for the single mount are +45/−10 deg. This gun is widely used for coast defense in the PRC, and possibly also in the Soviet Union.

◆ 115 mm

Caliber: 115 mm/55
Muzzle Velocity: 780 m/sec (HE-frag shells) (2560 ft/sec)
Maximum Rate of Fire: 4 rnds/min
Elevation/Depression: +17/−4 deg
Maximum Range: 4800 m (5250 yds)

This tank gun is installed in Yaz-class river monitors. Figures above are for the U-5 TS gun as carried by the T-62 tank.

♦ 100 mm/70

Caliber: 3.9 in (16-kg (35.2-lb) shell)
Rate of Fire: 15–18 rnds/min/barrel
Muzzle Velocity: 915 m/sec (3000 ft/sec)
Maximum Range: 20,000 m surface; 8000–9000 m (effective AA) (21,900/8700–9800 yds)
Elevation/Depression: +85/−15 deg   **Weight:** approx 40 tons

100/70 is the triaxially stabilized mount of *Sverdlov*-class cruisers. Some mounts incorporate Egg Cup range-only radars (now being removed) for local control. The associated director is Round Top (stabilized) with Sun Visor (tracker) and/or Top Bow or Post Lamp. This mount resembles the prewar German triaxially stabilized 105 mm/65, in which the guns elevated through the roof of the mount.

♦ 100 mm

100-mm guns on the cruiser *Kirov*. (U.S. Navy)

Single 100-mm gun. (*Sea Power*)

Caliber: 100 mm/70   **Rate of Fire:** 80 rnds/min
Maximum Range: 15,000 m (effective range 8,000 m) (16,400/8700 yds)

This is the automatic single-barreled water-cooled mount on *Kirov, Udaloy* class, and Krivak-II and -III.

♦ 100 mm/56

Caliber: 3.9 in/56 (15.6-kg shell, 28-kg fixed rnd) (34.4/62 lbs)
Rate of Fire: 15 rnds/min
Muzzle Velocity: 900 m/sec (2950 ft/sec)
Maximum Range: 16,000 m (effective range 10,000 m) (17,500/10,900 yds)
Elevation/Depression: +85/−5 deg
Weight: 13.5 tons (single mount)

This obsolescent single shielded mount is found on Riga-class frigates and Don-class submarine tenders. 100/56 was later manufactured in China. The original maximum elevation was 40 degrees. This mount was formerly used as a secondary battery for cruisers and was modernized in 1947. Electrically driven, the gun can fire in automatic, local, or manual modes. The breech is a horizontal sliding block. A twin version was designed about 1940 for the abortive Soviet battleship program. China now manufactures an autoloading twin version (see above).

The Soviet designation for the single mount is Bu-34. The associated director is Wasp Head with (in a few PRC ships) a Rice Lamp radar. Older Soviet ships used Cylinder Head to control this gun.

♦ 85 mm

Caliber: 85 mm/52 (9.6-kg shell, 13-kg fixed round) (20.9/28.7 lbs)
Rate of Fire: 10 rnds/min/barrel
Muzzle Velocity: 850 m/sec (2785 ft/sec)
Maximum Range: 15,000 m (effective range 8–9 thousand surface, 6000 m air) (16,400/8700–9800 yds)
Elevation/Depression: +75/−5 deg (maximum 85 deg in single version)
Weight: 5.5 tons (single)

This obsolescent twin mount survives on unmodified *Skoryy*-class destroyers. A single mount (maximum elevation 85 deg, elevation rate 8 deg/sec) is used by the PRC and other communist navies, arming smaller craft such as *Kronstadt*-type subchasers. The reported Soviet designation is 90K (twin mount HAM 39-3).

The modernized single mount (in use since 1948) is manually driven under local control. The twin mount is electrically driven; ammunition supply through the mount limits elevation to 75 degrees.

(*Below*) The Soviet 100-mm/56 mounted on board a Riga-class frigate, May 1984. The director is a Wasp Head, carrying a Sun Visor radar; and the main air-search radar is Slim Net. The guns aft are twin 37 mm, comparable to the old U.S. twin 40-mm Bofors. There are four torpedo decoys (of two types) on the fantail. The rocket launchers are RBU 2500s. (U.S. Navy)

(*Above*) Twin 76.2/60 guns arm this Mirka-class ASW corvette. There are torpedo decoys stowed on deck aft, four RBU-6000 rocket launchers, and 40-cm torpedo tubes. (U.S. Naval Institute)

◆ 76.2 mm/60

Caliber: 3 in (6.8-kg shell, 16-kg fixed round) (15/35 lbs)
Rate of Fire: 45 rnds/min/barrel
Muzzle Velocity: 900 m/sec (2950 ft/sec)
Maximum Range: 15,000 m (effective at 11,000 m; effective for antiaircraft at 6–7 thousand m)
Elevation/Depression: +85 deg
Ammunition Capacity: 43 (per barrel)
Weight: approx 25 tons (rotating mass)

Two Yaz-class gunboats, probably on the Amur, show their tank-type 76.2-mm guns. The guns aft are machine guns; later ships of this type have the standard twin 25-mm (over and under) mount. (TASS via SOVFOTO)

A Tarantul-class missile boat of the Soviet Baltic Fleet fires her single 76.2-mm gun. The radome atop her mast is Light Bulb, probably a missile data link. Below it is a Bass Tilt fire-control radar, and the big radome is Band Stand. The missiles are SS-N-2Cs. (TASS via SOVFOTO)

The caliber is 3 inches, not 76 mm. This weapon is installed on board Kara- and Kynda-class cruisers; Kashin-class destroyers; Krivak-I–, Koni-, Petya-, and Mirka-class frigates; *Smoln'yy*-class training ships; and *Ivan Susanin*–class icebreakers. The 76.2/60 was introduced in 1961. The mount is semiautomatic, like the U.S. twin 3 in/50; rounds are hoisted 43 at a time (per barrel) into the gunhouse. The gun is not water-cooled, but standard practice is to use a fire hose to cool down the barrel after an engagement. The turret has an unusually deep cleft, so that the guns can be mounted aft of the center of the trunnion, for a high angle of elevation. The associated fire-control radars are Hawk Screech and Owl Screech.

♦ 76.2 mm/60 Single Mount

Caliber: 3 in/60 **Rate of Fire:** 120 rnds/min
Maximum Range: 14,000 m surface; 6–7 thousand m (air target) (15,300/6600–7700 yds) **Elevation/Depression:** +85 deg

This automatic single mount, with on-mount crew, is found on Grisha-V– and Parchim-II–class light frigates; Nanuchka-III–, Pauk-, and Tarantul-class corvettes; Matka-class missile hydrofoils; and the one Slepen-class patrol boat.

The associated fire-control radar is Bass Tilt.

♦ 76.2 mm/55 Single Mount

Caliber: 3 in/55 (6.6-kg shell, 11.2-kg fixed round) (14.6/24.7 lbs)
Rate of Fire: 17–20 rnds/min
Muzzle Velocity: 815 m/sec (2675 ft/sec)
Maximum Range: 13,500 m (14,600 yds)
Elevation/Depression: +85 deg **Weight:** approx 5 tons

This weapon was introduced in the Soviet Navy in 1936 but is now used only by North Korea. The shield is similar to that of the Soviet 85-mm gun (90K), and the 76.2 Single Mount uses a vertical sliding-block breech.

♦ 76.2 mm/48 Single Mount

Caliber: 76.2 mm/48
Muzzle Velocity: 680 m/sec (2230 ft/sec) (HE shell)
Maximum Rate of Fire: 4–6 rnds/min (claimed 15 rnds/min max)
Elevation/Depression: +30/–4 deg
Maximum Range: about 800 m effective range, point-blank (about 870 yds)

The PT-76 tank turret gun (D-56TM) is found in Shmel-class river monitors.

♦ 57 mm (twin automatic mount)

Caliber: 57 mm/80 (2.7-kg shell, 5-kg fixed round) (6/11 lbs)
Rate of Fire: 120 rnds/min/barrel
Muzzle Velocity: 1000 m/sec (3280 ft/sec)

Twin automatic 57-mm guns on board a *Moskva*-class helicopter carrier, with a Head Lights SA-N-3 fire-control radar visible above the bridge. The small navigational radar below it is Don-2. (U.S. Navy)

Maximum Range: 12 km horizontal, 6.7 km vertical (13,100 yds/ 22,000 ft); effective ranges about 9000 m horizontal, 5–6 thousand m vertical (9800 yds/16,400–19,700 ft)
Elevation/Depression: +90/–10 deg
Weight: 25 tons (without ammunition)

This fully automatic mount is found on *Moskva*, Kresta-I and -II, Poti, Grisha, Nanuchka-I, Turya, Ropucha, Urga classes, etc. The barrels are water-cooled. The 57 mm first entered service in 1963. Unlike the various forms of ZIF-31B, this mount is fully enclosed, with a metal shield; ammunition supply is presumably fully automatic. Control is generally by a Muff Cob radar director. In some classes, later units have the newer 76.2 mm/60 in place of this weapon.

The Soviet designation is ZIF-72 (the Indian Navy reports an AK-257 designation for the mount on its frigate *Ganga*).

57 mm/80 Soviet-type twin mount on board the Indian frigate *Ganga*. The mount is designated AK-725 in Indian service. (*Ships of the World*)

♦ 57-mm Antiaircraft Gun

Caliber: 57 mm/70 (2.8-kg shell, 6.3–6.6-kg round) (6.2/13.9– 14.5 lbs) **Rate of Fire:** 120 rnds/min/gun
Muzzle Velocity: 1020 m/sec (3350 ft/sec)
Maximum Range: 4500 m vertical (14,700 ft)
Training Rate: 30 deg/sec (elevation 25 deg/sec)
Elevation/Depression: +90/0 deg
Weight: 28,000 kg quadruple mount; 6000 kg single mount; 14,500 kg twin mount (61,700/13,200/32,000 lbs)

Quadruple 57-mm guns on board a Krupny-class missile destroyer. The mast radomes are presumably a pair of Top Hat jammers with the associated Bell-series ESM above. (U.S. Navy)

This weapon exists in single (e.g., modified *Skoryy* class), twin, and quadruple (Kanin, Kildin classes) forms. In the quadruple mount the guns are in superimposed pairs. This weapon entered service in 1958 and was a navalized version of the

57-mm/70 M-50 used by the Soviet Army. That gun in turn was developed from a 55-mm antiaircraft gun under development in Germany late in the Second World War.

Like earlier Soviet naval antiaircraft guns, this one loads from clips. Heating and clip-feeding would probably limit its effective rate of fire to 90 rounds/min. The associated fire-control radar is Muff Cob.

The Soviet designation is ZIF-31B.

The PRC Navy uses a water-cooled version of this weapon, designated Type 76. Muzzle velocity is 1000 m/sec (3280 ft/sec), and maximum horizontal and vertical ranges are 15,000 and 10,000 m. Rate of fire is 140–160 rounds/min, and elevation limits are +85/−5 deg. Maximum laying speeds are 25 deg/sec both in train and in elevation, but the mount can sweep (i.e., can move less precisely) at 40 deg/sec both in train and in elevation. Total mount weight is 10,500 kg (23,140 lbs). No working circle data are available, but the mount's length is 6.583 m and width is 3.36 m (height is 2.264 m).

◆ 45 mm

Caliber: 45 mm/85 (2.2-kg shell)
Rate of Fire: 300 rnds/min/mount
Muzzle Velocity: 900 m/sec (2950 ft/sec)
Maximum Range: 4000 m effective (4400 yds)
Elevation/Depression: +90/0 deg **Weight:** 12 tons

This obsolescent quadruple-mounted gun is found in Sam Kotlin, Kotlin, and one modernized Kotlin. Single barrels are mounted on board some Sasha-type minesweepers. This weapon entered service about 1952–53 and can be recognized by the prominent muzzle flash hider, similar to that of a Bofors 40-mm gun.

The quadruple mounts are controlled by Hawk Screech radars.

◆ 37 mm

Caliber: 37 mm/63 (0.74-kg shell, 1.8-kg round) (1.6/4.0 lbs)
Rate of Fire: 160 rnds/min/gun twin; 130 rnds/min/gun single)
Muzzle Velocity: 880 m/sec (2890 ft/sec)
Maximum Range: 9500 m (10,400 yds)
Training Rate: 20 deg/sec (elevation 15 deg/sec); powered mounts
Elevation/Depression: +85/0 deg
Ammunition Capacity: 5-round clips
Weight: 6170 lbs single mount, 8375 lbs twin mount

Soviet single air-cooled 37-mm/63 gun. (TASS from SOVFOTO)

This obsolescent prewar weapon is found in twin mounts on board some *Sverdlov*-class cruisers, *Skoryy*-class destroyers, Riga-class frigates, and T-43–class minesweepers. There was also a single mount, now extinct in Soviet service. The single guns were air-cooled, with the usual Bofors-type recoil springs surrounding the bases, and barrels had to be changed after about 100 rounds. The twin mount, introduced in 1948, is similar in layout to the standard U.S. twin 40 mm of the time, with liquid-cooled guns. Loading is by five-round clip. The Soviet designations are 70-K for the original single mount, V-11M for the initial production twin naval mount, and V-47M for later twin mounts with water-cooled barrels. It appears that V-47M was the widely used postwar version. A quadruple version was begun in 1939–40 but appears not to have entered service.

This gun is derived from a Bofors 25-mm gun of 1933, sold to the Soviet Union some years later. Because the 25-mm gun was very similar in design to the Bofors 40 mm of 1934 (the ancestor of the standard World War II 40-mm gun), the 37 mm is very similar to the Bofors 40 mm/60, with different ancestry. The 37 mm fires ammunition derived from the Colt-Browning 37 mm, which was inferior to the contemporary Bofors 40-mm round. This weapon was developed in preference to a turreted twin 45-mm automatic gun, on which work began in 1937–38.

This mounting is standard in the PRC Navy in both single and twin mounts. The mount was produced in China, but without the cross-stabilization standard in many Soviet mounts.

Soviet twin liquid-cooled 37 mm/63. (TASS from SOVFOTO)

◆ 30-mm Gatling

Caliber: 30 mm/65
Rate of Fire: 3000 rnds/min/mount (probably 1000 rnds/min effective rate)
Muzzle Velocity: 1000 m/sec (3280 ft/sec)
Maximum Range: 2500 m (maximum altitude probably 500–600 m) (2700 yds; 1640–1970 ft)
Elevation/Depression: +90/−10 deg

This six-barreled Gatling gun has a mount similar to that of the twin 30-mm weapon. The 30-mm Gatling, generally controlled by Bass Tilt or by a remote Kolonka-II visual director, is the standard current Soviet close-in defensive weapon.

The designation ADMG-630, which frequently appears, is a NATO rather than a Soviet name (Air-Defense Machine Gun 6 × 30). The Soviets probably call the gun AK 630. It first appeared in the summer of 1970.

30-mm Gatling guns on board a Kresta-II–class cruiser, with two Side Globe jammers visible to the left; and an optical sight (presumably equivalent to the old U.S. Mk 51) is the tub to the right of the jammers. (U.S. Naval Institute)

◆ New Close-In Weapons System

The cruiser *Kalinin*, the third unit of the *Kirov* class, completed in 1989, carries a new close-in weapon in place of the AK 630 of earlier units of this type. Each mounting carries a pair of guns under paired missile launchers. The missiles are paired vertically or horizontally, in different mountings; these alternatives are probably being compared to see which provides the least mutual interference.

A large radar antenna occupies the center of the mount, flanked on the right by a similar but smaller antenna. Each is much higher than it is wide, producing a beam narrower in the vertical than in the horizontal. That configuration might be extremely desirable for a system intended to detect and track low-flying missiles, postponing the onset of multipath problems. The combination of very similar large and small radar antennas in Soviet naval practice is generally associated with command guidance, and in this case there is a small dish (presumably to transmit the commands) between the two main radars. The left side of the mounting carries what appears to be an electro-optical device, possibly a television tracker or a laser, and there are small radomes on the lower part of the mounting. Other navies find a television or IR tracker very useful in avoiding multipath problems when engaging low-altitude targets (such as sea-skimmers).

The combination of guns with missiles on the same mount recalls the recently introduced Soviet Army's 2S6 self-propelled antiaircraft weapon, which appeared in 1986 and is now replacing the earlier ZSU 23-4 quadruple mount. The 2S6 carries a combination of SA-19 missiles (which may be laser-guided) and a pair of new 30-mm cannon, part of a new family of weapons that includes the guns on board the Hind-E attack helicopter, the Su-25 Frogfoot ground-attack fighter, the MiG-29, and the Su-27 Flanker. These are all single-barreled guns, the barrel also supporting a tube for cooling and a thick cable for a muzzle reference (muzzle-velocity measurement) system. These weapons, therefore, look like three-barreled Gatlings, which they are not. The new naval system differs substantially from the army's 2S6 (which resembles the German Gephard antiaircraft tank with missiles added), and its guns appear to be shorter. However, Soviet standardization practice suggests that all of these guns are probably part of the same family.

No NATO designation for the *Kalinin* system has been published.

◆ 30 mm twin mount (AK 230)

Caliber: 30 mm/65 (0.54-kg shell, 1.0-kg round) (1.2/2.2 lbs)
Rate of Fire: approx 1050 rnds/min/barrel (effective rate 200–240)
Muzzle Velocity: 1050 m/sec (3440 ft/sec)
Maximum Range: 4000 m (4400 yds)
Training Rate: 70 deg/sec (elevation 55 deg/sec)
Elevation/Depression: +100 deg
Ammunition Capacity: 100 ready use, 600 magazine
Weight: 3.5 tonnes without ammunition (7715 lbs)

30-mm Twin Mount (AK 230). (*Sea Power*)

Soviet-type twin 30-mm gun mount on board the Indian frigate *Ganga*. (*Ships of the World*)

This widely used light weapon is widely exported. The unmanned mount is fully enclosed, stabilized, and power-driven. The gun tubes are liquid-cooled, and the guns are gas-operated. This mount is normally controlled by a Drum Tilt radar or by a remote Kolonka-I optical director. The gun is a revolver, with a four-round rotating breech.

AK 230 is the Soviet designation. This weapon appeared in 1959, as a successor to the earlier twin 25 mm. AK 230 is still in production, primarily for export.

This weapon is produced in the PRC under the designation Type 69. Elevation limits of this version are +87/−12 degrees, and the mount trains at 70 deg/sec and elevates at 50 deg/sec. Total weight is 1800 kg (3967 lbs): the weight figure above may include ammunition. Overall dimensions: 3.110 × 2.100 × 1.462 m.

◆ 25 mm twin mount

Caliber: 25 mm/60 (0.25-kg shell, 0.7-kg round) (0.55/1.5 lbs)
Rate of Fire: 450 rnds/min; effective rate 270–300 rnds/min (also given as 150–225 rnds/min/barrel)
Muzzle Velocity: 910 m/sec (2980 ft/sec)
Maximum Range: 3000 m; effective range 2300 m (3300/2500 yds)
Training Rate: 40 deg/sec (elevation 70 deg/sec) under hydraulic power (manual rates are 15 and 25 deg/sec, respectively)
Elevation/Depression: +83/−10 deg
Ammunition Capacity: 130 rnds **Weight:** 1.5 tons

Twin 25-mm antiaircraft guns on board a P-6–type motor torpedo boat, about 1962. (TASS from SOVFOTO)

Widely used for light craft, this weapon consists of two superimposed guns, with an on-mount optical sight. For example, this weapon arms Komar-class missile boats. It is still manufactured in China (PRC). The two machine guns are belt-fed from boxes on the left side of the mount, the gunner sitting on the right side. Guns are air-cooled, with prominent recoil springs around the bases. Normally, coupled 65-round belts are used, but the weapons can also be fed from 7-round clips.

This weapon is a Soviet version of the Bofors 25 mm, from which the 37-mm antiaircraft gun was developed. The Loginov design bureau, which was responsible for both weapons, actually concentrated on the 37-mm version (which entered production in 1939), and only in 1939 began to adapt the 25-mm version (Model 1940). Production began in September 1941. The twin-barreled naval version (2M-8) entered service in 1952; it was a heavily redesigned derivative of the army gun. The designation 2M-3 110PM has also been reported for this weapon.

The twin 30-mm mount (AK 230) was developed to replace this gun.

This weapon is produced in the PRC under the designation Type 61. The Chinese version has a maximum elevation of 85 degrees. Total weight, including ammunition (65 rounds per gun), is 1735 kg (3824 lbs); overall length (at zero elevation) is 2.810 m, and maximum width is 1.974 m.

◆ 23-mm Machine Gun

Caliber: 23 mm/87   **Rate of Fire:** 1600 rnds/min/barrel
Muzzle Velocity: 970 m/sec (3180 ft/sec)
Maximum Elevation/Depression: +90 deg
Maximum Range: 3000 m (maximum altitude 2000 m) (3300 yds; 6600 ft)

This weapon appeared on board Pchela-class border patrol hydrofoils, all now retired, in a twin enclosed turret that resembles that of AK 230. This machine gun may survive on board river gunboats. It was introduced in 1965.

◆ ZU-23

Caliber: 23 mm/81
Rate of Fire: 1000 rnds/min/barrel (cyclic); effective rate 200 rnds/min/barrel
Ready-use Ammunition: 50 rnds/gun (box magazine)
Muzzle Velocity: 970 m/sec (3180 ft/sec)
Maximum Elevation/Depression: +90/−10 deg
Maximum Range: 7000 m; effective range 2800 m (7700/3000 yds)
Training Rate: Manual   **Weight:** 893 kg (1968 lbs)

This twin-barreled army weapon is used by both the East German (e.g., on board *Libelle*-class light torpedo boats) and Polish (e.g., on board some *Krogulec*-class minesweepers) Navies. It has replaced the Sea Cat launcher on board Iranian *Saam*-class frigates. The Indian government armed some of its merchant ships with this weapon during the Iran-Iraq War. The barrels are air-cooled.

◆ 14.5-mm Machine Gun

Caliber: 14.5 mm/93   **Rate of Fire:** 600 rnds/min/barrel
Ready-use Ammunition: 150 rnds/gun (linked belt)
Muzzle Velocity: 1000 m/sec (3280 ft/sec)
Maximum Elevation/Depression: +90/−5 deg
Maximum Range: 7000 m (7700 yds)

Twin 14.5-mm machine guns forward, on board a Pchela-class patrol boat. Although this class has been discarded, the same mount is used on board the replacement Zhuk class. The radar is Pot Drum. (U.S. Naval Institute)

This light antiaircraft mount is no longer in widespread Soviet service but has been license-produced in China and serves on board Chinese Riga-class frigates, *Kronstadt*-type patrol vessels, *Huchuan*-class torpedo boats, and *T-43*–type minesweepers. This gun may no longer be in production. At one time it was described as a 12.7-mm machine gun; it replaced the earlier Degtyarev DHSK 38 12.7-mm gun on a one-for-one basis, beginning some time after 1945. The earlier gun used a 50-round metal belt and fired 300–500 rounds/min (0.043-kg bullets, muzzle velocity 814 m/sec [2671 ft/sec]).

The Soviet designation is 2M-7. In Soviet-made mounts the guns are superposed. The Chinese build a version in which the guns are side by side, e.g., in Huchuan-class hydrofoil torpedo boats. The Chinese version has been exported to Romania.

The PRC version is designated Type 82. It fires API (990 m/sec muzzle velocity) and API-T (tracer) (1000 m/sec) rounds. Effective range against air targets is 2000 m; against surface targets, 2200 m. Effective rate of fire is 150 rounds/min per gun. Elevation limits are +85/−10 degrees. Working circle radius is 1.757 m (69.2 inches). Total weight, without ammunition, is 600 kg (1320 lbs). Magazine capacity is 150 rounds.

There is also a modern twin enclosed 14.5-mm machine gun, in Zhuk-class patrol boats, which have been widely exported.

UNITED KINGDOM

◆ 4.5-in Mk 5

Caliber: 4.5 in/45 (114 mm; 55-lb projectile)
Rate of Fire: 14 rnds/min (firing cycle 4.3 sec)
Muzzle Velocity: 2460 ft/sec   **Maximum Range:** 20,750 yds
Training Rate: 20 deg/sec (elevation 20 deg/sec)
Elevation: +55 deg
Ammunition Capacity: none on mount
Weight: 33,562 lbs   **Working Circle:** 188-in radius

This single open mount survives on board "Tribal"-class frigates in the Indonesian Navy and on board the Malaysian *Rah-*

(*Above*) A "Tribal"-class frigate displays her 4.5-in Mk-5 gun, forward. The director is MRS 3, carrying a Type-903 radar. This particular ship, HMS *Mohawk*, no longer exists, but three sisters survive in the Indonesian Navy. (HMS Excellent)

mat. No examples of the earlier British destroyers with single guns survive. The mounting itself was a converted 4.7-in CP XXII.

The rates of train and elevation listed above apply to the gun when it is under power control. The gun can also train and elevate under manual control, at slower rates.

◆ 4.5-in Mk 6

>**Caliber:** 4.5 in/45 (55-lb projectile, 30–33-lb cartridge)
>**Rate of Fire:** 10–12 rnds/min/barrel (theoretical rate 24 rnds/min/barrel)
>**Muzzle Velocity:** 2460 ft/sec (derated to 2350 ft/sec in practice)
>**Maximum Range:** 20,000 yds (maximum altitude 19,700 ft)
>**Training Rate:** 25 deg/sec (elevation 25 deg/sec)
>**Elevation/Depression:** +80/−15 deg
>**Ammunition Capacity:** 80 shells, 45 cartridges in gun bay
>**Weight:** 98,560 lbs (revolving mass)
>**Working Circle:** 218 in (radius)

This postwar, enclosed semiautomatic twin mount is found on many frigates and on ex-British "County"-class destroyers now transferred to other navies. At the end of 1988, only two of these mounts survived in Royal Navy service, on board the frigates *Achilles* and *Ariadne*. This weapon is roughly equivalent to abortive U.S. 5-in/54 semiautomatic twin mounts designed at the end of World War II, the rate of fire being somewhat slower. The very high rate of fire initially expected could not be realized in practice because the power rammer was unsuccessful; the guns had to be hand-loaded. A figure of 18 rounds/min/gun was sometimes achieved.

Unlike previous types, this gun was designed from the outset for automatic aiming and for a high rate of fire. The weapon had many novel features, notably a loading tray, with which the gun recoils, and a rammer, which is pushed clear of the gun's axis by the vertically closing breechblock. Welding was used extensively for the first time in British gun-mount construction. The training mass was entirely supported on a cantilevered structure that provided a circular gun bay clear of obstructions, for much easier transfer of ammunition to the revolving structure. This mounting was also unusual in using hydraulic rams for elevation. Ammunition was supplied by two magazines; the revolving structure had one cartridge hoist and two shell hoists per gun, so that two types of ammunition could be used. The gunhouse plating is 0.375 inches thick.

The only surviving examples of the earlier twin Mk 4 are two mounts on board the Iranian destroyer *Damavand* and two on board the Pakistani *Badr*, the sole surviving examples of the "Battle" class. This mounting weighed 46.3 tons, 11.2 tons of which were accounted for by a 0.5-in gunhouse. Elevation limits were +80/−5 deg.

Mk 7 would have been similar to Mk 6, for the *Malta*-class carriers and the *Lion*-class battleships, all of which were canceled at the end of World War II.

◆ 4.5-in Mk 8

>**Caliber:** 4.5 in/55 (46-lb HE shell, complete round 80.5 lbs)
>**Rate of Fire:** 25 rnds/min   **Muzzle Velocity:** 2850 ft/sec
>**Maximum Range:** 24,000 yds
>**Training Rate:** 40 deg/sec (elevation 40 deg/sec)
>**Elevation/Depression:** +55/−10 deg
>**Ammunition Capacity:** 16 rnds
>**Weight:** 25.75 tons total (rotating mass 15.1 tons)
>**Working Circle:** radius 19 ft 11 in

This modern British unmanned single 4.5-in mount is installed on many current British frigates and destroyers. It is approximately equivalent to the U.S. 5-in/54 Mk 45, firing relatively slowly. The shield is fiberglass. Ready-service rounds are carried vertically, in an indexing feed ring, two spaces 180 degrees apart normally being kept free for special types of ammunition, such as star shell. Mk 8 can open fire in 10 seconds from the shut-down state. The developers considered rapid response more important than rapid rate of fire in self-defense against missiles, since each proximity-fuzed shell should be quite lethal, and since there would not, in any case, be much time for many rounds to hit. For the same reason, the gun is provided with a single multipurpose shell suitable for both air and surface action. Fuze mode is selected electronically just before the shell is rammed.

The gun itself was designed by the Royal Armament Research and Development Establishment (RARDE); modeled on the army's Abbot 105-mm howitzer, the gun has a muzzle brake and a fume extractor. The Royal Navy required that Mk 8 be able to sustain fire for 7.5 minutes (90 rounds). Water-cooling

(*Above*) The Thai frigate *Makut Rajakumarn* is shown in 1981, armed with two Vickers 4.5-in Mk-8 guns, controlled by a Signaal WM-22 forward, with a second fire-control radar aft for her Sea Cat missile. She has since been modernized, with a new air-search radar (in place of DA-05); the Sea Cat and its director were removed. The surface-search radar shown is a Decca 626. (Royal Australian Navy)

was rejected because it would have added too much weight, and the barrel had to be specially designed for sustained firing without cooling by water. Vickers designed the mounting.

It was reported in 1987 that the Royal Navy had shown some interest in a study of extended-range (base-bleed) ammunition, promising about 27-km range.

◆ **4-in Mk 19**

> **Caliber:** 4 in/45   **Rate of Fire:** 12 rnds/min/gun (firing cycle 5 secs)
> **Muzzle Velocity:** 2660 ft/sec   **Maximum Range:** 19,850 yds
> **Training Rate:** 20 deg/sec (elevation 20 deg/sec)
> **Elevation/Depression:** +80/−10 deg
> **Ammunition Capacity:** none on mount
> **Weight:** 17.8 tons   **Working Circle:** 141-in radius

One twin mount survives on board the Malaysian frigate *Hang Tuah*, and two similar guns arm the Egyptian sloop *Tariq*. Mk 19 was once an extremely common weapon. The two guns share a common cradle, but each fires separately, with a separate recoil system.

(*Below*) The Chilean destroyer *Almirante Riveros* shows the special Vickers 4-in guns manufactured for her. The radar at her masthead is SNW-12, with an SNW-20 slotted waveguide below it. She was later fitted with a Plessey AWS-1 aft but still retains the two Marconi radars forward. (Vickers)

Twin 4-inch gun. (Public Archives of Canada)

◆ **Vickers 4 in**

> **Caliber:** 4 in/62 (32-lb projectile)
> **Rate of Fire:** 50 rnds/min (service rate probably about 40)
> **Muzzle Velocity:** 2953 ft/sec
> **Maximum Range:** 18.5 km (maximum altitude about 12,000 m)
> **Elevation/Depression:** +85/−7 deg
> **Ammunition Capacity:** 56 rnds (two 28-rnd hoppers)
> **Weight:** 47,040 lbs

As originally conceived, this mount would have carried the same gun as the standard Mk 19, in a mounting similar to that of an abortive 5-in automatic gun designed by Vickers. The original weapon, developed from the army's new mobile 4-inch high-velocity antiaircraft gun, was proposed about 1953 for the projected (abortive) rearmament of the Argentine training cruiser *La Argentina,* and also for Peruvian and Chilean ships. Other potential buyers at this time were Israel and Venezuela, to use the gun either as the main battery of a 1200-ton escort or 2000-ton fast escort, or as the secondary battery of a 2600-ton destroyer also armed with 4.7-inch antiship guns.

The unusual feature of the mounting is that it loads through the trunnions, the shells being carried in two 28-round hoppers between the trunnions. The hoppers could be topped up to maintain a rate of about 30–40 rounds/min (Vickers claimed 50 rounds/min, but the DNO (Director of Naval Ordnance) of the day was skeptical). Weight, with the standard 45-caliber 4-inch barrel, was 19 tons empty (plus 1.6 tons of ammunition), and elevating limits were +85/−7 deg.

These guns arm the two *Almirante Rivero*–class Chilean destroyers and were being rehabilitated in Chile in 1987–88.

There was also a proposed 105-mm version, for the Argentine Navy; that version would have weighed 53,760 lbs and was rated at 40–46 rounds/min.

◆ 3-in Mk 6

Caliber: 3 in/70
Rate of Fire: 95–113 rnds/min/gun (designed for 120 rnds/min/gun) (15-lb shell) **Muzzle Velocity:** 3400 ft/sec
Maximum Range: 19,500 yds
Training Rate: 60 deg/sec (elevation 30 deg/sec)
Elevation/Depression: +90/−15 degrees
Ammunition Capacity: 161 rnds/gun (two hoppers per gun, 100 and 38 rounds, with others in the system); total 2000 rnds in the magazine
Weight: 83,150 lbs (revolving mass, including 34 rounds/gun)
Working Circle: radius 234 in

Twin 3-in mount Mk 6 on board the Canadian frigate *Chaudière.* (Nat. Def. Photograph Canada)

This mount was designed in Britain but survives only on board seven active Canadian frigates. Mk 6 used the same ammunition and the same gun tube as the U.S. twin 3 in/70 but was less ambitious in concept and, perhaps as a result, was much more successful. In the Royal Navy, Mk 6 was the intended main battery of the postwar frigates, but it was not ready in time, and the twin 4.5-inch Mk 6 was substituted.

The guns are water-cooled. There are two hoists on the nonrotating structure (25 rounds/min), and the hoists top up the hoppers that rotate with the guns.

◆ 40-mm Mounts

Caliber: 40 mm/56.3 (1.97-lb shell)
Rate of Fire: 120 rnds/min (140–150 with gun horizontal)
Muzzle Velocity: 2890 ft/sec
Maximum Range: 10,750 yds (but shells generally self-destruct at 3000–3500 yds)
Training Rate: 35 deg/sec (elevation 28 deg/sec; 35 deg/sec in Canadian-built mountings)
Elevation/Depression: +90/−15 deg (Mk 5)
Ammunition Capacity: twelve clips on mount (48 rnds); Mk 9 has six clips on the mount (plus the clips in the gun).
Weight: 6.397 tons

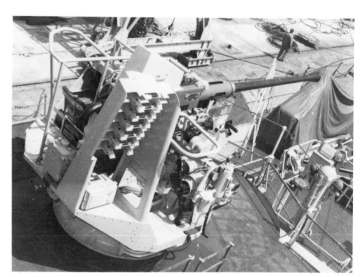

Standard British single 40-mm gun, probably Mk 7. The rack is for spare clips. (National Maritime Museum)

Single 40-mm mount Mk 9, on board a British minesweeper. (A. Wetback)

Data above apply to the Mk-5 twin power mount.

The Royal Navy still uses a few 40-mm Mk 7 and Mk 9 mounts, carrying the standard World War II 40-mm L60 gun (see the Swedish Bofors 40 mm/60 above for details). The Royal

Navy expected to adopt the postwar 40 mm/70 but bought Sea Cat missiles instead; the British Army did buy the L70 gun.

Mk 5 was the standard twin mount (water-cooled guns) with remote power control. There was also a Mk-6 sextuple mount, now extinct, the only British naval Bofors that did not use the standard gravity-feed clip. Instead, each gun had a 36-round ammunition tray operated by gun recoil.

Mk 7 is an adapted army single air-cooled mounting, with a light alloy structure and a splinter shield. Using one-man laying and a gyro sight, with a separate loader, Mk 7 is hydraulically driven, with the motor and pump on the revolving structure. Elevation rate is reported as 45 deg/sec, and total weight is about 3 tons. Mk 8 was an unsuccessful interim design with battery power. Mk 9 is a refurbished Mk 7 with electric rather than hydraulic drive. Mk 9 was used in the Falklands.

The Australian Maribyrnong Ordnance Factory remanufactures a modified Mk 7, designated 40/60AN, which has a much longer service lifetime between overhaul (demonstrated as 6 years, compared to 9–11 months for Mk 7). The Australian gun entered service about 1984. This mounting was designed specifically for the Australian *Fremantle* class patrol boat. Total weight is 1520 kg (3350 lbs). Elevation limits are +90/−5 degrees. Training rate is 40 deg/sec; elevation rate is 20 deg/sec. Existing Mk 7 mountings are converted by discarding old components, which are difficult to maintain, and by replacing them with modern power, hydraulic, and control systems. For example, the hydraulic power pack is fully enclosed for greater protection. The electrical box was relocated below decks.

The British version of the Bofors gun could accommodate two four-round clips (or ten rounds, with two loose between the clips), and it was claimed that a single loader could work fast enough for the gun to fire a burst of 24 rounds.

◆ 30-mm A32

    Caliber: 30 mm/75 (Type 831L cannon) (0.36-kg shell; 1.0-kg complete round) (0.8/2.2 lbs)
    Rate of Fire: 600 rnds/min/gun **Muzzle Velocity:** 3540 ft/sec
    Effective Range: 3300 yds (maximum 11,100 yds)
    Training Rate: 90 deg/sec (elevation 60 deg/sec)
    Elevation/Depression: +80/−15 deg
    Ammunition Capacity: A version: 160; B version 320
    Weight: 3740 lbs without ammo or gunner; ammo weight is 352 lbs (A) or 704 lbs (B) **Working Circle:** 8.25 ft (2.57 m)

This BMARC mount, for twin Hispano-Suiza guns, predated the twin Oerlikon that the company later marketed (BMARC was a Hispano-Suiza subsidiary, and Oerlikon later took over Hispano-Suiza). A32 is similar in overall configuration and was presumably adapted to the Oerlikon gun. The mount was designed in 1967, and two prototypes were produced for Finland (delivered 1968: one Series A, one Series B).

In the A version, the ready-service ammunition boxes elevate with the mount. In the B version they do not.

◆ 30 mm (Type GCM-A01)

    Caliber: 30 mm/75 **Rate of Fire:** 1300 rnds/min
    Muzzle Velocity: 1080 m/sec (3540 ft/sec)
    Maximum Range: 10,000 m (33,000 yds)
    Training Rate: 75 deg/sec (elevation 50 deg/sec)
    Elevation/Depression: +80/−15 deg
    Ammunition Capacity: 160 rnds/gun (A03-1: 160 or 250 rnds/gun; A03-2: 250 rnds/gun; A03-3: 320 rnds/gun)
    Weight: 2000 kg (A02); A03-1: 2150 kg; A03-2: 2050 kg; A03-3: 1900 kg (4410/4740/4520/4190 lbs)
    Working Circle: 2520 mm (99.2 in)

For this BMARC/Oerlikon project, Oerlikon provided the twin 30-mm guns and their new APDS ammunition, announced in 1975. The mount is gyro-stabilized and power-driven, with either local or remote control. The guns are twin 30-mm Type KCB cannon. BMARC (British Manufacture and Research Co.) was part of the Oerlikon-Buhrle Group, hence the use of Oerlikon guns as part of the weapon.

The original A01 version was introduced in 1968. A02 entered British naval service as an emergency close-in defense gun during the Falklands War, the Royal Navy buying eight of the

GCM-A02 version. The current version is A03. The version in the Brunei fast patrol craft built by Vosper Singapore in 1978 is GCM-B01, controlled by a Sperry Sea Archer 1.

BMARC also marketed the twin 35-mm Oerlikon gun (Type GDM-A; see the Swiss guns above).

30-mm GCM-A01 twin mount. (Oerlikon)

30-mm GCM-A01 twin mount. (A. Wetback)

◆ Laurence Scott LS-30B (DS 30)

    Caliber: 30 mm **Rate of Fire:** 650 rnds/min
    Muzzle Velocity: 1080 m/sec (3540 ft/sec)
    Training Rate: 55 deg/sec (elevation 55 deg/sec)
    Elevation/Depression: +65/−20 deg
    Ammunition Capacity: 160 rnds
    Weight: 1.2 tons (with ammunition)

LS-30B is a stabilized single mounting that carries the Oerlikon 30-mm KCB cannon. Twenty-five were ordered in September 1984 to arm "Duke"-class frigates and to replace some existing Bofors 40-mm/60 guns in Mk-7 and Mk-9 mounts, and the gun entered service in 1987. The mount was conceived as a gun adaptation of an existing optical director. Power-operated and gyro-stabilized, the gun is controlled by joystick. The original version, LS-30R, carried a 30-mm Rarden gun (as used on land) with a 21-round magazine. An alternative version, carrying a Mauser cannon, was designated LS-30F.

There were three versions of the basic mounting: Mk I, controlled locally by an operator with a joystick; Mk II, controlled remotely by the director; and Mk III, with an added digital predictor. The Rarden Mk I version was tested on board HMS *Londonderry* in 1981. Overall system dispersion was less than 3 mrad in sea-state 5, and in one trial a towed 2 square-meter target was hit 80 percent of the time at 1000–1300 m in poor visibility. This mount weighed 800 kg including gun, with a 2.2-m working circle (radius), and training/elevation velocities of 30/35 deg/sec; elevation limits were +70/−20 deg. The gun could fire a 6-round burst, or 21 rounds if an extra magazine was fitted.

This mount was redesignated DS 30 in 1986, the manufacturer having been renamed Defense Equipment and Systems, Ltd. The company offers versions of the basic mount armed with a variety of guns: DS 30B (30-mm Oerlikon KCB cannon), DS 30E (30-mm EBO-Mauser cannon), DS 30F (Mauser 173 Model F), and DS 30R (30-mm Rarden cannon). There is also a DS 25M carrying the U.S. M242 Bushmaster 25-mm cannon, a weapon also used by the U.S. Navy. As of 1987, DS 30E was being evaluated by the Greek Navy, and a NATO coast guard was evaluating the DS 25M. The Royal Navy uses DS 30B. Sea trials, on board the minesweeper *Cottesmore*, were completed at the end of October 1986.

DS 30B automatic cannon. (A. Wetback)

◆ L7A2

Caliber: 7.62 mm **Muzzle Velocity:** 838 m/sec
Maximum Rate of Fire: 625–750 rnds/min
Maximum Elevation/Depression: +45/−10 deg
Ammunition Load: 200 rnds **Maximum Range:** 1800 m
Weight: 10.9 kg (gun alone, empty)

L7A2 is the standard British light machine gun, and its role in the Royal Navy is broadly analogous to that of the U.S. 0.50. L7A2 serves as a policing weapon on board "Ton"-class minecraft, and the "Isles"- and "Castle"-class offshore-patrol vessels. It was also pintle-mounted on board larger ships, e.g., for close-in defense. The gun, which is a standard air-cooled infantry machine gun, can be mounted on a pedestal, a buffered tripod, or a bulwark pintle.

This gun is based on the Belgian FN MAG.

◆ GBN 155

Caliber: 155 mm/52 **Maximum Rate of Fire:** 12 rnds/min
Maximum Range: 24,000 m (26,200 yds)
Weight: 13,550 kg (29,860 lbs)

This modified 155-mm/52 gun-howitzer (GBT) was exhibited by VSEL (and later by the Royal Ordnance Factories (ROF)) at the RNEE 1983 and later shows, as a future naval gunfire support weapon that would use ammunition widely available for ground forces. This project lost much of its rationale when the Mk-8 4.5-inch gun was incorporated in the Type-23 frigate. However, in 1988 ROF is considering a joint venture with the U.S. company FMC to market 155-mm naval guns, perhaps using FMC's vertical loader.

◆ 105-mm Autonomous Patrol Gun

Caliber: 105 mm/51 **Muzzle Velocity:** 2400 ft/sec (HE)
Rate of Fire: 12–14 rnds/min (hand-loaded)
Training Rate: 30 deg/sec (elevation 10 deg/sec)
Maximum Range: 6000 m (6600 yds)
Elevation/Depression: +45/−12.5 deg
Ammunition Load: 30 rnds
Working Circle: swept radius 14 ft 9 in **Weight:** 6 tons

This adapted L7 tank gun, developed by the Royal Ordnance Factories, was first displayed in 1980. The 105 mm could be fitted in patrol boats from 35-m length up. Cost was estimated at £600,000 in 1981. The muzzle velocity given above is for high-explosive (full-caliber) shells; with discarding sabot shells the tank gun attains about 4800 ft/sec. Presumably naval operators would not use such shells. Although sales were not forthcoming, the weapon is interesting as a Western equivalent of the standard Soviet practice for river patrol boats. No current Western river-gunboat weapon of this type is in service, although the U.S. Navy did use tank-type howitzers in Vietnam, on board monitors.

UNITED STATES

◆ 16 in/50

Caliber: 16 in/50 (2700-lb AP shell, 1900-lb HC shell)
Muzzle Velocity: 2425 ft/sec AP; 2690 ft/sec HC
Rate of Fire: 2 rnds/min/gun
Training Rate: 4 deg/sec (elevation 12 deg/sec)
Maximum Range: 40,185 yds AP; 41,622 yds HC
Elevation/Depression: +45/0 deg (depression 2 deg in turrets I, III)
Working Circle: 36 ft 4.5 in
Weight: 1701–1708 tons (per turret) without ammunition

16-in/50 salvo. (Edward J. Bonner)

The 16 in/50s are now the most powerful naval guns in the world, the sole active survivors of the battleship era. The guns are mounted separately and elevate separately. Each gun loads at a fixed 5-degree elevation. After firing, each gun depresses to its loading elevation and then elevates again to fire. Each turret has a crew of 77, plus 30–36 total in the six magazines. The AP round will penetrate 30 feet of concrete. In Vietnam single HC rounds were used to clear 200-yard-diameter landing zones in triple-canopy jungle; the rounds made craters 50 feet wide and over 20 feet deep. The most important technical innovation of the Vietnam period was "Swedish additive," which was wrapped around the charge and which, when burned, reduced barrel wear. During Vietnam, too, some work was done on extending the gun's range. In the spring or summer of 1967 there was a proposal that saboted 280-mm shells (left over from the army's "atomic cannon" program, but nonnuclear) be fired, to ranges as great as 100,000 yards. The Naval Ordnance Station, Indian Head, proposed a $4-million, 18-month program to modify 23,000 such projectiles. There was, however, concern that stable flight could not be assured, and that fuzes could not survive the heat of very high velocity flight. However, exploratory shots were fired at Yuma (up to 60,000 yds) and in Barbados (in the latter case, from two surplus 16-in/45 tubes welded end to end). In February 1969 the Barbados gun fired an 835-lb shell at 40 degrees of elevation (4230 ft/sec) to 74,650 yds; in November 1968 the gun fired a 745-lb shell (4550 ft/sec) to 83,850 yds. It was estimated that at 45 degrees of elevation the light shell would reach 102,000 yds (93,000 yds at 40 degrees). The program died, presumably when the *New Jersey* was deactivated. However, these ranges are about what would be needed by a ship well offshore (i.e., over the horizon) to reach a V-22 landing zone inland.

As of 1981, when the battleships were being reactivated, the reported stock of ammunition was: 15,500 HC (high-capacity) shells, 3200 AP shells, and 2300 BL&P (blind-loaded training) shells. A total of 12,500 full-service and 12,600 reduced charges were on hand. As a measure of consumption, USS *New Jersey* fired 771 rounds during World War II, 6671 during the Korean War and her midshipman cruises, and 5688 during the Vietnam War. As of 1986, it was expected that new 16-inch shells would have to be manufactured for delivery in 1990; the last new 16-inch shells had been made during the Korean War.

There are now four special-purpose shells using the 16-inch HC (1900-lb) body but containing submunitions. Mk-143 HE uses an army proximity fuze. Mk 144 carries 400 M43A1 wedge (antipersonnel) grenades and is time-fuzed. Mk 145 is a time-fuzed high explosive. Mk 146 uses the time fuze and carries 666 shaped charge (SADARM) bomblets (M42/M46/M77 dual-purpose antipersonnel/antimatériel).

An operational requirement for improving the 16-inch guns was approved in May 1986. It includes the development of a new 13-inch subcaliber cargo shell carrying about 600 dual-purpose antipersonnel/antimatériel submunitions (SADARM) to a considerably greater range than the 16-inch shell can achieve. Although the 13-inch shell is much lighter and is of smaller diameter, it has a cavity about as large as that of the full-caliber shell. Other army submunitions are being evaluated. The design of the 16-inch sabot and the 13-inch body were begun in FY86; tests are expected in FY90, and the lead ship should receive the first shells that year, with approval for full production expected in FY92. The shell acts as a bus and can carry other loads: possibilities include chaff, smoke, and land mines (which are already carried by shells on shore).

The sabot shell was chosen for extended range because it was simpler than a proposed rocket-boosted projectile. There have been recurring proposals for a ramjet shell, a gun-launched missile, but they have been put aside because of their inherent complexity.

The other major element of the program is the integration of a digital gun computer, a Mk 160 similar to that of the *Arleigh Burke*, into the Mk-38 fire-control system. The digital computer can make allowances for the different ballistics of the new shells, and in future it may be connected to a shell-tracking radar that will measure the actual muzzle velocity of the guns on a round-by-round basis, so that ballistic corrections can be applied. Neither improvement would have been possible with the old analog computer, in which ballistic formulas are represented by the complex shapes of cams.

When the guns were brought back into service, there were initial problems with powder, i.e., with the consistency of fire on a round-to-round basis. The problem is reflected in variations in muzzle velocity. Powder of the World War II era was expected to produce a variation of no more than plus or minus 10 ft/sec; service figures were plus or minus 5 ft/sec. During the Korean War typical figures were plus or minus 14 ft/sec, and during operations off Lebanon this deteriorated to plus or minus 32 ft/sec. The reworking program restores the powder to the original standard of plus or minus 10 ft/sec.

Existing powder supplies were reblended during 1986, to improve the gun's accuracy. At that time the navy held large stocks of bulk 16-in/45 powder, plus prebagged 16-in/50 powder. The choices were either to remix and reload the 16-in/50 bags

(but matching lots was difficult because the bags had differing histories) or to bag the bulk-stored 16-in/45 powder. Since the bulk-stored powder had more uniform characteristics, it was used. There is a small difference in composition between 16-in/45 and 16-in/50 powder, but it was possible to bag the former to 16-in/50 specifications and to impose sufficient quality control to come within the original specification for muzzle velocity noted above. New powder production will not be needed for some time: as of 1985 the navy had about 12 million pounds of 16-in/45 powder on hand. This material does not deteriorate, but it does age, partly because its volatile components vanish in the first few years. Afterward, change is more gradual.

As modernized, each turret carries a DR-810 radar that measures the muzzle velocity of each gun. This data makes it easier to predict the velocity of the next shot (since it reflects the state of wear of the gun tube on the last shot). The radar elevates to follow gun elevation, and gun velocity is displayed in the turret and printed out in each plotting room. The radar occupies a small radome directly on the roof of each turret, over the center gun; the radar aft is on a short tripod. There are also two HP-85 digital computers. Computer IBC 1 calculates expected initial velocity based on measured gun erosion, powder temperature, and history of initial velocities; the output is compared with radar velocity data. Computer IBC 2 corrects for trunnion height, target height, earth curvature and rotation, ballistic density, and air temperature, calculating fuze time setting for projectiles (Mks 144, 145, and 146) that require it.

The combination of better powder and this degree of detailed calculation makes for considerable accuracy at very long range. For example, firing off Crete on 23 November 1987, *Iowa* fired fifteen 2700-lb AP rounds (five from the right gun of each turret) at a range of 34,000 yds. The pattern size was 219 yds (0.64 percent of total range), and fourteen of the fifteen shells were within 250 yds of the center of the pattern; eight of the fifteen were within 150 yds. Shell-to-shell dispersion was 123 yds (0.36 percent of range).

Considerable effort has been expended to reduce wear on the barrels. The 16-in/50 gun was designed to fire 290 full-charge armor-piercing rounds before tube replacement (the lighter HE shell is equivalent to only a fraction of the full armor-piercing round). During the Vietnam War, the battleship *New Jersey* used a titanium-dioxide jacket that reduced the wear per full-service round to the equivalent of 0.26 such rounds. A newer wax and polyurethane jacket does significantly better. One jacket is used around each bag of the propelling charge; the jacket forms a gaseous layer that protects the gun's bore. These jackets have been so successful that mechanical fatigue, rather than erosion, is now considered the limiting factor in liner lifetime; the 16-in/50 Mk-7 gun is now rated at 1500 FER (fatigue equivalent rounds). Even so, there was some concern at the beginning of the program that insufficient barrel liners remained. However, as of 1986 there were 35 new barrels on hand (one with a used liner), and also at least ten new liners.

◆ 8-in/55 Rapid-Fire

Caliber: 8 in/55 **Muzzle Velocity:** 2700 ft/sec HC; 2500 ft/sec AP
Rate of Fire: 10 rnds/min/gun
Training Rate: 5 deg/sec (elevation 8.2 deg/sec)
Maximum Range: 31,350 yds HC; 30,100 yds AP
Elevation/Depression: +41/−5 deg
Working Circle: 23 ft 3.0 in **Weight:** 451 tons

These guns, the sole survivors of a type that once armed many U.S. cruisers, remain in reserve on board the *Des Moines* and *Salem*. The guns are mounted in triple turrets. Work began in May 1943, after the development of a twin automatic 6 in/47 had shown that a large gun could be made to fire rapidly, i.e., about 10 rounds per minute. This high rate of fire was achieved by all-angle loading with semifixed (i.e., cased) ammunition, all ammunition being power-handled. The mount was considered quite successful in service, suffering only one bad accident (which, however, knocked out the No. 2 turret of the cruiser *Newport News*).

Triple 8-in/55 automatic turrets on board one of the two surviving *Des Moines*–class cruisers. The ship on the right is the *Newport News*, which has been stricken. Although these ships have been out of service for over a quarter-century, they are in excellent condition. The smaller guns are twin 5 in/38s and twin 3 in/50s; the latter would presumably be landed if the ships were recommissioned.

The abortive single 8-in/55 gun, as tested on board the destroyer *Hull*. (U.S. Navy)

◆ Major Caliber Lightweight Gun (Mk 71)

Caliber: 8 in/55　**Muzzle Velocity:** 2700 ft/sec
Rate of Fire: 12 rnds/min　**Ammunition Capacity:** 75 rnds
Training Rate: 30 deg/sec (elevation 20 deg/sec)
Maximum Range: 31,350 yds (no rocket boost)
Elevation/Depression: +65/−5 deg
Working Circle: radius 394.5 in
Weight: 191,860 lbs above decks (32,611 lbs below decks)

This single 8-in/55 rapid-fire gun was developed during the 1960s, to provide the fleet with a counter to Soviet-supplied shore batteries that might otherwise outrange the existing 5-in/54 gun. Mk 71 was designed to fit the new *Spruance*-class destroyer (replacing the forward gun; there was insufficient hull depth and volume under the after mount), but the project was canceled in 1978. To some extent the reactivation of the battleships, with their 16-in/50 guns, was considered an alternative way of providing the marines with sufficient gunfire support. The gun remains interesting as an indication of what a future fire-support weapon might be like.

This gun was conceived as a 175-mm weapon, to use the army's then-standard ammunition, but Mk 71 was developed in 8-inch caliber to exploit the navy's large ammunition stocks. The gun was not expected to fire the army's standard 8-inch howitzer rounds.

The one example built was tested on board the destroyer *Hull*. There were complaints at the time that the gun was not as accurate as required, but in fact it was expected to use a new laser-guided shell rather than standard unguided ammunition.

A variety of other fire-support guns were proposed during the 1960s and early 1970s, including a smooth-bore 13-inch low-recoil gun and a low-recoil 8-inch gun in a mount that did not penetrate the deck. Neither got far enough to receive a Mark number.

Congress tried to revive interest in a specialized Landing Fire Support ship during the 1980s, and one option for its armament

was a modernized 8-inch gun (8 in/60). It would have achieved greater range partly through improved charge design.

◆ 6 in/47

Caliber: 6 in/47 (105-lb HC shell, 130-lb AP)
Muzzle Velocity: 2800 ft/sec HC; 2500 ft/sec AP
Rate of Fire: 10 rnds/min/gun (rating: 3 rnds/min/gun)
Training Rate: 10 deg/sec (elevation 11 deg/sec)
Maximum Range: 24,010 yds
Elevation/Depression: +60/−5 deg (load at angles up to 20 deg)
Working Circle: 21 ft 7.5 in
Weight: 154–167 tons (for different turrets in the ship)

Only one ship still carries these triple mounts, the Chilean cruiser *O'Higgins* (ex-USS *Brooklyn*). The guns are semiautomatic, and they elevate together. The ammunition is semifixed. The gun's lifetime is about 750–1050 rounds at full charge. The associated director is Mk 34, similar to the battleship Mk 38. The crew per turret is 3 officers and 52 enlisted men, compared with 17 enlisted men for the semiautomatic Mk 39 5 in/54, and with 6 enlisted men for the abortive automatic 8 in/55.

◆ 5-in/54 Mk 42 and Mk 39

Caliber: 5 inch/54 (70-lb shell)　**Rate of Fire:** 40 (derated to 28)
Muzzle Velocity: 2650 ft/sec
Maximum Range: 25,900 yds (Time of flight to 10,000 yds at 6-deg elevation is 15.8 sec.)
Training Rate: 40 deg/sec (elevation 25 deg/sec)
Elevation/Depression: +85/−7.5 deg
Ammunition Capacity: 40 (automatically loaded)
Weight: 145,930 lbs (Mod 0)　**Working Circle:** radius 269 in

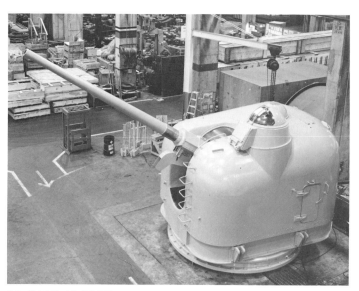

5-in/54 Mk 42. (FMC)

Data are for Mk 42.

Mk 42 was the standard U.S. single 5-inch gun mount of the postwar era, conceived as an automatic equivalent of the twin 5-in/38 with the same rate of fire (but firing a more powerful round). Later versions required fewer men: 13 in Mod 9, compared with about 20 in earlier types. For example, remaining mounts use a single joystick control, whereas the original mount had separate pointer and trainer.

In all variants, the gun is fed by two parallel two-stage hoists, each extracting ammunition from a loader drum. Shells and cartridge cases are loaded separately into the drums, each of which holds 20 complete rounds. Shell and cartridge case are transferred together from drum to lower hoist, then to an upper hoist, and then to a transfer tray (on a cradle) that swings up parallel to the breech; the left and right hoists operate alternately, so that one places a round in the right cradle while the other descends to pick up another. Each transfer tray contains a fuze setter; it drops into position between rammer and breech to load the round. Having loaded, the tray pops up to avoid the gun's recoil, and an empty case tray moves into position to receive the ejected case. The entire process is complex mechanically, and the Mk 42 acquired a reputation for jamming during protracted firing, e.g., on the gun line off Vietnam: hence the current derating to about half the originally projected rate of fire. Mk 42 Mod 10 has a special trouble-shooting status board.

A laser-guided 5-inch shell, Deadeye, was developed by Martin-Marietta, primarily for shore bombardment. Initially Deadeye was to have been guided by a shipboard laser designator incorporated in the Seafire (EX-121) director; but when Seafire was canceled, shell development continued, the designator being a marine mobile unit, MULE. Deadeye could also respond to a helicopter-borne designator. The shell was rocket-boosted for additional range. Deadeye was tested at sea on board USS *Briscoe* in 1981, and the first 300 rounds were scheduled for delivery in FY89, with another 15,100 planned. Delays between 1981 and 1989 were largely caused by disagreements about the cost per round, and the program died in the FY89 round of budget cuts.

The guided shell was 60.97 in long, with pop-out fins at its nose (for guidance) and at its base (for stability), and Deadeye weighed 104.7 lbs. The standard 5-inch/54 round, including its cartridge case, is 60.93 inches long; the shell itself weighs 57.3 lbs (carrying 7.9 lbs of high explosive). The shell could be either a shaped charge or fragmentation warhead. Given the great length, the guided shell had to be double-rammed: once for the shell and once for the separate cartridge case. That requirement roughly halved the rate of fire, and the need to accommodate markedly longer shells accounts for the FMC proposals for vertically loaded guns, described below. The estimated range of the rocket shells is 40,000 yds, compared with 20,000 yds for a conventional shell. With the demise of Deadeye, vertical loading is a much less urgent issue.

There was also an IR-guided shell, developed nearly concurrently with Deadeye, which would have been used as a secondary antiaircraft round. This shell did not enter production, although there is an IR fuze. The rationale was that there were numerous existing antiaircraft weapons, and that, with a warhead much smaller than that of Sea Sparrow, the shell would not have been worthwhile.

Finally, there is a rocket-boosted 5-in/54 shell, Mk 58 (the standard shell is Mk 65), weighing 58 lbs and carrying 3.8 lbs of explosive. With cartridge case, the full round is 61.25 in long. The solid-fuel motor burns for 34 seconds, and the maximum range against a surface target is 31,090 yds, compared with 23,690 yds for the conventional shell.

In 1988 a 5-inch cargo projectile was under development, to carry chaff and other loads (presumably submunitions).

The current program for ammunition development includes a super charge that increases range for the high-fragmentation 5-inch shell and that also gives two to four times the barrel life of the existing charge (the super charge is also under development for the 3-inch gun). This new LOVA (low-vulnerability ammunition) charge will also reduce a ship's vulnerability to fire and blast because rounds in a magazine will be less likely to cook off. A multifunction fuze (remotely set point-detonation, time, or multiproximity) is being developed, so that a single fuze can serve for all air and surface targets. The existing IR fuze is being improved to deal with cooler targets and to reject background clutter more effectively.

Mk 39 is a semiautomatic single 5-in/54 mount that survives on board three former Japanese destroyers, now reclassified as auxiliaries (*Akizuki* class). These weapons were removed from the U.S. aircraft carriers *Midway* and *Franklin D. Roosevelt*. The gun is the same as that in the Mk-42 mount, but the rate of fire is about 15 rounds/min because of manual loading. The mount weighs 87,500 lbs. The shield is 0.75 inches thick. Elevation limits are +85/−10 degrees, and the mount trains at 30 deg/sec (elevation rate 15 deg/sec). The working circle's radius is 276 inches.

The 5-in/54 Mk 42 has been manufactured under license in Japan (by the Japan Steel Works) since 1965.

♦ **5-in/54 Mk 45**

Caliber: 5 inch/54 (70-lb shell)
Rate of Fire: approx 20 rnds/min (17 measured in test)
Muzzle Velocity: 2650 ft/sec   **Maximum Range:** 25,900 yds
Training Rate: 30 deg/sec (elevation 20 deg/sec)
Elevation/Depression: +65/−15 deg
Ammunition Capacity (on-mount): 20 (10 guided rounds)
Weight: 47,820 lbs (no lower hoist)
Working Circle: radius 261 in

5-in/54 Mk 45, USS *Mississippi*, June 1988. (Stefan Terzibaschitsch)

Mk 45 is the slower-firing, low-manning replacement for Mk 42. Mk 45 was intended as the simplest of a family of such weapons, some of which would have fired as rapidly as Mk 42, and some of which might have had twin barrels, but only Mk 45 ever entered service. Mk 45 is remotely controlled; personnel requirements are one gun captain, one panel operator, and four ammunition loaders, all below decks.

Compared with Mk 42, Mk 45 has a greatly simplified mechanism. There is only a single loader drum, and it includes the fuze setter. Some guns have no separate lower hoist; when a lower hoist is present, it feeds the drum. Rounds are loaded into a single cradle, which swings from the vertical up into position behind the vertical breechblock, which rises to open. The round is rammed, and the block drops to close. The empty case is ejected when the gun counterrecoils, the empty case tray being mounted atop the slide. Misfired rounds are removed automatically, compared to manual procedures for Mk 42 and for the earlier 5 in/38.

The barrel's lifetime is 7000 rounds, compared with 3070 for the earlier gun tube of the Mk 42. About 1974, Mk 42's barrel life was rated at 2000 rounds.

Mod 1 allows the operator to change the type of ammunition remotely, whereas in Mod 0 such a change requires special procedures. Mod 1 also incorporates an electronic fuze-setter in addition to the earlier mechanical unit. The loading station is lowered to make room for the longer guided shells. In 1982, when Mod 1 was first tested, six different projectiles were planned: high capacity (HC), white phosphorus (WP), star shell (SS), illumination 2 (SS2), semiactive laser (SALGP, Deadeye), and IR guided (IRGP). The last two were later canceled. There were also seven fuzes: mechanical time (MT), controlled variable time (CVT), point detonating (PD), point detonating delay (PDD), infrared (IR), proximity (VT), and electronically set fuze (ESF). Mod 1 was first fitted to the destroyer *Briscoe*, in February 1980, and was to replace all existing Mod-0 guns.

♦ **5 in/38 (Twin Mount)**

Caliber: 5 in/38 (54-lb shell)   **Rate of Fire:** 10–15 rnds/min/gun
Muzzle Velocity: 2600 ft/sec
Maximum Range: 16,500 yds surface; 11,900 slant (time of flight to 10,000 yds at 11-deg elevation: 22 sec)
Training Rate: 25 deg/sec (elevation 15 deg/sec)

Elevation/Depression: +85/−10 deg
Ammunition Capacity: none on mount   **Weight:** 95,700 lbs
Working Circle: 11 ft 11 in

The 5 in/38 was the standard U.S. Navy dual-purpose gun of World War II. In very limited service in the U.S. Navy now (twin mounts on board the battleships), 5 in/38 remains on board many ex-U.S. destroyers in other navies. Data above are for the twin destroyer mount, probably the most common surviving type (*Gearing-* and *Sumner*-class destroyers). The weight given is for a 0.125-in shield; with an 0.5-in shield, the gun weighs 105,600 lbs. The corresponding battleship mount, with a 2.5-in shield, weighs 169,000 lbs. The usual crew for a twin mount, including loaders below decks, was 26 (13 on the mount itself).

A 5-in/38 rocket-assisted projectile (Mk 57) was developed during the Vietnam War. Including cartridge case, the projectile is 51.5 in long and has a maximum surface range of 23,770 yds. The rocket burns for 40 seconds, and the shell carries 3.5 lbs of explosives. Corresponding figures for the standard 5-in round (Mk 66) are 50.14 in, 41.6 lbs (shell only), range 14,000 yds, and explosive content 7.9 lbs.

The barrel's service life is 4600 rnds. Regunning time is 8 hours per gun, compared to about 1 hour for the 5-in/54 Mk 42 or Mk 45. There are no ready-service rounds on the mount.

5-in/38 twin mounts on board the recommissioned battleship *New Jersey*, with their Mk-37 director above them. The masthead director is Mk 38, to control 16-inch guns; and an armored box launcher (for Tomahawk) is visible between the two funnels, forward of the Phalanx platform. (General Dynamics)

♦ 5-in/38 Mk 30

Caliber: 5 in/38 (54-lb shell)   **Rate of Fire:** 15 rnds/min/gun
Muzzle Velocity: 2600 ft/sec
Maximum Range: 16,500 yds surface; 11,900 slant (time of flight to 10,000 yds at 11-deg elevation: 22 sec)
Training Rate: 38.74 or 34 deg/sec (elevation 15 or 18 deg/sec) (GE or Ford controls, respectively)
Elevation/Depression: +85/−10 deg
Ammunition Capacity: none on mount
Weight: 40,900–41,400 lbs (33,500 lbs for the open mount)
Working Circle: 11 ft 11 in

This shielded single base-ring mount corresponds to the twin mount described above. In the U.S. Navy, this mount remains on board only FFG 1– and FF 1040–class frigates, which are being transferred abroad. Mk 30 also survives on board many ex-U.S. destroyers and destroyer escorts. Some auxiliaries have open base-ring mounts (Mk 37): 34,700 lbs, 30/15 deg/sec training/elevation rates.

♦ 5 in/25

Caliber: 5 in
Shell Weight: 53.85 lbs
Muzzle Velocity: 2200 ft/sec
Maximum Range: 14,500 yds; maximum altitude 27,400 ft (dual-purpose version only)
Elevation Limits: +85/−15 deg (+40/−10 deg)
Rate of Fire: 20 rnds/min (max)
Training Rate: 20 deg/sec; 30 deg/sec in elevation (manual: 1.5 and 2.5 deg per handwheel turn, respectively)
Weight: 23,270 lbs (14,000 lbs)
Working Circle: 121.5 in (99 in) (radius in both cases)

Data apply to the Mk 10 antiaircraft gun in a Mk-27 mount; data in parentheses refer to the wet submarine gun in the Mk-40 mount. Rated life of the gun bore was 3000 rounds (as reported in 1944).

These guns are survivors of a once numerous group of weapons. Unlike the 5 in/38, the 5 in/25 fires a fixed round, just at the limit of quick handling by a single man. The 5 in/38 was developed from the 5 in/25 by increasing cartridge weight (hence muzzle velocity) for better surface performance. Both versions of the 5 in/25 are semiautomatic guns with vertical sliding-block breechblocks.

There are two types, an antiaircraft gun that survives on board the Chilean cruiser *O'Higgins*, and a wet submarine gun that survives on board several Peruvian submarines built in the United States. In addition, U.S. World War II–built fleet submarines; including those subject to "fleet snorkel" conversion, retained provision to mount one or two 5-in/25 wet guns. Guppy conversion presumably entailed streamlining to the extent that external gun foundations were eliminated, but the supporting structures below decks survived. Although no ex-U.S. submarines currently mount 5-in/25 guns, it seems likely that navies possessing such submarines retain these weapons and can mount them for special purposes, as the Royal Navy mounted 4-in guns on board its own streamlined submarines during the confrontation with Indonesia.

♦ 3 in/50

Caliber: 3 in/50 (15-lb shell)   **Rate of Fire:** 45 rnds/min/barrel
Muzzle Velocity: 2700 ft/sec
Maximum Range: 14,600 yds (time of flight to 6000 yds at 5-deg elevation: 12 sec) Maximum altitude is 30,400 ft.
Training Rate: 24 deg/sec (elevation 30 deg/sec)
Elevation/Depression: +85/−15 deg
Ammunition Capacity: No ready-use ammunition on mount (but each barrel can have 5 rounds in its loader). Typically 200 or 300 rounds in ready-service locker, another 1200 in magazine.
Weight: 31,435–32,400 lbs, depending on version
Working Circle: radius 120 in

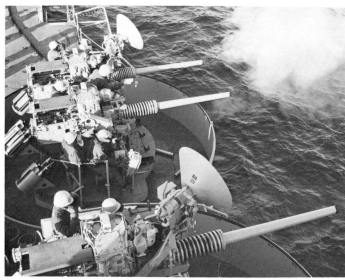

Twin 3-in/50 mounts, with the dishes of SPG-34 radars atop them. The associated Mk-63 directors were mounted separately. (U.S. Navy)

Data are for the twin automatic 3-in/50 Mk 33, once very widely used in the U.S. Navy and in several other navies. This weapon was developed specifically to deal with Kamikazes; in 1945 it was the smallest gun that could fire a proximity-fuzed shell. Although there is no magazine as such on the mount, the loaders continually refill the five-round revolving loading drums that actually feed the guns. There is no rammer as such; instead the loader, which is an independent electrically driven device, catapults each round into the chamber, the breech-closing mechanism being triggered by the edge of the cartridge case as it trips one of the ejectors. Once a round is in the breech, the loader cycle is stopped until the gun fires and ejects that cartridge case. This unusual arrangement was adopted because the gun itself is the earlier semiautomatic weapon adapted as simply as possible to automatic fire; in effect the loading and triggering cycle has been automated, without any basic redesign. That simple automation in turn limits the ultimate rate of fire. Because firing is automatic once a round has been catapulted into the chamber, the gun is unloaded whenever it is not firing: the loader has six slots, but only five can be occupied.

The original version of the twin automatic mount was Mk 27; Mk 33 is more common. Many mounts are enclosed in fiberglass gunhouses. There is also a single version (Mk 34), weighing, typically, 17,000 lbs.

The barrel's life is 2050 rounds.

This gun is usually controlled by a Mk-56 director; others, with a Mk-34 (SPG-34) radar dish on the mount, are controlled by the Mk-63 system. Except for two escorts (the FF 1037 class), the U.S. Navy has removed all remote fire-control systems for these weapons from its ships, leaving the guns entirely locally controlled.

The 3-in/50 automatic gun was initially provided to Japan under the Military Assistance Program (MAP). From 1957 on the gun was manufactured under license by the Japan Steel Works.

Some surviving World War II ships (two in the U.S. Navy) and many coast guard ships are armed with the earlier single semiautomatic 3-in/50 mount (Mk 26) from which this weapon was derived; Mk 26 has the same ballistics. Its rate of fire is 15–20 rnds/min, and, because of the slower rate of fire, the barrel's life is rated as 4300 rnds. The working circle's radius is 96 in.

◆ 3-in/62 Mk 75

Caliber: 76 mm/62   Rate of Fire: 80 rnds/min
Muzzle Velocity: 3000 ft/sec
Training Rate: 65 deg/sec (elevation 35 deg/sec)
Elevation/Depression: +85/−15 deg
Ammunition Capacity: 80 (ready-service)
Weight: 16,500 lbs above decks; 763 lbs below decks
Working Circle: radius 208 in

(Below) The frigate Perry shows her 3-in/62 (Mk-75) gun and her two-channel fire-control system: an egg-shaped Combined Antenna System forward, and a Separate Tracking and Illuminating Radar (STIR) abaft her lattice mainmast. (U.S. Navy)

This U.S. version of the Italian OTO-Melara 76/62 is manufactured by FMC (and by OTO Melara itself since FY86) and mounted on board U.S. frigates and missile hydrofoils and Saudi patrol craft. This gun, generally controlled by a Mk-92 fire-control system, is manned by three enlisted men. Compared to the 3 in/50, the 3 in/62 carries a much larger supply of ready-service ammunition, allowing the gun to fire long bursts without reloading. Because it is very nearly unmanned, it can fire at very short notice. The muzzle brake reduces recoil by about 35 percent. There is also a tank-type bore evacuator. Compared with a 5-in gun, this weapon's one great defect is that it cannot fire any of the more sophisticated munitions.

The gun can be arranged to use one, two, or three loading drums (40, 80, or 115 rounds). Rounds pass up a hoist, from which they are stripped by a pair of rocker arms. The arms in turn feed a revolving four-round feeding drum above the loading tray. The tray pivots back and up to strip a round from the loading tray, then moves into alignment with the breech so that the round can be rammed. As in the Mk-42 mount, two rocker arms are needed to maintain a high rate of fire, one swinging up while the other swings down.

The 3 in/62 is manufactured under license in Japan (by the Japan Steel Works).

◆ 81-mm Mortar Mk 2

Caliber: 81 mm (53 lbs for package of 3 rounds)
Muzzle Velocity: 787 ft/sec
Rate of Fire: 10 rnds/min trigger; 18 rnds/min drop-fire, 45-deg elevation
Maximum Range: 3987 yds
Elevation/Depression: +71.5/−30 deg   Working Circle: 108 in

81-mm mortar Mk 2. (U.S. Navy)

This weapon can be mounted alone or in combination with a 0.50-caliber M2 machine gun, in a piggyback mount. In contrast to mortars for land service, this mortar is either trigger- or drop-fired, and it can, therefore, be fired at zero elevation. Mk 2's recoil mechanism reduces deck loads when the gun is fired. Mk 2 uses army ammunition.

Mod 1 is the piggyback version carrying the 0.50-caliber machine gun; total weight is 722 lbs.

♦ 60-mm Mortar

Caliber: 60 mm (49 lbs for package of 10 rnds)
Muzzle Velocity: 500 ft/sec
Rate of Fire: 10 rnds/min trigger; 18 rnds/min drop mode, 45-deg elevation   **Maximum Range:** 1850–2000 yds
Elevation/Depression: +80/−20 deg   **Working Circle:** 114 in
Weight: 177 lbs

This mortar is a smaller version of Mk 2. None of these weapons remain in U.S. service; but many were produced for the Vietnam War, and they may remain in service in Southeast Asia.

♦ 40-mm Guns

Caliber: 40 mm/56.3 (1.985-lb shell)   **Rate of Fire:** 160 rnds/min
Muzzle Velocity: 2890 ft/sec
Training Rate: 24 deg/sec (elevation 30 deg/sec)
Elevation/Depression: +90/−15 deg
Weight: 24,900 lbs (13,000–14,000 lbs)

A quadruple 40-mm mount on board the cruiser *Portland*, 1944. Although the ship is long gone, some of these mounts survive. The boxes cover the paired feeds of the two guns. (U.S. Navy)

The U.S. Navy developed three principal Bofors mountings: a water-cooled twin mount (Mk 1), a quadruple (dual-twin) mount (Mk 2), and an air-cooled single mount based on the army's version of the gun (Mk 3). Mk 4 was a lightweight quadruple mount produced in small numbers in 1945. Very few of these weapons remain in U.S. service, but they were widely exported. Data above apply to the quadruple mount (twin mount data in parentheses). The only Mk 2s remaining in U.S. service are two on board USS *Sphinx* (ARL 24), controlled by two Mk-51 Mod-2 fire-control systems.

Mk 3 was originally a hand-operated gun for submarines and PT boats, but many of these guns were converted to power drive (4200 lbs rather than the original 2440 lbs, with performance comparable to Mks 1 and 2, above).

Mk 3 Mod 9 is a rebuilt single army-type gun for one-man operation on board patrol craft. This version is power-operated and stabilized and autoloaded (48-round magazine). The first

two were converted, by an ordnance depot, under the FY82 program. These guns were installed on board seventeen PB Mk III Sea Spectre patrol boats. Their loading drums were usually removed because they interfered with vision from the pilot house. This weapon is being replaced by the 25-mm Mk-88 Bushmaster described below.

The new single 40-mm mount Mk 3 Mod 9, on board a 65-foot Patrol Boat Mk 3. The object above the gun is the autoloading magazine. (U.S. Navy)

♦ 40-mm Grenade Launcher Mk 19

This short-range machine gun is used on board riverine and coastal craft and on larger ships to defend against saboteurs and boarders. Operation is by blow back, and the gun fires 400–450 rounds/min at a muzzle velocity of 800 ft/sec. Maximum range is 2400 yds (35-deg elevation), and effective range is 1780 yds (15-deg elevation). A 24-round box of ammunition weighs 21.5 lbs.

Mk 19 was developed during the Vietnam War and remains in production.

There was also a family of shorter-range grenade launchers, with a muzzle velocity of 215–230 ft/sec (maximum range 385–440 yds, effective range 350 yds): Mk 18 and Mk 20, rate of fire continuously variable from single shot to 250 rounds/min. These launchers were effectively rapid-fire versions of the army's M79 grenade launcher. Like Mk 19, they were externally powered.

♦ EX-74/Emerlec-30

Caliber: 30 mm   **Rate of Fire:** 1100 rnds/min (selectable rate)
Muzzle Velocity: 3543 ft/sec   **Maximum Range:** 3500 yds
Training Rate: 90 deg/sec (elevation 80–85 deg/sec)
Elevation/Depression: +80/−15 deg
Ammunition Capacity: 985 rnds/gun
Weight: 3469 lbs (full system 4156 lbs without ammunition)
Working Circle: 88 in

This Emerson Electric mount carries one 30-mm Oerlikon gun on each side of a cab in which the operator sits. EX-74 was originally developed for the U.S. CPIC coastal-patrol boat (of which only a prototype was ever built), but a developed version of the mount was later very successfully exported, as the Emerlec-30, to Ecuador, Greece, Malaysia, Nigeria, the Philippines, and South Korea. As of January 1988, over 150 Emerlec-30s had been delivered. The principal difference between the U.S. Navy's version and the exported version is that the navy's gun did not penetrate the deck, whereas export guns have below-decks magazines.

Emerlec-30's characteristics generally follow those above, but the claimed rate of fire is 1200 rounds/min and weight without ammunition is 4200 lbs. Working circle is 94 in. Training rate is 80 deg/sec (elevation 80 deg/sec). The gun is an Oerlikon (Hispano-Suiza) 30-mm cannon, with a barrel life of about 5000 rounds.

In the U.S. CPIC, the Emerlec-30 was controlled by GFCS Mk 93, which incorporated the Kollmorgen Mk 35 periscope director.

Emerlec-30 gun mount. (Emerson Electric)

◆ EX-83

This powered mount carries a 30-mm GAU-8/A Gatling gun. EX-83 forms the basis of the Dutch Goalkeeper close-in weapons system and was proposed as the basis of the French Satan system. The Dutch selection of the EX-83 mount was apparently based on successful trials at Den Helder, early in 1980, using an EX-83 controlled by a Signaal Flycatcher radar tracker (which is similar to STIR and thus to the VM40 proposed for Sea Wolf missile control). Success in these tests demonstrated both the pointing accuracy of Flycatcher and the tight dispersion of the 30-mm gun.

These tests were for land-based air defense, but they were clearly applicable to the naval close-in defense problem.

EX-83 is also the basis of the French SAGEM and SAMOS. There was also a proposed VSEL (Vickers) Sea Dragon carrying a Marconi tracker radar above the gun mount proper (1983), and there was a projected Israeli version. The U.S. Navy tested the EX-83, controlled by the Mk-86 fire-control system, on board the destroyer *Merrill* (DD 976) in 1981. For details of the EX-83 gun and mount, see the Goalkeeper entry above.

◆ 25-mm Automatic Cannon Mk 38 (Bushmaster)

Caliber: 25 mm/87 (1.1-lb round)   **Muzzle Velocity:** 1100 m/sec
Rate of Fire: single shot, 100, or 200 rnds/min
Training Rate: manual mount   **Maximum Range:** 6800 m
Elevation/Depression: +55/−20 deg
Ammunition Capacity: 150 linked cartridges
Weight: total gun weight (no mounting) 240 lbs; total mounting weight 1250 lbs

Bushmaster is the naval version of the "Chain Gun," an externally powered weapon developed by Hughes for the U.S. Army. The Chain Gun was originally a 20-mm, then a 30-mm (Aden ammunition) gun firing linkless ammunition at up to 900 rounds/min. Procured by the army as M242, the gun is desig-

nated Mk 38 for naval service; the pedestal mounting, Mk 88. The 25-mm gun is credited with a barrel life of 25,000 rounds; dispersion is 0.5 mil.

The name derives from the use of a loop of standard industrial double-row roller chain, carried horizontally, to drive the bolt back and forth. The length and width of the chain are determined by the length of the round and by the desired rate of fire. The chain runs at constant speed, carrying a shoe that drives the bolt. When in line with the bolt, the shoe pulls back and forth, locking and opening the bolt. When the shoe travels to one side (along the belt, perpendicular to the gun's axis), the gun has time to fire or to eject a fired cartridge (depending on where in the cycle this travel occurs). The feed to the gun is powered by the same motor that drives the chain.

Development and procurement of the Chain Gun was originally approved in December 1971. In 1977 the chief of naval operations approved procurement to replace existing obsolete Mk-16 20-mm guns, which were difficult to support (they required overhaul every 6500 rounds) and did not use standard NATO ammunition; many existing rounds were considered unsafe.

This weapon, already in large-scale production for the army, was operationally evaluated for naval use in the summer of 1987, and by mid-1988 over 5000 had been delivered to the U.S. Army. Bushmaster replaces existing U.S. Navy 20-mm cannon. The Mk 88 mount is not stabilized and is hand-aimed; it cannot, therefore, make very many hits when mounted on a lively small combatant. As of mid-1988, many Mk 88s were in service in the Persian Gulf, and they also equipped the Mark-4 patrol boats in the Panama Canal Zone. As of August 1988, the Naval Sea Systems Command planned to buy 460 Mk 88s.

25-mm Bushmaster (Mk-38 gun on Mk-88 mount). (McDonnell-Douglas Helicopter Co.)

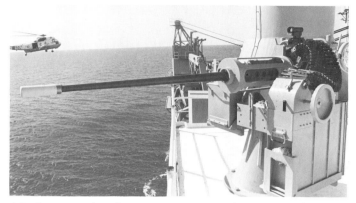

A Bushmaster on board USS *Mount Vernon* in the Persian Gulf, October 1987. (U.S. Navy)

◆ L-CAT 25

Caliber: 25 mm   **Training Rate:** 80 deg/sec (elevation 60 deg/sec)
Maximum Range: 3000 m (effective range)
Elevation/Depression: +60/−20 deg
Ammunition Capacity: 400 rnds   **Weight:** 1500 lbs empty
Working Circle: diameter 130 in

Emerson's single stabilized 25-mm gun mount, suitable for small patrol boats, was announced in 1984. It was developed as a result of a U.S. Navy project to define the characteristics of a standard minor-caliber mount. Empty weight is less than 680 kg, and the mount bolts to the deck. Control may be either manual or remote. Drive is electric rather than hydraulic, for simpler maintenance.

Data above refer to the remotely controlled 25-mm mount carrying the M242 Bushmaster. In the manned version, the gunner replaces one of the two 200-round ammunition boxes. This mount can also carry the Oerlikon KBA (570 rounds/min), which has about three times the recoil force of the M242.

Only a prototype was built, but L-CAT is interesting as an approach to the problem of installing guns on small combatants. At the 1986 Italian naval exhibition (Mostra Navale), Oerlikon Italiana showed a scale model of the mount, carrying a 25-mm KBA. The company was trying to interest the Italian Navy in license production, on the theory that 25-mm guns would be attractive to many navies, to arm small combatants, but that most of the combatant operators would find a stabilized mount much more attractive than the standard unstabilized Mk 88.

The U.S. Navy tentatively assigned a Mk-89 designation to this mounting.

◆ Sea Vulcan 25

Caliber: 25 mm   **Muzzle Velocity:** 3400 ft/sec
Rate of Fire: selectable, 750 or 2000 rnds/min
Training Rate: 1.6 rad/sec (train and elevation)
Ammunition Capacity: 500 rnds
Elevation/Depression: +85/−25 deg
Working Circle: radius 64.0 in   **Weight:** 2800 lbs fully loaded

General Electric's private-venture gun mount carries the lightweight 5-barrel 25-mm aircraft Gatling gun (GAU-12/U). Sea Vulcan was proposed for the abortive SWCM (surface-effect SEAL delivery craft), rejected, then restored to the program before the SWCM program itself died. The mount may appear on future U.S. small combatants, e.g., on whatever SWCM replacement emerges. Compared to the present 25-mm Bushmaster, Sea Vulcan 25 offers a much higher rate of fire and, more importantly, a stabilized line of fire suited to lively small craft. The mount was very successfully tested in 1987 on board the SES-200 surface-effect boat. The power-driven mount can incorporate an infrared camera for accurate target tracking or can be controlled by a lightweight off-mount director. Although the version tested in 1987 carried only the 25-mm gun, full-size models displayed in the past have carried two Stinger missile tubes.

General Electric claims that Sea Vulcan 25 can kill targets, presumably corresponding to a small missile, at 2000 meters (it

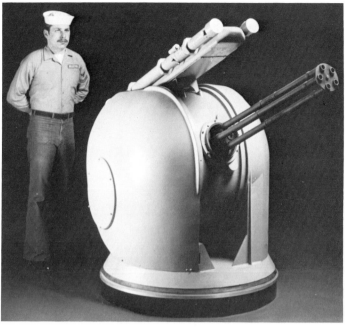

Sea Vulcan 25. (General Electric)

has published a photograph of the destruction of a Lynx drone at 500 m). In tests, Sea Vulcan was controlled by a Mk 24 optical director and an electro-optical director. Dispersion is 2.23 mrad. Claimed reliability is 7000 MRBF or 200 hours MTBF (nonfiring).

◆ Zenith 25/30

This projected General Electric turret on a canted mount is similar in concept to the Sea Zenith employed in the Swiss

Sea Zenith. (General Electric)

Seaguard system but carries a 25-mm GAU-12/U (as in the AV-8B) or a 30-mm GAU-8 gun. Zenith was announced in 1982. Sea Zenith was proposed either as main armament for a small combatant, or as the gun element of a ship's close-in defensive weapons system.

In Zenith 25, the ammunition feed has been modified so that it can operate (at 2000 rnds/min) at any angle of gun elevation. The manufacturer hopes to increase this rate to at least 3000 rnds/min, or to 4000 by scaling down the linkless feed of the GAU-8. Total weight is 4000 lbs, and the training/elevation rate is 1.6 rad/sec. Working circle radius is 68 inches (base radius 36 in).

◆ AAI Naval Gun Mount

AAI Corporation is developing a naval version of the Minor Caliber Weapons Station (MCWS) under development for U.S.

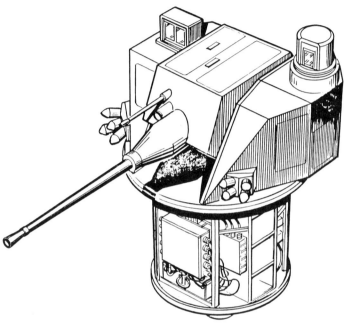

AAI Minor Caliber Weapons Station in brassboard form, for tests on an armored vehicle during 1987–88. The primary weapon is the 25-mm Bushmaster (200 rounds HE, 87 rounds AP); the secondary is the EX-34 7.62-mm machine gun (665 rounds); and the small projections are M243 smoke-grenade launchers (total of 8 grenades). (AAI)

The AAI naval gun mount. (AAI)

Marine Corps vehicles. This version will be electrically driven, with two- or three-axis stabilization, and will carry a 25-mm or 30-mm gun, plus perhaps a Stinger-missile launcher. Elevation limits will be −8 to +60 degrees (slew rates up to 60 deg/sec), and the mount will carry 400 rounds of 25-mm ammunition, or 150 to 200 rounds of 30-mm, plus up to two twin-rail missile launchers. AAI proposes two configurations: through-deck (2200 lbs) and above-deck (2500 lbs), each with 100–500 lbs of remote-control equipment and displays. Possible applications include future small combatants and landing craft.

◆ Phalanx (Close-In Weapons System Mk 15)

Caliber: 20 mm/76 (0.22-lb round)
Rate of Fire: 1000–3000 rnds/min **Muzzle Velocity:** 3650 ft/sec
Maximum Range: 6000 yds (effective range 1625 yds)
Training Rate: 100 deg/sec (elevation 86 deg/sec)
Elevation/Depression: +80/−20 deg **Ammunition Capacity:** 989
Weight: 12,000 lbs above deck, 466 lbs below deck
Working Circle: diameter 216 in

Phalanx (Close-in Weapons System Mk 15). The drum magazine is under the gun. (U.S. Navy)

Phalanx is the standard U.S. Navy close-in weapons system, using bursts of depleted-uranium penetrators to destroy or fuze incoming antiship missiles. The weapons system's designation covers the mount plus integrated radar; the mount proper is Mk 72.

Phalanx combines a 20-mm Vulcan automatic cannon with a (search and track) Ku-band radar that has two antennas but one transmitter. The radar automatically detects and tracks incoming missiles. In the search mode, the radar uses unambiguous doppler/ambiguous range, switching PRF to achieve range resolution in three range-coverage zones. During target acquisition, the system again uses unambiguous doppler/ambiguous range and a derived search range, bearing, and speed to search a "basket" provided by the search radar. Normally there is no operator intervention: the system decides automatically to engage, and the operator has a veto.

When the gun begins to fire, the radar also tracks outgoing bursts of fire, predicts their point of closest approach to the

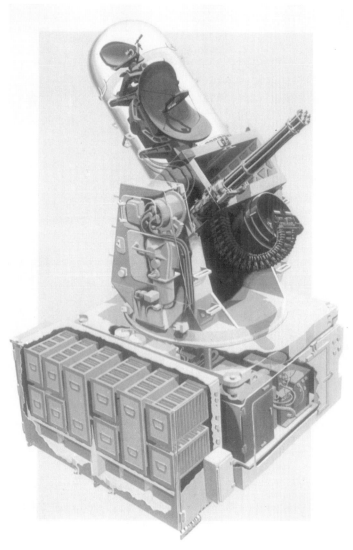

Phalanx. (General Dynamics)

incoming target, and corrects the aim of the following burst(s). This electronic spotting uses variable PRF with selected spectral (frequency) line tracking to measure the projectile stream's angular error. The manufacturer, General Dynamics, claims that this closed-loop spotting system improves lethality by as much as an order of magnitude. This self-contained fire-control system was originally designated Mk 90, although that designation has been dropped in favor of the Mk-15 designation embracing the entire system.

Phalanx was designed so that it can be rigged to engage surface targets designated by conventional optical target designators. However, that configuration is officially discouraged; ships are expected to use dedicated light guns, such as single 20s or Bushmasters, for self-defense against small surface craft.

This system was first proposed in 1968 as part of the early antiship-missile defense program prompted by the *Eilat's* sinking; a feasibility contract was awarded to General Dynamics in 1969. The first closed-loop spotting system was demonstrated at White Sands in 1970, and a prototype was demonstrated on board the missile destroyer *King* in 1973. There were, however, doubts as to whether Phalanx could destroy incoming cruise missiles. They were resolved, and full-scale production was authorized in 1977, the first installation (on board the carrier *America*) following in 1980. The 400th system was delivered in 1985.

Some difficulties were encountered in service. Block 0 guns suffered from sea corrosion, a problem corrected by construction of special "maintenance shelters" around parts of the mount. In addition, it takes 10–30 minutes to reload the ammunition drum.

Phalanx Block I (authorized for limited production in 1986) provides 50 percent more on-mount ammunition. This version is also designed to engage diving targets at steeper angles. The two-dimensional scanning antenna of Block 0 is replaced by a four-plate back-to-back antenna that continuously searches up through the zenith. In addition, a positive cease-fire function matches burst length to target characteristics, to conserve ammunition so that more targets can be engaged before reloading. Current developmental work is intended to counter faster, lower-altitude maneuvering targets with reduced radar cross sections. Block I was operationally tested at China Lake 3 December 1981–21 May 1982.

In 1983 a modified Phalanx, carrying a four-barrel 30-mm GAU-13 gun, was proposed for the Royal Navy. The Signaal Goalkeeper was chosen instead, but the proposal shows to what extent the existing Phalanx could be up-gunned (re-equipped with a more powerful gun) with minimum modification. In 1988 it was reported that General Dynamics was considering two up-gunned versions of Phalanx, one with a four-barrel 30-mm gun and one with twin 25-mm guns.

In 1987–88 the follow-on system was nominally designated CIWS-2000. In January 1988 a Congressional conference committee refused further funding for CIWS-2000 until the U.S. Navy had evaluated Goalkeeper. Admiral Metcalf, the outgoing chief of surface warfare, had already tried to cancel CIWS-2000 in the fall of 1987, arguing that the system represented an insufficient advance over the existing Phalanx, and that more revolutionary, rather than evolutionary, counters to attacking missiles were needed. That argument may reflect interest in such exotica as chemical lasers and directed-energy weapons.

◆ Sea Vulcan 20 (EX-84)/20P

Caliber: 20 mm   **Rate of Fire:** 750/1500 rnds/min
Muzzle Velocity: 3380 ft/sec
Training Rate: 80 deg/sec (elevation 60 deg/sec)
Elevation/Depression: +55/−10 deg
Ammunition Capacity: 500 rnds   **Maximum Range:** 6000 yds
Working Circle: 130 in   **Weight:** 318 kg empty, 465 kg loaded

Sea Vulcan 20 on board the Thai Hyuscat-18 fast patrol boat. (Tecnautic)

Data apply to Sea Vulcan 20.

Sea Vulcan 20 is a powered turret mount for a three-barrel M197 Vulcan machine gun, for use on small craft. The turret itself is also designed to carry the 7.62-mm mini- (Gatling) gun and the M19 40-mm grenade-launching machine gun. Many components are identical to those used in the UTS turret of the AH-1 attack helicopter. The system is remotely controlled with its own on-board ballistic computer (to process target-designation data from another source). One EX-84 mount was built and tested in June 1981 on board a U.S. PB Mk III, but the weapon did not enter U.S. service.

A Sea Vulcan 20 was mounted on board the Thai Hyuscat-18 patrol vessel, controlled by a Kollmorgen Mk-35 periscope director. Total weight was 800 lbs empty or 1167 lbs with ammunition, and training and elevating rates were 60 and 50 deg/sec, respectively. As installed on board the Thai patrol boat, the mount also carried a mock-up of a two-missile SAM launcher on an extension of the elevation gimbal shaft. The mount could carry Stinger, Mistral, Blowpipe, Javelin, or RBS 70. This mount (less the missiles) was retrofitted into existing Honduran Navy patrol craft (85-, 105-, and 106-footers) in 1986–87. In addition, two Sea Vulcans were installed on board the Boeing commercial Jetfoil operating as tender to the larger Saudi royal yachts. The hydrofoil is also armed with Stingers.

Sea Vulcan 20P is a much simpler pintle mount (originally designed to carry a twin 20-mm cannon) carrying the same three-barrel gun and a 300-round ammunition box. Total weight is about 500 kg without ammunition, and elevation limits are +75/−10 deg. Although this mount is not in U.S. service, it has been bought by the Japanese Maritime Self-Defense Force. The South Korean Navy uses this gun in its own specially weatherproofed mounting.

Both the gun and the Sea Vulcan mount are manufactured by General Electric.

◆ Other U.S. 20-mm Mounts

Although early U.S. 20-mm guns are capable of antiaircraft fire, they are primarily surface weapons. These guns are now being replaced in that ASUW role by the 25-mm Bushmaster or Chain Gun (see the Strike/Surface Warfare section), which clearly is a surface weapon. Some single 20-mm guns of U.S. design also survive in foreign navies.

World War II mounts carried a Mk-4 (Oerlikon) gun, using an 80-round drum magazine. This gun had a cyclic rate of 450 rounds/min and a muzzle velocity of 2730 ft/sec. Effective range was 2000 yds (maximum range 4500 yds at 35-deg elevation). This gun was blow-back operated.

The newer 20-mm guns are Mk 16s, modified aircraft guns (Hispano-Suiza HS404, designated M3) that are slightly lighter (116 vs. 150 lbs) and shorter (78 vs. 84 in), and that are fed by box magazines carrying disintegrating link belts. The ammunition and muzzle velocity are the same, but cyclic rate is 600–650 rounds/min (reduced from the 800 rounds/min of the aircraft gun). These guns are operated by a combination of gas and blow back. Mk 16 also has a special oiler to lubricate its ammunition. Mod 5 adds a hand-pulled stepped mechanical trigger. Mod 4 has an electrical trigger mechanism.

About 5000 Mk 16s were delivered during the Vietnam War, and Mk 16 is a standard coast guard weapon. In recent years many M24 (air force version of M3) aircraft cannon have been cannibalized for Mk 16 conversion.

The then Naval Ordnance Systems Command developed a series of alternative 20-mm guns in the late 1960s and early 1970s, but ultimately adopted the 25-mm Chain Gun instead.

Single 20-mm World War II–type Oerlikon, as still used on board some British (and other) warships, photographed in 1988. (A. Wetback)

In the list below, Mk 10 and Mk 24 were the World War II single and twin mounts. Mk 67 was the standard mount for the Mk 16 gun, introduced in 1971 on board USS *Tarawa* (LHA 1). MK 68 was a stop-gap until Mk 67 could enter production; Mk 68 was tested in 1970 on board a radar-picket ship.

Only Mk 67 and Mk 68 are in current U.S. service; earlier mounts survive abroad.

◆ 0.50-Caliber Machine Gun (M2)

This standard U.S. heavy machine gun is used on board many coastal craft. Total weight is about 87 lbs, and total length is 65 in. The gun is recoil-operated, and it fires 450–550 rounds per minute. Muzzle velocity is 2900 ft/sec (nominal), and effective range is 1500 yds. Maximum horizontal range is 7400 yds (35-degree elevation). A 100-round disintegrating-link belt weighs 30 lbs. This gun is often combined with an 81-mm mortar in an over-and-under mount.

Many surface combatants and auxiliaries have pedestal mounts on which shielded 0.50-caliber machine guns can be placed, for defense against small boats and swimmers. Sometimes these weapons are mistaken for larger 20-mm cannon. Typically small ships carry two, destroyers and cruisers carry four, and larger ships carry eight of these machine guns.

Photographs of U.S. warships in the Persian Gulf sometimes show 7.62-mm machine guns (M60) on bridge wings.

MOUNT CHARACTERISTICS

	Mk 10	Mk 24	Mk 67	Mk 68
Gun	Mk 4	2 × Mk 4	Mk 16	Mk 16
Weight	970 lbs	1216 lbs	475 lbs[a]	775 lbs[a]
Working Circle	106 in	120 in	114 in	119 in
Elevation/Depression Limits	+90/−15 deg	+85/−15 deg	+75/−30 deg	+70/−45 deg
Ammunition	60 rnds	2 × 60 rnds	385 rnds	400 rnds

[a]Weight without ammunition.

0.50-caliber flexible pedestal mount (Mk 26 Mod 7). (U.S. Navy)

A 0.50-caliber machine gun on board USS *Mount Vernon* in the Persian Gulf, October 1987. There are supports for a splinter shield, which has not been fitted in this case. U.S. ships in the Gulf were also provided with M60 light (7.62-mm) machine guns. (U.S. Navy)

♦ 7.62-mm Mini-Gun

This miniature Vulcan weighs 60 lbs, including the drive motor and de-linking feeder. Total length is 30 in. Muzzle velocity is 2800 ft/sec, and effective range is 1200 yds (maximum 4000 yds). Cyclic rate is 2000 or 4000 rnds/min, and a 1000-round belt weighs 64 lbs.

The gun is designated Mk 25 in U.S. naval service and is the GAU-2B/A aircraft weapon adapted for surface use, mainly by Special Forces (SEALs).

♦ 155-mm (6.1-inch) Vertical-Loading Gun

This weapon was proposed by the FMC Corporation, the manufacturer of the U.S. 5 in/54 and 3 in/62, in 1981, to fire the army's existing standard rounds. The marines saw this weapon as a replacement for the 8-in/55 lightweight fire-support gun, which had been canceled in 1978. However, the 155 mm was rejected. Although the army's existing special-purpose rounds had been proven on shore, many of them could not be used in the naval electromagnetic environment without extensive and costly modifications. The Marines, therefore, had to be satisfied

with a combination of the existing 5-inch guns and the revived 16 in/50s of the battleships.

The FMC project remains interesting for its unique loading system. All other naval guns load either at a fixed angle near the horizontal or at a variable elevation angle. For the 155 mm, FMC proposed loading vertically, the gun forming, in effect, a continuation of the loading hoist. Projectile and charge were loaded onto separate horizontal trays in the magazine, and then each tray rotated to the vertical, so that shell and powder rose in the proper sequence toward the breech. Shell and powder were there rammed together. After firing, the gun elevated so that its breech was in line with the empty-case door, ejected the case, and then continued to elevate to the vertical. The main advantage was that the gun could fire projectiles of differing lengths; inserting long guided projectiles greatly slowed the rate of fire of the existing 5 in/54. The usual loading tray was eliminated completely from FMC's design.

In 1981, FMC estimated that the mount could be ready in six years (three for development, three for production), that it would weigh less than 50,000 lbs (revolving weight 43,000 lbs), and that it would be cheaper and more reliable than the 5 in/54 (MRBF about 1320 rounds). The gun would have been a 155 mm/50, and elevation limits would have been +75/−10 deg (training rate 30 deg/sec, elevation rate 50 deg/sec). The conventional 155-mm shell would have weighed 103 lbs, the guided shell 225 lbs; and FMC claimed that the sustained firing rate would have been 10 rounds/min.

FMC has also proposed a vertical-loading 8-inch gun. Recent (1988) FMC advertisements show a projected advanced 5-in/54 gun, which may be a vertical-loader.

♦ Combustion-Augmented Plasma (CAP) Technology

This high-energy gun technology was announced by FMC in 1987. This type of gun is a hybrid between an electrothermal (ET) and a liquid-propellant (LP) cannon; about 20 percent of muzzle energy is derived from an electrically generated plasma, and 80 percent from a conventional chemical reaction, as in other liquid-propellant guns. Compared to a pure electromagnetic gun, the CAP gun requires about a third as much electrical generating power. Compared to other new-technology guns (such as rail guns), the main disadvantage of the system is its complexity. On the other hand, the CAP gun has the shortest barrel (for a given performance) of a series of weapons, including pure liquid propellant guns and advanced conventional guns.

In this type of weapon, a sudden discharge of electricity heats the propellant in the breech to 5000 degrees C and causes an ion plasma to form. The oxidant is then added. The resulting combustion is more rapid than usual and adds about 25 percent to the muzzle velocity of the weapon. That increase in velocity approximately doubles the range of the gun and, at short ranges, greatly increases the energy of the shell. In addition, because time of flight is reduced, fire control may be simplified, e.g., in antimissile defense. In the 1987 announcement, FMC showed its version of CIWS 2000, which carried two rather than six barrels.

The first experiments used 10-mm projectiles, but later 30-mm were fired, and FMC expects to fire 90-mm projectiles. All of these experiments used liquid propellants, although a conventional solid propellant might also be used.

As of 1987, FMC was applying its CAP technology to an air force–funded hypervelocity ammunition technology (HAT) program, in which a sideways-pointing antitank gun is to be mounted on board a C-130 or successor gunship that would fly just behind the battle line. CAP was also proposed as part of a hybrid rail gun for antimissile defense, to be used to inject a projectile into the electric gun.

♦ Liquid-Propellant Gun Technology

For some time General Electric has been developing the technology for liquid-propellant guns for the U.S. Defense Department, both for ground and for naval missions. By 1983 GE had demonstrated its new regeneratively pumped direct-injection-combustion technique in a 105-mm test gun. Although not yet applied to a naval weapon, this technology is potentially important enough to be included here.

Interior ballistics are controlled by metering the propellant into the combustion chamber. Thus, to a considerable extent, a gun's muzzle velocity, hence range, can be varied without varying the elevation angle. Bulk stowage of propellant greatly reduces the weight and bulk of ammunition, and quicker loading of propellant can greatly increase the rate of fire. In the GE system, once the first round has been fired, the pressure in the combustion chamber is used to pump in the next load of propellant (hence the regenerative name).

SHIPBOARD ELECTRONIC WARFARE

This section includes two very different classes of systems: chaff or decoy launchers and electronic intercept/jamming devices. There are also a few towed or floating decoys and some electronic intelligence devices.

A chaff launcher can have one or more of three distinct functions. Firing at long range, the launcher can provide a targeting radar or an incoming missile with multiple targets. If all targets must be engaged, the attack is diluted, and close-in weapons have a better chance of dealing with those weapons that do lock onto the ship herself. The usual counter-countermeasure is MTI (moving-target indication). A radar easily distinguishes an airplane from chaff because the real target is moving so much faster. Such a distinction is much more difficult to make if the target is a ship. The second, intermediate-range function is to seduce the missile seeker away from the ship target onto a decoy cloud. The missile seeker is designed to avoid such seduction by using a range-gate, i.e., by reacting only to signals within a narrow band of ranges around the expected target's position. An active ECM transmitter (range-gate stealer or range-gate pull-off) is used to move the missile's seeker into the chaff cloud some distance from the ship. Finally, there is a last-ditch tactic, centroid seduction. The missile's seeker generally homes on the centroid of the target's return, seeing the ship target as a complex array of point and corner reflectors. If a large chaff cloud is added, it moves the centroid up and away from the ship target, and the missile may pass overhead or to one side. Success in this mode depends upon the reflective cross section of the chaff cloud compared to that of the ship proper. If the cloud is designed merely to move the centroid up, that countermeasure may be countered by a radio altimeter that keeps the incoming missile at low altitude.

Chaff (and IR decoys) may be launched by rocket or mortar. Rockets provide longer range (for the dilution role) and do not impose any load on the surrounding deck. However, they are relatively large, and a designer must protect against their back blast. Mortars are more compact, as is their ammunition. Both types exist in considerable variety.

ECM devices fall into two broad categories, intercept receivers (often termed ESM, electronic support measures) and active countermeasures (jammers and more sophisticated deception devices). ESM includes not only attack warning but also passive detection of air and surface forces beyond the sensor's horizon. Although such detectors may be considered more as antiship targeting devices than as self-protection, they are most conveniently included here. Attack warning requires, at most, coverage of the standard air-to-surface radar (X-) and missile-seeker (X- and K-) bands. Over-the-horizon detectors of surface ships may exploit both the sea-wave emissions of P-band air-search radars and HF communications.

These devices can also be divided into wide-open and narrow-beam scanning types. A wide-open detector will pick up very short signals, but it may lack sensitivity in any one direction, and it will also generally lack directional precision. A narrow-band scanner will provide good directional data and may achieve great sensitivity; but with a finite scanning rate, a narrow-band scanner may miss a very short transmission. In the past, British practice has generally favored wide-open detectors using fixed antennas (and measuring signal direction by phase comparison); U.S. practice has favored rapidly scanning directional antennas (as in SLR-12). Current U.S. practice employs electronic scanning, in which a wide-open antenna can form numerous narrow beams continuously and simultaneously (e.g., SLQ-32).

Active countermeasures employ a variety of tactics, from simple noise (barrage) jamming up through false-target transmitters sequenced to confuse scanning radars. There are also multi-antenna antimonopulse techniques. For many years U.S. escorts were fitted with blip enhancers intended to make it difficult for an approaching antiship bomber to distinguish them from the accompanying carrier. Reportedly the implicit missile-absorber role was less than popular, but this measure suggests the subtlety of electronic warfare. Currently the U.S. and Royal Navies use floating decoys, which are called "rubber ducks" in analogy to hunters' decoys.

AUSTRALIA

◆ Winnin

Winnin is a hovering rocket that carries an active jammer. By hovering, the decoy prolongs its life and, thus, better simulates the behavior of a real ship. The key technology is a variable-thrust solid-propellant rocket, whose thrust automatically decreases as the weight of the decoy decreases through burning. Servo tabs in the rocket's exhaust control the rocket's direction. Winnin is fired in a precomputed direction but can also receive control data while in flight. This degree of control simplifies launching arrangements, since the decoy can fly in the required direction whatever its initial launch path.

Winnin was conceived in 1974 and first flew in 1981. The concept was developed by the Weapons Systems Research Laboratory at Salisbury, South Australia, and by the Government Aircraft Factories in Melbourne. In 1985 the Australian government was running trials while soliciting industrial interest. The rocket is now called "Hoveroc," and its tubes will be added to the existing U.S.-type Mk-137 SRBOC tubes. In this form the rocket can carry an IR payload in addition to the active-radar decoy.

CANADA

◆ CANEWS (SLQ-501)

MEL's system for the Canadian "City" class was first tested in the fall of 1981. CANEWS embodies the MEL instantaneous-frequency-measurement (IFM) device also used in the British Abbey Hill system (see below) and claimed, in 1983, to be the only one of its type manufactured in Europe. Some accounts suggest that CANEWS is a derivative of the British UAA-1.

Radar intercepts are compared with a library, providing automatic classification within 2 seconds of an intercept. The system covers 1–18 GHz in five bands, each with its own receiver (eight horns, wide open in frequency, for full 360-degree coverage, a bearing accuracy of better than 4 degrees, and a frequency accuracy of 5 MHz). The system can be expanded below 1 GHz if desired. Two UYK-20 computers are used, to process up to 500,000 pulses/sec; the library stores up to 2000 emitter modes, tied to geographical area. The operator can add up to 128 emitters (a "regional" file, of radars most likely to be encountered). There is also a smaller preprogrammed threat library. CANEWS was described as fully automatic, unlike the British Abbey Hill.

The antenna weighs less than 200 kg. It consists of eight boxes, each covering 45 deg and each carrying four radomes, for four frequency bands. The two highest-frequency radomes are side by side, with intermediate- and lower-frequency radomes below. Four Band-0 (low frequency) units are located between the pairs of 45-degree boxes. Each antenna feeds a wide-open receiver; in addition, there is an omnidirectional antenna feeding an IFM.

CANEWS antenna array. (MEL)

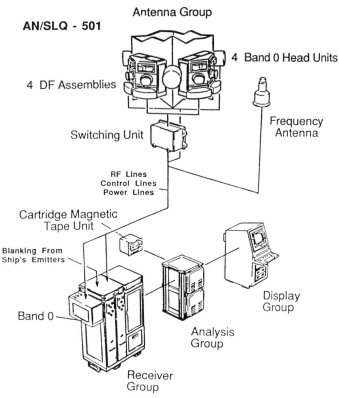

CANEWS, SLQ-501. (MEL Defense Systems)

Work began in 1973, the MEL proposal being accepted in 1976; the first set was delivered in July 1980. It was tested on board the Canadian frigate *Terra Nova* that October. CANEWS was selected for the Destroyer Life Extension Program and then for the "City" class. Successful sea trials of a production set were reported in mid-1983. The first operational installation was on board the frigate HMCS *Huron*, in 1986; and by early 1987 CANEWS was also on board HMCS *Gatineau* and *Huron*, with four more installations planned. The new "City"-class frigates will carry communications intercept-and-DF equipment in addition to CANEWS, and also the MEL RAMSES (SLQ-503) noise/deception jammer.

MEL Defense Systems (of Canada) was set up specifically for this program.

◆ SLQ-503 (RAMSES)

This MEL system is combined with CANEWS (SLQ-501) in new and modernized Canadian destroyers. RAMSES is an acronym for Reprogrammable Advanced Multimode Shipboard Electronic-Countermeasures Systems. RAMSES can operate either under SLQ-501's control or independently. Software-controlled, RAMSES can jam several threats simultaneously. MEL claims that RAMSES is effective against monopulse radars, even though it uses only two antenna assemblies, one to port and

one to starboard. Each incorporates a pair of radomes, presumably for two different frequency ranges.

◆ Model 100

This naval direction-finder, manufactured by General Precision Industries, covers 10 kHz to 180 MHz. For LF/HF Model 100 uses a pair of multiturn switched loops (sense from balanced dipoles); for VHF the system uses 16 monopole elements that can be arranged as crossed-Adcock and parallel-dipole arrays for both horizontal and vertical polarization. There is also a ground mobile version, Model 109. This system dates from the early 1970s.

◆ CCP

Canadian ULQ-6 ECM systems are currently being upgraded by addition of Telemus Electronic Systems's Coherent Countermeasures Processor (CCP), a deception jammer operating between 2 and 18 GHz. It incorporates a 500-emitter library and can deal with coded and pulse-compressed waveforms. Telemus is also offering a system to improve the signal deinterleaving capacity of current broad-band ESM systems, and the company has received a study contract for a low-cost off-board active decoy.

CHINA (PRC)

At the ASIANDEX exhibition in Beijing in the fall of 1988, the China Shipbuilding Trading Co. displayed a radar noise jammer (EAJ-7), a decoy launcher (ERC-1), and a tactical data system (ECIC-1). No details of these devices are available.

The China National Electronics Import and Export Corp. offers a submarine radar ESM device, Type 921-A. It provides bearing accuracy within about 30 degrees for signals at 2–18 GHz in four bands. There is no IFM. The antenna unit is a dome, 560 mm (22 in) in diameter and 515 mm (20 in) high, weighing 80 kg. The four-band operation and lack of Western-style displays suggests that this system may be derived from Soviet ESM technology (as in Watch Dog) obtained prior to the Sino-Soviet split of the late 1950s.

The same company offers a surface-ship radar-warning receiver, RW-23-1, operating over the same four bands, and storing parameters of up to 15 radars. The system employs two antennas, one on either side of the ship.

FRANCE

<small>ELECTRONIC SYSTEMS</small>

◆ ARBB 32

Électronique Serge Dassault conducted the first design studies for this shipboard jammer in 1967, and ARBB 32B entered production in 1974. Two prototypes (ARBB 32A) and ten ARBB 32B were manufactured in 1974–79, and they were installed on board the major French warships: the cruiser *Colbert*, the *Suffrens*, the *Aconit*, the *Tourvilles*, and the first three ASW C70-class corvettes. ARBB 32 was limited to range-gate pulloff, and in 1979 the French Navy asked ESD to develop a more sophisticated jammer, which became ARBB 33.

A few ships have the older ARBB 31.

◆ ARBB 33

Électronique Serge Dassault began design studies for this electronically steered multiple-threat shipborne jammer in 1979; the prototype was completed in 1983, and series production began in 1986. In current form, the system employs a pair of semicylindrical radomes (height 2.2 m, diameter 1.2 m, weight less than 500 kg), port and starboard, each of which contains upper and lower dielectric windows, containing the transmitting and receiving antennas, respectively. The antennas are electronically scanned, and there are 36 ten-degree lobes on each side (so that the direction of jamming can be controlled to within 5 degrees). Jamming power is 100+ kW.

A major advantage claimed for ARBB 33 is its ability to counter target-designation radars as well as fire-control and missile-seeker radars. System functions are threat detection/classification; data transmission to a combat system; and jamming, either automatically after detection, or controlled by the electronic-warfare system. Typically, jamming is coordinated with decoy firing.

The detector operates over H-, I-, and J-bands, measuring frequency, pulse width, PRF, and direction (accuracy within 5 degrees); reaction time is less than 500 msec. The jammer operates over the same bands and can deal simultaneously with two (optionally four) threats. Its primary operating modes are continuous noise, pulsed noise, synchronous false echoes, asynchronous false echoes, and range-gate pull-off (e.g., onto chaff). The jammer uses dish antennas for higher gain compared to the planar antennas of ARBB 32 and other systems. The bands are chosen to cover missile seekers, fire-control radars, and target-designation radars.

◆ ARBR 16/DR 2000

The current standard surface-ship ESM system is made by Thomson-CSF. ARBR 16 works either with an ARBB 31 or 32 jammer (*Jeanne d'Arc, Colbert, Suffren* class, the F67-class frigates, the *Aconit,* and the first three C70 ASW class) and Syllex medium-range chaff; or with DAGAIE chaff launchers (eight Commandant Rivière class and the A69 class).

ARBR 16 is a modified DR 2000.

DR 2000 is an F-band analysis receiver for warning, for surface ships (2000S, with 27-kg antenna) and for submarines (2000U, with 34-kg antenna and, as an option, a 14-kg periscope antenna). DR 2000 is designed to detect pulse and CW signals, including those of frequency-agile radars, and it has a 500- or 1000-signal library against which the video signal (or an optional printout) can be compared. An automatic alarm is provided, either to begin jamming or to dive the submarine. Data output: band, PRF, pulse width, power level, antenna rotation period, jitter, and bearing.

There are six D/F antennas plus an omnidirectional antenna, and a frequency-determining unit (indicating whether a signal is in S-, C-, X-, or Ku-band).

DR 2000 is typically combined with Dalia 500 (500 threat modes) or Dalia 1000 (1000 threat modes). DR 2000 is to be replaced by DR 4000.

DR 2000 was adopted by the German Navy for its Type-343 minesweepers and controls two Silver Fox chaff launchers. As of May 1980, 165 DR 2000–series systems had been ordered; by1988, this number had increased to more than 400. The DR 2000U submarine version is operational in 25 navies.

A new DR 2000U Mk 2 reduces size and increases performance. It covers the D–J-bands, and DF accuracy is about 6 degrees. Total weight is about 90 kg.

◆ ARBR 17/DR 4000

Thomson-CSF's ESM system (covering D–J-bands) for surface ships was announced in 1984 for the new generation of French warships, including the nuclear aircraft carrier *Charles de Gaulle* and the *Cassard*-class air-defense frigate. In these ships ARBR 17 cues the ARBB 33 jammer and the chaff launchers. In the new FL25 frigate, announced in 1984, ARBR 17 was intended to cue the two Dagaie chaff launchers. There are two antennas, an omnidirectional unit (initial detection, IFM, and threat analysis), and two eight-port directional arrays slightly below on the same mast (for D/F and more accurate frequency analysis).

The first ARBR 17 was installed on board the missile frigate *Cassard* in 1986.

DR 4000 is the export version. Compared with DR 2000, DR 4000 gives wider frequency coverage (C- through J-bands). There are three basic versions: 4000S for ships, 4000U for submarines, and 4000A for aircraft. The antenna array consists of one omnidirectional antenna and two groups of six directional antennas (one each for the high and low bands, respectively H–J and C–G). Analysis involves ten radar parameters, to reduce the chance of mistaken identity. The system triggers an alarm if it detects a preset threat radar, such as a missile seeker, requiring instant attention. DR 4000 can process 15 tracks automatically, and can track 40 emitters under operator control.

The display shows both raw video and a generated picture, using the usual NTDS symbols supplemented by three-color coding to indicate particularly urgent threats (red is most urgent), on the theory that color should be used only to trigger an immediate response from an operator. Also showing jammer and decoy use, the display can be used for overall EW management.

DR 4000U has been adopted for the new Brazilian Type-209 submarines. Claimed DF accuracy is 5–6 degrees, the antenna array consisting of an omnidirectional antenna (for IFM) and two six-port assemblies, one for C–G-bands and one for H–J-bands.

◆ Alligator

Alligator is Thomson-CSF's dual-mode (noise/deception) X-band jammer. Its antenna weighs 120 kg; its transceiver, 320 kg.

◆ Dalia

Thomson-CSF's radar analyzer works with the DR 2000 receiver, operates over the E–J-bands, and uses instantaneous frequency measurement. Signals are compared to those in a 500–1000 signal library (the suffix, 500 or 1000, indicates the size of the library; Dalia 1000 was announced in 1976). Identification is based on the characteristics of three consecutive pulses, and as of 1976 Thomson-CSF claimed that any pulse train could be identified within 1.5 seconds. When a signal matches several in the library, all are displayed, each with a "confidence level." Thomson-CSF designates the Dalia/DR 2000 system THV 433 or TMV 434.

◆ DR 3000

This system is under development (1988) and should be available in 1990–1991. About half the weight of DR 2000U, DR 3000 covers the D–K-bands, with an accuracy much better than 6 degrees. The antenna is the new lightweight type introduced in DR 2000U Mk 2.

◆ DR 3012 (Arial)

This broad-band omnidirectional radar receiver for surface ships and submarines is made by Thomson-CSF. DR 3012 normally operates with an Arial 15 analyzer, intended for small ships operating briefly in low-threat environments. The system's memory is manually programmed with about 15 radar modes.

◆ ELISA

The latest Thomson-CSF ESM/ELINT system can also work with DR 4000. ELISA is an acronym for ELINT, Search and Analysis. ELISA covers the C–J-bands (500-MHz instantaneous bandwidth) and is considered sensitive enough to detect a radar's sidelobes or diffused lobes. Signals may be designated to this system by a DR 4000 operator; ELISA carries out detailed analysis using superheterodyne techniques. Search parameters, including those of friendly radars (which are to be locked out) can be programmed in. The plasma display shows a series of histograms (DF, amplitude for scan rate, pulse width, and pulse repetition interval); the operator positions markers in each histogram to read out the measured radar parameters, which are displayed below the four histograms.

◆ Janet

Thomson-CSF's shipboard I/J-band jammer is usually associated with DR 4000. Janet provides both noise and deception signals, either in sequence or simultaneously. Each jammer is computer-controlled for automatic response, and each can deal

Janet jammer on the foremast of a Saudi *Al Madinah*-class frigate (the two round radomes mounted one atop the other). The DR 4000's array is at the masthead, and the radar visible is Sea Tiger. The DAGAIE decoy launcher (without its "suitcases") is on the platform below the top of the superstructure. (Thomson-CSF)

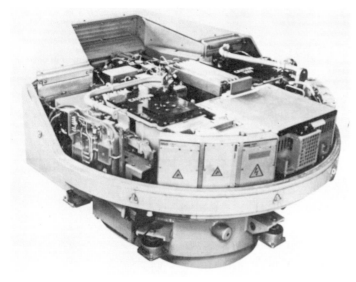

Janet. (Thomson-CSF)

with several simultaneous threats. The complete system includes up to four jamming modules, each incorporating an IFM receiver and a two-horn antenna for signal acquisition and for monopulse signal tracking (azimuth and frequency, not elevation). The jamming transmitter is a TWT, and there is a separate mechanically scanned jamming antenna (10-degree-sector coverage). Under favorable conditions, a module can jam three threats simultaneously.

Reception is sufficiently insulated from jamming transmis-

sions so that the system can receive the signals it is attacking while jamming; there is no look-through pause in the jamming. Thus, Janet can deal with frequency-agile radars, which can defeat the usual jam/see-through systems.

Jamming modes include noise, pulsed noise, self-masking, various forms of deception, and blip enhancement.

Janet is part of the electronics suite of the Saudi *Sawari*-class frigates.

◆ NEWSY/NADS

NEWSY, the Naval Electronic Warfare System, is intended for the C70AA class and the carrier *Charles de Gaulle*. NEWSY uses a dedicated computer that monitors an ARBR 17 ESM system (D–J-bands) and operates an ARBB 33 jammer and chaff/IR decoy launchers (DAGAIE and SAGAIE).

NADS is the export version of NEWSY.

◆ SAPIENS

SAPIENS is Thomson-CSF/CSEE's surveillance alarm and protection, intelligence EW naval system. There are three versions. SAPIENS 1, for small craft, uses Dalia and a 1000-emitter library, DR 2000 receiver, and DAGAIE launcher. SAPIENS 2 uses DR 4000S with IFM and can detect low frequency radars. SAPIENS 3 has a noise and deception jammer.

◆ Shiploc

Shiploc is a small-ship version of the Thomson-CSF Sherloc (TMV 011) airborne radar detector.

◆ TMV 026

TMV 026 is for fast patrol boats, to interface with the Vega fire-control system as well as with Signaal's fire-control systems. Connected with the DR 2000 and Dalia 500, TMV 026 provides coverage of the E–G-bands.

◆ TMV 430

This ESM suite was designed for fast patrol boats but is adaptable to submarines and to larger surface ships. It comprises a DR 2000 broad-band receiver, an analysis/identification/warning receiver such as the Thomson-CSF's Dalia 500 or DR 3012, a noise/deception jammer (such as Alligator 5), and a printer.

Expendables

◆ DAGAIE

This short-range decoy system stands alone on small warships and complements SAGAIE on board French destroyers and larger ships. DAGAIE is sometimes marketed as Squid. The trainable launcher carries ten suitcase-type charges, each 24 × 31 × 5 inches (up to 110 lbs). In small ships, one launcher is mounted on the centerline; larger ships have two launchers. Each suitcase in turn contains either IR or radar decoys fired by mortar, the IR decoys reaching various altitudes and then descending in sequence by parachute to prolong their individual and net effect. Given a warning signal, calculation time is less than 0.2 seconds, and each launcher slews at 1.2 rad/sec.

The manufacturer, CSEE, credits the system with the capability to deal with up to 5 incoming missiles in less than 10 seconds (i.e., one IR and one radar suitcase per missile). A suitcase contains 33 predirected mortars (34 for IR). For IR, there are 10 initial-action and 24 continued-action charges. The initial-action charges operate very close to the ship and break up IR tracking. The delayed-action charges extend the net operating life of the decoy and ensure that the chaff cloud is colocated with an infrared source. Alternative suitcases "A" and "B" can be used to deploy clouds at different altitudes, maximum altitudes being 150 and 300 ft, respectively. Combining both types gives a very large cloud, with a radar cross section of up to 24,000 square yards. A special suitcase (Type D) provides a smaller cloud (3600 square yards) for small vessels.

The radar decoy's bloom time is less than 2 seconds, 132 blooming points being distributed per suitcase, to form a radar

BLOCK DIAGRAM

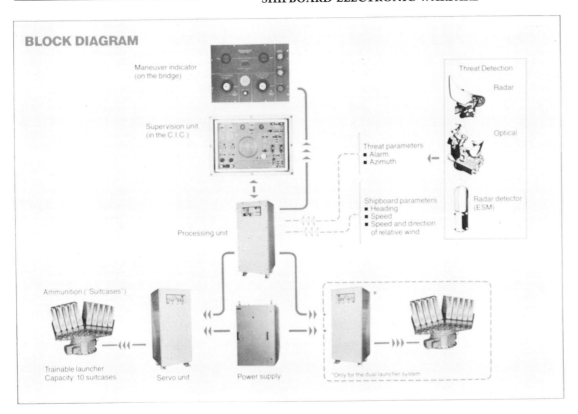

DAGAIE system. (Compagnie de Signaux et d'Entreprises Électriques)

reflector over 5500 square yards in area, covering H- through J-bands and lasting longer than 10 minutes. The IR decoy's duration is 30 seconds, the emitting surface having an area of 360 square yards at an altitude of 45 feet. Individual decoys hit the water at 1 second intervals, after having drifted with the wind.

There is also a 6-suitcase version (990 lbs rather than 1100 lbs for the 10-suitcase launcher).

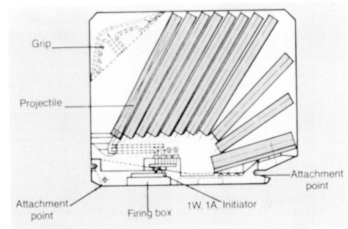

The DAGAIE "suitcase."

DAGAIE launcher. (Compagnie de Signaux et d'Entreprises Électriques)

DAGAIE fires. (Compagnie de Signaux et d'Entreprises Électriques)

The system provides recommended helm orders for evasion based on the expected decoy disposition.

In large warships (frigates and above), DAGAIE is generally used in conjunction with SAGAIE, providing close-range backup. DAGAIE was developed to meet a 1974 French Navy requirement for antimissile self-defense for ships; DAGAIE had to be able to cope with attacks distributed around the horizon and had to be quick acting (reaction time about 5 seconds).

The large-ship DAGAIE launcher is designated AMBL-1B.

A new version, DAGAIE Mk 2, was announced in 1986. It has a more powerful computer and digital/analog, rather than pure analog, interfaces. Mk 2 can, therefore, be integrated with a computer-based combat information system such as SENIT or NTDS. Mk 2 is also designed to fire new chaff and IR rounds requiring more complicated software, such as dilution decoys. A new medium-range REM rocket can be carried in a standard-sized suitcase (four per suitcase), fired individually. Each round has a radar cross section of about 1000 square meters and deploys 800 m from the launcher. The basic DAGAIE launcher can still carry the earlier types of suitcase.

◆ LAD

Leurre Actif Decale, or launched active decoy, was the subject of a 1986 competition between Thomson-CSF and ESD. LAD is to be fired from both DAGAIE and SAGAIE launchers, and maximum dimensions are 127 mm × 1.76 m (weight 27 kg). LAD will be launched and deployed in 8 seconds and should operate for 60 seconds. The dimensions make it compatible with the U.S. Mk 36 SRBOC launcher. In 1988, LAD was described as a centroid decoy, carrying a mini-TWT wide-band transmitter (10 kW, 40-second operation). ESD reportedly prefers deception (presumably by means of a repeater); Thomson-CSF, a noise jammer (which is simpler to implement and may overcome pulse coding). As of 1988, there was no official program, and LAD was being referred to as RAD (Remote Active Decoy). Each round was likely to be both complex and expensive, and there was some interest in an RPV-carried (reusable) solution.

◆ MAGAIE

A lighter version of SAGAIE, MAGAIE carries only three suitcases. There is only one type of ammunition (chaff/IR combined); as in DAGAIE, the mortars are trainable but are fixed in elevation. Operation is fully automatic, based on an attack alarm from an ESM detector, a search radar, or an optical director. The threat sensor provides bearing, and the ship also provides relative wind direction and velocity and ship's heading and speed. Once the decoys have been fired, the system provides recommended helm orders for evasion (favorable course, emergency maneuver, recommended course). Average reaction time is 5 seconds.

The 400-kg launcher slews at 1.2 rad/sec, with a working circle of 400 mm. Each ammunition suitcase weighs 65 kg (630 × 785 × 135 mm).

The name means antimissile self-defense decoy mini-system (*Mini-dispositif d'Autodéfense pour la Guerre Antimissile Infra-rouge et Électromagnetique*).

◆ REM

This new medium-range chaff round was introduced in 1988; as of early 1988, the French Navy had not yet decided whether to adopt this chaff. REM can be launched to 250, 500, or 750 m (altitude 50 m) in less than 5 seconds, providing a radar cross section of 1200 square meters (H–J-bands) for about two minutes.

◆ SAGAIE

SAGAIE is a long-range radar and infrared decoy system (*Système d'Autodéfense pour la Guerre Infra-rouge et Électromagnetique*). It is intended to deal with missiles approaching around the entire horizon, confusing the enemy's targeting radars at long range and, in combination with DAGAIE, confusing missile seekers. A typical installation consists of two ten-tube trainable and elevatable launchers (one on each side), fired from CIC. Each 40-kg rocket carries a 24-kg payload and flies at 250 m/sec (average). The chaff (EM) version fires projectiles radially, to create a large chaff cloud. The subprojectiles of the IR version contain parachutes that lower them in sequence, to prolong the effective life of the IR decoy. Each rocket is fired from its shipping container (330 × 1800 mm, 30 kg containing a 170 × 1740 mm, 40-kg rocket); the entire launcher weighs 1900 kg (empty) and has a working radius of 1.6 m. Range is 8 km for chaff or 3 km for chaff/IR decoys.

Used alone, the decoys provide confusion and distraction. With a jammer, they can dilute an attack and cause missiles to home on a false target after the real target has been concealed or after the missile has been distracted by gate-stealing.

SAGAIE will be mounted on board French frigates, destroyers, and aircraft carriers. It will also be installed on board the new Italian *Animoso*-class missile destroyers. In French service, this system is replacing the modified British eight-barrel Knebworth-Corvus system (Syllex). The prototype was tested on board the trials ship *Île d'Oléron* early in 1986, and the first production installation was on board the destroyer *Cassard* (the second was the carrier *Foch*).

Work is proceeding on a future single system to replace both DAGAIE Mk 2 and SAGAIE.

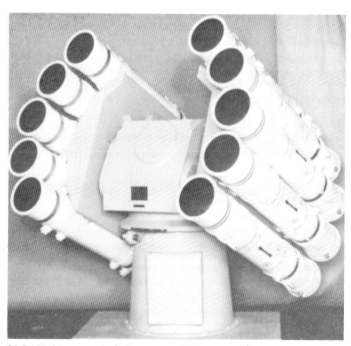

SAGAIE. (Compagnie de Signaux et d'Entreprises Électriques)

GERMANY (WEST)

ELECTRONICS

◆ FL1800S/FL400

FL1800 is the AEG system in German Type-122 frigates and the replacement for the U.S. WLR-6 in the German missile destroyer upgrade of 1986. FL1800 is also fitted in Type-143A missile patrol boats.

FL1800S covers 7.5–17 GHz. This system is designed to engage a large number of close-in emitters automatically, e.g., a short-range missile attack in the North Sea or in the Baltic. A very high processing rate is achieved by preprocessing before signals are entered into the main computer.

In a Type-122 frigate, the D/F array is mounted at the head of the lattice mast amidships, the omnidirectional antenna (for

The German frigate *Rheinland-Pfalz* carries the FL1800S ESM system (omnidirectional mast between the two fire-control systems atop her bridge, directional arrays at her masthead. (M.O.D., Bonn)

frequency and other signal characteristics) on a pole atop the bridge. The omnidirectional antenna consists of five antennas (for five bands) stacked vertically. Each DF array consists of a series of planar antennas mounted on a common base, again to cover five bands. The associated quartet of jammers is mounted on a frame at the base of the housing under the Signaal WM25 radome, on the foremast.

FL400 is a smaller derivative, for export. There are three modules: FL400A, for ELINT; FL400U, for ESM; and the FL400G jammer. Normally FL400U drives FL400G. These systems were all designed for small patrol boats, but they have also been offered for ground use.

FL400A uses an enclosed masthead radome containing three omnidirectional antennas over a rotating high-gain reflector for direction finding. The fixed antennas feed an IFM. The frequency range is 0.5–18 GHz, with an optional extension to 40 GHz (higher frequencies are down-converted into the standard range for analysis). FL400U covers the same frequency range, and it is not clear to what extent the FL400U antenna differs from that of FL400A; FL400G is a 20–60 kW noise and deception jammer (7.5–17.5 GHz).

◆ ASDF

AEG's Advanced Shipborne Direction-Finder was introduced in 1985 to achieve high bearing accuracy (particularly in HF) by suppressing reradiating fields to eliminate ambiguities almost completely. Special wide-band antennas, with nulls at various bearings, can help eliminate receding targets. The A1288 antenna consists of a crossed-loop unit plus a parallel-loop unit to create nulls directed at the presumed locations of fields reradiated by the ship. The processor is designated PST1288.

EXPENDABLES

◆ Hot Dog/Silver Dog

The 76-mm IR (Hot Dog) and chaff (Silver Dog) grenade decoys are made by Buck-Wegmann. Payloads: 0.9 lbs for Hot Dog, 1 lb for Silver Dog. Silver Dog blooms in about 2 seconds. The twelve launchers (in four groups of three) are set at 45-deg elevation and 30-deg train.

Hot Dog/Silver Dog decoy launchers. (Wegmann)

◆ SCHALMEI

AEG-Telefunken's radar (G–K-band)/IR (medium-range) decoys are fired by a trainable launcher, typically one each port and starboard, each holding two 10-tube GRP magazines of chaff or

IR rockets. Each magazine can be elevated independently between +13 and +63 degrees, and the entire mounting is trainable (in 5-deg steps from 0 to 110 degrees relative to the ship's centerline). The 70 mm × 560 mm (2.5-kg) rockets are launched either singly or in salvos of two or three at 60-msec intervals. There is also an 800-mm decoy rocket with twice the chaff payload. Reloading is by replacement of a magazine (570 × 587 × 230 mm, 40 kg).

This system has a low magnetic signature and is, therefore, suitable for MCM craft.

INDIA

In 1986 India announced that its Armament R&D Establishment at Pune had developed a multibarrel medium-range chaff launcher, which either is, or will be, used on board Indian ships.

INTERNATIONAL

◆ Sea Gnat

NATO's program for a chaff/IR decoy, Sea Gnat is compatible with the U.S. SRBOC (Mk-36) launcher. The decoy deploys chaff and also a hot gas bag (for IR), the two drifting together in the wind. In Britain, the contractors are Hunting Engineering (fire control by Thorn EMI), and the launcher is DLB (to be replaced by DLJ). As fitted to a British Type-22 frigate, Sea Gnat employs either the U.S. Mk 36 or a pair of eight-barreled launchers on each side, all eight barrels apparently sharing the same elevation, the two launchers at two different (fixed) bearings.

Decoys associated with Sea Gnat include the U.S. Mk 214 seduction cartridge and Mk 216 distraction cartridge. Hycor developed an IR cartridge under this program, M-BIRD (Balloon Infrared Decoy), a balloon that floated on the water. M-BIRD did not enter production. The new Sea Gnat cartridges are scheduled to enter U.S. service during 1989.

ISRAEL

ELECTRONIC SYSTEMS

◆ EL-1040

Elta's system is found in Taiwanese (GRC) FRAM-II destroyers.

◆ EL/L-8303

Elta's computerized ESM system is for ship, air, and ground applications. EL/L-8303 intercepts, digitizes, identifies, and records signals in the 2–18 GHz range, with an optional extension to cover 0.5–2 GHz; this system can interface with ECM and chaff systems for manual or automatic operation. Features include direction finding, a combined alphanumeric and graphic (bearing/threat level) display, and comparison with a built-in emitter library. Accuracy: 5 deg in bearing, 1 MHz in frequency; nominal reaction time is 1 second. Sensitivity (narrow-band) is −80 dBm, and dynamic range is 60 dB.

◆ EL/L-8310

Elta's ESM receiver is for 0.5–18 GHz (with optional extension to cover 0.06–40 GHz).

◆ EL/L-8312

Elta's computerized ELINT/ESM microwave reception and classification system (computer-controlled autoscan, signal acquisition, and display) covers 0.5–18 GHz (optional extension to 60 MHz–40 GHz range). EL/L-8312 is a monopulse DF system. It is operated by one man. EL/L-8312A is an airborne ELINT/ESM system. This system employs the EL/L-8310 receiver, the EL/L-8320 pulse analyzer, the EL/L-8610 computer, and the EL/L-8570 display.

◆ MN-53

ELTA's passive intercept is used in Israeli Navy and South African *Reshev*s and Israeli *Romat*, *Aliyah*, and *Sa'ar*-II and -III–class missile patrol boats. Reportedly the ESM/ECM system was designed by the Italian firm Elettronica and manufactured by Elta. Radar parameters measured are band, PRF, pulse width, and PRF wobbulation. Elta claims that MN-53 reflects Israeli experience during the 1973 Yom Kippur War. The NS-5000 is an alternative.

◆ NS-9000 Series

These AEL Israel (Elisra) EW systems were announced in 1982. NS-9001 is an automatic electronic-intelligence (ELINT) gathering system to map emissions (0.5–18 GHz). The display shows frequency vs. bearing. Direction-finding accuracy: 10 degrees in X/Ku-bands, 3 degrees in S/C-bands. Frequency measurement: 2-MHz resolution. Sensitivity: 70 dBm (omni), 80 dBm (sector). Modes: instantaneous direction finding (IDF), monopulse direction finding (IDF), and search (SDF).

NS-9002 is a simulation van, which can generate up to 256 emitters (frequency resolution 1 MHz, PRF 125 pps up to 250,000 pps, scan rate 100 Hz track-while-scan to 20-second search).

NS-9003 is an automatic computer-controlled ESM system. Direction finding is monopulse, and the system incorporates an IFM. NS-9003 can be used to trigger chaff, flare, or ECM responses (typically by NS-9005). Direction-finding accuracy is 1 deg in X/Ku-bands and 3 deg in S/C-bands. This version was originally developed for the hydrofoil *Shimrit*.

NS-9004 is an ESM system for submarines.

NS-9005 is a noise and deception jammer (2–18 GHz) that uses steerable antennas to engage multiple threats simultaneously, using spot, barrage, or swept noise, or RGPO, RGPI, AGPO deception. NS-9005 can also produce false targets.

NS-9007 upgrades existing EW equipment.

NS-9008 is an automatic repair facility.

NS-9009 is a compact version for small patrol boats of up to 200 tons. It uses a wide-open receiver for dense (over 200,000 pulses/sec) electronic environments (2–18 GHz). DF accuracy is 8 degrees, and sensitivity is 35 dBm. The operator has both a tabular read-out and a polar display. Visual and audio alarms are activated when specific threat signals are recognized. This system can control chaff launchers, and it can be upgraded to provide IFM.

A faster version of 9003, NS-9010 uses distributed microprocessors for dense environments (over 250,000 pulses/sec). It is used against radars in the 2–18 GHz range. It employs monopulse switching direction finding (instantaneous direction finding is optional). NS-9010 uses a multibeam static-antenna array. Accuracy is 3 deg in X/Ku-bands and 5 deg in S/C-bands.

NS-9025 is an airborne standoff jammer for naval and ground applications.

NS-9034, a specialized submarine ESM suite for a moderate pulse environment (about 100K pulses/sec), uses six spiral antennas (2–18 GHz), an optional coarse DF array (Elbit-supplied RKR lenses, 7.5–18 GHz), and an omnidirectional array (2–18 GHz) on the periscope mast. Coarse DF accuracy is 6 degrees, fine accuracy 1 degree, and elevation coverage +30/−10 deg.

A typical integrated ECM suite consists of NS-9010 controlling an NS-9050 jamming and deception system.

All of these systems were announced in 1982. As of 1985, they had been exported to at least three countries and were in Israeli Navy service.

◆ SEWS/Rattler

Rafael's Shipboard Electronic Warfare System is in current Israeli service. The ESM portion employs monopulse direction finding (for instantaneous direction finding) and IFM, over 1–18 GHz; signals are automatically compared to an emitter library, on the basis of frequency, bearing, amplitude, time of arrival, pulse width, scan rate, and pulse coding. The display shows the true and relative bearings of detected emitters. The ECM response is either automatic or operator controlled, and the system incorporates a multibeam array transmitter (MBAT) jammer so that it can engage several targets simultaneously (and so that it can steer its beam very rapidly). This system can also control the Rattler jammer.

Rattler is a Rafael jammer for air, ground, and naval applications. It can engage up to three radars simultaneously, over 2–18 GHz. One high-powered broad-band amplifier is time-shared among the three channels, excited by a lower-powered microwave source. Output power is reportedly greater than 400 watts.

◆ SPIRTAS DS 35

Elop's IR target-acquisition system for missile boats is designed to respond to the low-flying antiship missile threat. SPIRTAS classifies targets using their IR signatures and provides a synthetic display of the system's entire field of view, together with threat-evaluation data, an enlarged FLIR display of a selected area, and an auxiliary display showing the intensity of selected targets. SPIRTAS can be used together with a laser range-finder or a radar.

◆ TIMNEX 4 CH

Elbit's ESM/ELINT system for the 2–18 GHz range has channelized IFM and automatic classification. Mk 1 has been in service on board *Gal*-class submarines since 1982, and Mk 2 will be fitted in the Taiwanese submarines built in the Netherlands. A related ESM system is probably being fitted to Australian *Oberons*, and Elbit and Kollmorgen are responsible for the ESM suite planned for the next-generation Israeli submarine.

The TIMNEX 4 CH is optimized for ELINT rather than for threat warning. In the Mk-2 version, the system has four-channel IFM associated with an enlarged DF array covering its frequency range (expandable to 0.5–40 GHz). There is also a miniature DF mast atop the periscope, for threat warning (8–18 GHz, accuracy 3–5 degrees).

EXPENDABLES

◆ Automatic CM-Dispensing System

Elbit's shipboard launcher for chaff and flares selects and launches countermeasures on the basis of the threat's character, range, and bearing. There is a manual back-up.

◆ Chaff Rockets

Israel's chaff rockets were developed as a complement to the Gabriel missile. The designed range of the missile was much shorter than that of the Styx missiles of the Arab navies, so the Israeli strategy was to induce the Arabs to fire first—and to miss—using a combination of active and passive countermeasures. Reportedly the long-range chaff was fired to induce enemy boats to shoot. A combination of short-range chaff and radar-absorbing material on portions of the Israeli boats caused the incoming missiles to miss their targets.

The short-range rockets are fired from six-round launchers on machine-gun mounts or from fixed 24- or 45-round launchers; the rockets weigh 7 lbs (payload 3.9 lbs). Dimensions are 90 × 640 mm. The long-range rockets are fired from single- or double-barreled launchers located on ships' superstructures. These rockets use two-pulse (boost-sustain) rocket motors and are actuated by an altitude fuze. Rocket weight is 9.4 kg; and 1.3 kg of chaff are carried, dispensed by an altitude fuze. Dimensions are 89 × 922 mm.

The six-barrel launcher is now being marketed in the United States under the designation LADS.

◆ Beamtrap

Beamtrap, manufactured by Rafael, is a short range ESM/chaff rocket announced in 1988, presumably as a replacement for the earlier Israeli short-range chaff rockets. Weight is 6.5 kg (chaff payload 3.75 kg); dimensions are 115 × 804 mm. These rockets are fired from a six-barreled launcher, whose elevation is fixed.

ITALY

◆ BETA

Elettronica's ESM system is found in the Spanish *Descubierta* class. BETA is not integrated into the combat systems. This system employs a pair of the standardized Elettronica D/F antennas (spinners in cylindrical stabilized radomes).

◆ CO-NEWS

Elettronica's communications ECM system (VHF/UHF) is installed in the *Maestrale* class. This system, designed for continuous surveillance and intercept, measures bearings and classifies emitters. CO-NEWS uses a high-scan-rate receiver and a fast automatic direction-finder. The antenna consists of three arrays, each consisting of four vertical dipoles (to cover the full VHF/UHF range) and a switching matrix; intercepted signals are demodulated for surveillance.

◆ ELT 116

Elettronica's radar interceptor is used as part of an ESM or ECM system. Typically such a system covers 2–18 GHz and uses a four-channel IFM receiver, whose outputs are displayed on two CRTs. The system can discriminate between pulsed and CW signals, and an automatic-warning module with a lamp alert can be added. The module can be set to respond to up to 32 emitters. Frequency measurement is accurate to within 0.2 percent, and sensitivity is −70 dBm.

◆ ELT 123

Elettronica's basic ESM module is similar in principle to ELT 116 above. ELT 123 provides direction finding for both pulse and CW signals and can be programmed to provide automatic warning of particular threats. In the FARAD system, ELT 123 passes its data automatically to an ELT 261 for analysis.

◆ ELT 124

ELT 124 is used for threat warning and D/F; see THETIS.

◆ ELT 128

This communications direction-finder is for air, ground, and naval service on the HF, VHF, and UHF bands. ELT 128 automatically finds the direction of an emitter and provides technical analysis of modulation. The HF antenna consists of half-dipoles or ferrite crossed loops (mobile applications); for VHF/UHF, the device uses an array of active dipoles.

◆ ELT 211

This ESM system is for Newton (see below).

◆ ELT 224

See THETIS below.

◆ ELT 261

Elettronica's radar analysis module (see FARAD below) provides automatic tracking and automatic analysis of intercepted signals, with continuous surveillance on a panoramic display.

◆ ELT 311

ELT 311 is Elettronica's manually operated jammer. Jamming techniques include noise, deception, automatic, and semiautomatic. For example, the jammer can use spot noise or modulated spot noise against search and tracking radars (conscan types). There are look-through and time-gated circuits for control.

◆ ELT 318

Elettronica's dual-band CW noise jammer operates with either medium- or high-gain antennas. Using variable modulation techniques, it jams search radars and can adapt to new threats. It normally uses one or two ELT 828 stabilized-antenna assemblies.

◆ ELT 361

Elettronica's dual-band CW noise jammer is capable of spot and barrage jamming; see FARAD below.

◆ ELT 511

Elettronica's manually operated jammer is used as part of an ECM system.

◆ ELT 521

This Elettronica high-powered deception jammer uses either directional (in conjunction with a D/F system) or omnidirectional antennas.

◆ ELT 711

Elettronica's radar-identification module is used as part of an ESM or ECM system.

◆ ELT 712

Elettronica's programming unit is used as part of an ESM/ECM system.

◆ ELT 716

Elettronica's data-transmission module is used as part of an ESM or ECM system.

◆ ELT 814

ELT 814 is Elettronica's omnidirectional antenna. It is a broadband cone, the radome covering a spiral antenna. Similar units include the Selenia RQN-1A and the U.S. AS-1174/SLR. Frequency coverage is determined by the angle of the cone, and bandwidth by the rate of spiral around the cone.

◆ ELT 828

ELT 828 is Elettronica's directional antenna. It was reported in 1987 that PRC's Jianghu-V frigates were being fitted with Elettronica EW suites including this antenna. Elettronica uses two sizes (to cover two bands) of spinning D/F antennas in stabilized, cylindrical radomes.

◆ FARAD

FARAD is Elettronica's system for small ships. It conducts signal intercept and self-protection and consists of ELT 123 (basic ESM), ELT 261 (analysis), ELT 521 (deception jammer), and ELT 361 (noise jammer), with an ELT-828 antenna. ELT 123 is the core unit, with others added as needed.

◆ GAMMA

Elettronica's ECM suite covers the 2–18 GHz range in four bands. The four outputs are displayed on two CRTs that can discriminate between pulse and CW signals. Two other CRTs display signal-analysis data, and a fifth gives D-band data. Several jammers are provided, including radar-angle jamming to confuse track-while-scan radars.

◆ INS Series

Selenia's Integrated Naval Systems, INS-1, is for small ships such as fast patrol boats. INS-3 is for large ships. INS-1 consists of an RQN-1 radar detector, a PAW-1 pulse analyzer (with warning), and an optional TQN-1 jammer and an RIN-1 identification unit.

RQN-1 employs an omnidirectional cone antenna (for wide frequency range) plus an array of directional antennas, measuring signal source bearing, pulse width, PRF, and band (L, S, C, and X: a lamp indicates the band). There is no IFM. Coverage is 1–12 GHz (but the system works up to 18 GHz), and nominal sensitivity is 48 dBm. Directional accuracy is 5 degrees for the 2–12 GHz range, PRF is measured to within 10 percent for 50–10,000 pps (displayed on a 3-inch CRT), and pulse width is measured to within 10 percent between 0.3 and 5 microseconds. Bearing is indicated by a CRT strobe.

The intercept and direction-finding antenna of an Italian INS-3 installed on the Indian frigate *Godavari*, 1986.

INS-5 is the latest of a series of Selenia jammers. They are generally mounted on masts, without radomes. (Selenia)

The designation INS-3 indicates Integrated (ESM-ECM) Naval System, third generation. Selenia characterizes the first generation as having separate analog video displays for D/F and frequency measurement and as using a digital analyzer. In dense environments, it could be difficult to correlate a strobe with the associated pulse characteristics. Second-generation systems introduced a frequency-bearing (situation) display, for quick analysis and unique D/F-frequency correlation. A system of this type was successfully tested on board an Italian corvette but did not enter production. However, the second generation led directly to INS-3, whose main feature is automatic data extraction, done by a processor that carries out automatic analysis in real time and that controls active countermeasures. Compared with the second-generation display, INS-3's associates an identification symbol with each intercept. The processor maintains an active radar file of up to 64 emitters and can provide warning of up to 32 preprogrammed threats. There are two intercept channels, to cover the full 1–18 GHz range. For DF, there are eight fixed antennas surrounding the omnidirectional antenna feeding the IFM processor. Directional accuracy is 5 degrees.

INS-3 is built around a digital interceptor (RQN-3), with instantaneous frequency measurement for 1–18 GHz and with automatic control of chaff launchers. It is usually associated with the RIN-1 digitally augmented display system, which includes an RQN-3B for automatic detection, analysis, and tracking. Threat library capacity is 3000.

The ECM section is designated TQN-2; it receives data for automatic reaction (noise and pulse jamming, as well as chaff and flare control). The stabilized jamming antenna automatically tracks its target by two-channel monopulse (the DF array provides coarse data) and emits noise over a range of 6–18 GHz. Beamwidth is 3 degrees. There is a second 6-degree beam used to avoid the nodding effects due to multipath reflection at low elevation angles. A separate ULQ-2 deception unit can be added, to modulate the jamming signal for range and angle deception. The system can also provide passive tracking data to other self-defense weapons.

INS-3 is based on a helicopter system, IHS-6, which uses an RQH-5 receiver and a TQN-2 jammer.

The latest system in the series is INS-5, employing the RQN-5 receiver and the TQN-2 active jammer of the INS-3 system. The system can track up to 50 emitters, and its threat library contains 3000 emitters. Emitters are tracked both in bearing and in elevation (as in the case of aircraft and missiles).

◆ NETTUNO

Elettronica's ECM system is found in the hydrofoil *Sparviero.*

◆ Nettunel

Nettunel is the Elettronica ECM system of the Spanish *Oliver Hazard Perry*–class frigates. Just below the TACAN antenna are eight D/F panels, and below them are four omnidirectional antennas on the crosstrees, similar to those of Newton (ELT 211). However, where Newton uses two pots and two cone antennas, Nettunel uses three pots and one cone. There are also two large boxes on the superstructure and two smaller boxes, one at each yardarm end (about half the size of the main boxes). All are roll-stabilized: these boxes are presumably the jammers. Each carries two cylindrical dielectric lenses, side by side, in front of transmitting arrays. The small yardarm boxes are D/F antennas, presumably for lower frequencies than those collected by the antennas at the masthead. The two lenses help focus incoming radiation onto two phased-array antennas for high-angular resolution; each box covers 180 degrees. The Italian carrier *Garibaldi* uses similar box-lens D/F antennas, although she carries four.

◆ Newton

Elettronica's ESM system in the *Maestrale* and *Minerva* classes, Newton employs the ELT-211 receiver. Four omnidirectional antennas cover all the usual bands, and a DF antenna localizes a detected threat. The mast-mounted portion of the receiver weighs 120 lbs (total 800 lbs). The ECM portion of the system consists of the ELT-814 receiver/transmitter omnidirectional antenna, two ELT-828 antennas, an ELT-318 noise jammer, and an ELT-521 deception jammer.

Newton B is intended for 250–650 ton craft. This ESM system integrates with the combat and fire-control systems.

Newton and Newton B were first shown in 1980.

◆ MM/SPR-A

Elettronica's ESM system for the Italian Navy is presumably a version of one of the commercial systems listed. Coverage is 1.0–10.5 GHz, using four fixed omnidirectional antennas to achieve wide-open performance in bearing. The system employs crystal video receivers; it has no associated IFM. Emitter bearing is indicated by a strobe on the CRT display.

This system appeared in the late 1970s.

◆ RQN Series

Selenia's signal receivers are associated with digital data-analysis threat libraries. RQN-1 operates over 1–12 GHz; –1A over 1–18 GHz. Outputs are bearing, frequency band, pulse width, and PRF. Directional accuracy is 5 degrees. With the addition of a special module, RQN-1 can provide automatic warning of up to eight selected threats. Sensitivity is 48 dBm. RQN-3 uses an IFM, and its sensitivity is 65 dBm.

◆ THETIS

Elettronica's submarine ESM system provides threat warning (via frequency measurement) and direction finding. The name means Threat Evaluation Tactical Information System. THETIS is available in two configurations, ELT/124-S and ELT/224-S. The basic system gives threat warning and direction finding only; the more sophisticated version also gives full ESM (it adds an IFM receiver and full ESM display). Both versions use the same D/F antenna (one conical spiral omnidirectional antenna plus eight plane-spiral D/Fs assembled in a single casing to withstand pressure), and both can be fitted with a separate omnidirectional antenna (ELT/724-S) with pre-amplifier, which can be mounted on the attack or search periscope for primary warning before surfacing.

◆ Breda 105-mm Rocket Launchers

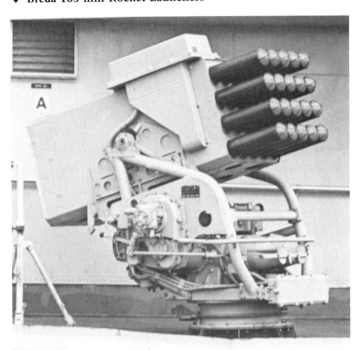

Breda's 105-mm rocket launcher, for both decoys and shore bombardment. (Breda)

There are two types, a 20-rocket trainable and elevatable launcher and a light-chaff launcher.

The twenty-tube heavy launcher is part of the SCLAR system, which has been successfully exported. A full SCLAR consists of two rocket launchers, a control unit (UCLAR, built by Elsag), and 105-mm SNIA rockets. The launcher consists of four horizontal rows of tubes; weight is about 1150 kg empty or 1750 kg loaded. The launcher trains at 60 deg/sec and elevates at 30 deg/sec (limits +55/–3 degrees). Firing rate is approximately one rocket/second. Working circle is 1.38 m.

This launcher can also fire illumination and bombardment rockets. Rocket types are chaff distraction (range 12,000 m), chaff seduction (5000 m), IR seduction (5000 m), illumination (4000 m), bombardment to support a landing force (11,000 m), and coastal bombardment (11,000 m). Rockets are carried in waterproof containers with frangible heads. The launcher itself can be modified to accommodate 81-mm or 127-mm rockets (e.g., 24 × 81 mm or 12 × 127 mm).

The light-chaff dispensing system uses only short-range rockets, for distraction or seduction; this system is intended for craft too small for the twenty-tube launcher. Rockets are carried packed in their fiberglass shipping containers, and the six tubes of each launcher (port and starboard) are fixed in elevation (35 degrees) and in train (45 degrees from the centerline), in a chassis fixed on the deck. Typically four tubes face onto each bow, and two onto each quarter. The system can fire one rocket onto each bearing, or four onto all four bearings (045, 135, 225, and 315 degrees), or two onto the two bow bearings.

Each six-round launcher weighs 105 kg empty or 145 kg loaded. Each short-range rocket weighs 5.2 kg; and when fired at a 35-degree elevation, the rocket reaches a maximum altitude of 100 m (300-m range) in 4.426 seconds, and falls into the water in 9 seconds (range about 560 m). The rocket is designed to burst at 80 meters (to ensure a cloud duration of about 2 minutes, with a reflecting area of 800–1200 square meters on I/J-bands).

JAPAN

◆ Fleet ECM Policy (1988)

Electronic warfare systems on board the Japanese destroyer *Asagiri*. The masthead radar is OPS-28, the cruise-missile detector analogous to the U.S. TAS Mk 23; OPS-28 is used in conjunction with the radome-enclosed FCS 2-12E aft, which controls the Sea Sparrow (launcher on the stern). The fire-control radar forward is FCS 2-21A, and the air-search radar is OPS-14C. NOLR-6 combines equipment on both masts. (Japanese Maritime Self-Defense Force)

Electronic warfare systems of the missile destroyer *Hatakaze*. NOLQ-1 combines the masthead array, the antenna just forward of the main air-search radar (SPS-52C), and the flat array at the base of the big lattice mast. The two-dimensional radar aft is OPS-11C, and the slotted array at the masthead is the OPS-28B anti–sea-skimmer set. (Japanese Maritime Self-Defense Force)

The main current systems, with their U.S. equivalents, are:

NOLR-6 very similar to WLR-8

NOLQ-1 very similar to the U.S. SLQ-32(V)3

NOLQ-2 currently under development

OLR-9 very similar to WLR-11

OLT-3 very similar to SLQ-17

ZLR-3/5 warning receivers, very similar to WLR-8

ZLR-4/6 ESM systems, very similar to WLR-1G

Surface units will have the following systems:
DDH, DDG—NOLQ-1 (ESM/ECM), Mk 36-2 SRBOC
DD—NOLR-6 (ESM), OLR-9 (WR), OLT-3 (ECM), Mk 36-1 SRBOC
DE—NOLR-6 (ESM), OLR-9 (WR), Mk 36-1 SRBOC

After JFY88, NOLR-8 will replace NOLR-6 and OLR-9. New ships after JFY90 will have NOLR-8 and Mk 36 SRBOC.

Submarines have ZLR-4/6 (ESM) and ZLR-3/5 (WR); new submarines after JFY88 will have NZLR-1.

Aircraft:
—P-3s have ALQ-78 or ALR-66(V3)
—P-2Js have HLQ-101 (domestically developed)
—SH-3Hs have ALR-66(V1)
—SH-60Js have HLR-108 (domestically developed)

NETHERLANDS

Signaal and the British MEL company are both members of the PEAB group, and the equipment of these two companies is often intended to operate together.

◆ RAMSES/Scimitar

Ramses jammer (two radomes, separated vertically, with radiation-reflecting plates between them) on board the former Dutch cruiser *de Ruyter*, now in Peruvian service. The radar above is DA-08. (Signaal)

Signaal's Reprogrammable Multimode Shipborne ECM system is a noise and deception jammer (I/J-band) that uses a pair of egg-shaped masthead or yardarm radomes (350-mm diameter × 1100 mm; 25 kg each). The antennas inside rotate and are stabilized. Within each radome, the upper antenna is the transmitter, the lower the receiver. Noise jamming is used against target-acquisition radars, and a deception repeater against missile seekers. Signaal claims that the noise jammer may be effective at ranges as great as 180 or 200 km.

A NATO version of RAMSES, Scimitar is a reprogrammable noise and deception jammer for the 8–16 GHz band, intended primarily to deal with missile seekers and target-indication radars. Jamming modes include noise (either spot or wide band), range-gate seduction, inverse scan gain, and false-target generation. Power output is 1.0 kW in pulse mode and 100 W in CW mode (later increased to 1.5 kW and 150 W). Scimitar can jam several radars (with different characteristics) simultaneously, as long as they are all in its beam. The two antennas can track two separate radars simultaneously. Beamwidth is 7 × 7 deg (gain 23 dB) and frequency sensitivity is 60 dBm.

Scimitar, with its own receiver, can be used as a stand-alone system if the associated ESM system fails.

See also the Canadian SLQ-503 above.

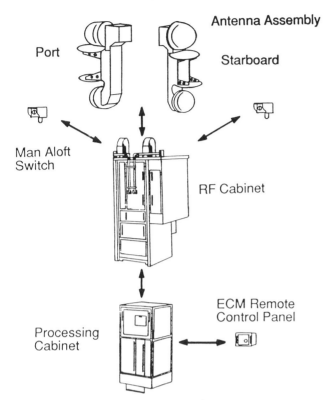

RAMSES, SLQ-503. (MEL Defense Systems)

◆ Rapids

Signaal/MEL's system for passively identifying radars (ESM) covers 2–18 GHz and uses phase comparison for direction finding. Rapids provides automatic threat warning and can be used to trigger countermeasures. Operation can be either automatic (using a threat library) or manual, the screen showing scan type, frequency, PRF, pulse width, scan rate, signal

Rapids ESM arrays around a mast (under the DA-08 radar) on board a Dutch *van Heemskerck*–class missile frigate. The different-sized radomes correspond to different bands. (Signaal)

strength, and bearing. The receiver is wide open, so it can provide data after the first pulse. Up to six warning channels can be programmed with frequency, PRF, pulse width, and triggering amplitude. A special feature warns of automatic lock-on and can record up to three simultaneous lock-ons (i.e., signals with constant bearing and relatively constant amplitude and frequency, within specified limits). The lock-on circuits monitor the 7.5–18 GHz band. The library can store up to 256 radars, with up to 6 modes per radar parameter. Bearing accuracy is 3 degrees.

See also the British (MEL) Manta system below.

◆ Sphinx

Signaal's ESM system intercepts and identifies pulsed radar transmissions (1–18 GHz), using a sensitive IFM with digital output. Sphinx automatically warns of radar lock-on and automatically analyzes and tracks selected signals. Selected signals tracked in bearing, or selected sectors, can be blanked. Sphinx exchanges data with associated ECM and combat systems. Frequency coverage can be extended to 33–40 GHz.

The Dutch frigate *Van Kinsbergen* shows a Sphinx ESM array around her foremast, under the egg of her Signaal WM-25. The surface-search radar is ZW-06. (L&L Van Ginderen)

NORWAY

◆ SR-1A

This shipboard radar-intercept receiver (2.5–18 GHz) is made by Nera A/S. The antenna consists of a rotating antenna in a radome and a fixed octagonal horn array. The spinning antenna gives a bearing accuracy of 3.5 degrees, compared with 22.5 degrees for the omnidirectional horns at the base. The system as a whole can measure PRF between 200 Hz and 10 kHz, and pulse widths between 0.2 and 10 microseconds. The spinner can rotate at up to 500 rpm, the speed varying automatically to avoid synchonizing rotation with that of the transmitting antenna (and thus losing all signals). The display is a CRT, showing a deflection pattern of multiple radial lines corresponding to the rotation of the spinner; the longest lines give the direction of the emitter, and this data can be read off as either relative or true bearing.

This system dates at least from the mid-1970s.

◆ NE-10A

The Nera A/S broad-band submarine warning receiver operates between 2.5 and 11 GHz (usable up to 18 GHz). It covers the entire hemisphere over the antenna, and PRFs of 0.1–10 kHz. The system does not discriminate among signals: it emits its audible warning when it receives any pulsed radar signal over its bandwidth.

This system dates at least from the mid-1970s.

♦ VS-30

Nera's radar search receiver, ca. 1976, uses fixed wide-open ports to cover the 2.5–18 GHz range, with instantaneous measurement of PRF, pulse width, and bearing. There are five versions, with three types of antennas and four display and output arrangements. A typical unit consists of three tiers of horns, eight per tier, alternating horizontal and vertical polarization.

SPAIN

About 1976 the Spanish Navy installed a strategic ELINT system on board the fast attack vessel *Alsedo*, which typically patrols southern Mediterranean waters near the Straits of Gibraltar and off the North African coast.

SWEDEN

ELECTRONIC SYSTEMS

♦ EWS 900CA

Saab's ECM system is intended primarily to counter antiship missiles fired at fast strike craft. The associated computer evaluates the threat, fires chaff rocket decoys, and calculates the appropriate evasive maneuvers. The system is controlled from a PPI and can be operated from one of several locations on board, by the first operator to recognize the incoming threat (radar-warning operator, radar operator, officer of the deck, lookouts).

The decoys are unusual in that, instead of using pyrotechnics, they are launched by compressed air; chaff charges for several frequency bands are available. Each launcher has eight 40-mm tubes arranged around an air reservoir; their angles of elevation and divergence are adjustable. Chaff is pneumatically dispersed at an altitude of about 100 m, 0.6 seconds after launch. Muzzle velocity is 70 m/sec.

This system entered service in 1980 on board Swedish *Hugin*-class missile boats. In Swedish service EWS 900CA was superseded by the Saab-Scania EWS 905.

♦ EWS 905

Saab-Scania's dual-mode ESM/warning system identifies targets detected by search radar; this system is found on board Swedish

EWS 905 masthead array. (Saab)

fast attack craft *Stockholm* and *Hugin* class. EWS 905 automatically commands shipboard chaff launchers and other self-defense measures. The display shows bearing, frequency band, pulse interval, pulse width, and scan time, as well as the major evaluated threats. Up to fifty emitters evaluated as less threatening are stored and can be called up. There are three operating modes: alert (all bands covered, with the system concentrating on a single threat sector; the sector and frequency are displayed); decision (the antenna rapidly scanning a selected sector; bearing, band, pulse interval, and pulse width are displayed); and surveillance (the antenna slowly scanning the selected sector; the above parameters plus the target antenna's rotation rate are displayed).

♦ 9EW300/400

PEAB's integrated ECM systems, designed for, respectively, patrol vessels and small frigates, were announced in 1987. These systems combine a new Philax trainable chaff launcher with new lens and omnidirectional antennas and laser-warning receivers. In the *Goteborg* class, the directional lens antennas are mounted on the fore and after surfaces of the mast, just below the search radar.

The PEAB 9EW300 EWS system includes up to eight chaff/IR magazines on a trainable launcher. (Saab)

EXPENDABLES

♦ Bofors Rockets

Chaff rockets (57 mm) can be fired from rails rigged to existing Bofors gun mounts, using the existing gun-control system. Rocket dimensions are 57 × 1385 mm (16.5 lbs carrying 2–2.2 lbs of chaff), with maximum velocity of 420 m/sec; range at 30-deg elevation is 1400–6000 m. Time to bloom is 30 seconds, and the chaff cloud lasts at least 6 minutes, forming a radar target similar to that of a 2000–3000 ton ship.

There is also a long-range 103-mm rocket (payload 2.4 kg, range 10,000 m).

♦ Philax 105/106

The Philips (PEAB) chaff-launching system is rather larger than that associated with the Saab EWS 900CA. Philax 106 carries IR decoys. The system employs two launchers (four in larger ships), each consisting of four 40-kg boxes; each box contains 36 chaff grenades (four nine-grenade salvos). The grenades of the salvo (each carrying 0.175 kg of chaff) are launched by a single ejection charge, and they rise at varying angles to form a 1000 square-meter chaff decoy about 2 seconds after firing (about 20 m from the launch point, at a height of 50 m) and remain effective for about 20 seconds.

In Philax 106, one of the normal four magazines is replaced by three IR decoy containers, each holding 21 decoys. Deployment is much like that of the French DAGAIE system, but the decoys are not the same. The first five IR grenades form an initial decoy near the ship (about 10 m away), then two remaining groups of eight each are fired on varying trajectories, with parachute descent, to merge with the chaff cloud about 10–15 m above the sea surface. The decoy lasts about 25 sec.

The Philax launcher, plus a computer to achieve optimum decoy effect, is designated 9CM200 (four sets of launchers) or 9CM100 (two sets of launchers) by PEAB.

MEL in the United Kingdom is a member of the PEAB group, and its Protean is almost identical to Philax.

◆ 9CM Series

PEAB's chaff systems are intended for integration with the 9LV series of fire-control systems. The 9CM Series are based on a combination of the Philips Philax system (see above) and a threat-warning system: Matilda for 9CM100; Rapids, Phoenix II, or Cutlass for 9CM200. Data from an ESM/threat-warning module and from fire control are fed to the 9CM computer, together with the ship's heading, speed, and roll angle; the ship's radar cross section and IR signature; and wind direction. 9CM200 uses a fixed quadruple chaff/IR launcher.

TAIWAN (GRC)

◆ ECM Systems

The chief warning systems are the U.S.-supplied WLR-1 and the ARGO 680/681, the latter equipping ships updated with Honeywell H-930 fire-control systems. Surviving WLR-1s have been modernized to cover the J-band, to deal with new PRC missiles with J-band seekers (such as C801 and FL-1).

Reportedly the latest Taiwanese ECM system was derived from the unsuccessful Hughes contender for the Design-to-Price EW suite, SLQ-31. As of 1982, about 10 were on order, for Weapons System Improvement Program 3 (*Gearing*-class destroyers). This ECM system may have been an ESM system supplemented by a stand-alone jammer; Raytheon claims that its Sidekick (see the U.S. SLQ-32 entry) was originally evolved to meet a Taiwan Navy requirement.

◆ Chaff Rockets

The standard Taiwanese destroyer chaff launcher is CR-201, a 16-barrel 126-mm device similar to the 105-mm Italian Breda SCLAR. The rocket was developed from the abortive army Kung Feng (KF-4) artillery round. Four launchers are mounted on board each destroyer and large frigate. As in SCLAR, there are both long-range distraction rounds and short-range break-lock rapid-bloom rounds.

A Taiwanese (GRC) destroyer, firing her Hsiung Feng I missile, shows a CR-201 trainable chaff rocket launcher in the foreground. (Fu S. Mei)

USSR

◆ Bald Head

Bald Head is the ESM in Alfa-class submarines.

◆ Bell Series (Bell Clout, Bell Shroud, Bell Squat, Bell Thump)

These surface-ship ESM antennas, located in small radomes, are generally associated with jammers and presumably are used for accurate direction finding, to direct the jammers. For example, each Side Globe or Foot Ball has an associated Bell-series antenna.

◆ Brick Group (Brick Spit and Brick Pulp)

These passive threat-intercept and -warning systems for submarines were delivered from the late 1960s on, beginning with Victor and Charlie. Many submarines have only Brick Pulp. In Delta-I/II, Brick Pulp is supplemented by Squid Head. In contrast to Stop Lights, this group have radome-enclosed antennas. They are, therefore, probably U.S.-style rapidly spinning antennas rather than British-style wide-open DF systems. The advantage of the rapid spinner is that it has very high gain, so that it can detect an airplane at a great distance, though it may well miss an intermittent transmission. The long-range detection would seem the more likely option for a submarine because an approaching airplane will use its search radar almost continuously.

◆ Foot Ball/Bell Thump

This system apparently replaces Side Globe in the cruiser *Frunze* and the carrier *Novorossisk*. The four antennas on each side are paired horizontally and vertically, one vertical pair at each corner of a tower mast. Each big Foot Ball radome has a smaller Bell Thump attached to it.

◆ Rum Tub

Rum Tub is reportedly a wide-open ESM system, dividing coverage into 90-degree segments. Each radome is split horizontally into a wider base and a narrower top, and each segment is further split into segments (five at the base, six at the top), each segment showing two square plates, one above the other. The effect is quite unlike that of earlier Soviet radomes and may indicate adoption of electronic scanning (by lens) as in the U.S. SLQ-32.

◆ Side Globe

Side Globe is reportedly a broad-band jammer; each antenna of the system covers a separate band. Side Globe was a standard Soviet heavy-ship system of the late 1960s and later, in the *Moskva*, Kresta-I and -II, Kara, and *Slava* classes, and in the large cruiser *Kirov*. Generally four domes, in vertical pairs,

A pair of Side Globe radomes is visible on the mainmast of this Kara-class cruiser, with the associated Bell-series radome visible below them, and another pair (presumably lower-frequency) visible to the right. The larger radome on the lattice foremast is probably a wide-open ESM receiver. The guns are twin 76.2 mm. (U.S. Navy)

are mounted on each side of a tower mast or mack. Each dome is associated with a Bell-series radome (see above).

This system is being replaced by Foot Ball/Bell Thump.

◆ Stop Light

This submarine ESM array was introduced about 1957. It is installed in submarines of that vintage (Foxtrot, Golf, Hotel, Echo, November). The Soviet name is Machta. This system is roughly analogous to Watch Dog, but there is only a single (octagonal) radome with the four tiers of horns (eight horns per tier, or band). A radome on top presumably houses an S-band dipole; the horns cover the X-, C-, and S-bands (probably 2.5–10 GHz). DF accuracy is probably about 10 degrees. This system was replaced by Brick Group in submarines completed from the late 1960s on (Tango, Charlie, Victor, Yankee).

◆ Top Hat A, B

This Modified *Skoryy*-class destroyer carried a Top Hat jammer on her mainmast and two smaller radomes just abaft her bridge. Presumably they covered rotating direction-finding antennas used to direct the jammer. The mainmast radar is Slim Net. (U.S. Naval Institute)

The first Soviet naval jammers, Top Hat operated in a 500-MHz band around 9370 MHz, with an output (in the original version) of 150 watts CW using noise-modulated AM. There was a directional antenna (4-degree beam, 24–28 dB gain). In a few cruisers and destroyers Top Hat replaced a radar. Top Hat first appeared about 1962. It was replaced by Side Globe.

In Modified *Skoryy*s, the jammer was mounted on the centerline, and two shallow cylindrical radomes (which presumably contained the directional ESM antennas supporting the system) were mounted on the sides of the ship.

◆ Watch Dog

The first Soviet ESM system, Watch Dog was introduced about 1957 and is still in service. Watch Dog is apparently a wide-open system, its array consisting of a cylinder carrying four tiers of microwave horns (eight per tier). Typically a ship carries one array on each side, each backed by a reflector. Presumably each horn is tuned to a fairly narrow band, for a combination of threat warning, direction finding, and identification, over a 1–12 MHz band. In a Kotlin, for example, Watch Dog is mounted on the radar platform on the foremast. This system was apparently enclosed in radomes in later ships.

EXPENDABLES

Twin-tube trainable or 16-tube fixed chaff launchers are mounted on board many ships. There is also a spherical floating radar decoy containing a corner reflector.

UNITED KINGDOM

◆ Royal Navy Decoy Outfits

Current systems are:

DLA 6-tube Sea Gnat multipurpose decoy rocket launcher

DLB Plessey Shield 6-tube launcher, equipped to fire Corvus chaff or IR decoy rockets

DLC Knebworth/Corvus 8-tube 3-inch launcher, often with 50-mm flare launcher atop

DLD U.S. Hycor Mk-137 6-tube launcher for U.S. SRBOC Mk 36; several configurations

DLE Plessey Shield for RFA auxiliaries

Chaff launcher on board the cruiser *Kerch*, 1989. This is the standard Soviet unit for ships of large destroyer size and above, generally mounted aft. Many older ships, including cruisers, still lack chaff launchers. Smaller ships use non-reloading units with more barrels, e.g., 16-barrel launchers in *Parchim*– and *Grisha*-V–class light frigates, in Pauk-class corvettes, and in Tarantul-, Nanuchka-, and Sarancha-class attack boats. The chute visible to the left is used to drop duds over the side. (Eric Grove)

DLF Irvin "Rubber Duck" floating corner reflector; also in U.S. service (DLF-2 launches the successor "Replica" decoy.)

ELECTRONIC SYSTEMS

◆ Type 668/669

These jammers, associated with the UA-8/9 ESM system, were introduced in the early 1960s. The third member of the family

The boxes on the side of the foremast of this *Leander*-class frigate are Type-668/669 jammers. The foremast antennas are Type 994 and a surface-search set (978 or 1006); the mainmast antenna is an independent IFF interrogator, Type 1010. (Author)

was Type 667 (Cooky), a high-powered spot noise jammer (covering a 20-MHz band in S-band, and a 40-MHz band in X-band, in each case with a trainable 30-degree beam). By 1958, trials of Type 667 had shown that it could screen a carrier to a range of about 30 nm in S-band, or 10 nm in X-band, or screen a destroyer to 5 nm in S-band (and completely in X-band). The hope was that Cooky would screen a task force within an area roughly comparable to surface-to-air missile range, forcing enemy missile bombers (the AS-1 was the principal threat at the time) to approach so closely that the defending missiles could shoot them down. Types 668 and 669 were probably more sophisticated versions of Cooky, to include C-band jamming and pulse repetition (which was not yet available to the Royal Navy in 1958). The figures for Type 667's performance probably approximate those to be expected of the later 668/669.

◆ Type 670

Racal's jammer, code named Heather, is intermediate between early systems such as 668/669 and the UAF-1 jammer. Racal has supplied 27 sets for Type-42 destroyers and *Leander* Batch-3 and Type-22 frigates.

Jammers on a *Leander*-class frigate, 1988. (A. Wetback)

Radomes of Type-670 jammers, HMS *Bristol*, 1988. (A. Wetback)

Type-670 jammers on board a Type-22 frigate. The masthead DF array, which is the U.S. AS-3112/SRD-19, is part of the Classic Outboard passive location system. Reportedly this system, which also includes deck-edge antennas, is installed on board several Type 22s. The array is a direction-finder, covering the VHF range in three bands. The upper two bands are covered by Adcock arrays, the lower by crossed loops. The entire array is 85 inches high. The two cylindrical objects below the array are UHF receive and transmit antennas. (A. Wetback)

◆ Type 675 (Guardian/Millpost)

Thorn EMI's low-cost intercept system replaces Type 670. The first contract was announced in 1983. Guardian is an intercept system and associated jammer for both area (i.e., anti-surveillance) and point defense. Area defense is by pulse or barrage noise jamming; point defense (against missiles that have already locked on) is by range-gate pull-off and amplitude pull-off. Guardian can deal with several simultaneous threats. It employs two stabilized antennas (port and starboard or fore and aft), each including a DF receiver and transmitting antennas. The jamming antennas are mechanically steered for full azimuth cover and for elevation cover up to 50 degrees. Each antenna consists of a pair of boxes around a pedestal, each box bearing two oblong antennas, one over the other. Bearing and threat data are fed by the associated ESM system, searching its own library for appropriate jamming techniques. Guardian can also use its own DF receivers to operate autonomously, classifying incoming signals. Because it incorporates a separate receiver, Guardian can remain open to new threats while jamming existing hostile signals.

Guardian is the commercial name; the British naval designation is Millpost. Type 675 has been ordered to equip Type-22 frigates, Type-42 destroyers, and the *Invincible*-class aircraft carriers. It became operational in 1987.

◆ CXA

CXA is a communications-band (LF to A-band) direction-finding and threat-warning receiver found on board British nuclear attack submarines; it is an AEG-Telefunken Telegon. In British service CXA is arranged so that it can be augmented as required for signals or communications intelligence.

♦ FH 4/5

The standard HF/DF was developed during World War II; the characteristic "bird cage" antenna is still very widely used.

The standard FH 4 "birdcage" antenna at the foretop of a *Leander*-class frigate, 1986. (Author)

♦ UA-1/UA-4

UA-1 was the first postwar British S-band DF set, for surface ships, ca. 1956. The antenna consisted of four horns mounted around a mast, other sets of four each being added later to cover the C- and X-bands. The receivers were crystal videos without RF amplification, and the display showed intercepted signals as radial lines showing direction. Direction finding was by amplitude comparison, and a loudspeaker gave the PRF as an audible note. Operators tried to recognize radars by the combination of PRF and timed scan rate (antenna rotation rate).

These systems used arrays of horn antennas, four per band, at the masthead.

UA-2 and UA-3 were related systems for radar-picket destroyers, and UA-4 was a submarine-mounted equivalent, used primarily for warning.

♦ UA-8/9/10 (Porker)

These older passive intercept systems (1–10 GHz) were derived from the original MEL IFM system, Pendant, which appeared in the late 1950s. UA-8/9/10 are analog systems, and the display is a polar plot of frequency against bearing. The digital successor to these systems is the MEL Susie (see below). Compared to UA-1/4, these sets use broader-band superheterodyne receivers of greater sensitivity. UA-8/9/10 also introduced facilities for isolating and analyzing specific signals, using a library of known signal characteristics to identify them. Finally, these sets introduced pulse blanking, so that they would not pick up pulses from the ship's own radars (which would have swamped the much weaker pulses from distant radars). UA-8/9/10 have four-channel amplitude-comparison DF systems similar to those of UA-1/4.

UA-8/9 cover S- and X-bands and are typically mounted together on a masthead, with their arrays superimposed. UA-10 covers C-band. Each of the three sets covers a 500-MHz range.

♦ UA-11/12

UA-11/12 are Racal ESM sets for British SSBNs and SSNs, respectively. The associated array normally surmounts the dedicated ESM mast. UA-11/12 is used for precision bearing- and frequency-measurement, but reportedly its operation is slower and requires much greater operator concentration than does a more recent set. UA-11/12 dates from the 1970s. These sets are being replaced by Outfits UAB and UAC.

♦ UA-13

This passive array (12–18 GHz) on *Ariadne, Cleopatra,* and *Phoebe* consists of a conical D/F antenna at the masthead, with projecting dipole arrays.

UA-13 is the array at the masthead of the Dutch frigate *Hadda* (now discarded), with the British UA-8/9 below it. The foremast radar is DA-05/2, and the mainmast carries LW-03. The director over the bridge is M-45 (for the 76-mm gun), and the two after directors are M-44 (for Sea Cat, visible aft). The slotted-waveguide antenna is Decca TM 1229C. (U.S. Naval Institute)

♦ UA-15

Racal's add-on to existing Royal Navy ESM systems extends coverage to the 12–18 GHz band.

♦ UAA

See Abbey Hill below.

♦ UAB/UAC

UAB/UAC are Racal ESM sets for British SSBNs and SSNs, respectively. UAC has been installed on board *Trafalgar* and *Swiftsure* classes since 1985 and will be on board the new *Upholder*s UAC-3 will be on board the new Trident missile submarines. In existing submarines, outfit UAB is being replaced by the Racal outfit UAP.

♦ UAF-1

The Type-23 ("Duke"-class) ESM suite by Racal is the first Royal Navy ESM system to employ color displays. The antenna is an eight-port array atop the foremast. Racal has proposed a modified UAF-1 for the NATO frigate, in collaboration with AEG.

◆ UAG-1

UAG-1 is an ESM/chaff-triggering system for patrol craft up to fleet auxiliaries. The requirement for this system was issued about 1983. Marconi was chosen, and the first application will be the new *Fort*-class AOR; UAG may also be installed on board the new LPD, the aviation training ship, and the proposed aviation support ship. This system is based on Mentor (see below); Mentor A was tested on board an RFA in 1987.

◆ UAH

UAH is *Oberon*'s ESM suite; see Manta below.

◆ UAJ

Racal's ESM suite for *Oberon*s is a modified Porpoise. UAJ uses the same display and processor as the Cutlass surface-ship set.

◆ UAL

Churchill-class SSNs' suite is similar to UAH (and, therefore, to Manta). UAL will also probably be retrofitted in other British nuclear attack submarines.

◆ UAP

UAP is an ESM suite by Racal; see Sabre below.

◆ UAR

UAR is the ESM suite for royal fleet auxiliaries, such as the new *Fort*-class AOR.

◆ Abbey Hill (UAA-1)

Abbey Hill (UAA-1) DF antennas under the platform of a Type-992Q radar antenna. The round objects on the small yardarm are presumably the associated omnidirectional antennas feeding the system's IFM. There are four tiers of DF antennas, corresponding to four bands. (A. Wetback)

Abbey Hill is the ESM system developed by MEL for the Type-42 destroyer, then for Type-22 (and, later, Type-21) frigates. Abbey Hill is also being fitted to most earlier types. Frequency range is 1–18 GHz. UAA-1 is the passive reception and pulse-measuring portion of the system, using the MEL IFM. UAA-1 in turn was designed to work with a constant-beamwidth antenna with a direction-finding accuracy of better than 3½ degrees, compared to 15 degrees for other systems.

MEL IFMs operate between 0.7 and 18 GHz in a variety of ranges and can exploit pulses with durations as short as 0.05 microsec. There are two ranges: binary, for high integrity in dense signal environments, and quaternary, for less demanding situations.

The intercept and D/F antenna is a series of ports (radome-covered horns) typically mounted under the masthead radar antennas, and covering four bands (probably eight per band). Frequency-measurement accuracy is reportedly 1.5 MHz, and bearing accuracy better than 3 degrees.

In Abbey Hill, UAA-1 is combined with an EMI threat-identification system and, reportedly, with an EMI jammer code-named Millpost. At least in the original form, Abbey Hill made a tentative identification of a received signal, but the system also provided raw data so that the operator could decide for himself. In 1981 it was reported that the Royal Navy considered the signal environment in the North Atlantic too dense for anything but fully automatic operation and so was seeking an updated version of the threat-identification system.

◆ Masthead Repeater

This countermeasure was introduced in the 1960s to provide protection against Styx and similar missiles, which steer in both altitude and bearing. The repeater pointed back toward the sea surface to provide a false target some distance from the ship, toward the incoming missile. This type of countermeasure is not effective against a sea-skimmer, which approaches at fixed altitude and has a radar that does not look down; but the repeater should be effective against diving missiles, such as AS-4/6.

◆ Cutlass

Cutlass is Decca's combined ESM/ECM suite for a very dense signal environment (up to 500,000 pulses/sec, as in the Middle

An Egyptian *Ramadan*-class missile patrol boat equipped with Cutlass ESM gear. The masthead array is presumably associated with Cutlass B1; below it are two air-backed spirals. The big foremast radar is a Marconi S820; the smaller S810 has not yet been mounted on her mainmast. (Giorgio Arra)

East or Europe); Cutlass operates in the 2–18 GHz range, using two digital bearing and frequency discriminators (2–7.5 and 7.5–18 GHz). Signals are automatically compared with a 2000-radar library, and the results displayed in tabular form, with threats automatically ranked. The display can show up to 150 threats on 5 pages, and the 30 most important threats are displayed automatically. The display also shows the level of confidence to be applied to the identifications. Selected digital data can be sent to other systems (e.g., antiship-missile fire control). Signal analysis is by instantaneous frequency measurement, the ESM receiver operating on two channels (frequency and bearing). The bearing channel can be used for weapons direction. A typical installation, providing all-around coverage from the masthead, consists of an omnidirectional antenna (to provide an input to the IFM) and six ports for direction finding by amplitude comparison. Cutlass B1, which achieves much greater precision in direction, uses a 32-element array for phase-analysis direction finding (2-degree rather than 7-degree accuracy). The more accurate direction-finder suffices to target antiship missiles such as Harpoon.

Cutlass generally provides (a) bearings over the entire 2–18 GHz range, with preamplification over 4–18 GHz; (b) IFM over the whole range; (c) signal processing/library look-up; and (d) CW bearing and frequency measurement over 2–18 GHz. As of 1988, frequency and bearing accuracies of 5 MHz and 5 degrees were being claimed, over the 0.6–18 GHz range.

Cutlass can incorporate its own responsive noise jammer, which can track the target, and can provide either spot or barrage noise. Cutlass can also be integrated with chaff launchers and with self-defense weapons such as Sea Wolf. In a typical installation, Cutlass operates with a Cygnus directional jammer.

The system is modular so that it can fit ships ranging in size from fast attack craft to frigates. As of 1985, over 40 Cutlass systems had been exported, and this figure had risen to nearly 100 as of early 1988.

Cutlass was adopted in modified form for the Type-23 frigates (as UAF-1). Porpoise is a modified version.

◆ Cygnus

Racal's ECM system uses a narrow-beam tracking jammer (1–18 GHz). Cygnus was designed specifically to operate with the Cutlass ESM system, operating over a variable bandwidth for spot or barrage jamming. Cygnus has two separate antennas but one transmitter, so that the system can jam two targets on a time-shared basis at maximum power. The associated IFM tunes the jammer within microseconds of the receipt of a pulse. Radiated power is reportedly over 300 kW, which suffices to counter aircraft-surveillance and missile-guidance radars.

In 1988 it was reported that the latest version operates over the 8–18 GHz band (300 kW minimum power, 480 kW in mid-band), with 1 degree tracking accuracy.

Users include the navies of Kuwait, Bahrein, Qatar, Abu Dhabi, and Oman.

◆ Guardian

See Type 675 above.

◆ Hermes

Hermes is Marconi's airborne, shipboard, or ground ESM system.

◆ Manta/Sceptre/UAH

Manta, an ESM system for submarines, was derived from MEL's Rapids and was announced in 1983. Manta covers the 2–18 GHz range, providing automatic detection, analysis, and identification, and can feed into a tactical data system. The operator can override the threat library if the system picks up an unassigned signal. The capacity of the threat library is 2000 modes, and the operator can add another 100. The system intercepts signals at elevations between −10 and +30 degrees, with horizontal, vertical, and circular polarization; 50 nanosec–100 microsec pulse

width; and 0.02–40.0 second scan period. Bearing accuracy is about 2 degrees, sufficient for torpedo fire.

In 1987, MEL announced that it was working with Philips to extend coverage into the Ka-band (27–39 GHz).

UAH, for the modernized *Oberons*, is a version of Manta.

Sceptre is a version for surface ships, announced in 1985. It employs a boom-mounted omnidirectional antenna and a pair of mast-mounted DF half-arrays, each carrying three sets of three antennas (for three bands). The typical display consists of two side-by-side CRTs, one showing frequency against bearing, the other a series of best fits to library data.

Sceptre 0 is for fast patrol craft; Sceptre X for corvettes and frigates; Sceptre XL for destroyers and carriers. Sceptre X covers the 2–18 GHz range, provides a bearing accuracy of 6 degrees, and handles up to 1 million pulses/sec.

◆ Matilda

MEL's Microwave-Analysis Threat-Indication and Launch-Direction Equipment is a lightweight low-cost intercept system for patrol craft and was announced in 1981. The design targets were £70–75 thousand and a masthead weight of 5 kg (to be reduced to 3–3.5 kg). The antenna is designed to provide a broad vertical beam, to detect both sea-skimmers and steeply-diving (but not vertical) missiles. Typical coverage is 7.5–18 GHz. Frequency resolution: 1.5 GHz. Pulse-width range: 0.1–6.4 microsec (resolution 0.2 microsec). Bearing resolution: 45 degrees. Sensitivity is −30 dBm, and dynamic range is 40 dB. Antenna gain (7.5–18 GHz range) is 6–8 dB.

Besides automatic threat recognition, Matilda provides a synthesized-voice warning of the impending attack, as well as advice of correct evasive action, within one second of detection. A lamp indicates the sector from which the threat is coming, and Matilda can be connected to trigger an ECM system.

The system is optimized against locked-on or tracking radars. It avoids false alarms by scanning the rate at which incoming signals arrive, initiating action only when (i) more than 250 pulses of similar bearing, pulse width, and amplitude arrive in less than 500 msec, or (ii) when continuous CW has been received for more than 100 msec. These conditions do not apply to secondary threats such as track-while-scan radars.

The antenna consists of four spiral antennas (to intercept signals of any polarization), arranged in two matching halves that are clamped around a mast, each a tube about 115 mm in diameter.

As of 1985, twelve Matildas had been ordered by the Royal Navy, to be integrated with Wallop's Barricade-series chaff launchers. Matilda E, an uprated version, was installed on board British "Hunt"-class minesweepers before they were sent to the Persian Gulf in 1987. Matilda E had been tested on board HMS *Dumbarton Castle* in 1986. This version will also be part of the PEAB EW system of the Finnish *Helsinki 2*–class fast attack craft.

◆ Mentor

This family of shipboard ESM systems, by Marconi, was announced in 1985 and was designed for small craft such as hydrofoils and minesweepers. The installation comprises an omnidirectional antenna and 4, 6, or 8 DF antennas. The system can be extended to millimeter wavelengths. Its library contains 3000 emitter modes, and it can have up to 100 programmable threat-warning channels. The display shows emitters in tabular form (typically track number, identification, bearing, frequency, pulse repetition interval, and pulse width) as well as automatic warning information.

Mentor is built around a special-purpose digital signal processor that transforms incoming video for library comparison.

Mentor 1 is a simple missile warner (7.5–18 GHz, 9-degree bearing accuracy, −45-dBm sensitivity). Mentor 2 is a surveillance system (1–18 GHz, 6-degree bearing accuracy with 1-degree accuracy optional, −65-dBm sensitivity). Coverage can be extended into the MMW range. The masthead unit consists of three omnidirectional antennas and six DF antennas, presumably to cover three bands.

Extended versions are available for surveillance and for target acquisition (for the use of over-the-horizon missiles). Comparative characteristics, which are presumably typical of ESM devices, follow:

	Warning	Surveillance	Acquisition
Range	6–8 GHz	1–2 GHz	0.5–40 GHz
Accuracy	9 deg	6 deg	1 deg
Channels	4	6	6 plus dish antenna
Sensitivity	−45 dBm	−65 dBm	−65 dBm
Dynamic Range	45 dB	55 dB	65 dB
Amplitude Resolution	1 dB	1 dB	1 dB
Parameters in Library	1000	3000	3000
Processing Time	1 sec	1 sec	1 sec

Three versions, Mentor A, B, and C, were announced about 1987; they are export variants of UAG (see above). They cover the 1–40 GHz range, and their bearing accuracy can be as good as 1 degree. Mentor A and B are described as inexpensive variants of Marconi aircraft systems, something between an RWR and a full ESM suite. Mentor A identifies threat radars by their PRFs.

◆ MIR-2

MIR-2 is the MEL ESM system for aircraft and small ships, for the 600 MHz–18 GHz range. MIR-2 uses six antennas, flush or externally mounted. The display shows frequency band, bearing, and amplitude activity; the operator can strobe to obtain true bearing and PRF.

See also Orange Crop in the Strike/Surface Warfare section.

◆ Porpoise (UAJ)

Racal's automatic ESM equipment for submarines (2–18 GHz in two bands: 2–8 and 8–18 GHz) is based on Cutlass. Parameters measured are bearing, frequency, signal strength, pulse width, and time of reception. Porpoise has a 2000-signature library, corresponding to about 400 radars (operating in different modes); and the operator can feed in another 100. The display shows emitters in order of threat priority, either in graphic (track) or tabular form. The highest priority emitters trigger both audio and visual alarms. The tabular display can show 25 tracks at a time, 150 in all being stored. Priority is based not only on the character of the emitter, but also on a calculation of the submarine's probability of detection, given the level of radar reflection from the masts, including the snorkel, and the sea-state.

Racal designed the Porpoise's mast specifically for the German Type-209 submarine, the most widely exported type. That boat required a nonretracting telescoping design. The antenna head is made of titanium, with an omnidirectional antenna (for IFM) surmounting two rows of directional ports for the two bands (six in each row, spirals for the low band and horns for the high band). Signals are amplified in the head proper before being transmitted into the hull of the submarine for analysis.

Porpoise 2 is an improved version (DF accuracy 3 rather than 5 or 6 degrees).

◆ RCM

Decca's RCM-series jammers were introduced in 1975 to work with other Decca equipment, such as the RDL series. RCM-1, which operates with the RDL-2 series, covers the 8–10 GHz range (using a high power CW TWT). RCM-2 series has its own IFM receiver and can handle several targets; two bands (5–9 GHz and 9–16 GHz) are available. The installation consists of transmitting and receiving antennas covered by a radome (two radomes on larger ships). If a particular ESM signal is chosen, the system sets a 100-MHz slot around it, the receiver searching within the slot to find the target frequency very accurately. The antenna trains and elevates.

The RCM-3 gate-stealing jammer is now being added to large British surface combatants. The Nigerian MEKO frigate is fitted with the RCM-2 jammer (and the RDL-2 intercept receiver).

◆ RDL

Decca's RDL-series ESM system is used primarily to detect the enemy's radar-controlled weapons systems. Work began in 1968, the system being intended for Third World navies needing

The Brazilian frigate *Uniao* shows the antennas of Decca RDL-2/3 at her masthead, with a Signaal ZW-06 surface-search radar below, and an Orion RTN-10X fire-control radar below that. The weapon forward of her bridge is a two-barrel Bofors 375-mm rocket launcher, and the air-search radar is AWS-2. Such international combinations are increasingly common. (Vosper Thornycroft)

RDL 2/3 intercept and DF arrays around the foremast of a Brazilian frigate, 1986. Each array is split to fit around the mast.

something less expensive and less sophisticated than existing Western ECM systems. By 1980, over 100 were operational in over 30 navies.

RDL covers a fraction of the 1–18 GHz band, the particular range depending on the version selected. The typical output is bearing, frequency, automatic pulse analysis, and alarm. The antenna consists of two semicircular units that wrap around a mast (so that it need not be positioned at the masthead); more can be added to expand frequency coverage to match specific threats.

RDL-1BC, for fast patrol boats, provides frequency band, bearing, automatic pulse analysis, and warning. RDL-2ABC, for larger warships, adds frequency measurement, visual pulse analysis, and RF amplification of the signal in the analysis channel for greater range and more effective analysis.

RDL-2AB 6AC covers the entire 1–18 GHz range, with IFM and automatic pulse analysis.

RDL-4BC is a semiautomatic threat-warning system for submarines; RDL-1BC S is a simpler system for submarines. The submarine antennas consist of sixteen separate encapsulated elements (rather than a single encapsulated array) and cover up to the 2.5–20 GHz range.

◆ Sabre/Sea Lion

Racal's ESM system (Sabre for surface ships, Sea Lion for submarines) employs the company's SADIE signal processor and 14-inch color raster display, both of which are also used in UAP and in the airborne Orange Reaper. Sabre is a development of the earlier Cutlass, covering the 0.6–40 GHz band with selectable bearing accuracy of 2 or 8 degrees.

Sabre has been selected for the Danish Stan Flex 300, and Sea Lion for Danish submarines. These systems reportedly appealed to the Danes because of very fine DF accuracy, allowing them to distinguish individual targets on a crowded coast.

◆ SADIE

Racal's Segregation, Association, Deinterleaving and Identification Equipment processor, for ESM, has separate elements for pulse segregation; for known emitter monitoring; for new emitter analysis; and for ESM processor control. The segregator recognizes pulses from emitters already characterized and segregates those pulses from new ones. That segregation allows the system to concentrate on new signals, so that the system can function in very dense environments. The segregator uses the maximum number of monopulse parameters, e.g., frequency, pulse width, bearing, modulation flags, expected time of arrival, and expected amplitude. The monitor receives this data, including emitter number and whole pulse record, accumulating pulse parameters for each emitter and deriving exponential averages for the key parameters. The analyzer deinterleaves and characterizes emitters.

◆ SARIE

EMI's Selective Automatic Radar Identification Equipment, manufactured for the Royal Navy and for NATO navies, complements existing ESM systems. SARIE is an automatic ESM library look-up device (operating time about 0.1 second) that accepts video from a receiver and displays the results of analysis (PRF, pulse width, and scan period) in alphanumeric form together with an assessment of the confidence of the identification. The system can also accept data on frequency, frequency agility, modulation, and scan type as aids to identification and will indicate PRF jitter. SARIE II contains data on up to 1000 radars, presenting data in tabular form.

SARIE I, in production 1973–79, was sold to the Royal Navy and to other NATO navies; about 75 copies were made. Production of SARIE II began in 1979, and many were exported.

◆ Scorpion

Racal's wide-beam jammer is capable of dealing with five targets simultaneously (to be expanded to eight in later versions) in the 7.5–18 GHz range, with up to 50 kW of radiated power. The dual beam (wide/narrow) antenna weighs less than 100 kg, and the jammer operates in continuous, burst, cover, conscan, and RGPO modes.

◆ Sea Saviour

Racal's radar-warning receiver (8–18 GHz) is designed for small combatants such as minesweepers. It uses a four-port antenna, measuring bearing by comparing signal amplitude at the different ports to achieve 45-degree accuracy. Warning is by both digital readout and audio alarm. This system can also be programmed to fire decoys from systems such as Barricade.

◆ SPRAT

Racal's threat-warning system (8–18 GHz), designed for submarines, is mounted on the periscope. Detected pulses pass via the periscope cabling to an indicator in the control room; that indicator in turn uses LEDs to show the signal level, and a loudspeaker gives a corresponding audio alarm.

◆ Susie

MEL's solid-state ESM system has a frequency range of 2–18 GHz. Data are displayed in alphanumeric form. Susie automatically correlates frequency band, pulse width, and bearing, and displays these data together with PRF and signal strength. The operator can arrange for automatic tracking of selected targets and for an automatic lock-on alarm (i.e., missile alarm). Bearing antennas have eight ports, for high accuracy. There are three versions, for fast patrol craft, frigates, and large warships. Antenna weight is 154–300 kg, depending on the version.

Susie-1 is intended for small warships. It equips the Dutch-built Indonesian frigates and is connected to chaff launchers. Susie-1F (for medium-sized ships) is a redesigned Susie-1, providing accurate frequency measurement.

Susie-2 is intended for medium-sized ships. The main improvement is to display precise frequency rather than frequency band; coverage extends down to 1 GHz. A threat library can be added.

Susie-3 is more sensitive and more accurate. As of 1981, it was in service on board at least one foreign warship.

Susie was designed so that it could be used to control a Scimitar jammer.

◆ Triton

Dalmo-Victor's threat-warning system for fast patrol boats was announced in 1984. Triton weighs 5.9 kg and provides voice warning of missile seekers and also of unknown threats. There is also a visual display, and the threat library can be quickly reprogrammed on board.

◆ Type 242

Racal's integrated ESM/ECM system was announced in 1987 (the number is Racal's, not the Royal Navy's); 242 has already been ordered by the Sultan of Oman's Navy. This system combines modified Cutlass and Scorpion in a single console, and Racal describes 242 as one-fifth the weight of its predecessors (as well as cheaper and more reliable). The jammer is driven by the frequency-measurement unit of the ESM system, and the ESM data processor feeds the jammer directly. The processor is the new SADIE (see also the entry for Sabre/Sea Lion), which can handle pulse densities greater than 1 million/sec.

EXPENDABLES

◆ Barricade/Super Barricade/Stockade

Barricade, a lightweight chaff launcher made by Wallop Industries, fires spin-stabilized 57-mm rockets from a stacked series of six open frames (three rockets per frame), which point in various directions at different elevation angles, to form a large chaff cloud. The lower three sets of tubes are angled at 60 deg to each other for full azimuth coverage by long-range Stockade rockets (range 400–2000 m). The upper three sets fire short-range Pallisade rockets to 60 m from the ship to form a large overhead decoy for centroid seduction. Typically one set of 110-kg launchers is fitted to each side of a ship. Decoys are both chaff and IR. The original rocket had a range of 2000 m and carried a pound of chaff; that rocket dispersed its load centrifugally, spinning at 9000 spins/sec. Control is by a microprocessor that chooses the appropriate mode (distraction, dump/range-gate pull-off, confusion, seduction/centroid) and that also provides a recommended course to steer.

In 1981 Wallop announced a new 500-m rocket.

Super Barricade fires a larger rocket than Barricade, to cover a larger ship.

Stockade is a related lightweight chaff launcher for fast patrol boats. Unlike most chaff launchers, Stockade consists of frames, inside which are launch tubes containing 57-mm fin-stabilized rockets. The launcher itself weighs only 10 kg unloaded. Each assembly consists of three frames holding nine rockets, pointed in three directions and elevated; together the rockets form a chaff cloud with a radar signature approximating that of a corvette. Typically one launcher is mounted on either side of a ship.

The rockets burst at an altitude of 70 m, at ranges of 400–1500 m. The associated IR decoys ignite at 1000 or 1500 m and burn for 30 seconds. As of 1980 longer-range (5000 m) and hotter IR decoys were under development.

Wallop also offers Stockade-Seaflash: a remotely controlled boat launches the Stockade chaff rockets, usable at ranges as great as 20 km. The boat carries two decoy launchers (18 barrels).

Corvus chaff launcher, with flare projector on top. (A. Wetback)

Barricade chaff launcher. (A. Wetback)

◆ Corvus

Plessey-Vickers's chaff-decoy rocket launcher consists of eight tubes: two sets of three at right angles, and one set of two, above, bisecting that angle; all tubes are at a fixed elevation of 30 deg. The usual pair of port and starboard launchers is considered sufficient to deal with three attacks. In 1979 a new Plessey BBC (broad-band chaff) round (101.6 × 1580 mm, 21.8 kg including a 6.8-kg payload) replaced the earlier Knebworth. At the time the BBC round carried the heaviest payload available in a rocket of its dimensions. Chaff is dispensed in one of three

A Corvus launcher, with its rocket flare (illumination) launcher on top.

modes to cover the G–K bands; dispensing range is set by a fuze adjusted manually before launching. At a threat wavelength of 2.6 cm, 2.5 seconds after bursting, the BBC rocket produces a 1200 square-meter radar target that, given the enhancement effect of echoes off the sea surface, is equivalent to a 12,000 square-meter ship's radar target.

There is also an associated IR decoy. One version, by Plessey, uses the chaff rocket as a buoy, with the IR flare on top.

The prototype 6-barrel launcher went to sea on board HMS *Arethusa* in 1968. This system was exported to the Dutch, Brazilian, French, and other navies.

Many standard Corvus 8-barrelled launchers carry a single Attwell 2-inch rocket-flare launcher atop them. This launcher is manually fired. There is also a single stand-alone rocket-flare launcher, manually trainable on its own pedestal.

◆ EPO Naval Rocket Launcher

Evershed manufactures this two-axis, stabilized, multibarreled launcher of chaff and IR flares. Targets can be designated from the ship's fire-control system.

◆ Protean

Protean is a chaff grenade launcher that is similar in principle to the Swedish Philax. A typical installation consists of two or four launchers, each carrying four reloadable magazines (36 chaff grenades each, 144 per launcher). Launchers are fixed in train and elevation; they fire grenades in groups of nine (up to four simultaneously). One or more chaff magazines can be replaced with IR grenades. Time to deploy a grenade cloud is 5 seconds; height is 40–60 m (flight time 1 second). Grenades weigh 0.35 kg, and they can be made in various wavelengths. In 1980, Protean equipped several fast patrol boats, as well as the Nigerian Mk-9 corvettes.

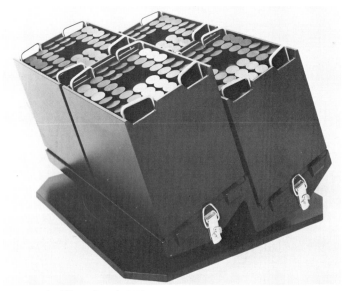

Protean chaff launcher. (MEL)

◆ Radamec

This trainable, two-axis, stabilized decoy launcher (chaff/IR flare) uses interchangeable pods mounted amidships. Targets are designated by the ship's fire-control system. The manufacturer is Radamec Defense Systems of Chertsey, Surrey.

◆ Replica (DLF-1/Rubber Duck/SLQ-49)

Replica is an inflatable buoyant structure that supports a fabric-backed octahedral corner reflector; Replica operates as a distraction/seduction decoy. To a radar, the result looks very much like a ship. Replica, a substantial physical structure is inherently broad-band, unlike chaff, and is considered effective for up to three hours in sea-state 4. The standard decoy is carried in two 1.14 m long containers, similar to those used for life rafts, on inclined ramps. When the containers are released (either manually or automatically), they begin to inflate before hitting the water. The two decoys remain connected by a 4–5 m line, and the lid of one of the two containers remains connected

as a drag anchor, to keep the line taut (and thus to prevent the two decoys from collapsing together). Each decoy is about 2.5 m from apex to apex. Inside, the decoy has silver-coated nylon mesh suspended from aluminum-alloy tubes. Replica can be set to self-destruct or to be activated by remote control.

Reportedly this system was based on a Soviet decoy, which is similar but spherical (about 2.5 m in diameter).

The Royal Navy's name is Rubber Duck, and this decoy has also been adopted by the U.S. Navy, as SLQ-49. In April 1987 the U.S. Navy reportedly tested an air-launched version of Replica, comparable in size and shape to a Mk-46 torpedo. At that time the navy was also testing an improved version of the basic SLQ-49.

Irwin Replica radar decoy, stowed (left) and deployed (right). (*Ships of the World*)

◆ Seafan

Vickers-Plessey's 105-mm decoy rocket launcher, for small craft such as fast attack boats, was originally conceived as a smaller equivalent to Corvus, for rapid installation on board merchant ships that might have to operate unescorted (albeit in convoy) during a period of rapidly escalating prewar tension. Seafan employs a 200-kg (vs. 762-kg for Corvus) six-round fixed launcher. As originally proposed, Seafan was to have been fired from a lightweight triple launcher, and it was claimed that an existing Corvus launcher could fire 15 Seafans.

In 1977 Plessey announced a new Seafan rocket to dispense broad-band chaff (105 mm × 979 mm, 17.26 kg, carrying 4.1 kg of chaff). Elevation was fixed at 25 degrees, so that the rocket would begin to seed the chaff cloud while still rising. The resulting triangular chaff cloud was expected to last longer than most. A 0.33-second fuze setting would produce a cloud between 24 and 155 m from the ship, and between 10 and 61 m high. After 2.5 seconds, this cloud (from a triple launcher) would have a reflecting area of 2500 square meters, reaching 4100 square meters in 10 seconds and lasting about 3 minutes.

The key to reduced rocket size was a multinozzle motor using wraparound fins; Vickers claimed that Seafan would be considerably smaller than the existing Knebworth rocket. The advent of this rocket in turn led Plessey to develop the Shield broad-band decoy system, using the original Corvus tubes instead of smaller-diameter ones.

There is also an associated IR decoy, the Vickers Honeydew hot-spot round, which is a spar decoy. A hot spot is held above the water by the bulk of the rocket, which acts as a spar buoy. As long as the hot spot lasts, it has a considerably stronger IR signature than a ship and will, therefore, decoy an approaching missile.

◆ Shield

Plessey's broad-band chaff decoy system employs port/starboard sets of parallel- or crossed-barrel six-tube launchers and variable-range rockets to distract or seduce incoming weapons (seduction is by moving the target's centroid). Chaff can be deployed at ranges from 35 to 2000 meters, each 4-inch (102-mm) broad-band chaff (BBC) rocket carrying about 6.5 kg. Variable chaff range is obtained by setting a time fuze (0.5–12 seconds) that ignites a secondary gas generator in the nose, unlocking the nose and spraying out the chaff packs. There is also an IR decoy, the rocket having a range of 40–160 m. Each carries seven

Shield launcher. (U.S. Naval Institute)

Shield launcher being loaded. (Plessey)

IR submunitions, to cover a large physical area in the 3–5 and 8–14 micron bands.

Each launcher carries two three-rocket modules, either parallel or crossed at an 80-degree angle, and fixed in elevation at 30 degrees. The launcher is strong enough to carry three modules, so that in the crossed-launcher case the number of forward-aligned barrels can be doubled. Plessey recommends the crossed-barrel launcher for corvettes or smaller vessels, and a pair of parallel-barrel launchers for larger ships.

Three different tactics can be used. In the distraction mode, up to four separate chaff clouds are deployed in a pattern around the ship, up to 2 km away, in hopes of attracting incoming missiles and diluting the incoming attack. The manufacturer states that only a rocket system can execute this tactic, since no mortar can provide the necessary range. A second mode, dump decoy, is used in conjunction with an active ECM system such as Decca's Cutlass. The missile's range gate is distracted onto a chaff cloud about 400 m from the ship. Actual range depends upon ECM characteristics. For example, if the fuze is set at 2.5 seconds, the burst will occur at 400 m at an altitude of 145 m; by 2.5 seconds after burst, the chaff cloud will be ship-sized. Typically such a chaff decoy is placed abaft and to

one side of the real target. Finally there is centroid seduction, a last-ditch defense. The chaff cloud is superimposed on the missile's image of the ship. Because the missile tends to home on the centroid of this image, and because the chaff cloud is more reflective than the ship itself, it may lock onto the cloud. The radar cross section of the cloud is further increased by reflections off the sea surface, because of multipath propagation. If the fuze is set at 1.5 seconds or less, the cloud can extend between 90 m and 395 m in range, and between 25 and 138 m in height. The reflecting area 2.5 seconds after burst is 3000 square feet, expanding to 5500 square meters 10 seconds after burst; the cloud remains in place for up to 5 minutes.

Shield is designated DLB (DLE when adapted to royal fleet auxiliaries). The basic launcher is sometimes used to fire IR decoys as well as chaff rockets. Plessey offers a containerized version, incorporating two six-barrel launchers, to protect merchant ships. This version includes a 24-round ready-use locker but apparently not the associated ESM warning device.

Shield 2 is an automatic version for export; it has been adopted by Brazil, Canada, and one unidentified Southeast Asian customer. The Royal Navy's version is manual. The Canadian ships will fire P6 IR rounds (using the same pyrotechnic material as in the German Hot Dog), and P8 chaff rounds (adapted BBC, with a larger payload and a programmable electronic fuze). P6 fires seven submunitions ejected between 40 and 160 m from the ship.

◆ **SIBYL**

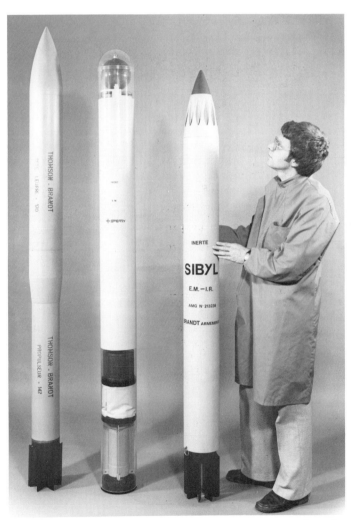

Sibyl decoy rockets, with the combined chaff/IR round on the right. (British Aerospace)

British Aerospace/Thomson Brandt's joint venture was announced in 1982. It uses a combination of rocket chaff/IR decoys and off-board ship-controlled jamming. The launcher has 12 tubes (4 tubes for smaller craft), is trainable and elevatable (limits +80/−20 degrees, with automatic loading at 90 degrees), and is stabilized in two axes. There are seven types of ammunition—floating active decoy (simulating a ship's radar, to seduce ARMs); remotely controlled off-board jammer; long-lifetime chaff decoy; combined IR/chaff decoy; "hot balloon" decoy carrying chaff; a radiation-absorbing decoy covering the spectrum from the visual to 14 microns; and a practice round—in two sizes, 170 mm and 263 mm. Effective range is zero to 8.5 km.

◆ Siren

Marconi's expendable 130-mm (1.8 m long, 28 kg) active-decoy round was announced in 1985 as the world's first intelligent off-board ECM jammer. Siren is parachute-retarded and is intended to seduce incoming missiles. Typically it is fired in company with chaff and IR rounds, selected by a central processor. At a preset distance from the ship, Siren switches on its own receiver, transmitter, and control electronics, using the range-gate pull-off seduction technique. The decoy is fired to a position 400–500 m from the ship, and Siren takes more than a minute to descend by parachute.

◆ SWORD

This alternative to the Wallop Barricade was announced at RNEE 1985. SWORD is manufactured by Pains-Wessex and uses 51-mm rockets in three groups of three sets of rails; like Barricade, SWORD has no tubes as such. The name means Small-Warship Operational Reconnaissance and Decoy (reconnaissance refers to an illuminating rocket for which the launcher was first designed (to provide multishot illumination)). Barrels can be fired either individually or in salvo, either manually or automatically.

◆ TOAD

Marconi's Towed Off-board Active Decoy was developed to protect tankers in the Persian Gulf. TOAD is a small boat, carrying a receiver, signal processor, and jammer (presumably a blip enhancer), that the tanker tows astern. Power is provided by onboard batteries recharged by wind-driven generators and solar cells. Although TOAD was reportedly sold to tanker operators in the Gulf, there have been no reports of its effectiveness.

UNITED STATES

ELECTRONIC SYSTEMS

◆ BRD-7

This radio direction-finder for submarines uses an antenna on the General-Purpose Periscope ECM antenna group; BRD-7 also contains an internal DF antenna. The DF antenna is typically mounted atop the snorkel air induction mast. BRD-7 may be connected to the periscope ECM antenna group.

◆ SLA-12

SLA-12 is the EW antenna group used with ULQ-6 and SLQ-22, -23, and -24. SLA-12 uses the AS-1751A/SLA-12 trainable-antenna group and the complementary AS-1750A fixed-antenna group, one each of the latter being mounted above and below the trainable AS-1751A. A complete installation consists of sets of all three antennas located port and starboard. Although this system is no longer widely used in the U.S. Navy, SLA-12 was transferred to many friendly navies on board former U.S. destroyers and frigates. It is recognizable by the latticework support holding all three antennas away from the structure of the ship; in FRAM destroyers SLA-12 is the antenna set on the after deckhouse.

Of the two AS-1750 antennas, the lower one is used to transmit and the upper to receive. Each consists of a microwave horn covered by a radome, and each covers 180 degrees in azimuth. Power rating is 25 kW peak, 1000 watts average. The trainable AS-1751 consists of two trainable antennas. The upper one consists of a conical receiving horn flanked by skewed direction-finding horns. The lower antenna is a transmitting horn. The

transmitter may use either a narrow high-gain (8-degree beam) or a wide low-gain (17-degree beam) horn antenna.

◆ SLA-15

Analogous to SLA-12, SLA-15 has a different frequency range. SLA-15 is used as part of ULQ-6. SLA-15 consists of a trainable AS-2431 antenna flanked above and below by two AS-2430 fixed auxiliary antennas; one unit is mounted on each side of a ship. As in SLA-12, one fixed antenna is a receiver, the other a transmitter. Beam size is 17 × 155 deg. AS-2431 consists of a receiver and a narrow-beam (9- or 18-degree) transmitter. Peak power is 25 kW in both subunits.

SLA-18 is a supplemental antenna system consisting of two AS-2430s, but without the rotatable element of SLA-15.

◆ SLD-1A

This shipboard microwave direction-finding antenna is chiefly used as the auxiliary search antenna of the SLQ-26 system. SLD-1A employs two AS-2854 antennas, installed port and starboard. Each antenna is a four-horn array, switching electronically to scan 180 degrees. Each antenna is 9 in high, 27⅜ in long, and 18¾ in deep.

Earlier installations used an AS-2308 antenna.

◆ SLQ-12

This automatically tuned jammer by Scope, Inc., is part of SAMID (Ships Anti-Missile Integrated Defense program).

◆ SLQ-17/29

SLQ-17 on board a carrier. (Hughes)

Hughes's jammer/deception system for carriers replaces the earlier ULQ-6. SLQ-17 is automated, tracking threats and providing a combat system with identification information. Originally unreliable, SLQ-17 was unpopular. However, in 1985 Hughes claimed that the system had been cured, that its MTBF (mean time between failure) had improved from 20–30 hours to 250 hours (availability increased from 25 to 97 percent). Nevertheless, to increase standardization, SLQ-17 is being replaced by SLQ-32(V)3.

SLQ-17 employs an AS-2963 multibeam, electronically steered, phased-array antenna. The roll-stabilized antenna uses flared horns for transmission and slotted waveguides for simul-

(*Above*) USS *Enterprise* shows an SLQ-17 antenna outboard of her angled deck, on a trellis mast, February 1986. (Hughes)

taneous direction finding; the entire assembly fits into a box with radome windows. Dimensions: 68 in high × 71¼ × 50 in deep; each array weighs 1200 lbs.

SLQ-29 is a combined WLR-8/SLQ-17 package installed on board twenty U.S. warships about 1976.

◆ SLQ-19/26

RCA's shelter-housed deceptive jammer was developed in response to the *Eilat* incident, as a Quick Reaction program (QRC 68–9). Later incorporated in SLQ-29, SLQ-19 could automatically recognize and respond to the main threat missiles of the time: Styx, Shaddock, and Samlet (AS-1/SSC-2). When integrated with an NTDS system, SLQ-19 is redesignated SLQ-26. These systems use the SLD-1A microwave DF set and the ULQ-6 antennas.

This system was replaced by SLQ-32 and by SLQ-17.

◆ SLQ-21

American Electronic Laboratories' signal processor, for electronic warning in a very dense signal environment, operates either manually or fully automatically. SLQ-21 was installed on board *Spruance*-class destroyers and *California*-class cruisers.

◆ SLQ-25

SLQ-25 is a NIXIE acoustic countermeasure; see the ASW section.

◆ SLQ-27

Shortstop was an attempt to develop a standard, integrated surface-ship electronics warfare system. Because it was too expensive, Shortstop was canceled in favor of a new design-to-price EW system, which became SLQ-32.

◆ SLQ-32/Sidekick

SLQ-32, manufactured by Raytheon, is the current standard U.S. Navy ECM system. It was the successful competitor in the 1975–77 Design-to-Price Electronics-Warfare System (DPEWS) competition, beating the Hughes SLQ-31.

This system uses an internal library to automatically detect and categorize threats. The (V)3 version can also jam. Other versions are used to trigger such defensive reactions as chaff and weapons firing. Reportedly SLQ-32 does not automatically steer a ship away from its own chaff cloud, as some foreign systems may. Versions are: (V)1, radar warning on H- through J-bands, for auxiliaries and amphibious ships (most will be upgraded to (V)2); (V)2, radar warning on B–J-bands, for newer destroyers and frigates (replaces WLR-1 where fitted); and (V)3, radar warning on B–J-bands and jamming/deception on H–J-bands, for carriers, cruisers, DDG 37 class, and major amphibious ships. Modular design allows for upgrading from one variant to the next.

The system is designed to handle three frequency bands: (V)1 is limited to band 3 (missile seekers), and (V)2 and (V)3 are extended to bands 1 and 2. The band-3 receiver is wide-open in direction and in frequency, using two stabilized-lens direction-finders (each covering 90 degrees) and a semi-omnidirectional antenna that senses the dominant pulse in the incoming energy for instantaneous frequency analysis. For band 2, (V)2 adds two more lens arrays and another semi-omnidirectional receiver. For band 1, (V)2 uses four masthead spiral antennas, typically two

SLQ-32 on board USS *Mississippi*, June 1988: the three radomes are for three frequency bands. (Stefan Terzibaschitsch)

SLQ-32 integrated polar display, showing own-ship and friendly emitters in the center circle, hostile missiles in the broad middle ring, and hostile nonmissiles (such as ships) in the outer ring. That arrangement corresponds roughly to frequency, since missiles (with the smallest available space for antennas) generally operate at the highest frequencies, and the least urgent threats, ships, operate at the lowest. Engagement data and further emitter data for analysis and identification are displayed around the edges of the 8 × 10 inch CRT. (Raytheon)

each port and starboard. The (V)3 transmitters are located in the bottom of each box. The band 1 antenna is AS-3316, and is unique to the SLQ-32.

The (V)1 antenna assembly weighs 1560 lbs, (V)2 2400 lbs, and (V)3 5000 lbs. Band 1's lens antennas are 25 × 13 × 18 in (30 lbs).

The jammer, consisting of a beam-forming lens fed by a 35-element linear horn array, is capable of forming 64 beams on either side of a ship.

Coarse frequency data (from the IFM) and amplitude data (from the DF array) are combined in a direction/frequency correlator; time-of-arrival data is added to form a pulse word, stored by frequency and angle in an emitter-file memory. If three or more identical pulses are received within a programmable interval (up to 32 msec), the digital tracker decides that a new emitter is present, and additional data are collected for analysis. PRF, scan type, scan period, and frequency are all extracted.

The initial-development contract was awarded in May 1977, with first production deliveries in June 1978 (final sea trials were on board the cruiser *Leahy*). Raytheon offered a series of crystal video receivers plus an IFM; Hughes offered a scanning superheterodyne. The key advantage of Raytheon's proposal, however, was reportedly its multibeam array, which could handle multiple threats simultaneously. Each beam offers the gain of the entire array; and by using all beams simultaneously, SLQ-32 can carry out uninterrupted surveillance over the entire horizon. In the jammer, an individual microwave amplifier (TWT) is inserted ahead of each array element (a total of 140), for a total reported radiated power of 1 MW. Jamming modes include range-gate pull-off (RGPO) and azimuth-gate pull-off (AGPO), the latter jamming CW missile-guidance radars. It is claimed that the system can jam 75 hostile threats simultaneously, each with a tailored countermeasure.

As a result of the attack on the frigate *Stark*, existing SLQ-32(V)2s on board frigates (FFG-7 class) are being modified with a separate jammer, designated Sidekick. Raytheon had already developed such a system for the Taiwan Navy some years ago; the company took about three months from initial request (seven weeks from contract award) to first installation. No for-

mal designation for the Sidekick jammer or for the modified SLQ-32 had been announced as of early 1989.

A (V)4 version for carriers, to replace the current SLQ-17, will employ fiber optics.

◆ SLQ-33

See the ASW section.

◆ SLQ-34

This new-generation (1986) cover and deception system uses two small antennas, one for reception and one for transmission (about 30 lbs each, approximately 20 × 15 × 15 inches). They will probably be masthead-mounted.

◆ SLQ-35

See the Mine Warfare section (countermeasures).

◆ SLQ-36

See the ASW section (torpedo countermeasures).

◆ SLQ-37

See the Mine Warfare section (countermeasures).

◆ SLQ-39

Chaff buoy.

◆ SLQ-41 through -47

Active expendable EW buoys.

◆ SLQ-48

See the Mine Warfare section (countermeasures).

◆ SLQ-49

SLQ-49 is an inflatable decoy or "Rubber Duck"; it is the U.S. version of the British DLF. See above for details.

◆ SLQ-50

SLQ-50 is E-Systems's surface-ship terminal for the Battle-Group Passive Horizon-Extension System (BGPHES), the airborne passive electronic-intelligence collector. The original contract was awarded in 1984, and the first SLQ-50 was shipped for installation in 1987. SLQ-50 consists of four UYK-44 computers and three UYQ-23 terminals connected by a Militarized Local Area Network (MLAN).

◆ SLQ-51

The advanced electronics-warfare system will replace SLQ-32. SLQ-51 is to counter all threats, including monopulse seekers. The preliminary design was completed about 1985.

◆ SLR-12A

This wide-band shipboard EW direction-finder uses a rotating directional microwave antenna in a radome. The antenna itself (AS-2209, formerly AS-1789) is a small paraboloid feeding a horn in the upper part of the radome. The antenna is mast-mounted.

◆ SLR-16

This HF SIGINT receiver uses SRD-19 arrays. SLR-16 automatically seeks and acquires signals, then selects those of interest for further analysis while avoiding set frequencies of no interest, e.g., those used for friendly communications. SLR-16 and SRD-19 are used together in the Classic Outboard (SSQ-72) system.

◆ SLR-21

This ESM system for small ships, made by EM Systems, was announced in 1978. The broad-band DF antenna consists of four cavity-backed spiral antennas, with four crystal video receivers, apparently with associated IFMs. Frequency range is 2–18 GHz, and the claimed direction-finding accuracy is better than 10 degrees. SLR-21 is an automatic table look-up system, and in 1978 the manufacturer claimed that SLR-21 could cope with up to 200,000 pulses/sec. The display is a table of parameters of the detected emitters.

SLR-21 was developed specifically for the *Pegasus* class, with a projected unit cost of $30,000.

◆ SLR-22

A cover and deception device for carriers, SLR-22 was developed about 1985.

◆ SLR-23

An intercept direction-finder in the J-band, SLR-23 works with WLR-1 and SLQ-32.

◆ SRD-19

SRD-19 is a system for exploiting SIGINT (LF/MF/VHF) and is part of the shipboard Classic Outboard (SSQ-72) system. SRD-19 uses 24 small deck-edge antennas in three groups of eight (LF/MF–HF). These antennas include standard communications antennas (for target acquisition and reference: one combination would be a 10–30 MHz inverted cone, a 35-foot 2–35 MHz whip, and two broad-band discages), and an Adcock-type VHF D/F array (dipoles and crossed loops) mounted in three tiers on the masthead. SRD-19 is often used with SLR-16. In that application SLR-16 has priority over the direction-finding functions.

The deck-edge antennas are electronically switched in sequence to form receiving beams. The masthead array (AS-3112/SRD-19) includes both a wide-open directional system and a wide-band target-acquisition/reference system.

SRD-17 (AS-3202) deck-edge antenna, USS *Mississippi*, June 1988. (Stefan Terzibaschitsch)

◆ SSQ-70

SSQ-70 is a system for collecting operational intelligence.

◆ SSQ-72

See SRD-19 and SLR-16 above.

◆ SSQ-74

A van-mounted radar and communications simulator, SSQ-74 is called ICADS (Integrated Cover and Deception System). SSQ-74 may be temporarily installed on a destroyer's weather decks; ICADS has a gross weight of 18,000 lbs (1974). This system is now being modernized. The current prototype is on board USS *Comte de Grasse.*

◆ SSQ-82

SSQ-82 controls a ship's electronic emissions (MUTE: Multiple Unit for Transmission Elimination). By centralizing control of all electronic emissions on board a ship, MUTE makes full electronic silence possible.

◆ SSQ-91

SSQ-91 is the communications simulator in the *Kidd* class.

◆ SSQ-93

SSQ-93 is a ship-simulation acoustic buoy.

◆ URD-9

URD-9 is a radar D/F (225–400 MHz)

◆ URD-27

URD-27 is a broadcast-frequency D/F for SIGINT (250 MHz–18 GHz)

◆ ULQ-6 and SLQ-22/23/24/30

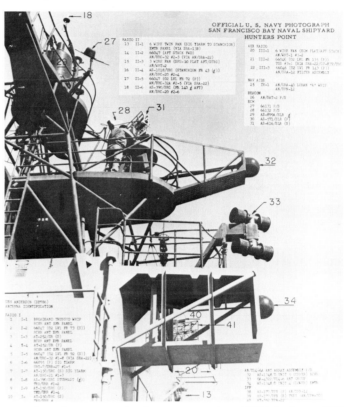

ULQ-6A and some associated antennas, on board USS *Anderson* (DD 786), 1969. Although superseded in U.S. service by SLQ-17 and -32, these systems remain on board many ex-U.S. ships. Numbers 32 and 34 are AS-1348/Us; 33 is OA-4322/ULQ-6 itself, the trainable deception jammer. Number 31 indicates AS-616/SLR, which is usually enclosed in a radome. U.S. ships always carried three DF antennas in radomes: AS-616 (shown), AS-899A (barely visible, on the centerline), and AS-571 (not visible, on the other side of the ECM platform). Number 27 is the "derby," 66131, which works with the "sword" (not visible here) to provide wide-open interception. (U.S. Navy)

ULQ-6 is a deception repeater/jammer for cruisers and destroyers, often found on board ships transferred abroad. ULQ-6 has been almost completely superseded in U.S. service by SLQ-32. For details of the antenna system, see SLA-12 and SLA-15 above.

ULQ-6 was used in combination with chaff launchers: the jammer would break a missile's track, which would then transfer to the chaff cloud (see the account of U.S. chaff rounds below). ULQ-6 was the basis of the ECM/chaff systems added to U.S. warships on an emergency basis during the Vietnam War, both in the Western Pacific and in the Mediterranean.

This system currently equips Canadian frigates. In 1987 an additional coherent countermeasures processor (CCP), to be added to ULQ-6 on board all 17 Canadian frigates, was announced. CCP contains its own 500-radar threat library and can deal with such ECCM techniques as pulse coding and pulse

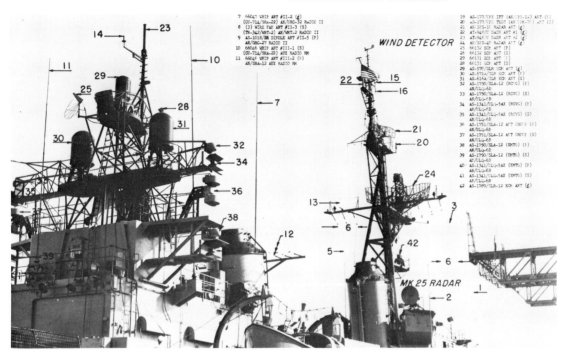

ECM arrays associated with ULQ-6B, on board the destroyer *Hamner*, 1965: (32) AS-1750/SLA-12; (34) AS-1341/ULQ-5AX (receiving); (36) AS-1751/SLA-12; (38) AS-1750/SLA-12 (transmitter). The big radomes are direction-finders containing spinning antennas: (29) AS-570/SLR; (30) AS-571A/SLR; (31) AS-616A/SLR. Number 25 is a "sword" (66132), and number 28 is a "derby" (66131). Antenna 42, on the foremast, is AS-1789/SLR-12. (U.S. Navy)

ULQ-6 on board the Canadian Tribal-class frigate *Iroquois*, 1986. The arrays differ from those in U.S. ships, but the system is the same. The arrays are visible along the barbette under the Signaal "egg" on the near side of the ship. (Author)

compression. Instantaneous bandwidth is up to 550 MHz. CCP is manufactured by Telemus Electronic Systems.

SLQ-22/23/24 are high gain versions of ULQ-6, using the same SLA-12 or -15 antennas. SLQ-30 is an updated ULQ-6 by Kuras-Alterman (TRUMP, or Threat-Reactive Update and Modernization Program).

◆ WLQ-4

The *Sturgeon*-class submarines' ESM system (Sea Nymph) was developed by GTE-Sylvania. WLQ-4 searches automatically for unknown signals. Presumably it was developed for electronic reconnaissance: in 1975, it was revealed that for some time *Sturgeon*-class submarines had been employed in that role.

◆ WLR-1/WLR-11

WLR-1 was the standard U.S. radar-warning system of the 1960s, for both surface ships and submarines. As such it has been transferred to many friendly navies, and it continues in U.S. service. WLR-1's chief disadvantage was that the operator had to search manually through the frequency range(s), so he could easily miss transient signals. That limitation was acceptable for electronic intelligence gathering but not for quick reaction to an incoming missile. On the other hand, WLR-1 was liked for its resolution and for its very wide bandwidth covering VHF through SHF (50 MHz–10.75 GHz). WLR-1 simultaneously finds the direction of a selected signal and displays information. Systems now in U.S. service are being upgraded to WLR-1H, which scans automatically and covers a wider bandwidth (0.55–20 GHz).

WLR-1 uses a combination of wide-open fixed antennas (NT-66131 for UHF (300–3000 MHz) and NT-66132 for VHF (40–300 MHz), the "derby" and "sword," respectively; and the AS-1174 (or AS-3200) for UHF/SHF, a tape-wound cone) and rotating direction-finding antennas in radomes (AS-571, AS-616, and AS-899; in some cases the roles of AS-571 and -616 are combined in a single AS-1023 antenna). In FRAM destroyers the radomes are typically located atop the after deckhouse, near the ULQ-6 arrays. The sword/derby combination has been in service since World War II and is used in the Royal Navy as well. Scan rates for AS-571 and -616 are 0–250 rpm; for AS-899, 300 rpm maximum. Beamwidths: AS-571 (300–600 MHz), 50 × 90 deg at lowest frequency to 30 × 70 deg at highest, combining vertical and horizontal dipoles; AS-616 (550–2600 MHz), 35 × 85 deg to 20 × 70 deg on low band and 35 × 70 deg to 20 × 50 deg on high band (vertical horns 20 × 95 deg to 10 × 65 deg on high band); AS-899F (1 GHz–20 GHz, i.e., bands 6 through 10), 40 deg in horizontal width at lowest frequency, 4 deg at highest.

AS-571 uses a double-sided high-gain dipole array, one side of the array acting as a reflector and the other as a planar surface. Three dipoles are mounted vertically on the planar surface, and two are mounted horizontally on the corner reflector, so that the antenna can receive both vertically and horizontally polarized signals, although only one polarization is selected at any one time. AS-616 uses similar dipoles, six arranged horizontally on one side and three, vertically, on the other, to intercept signals in the lower UHF band. Below the dipoles it carries waveguide horns, four mounted vertically on one side and four horizontally on the other, to receive signals from the higher UHF band. The radome is identical to that of AS-571 (diameter 45 $^{11}/_{32}$ in, height 62 in), but the antenna inside is much heavier (total weights are 250 lbs for AS-571 and 425 lbs for AS-616).

The current AS-899F is a more complex antenna, consisting of a stationary spiral feed, a multiplexer, and a reflector tilted at about 45 deg so that it always focuses signals on the stationary feed. This type of construction is quite common in the spinning ESM antennas developed during the 1950s and 1960s. Earlier versions were more complex, with four feed horns, two at the top and two at the bottom of the antenna, and a spinning reflector, angled at 45 deg. These antennas were more limited in frequency response (to bands 7, 8, and 9, because the horns were not broad-band antennas). AS-899F is 34 in in diameter and 82 in tall and weighs 268 lbs. AS-1174 is an ominidirectional broad-band antenna, for UHF through low SHF in three bands (designated 6, 7, and 8: 300–2450 MHz, 2450–4375 MHz, and 4375–7350 MHz). It employs two strips of aluminum tape spiraling up a fiberglass cone; a triplexing filter separates signals from the three bands. The basic frequency of the antenna is determined by its apex angle; bandwidth is determined by the tightness of the spiral. The antenna itself is 16.5 in in diameter and 41.5 in high (weight 11.25 lbs). Existing AS-1174s are being replaced by AS-3200s, which are very similar in shape but are larger, with four spiral copper bands (diameter 30.3 in, height 45 in, total weight 45 lbs.)

WLR-11 is an IFM system. It also adds capacity through J-band to the basic WLR-1 system. WLR-11 uses the same antennas, for the 7–18 GHz frequency range. WLR-11 is being added to existing WLR-1 systems, the designation of the new configuration being WLR-1G. It incorporates an automatic lookup feature. For its IFM function, WLR-11 adds a further omnidirectional antenna, AS-2918/S, a fiberglass cylinder housing a biconical horn, a polarizer, and a diplexer. The horn consists of two cones, apex to apex, with a small gap between, this region forming the antenna aperture. The pattern is omnidirectional and is at least 25 degrees wide in elevation. The diplexer breaks received signals into two bands: 7–11 GHz (low pass) and 11–18 GHz (high pass). The entire antenna is only 6.3 in in diameter and 24 in high (the attached preamplifier is considerably larger than the antenna proper), and it is typically mounted on a yardarm or other high horizontal position. The manufacturer is ARGOSystems.

A "sword" antenna typical of those feeding the WLR-1 pulse analyzer. This one is on board a British ship, but U.S. "swords" (i.e., monopoles emerging from ground planes consisting of a few wires) are identical. WLR-1 also employs higher-frequency "derby" antennas, which are analogous in design. (A. Wetback)

♦ **WLR-3**

WLR-3 is a radar-warning and signal collection system for surface ships and some submarines.

♦ **WLR-4**

WLR-4 is an ESM receiver, part of Shortstop.

♦ **WLR-5**

WLR-5 is an acoustic intercept receiver.

♦ **WLR-6**

WLR-6 is a reconnaissance signal-collection system. In submarines, this device is called Waterboy.

♦ **WLR-8**

WLR-8 is a radar-warning system for sequential or simultaneous scan over the 50 MHz–18 GHz spectrum. WLR-8 measures signal direction, frequency, modulation, PRF, pulse width, amplitude, and scan rate. There are four configurations: (V)1 for submarines, (V)2 for the *Los Angeles* class (550 MHz–20 GHz), (V)4 for carriers, and (V)5 for Trident submarines. It was reported in July 1980 that the entire DF subsystem of the carrier version would be replaced, and new lightweight antennas fitted.

WLR-8 employs seven electronically swept octave-band superheterodyne receivers, to achieve high sensitivity and accuracy. All but the lowest frequency band (which is veractortuned) are YiG-tuned. Three more tuners are available as reserves, or for expanded frequency coverage. The system can operate with any of the U.S. Navy's standard rotating DF antennas, either manually or by computer control.

The display is a five-trace CRT: the upper two traces, which can be switched to any tuner, show amplitude vs. frequency. The next two are A-scans for manual PRF (actually pulse repetition interval, the inverse of PRF) and pulse width measurement. The last is used for signal analysis.

WLR-8 was conceived in 1968, and in 1971 GTE-Sylvania won a design competition, beating Watkins-Johnson, ITT, and Loral. The requirement was urgent because the Shortstop antimissile ECM program had just been canceled because of its high cost. Originally three versions were planned. WLR-8(V)1, which was not built, was the basic computer-aided surveillance system. (V)2 added an automatic signal acquisition; a parameter measurement; and a threat-alarm function, Scan Lock. (V)2 was intended specifically for submarines. (V)3, for destroyers and larger surface ships, was (V)1 plus an interface to general-purpose computers. (V)3, in turn, was superseded before production by WLR-8(V)4 Mod 1, which benefitted from submariners' experiences. Improvements included a Threat Early Warning (TEW) operating mode and more automatic signal-parameter measurement. (V)2 was updated to include many of the features of (V)4 Mod 1.

♦ **WLR-9**

WLR-9 is an acoustic intercept system; see the ASW section.

♦ **WLR-10**

WLR-10 is a radar-warning system. In its (V)1 version, it consists of a tuner assembly (4 tuners) and a receiver-processor. Each transmission received is converted to audio intelligence data, primarily monitored and recorded on magnetic tape. WLR-10 shares a periscope antenna with WLR-8.

♦ **WLR-13**

WLR-13 is an IR/EO-warning receiver.

♦ **APECS**

Advanced Programmable Electronic Countermeasures System is a multibeam integrated ESM/ECM system that gives elevation and azimuth data on each pulse by monopulse techniques. The phased-array transmitter antennas (two modules per system, port and starboard) can engage multiple targets simultaneously. This system, manufactured by ARGOSystems, is light enough for installation on fast patrol boats.

◆ APECS-II

APECS-II is a surface-ship electronic-warfare (ESM and ECM) system for ships displacing up to 8000 tons. In 1988 APECS-II is in production for four navies. It employs a phased-array multibeam (16-target) antenna covering 360 degrees in azimuth and up to 30 degrees in elevation, with high radiated power both in pulse and in CW modes. Compared to older phased-array designs, APECS has polarization diversity (to counter monopulse threats), is easier to install (because it requires neither external waveguide nor water cooling), and can handle complex signals. For example, it can deal with frequency/PRF-agile seekers by tracking the leading edges of their pulses, not waiting until the full pulse has been received before sending the countering signals. Frequency coverage is 0.5–18 GHz.

The ESM portion of the system is the AR-700 receiver, including an upgraded version of the ASP-32 signal processor. The ECM portion is controlled by a multiprocessor-driven power-management unit and radiates from two stabilized transmitters. Because control is software-based, ECM tactics can be tailored to specific threats. The two basic operating modes are transponder (in which the appropriate response signal is preset) and deception (in which the response signal is constructed in response to the details of the received signal). The two techniques can be run in sequence, and the entire system can operate fully automatically, semiautomatically (the command to radiate is under operator control, but everything else is automated), or manually.

This system is manufactured by ARGOSystems.

The first APECS II was delivered in 1986. The II/AR-700 suite will be carried on board the new Portuguese MEKO frigates, and APECS II was selected in 1987 for the Dutch *Karel Doorman* class, in place of a more expensive Signaal system.

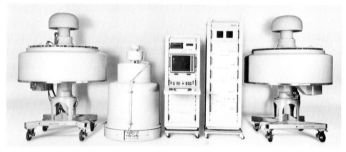

ARGOSystems APECS-II electronic warfare system for surface ships, showing the two jammers, the radome-enclosed ESM array, the indicator, and the rack of electronic equipment. (ARGOSystems)

◆ ARGO 680/681

This system is found on board some Taiwanese (GRC) destroyers. This system employs a single mechanically scanned D/F antenna to cover the E–J-bands. ARGO 680/681 uses electronically scanned antennas for frequency fixing, which is much faster than with WLR-1.

◆ AR-700-S5

AR-700-S5 is an ESM system for submarines that provides threat warning, surveillance, and targeting information using signals in the 2–18 GHz band. Direction finding is by monopulse rather than by a rotating antenna, and the system is also wide open in frequency, using paralleled digital IFM receivers. Bearing accuracy is 5 degrees (rms). The embedded signal processor, an ARGOSystems ASP-32, can track up to 200 signals simultaneously, identifying them by reference to a library. The system's frequency range can be extended to 40 GHz.

A miniaturized version of the mast assembly, 6.5 inches in diameter and 11.8 inches high, has been developed.

This system is manufactured by ARGOSystems.

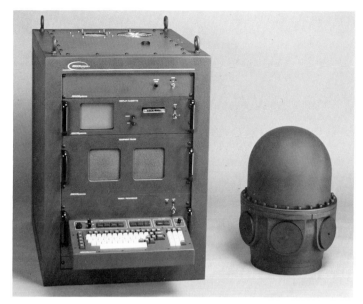

ARGOSystems's AR-700 ESM system for submarines, with the indicator on the left and the antenna on the right. Three D/F ports are visible on the antenna. (ARGOSystems)

ARGOSystems miniaturized ESM antenna for submarines. (ARGOSystems)

◆ CAROL

ARGOSystems's intercept receiver and deception transmitter is designed for the new Swedish *Goteborg*-class missile corvettes.

◆ EW-100/200/300

These threat-warning suites are designed for fast patrol boats. EW-100 is the basic system; EW-200 is improved; EW-300 is an integrated suite. All provide 360-degree cover in azimuth and 60 deg in elevation, are based on a 16-bit programmable computer with 1-second reaction time, and have a library of 75–100 emitters. EW-300 weighs 300 lbs and covers the D–J-bands.

These systems are manufactured by Loral.

◆ FERRET

An austere submarine ESM set by GTE, FERRET uses an Israeli front end and covers the entire 1–40 GHz band. The narrow-band subsystem (1–18 GHz) uses up to four superheterodyne receivers for precise analysis. Claimed DF accuracy is 5–10 degrees. Frequency resolution is 125 kHz (narrow-band) and 5 MHz (broad-band).

◆ GUARDIAN STAR

Sperry Marine's automatic ESM direction finder (ADF/ESM) is for small patrol combatants. The Mk 3(V) version, announced in 1987, combines omnidirectional and monopulse direction-finding antennas (six spirals) with an RF digital frequency-discrimination (DFD) unit. Guardian Star is interesting as an example of the capabilities that are possible using modern high-density electronics with distributed (rather than concentrated) microprocessors.

The antenna, with its radome, is 36 cm high and 15 cm in diameter (14 × 5.9 in) and weighs 5 kg. The associated digital interface unit weighs 33.5 kg. The display is a 48-cm-diagonal raster-scan color unit. The system as a whole illustrates the high density of modern electronics. The digital unit converts each received pulse or CW signal into digital form. The display sits atop a processor that sorts pulses and compares them with library entries. Output can include platform identification and threat-level determination based on library matching. Sperry describes the library (containing 1000 emitter modes) as uniquely structured for ease of automatic identification; the operator can load the library with specific emitter characteristics, or the load can be from some separate electronic data base. The operator has a scratch library with a capacity of 50 emitters.

The display is normally a polar plot (emitter frequency vs. bearing), but because the display is digital it can also show emitter frequency vs. amplitude. Typically the display also provides tabular data on particular emitters (e.g., name if identified, bearing/confidence level of bearing determination, frequency/amplitude, PRF/pulse modulation, scan rate/threat level, and platform/use if library matched). The operator interacts with the display by means of a touch screen and a keyboard.

The system covers frequencies 2–18 GHz (frequencies are determined within 7.5 MHz), PRFs 100–300 kHz (determined to within .002 percent), pulse widths 0.1–100 microsec (measured to within 0.05 microsec), and scan rates 16 msec to 40 sec (determined within 10 percent). Elevation coverage is within a 30-deg cone. Sensitivity is −60 dBm across the entire bandwidth. Claimed false-alarm rate is less than one per hour, and the manufacturer claims a probability of detection greater than 99 percent (Sperry claims a probability of intercept of unity if 6 successive pulses are received). The system can track 250 emitters simultaneously. Emitter throughput is less than 1 second, and the display is updated 50 times per second. Sperry claims a bearing accuracy of 10 deg for 2–8 GHz, and 5 deg for 8–18 GHz.

Sperry offers several optional extensions. The frequency range can be extended down to 0.5 GHz and up to 40 GHz. Frequency precision can be improved. The system can be extended to receive communications (VLF through UHF). Guardian Star can be connected to control chaff and flare launchers and to correlate with a radar; Guardian Star can also be modified to estimate target range by target-motion analysis (analogous to submarine ranging by target-motion analysis).

◆ PHOENIX II

ARGOSystems's ESM/DF system (1–18 GHz in five bands) is for ships of fast-patrol-boat size and larger. Announced in 1984, PHOENIX II was ordered for the Colombian HDW corvettes and the Indian Type 1500 submarines, among others. PHOENIX II uses a combination of omnidirectional, monopulse, and directional antennas and IFM receivers. All signal processing and identification is automatic.

◆ Protector

The Kuras-Alterman family of naval ECM systems was announced in 1981. Protector uses SLQ-30 technology. Protector I is the basic suite for missile warning and track breaking on fast patrol boats through frigates. Protector II adds fully automated ESM plus direction finding in the H/I- and J-bands; Protector II is for fast patrol boats through frigates also. Protector III provides high-power noise jamming from multibeam lens-array antennas, as well as automated ESM, direction finding for missile warning, track-breaking ECM, and chaff hand-off; this version is for frigates and larger ships. The basis of the system is a proprietary multisignal IFM receiver. The overall reaction time of the automated system is 2 seconds in either the 7–12 or the 7–18 GHz bands. Jamming techniques include angle, range, and velocity-repeater deception, plus spot, swept-spot, and barrage noise. Power ranges from 10 kW (semi-omni sector) to over 200 kW for a multibeam lens array covering a 360 × 20 degree sector. In 1981 a monopulse jamming system was being developed. Protector I employs two receiving and two transmitting antennas (weights, respectively, 13 and 45 kg each; each is 130 × 80 × 115 cm). Protector II uses a rotating antenna (166 kg) plus pairs of receiving and transmitting antennas (20 and 65 kg; respectively, 50 × 50 × 30 cm and 130 × 115 × 115 cm). Protector III uses two receive/transmit antennas (225 kg each, 76 × 102 × 112 cm).

◆ S2150

S2150 is EM Systems's fully automatic ESM system for small ships and submarines. The S2150-01 version operates over the 2–18 GHz range, with a direction-finding accuracy of 10 degrees.

◆ S3000

S3000 is EM Systems's surveillance system for submarines. S3000 is installed in British *Oberon*-class and nuclear submarines. S3000 uses a high-gain scanning antenna plus an omnidirectional antenna and IFM receiver; the operator selects scanning, sector-scan, or pointing modes for the directional antenna. There is an associated threat library and an automatic threat-alarm feature. Presumably S3000 is an ELINT system.

◆ Sea Sentry

Kollmorgen's ESM system for submarines and surface ships was announced in 1980. Versions I and II are for surface ships, with version III for submarines. The basic system covers the 1–18 GHz range, with automatic detection and direction finding (accuracy better than 10 degrees). A 150 MHz–1 GHz receiver is available as an option, so that all communications bands can be covered. Sea Sentry I is a simple ESM system to support fire control in fast attack craft. Sea Sentry II is more sensitive and can incorporate an IFM or superheterodyne receiver. Sea Sentry III is designed for full integration with a submarine's combat system, using both the periscope and its own antenna (multiple arrays and microwave receivers on a mast). The General Instruments DF/threat processor has a 128-emitter threat library, and it can be supplemented by additional ELINT information collected by the Sea Sentry III system. Up to 35 emitters can be processed simultaneously, and 15 displayed. The user assigns a priority to each threat radar, CW (fire-control) radars having the highest. Threat surveillance is automatic, and there are two modes: (i) surveillance, as a wide-open receiver providing all-around cover; and (ii) search, in which frequency is measured and direction is more accurately measured. The system measures both CW and pulse signals, displaying threat identity, bearing range, and other signal data on its CRT. Direction-finding accuracy is about 10 degrees.

Kollmorgen claims that Sea Sentry III (Model 962U) is the first completely automatic broad-band radar-threat detection-and-analysis system integrated into a submarine's surveillance periscope. Sea Sentry III detects and identifies signals in the 100 kHz to 1 GHz range, and detects, determines the bearing of, and identifies signals in the 1–18 GHz range. The antenna consists of three omni and four DF spirals that collectively receive 100 kHz to 18 GHz signals. The LF omni units are a voltage probe antenna; a top-loaded electric-field probe connected to an impedance-matching transistor amplifier, housed within a dielectric radome on top of the array; a sleeve/stub, a thick quarter-wave monopole above a ground plane around the spiral antennas and receiver components; and a biconical omni housed within the dielectric radome below the VPA. The four DF spirals are identical and mounted spatially around the cylinder to provide 360-degree coverage in 90-degree segments. Four identical microwave receiver channels are housed within the antenna array, each receiver fed by one of the DF antennas. A four-digit LED readout displays the threat's center frequency, within 15 MHz; threat characteristics are presented on a radar-parameter digital display.

Although only one version is for submarines, Sea Sentry is intended primarily for a submarine's use; Kollmorgen is a periscope maker. Argentina bought Sea Sentry III for its TR 1700 submarines, and India bought both the system and the company's periscope.

◆ SLR-600 Series

These private-venture ECM systems are made by General Instrument Corporation specifically for fast patrol craft. SLR-600 is an ESM system for fast patrol craft; it is highly automated for ships with small crews. It uses IFM techniques and combines a broad-band (E- through J-band: 2–20 GHz) receiver with a fast processor for rapid response. Automation requires the system itself to decide which radars it is detecting: the display shows radar identifications, based on data in the threat library, as well as the details of pulse width, PRF, and scan rate for radars that do not fit the library's information. The operator can select data on any specific radar for read out, and the system provides an alarm if a specific threat radar is detected. SLR-600 responds to tracking radars within one second and to scanning radars within two.

SLR-600, a navalized version of the ALR-66 radar-warning receiver, uses a four-antenna array to measure direction with an accuracy of 15 degrees.

SLR-610 is much the same system with expanded frequency coverage (C–J-bands, 6.5–22 GHz) and with a different display (presumably making greater use of the operator).

SLR-640 is an improved SLR-610, adding accurate directional information. The dual CRT display shows both a polar plot of detected signals and a detailed parameter readout on a selected list of detected emitters. ALR-646 is a similar airborne system.

SLQ-630 is a jammer.

SLQ-650 (INEWS, Integrated Naval EW System) is a fully integrated system consisting of an SLR-640 receiver and an SLQ-630 jammer. The monitor shows both the threats being jammed (monitored by the ESM system) and the type and level of jamming. The system can track up to 100 targets continuously, presenting their parameters in tabular form (20 to a page) and also displaying them in polar form. The system automatically selects the highest-priority threats and passes their data

to the jammer, which uses a high-gain steerable antenna. Several emitters can be jammed simultaneously: modes include range and angle deception.

◆ SR-200

SR-200 is a shipboard ESM receiver with automatic frequency measurement (0.5–18 GHz, with optional extension to 40 GHz). The frequency range is broken down into four bands (C/D, E/F, G/H, I/J, with an optional extension into K). This receiver is intended for fast patrol boats and is designed to provide sufficiently accurate direction finding to support the targeting of antiship missiles. SR-200 is designed to operate in a dense pulse environment. The antenna array consists of an omnidirectional antenna and a rotating multihorn (for multiband) DF antenna. The omnidirectional antenna hands over the signals it intercepts to the DF antenna, which in turn provides signals for analysis. SR-200 provides an alarm based on the identity of an emitter. The display is either a PPI (strobes) or tabular. SR-200 can also be adapted to provide ESM data to a conventional radar display.

To measure direction of arrival, SR-200 uses a rotating antenna with sidelobe blanking. The receivers use wide-open IFM, for rapid intercept and acquisition. Automatic signal processing is employed to achieve rapid identification in a dense environment. The signal processing technique is azimuth-oriented spatial sampling. There are three receivers: IFM, TRF (tuned RF), and logarithmic video. Outputs are digitized pulse by pulse. The IFM is fed only by the narrow-beam directional antennas; the other receivers are fed by the omnidirectional antenna (TRF can be either).

The design emphasizes angular accuracy, which is required to estimate the range to a potential target. Range can be obtained by observing the change of bearing angle as the ESM platform moves along a baseline. The system can get within 10 percent of the range by measuring the bearing angle within 1 degree. For shorter ranges (within radar range), the ESM system can be used to point a ranging radar; accurate pointing permits very short radar transmission, and so minimizes the risk of counterdetection.

Parameters: RF, PW, PRI, scan, DF, amplitude
Capacity: 500,000 pulses/sec, can display 58 active tracks

As measured in 1980, the system's performance was typically better than 2 degrees on a single pass, and better than 1 degree on multiple passes. The accuracy above is measured at 1000 PRF. In a test in August 1980, SR-200 outperformed the requirements listed above. At 1 GHz, the requirement was 10 deg, but the system achieved an accuracy of about 3 degrees; at 3 GHz the requirement was 5 deg, but the system was actually accurate to about 1 deg. At 6 GHz the measured accuracy was about 2 deg (the same at about 2 GHz); at 13 GHz it was about 1 deg (requirement was 2 deg).

SR-200 is manufactured by Sanders Associates.

EXPENDABLES

◆ Mk 33/34 Launcher (RBOC)

RBOC was the Hycor Rapid-Blooming-Chaff launching system. Mk 33 was for frigates or destroyers (four launchers); Mk 34, for corvettes, fast patrol boats, or hydrofoils (two launchers). The launcher itself is Mk 135. This system has now been re-

PERFORMANCE OF SR-200

	Band 1 (0.5–2.0 GHz)	Band 2 (2.0–4.0 GHz)	Band 3 (4.0–8.0 GHz)	Band 4 (8–18 GHz)
Direction of Arrival accuracy	7.5 deg	5 deg	4 deg	2 deg
Frequency accuracy	9 MHz	9 MHz	17 MHz	21 MHz
PRF range	75–100 Hz	125–100 kHz	250–100 kHz	500–100 kHz
PW range	0.2–100 microsec	0.2–100 microsec	0.1–100 microsec	0.1–100 microsec

placed in U.S. service by Mk 36, but it was exported. These launchers were either automatically or semiautomatically controlled by the ship's ESM system. Each launcher was a six-barreled mortar fixed in position: the barrel elevation angles were 55, 65, and 75 degrees (by pairs). The standard Mk 171 chaff cartridge provided short-range protection, to about 150 yds (slant range). For longer ranges (about 1000–1500 yds), a rocket motor could be added to the cartridge.

Decoys included chaff (2–20 GHz range), an IR decoy (HIRAM), and a combined decoy (Gemini, a parachute-suspended flare).

A Gemini decoy. (Hycor)

In 1977, a typical cartridge outfit for two six-barrel launchers was 32 Mk 171 and 16 HIRAM (IR) decoys, plus two Mk 173 test cartridges.

◆ Mk 36 SRBOC

The Super Rapid-Blooming-Chaff launcher fires 130-mm cartridges. Mod 1 with two 6-tube launchers is for ships under 140 m; Mod 2 with four launchers, for ships over 140 m. All use Mk 182 chaff-dispensing cartridges, which climb to 244 m. A "Torch" IR decoy is being developed for use with Mk 36 SRBOC, and the NATO Sea Gnat rocket chaff dispenser may be adopted. Cartridge types are Super Chaffstar, Super Hiram III/Super Hiram IV (IR), and Super Gemini RF/IR.

Loading a Mk-33 RBOC. (U.S. Navy)

A Mk-36 SRBOC launcher. (U.S. Navy)

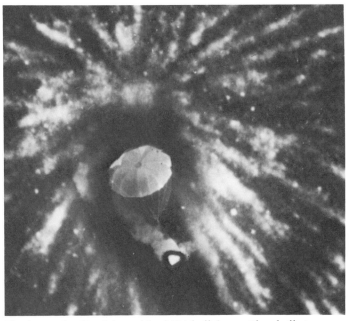

The burst of a Gemini combined IR/chaff decoy. The chaff streamers blow apart, while the infrared flare descends slowly on a parachute. (Hycor)

Mk-36 SRBOC launcher. Versions exist with the tubes either splayed, as here, or in rows of two. (Hycor)

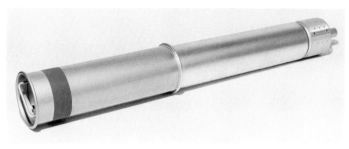

A Super Chaffstar decoy for SRBOC. (Hycor)

◆ AEB

The U.S. Navy's Active Expendable Buoy is similar in size to an A-size sonobuoy and contains a receiver, power supply, TWT, programmable signal processor, and deployable antenna. In June 1984 Dalmo Victor received a contract for 45 test buoys. Operational evaluation was completed in FY87, and a cost-reduction program began in FY88. AEB is deployed from aircraft or ships. This buoy counters enemy command/control; an advanced multipurpose buoy, now under development, will counter surveillance and targeting radars and missile seekers into the 1990s.

◆ AED

AED is the U.S. Navy's Active Expendable Decoy.

◆ CAD

CAD is a ship-fired radar simulator, made by Brunswick Defense. CAD hangs from a parachute and mimics the emissions from search radars. The program was jointly funded by the air force (for land application) and the navy, but funding was suspended just as the program was about to enter full-scale engineering development, about 1987.

◆ HIRAM

Hycor's IR Anti-Missile decoy for RBOC launching (112 × 417 mm, 4.1 kg) is a floating (spar buoy) IR decoy, sufficiently bright to duplicate the radiant intensity of even a large ship. HIRAM-2 (8 × 35 in, 29.4 lbs; the decoy extends beyond the mortar's muzzle, and the portion in the mortar is of 112-mm diameter) uses liquid (similar to JP-5) rather than solid fuel, to burn longer (1 min rather than 0.5 min) with a brighter and higher flame (3 m high), to protect against IR missiles seeking their targets in either of the two typically used wavelength ranges (windows). HIRAM-2 will strike the water about 150 m from a ship in 5–7 seconds. HIRAM was announced in 1980, for deployment in 1981.

Hiram IV decoy (with "IR" marking). (Hycor)

◆ LODED

NRL's project for a Long-Duration Expendable Decoy was announced in the early 1980s. LODED was a slow-flying aircraft, planned for an endurance of 12 hours and a payload of 40 lbs. Only a scale model, slightly over half scale, was built. It had tandem wings and a pusher propeller. It had no tail as such: the forward wings pivoted together for pitch control; and the after wings pivoted separately for roll control, and together for pitch trim. The power plant was a 1-HP 2-stroke engine driving a 2-blade propeller. Dimensions: span 5 ft 8 in × length 4 ft 1 in, maximum body width 6.75 in, propeller diameter 11 in. Weight: 25 lbs loaded (8-lbs fuel, 10-lbs payload). Launch speed was 33 kts. This project is interesting as an example of the way an RPV can be used for a ship's protection.

◆ TORCH

TORCH is a replacement for the earlier SOID. A quick-reaction off-board IR decoy launched by SRBOC, TORCH burns while floating on the water.

◆ Standard U.S. Chaff Cartridges

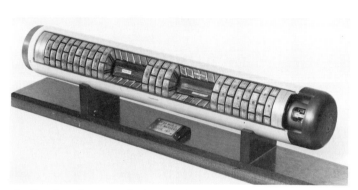

Chaff packaged in an early decoy: Mk 84. (Hycor)

Chaffstar I decoy (with "RF" marking). (Hycor)

The first U.S. chaff cartridge, the Mk-76 Chaffroc, was fired by Zuni (5-inch) rocket, using a modified aircraft launching pod. Its 10-kg payload was burst open by a time fuze, at up to 15-km range. The theoretical cross section was 60,000 square meters, but because all the chaff was released at one point, the effective cross section was 1000–2000 square meters. Mk 76 was in service in 1965–69.

Mk 76 was succeeded by the Hycor Mk 84 (1969–71); it used a new packaging and deployment technique. About a third more chaff was carried, and it was in hundreds of packages (cassettes), that rapidly bloomed in patterns 100 m in diameter. Total radar cross section was about three times that of Mk 76. However, Mk 84 was expensive; only about a third of its weight went into chaff; it was too large for a small ship; a separate jammer (ULQ-6) was needed to shift the missile tracker from ship to chaff cloud; and chaff deployment/track transfer took too long.

The next step was a mortar with a seduction round, RBOC (Rapid-Blooming Off-board Chaff) Mk 171 (1972–74). Hycor delivered the first eleven sets of Mk 33 mortars early in 1972. Mk 171 carried much more chaff, using a new plastic-film wrap to subdivide the load. The initial mortars were delivered to the fleet off Vietnam and were, therefore, called Westpac. The developed version, Mk 171, entered service in 1974. Radar cross section was about seven times that of Mk 76. Mk 171 could be made for any frequency from 2–20 GHz. Mk 173 is a reusable inert test cartridge. Hycor markets Mk 171 as Chaffstar.

Mk 171 was intended to protect destroyers; and a new round, Mk 182 (Super RBOC, 130 mm rather than 112 mm), entered service in 1977. SRBOC carries about four times the payload of Mk 171, in two stages (macrocassettes for first stage deployment, and plastic wraps within each macrocassette for second-stage deployment). Radar cross section is about 13 times that of Mk 76. Mk 182 is currently the standard U.S. chaff round.

The next stage is Mk 214, development of which was completed in 1986. Mk 214 provides about 26 times the radar cross section of the original Mk 76.

♦ **ALEX**

A shipboard decoy (chaff or IR) system made by Hycor, ALEX is available in two calibers (130.2 and 112.8 mm) and with two to twenty launchers that have automatic round selection and sequencing. ALEX can use all current U.S. Navy cartridges, as well as the Chaffstar, Gemini, HIRAM, and LOROC series.

♦ **Chaffstar II**

Announced in 1986, Hycor's chaff cartridge produces a much larger chaff cloud than Chaffstar (Mk 171). Chaffstar II is much longer than Chaffstar (112.3 × 1067 mm, 18.2 kg vs. 112.3 × 412.1 mm, 4.15 kg) and, therefore, must be launched from an RBOC II launcher with barrel extenders. Muzzle velocity is 200 ft/sec, and the typical cloud is 328 ft (100 m) in diameter, with an area of 7850 square meters. Payload weight is 8.2 kg (18 lbs).

♦ **LOROC**

Hycor's long-range off-board countermeasures chaff decoy can be launched from a lengthened RBOC II launcher and has an additional booster rocket. LOROC is launched to burst 1.0–4.5 km away from the ship for distraction. Dimensions: 112 × 1200 mm, weight 14.75 kg, payload weight 2.3 kg.

LOROC chaff decoy. (Hycor)

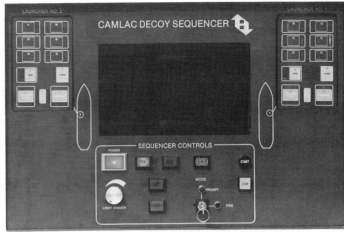

A typical CIC control panel for chaff launchers. This system is CAM-LAC, by Hycor, controlling two six-barrel launchers that are loaded, in this case, with a mix of RBOCs and LOROCs. (Hycor)

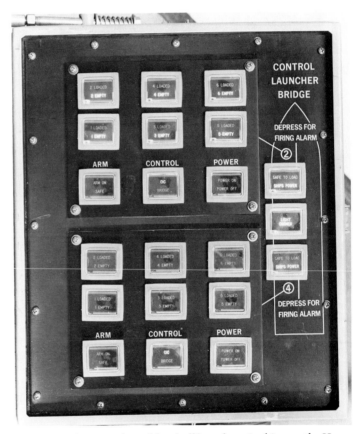

A typical bridge control panel for chaff launchers, in this case the Hycor CAMLAC. There are two launchers, and the lower set of buttons indicates that control is being exercised from CIC rather than from the bridge. (Hycor)

ANTISUBMARINE WARFARE

Antisubmarine warfare is carried out by three almost distinct forces: long-range maritime-patrol aircraft, which are cued by underwater surveillance systems or other very long range intelligence; surface ships, which may themselves launch helicopters (or cue aircraft); and submarines on patrol in likely areas of enemy submarine concentration, which rely largely on passive sonars and on long-range heavy torpedoes.

At this writing, the only ASW sensors effective beyond a few hundred yards are acoustic. Numerous (and expensive) attempts to develop nonacoustic sensors have not succeeded, except under very specialized conditions; and there is every evidence that the world's navies must continue to rely on acoustics. Nonacoustics is attractive because, at least in theory, a nonacoustic sensor can be operated continuously by an airplane or even a satellite. Acoustic sensing demands that the sensing platform put something in the water, either an expendable sonobuoy or a hull or towed sonar. Because sonobuoy fields must be of limited size and density, an airplane's search rate is inherently limited. In addition, the finite supply of sonobuoys always limits possible searches.

Generally there is a surface layer in the sea, kept at constant temperature (hence constant sound velocity) by mixing due to weather; this surface layer acts as a waveguide. The surface layer is about 300–600 feet deep in the North Atlantic, for example, depending on weather conditions. Within this layer, sonar acts much like radar, with signals propagating in nearly straight lines.

Below the layer, the velocity of sound varies with the depth, so rays of sound tend to bend, just as light passing through a complex medium will be refracted. One effect of this bending is to limit drastically the detection range of a surface ship against a submarine below the surface layer. For a hull-mounted sonar, the maximum (direct-path) range in the surface layer is about 20,000 yards, and ranges are often considerably shorter. Whether a given sonar can realize such maximum performance depends upon the sonar's power and frequency.

If the sonar's signals can propagate far enough, and if the water is deep enough, they bend down to a region of minimum sound velocity and then refract back up. The signals focus in a convergence zone around the ship, at a range set by water conditions. The convergence zone forms an annular ring around the ship, and additional convergence zones form at multiples of this first range. The typical range to the first convergence zone in the North Atlantic, for example, is 35 nm, and additional zones are found at 70, 105, 140, etc. Each zone may be 5 nm wide, and the sonar detecting a submarine in a convergence zone cannot distinguish positions within that zone. As a result, weapons cannot be fired on the basis of very long range detection. Instead, some platform must search the area in the zone within which the submarine may be located, to reacquire the target before attacking.

Two other acoustic paths deserve mention here. One is bottom (or surface) bounce: both the bottom and the surface can function as acoustic mirrors. In the late 1950s it appeared that bottom-bounce propagation could help fill the gap between relatively short direct-path ranges and long convergence-zone ranges; maximum bottom-bounce range was about 40,000 yards. Bottom bounce later lost much of its popularity because the sea bottom in much of the world turned out to be much more absorptive than had been expected.

A submerged submarine (or, in theory, a submerged variable-depth sonar) can use surface-bounce propagation. Presumably U.S. submarine sonars are spherical (i.e., can both depress and elevate their beams) specifically to exploit surface- as well as bottom-bounce propagation. Soviet submarines, such as Victors, have bow torpedo tubes and are presumably, therefore, limited to chin sonars, which are unlikely to make much effective use of surface-bounce propagation. That limitation in turn may be related to an emphasis on operation at shallow depths. Surface-bounce propagation is somewhat limited by weather, since reflection will be much less efficient if the surface is rough on the scale of sonar wavelengths, i.e., several feet.

Undersea warfare is complicated because sound does not travel in straight lines. It is, therefore, important to be able to predict that path. This display is a sonar ray-path predictor; the sound velocity profile is at left, and the corresponding prediction is at the right, for a sonar deep in the water. There is a combination of convergence zone refraction and reflection off the surface. (Thomson Sintra)

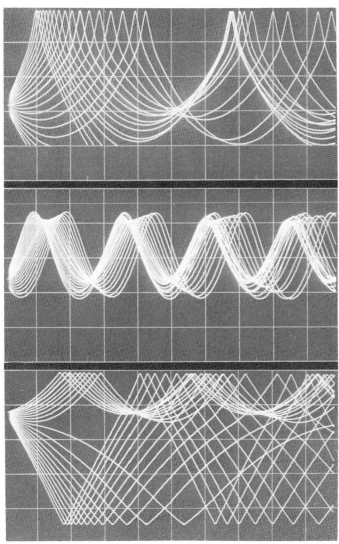

Typical sonar transmission patterns are shown on a ray-path predictor. All are from submerged sonars (variable-depth sonar or a submarine). At top, the rays bounce off the surface and curve around because of the convergence-zone phenomenon. The middle picture shows the effect of refraction in bending sonar rays up and down; this effect is the convergence-zone phenomenon. The bottom picture shows rays trapped in the surface duct at top, and bouncing off both the surface and the bottom. Whether a ray is trapped depends on the angle with which it is projected. (Signaal)

Both bounce paths are inherently limited in range because the sound ray must pass steeply enough through the various layers to avoid refraction and trapping, a phenomenon equivalent to that of the critical angle in optics. Actual range must depend on the bottom depth (or, in the case of surface-bounce, on the depth of the source), but for surface ships under average conditions the usual assumed maximum range is 40,000 yards. That figure may be based in part on an estimate of the loss to be expected in reflection off the bottom.

The other alternative is the reliable acoustic path (RAP), essentially the vertical path from bottom to surface or vice versa. No matter what the acoustic layering of the sea, a signal propagated perpendicular to the layers should pass through without distortion. There should also be a small angle around the vertical in which signals can pass with little loss or distortion. If the sound source or detector is deep enough, even that small angle can subtend a very considerable distance at the surface. RAP is hardly new, as it explains the successful operation of echo-sounders. However, the widespread application of RAP to sonar operation is relatively recent because an RAP sonar generally has to be quite deep.

In relatively shallow water, inside the 100-fathom (600-ft) curve, convergence-zone propagation is impossible. Hull sonars suffer from multiple bottom bounces, so detecting real targets is very difficult. However, a very high frequency upward-looking RAP sonar can function effectively. A sonar source well below the surface, moreover, can send out a horizontal beam that can avoid bouncing off either bottom or surface. Horizontal transmission is probably one mode of operation of the new low-frequency helicopter dipping sonars.

Sonar may be active or passive. Active operation has the advantage of imposing a signature on a submarine, and thus of overcoming silencing; but active operation reveals the presence of the searcher, and range is limited by the amount of energy that can be poured into the water. Passive operation depends upon picking up relatively faint sounds against the background of a relatively noisy ocean. When passive signals can be picked up, extraordinary ranges can be achieved because of multiple convergence zones. In most cases, success with passive sonar has been the key to NATO's ASW dominance, with active operation virtually limited to homing torpedoes. That situation may now be changing.

The major development of the past few years has been the Soviets' progress in countering Western sonars. Countermeasures consist of both silencing submarine noises to reduce pas-

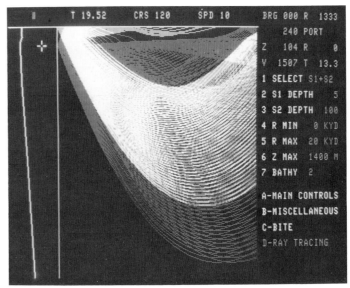

Given knowledge of the possible sound paths, sonar performance can be predicted. This typical modern display has the sound-velocity profile at left. Maximum effective range, read out at right, is 20,000 yds, and maximum target depth is 1400 meters (limited by refraction). (Thomson Sintra)

sive ranges and applying anechoic coatings to absorb active pings and, thus, to make active detection more difficult. The anechoic coatings cannot be very thick, so they are likely to be most effective against relatively high frequency sonars, i.e., against the sonars on board homing torpedoes.

The basis of passive operation, i.e., of all signal processing, is that the submarine's signals are regular, whereas the background noise is random. There are two fundamental approaches: the signal may be analyzed in spectral (frequency) terms, on the theory that over time the constant signature of the submarine will emerge; or the sonar can look instead at small volumes (cells) of ocean, choosing a particular cell that is consistently louder than its neighbors on the assumption that it contains a noise source. Mathematically, the two approaches are Fourier-transform alternatives. Spatial processing (i.e., concentration on a cell or on a volume defined in terms of bearing angle) is equivalent to adding up (integrating) signals over a broad band of frequencies from sources within that cell or angular range. Spatial processing is, therefore, often described as broad-band. The alternative (spectral processing) is, naturally, described as narrow-band.

Narrow-band noise is produced by rotating devices, such as machinery and propellers or, for a diesel, the regular firing of the engine. In practice, each line of noise is accompanied by harmonics, weaker repetitions of the sound at progressively higher frequencies. A signal processor may concentrate on a harmonic, even though it is weaker, because it occurs in a quieter part of the background noise. Moreover, because listening arrays are limited in size, they will have better gain (i.e., better discrimination in direction) at higher frequencies. The better that discrimination, the less background noise is mixed with the signal of interest.

Broad-band noise is much less well defined. Examples might include the flow noise over the submarine's hull and the gurgling of piping inside the submarine.

The appropriate choice for analysis depends on several factors. The fainter the submarine's sounds (i.e., the better it is silenced), the longer the period of integration required to separate a regular acoustic signature from the surrounding noise. If the signature is not really constant, integration time is limited, perhaps below what would be required to overcome noise. In that case broad-band (spatial) processing may be a much better choice.

Both types of processing can be quite sophisticated, and both represent alternatives to active operation. After World War II, when submarines (particularly those snorkeling) were relatively loud, passive operation entailed essentially no integration: a sonobuoy (or, for that matter, a homing torpedo) had only to seek a noise noticeably louder than its surroundings. That operation was very simple broad-band processing. That era ended in the early 1950s, as submariners learned not to snorkel for protracted periods. The question then was whether passive ASW was still practical. The solution turned out to be low-frequency narrow-band processing and integration, which the U.S. Navy code-named LOFAR (Low-Frequency Analysis and Recording).

LOFAR was the basis for Western passive acoustics from the mid-1950s on, and for many years it was a closely guarded secret. The success of LOFAR depended in part upon knowledge of the detailed acoustic signatures of potential enemy submarines because signal processing could be much more effective if specific features of a target submarine's acoustics were known. During the 1970s, Soviet recording devices began to turn up in areas where NATO submarines operated, such as Norway and Puget Sound. Such devices are useful only in a LOFAR-acoustics context. In 1988 the U.S. Department of Defense provided confirmation by publishing a photograph of a Soviet equivalent of a U.S. LOFAR sonobuoy.

Many modern passive sonars use waterfall displays, in which the vertical ordinate is time. The horizontal scale is either frequency or bearing. In either case, the data flow down from the top of the display, which shows the short-term history of what the sensor receives. The beaming version, therefore, shows rela-

tive target motion. Signals that are constant in frequency stand out in a frequency waterfall (a LOFARgram, often shortened to "gram"). The observer integrates the data visually to separate the stable signals (which appear as more or less continuous ver-

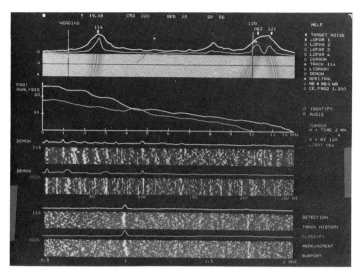

LOFAR was the most important ASW discovery of the first postwar decade. This passive sonar display has LOFAR at bottom. Frequency is read from left to right, and time from top to bottom. The dots of which the display consists indicate frequencies observed; the secret of LOFAR was that a consistent sound source would produce a line of such dots, whereas the random surrounding noise, though it might be louder at times, would fade into grayness over time. In effect, the observer integrated the spectrum over time by eye. However, modern electronics can also integrate, to produce the spectrograms shown between the bars of LOFAR data (the bumps corresponding to observed lines). The upper pair of LOFARgrams is marked DEMON, demodulated noise; it is data extracted from higher-frequency signals, on the theory that the consistent low-frequency signature of the submarine is superimposed on (modulates) its broad-band noise and can, therefore, be extracted by demodulation. The lower pair of LOFARgrams, at higher frequency, is extracted directly. The two graphs of "Fast Analysis" show the broad-band spectrum and may be used to estimate submarine speed. At the very top is a surveillance display, time against bearing, the spectrum having been integrated in frequency. Such an integral may emphasize transient behavior, which other displays will not show so clearly. The bumps at the top of this graph are approximate submarine locations, obtained by integrating again, this time over time. In effect, the top is a waterfall display. This basic technology is now common to all Western navies, though applications will vary in detail. (Thomson Sintra)

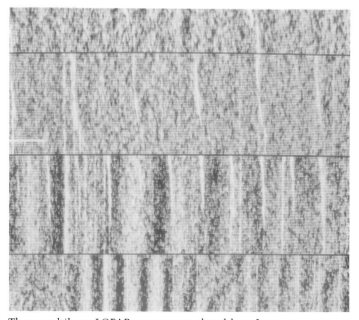

These multibuoy LOFARgrams are produced by a Lamparo processor. Each buoy is treated separately, and the vertical lines, light and dark, indicate steady frequencies against a noisy background. This is a CRT display; many systems use paper recorders. (Thomson Sintra)

tical lines) from the surrounding noise. The LOFARgram is, in effect, a spectrogram. Some systems record relative intensities at different frequencies at time intervals and then integrate over time to form a true spectrogram that is usable, for example, for automatic or semiautomatic target recognition.

Waterfalls are not suitable for active sonar displays since a waterfall cannot show range and bearing simultaneously. Therefore, active scanning sonars generally use PPIs. In cases of ODT transmission, the display often uses an expanding ring to represent the outgoing minidirectional pulse; in contrast, in a radar PPI, a line representing the directional pulse and its echo

revolves around the face of the scope. Many active sonars use B-scans, rectangular displays of range (vertical) vs. bearing. Compared with a PPI, a B-scan has the advantages of compressing distant targets into a limited space yet showing nearby targets clearly. Searchlight sonars use an A-scope and bearing indicator.

Armed with knowledge of the primary Western signal-processing technique, and probably driven by revelations of the effectiveness of NATO's detections of submarines, the Soviets have been able to achieve considerable silencing in their latest classes. The question, again, is whether passive signal processing has much of a future.

Three possibilities emerge, and as yet it is impossible to choose between them. One is that improvements in LOFAR technology—e.g., by adding more spatial discrimination, by tightening discrimination between nearby frequencies, or just by increasing integration time—can solve the problem. The United States' new LOFAR array sonobuoys and continued investment in towed passive arrays typify this approach. If this approach succeeds, the current situation, that Soviet submarines can be detected at long range without revealing the presence of NATO forces, will basically continue.

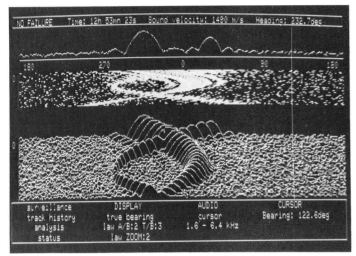

This view is a passive-detection display of a Thomson Sintra sonar; the original is in color. At any one time the spectrum can be integrated to provide a graph showing the directions from which the loudest noises come (as at the top of the display). These lines are not quite like the lines of the usual waterfall, showing more gradation. The bottom of the display shows these integrals as they have changed over time, to indicate target maneuvers. The result is like a waterfall but more finely graded. (Thomson Sintra)

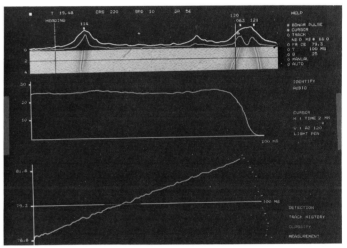

These typical sonar-intercept displays are shown below a waterfall display giving target motions as detected passively (three targets are shown). The middle display shows intercepted pulse duration. (Thomson Sintra)

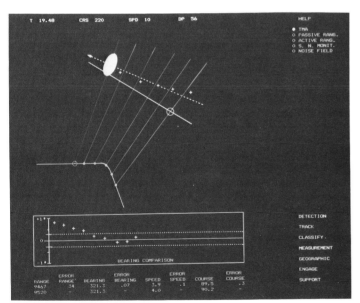

As a submarine maneuvers, a nearby target changes bearing. The change can be used to measure the target's range. Modern computer-assisted submarine combat systems do this target-motion analysis automatically, sensing changes in own-submarine course and speed. This Thomson Sintra passive-ranging display shows the assumed target path at top and the own-submarine maneuver at bottom; the graph at the bottom shows how target bearing has changed during the maneuver. The ranging algorithm assumes that the target is following a steady (but unknown) course. The upper right-hand corner indicates that the operator can choose instead passive ranging by triangulation or active ranging. Target-motion analysis requires time: the longer the analysis, the better the range accuracy. Modern computer-aided systems tend to be much faster than older manual plots, using essentially the same techniques. (Thomson Sintra)

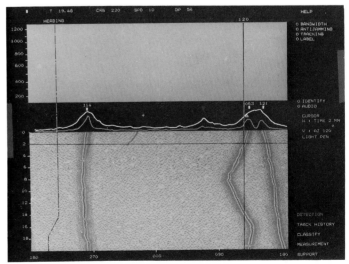

Sonar detection (waterfall) displays show heading against time. The dots in the background are noise. Only real target tracks, however, are consistent, so they can be distinguished. The graph at the top of the display integrates over time. This particular display can switch (by light pen) between detection (as here), track history (i.e., summary of relative motions of targets), classification (by sound spectrum), measurement, and support (sound ray-path and sonar-performance prediction). (Thomson Sintra)

Another possibility is that low-frequency narrow-band passive sonar will lose its capability, so that passive operation will be reduced to medium-frequency flow noises. In that case, it will pay to abandon expensive signal processing in favor of mass producing relatively simple (broad-band) sensors of flow noise and strewing them about the estimated position of a submarine. This approach would seem to be the basis of the new low-cost sonobuoy. An intermediate possibility would be to distinguish regular features of broad-band noise and, thus, to retain longer-range operation at a cost in processing complexity.

The third alternative is to abandon passive operation in favor of very low frequency, i.e., very long range, active operation. In that case the existing low-frequency systems would be retained, but they would function as the receivers in bistatic sonars, receiving echoes from the pings of relatively simple noise sources. Several active towed arrays, described in these pages, typify this approach.

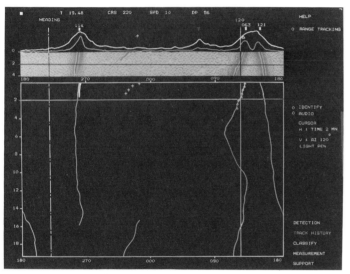

This display is for passive tracking. Three noise peaks have been identified, and the system provides their tracks over time (vertical axis). At the bottom, two more tracks have been added, and one of the original tracks has disappeared. This system can operate automatically, as long as the targets produce enough noise at any one time for the waterfall to identify them unequivocally. Problems arise only if the targets are so quiet that the operator has to choose among several possibilities. (Thomson Sintra)

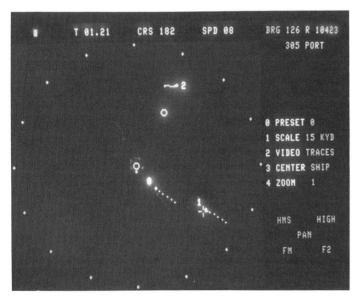

Automatic (active) detection and tracking can be applied to sonar as well as to radar. This Thomson Sintra display shows two actively tracked targets, each marked by successive echoes (the dots); the readout gives the targets' current bearings. Sufficiently loud passive targets can be tracked automatically in bearing, once an operator places a cursor on their current positions. (Thomson Sintra)

Driving the development of ASW weapons, sensors, and tactics are the basic facts of sonar operation: sound propagates farthest at low frequency and sound tends not to propagate in straight lines. Lower frequency means longer wavelength, and a sonar operating at that lower frequency must be larger to maintain the same gain (directionality). World War II sonars operated at high frequency (20–30 kHz) to assure directionality even with relatively small transducers. Medium frequency might loosely be defined as the range from 5 to 15 kHz, and low frequency as about 1 to 5 kHz. However, some navies regard 5–7 kHz as low frequency and so describe their sonars. Operation below about 1 kHz generally requires devices, such as towed arrays, different enough from conventional sonars for another differentiation to be made, e.g., very low frequency. Another way to draw this distinction would be to associate high frequency with short direct path ranges and with sonars essentially limited to the surface layer. Medium frequency sonars can detect submarines below the (surface) layer at useful ranges, and, if properly designed, they can use the bottom-bounce path. Low frequency means convergence-zone propagation, at least potentially. On this basis 5 kHz is low-frequency in the Mediterranean, but about 3 or 3.5 kHz is required for low-frequency operation in the Atlantic and the Norwegian Sea. The history of sonar since 1945–50 has been a series of jumps down in frequency and, therefore, up in range. The velocity of sound in water is about 4700 ft/sec, so that 30 kHz equates to a wavelength of about 1.8 inches. A typical World War II maximum operational range was 2500 yards. Postwar sonars, such as the U.S. SQS-4, operated at about 10 kHz (about 5.5-in wavelength) and could achieve ranges of about 5000 yards. A drop to about 5 kHz (wavelength about one foot) bought twice the range in sonars such as the U.S. SQS-23. Sonars such as the U.S. SQS-26 operate at still lower frequencies, about 3 kHz (wavelength about 1.5 feet), and are credited with direct-path ranges of about 20,000 yards. All of these figures are nominal, keyed to specific idealized conditions and useful more for comparisons between sets than for predictions of actual performance. Actual performance depends not only on water conditions but also on such considerations as the energy output of the sonar, the efficacy of its signal processor, and the character of the dome through which the energy must pass. SQS-26, whose dome is about the size of a 60-foot personnel boat, represents an upper limit for conventional hull sonars.

Beyond increasing the size of the dome, there are two choices for increasing a sonar's performance. One is to spread the sonar over a longer portion of the ship's hull, as a conformal array. That configuration has been tried, but so far it has not been effective. The other possibility is to remove the sonar from the hull altogether and tow it astern in the form of a linear or towed array.

It may be much more difficult for the Soviets to eliminate the lowest-frequency narrow-band sound, so longer arrays, working at lower frequencies, may effectively counter Soviet silencing. In that case, the practical limit on frequency is probably the array length that can be towed without kinking, i.e., without losing beam coherence. For a surface ship, there is really no effective limit on the array's length, although a very long array would be relatively heavy and, hence, difficult to pull back on deck. For submarines, a very long array may be too bulky to house. That bulkiness is a particular problem in many Western submarines, which have either a single hull or else very limited space between their double hulls: hence the vital importance of thin-line arrays, which can be substantially longer than the existing thicker array.

The technological problem here is twofold. First, the thicker the array, the less flow noise per unit area that the array must overcome. Therefore, for a thinner array to be effective, it must be backed by better signal processing. Second, the array must accommodate both a string of transducers and the wire(s) carrying their signal(s) back to the ship. Conventional thick-line arrays, which have been in service since the late 1960s (at least in the U.S. Navy), are built up of transducer elements in an oil-filled casing. Each element has its own output wire, and the wires are fed back through the multicore towing cable. A thin-line array needs more compact elements and, ideally, a multiplexed-signal transmitter cable. Recently there have been suggestions that fiber optics can solve both problems. The optical path through the fiber changes if it is subjected to distortion, e.g., by a passing sound wave. This path can, moreover, be monitored by maintaining a standing optical wave in the fiber (using a laser). Optical fibers are much smaller than conventional wires, so multiplexing might be unnecessary. It is also possible that the optical signals so produced could be processed optically, using an array of fibers in a specialized computer; thus, many or all of the usual signal converters could be eliminated.

Arrays and their associated processors are generally described in terms of the number of octaves they cover. As in music, an octave is the range between a tone and the one having twice the first's frequency (i.e., half the first's wavelength). For example, different versions of the Ferranti processor cover either two or five octaves. Each octave may surround a single line, so that a two-octave system may be intended to seek two particular lines in a target's spectrum. Additional octaves are added by adding hydrophones to each end of the two-octave array (to achieve the same sort of directionality at a lower frequency). One sub-array will typically cover one octave, e.g., 50–100 Hz, centered on 75 Hz. The center frequency will be chosen in the expectation that useful signals will occur nearby. If the signals are narrow-band, they are often accompanied by higher harmonics, i.e., by signals at multiples of the original frequency. Thus a line at, say, 70 Hz might be accompanied by others at 140, 210, 280 Hz and up. Peculiarities of transmission might even make some of the higher harmonics stronger than the original signal. Thus, it is important to provide a towed array with capability at several ranges of frequency, and also with the software to correlate a line at one frequency with its possible harmonics.

Useful (i.e., directional) reception at very different ranges of frequency is achieved by nesting the transducers, each of which has a very broad range of frequency responses. A single unit of the array may be long enough to provide good directionality for signals at the highest frequency (i.e., shortest wavelength) with which the system deals. That unit becomes the middle subunit of a second, longer sub-array used at a lower frequency. Typically, all the sub-arrays are built of identical basic units, so in this case the second sub-array is three times the length of the first, operating at a third of the first's base frequency. The two are nested, the units of the first sub-array working simultaneously at both frequency ranges. Forming the middle of the lower-frequency array, the first is said to nest in the second. Adding two more units to the ends of the three-unit array gives a third array five times the length of the first, operating at a fifth its frequency.

If the first sub-array was designed to work in the range around 600 kHz, the second would be centered on 200 kHz and the third on 120 kHz. The U.S. SQR-18A reportedly consists of eight identical subunits, two of which form the highest-frequency sub-array. The combination of those two with the two at their ends forms the next lower-frequency sub-array (at half the highest frequency). If the next two are counted, then the next-lower sub-array consists of six basic units, at one-third the highest frequency. All eight basic units form the lowest-frequency receiver, working at a base frequency a quarter that of the highest-frequency sub-array.

In each case, the sub-array is imagined as built out fore and aft from the center of the array as a whole. That design greatly simplifies beam-forming. Beams are formed by adding the outputs of the sub-elements of the sub-arrays in proper phase, and that addition changes least from frequency to frequency when the array is handled symmetrically.

Current towed arrays are passive receivers of sounds made by submarines; but as the submarines become quieter, it becomes attractive to provide an active sound source, generally in the form of a flex-tensional transducer operating at about 150–600 Hz (wavelength about 7.5–30 feet). The array would then act as the receiver of a very low frequency sonar.

Systems vary from navy to navy partly because different navies operate under very different acoustic conditions, and partly because navies perceive their missions very differently. For example, the Royal Navy operates its frigate-towed arrays largely for surveillance. They must, therefore, be relatively long (to work at the low frequencies at which sound propagates most effectively); and the ships must be very carefully silenced. By way of contrast, the U.S. Navy operates separate surveillance arrays (the SURTASS program) and separate tactical arrays, the latter for defending battle groups or convoys. U.S. tactical arrays can, therefore, be shorter, and they can tolerate worse acoustic conditions.

Sea conditions modify sonar choices. In summer, the surface layer in the Mediterranean, for example, may be only about 50 feet deep, so hull-mounted sonars become nearly useless. That condition explains the long-standing interest of the French and Italian Navies in variable-depth sonars, which can operate under the layer. In the Mediterranean, too, the deep sound-channel is much shallower than in the Atlantic, and the convergence zone is much closer. In consequence, there is little point in using very low frequency sonars, and neither the French nor the Italians have gone as far as the U.S. Navy in the development of lower-frequency sonars. Other warm areas, such as the Arabian Sea, also have shallow surface layers, heated by the sun and often not mixed with deeper, cooler water. The Baltic is notorious. Because so many rivers empty into that sea, its acoustics are dominated by alternating layers of different salinity, from which sonar pings reflect. That condition is one reason the Swedish Navy effectively abandoned ASW in the 1960s, and also one reason why it has been so difficult to determine whether the Soviets really are operating midget submarines in shallow Swedish waters. On the other hand, the Arctic Ocean is at a nearly constant temperature, so that the surface layer extends down to the bottom, making for very much longer effective ranges. Presumably the only problem is the reflection and refraction of sound in the presence of large masses of ice. Special sound conditions may also be caused by particular marine life or particularly heavy shipping lanes or fishing areas. Other special conditions obtain in other areas, such as the South China Sea or the waters around Australia, and these conditions help explain why different navies have adopted such different approaches to essentially the same sonar technologies.

Some technological points require explanation. Virtually all modern sonars scan. They may send out directional pings, but they do not wait for the ping to return before looking in another direction. Reception is separated from transmission because the sonar can receive in all directions, either in quick sequence (with a scanning cycle much shorter than the ping's length, so that the sonar is in effect looking in all directions all the time) or actually simultaneously. Because the sonar need not continue to stare in one direction before looking elsewhere, the scanning rate is independent of the expected time between ping and echo (i.e., independent of range), and a sonar can search a large volume with a reasonable probability of detecting a target.

A scanning sonar consists of an array of more or less omnidirectional transducers, achieving directionality by combining the signals from several adjacent transducers in the appropriate phase relationship, much as a phased-array radar works. This idea is not new: as long ago as World War I, linear hydrophone arrays formed beams using delay lines (which were sometimes called "artificial" or "electrical" water because the lines corresponded to effective water paths to different elements of the array). In older sonars this phasing is accomplished by rotating a commutator within the array, the commutator carrying the appropriate (beam-forming) phase relationship. However, the commutator inevitably adds to the noise of the system, and a commutator-scanned sonar will miss some transient sounds.

The alternative is to store the appropriate phase relationships electronically and then feed the signals from the transducers through a digital memory, adding and subtracting to form all the beams the commutator would have formed. In U.S. practice this process is called DIMUS (digital multibeam steering) or beam-preforming (as opposed to mechanical beam-forming, in which delay lines impose the appropriate phase relationships at the time of reception). A commutator sonar beam-forms; a DIMUS sonar beam-preforms.

Beam-forming by commutator works only if a sonar is sufficiently symmetrical (e.g., cylindrical) that the fixed phase relationship between adjacent transducers produces a beam anywhere in the transducer. Beam-preforming is clearly easiest for a symmetrical sonar but can also work for a more complex shape. In addition, the relationships can be adjusted to meet changing operational or water conditions (adaptive beam-forming), since the relationships may be software-controlled rather than hard-wired. Thus beam-preforming is a prerequisite for building complex conformal sonar arrays. Beam-preforming can also be used to project or to receive multiple beams, just as a phased-array radar can produce several beams simultaneously.

The first scanning sonars sent out omnidirectional pulses (ODT, omnidirectional transmission). These sonars had the advantage of effectively matching their transmissions with omnidirectional reception, but the power available in any one direction was limited. One modern alternative is RDT, rotationally directed transmission, the sonar sending out concentrated pulses along each bearing while scanning through all transmission directions, like a 360-degree radar. The drawback to simple RDT is that it does not scan through all directions quickly enough. Some sonars employ tribeam transmission, scanning three transmitting beams that are 120 degrees apart.

Sonars are sometimes classified as search or attack, or a single sonar may operate in both modes. Attack always implies a narrower beam capable of tracking a target sufficiently well for weapons to be aimed. The required standard of aiming depends on the lethal envelope of the weapon. A mortar or rocket launcher, whose bomb has only a very limited lethal range, generally requires three-dimensional ballistic information, including the underwater equivalent of height-finding. A homing torpedo, delivered either over the side or by rocket or missile, may need little more than an initial range and bearing, although the target's depth may still be important for predicting a target's position.

Most ASW surface ships armed with mortars or rocket launchers in the early postwar period were provided with separate search and attack sonars, and some ships still show this distinction. On these ships, the attack sonar has a narrow beam that can both train and elevate. In more recent sonars, the beam can be depressed electronically, since each vertical stave (an element that resembles and is named after a barrel stave) consists of several fairly nondirectional transducers that can be phased relative to each other. In large sonars the beam can be elevated fairly precisely. However, in a few cases there is only one fixed elevation or perhaps two alternative elevations. For example, a 24-stave sonar credited with 48 beams probably produces a fan of 24 beams at one elevation and 24 at one other. It is impossible for any modern stave sonar to depress its beam continuously so as to match the motion of a target precisely.

A few sonars still employ searchlight operation, which was standard through the end of World War II: they concentrate their energy in a single directional pulse and have only a single receiver. They must ping in one direction, and listen for an echo, before they shift to another direction. That requirement severely limits the search rate. All specialized attack sonars are searchlights capable of depression.

There is also an intermediate case, a flat-plate sonar that scans a limited sector. Compared to an ODT scanner, the flat-plate sonar provides a stronger ping and may achieve a tighter beam over the scanned sector. Such sector scanning might be justified for a ship operating as one of several escorts in a screen.

Many of the sonar entries mention alternative range scales. They equate to alternative pinging rates. As in a radar, a sonar cannot easily distinguish a ping returning from a very distant target (after another has been sent out) from the echo of a nearby

object: the problem of the second-time-around echo (STAE). Therefore, a sonar operator will set his ping rate beyond the maximum range he expects to achieve. On the other hand, the operator will try to get as many pings as he can, to increase the probability of detection, typically using some type of sonar-performance predictor to set his ping rate.

As in radar, the length of the sonar's pulse determines the precision with which nearby objects can be distinguished. The length of sonar pulses is typically measured in milliseconds (thousandths of a second), compared to microseconds (millionths) for radar pulses.

Torpedoes, both antiship and antisubmarine, are listed in this section because so many weapons are dual-purpose. They deserve some comment. Three kinds of torpedoes' seekers are in current use: active pingers, passive, and wake-followers (or wake-homers). There are also straight-runners, pattern-runners, and command-guided (wire-guided) weapons.

Until World War II, all torpedoes were straight-runners, analogous to artillery shells. In many cases these torpedoes could be turned through an adjustable gyro angle after leaving the tube, but then they ran as straight as possible. Effective range was, therefore, limited by the accuracy of the torpedo and by the ratio of the torpedo's speed to the target's speed. Since the main method of torpedo warning was visual observation of the wake, it was often argued that a wakeless (electric or oxygen) torpedo could be fired at a faster or more distant target, in the expectation that evasive action would not be taken. The main countermeasure to such torpedoes was zig-zagging (whether or not the torpedo was detected), in the hope that the firing platform would be unable to anticipate the target's maneuver.

Straight-runners were generally fired at designated targets. Weapons fired beyond the effective single-target range were said to be fired "into the brown," i.e., into the mass of targets in hopes of hitting one (this was also called a "browning shot"). One way to increase the efficacy of such a shot was to program the torpedo to weave back and forth in the mass of target ships until exploding under one of them. The most common pattern-runners zig-zagged (the French even designated their pattern-runners in a Z series); but the Germans, Italians, and probably the Soviets produced aerial torpedoes that circled. Pattern-runners are still an economical way of attacking convoys from a safe distance. Wake-following (see below) was conceived as an improvement on simple pattern-running.

The alternative was to provide the torpedo with a homing system so that the weapon could convert a miss (due to firing at excessive range) into a hit. During World War II, the Germans developed passive homing torpedoes as antiescort weapons, and the Allies developed much the same technology for ASW. At that time, both submarines and surface ships were loud enough

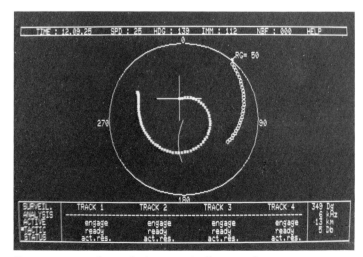

Once targets can be tracked automatically, a combat system computer can help evaluate threats as a decision aid. It can also superimpose torpedo operating limits on the display, to show which targets can be engaged. (Thomson Sintra)

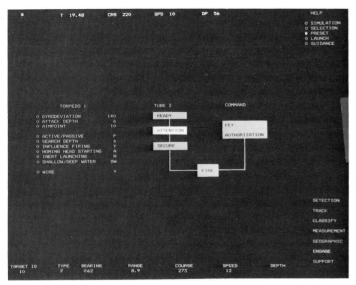

A typical torpedo fire-control display shows target data at the bottom (bearing, range, course, speed) and torpedo parameters at left (gyro angle, attack depth, aim point along the length of the target, the choice of active or passive homing, search depth, the choice of whether to use a proximity [influence] fuze, the enable range of the seeker, the type of launching, and whether the water is deep or shallow). In this case the torpedo is a wire-guided F17, fired against a slow (12-knot) surface target, so the choice is for passive homing and a search depth of 6 meters and a proximity fuze. The torpedo is fired at a 140-degree gyro angle: the submarine is almost beam-on to the target. (Thomson Sintra)

to attract such weapons. Later, however, the development of antiship and antisubmarine torpedoes diverged.

Antiship torpedoes almost have to be passive homers for two reasons. First, the water's surface acts as a mirror, and an active homer near the surface can easily be attracted into it. Second, a surface ship does not provide much of an echoing target (distinct from the surrounding surface, that is).

As long as submarines were relatively noisy, it was not too difficult to design a torpedo to home on their loud noise. It is much more difficult to design a torpedo to listen for subtle low-frequency (long-wavelength) sounds, to automatically decide that it is hearing a submarine, and then to steer for the source of that noise. As submarines became quieter, then, torpedo designers had to turn to active operation, incorporating powerful high-frequency sonars in the noses of the weapons. This development was accepted most readily in the United States. Active homing automatically alerts the submarine target, and U.S. designers have assumed that an alerted submarine will run off at maximum speed. They have, therefore, required torpedoes fast enough to catch up, the rule of thumb being that the torpedo must be 50 percent faster than its target.

Until recently, European torpedo designers preferred what they called a covert approach, homing passively at relatively low speed. They argued that, unless alerted, a submarine commander would generally operate at low speed, and that a relatively slow (and very quiet) torpedo might well catch him unaware. Consequently, many European torpedoes employ inherently quiet electric motors, at the cost of high speed. It now appears that submarines, at least Soviet types, will increasingly be too quiet for the covert approach to work, and, therefore, that all future ASW torpedoes will be fast active homers. In turn, torpedo design will be substantially more difficult. This evolution is exemplified by British practice. Tigerfish was a very quiet, relatively slow torpedo. Its successor, Spearfish, is being marketed as the fastest torpedo in the world.

On a more detailed level, the earliest homing torpedoes could be described as using two- or four-beam energy comparison (i.e., only left-right or a combination of left-right and up-down). Their signal processors were, in effect, hard-wired. During the 1960s it became possible to form multiple beams so that the torpedo's view of its surroundings was better defined. As in a shipborne

sonar, the narrower the beam, the better the torpedo's ability to reject the noise around a target. In some passive systems (such as the French E14), phase comparison replaced energy comparison. During the 1970s, new torpedoes were designed with software-controlled signal processors and seekers and with more sophisticated sonars, which could be doppler-enabled (i.e., which switched tactics depending on the target's velocity) and which could use coded sonar waveforms (to improve the signal-to-noise ratio, perhaps without increasing peak power, thus denying the target longer-range warning). The torpedo's acquisition range defines a cone within which the weapon can locate targets. The longer the range, the greater the band in depth equivalent to the angle of view of the torpedo's seeker. A torpedo with a narrow depth-band must describe a helical search path through the water, whereas one with a broader depth-band may be able to search at a single depth. The latter technique reduces the fraction of (limited) torpedo endurance that must be devoted to search, and also reduces the evasion time available to the target.

There is one other modern homing technique: wake-following. A surface ship's wake extends many ship's lengths aft, and the wake's boundaries can be detected relatively easily. A torpedo can be programmed to turn through a preset angle each time it crosses the wake, so that it takes a sinuous path toward the ship, around the wake (assuming that the torpedo enters the wake at an acute angle). If the torpedo can detect both wake boundaries, it can run up the wake itself, wasting less time in turning back and forth and, thus, giving itself a better chance of catching a fast target. Wake-following was invented in Germany during World War II (as a variation on pattern-running), and this program has been tried out by most of the major torpedo manufacturers since then (see the Soviet torpedoes and the U.S. Mk 45F). Wake-following has two great virtues. First, the wake is so massive a ship's signature that it is difficult or impossible to disguise or for a decoy to duplicate. Second, wake-homing is a specialized anti–surface ship technique; so it would be possible, in theory, for a wolf pack of submarines to fire wake-followers toward a targeted formation without fear of hitting one another. That safety would not be possible with conventional passive-homing torpedoes.

All homing techniques for torpedoes are effective only at relatively short ranges because limited torpedo dimensions cause frequencies to be high. However, shipboard or submarine sensors, which can operate at much lower frequencies, can reach out much further. One way to combine the two capabilities is to provide the torpedo with mid-course guidance in the form of a wire. Wire guidance can also be used to correct the course of a nonhoming torpedo attacking a maneuvering target, a technique used by the heavy Swedish torpedoes. This type of remote control was used as early as World War I by the Germans and was tried both in Germany and in Italy during World War II. In its simplest form, wire guidance is one-way, commands being issued by the submarine. However, in some recent applications, the wire is used both ways, the operator on board the submarine receiving the picture generated by the torpedo-borne sonar. The passive triangulation that results can be used to negate some countermeasures a target may take.

Torpedo homing naturally inspires the development of torpedo countermeasures. For a surface ship faced with passive homers, the natural countermeasure is a noise-maker whose output more or less duplicates that of a ship. There are two main technical problems. First, although the level of noise must be high enough to fool the approaching torpedo, the noise cannot be allowed to blank out sonar operation: generally, the signal output of the decoy must be controlled. Second, there is always some fear that, having attracted (but not destroyed) a torpedo, the noisemaker will merely lead the torpedo closer to the targeted ship. Most modern missiles (including torpedoes) have some form of re-attack logic, which causes them to try again after having been fooled once. The decoy must be far enough from the targeted ship that the torpedo, trying again, hears the decoy rather than the ship.

Countering a wake-follower seems altogether a bleaker prospect because no noise maker on earth can make anything that resembles a wake.

The point is that, to be effective, existing types of countermeasures must be closely matched to the weapons they counter. Against a torpedo, the alternative is a direct-kill countermeasure, an antitorpedo weapon. There have been several such programs since World War II, both in Britain and in the United States, but they have generally died because the problem of finding and killing a small torpedo is so very difficult technically, and is also very expensive.

From a submarine's point of view, acoustic countermeasures come in three varieties. First there are self-propelled submarine simulators, which may mislead the sonar operator and which may also attract passive-homing torpedoes. Then there are sonar transponders, either hull-mounted or ejected, which can confuse an active pinger. Finally, a submarine may eject bubble-makers, which will create a screen between the boat and an active pinger. Since the bubbles reflect pings, the torpedo will be unable to see into the screen and may home on the screen itself. What happens afterward depends on the torpedo's re-attack logic. The bubble screen may also be intended to obscure the submarine and its track from a longer-range sonar. In that case, a torpedo with a two-way wire may be steered around the bubble, to look beyond.

For example, in a submarine vs. submarine engagement, the targeted submarine will want, first, to break track. It must accelerate, and it will, consequently, make more noise. To cover that acceleration, the submarine can launch decoys and create a bubble screen. The targeted boat can also fire back (without wire guidance) at the pursuing submarine in hopes of escaping while the latter evades. If track-breaking fails, the targeted submarine can still hope to counter torpedoes fired by the pursuing submarine, either by firing back (to force the pursuer to break his guidance wires while counter-evading), by using decoys, or, more likely, by using both methods. It is also possible to imagine using hull-mounted transmitters, in appropriate sequence, to break lock, just as a surface ship would use a radar lock-breaker and chaff launchers.

Mines, including ASW mines, are listed separately.

Minehunting sonars, which may be used to detect bottomed submarines, are listed in the Mine Warfare section.

Surface-search radars, which are often used by ships and aircraft to detect periscopes and snorkels, are listed in the Strike/Surface Warfare section.

SONARS AND UNDERWATER FIRE-CONTROL SYSTEMS

AUSTRALIA

◆ ASSTASS

ASSTASS is the Australian Surface-Ship Towed-Array Sonar System. In 1986, the Royal Australian Navy decided against using frigates for long-range submarine surveillance, and in favor of buying a specialized surveillance towed array to be deployed on board inexpensive specialized ships, similar in theory to the U.S. SURTASS. A formal Naval Staff Target for such a system was formulated that year. Unlike SURTASS, ASSTASS would reportedly process its data onboard. In 1986 the total requirement was apparently for 8–12 ships. It was not clear whether the Kariwara thin-line wet end would be suitable for ASSTASS.

◆ Kariwara

The Australian-developed thin-line towed array is for use by surface ships or submarines. The requirement was stated in 1984–85, and the array was developed by the Australian Defense Research Center; trials began in 1987–88. The array is reportedly 30 or 40 mm in diameter, consisting of hydrophones 2 inches long embedded in a fully reelable ropelike matrix. The array is unique in being manufactured in continuous lengths, using rope-making techniques. The core, a buoyant polypropylene rope in which the electronics are embedded, is surrounded by a gel-filled weave of electrical conductors and Kevlar fibers, the whole being covered with a polyurethane sleeve.

Kariwara grew out of a five-year Australian-U.S. project, Boolee, of the 1970s. Boolee reportedly demonstrated the value of towed arrays in Australian waters; but the RAN found the existing 90-mm diameter fluid-filled type unsuited to its diesel-electric submarines and asked the Defense Science and Technology Organization (DSTO) to devise a light reelable array that could be stowed in a submarine casing. Reelability was presumably important because an Australian submarine would have to operate in shallow water. Sections of Kariwara's wet end were tested onboard the submarine *Oxley* in 1982. *Otama* began Kariwara trials in 1984, and *Otway* received the first clip-on operational version in April 1985.

◆ Mulloka

This Australian-developed replacement for British hull sonars such as 177 and 184 was developed in the early 1970s. The prototype was completed in 1975 and tested on board HMAS *Yarra* through 1979. The initial production contract was let in 1980, for five sets for the "River"-class frigates (installed 1983/84). In contrast to other Western sonars, Mulloka operates at a relatively high frequency, to produce a very narrow but powerful beam. The cylindrical transducer consists of 96 staves, each of 25 spot transducers, to produce very narrow beams. It forms beams digitally and uses random transmission to reduce warning to submarines, transmitting for 1–4 seconds and then listening. The object of the design is to achieve very solid coverage out to about 10 kyds, accepting virtually zero coverage at greater ranges. Mulloka uses the sort of high frequencies common during World War II, achieving much better range through superior signal processing.

Mulloka will be installed onboard the two U.S.-designed *Oliver Hazard Perry*–class frigates that are building in Australia, in preference to the U.S. SQS-56.

CANADA

◆ BQG-501

See Micro-PUFFS under U.S. sonars below.

◆ SQR-501

The Canadian towed array (CANTASS) uses a U.S. SQR-19 "wet end" and a Canadian (Computing Devices) signal processor. The requirement was stated in 1981, and in mid-FY84 the U.S. Navy offered six SQR-19s. The Canadians opted to develop their own dry end. CANTASS was developed in 1983–87. A system was tested onboard HMCS *Fraser* in 1986–88 under the designation ETASS. CANTASS is to go on board all twelve "City"-class frigates and also on board two modernized *Annapolis*-class frigates in 1990–95.

Canadian experiments using quarter-scale arrays began in 1980. The one-half scale ETASS was tested on board HMCS *Nipigon* in 1983 and on board HMCS *Iroquois* in 1984; in 1985 it was decided that ETASS would be fitted semipermanently on board HMCS *Fraser*, replacing her ASW mortar and several internal compartments. In this version the length of the tail was doubled, bringing ETASS up to full SQR-19 size. However, the handling system is much more primitive than that of the full CANTASS. The *Fraser* installation introduced a new third console, for a supervisor. He analyzes the collated information, leaving the two primary operators free to watch incoming data and to do primary search. This configuration proved successful enough to cause a change in the CANTASS design to incorporate the third position. Installation began in October 1986 and was complete by early December.

The first full CANTASS will be an SQR-19 tail combined with a commercial Motorola 68020/UYS-501 Teamed Architecture Signal Processor (TASP). Later examples will use a fully militarized 68020/UYS-501 by Computing Devices of Canada.

◆ SQS-501

See Type 162 under U.K. sonars below.

◆ SQS-502

The Canadian derivative of the British Type 170B is for Limbo fire control. See U.K. sonars below.

◆ SQS-503

This hull-mounted medium-frequency scanning sonar is found in Canadian frigates of the *Restigouche* and earlier classes and in the underway replenishment ships. SQS-503 equips the French *Foch*-class aircraft carriers.

◆ SQS-504

SQS-504 is a medium-frequency variable-depth searchlight sonar. The British Type 199 is a derivative. See the U.K. entry below for details.

Canadian work on variable-depth sonars dates from 1947, and a naval staff project, code-named Dunker, began in April 1949. The dipping sonar was particularly wanted to exploit a sound channel lying between the warm surface layer and the warm bottom layer on Scotian Shelf off the Canadian east coast. The first trials employed a dipping version of the British Type 144, on board the fleet minesweeper *New Liskeard*. It turned out that, with both the target and the sonar in the axis of the channel, ranges as great as 9400 yds could be achieved. Even when both were at the upper edge of the channel, range was 4200 yds, far beyond the performance of a hull-mounted Type 144. The early trials employed a transducer dipped from a stopped ship, and through the early 1950s work proceeded on viable towed bodies. They, too, carried Type 144 transducers.

Through 1953 the project concentrated on submarine detection in the shallow Gulf of St. Lawrence and off Halifax, where conventional hull sonars were often useless. In 1953, however, the project was redirected toward achieving maximum possible sonar range (for early warning) by placing the transducer at the optimum position under a much wider variety of conditions. By this time much work had been done on suitable towing bodies. The first fully developed experimental system, CAST/1/X electronics in a body designated TRILBY Mk V, was turned over to the Royal Canadian Navy on board HMCS *Crusader*, a destroyer.

CAST/1/X was re-engineered as SQS-504. In tests in 1958, off Bermuda, off New London, on the Scotian Shelf, and in the Gulf of St. Lawrence, it outperformed the hull-mounted Type 144 by a factor of five. This result led immediately to a decision to include SQS-504 (and the associated SQA-501 hoist) in the midlife modernizations of the *St. Laurent*–class frigates. In addition, CAST/1/X outperformed the contemporary British Type 192X experimental variable-depth sonar (which was then mounted on board HMS *Brocklesby*). Hence the British decision to adopt SQS-504 as Type 199.

Further development was concerned largely with handling gear, which caused particular problems in heavy weather. By 1964 there were complaints from sea that the system was useless, and a get-well program had to be instituted. The lessons learned at this time were applied to the VDS version of SQS-505 (which uses a hoist designated SQA-502). SQA-502 permits operation at higher speeds and at greater depths, and it is officially claimed that overall search capability is twenty times that of SQS-504. In early trials, it achieved a range of 27,500 yds compared to 5,000–7,000 yds for SQS-504.

◆ SQS-505

SQS-505 is the hull sonar in the *Iroquois* and *Halifax* ("City") classes. The *Iroquois* class has the same transducer in a variable-depth fish (SQA-502 hoist). In the first six "City"-class frigates, SQS-505 will be integrated instead with the SQR-501 towed array. The sonar was designed to be fitted in either a fixed or a retractable dome (in the former case, the transducer can be either fixed or retractable).

SQS-505 uses a 36-stave (10 elements per stave) cylindrical transducer operating at a nominal 7-kHz frequency. The sonar has 36 preformed beams (10 degrees each), and peak-power level is 5 kW. SQS-505 can also operate passively at 3.5–8 kHz. Target classification is by doppler, by a separate steerable audio channel, or by short-pulse imaging (ASPECT). This sonar can track multiple targets; and it can display a 12-ping history, a 5-ping history, or fine video. The transducer has a diameter of 1.2 m and is 1.2 m high (47.25 × 47.25 in). The hull dome is 14 ft long; the variable-depth body is 18 ft long and weighs 14,000 lbs (10,000 lbs submerged).

Range scales are 2, 4, 8, 16, and 32 kyds.

SQS-505 has been criticized for lacking true low-frequency capability, hence the shift to SQS-509 for later Canadian "City"-class frigates. SQS-505 TASP with digital acoustic processing and SHINPADS display was tested in an *Iroquois*-class ship in 1984. SQS-505 can track five targets while searching for more; it uses a 5-ping history (plus hydrophone effect) for initial detection and classification.

Development began, in the mid-1960s, for the *Iroquois* class, the sonar being developed in 1966–69. Ten units were bought for retrofit into older Canadian frigates in 1982/85. SQS-505 is also the hull sonar of Dutch "Standard" frigates; SQS-505A is the hull sonar of the Belgian *Wielingen*-class frigates. Four of the twelve Dutch sonars are a lower-frequency version, SQS-509. SQS-505 was originally chosen as the sonar of the U.S. *Perry* class (in preference to the larger and more expensive SQQ-23), but the generally comparable SQS-56 was substituted.

◆ SQS-507/HS-1000 Series

"Helen," a lightweight towed sonar, was developed specifically for the ASW hydrofoil *Bras d'Or*. Development began in 1963, and the sonar was delivered in 1968. This work, in turn, led to the HS-1000 series. SQS-507 was a smaller, simplified version of SQS-505.

The HS-1000 series is a joint Canadian Navy/Westinghouse of Canada development project for fast attack craft, based on experience with the SQS-507 towed sonar. HS-1001 is a lightweight variable-depth sonar; 1002 is a lightweight hull sonar; 1003 is a VDS for small ASW ships; 1007 is a medium hull or variable-depth sonar; and HS-1001/2, -1002/3, and -1007/7 are combination installations, the hull and variable-depth sonars sharing a common transmitter and signal processor. The variable-depth sonars use a 330-ft cable and can be towed at 35 kts. HS-1007 uses the same receiver, display, transducer, and variable-depth fish but an SQS-505 power supply, for four times the power of HS-1001 and -1002 in ODT mode, and 20 times the power in tribeam mode. HS-1001/2 operates only in ODT mode.

R&D began early in 1970, and a prototype was completed in 1972. The HS-1001 version was tested on board the U.S. hydrofoil *High Point* in 1980. Details of sales have not been reported, but in 1972 sonars of this type were reported in production for the West German Navy. That report may reflect projected installation in the abortive German hydrofoil (equivalent to the U.S. *Pegasus* class).

In 1985, two Westinghouse hull and three VDS sonars were reported sold to the Indian Navy, and the HS-series would seem to have been the most likely candidate. The VDS arrays were carried in fish built by Fathom Oceanology, Ltd., of Canada. Both hull and VDS use the same array, which has 21 staves.

◆ SQS-508

SQS-508 is the digital sonar developed about 1980 by Westinghouse Canada as a follow-on to SQS-505. SQS-509 was bought instead.

◆ SQS-509

A lower-frequency version of the SQS-505, SQS-509 is closely related to (but not identical with) the Dutch PH-36.

◆ SQS-510

SQS-510 employs the Canadian SQR-501 towed array instead of the variable-depth sonar of SQS-505.

◆ SCAN 515/525

Westinghouse Canada (originally Scannar Industries of Ontario) makes this shallow-water high-resolution ODT sonar for small ships. Announced in 1985 (for introduction in mid-1988), SCAN 515 operates at either 15 or 22 kHz (transducer diameter 21.95 or 13.5 inches), with a 4-degree vertical beamwidth (which can be tilted to accurately determine a target's depth). There are 256 preformed beams (presumably at a variety of elevations), and source level is 215 dB. Range scales are 100, 200, 400, 800, 1600, 3200, 6400, and 12,800 meters. A three-color display is used to distinguish between noise and targets (presumably, processed video).

Scan 525 is a related search-and-attack sonar using a 512-element circular thinned array, with a 6 × 6 degree beam, operating at 15 kHz.

◆ ASWDS

ASW Data System is used on board the "Tribal"-class and west-coast *Restigouche*-class frigates. It employs a Signaal computer to track up to 27 targets detected by an SQS-505 sonar, and (in the "Tribal" class) provides this data directly to the ship's CCS-280 combat system. In an Improved *Restigouche,* a second display is provided in the Operations Room, and data is transmitted in analog form to the plotting table, driving two contact lights, the plotters either using grease pencils or sitting at the ASW system console. In the latter case, one contact light is used for the contact, the other for the helicopter the ship is conning into position to reacquire and attack the contact.

The system was originally to have used half of the L-304 computer power of the CCS-280 system. However, the Signaal computer was purchased as an offset to a Dutch purchase of Canadian-built F-5 fighters, so the L-304 was only half utilized.

The Canadian Navy first became interested in a decentralized combat system (see CCS-280) during the development of the abortive ADACS system (for this system, see the entry, below, for the U.S. ASWCCS). ADAWS is UCS-280, the underwater warfare portion of CCS-280. The prototype ASWDS was tested on board HMCS *Terra Nova.*

FRANCE

Sonars

With the merger of Sintra-Alcatel into Thomson-CSF in 1987, Thomson Sintra is now the sole supplier of French naval sonars.

◆ SLASM

SLASM is the future (1990s) French ASW system, consisting of a very low frequency transmitter in a towed "fish," with a dual towed array receiving the resulting signals. The fish will also carry a medium-frequency transmitter (as in DUBV 43), and there will be a medium-frequency hull sonar. A dual towed array, as in the earlier frigates, will function both as a submarine detector and as a torpedo detector.

A French description of this system emphasizes the "deep integration" among elements, since the arrays, processors, and displays will have to shift functions, the displays allowing the operators to choose an optimum configuration (depending upon both physical oceanographic circumstances and the tactical situation).

Other automatic inputs will be sonar intercepts and helicopter-laid sonobuoys, both active and passive.

The modernized *Tourville* class will be the first to be fitted with SLASM. The first tests of the very low frequency active sonar were conducted on board the trials ship *Commandant Rivière* early in November 1987.

◆ DSBV 1

DSBV 1 is a torpedo-detection sonar (passive) found in postwar French destroyers and escorts, at least up through the *Commandant Rivière* class (where this sonar shares a dome with DUBA 3). DSBV 1 operates over the 5–40 kHz range and presumably shares some of the components of Velox (DUUG-1).

◆ DSBV 61 (DSRX 61X) (FLUTE)

DSBV 61 is the French towed array for surface ships. DSRX was the experimental version tested on board *L'Agenais.* Reportedly the array consists of 50 hydrophones at the end of a 1000-meter cable. The requirement was stated in the mid-1970s, and Thomson Sintra received a research contract in 1977, delivering the prototype in mid-1980. Trials were completed late in 1984, and DSBV 61 was approved for production early in 1985.

It was announced in January 1988 that the Netherlands would buy this array (rather than SQR-18) for M-class frigates. For the Dutch, the processor is derived from the Mangouste airborne processor and interfaces with a SEWACO-VII combat system.

◆ DSUV 2

This passive low-frequency (i.e., sonic) keel (bow) array of *Narval* (now extinct) and *Daphne* classes replaced the earlier G36. G36, in turn, was a 36-transducer array descended from France's standard prewar passive arrays, G12 and G16 (12 and 16 transducers, respectively). DSUV 2 is not a GHG-style array (like the U.S. BQR-2) but is much smaller, and the transducers are apparently spot hydrophones. DSUV 2 is associated with a correlator (GC 02) that automatically scans in bearing, registers all noise sources on a hard-copy printer, finds their direction, and tracks them automatically. This sonar system incorporates both a CRT display and an audio output.

DSUV 2B was first tested in 1977, and the first unit was installed in 1979 on board the submarine *Rubis.* DSUV 2B is now the primary sonar for French nuclear attack submarines, in combination with DUUX 5 (FENELON).

◆ DSUV 22 (Eledone)/Scylla/Type 2040

DSUV 22 is the passive hull array of the *Rubis* and *Agosta* classes.

Eledone is the commercial version of DSUV 22, adding other arrays to form an integrated modular sonar system for submarines. Eledone consists of some or all of: a passive bow array, an intercept array, flank arrays, a towed array, passive-ranging arrays, an active array, and a mine-avoidance sonar. The primary (search/attack) active sonar operates at 5 kHz (source level 215 dB for search) and incorporates an 8–11 kHz underwater telephone. Transmission is CW or FM, and the passive bow sonar is used for reception. The active transducer is a planar-array searchlight, active operation being used primarily for single-ping ranging at 5 kHz.

The bow transducer is 1.25 or 3.5 m (49.3 or 137.8 inches) in diameter and 0.8 or 3 m high (32 or 64 staves; a larger 96-stave version was also developed, but it was not sold), operating at up to 12 kHz in two or three frequency bands (e.g., 1–5 and 5–12 kHz for the smaller version). There are 128 preformed beams, for 360-degree coverage. Eledone can automatically track 4–12 targets, providing very accurate azimuth data. It can also provide audio output or spectral analysis in one or two directions. An optional associated intercept receiver operates at 2–80 kHz, i.e., from LF search to torpedo seekers. The transducer is typically mounted on the submarine's sail. Target emissions are analyzed using tunable low/high-pass filters. The associated PPI shows active transmissions in three bands (2–7.35 kHz, 7.35–27 kHz, 27–80 kHz) with an accuracy of 3–5 degrees.

The associated single-ping active sonar operates at 5 kHz (4-kW peak power) with an unambiguous range of 100–1400 meters. This sonar can also be used as a passive receiver (1–6 kHz) if the main hull array fails.

Eledone uses the same MIRTA 1500 series computers as do Beluga and Remora.

Scylla, the sonar system of the Australian Type-471 submarine, is an advanced version of Eledone, with the following arrays: cylindrical bow, flank, distributed passive-ranging, intercept, active (in the sail), mine-avoidance, and self-noise–monitor-

and 5.4 kHz, producing pulse⋮
Beams are 15 degrees wide (48 v⋮
is 96 kW. Accuracy in range is ⋮
of the range scale; accuracy in b⋮
in speed is less than 0.4 kts on⋮
the 0–30 kyds scale.

In the *Georges Leygues* class⋮
sonar is modified, and it tows ⋮
performance. This improvemen⋮
for DUBV 43.

♦ DUBV 24

DUBV 24 is a slightly less powe⋮
24C incorporates an SS 24 transc⋮
one of the first French preforme⋮
(8 transducers per stave); and ⋮
search/receive (3 ping), stepped⋮
mit/receive for attack, ODT for a⋮
and passive. In the ODT sea⋮
audio beams. Tribeam search us⋮

♦ DUBV 43

The towed variable-depth sonar⋮
erally operate in conjunction wi⋮
ical towing depth is about 300 n⋮
The transducer in the stabilize⋮
ments, 8 per stave). DUBV 43 ca⋮
or synchronized with DUBV 23, ⋮
The sonar operates on four fre⋮
15-degree beams (peak power 96⋮

In the *Georges Leygues* class, t⋮
than 600-meters depth. This incr⋮
to the period during the year whe⋮
full depth of the Mediterranean. ⋮
tactical array (TACTASS) 200 m⋮
is towed 3000 meters astern of the⋮
The TACTASS is fully digital, an⋮
gets (presumably once they have⋮
The offensive element of this syst⋮
Malafon is carried.

The DUBV 23/43 requirement ⋮
Alcatel used DUBV 24 as a build⋮
proved for service in 1969, and a⋮
in the early 1970s. Tests followed⋮
installed in 1978 on board the G⋮
was completed in 1983, for the ⋮
1988 DUBV 43 was being modifie⋮
a new transducer (developed by ⋮
processor (UTCS).

DUBV 43 fish, onboard the experimen⋮ (U.S. Naval Institute)

ing (astern of the flank arrays, on each side). The towed array is the Australian Kariwara.

For Type 2040, see U.K. sonars below.

Eledone passive attack (bow) array. (Thomson Sintra)

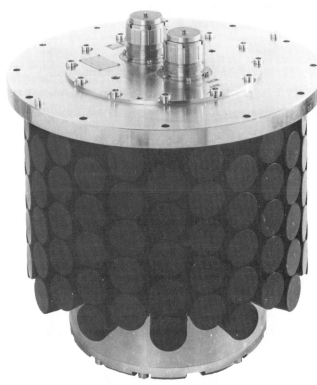

Eledone active array, typically located in the submarine sail. (Thomson Sintra)

♦ DSUV 23

DSUV 23 is a passive low-frequency hull array found on strategic submarines.

♦ DSUV 61

A towed array for strategic submarines, used primarily for evasion, DSUV 61 is comparable to BQR-15 and Type 2023. Tests were conducted in 1974–77, the first installations following in 1977–78. *Le Tonnant* and *L'Inflexible* were completed with this array, and the four earlier units were retrofitted.

Typical modern French submarine sonar-intercept array. (Thomson Sintra)

♦ DSUV 62

DSUV 62 is a towed array for attack submarines, used for passive fire control rather than evasion. Thomson-CSF received a research contract in 1975–76, after work was already proceeding on DSUV 61. The prototype was completed in 1979, tests following late in 1980, and approval for production in 1981. The first unit was installed on board the submarine *Rubis* early in 1983.

♦ DSUX 21

A multipurpose system for *L'Inflexible* and earlier strategic submarines, DSUX 21 consists of bow or flank passive arrays. It replaces DSUV 23 in all strategic submarines.

♦ DUAV 4 (HS 71)

DUAV 4 is Sintra-Alcatel's dipping sonar for the Lynx (WG-13) helicopter. Development began in 1968/69, and the sonar entered service in 1975. DUAV 4 is also used by the Dutch and Swedish Navies. It operates on three frequencies between 21 and 24 kHz (source level 119 dB), and the maximum depth is 495 ft. There are three operating modes: search (bearing and range), plot (bearing, range, and speed), and passive.

DUAV 4 is one of an HS-70 series of dipping sonars; HS 73 was announced in 1975 (for use on board French Navy Lynx helicopters). HS 73 uses a coherent processor to reject reverberation echoes in shallow water. HS 70 was an earlier dipping sonar derived from the first French Navy dipping sonar, DUAV 1.

The French and Swedish Navies selected DUAV 4 in 1976, the Dutch Navy following in 1978.

♦ DUBA 1

This searchlight attack sonar for postwar French destroyers (*Surcouf* class) and frigates is designed to control K-1 straight-running torpedoes (the French equivalent of Squid). DUBA 1B operated at 23–26 kHz, with a peak power of 2.5 kW, and 8- and 20-millisecond pulses; range scales were 0.75, 1.5, 3, 4.5, and 6 kiloyards. In a *Surcouf*-class destroyer, this sonar operated in conjunction with a DUBV 1 search set.

The only surviving examples are found on board the old missile destroyers *du Chayla* and *Dupetit Thouars*, controlling Bofors-type 275-mm rocket launchers.

◆ DUBA 2

This hull attack (searchli
French-built 174-foot subc
nisian and Yugoslav Navie
of the World War II U.S.
postwar version was equipp
at 8–30 kHz, with 8-, 20-,
sumably for search, since tl
attack). Range scales are 0
the limitations of high-freq

◆ DUBA 3

This high-frequency attack
mandant Rivière–class frig
SQS-17 is the associated s
(source level 126 dB), pulse
msec (100 yds), and frequer
reduced power). This sonar
search projector and with a
puts are elevation (target de
pler analysis of a single pin

◆ DUBA 4 (Premo)

Alcatel's search-and-attack
3. The mechanically stabil
has a diameter of 120 cm (9C
of 36 staves, for 36 prefor
Alternatively, the receiver c
Total peak power in the OI
also RDT and sector-scan tr
adds 8 dB to the transmissi
half-channels are correlatec
ing. Premo can also conduc
passively.

This sonar was announced
for the A-69 Avisos; but wh
was substituted.

◆ DUBA 25 (Thomson-Sint

This medium-frequency h
A-69–class Avisos and the
accommodate the big DUBV
or 10 kHz, with 30 or 90 mse

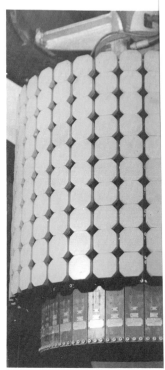

Tarpon low-frequency hull array.

plays include a 20-minute track history of any target, to assist in classification.

DUUX 5 uses two arrays, each consisting of three hydrophones on one side of the submarine's hull. Range is by triangulation, and the target's course and speed are estimated by TMA (target-motion analysis). DUUX 5 automatically and continuously measures the bearing of any loud noise source near the submarine and calculates the range of up to three contacts in a 120-degree sector on each side of the submarine. A fourth target can be tracked by means of an acoustic intercept receiver. DUUX 5 can listen on several frequencies between 2 and 10 kHz, and bearing resolution is 2 deg abeam and 4 deg at 60 deg fore or aft of the beam. Data can be transferred automatically to the submarine's fire-control system.

There are five standard alternative hydrophone units, ranging from 730 × 380 × 184 mm (DUUX 5–H1) to 1350 × 840 × 212 mm (DUUX 5–27H2). The latter version uses a beam-pre-

DUUX 5 array, one of three on each side of the submarine. (Thomson Sintra)

DUUX 5 display. Each half covers a 120-degree sector, with bearing running along the horizontal axis and time along the vertical. Radiated noise spectra can be displayed vertically on the right-hand side. (Thomson Sintra)

former (for resistance to countermeasures) with its large high-gain arrays (about 1 square meter, with ten-stave hydrophones).

DUUX 5 was developed for the French nuclear attack submarines. The contract to Sintra-Alcatel was let in the mid-1970s, the prototype being tested on board the submarine *Doris* in 1977. The first operational unit is in *Saphir*. A version of DUUX 5 is incorporated in the Eledone system.

◆ Baliste/Espadon

Thomson-CSF's sonar for fast patrol craft is a light multibeam search-and-attack set (11, 12, or 13 kHz). The company also produced an earlier sonar for the same market, Espadon (1975), operating at 14 or 16 kHz.

◆ Beluga

Thomson-CSF's export sonar for frigates was introduced in 1978. Beluga was a larger, lower-frequency equivalent to Diodon. Frequency is 6.75 or 7.8 kHz; power level is five times that of Diodon (source level 135 dB); and there are 48 preformed reception beams (ODT or 15-degree–wide SDT or steered-directional transmission). Range scales are 2.5–40 kyds, and bearing accuracy (for fire control) is 0.6 degrees. The 48-stave transducer has a diameter of 1.35 m and a height of 1 m (53.1 × 39.4 inches).

Because the number of beams is so great and the realistic range (20,000 yds) so high, the operator is assisted by an automatic signal extractor. All of the bearing-range cells are computer analyzed, and targets selected on the basis of their signal-to-noise ratio, spatial coherence, and time coherence. Numerous tracks are stored and analyzed on a scan-to-scan basis, and the sonar automatically tracks up to 12 targets. It displays the last 10 or 20 minutes of tracks and extrapolates for fire control. External data, such as helicopter positions, can be shown. The display is a two-color PPI showing raw video in orange and synthetic video (e.g., target tracks) in green.

There is also a passive detector (64 beams covering 220 degrees) that operates in parallel to the active sonar.

Another Thomson-CSF large-ship sonar, Lancon, was reported under development in 1982; presumably it was intended as a successor to Beluga.

◆ Diodon (TSM 2630)/Sorel (TSM 2630)

Diodon medium-frequency variable-depth sonar fish. (Thomson Sintra)

Thomson Sintra's medium-frequency sonar is for medium-sized ships. Diodon is the bow sonar, Sorel the same sonar in VDS form. They share common information handling and signal processing but can transmit separately. They operate at 11, 12, or 13 kHz, with pulses of 20 or 80 msec (CW or hyperbolic FM). FM pulses are pulse-compressed for reception. CW pulses are used for doppler processing. The stabilized transducer has 24 staves and uses 48 preformed beams for reception. Operating modes are ODT, RDT, SRDT (directional transmission confined

Diodon hull array. (Thomson Sintra)

to within five circuit boards. Estimated MTBF is 500 hours, and MTTR is 15 minutes.

Work began in 1969, and Diodon ran trials in 1971. Exports have included sets for four frigates for Portugal and four sets for Libya. TSM 2630 is an advanced version, in the Saudi frigates and in six Iraqi *Wadi*-class corvettes. Data given may refer to 2630 rather than to the original Diodon.

◆ FENELON

See DUUX 5 above.

◆ HS 12/SS 12/DIP 12/WS Series

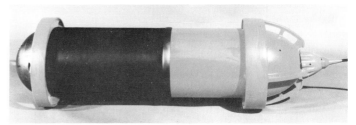

SS 12, the shipboard version of the HS 12 dipping sonar. (Thomson Sintra)

SS 12 fish (Thomson Sintra)

to a sector), and SDT. Transmission can be at reduced power. Maximum power source level is 123 dB. There are two signal processing modes: linear integration filtering (which can accommodate doppler speeds of up to 30 kts) and coherent processing (FM transmission, to reject reverberation). The coherent mode can show the fine structure of the target (range definition 1.5 m).

Generally all 24 staves are processed simultaneously (multiplexed). Range scales are 2–16 kyds. For attack, special precision circuits are used (range to within 1 percent, bearing to within 1 degree); data are displayed separately on a scope showing bearing within 10 degrees to either side, and range within one eighth of the chosen range scale, centered on the position of a surveillance marker on the main PPI. There is a separate doppler display (plus or minus 1 kt) for target following.

The signal processor can discriminate fast and slow targets (doppler). This sonar can be set for doppler enhancement (to eliminate reverberation) on one receiving beam, or on two adjacent beams for target following (beam comparison for accurate pointing). A target can be automatically tracked.

For the towed sonar, typical operating speed is 14 kts, and maximum towing speed is 20 kts. The fish is launched/recovered at 4–10 kts (10 minutes launch/recovery time).

Diodon employs the same display as DUBA 25 (Tarpon) and has the same function, but Diodon was intended to cost half as much: hence the choice of 24 rather than 36 staves, and the higher frequency for reduced size. Diodon was an early application of digital technology, for reduced overall volume, and has built-in fault-detection equipment that can isolate a fault

Thomson Sintra's helicopter dipping sonar is the fifth generation this company has produced. HS 12 was developed from the company's SS 12 variable-depth sonar for small ships.

HS 12 operates either actively (about 13 kHz, short CW pulse or FM slide) or passively (7–20 kHz), at depths as great as 300 m, with a figure of merit of 175 dB. The sonar employs 12 preformed beams, for a base directivity of 30 degrees. However, the display consists of four quadrants, north-stabilized, each obtained by processing the three adjacent beams. In this panoramic mode the operator can select a CW mode, in which each quadrant shows the target's range and the target's doppler (speed range plus or minus 40 kts). Alternatively, the operator can select FM processing (target range displayed precisely enough for the target's motion to be seen from sweep to sweep). There is also a sector mode for simplified target tracking, in which the three adjacent beams of the sector are displayed. The manufacturer claims a maximum range of over 10 km. In the dip cycle, the winch operates at 5 m/sec (average).

Construction is modular, for quick installation; HS 12 can be removed from any helicopter in less than 45 minutes. Total weight is 508 lbs (121 lbs for the dome; 42 lbs for a 300-meter cable; 158 lbs for the hydraulic winch; and 187 lbs for the display, control panels, and black boxes). The sonar dome itself is 10.3 in in maximum diameter and 33.7 in long and weighs 16 kg (33 lbs). The manufacturer, Thomson Sintra, claims that HS 12 is currently the lightest helicopter sonar in the world.

HS 12 is currently in Saudi service.

DIP 12 is a dipping version for surface-effect craft.

SS 12 is a hull and variable-depth searchlight sonar for fast attack craft and corvettes, operating in three frequency ranges around 13 kHz, using CW (rectangular or cosine-squared pulses) or FM pulses (source level 212 dB). SS 12 can automatically track two targets. The variable-depth fish can operate at 600 ft, and at speeds of up to 16 kts; it can also be used with SS 24. Alternative range scales are 2, 4, 8, and 16 km or kyds. This sonar is comparable to the TSM 2640 Salmon, which has been more successful in its market niche.

SS 12 is the basis for the CIT-Alcatel WS series of surface-ship sonars announced in 1976. WS 101 is the hull sonar, WS 110 the towed VDS, and WS 111 the combination of hull and VDS. All of these sonars employ a flat-plate transducer, and all are matched to the performance of the L3 torpedo. Although SS 12 operates at 13 kHz, these sonars are described as operating at 19, 21.4, and 23.8 kHz, using both CW and FM pulses. Signal levels are 111 dB for the standard transducer, 117 dB for a high-performance version in a fixed or retractable dome, and 116 dB for the same version in the towed fish. Range scales are 1.5, 3, 6, 9, and 12 kyds or km. The sonar can also listen at 10–26 kHz. It can track two targets simultaneously on its display.

SS 12 handling gear on board the patrol vessel *La Glorieuse*, 1985. (Thomson Sintra)

HS 12 on a Lynx helicopter. The dipping body and winch are on the left, the control panel on the right. (Thomson Sintra)

◆ HS 312S

Thomson Sintra's single-operator integrated helicopter dipping sonar/sonobuoy system includes the sonar fish and the integrated processor. The active sonar is similar to HS 12 but is more powerful (figure of merit of 177 dB), and the processor can handle 4 or 8 sonobuoys simultaneously. The latter figure is based on experience with the Lamparo airborne acoustic processor (see below).

◆ HS 70

Made for export, this dipping sonar is a solid-state (and more digital) version of DUAV 1. HS 70 is a searchlight sonar, its transducer consisting of four staves, rotated in 15-degree steps. There are three preset frequencies between 21 and 26.2 kHz. Output is 50 W or 1 kW, with 20- or 80-msec pulses. The beam is 20 × 10 deg, and the directivity index is 19 dB. Dipping depth is from a few meters to 50 m (but minimum depth for high-power transmission is 20 m). Range resolution at all ranges is 15 m.

HS 70 was announced in the late 1960s, and it is typical of the first generation of helicopter-borne sonars, which were all searchlights. The equivalent U.S. sonar was AQS-4.

HS 71 is the Lynx sonar, DUAV 4.

◆ Lamproie

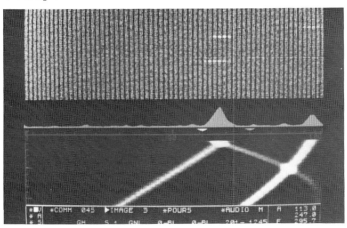

Lamproie combined narrow- (top) and broad- (bottom) band display for initial detection. The upper display is a LOFARgram, showing frequency (horizontal) plotted against time (vertical). The graph below is a series of time integrals of the highlighted areas of the LOFARgram. The lower (broad-band) display is a waterfall, showing potential target tracks, bearing (horizontal) being plotted against time (vertical). (Thomson Sintra)

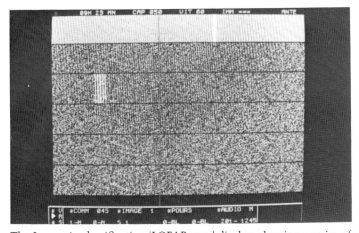

The Lamproie classification (LOFARgram) display, showing a series of six different frequency bands (separate horizontal bands) simultaneously. (Thomson Sintra)

Thomson Sintra's commercial towed array incorporates both wide- and narrow-band processing and automatic torpedo warning. The array proper is 74 m long, including the usual vibration-isolation dampers at each end. Diameter is 80 mm, and the casing is Kevlar. The array can be towed at up to 32 kts, and at depths as great as 1000 m (3280 ft). It can be towed by submarines (either in reel-in or clip-on configuration) and by surface ships (either in critical-angle or depressor-tow configurations, the latter for shallow water). The processor can operate simultaneously in several frequency bands, permitting comparison among different harmonics of the same signal, and the processor provides automatic threat (i.e., torpedo) warning while in the detection mode. Lamproie can track targets in either broad- or narrow-band mode, either automatically or manually, and can automatically reject narrow-band jammers. Classification resources are LOFAR, DEMON, and a special high-fidelity audio channel. The display is the usual pair of high-resolution color CRTs. This array is based on DUBV 62.

The wet end can be a critical-angle tow or it can be towed from a VDS fish.

Towed-array handling gear on board the frigate *Lamotte-Picquet.* (Thomson Sintra)

♦ Pascal

CIT-Alcatel's sonar for small to medium vessels was produced in the 1970s. This sonar has three transmission modes (probably ODT, RDT, and SDT) and panoramic or directional reception, with several signal processing modes for the latter. There are both hull and VDS versions. The transducer has 24 staves (24 receiving beams) and operates at 10 and 11.5 kHz (25- or 100-msec pulses, peak power 5 kW, repeating at 4, 8, 16, or 32 seconds). Range scales are 3, 6, 12, and 24 km.

Passive operation is at 2.5–15 kHz, one 500-Hz channel being chosen for processing.

The prototype was completed in mid-1972.

♦ Piranha (TSM 2140)

Piranha is a small-ship searchlight sonar. This sonar operates at 8, 9, or 10 kHz (pulses of 12.5, 25, 50, and 100 msec); and range scales are 1, 2, 4, or 8 km. The transducer, stabilized in pitch and roll, is a flat 32-transducer plate, producing a beam 20–26 degrees wide, normally depressed at −10 degrees but capable of depressing to −45 degrees to maintain close contact. Reception is on three beams: one for reference, one for depth, and one for bearing. Signal processing includes a split-beam mode for target following. Very high power (at the cavitation limit) is used to obtain long range and thus to compensate for the usual disability associated with searchlight operation.

Total weight is 510 kg. The standard fixed dome is 700 mm deep.

Piranha was announced in 1974.

♦ Remora

A smaller version of Diodon, Remora was under development in 1980, using newer technology. Remora used a 24-stave transducer, and the claimed performance was 80–90 percent of Diodon's at 60 percent of the cost. Claimed range was 6000–8000 m. This sonar could track three targets simultaneously. Like Beluga, Remora used a color display (orange for raw video, green for generated data, e.g., target tracks). The transducer's design

was similar to that of Beluga, but the sonar operated at 11, 12, or 13 kHz (passive at 10–14 kHz).

♦ Salmon (TSM 2640)

Thomson Sintra's lightweight high-frequency towed sonar for small patrol ships is dismountable. The 24-stave transducer (diameter 290 mm, weight 150 kg) operates at three frequencies around 12 kHz (217-dB source level). The operating mode is ODT with CW or FM pulses (which can be pulse-compressed). CW pulses are used for doppler (spectral) analysis. The transducer produces 48 beams with FM pulses or 24 with CW. Maximum instrumented range is 12 kyds.

This sonar can track three targets simultaneously, and Thomson Sintra describes its signal processing as particularly suited

Salmon high-frequency variable-depth sonar fish. (Thomson Sintra)

Salmon array. (Thomson Sintra)

to shallow water with substantial background noise and reverberation. The techniques in question are pulse compression with a high compression ratio (for sharp discrimination in range); high doppler resolution in the CW mode; normalization (adjustable gain, to reduce reverberation effects); and computer-aided detection. A flexible display also aids the operator.

The fish lowers to nearly 300 ft. It can be streamed at up to 20 kts (typical operating speed is 14 kts) and launch/recovery speed is 4–10 kts (time 10 minutes). The fish weighs 550 kg, and the towing/handling mechanical assembly weighs a total of 5.2 tons.

Development began in the late 1970s, the first unit being installed on board Swedish *Stockholm*-class fast patrol boats. Salmon was first tested in 1985. The *Goteborgs* are to have TSM 2643.

◆ SPDT-1A

This passive broad-band preformed-beam sonar for surface-ship torpedo detection is made by Safare-Crouzet. Classification is by analysis of a torpedo's radiated noise. SPDT means *Sonar Passif pour la Détection des Torpilles.*

SPDT-1A is currently (1988) being installed on board the first of eleven major French warships. This sonar uses the array of an active hull-mounted or a towed sonar. SPDT-1A operates at medium frequency. The system reportedly detects a torpedo at 10 km or more under favorable conditions; it does not measure range.

◆ Spherion (TSM 2633)

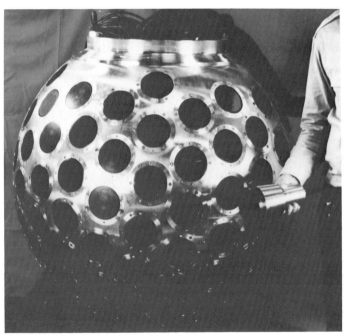

Spherion array. (Thomson Sintra)

A Thomson Sintra variable-depth sonar, Spherion is thus far in service only with the Royal Norwegian Navy. Spherion derives its name from its spherical shape. Like the much larger U.S. BQS-6, Spherion is covered with spot transducers, and presumably it can steer its beam both in azimuth and in elevation, for full three-dimensional performance.

Derived from the TSM 2630, Spherion consists of 160 transducers on a 1.15-m sphere, weighing 1830 kg. This VDS operates at 10–13 kHz (on three or four frequencies), using 10- or 15-degree beams. Source levels are 217 dB ODT and 227 dB directional mode. There is also a sector directional mode. There are 36 preformed beams stabilized in azimuth and elevation; all CW beams are subject to spectral analysis (768 doppler channels), and FM pulses are pulse-compressed (TB of 300). The signal processor can extract and maintain 25 tracks simultane-

ously. Criteria provided by the system for target analysis include apparent length, inclination, and doppler. As in TSM 2630, the display incorporates two identical high-resolution monitors. Total system weight is 6000 kg.

Spherion was announced in 1985.

TSM 2633 is an ES/LF hull-mounted version, operating at 6–8 kHz, also producing 36 preformed beams, with instrumented ranges between 2 and 24 km. There is a VDS version of TSM 2633; it is not clear whether the higher-frequency Spherion described above would be used as the complementary VDS. The Thomson Sintra brochure describing this sonar shows it installed on board what appears to be a Norwegian *Oslo*-class frigate, with a large spherical transducer in the bow sonar dome, and a much smaller transducer in a towed fish.

◆ SS 24

SS 24 is a hull and variable-depth sonar for corvettes and frigates. It operates at three frequencies around 5 kHz, forming 24 beams (15-degree beams) and using either CW or FM pulses. Source level is 223 dB (ODT) or 232 dB (RDT); source level for the variable-depth fish is 212 dB (as in SS 12). This transducer is being used to update the existing DUBV 24C, and the first units produced were incorporated into 24Cs in 1983.

◆ SS 48

This hull and variable-depth sonar (48-stave hull transducer, 24-stave VDS transducer) operates at three frequencies around 5 kHz. The two transducers produce, respectively, 96 and 48 preformed beams. Source levels (ODT/RDT) are 230/241 dB for the hull sonar and 228/237 dB for the VDS. Pulses are CW or FM, and in either case the sonar can measure doppler shift for classification and tracking. SS 48 can maintain track on twelve targets simultaneously.

Although SS 48 was developed entirely as a private venture (and although it has not been exported), the French Navy decided in 1983 to use SS 48's technology to upgrade the existing DUBV 23/43 combination.

◆ Velox-M7

This sonar-warning receiver for submarines is under development by Safare Crouzet as a private venture, to replace Velox-M5/DUUG-6B. M7 automatically gives an alarm when sonar signals are detected, and giving the bearing of the source and measuring the transmitter's frequency, relative level, pulse width, and PRF. M7 will also detect ultrasound communications and acoustic noise generated by surface ships.

◆ PVDF

In 1988 Thomson-Sintra announced a new material, PVDF, for passive sonar transducers. A continuous sheet of alternating piezo-electric film and metallic electrodes, to replace conventional ceramic hydrophones, PVDF is made in panels about 1.5 × 3 feet and about 2 inches thick. It will initially replace conventional flank-array hydrophones; sea trials reportedly show a better signal-to-noise ratio (hence greater effective range) than conventional hydrophones, with useful response up to 5 kHz. Theoretically PVDF should be effective up to 10 kHz. This improvement is important because, given the baselines involved, ranging requires the kind of accurate bearing data available only above 5 kHz. Below that frequency the bearing of a target can be obtained, but individual flank hydrophones do not differ enough in their bearing data to provide range by triangulation. PVDF is already in service on board Norwegian submarines and is planned for French ballistic-missile submarines. Existing spot hydrophones have to be isolated from water flow over the hull to achieve sufficient signal-to-noise ratios. They are, therefore, mounted in fairings, and the fairings in turn cause drag as well as noise due to flow disturbance. The flat PVDF panels can presumably be mounted directly on the outside of a submarine's hull.

UNDERWATER FIRE-CONTROL SYSTEMS

◆ DLA

Direction de Lancement d'Armes, a torpedo fire-control console for the Saudi *Al Madinah*–class frigates, controls four F17P wire-guided torpedoes fired from stern tubes. The console receives the essential data from the ship's combat system (target's bearing, range, heading, and speed); alternatively, DLA obtains this data directly from the ship's sonar. Two target tracks can be shown simultaneously, but only one torpedo can be controlled. If both targets must be attacked, one of the torpedoes must be fired on a preset track.

◆ DLT D3A

The standard French torpedo fire-control system is *Direction Lance Torpilles.* Versions in current service are the following:

D3A in *Agosta* class and modified *Daphne* class. All operations are controlled by an IRIS 35M computer.

L4C in surface ships.

S4E in *Daphne* class, controlling Z16, E14/15, and L3 torpedoes. S4D was in the modernized *Narval* class, now defunct.

Integrated sonar combat system of a typical French submarine, showing bow, flank, ranging, and towed arrays. (Thomson Sintra).

Agosta CIC, showing the torpedo fire-control system display (DLT), DUUX 5, and the panoramic (integrated) sonar displays. (Thomson Sintra)

CIC of a French nuclear attack submarine. The sonar is integrated with other sensors: the screen in the foreground shows an infrared periscope image and, it would appear, the image of a second target below it. (Thomson Sintra)

GERMANY (WEST)

SONARS

Virtually all West German sonars are produced by Krupp-Atlas Elektronik GmBH (KAE).

◆ DBQS-21 (CSU 83)

Compared to the earlier CSU 3-4, this system adds a flank array and a towed array. CSU 83 is the primary sensor of the new German SLW-83 submarine's fire-control and command/control system now being developed, and also of the ISUS (integrated-sensor underwater system) for export. CSU 83 was evaluated on board a Type-206 submarine during 1985, the German Navy ordering 13 sets for its SLW 83 integrated submarine combat system, twelve of them for Type-206A submarines being modernized and the other for a shore site. Others were ordered for the Norwegian *Ula* class, for the Swedish *Vastergotland* class, and for two Type 209s for Brazil.

The system consists of a passive bow array (0.3–12 kHz), a trainable active transducer (8 kHz, range 10 kyds, 30-deg beam), a passive flank array (10 Hz–2 kHz, range 50 kyds), a passive-ranging array (2–8 kHz, effective to 15 kyds), a towed array (100–800 Hz, maximum range 100 kyds), a sonar-intercept array (1–100 kHz, effective at up to 100 kyds), and two self-noise sensors (sail and machinery room, 0–12 kHz).

CSU is a commercial designation, meaning Compact Sonar for U-boats.

◆ DSQS-11

See the Mine Warfare section.

◆ DSQS-21/ASO80 Series

These are Krupp-Atlas's hull and variable-depth sonars for surface ships. DSQS-21A is for large destroyers. DSQS-21B for destroyers and frigates has 32 beams (variable-depth version has 64 beams). DSQS-21C for corvettes and DSQS-21D for small ASW patrol vessels have 32 beams in both hull and variable-depth versions. In each case a Z suffix, as in DSQS-21BZ, indicates that the transducer is electronically stabilized against roll and pitch. The transducer's diameter varies from 0.95 m (32 staves) in DSQS-21D, to 1.8 m (64 staves) in DSQS-21B, to 3.0 m (96 staves) in DSQS-21A for destroyers.

There are five selectable range brackets (2–32 kyds). Transmission modes are 5 and 50 msec CW; 50 msec FM; and 5/50, 50/50, and 300/300 msec CW/FM. The returning pulses are subject to processing optimized separately for each type (CW and

Console for a DSQS-21 sonar, showing a ray-trace indicator on the upper display and a PPI (plan position indicator) below it. (Krupp Atlas-Elektronik)

	Hull Sonar/VDS Array Diameters	Preformed Beams
ASO86	3.0/1.0 m	96/32 deg
ASO85	1.8/1.0 or 0.58 m	64/32 deg
ASO84	1.0/1.0 or 0.58 m	32/32 deg
ASO83	1.0/0.58 m	32/32 deg

Each has a stabilized beam option.

As of 1987, a total of about 50 DSQS-21s had been delivered to 15 navies. This sonar has also replaced the U.S.-supplied SQS-23s of the *Lutjens*-class missile destroyers.

KAE is currently developing a new hull sonar for the German F124 frigate and the NATO NFR-90. This system is to use a low-frequency hull transducer, an intercept sonar, and an active/passive towed array (with either a hull or towed active transmitter).

◆ SLW 83/ISUS

This integrated sonar suite uses the CSU 83 (DBQS-21) sonar plus tactical-data handling and weapons control. ISUS (integrated-sensor underwater system) is the export version. Each sonar can initiate a target track, the data then being supplemented by data from the other sonars. Each track is subject to automatic classification and TMA (for up to 24 targets), before being combined with periscope and ESM data in the tactical-data handling system (TDHS). The TDHS in turn generates a combat-situation display. The system can handle up to three simultaneous engagements, either from a single console or from several consoles.

These systems are modular, built up from multifunction consoles: two for a small submarine or up to six for a submarine of over 1800 tons. German Type-206A submarines have four consoles, two devoted to the CSU 83 sonar suite, one to CIC duties, and the other to fire control. Each console carries two 15-inch three-color CRTs, the lower screen functioning as a PPI and the upper carrying alphanumeric tables.

◆ CSU 2 and CSU 4

These searchlight sonars for submarines are tiltable and trainable. CSU 4 is an electronically scanned active sonar. These sonars are part of CSU 3-2 and 3-4.

◆ Krupp-Atlas CSU 3-2/CSU 3-4

An integrated sonar system for submarines, CSU 3-2 uses a fixed passive array and a searchlight active sonar that is mechanically tilted and rotated. Development began in 1963–64, and the first units (CSU 3-2 passive only) were installed in German Type-205 submarines in 1966–68, after which an improved version was exported. The AN526 passive array consists of a 96-stave horseshoe wrapped around the chin of the submarine, each stave consisting of three elements, and the entire array covering the sector back to 30 degrees on each side of the bow. Beams are formed by delay lines. In service, it was soon found that individual staves could easily be knocked out of alignment and that they were difficult to replace.

Accuracy was about 1 degree. Hydrophone output was in six bands between 350 Hz and 3.2 kHz, all six being displayed above the main PPI as an aid to frequency analysis and classification.

CSU 3-4 is an improved version of CSU 3-2, with a circular passive array (3-m diameter, 900 mm deep). Because this array, which is designated AN5039, is more symmetrical than the chin array, its beam-forming network is easier to manufacture, and the array itself is easier to align. Type-205 and Type-206 submarines in Danish, German, and Norwegian service use the AN5039 chin array.

CSU 3-4 is specially intended for shallow water. Able to track four contacts automatically, this sonar system provides target elevation angle to estimate range and optimum sound ray path. An audio channel improves classification. The active mode is displayed in 30-degree sectors (waterfall) on the CRT, with continual memory update. The cylindrical array is electronically

FM) of pulse. On the PPI display, fixed navigational points (such as cliffs) are shown in yellow, approaching targets are in red, and retiring targets in green. In active mode, the sonar can automatically track three targets simultaneously, giving their range, bearing, and radial speed (i.e., doppler). In the passive mode, three targets can be tracked automatically in bearing. There is also a sonar-intercept facility. This sonar incorporates geometric processing, new plots being correlated with past tracks to reduce the false-alarm rate. The track list is constantly thinned by checking and by assigning each track a confidence level.

This sonar began with a German Navy requirement for a sonar for the frigate (which became Type 122) that was planned for the 1980s; the export market was secondary. Krupp-Atlas began feasibility studies in 1972. Bids were solicited in 1976, Krupp-Atlas carrying out research and development between 1976 and 1979, leading to tests of DSQS-21BZ in 1979. It is intended primarily to operate in shallow water, often with a cluttered bottom.

The Taiwanese government has reportedly selected DSQS-21CZ for its new surface combatant (modified *Perry* class).

The export version of the DSQS-21 is the ASO80 (Type 80) series. ASO83 is a low-volume single-display system; ASO84 is DSQS-21; ASO85 has 64 preformed beams; and ASO86 has 96 preformed beams. There are variable-depth versions of each sonar. ASO84/5 equips Malaysian Type-1500 frigates.

ASO 84 to 86 are derived from DSQS-21; over 50 had been manufactured as of 1987, and all versions were compatible with a VDS. ASO83 is a smaller single-operator sonar intended for smaller surface craft up to corvette size. Dimensions are as follows:

SONARS AND UNDERWATER FIRE-CONTROL SYSTEMS

scanned. The intercept function can display up to eight pulses in the center of the CRT, plus data on bearing, frequency, signal level, and signal duration on one pulse. These pulses can also be presented on the audio channel. Two passive-ranging sonars, PRS 3-4 and PRS 3-15, can be added as options. In 1987 German production shifted to the CSU 83, which combines active, passive, intercept, and two flank arrays, a doppler log, and an underwater telephone.

◆ CSU 3-41

CSU 3-41 is an active-passive sonar for submarines (in Canadian *Oberons*). The active transducer in the sail replaces the original Types 187, 197, and 719.

◆ ELAC 1BV

ELAC 1BV was the first modern German-produced surface-ship sonar, a medium-frequency (range 7–10 kHZ) searchlight. It is installed only on board the *Hamburg*-class destroyers and *Thetis*-class corvettes; the *Koln*-class frigates are fitted with Dutch PAE/CWE sets. Since these ships are fitted with Bofors ASW mortars, 1BV is presumably tiltable to follow a target in three dimensions, serving simultaneously as a search and an attack sonar. ELAC is now a division of Honeywell and no longer produces stand-alone sonars.

◆ PRS (Passive-Ranging Sonar)

PRS is a passive complement to CSU 3-4 active/passive sonar. There are two types of PRS 3, each with six sets (3 each side) of hydrophones. Each PRS 3-15 array has 60 hydrophones in 15 staves; each PRS 3-4 array has 40 smaller hydrophones. Tracking can be either manual or automatic, following four targets simultaneously in manual mode. For automatic tracking, the system uses the auto–target-tracking (ATT) channels of the CSU 3-4. Targets can be tracked over a 170-degree arc on either beam (45–135 and 225–315 degrees relative to the bow). Targets are tracked at 2–8 kHz. The combination of large arrays and a wide frequency range makes for an accuracy of about 0.5 degrees over the highest performance arcs (45–135 and 225–315 degrees) of PRS 3-15.

A PRS sonar can be used as an independent sensor (for detection, automatic tracking, ranging, and course and speed evaluation), or the sonar can be controlled automatically by the main sensor's automatic tracking channels, to measure range and evaluate a target's course and speed.

This system, roughly contemporary with CSU-4, was developed in 1961–65 and tested in 1965–66.

◆ PSU 1-2

This sonar for small submarines was developed for passive detection and reception of underwater telephone signals. PSU 1-2 uses a cylindrical transducer with 64 preformed beams, presenting information on a CRT in true or relative bearing. PSU 1-2 can autotrack four targets and is intended for a 400–500 ton submarine.

INDIA

◆ APSOH

Bharat Electronics's Advanced Panoramic Sonar was first installed in the Indian-built frigate *Ganga* (completed 1986). APSOH has also been described as an ODT scanning sonar, developed by the Naval Physical and Oceanography Laboratory (NPOL) at Cochin.

ITALY

SONARS

◆ IP-64

This integrated active/passive sonar suite of the *Enrico Toti* class incorporates a JP-64 active sonar. IP-64 is an analog system; about 1982 the Italian Navy drafted a staff requirement for

a digital upgrade, retaining the same array, but replacing the existing operator console with one based on that of the NA-18 AAW fire-control system.

The system consists of a conformal passive array on the chin and an active circular array on deck. A passive range-finder (MD-64, consisting of three hydrophones on each side) can be added. Operation of all three units is analogous to the IPD 70 system, the submarine using her conformal array and her passive ranger to get into attack position and then obtaining a final range by single ping. As in the MD-70 system, MD-64 can lock onto a signal to produce continuous bearing data.

◆ IPD 70/S and SISU

IPD 70 is the integrated active/passive sonar of the *Sauro* class, using much IP 64 technology and, therefore, largely analog. IPD 70/S is a digital version for later ships of this type, the existing two-man console being replaced by a console based on that of the NA-18 AAW fire-control system.

There are three arrays: a conformal array of 46 barium titanate hydrophones wrapped around the lower part of the bow, for long-range detection and classification (220 Hz–7 kHz); a 36-stave cylindrical high-frequency array in the upper part of the bow for target tracking (8–15 kHz); and (optionally) a pair of line hydrophones down the hull for passive ranging (designated MD100/S when used alone). The high-frequency array can track four targets simultaneously; the passive linear arrays can range up to three noisy targets. Targets are tracked passively, and accurate ranges are then obtained by single narrow-beam (10-degree) high-frequency pings (peak power 10 kW, source level 130 dB). The same array can be used for active search (ODT or RDT) if required. There are two sonar interceptors: one using the main passive array (3–15 kHz), and the other a Velox M5 (see the French entry above for details) operating in the 2.5–80 kHz range, primarily to detect active-homing torpedoes approaching from abaft.

These sonars are made by USEA/Selenia. In export form they are designated SISU-1; SISU-2 is a modified version for small (600-ton) submarines.

The IPD 70/S can be integrated with the IN100A omnidirectional and directional LF intercept sonar, ISO100 omnidirectional HF intercept sonar, TS100 underwater telephone, and CM10 acoustic range predictor.

◆ MD 100/S

MD 100/S is an update of Selenia-Elsag's M100 passive range-finder for small to medium diesel-electric submarines. MD 100/S can operate separately or as part of IPD 70/S. MD 100/S employs two linear arrays, each consisting of three equally-spaced transducers on the port and starboard sides of the hull, and can track four targets simultaneously within 60 degrees of amidships (to either side). This sonar triangulates to obtain range and bearing on each target, using at least two transducers on either side, then uses TMA for the target's course and speed (either using own data or data from another sonar). The modification program parallels that of IPD 70/S. Trials were conducted in 1981–83, and this system is installed in Improved *Sauro*-class submarines laid down from 1983 on. MD 100/S is being retrofitted in earlier Italian *Sauro*-class submarines.

FIRE-CONTROL SYSTEMS

◆ DLB-1

DLB-1 is San Giorgio-Elsag's ASW fire-control system for surface ships.

◆ BSN-716 (SACTIS)

SACTIS is the standard current Italian Navy integrated submarine combat system, using a single central computer (in this case a Rolm MSE 14 with disk memory). The associated sensors are the IPD-70 sonar, Thetis ESM, and BPS-704 radar. Made by SMA, SACTIS incorporates the Elettronica ELT/810 sonar-performance predictor. There are two display groups (each with three screens). Each display is a 9×16 in CRT, and up to 30 targets can be displayed simultaneously. Individual track histories can be selected for presentation, with 10 available as filtered targets. There are four presentations: the general unfiltered situation; a tactical picture; a time-bearing display; and target-motion analysis. Sonar ray paths can be displayed, and own and target's sonar performance calculated. SACTIS can also accept both manually entered and Link 11 data.

SACTIS (Submarine Action Information System) is the export designation.

◆ SEPA Mk 3

SEPA Mk 3 is an integrated command-and-control system for submarines. Unlike the current SACTIS, SEPA is a federated system using three Elsag digital multifunction consoles, which predict acoustic performance, predict counter-detection range, collect and correlate sensor data, conduct target-motion analysis, evaluate threats, designate targets, and control weapons and countermeasures. Generally one console is used for command and control and for radar and ECM display. The other two control weapons.

◆ SICS

SICS (Submarine Integrated Combat System) is being developed by a consortium of Elsag, Whitehead, and SEPA (the Welse consortium). Like SEPA Mk 3, SICS uses several interchangeable consoles, which incorporate the system's computers.

JAPAN

Japanese submarines are equipped with license-built U.S. SQS-36J active sonars. Some surface ships have SQS-35J variable-depth sonars.

Development of a new tactical towed array, OQR-1, with performance to be superior to that of the U.S. SQR-19, was announced in JFY86. R&D work on a high-speed low-noise towed array began under the JFY87/88 program. There is also a surveillance towed-array project. A submarine-towed array, included in the ZQQ-5B system, was tested on board the submarine *Okishio* in 1987. In addition, work is proceeding on an improved low-frequency active sonar, using a new transducer and improved anechoic baffling.

◆ HQS-101

The dipping sonar for the PS-1 maritime-patrol aircraft operates at 5 kHz. PS-1 is unusual in that it lands to dip its sonar before attacking; other patrol aircraft merely drop sonobuoy fields. The -101C version solves the problem of noise interference (from the airplane's engines) by noise cancellation.

◆ OQS Series

The OQS Series are hull sonars for surface ships:

OQS-1/2/12/14 are license-built versions of the U.S. SQS-4/29; OQS-12 and -14 are developed versions, in the *Isuzu* class. OQS-12 is a modified SQS-31. Like some U.S. versions of SQS-4, OQS-12 or -14 can support a variable-depth sonar operating from the same sonar stack, using an OQA-1 hoist and fish equivalent to the U.S. SQA-10 (*Isuzu* class). The current VDS is SQS-35J. In *Shirane*, the VDS is used to tow an array.

OQS-3 is a license-built SQS-23 bow sonar. It is being replaced by OQS-4.

OQS-4 is an indigenous low-frequency design, in the *Asagiri-*, *Hatakaze-*, and *Hatsuyuki*-class destroyers, and the *Yubari-* and *Ishikari*-class frigates. OQS-4 is probably similar to SQS-23. Compared to OQS-3, OQS-4 has improved electronic components and better signal processing.

OQS-101 is an indigenous-design hull sonar, equivalent to U.S. SQS-53. OQS-101 is the hull sonar of the *Shirane* class and will be used in the Japanese Aegis destroyers.

◆ ZQQ Series

The ZQQ Series are hull sonars for submarines:

ZQQ-1 Oki passive sonar, comparable to the U.S. BQQ-2.

ZQQ-3 Oki Electric cylindrical (10-ft diameter) hull array.

ZQQ-4 Standard submarine passive suite incorporating a spherical bow array.

NETHERLANDS

SONARS

◆ CWE-10N

This 10-kHz searchlight surveillance sonar is installed for search on board German and Turkish *Koln*-class frigates and on board the ex-Dutch cruisers and destroyers in Peruvian service; CWE-10N may also still be on board the Argentine carrier *25 de Mayo*. The manufacturer was van der Heem, which was part of the Philips group and was later absorbed into Signaal. In destroyers and frigates, this sonar was associated with another, PAE (see below).

◆ HSS-15

Signaal's austere scanning sonar, announced in 1982, operates over the same 9.3–11.7 kHz range as PHS-32, for ranges of 4,000–6,000 m. HSS-15 was intended for ships displacing 100–800 tons.

◆ LWS-20

Signaal's sonar-intercept device uses four arrays to cover the four 90-degree sectors, the whole device being diagonal to the centerline of the submarine. Each face carries four hydrophone groups, for the four bands in the 2–80 kHz range. The display consists of two CRTs, one for bearing and one for frequency, plus fifteen LEDs to give signal strength (which provides a measure of range).

◆ LWS-30

The Signaal (HSA) passive sonar and sonar-intercept system for submarines was announced in 1973. LWS-30 could use existing transducers and hydrophone arrays. Capabilities included omnidirectional warning and multitarget autotracking, as well as torpedo warning.

Frequency ranges were: CRT display for 1.25–80 kHz (sonar intercept); torpedo warning from 20–80 kHz; direct audio for 1.25–10 kHz (synthetic audio produced for 10–80 kHz signals). All signals (1.25–80 kHz) are displayed on a CRT and are measured for analysis. The system was designed to track signals in three ranges: 1.25–2.5 kHz, 2.5–5 kHz, and 5–10 kHz.

Intercept ratio: between 1.25 and 10 kHz, 12.5 to 6 at 5-kts speed in sea-state 3; 9.5 to 5, when snorkeling. Between 10 and 80 kHz the respective ranges of intercept ratio are 5.5–3.5 and 5–3.

Detection range: 1.25–10 kHz at 5 kts in sea-state 3, 125–40 kyds; snorkeling, 100–35 kyds. At 10–80 kHz, 25–6 kyds at the lower end of the band and 20–6 kyds at the upper end. Signaal offered a 600-kg LF hydrophone array (height 800 mm, diameter adapted to ship dimensions) and a 40-kg HF array (200 mm × 280-mm diameter).

◆ PAE-1

Van der Heem's attack sonar (searchlight) is associated with CWE-10 (see above) and operates at 24 kHz.

◆ PHS-32

PHS-32 is Signaal (HSA)'s search-and-attack sonar for ships of 200 tons or more. The transducer can be fixed or retractable. PHS-32 can automatically track four targets simultaneously (i.e., has four pairs of range gates, with automatic video extraction and special software that filters the resulting target positions into an accurate target track for fire control). During sea trials in 1978, in bad weather (sea-state 4, ship rolling up to 25 degrees, and pitching up to 10 degrees), a submarine was automatically tracked out to 14,000 yds.

The system uses a fast-Fourier-transform processor to extract doppler information from echoes in each preformed beam. The B-scan display (bearing-range rather than PPI) is connected to a memory that stores doppler information. Signaal argued that the time-bearing waterfall made detection more likely than a conventional PPI, since the operator did not have to search ever-widening circles. In passive (LISTEN) mode, the sonar can display up to four targets in a 20-minute time/bearing format. The associated SMR-Mu computer operates the sonar and is accessible via a light pen.

The transducer consists of 30 staves (10 spot transducers each), with 60 preformed beams (effective beamwidth 12 degrees, with bearing accuracy of 1 degree; vertical beamwidth is either 12 or 20 degrees, switchable during reception). Modes of operation are ODT, TRDT (tribeam), LP (long pulse option), MCC (beam widened in the vertical to maintain close contact), and LISTEN (passive). This system can automatically track up to four targets simultaneously. Frequency is 9.3 or 10.5 or 11.7 kHz, with 600-Hz bandwidth. Pulse lengths are 12.5, 25, 50, 100, and 400 (optional long pulse or FM mode only) msec. Range scales are 1, 2, 4, 8, and 16 kyds; and range accuracy is 0.5–2 percent of full-scale range (range gate is 1/16 of the range scale). The system can maintain a time/bearing history for 20 minutes. The transducer's diameter is 730 mm, and total weight of the fixed hull outfit is about 7000 kg. The retractable hull outfit weighs about 2500 kg and can be lowered or retracted at up to 24 kts.

The display includes a ray path predictor, using a sound-velocity profile from an on-line XBT. PHS-32 incorporates built-in test equipment.

PHS-32 is in the Dutch-built Indonesian frigates, the South Korean *Ulsan*-class frigates, and the Nigerian *Aradu*. PHS-32 is the smallest of the PHS-32/34/36 sonar family that grew out of negotiations between Signaal and the Royal Netherlands Navy in the early 1970s. Design work on PHS-32 began in 1974, and hardware contracts were awarded from 1975 on. The first unit was tested in 1977–78.

◆ PHS-34

Signaal's hull sonar operates on four frequencies centered on 7 kHz. Modes are ODT, MCC (expanded vertical beam), RDT, SDT (synthetic searchlight), and DT. This sonar uses pulse compression for simultaneous detection of high- and low-doppler targets in a turbulent sea or in poor conditions. Pulses are CW and FM or CW/FM. The sonar can track twelve targets simultaneously, and it incorporates a passive time-bearing plot and range predictor. There is also an underwater telephone. Options include an XBT, different-sized domes, and a variable-depth fish.

PHS-34 was tested in 1977–78, but as of 1988 there have been no reported sales.

◆ PHS-36

This low-frequency bow sonar is a derivative of the PHS series and also of the Canadian Westinghouse SQS-509. PHS-36 operates at 5.5, 6.5, and 7.5 kHz (5-kW pulses, 15-degree beam) and in four active modes plus a passive mode. In the new M-class frigates, the sonar transducer is derived from that of the French DUBV 25, with PHS-36 electronics.

PHS-36 was first tested in 1979–81 and was first installed on board the frigate *Jacob van Heemskerck*.

◆ SIASS

Signaal's Submarine Integrated Attack-and-Surveillance Sonar System was first fitted to the Taiwanese *Hai Lung* class (the Dutch *Walrus* class uses a Thomson-CSF suite). SIASS-1 has its own consoles and can interface with other systems; SIASS-2 is integral with SEWACO (see tactical-data systems in the Surveillance and Control section). SIASS consists of a cylindrical bow array (96 staves, each with four transducers), a four-element HF acoustic-intercept array, a set of flank ranging arrays, and a cylindrical active transmitting array. Three square passive-ranging arrays (25 hydrophones each, arranged 5 × 5) are fitted on each flank of the submarine; they provide a total of 64 preformed receiving beams, counting both sides of the submarine. The bow array, with 96 preformed receiving beams, is used for narrow-band and broad-band listening, for low-frequency acoustic intercept, and as the receiver for active operation.

A full flank array, for low-frequency coverage, is available as an option.

The system can store up to 35 tracks, carrying out contact-motion analysis (TMA) on up to 20 of them. The broad-band systems of the cylindrical and flank arrays each provide four such channels, on eight preselected frequencies; there are 16 more for high- and low-frequency acoustic intercept sonars, and four more for the active sonar. In at least some cases, tracking is based on the automatic association of inputs from different sensors operating in different frequency ranges. Each sonar has an electronic classification library of up to 300 specific platforms (100 ship classes, 100 sonar types).

The output of each of the 160 receiving channels (beams) is subject to complex fast-fourier-transform analysis for LOFAR, the computer holding 15 minutes of history on each (total capacity 2 Mbytes). This history can be displayed either as broad-band (time vs. bearing, i.e., waterfall) or narrow-band (frequency vs. bearing, or frequency vs. time for one beam, or amplitude vs. frequency integrated over time). Signaal claims that the ability to call up LOFARgrams at will (using the 15-minute memory), rather than waiting for them to build up over time, allows their use for target detection rather than merely for target classification or monitoring. There are also enhanced classification channels, Zoom-LOFAR (high-resolution vernier analysis) and DEMON (demodulated noise, enabling the sonars to measure frequencies below 100 Hz by demodulating higher-frequency noise, such as flow noise or cavitation, to get at fundamental frequencies). DEMON allows measurement of blade and shaft rates.

The cylindrical and flank arrays can also be used for multi-target tracking, and different targets can be tracked in narrow- and broad-band at the same time, the broad-band track being by noise over a selected frequency interval, the narrow-band by specific frequency line (for automatic tracking of a crossing target). Active modes are single-ping (directional) and single- or multiple-ping ODT, and the active sonar can automatically track multiple targets.

Normally the passive-ranging sonar is slaved to the main cylindrical array in the bow, so that range can be calculated automatically once a broad-band contact enters the ranging sector. The method is measurement of wavefront curvature by frequency-domain correlation, and bandwidth is varied to reject specific noise sources.

The high-frequency intercept sonar operates up to 100 kHz, and uses a fast-Fourier-transform processor to detect, classify, and correlate contacts. The intercept sonar incorporates a threat library and can warn automatically of, e.g., torpedoes.

Work on the system began in the early 1980s, to provide a new system for export submarines. The first production models were completed in 1982/83, the first installation being on board the submarine *Walrus* in 1985. SIASS is also installed in the two submarines built in the Netherlands for Taiwan. The associated combat system is Spectrum.

UNDERWATER FIRE-CONTROL SYSTEMS

◆ M8 Series

Signaal (HSA)'s torpedo fire-control system for submarines can simultaneously track three targets, prepare fire-control solutions for three targets, and control three torpedoes. Maximum own-ship speed is 40 kts, maximum target speed is 60 kts, and maximum torpedo speed is 60 kts. M8 can control straight-running, homing/programmed, or wire-guided torpedoes.

This system was introduced as M8/O in 1955, in the Dutch *Dolfijn* class. Signaal developed a special solid-state digital computer for submarine fire control, which was introduced in M8/1, for the German Navy (Type-205 submarines). Instead of dials, tactical data was displayed on a PPI. Although problems were encountered, this display seemed far better than the earlier separate manual plot and rack-mounted instruments. M8/1 was, therefore, an early example of the integration of AIO and fire-control system. Because the computer was programmable, it could be used not only to calculate torpedo lead angles but also to process all sensor data to give target positions and vectors; it could simultaneously display sonar, radar, and periscope range and heading data. Programs were developed to compute positions (either active or passive), to evaluate periscope-bearing data (with estimates of range, heading, and course), and to evaluate passive bearings (TMA, based on a stereotyped own-ship maneuver).

Later versions, both for the German Navy and for all the German export submarines, were M8/5, M8/15, M8/16, M8/17 (to fit the very limited internal space of the *Dolfijn* class as rebuilt), and M8/18. The last of the series was M8/24, 1975 (as of 1974, a total of 85 M8 systems had been ordered, and nearly 70 had been delivered). The later M8/41 was renamed SINBADS (see below). These M8s are all centralized systems, a command and weapons-control console being fed by all the sensors (some of which have their own dedicated operator consoles).

Increased capability was generally achieved by adding special-purpose computers, and these computers ultimately added automated plotting capability for target-motion analysis (TMA), i.e., for plotting beyond what was needed for torpedo fire control.

◆ M9 Series

These ASW-torpedo fire-control systems for surface ships use a standard Signaal horizontal tactical-display console and a third-generation Signaal SMR-S general-purpose minicomputer (24-bit words, basic memory 4K expandable to 64K in 4K modules of RAM or ROM). These systems are also designated VM, e.g., VM9/41.

◆ SINBADS

Signaal's Submarine Integrated Battle and Data System can track automatically after a firm contact has been established, based either on continuous bearing data or on range and bearing supplied intermittently by an active sonar. There is also a semi-automatic mode allowing comparison of information from various sources; this mode is capable of detecting target maneuvers and of determining the target's new parameters after a maneuver. Target evaluation is based on a target-motion-analysis display (TMAD).

Like other combat systems of its time (the 1960s), SINBADS is built around a central computer, in this case optimized to process track data by Kalman filtering. The single operator can call up any one of three displays: a track display for target evaluation; a PPI for weapons control; and an alphanumeric display showing selected data. Alternatively, raw data from any particular sensor can be called up.

Weapons-control functions are (i) weapon assignment/torpedo setting; (ii) prediction for aiming; (iii) firing preparation; (iv) torpedo wire-guidance/monitoring. Up to three torpedoes can be assigned simultaneously, and SINBADS can track up to five targets simultaneously. Prediction includes continuous calculation of a torpedo's course (from assignment to end of run for guided torpedoes, or until firing for non-guided ones). The system automatically tests torpedoes before firing them.

Over 20 systems were exported between 1975 and 1985, to Argentina, Ecuador, Peru, Indonesia, Greece, and Turkey.

◆ GIPSY

GIPSY was designed specifically for the *Walrus* class. Unlike SINBADS, GIPSY provides a separate Signaal SMR-MU computer for each of seven interchangeable consoles. In addition,

there are two SMR-MU computers for system management (one on standby), and two SMR-MU computers for sonar-data handling. A 16-inch PPI presents sonar or radar video. Contacts can be displayed in time-bearing (waterfall) form, and their movements computed by target-motion analysis.

◆ SEWACO

SEWACO is a new-generation system for submarines down to 800 tons. First installed on board the Taiwanese (GRC) *Sea-dragon* class, SEWACO developed into Spectrum.

◆ Spectrum

This combat system, developed from SEWACO for the two Dutch-built Taiwanese submarines, integrates the full spectrum of combat system functions, including sensor operation. Spectrum is normally associated with the SIASS integrated sonar (see above). The system is digital and software-based and provides high-resolution spectral analysis in each preformed beam to improve the probability of detection and to assist in classification. Memory suffices to store the results of this analysis (LOFARgrams) for later display.

Spectrum is built around a data bus feeding three or four multifunction consoles. Sensor data are preprocessed before being fed into the data bus, to reduce the load on the consoles. The active transducer and cylindrical receiving array feed into a common processor (with separate preprocessors for active and passive operation); the passive ranger and acoustic-intercept arrays share a common processor (with separate front-end preprocessors); and the nonacoustic sensors (ESM, radar, periscope, and navigational aids) share a common processor. Each console is a SIGHT general-purpose work station with a 19-inch color screen and a smaller alphanumeric display. Input is by keyboard and a rolling ball, and each console contains two SMR-MU general-purpose computers. Besides sonar functions, the system carries out analysis of periscope data, maintains a plot, associates multiple tracks to reject false alarms, assists in navigation, and simulates sensor inputs for training. Two identical weapon-electronics cabinets each contain interfaces to control half the torpedo tubes (normally four each).

Spectrum can maintain 35 simultaneous tracks, and it can control four missiles (such as Harpoon) and four wire-guided torpedoes simultaneously.

NORWAY

SONARS

The only manufacturer is Simrad, which entered the military market after producing fish-finding and whaling sonars. The company announced details of four main types in 1975–76: SU, ST, SQ-D, and SK3-D, the largest being the SU-RS searchlight. Later the company announced the SS series.

◆ SK Series

SK3 is smaller than SQ-D. With a fixed dome, SK3 is designated SK3-D; in either case the transducer is retractable. Operating frequency is 30 kHz, and peak power is 1 kW; instrumented range is 1500 m.

SK12OR is a special high-frequency (120 kHz, 0.8 kW) research sonar with a 4.5-degree conical beam and pulses as short as 0.1 msec. There is also SL, a very short range (50 kHz, 1 kW, 1500 m) sonar.

◆ SQ Series

The SQ series operates at 27 kHz (SQ-D operates at 24 kHz and uses a fixed streamlined dome). Standard instrumented range is 2500 m (peak power 4 kW, which can be increased to 8 kW), and the beam is 12 × 16 degrees.

The Simrad SQ3-D/SF is in the Swedish *Hugin* class and in the Finnish Navy. SQ3-D/SF operates at 24 kHz (4-kW peak power) and has five range scales (maximum 2500 m). It can search automatically, the array training through 360 degrees in bearing and through 90 degrees in elevation. The usual sonar speed of a *Hugin* is 22 kts.

SQ-D is similar, but the transducer is retractable in a fixed rather than a retractable dome.

◆ Simrad SS105

This scanning sonar for the Norwegian Coast Guard (*Nordkapp* class) provides range and bearing data to the Kongsberg NAVKIS combat control system. The transducer consists of 48 staves and has 48 preformed receiving beams (each 10 degrees wide), using split-beam processing in each beam. Frequency is 14 kHz, and total output power is 15 kW. Transmission modes are ODT and tribeam, and the range scales are 2–16 km. LEDs are used to indicate the target's range and relative/true bearing and own-ship's speed, and there is an 11-inch CRT (PPI). The dome can be fixed or retractable, and the sonar can be used at speeds of up to 25 kts. Retraction, when it is provided, is by an unusual pivoting mechanism.

◆ Simrad SS240 Series

This sonar for small patrol boats, developed from SS304, was announced in 1986. SS240 is an active scanning sonar using preformed beams, with ODT, sector, and RDT modes. Both transmission and reception beams may be tilted from +10 to −20 degrees, and there is also an MCC mode with a broad vertical beam in both transmission and reception. The transducer is cylindrical (diameter 42 cm, weight 300 kg). Operation is at 24 kHz (7-kW pulses, pulse length 2–160 msec, both FM and CW). Instrumented ranges are 200–6000 m in 200-m steps. The PPI display shows echoes in eight colors to indicate various signal strengths. Target data, including range, bearing, course, and speed, are displayed in green; and the operator can select true or relative motion.

SS242 is the fixed-transducer version.

◆ SS 304 (Spira)

This searchlight sonar (operating at 34 kHz) was designed for small fast craft (down to 150 tons, up to 40 kts). The 17 pre-formed receiving beams cover an 85-degree sector with a single ping, and the transducer can be turned and tilted (limits +15 to −105 degrees) to cover the full 360 degrees. The beams are narrow in the vertical, for shallow water. The display uses 6 colors to provide a true-motion picture of the underwater situation. Maximum instrumented range is 4000 m. This sonar is used on board Swedish *Goteborg* class and *Stockholm*, in combination with the French-supplied Salmon.

This sonar was developed from the SM600 fish-finder, which was demonstrated to the Norwegian Navy in December 1982 on board a fishing boat.

◆ ST

ST, announced in 1976, uses a pressurized rubber membrane dome. When the internal pressure is relaxed, the dome lies flush with the hull. The sonar operates at 21 kHz, and peak power is 8 kW. Internal pressure is sufficient to allow the sonar to be used at up to 15 kts. ST3 has a split-beam transducer, for bearing and tilt accuracies of 1 degree. This feature can be switched off, the sonar reverting to ST operation.

◆ SU Series

This series are frigate searchlight sonars. SU-RS, the Stabilized Survey Sonar, has a retractable dome and can operate at over 20 kts. SU-RS trains through 360 deg and can tilt +20 to −110 deg. It is azimuth stabilized and also stabilized against pitch and roll. SU-RS operates on one of four working frequencies (12, 14.5, 18, or 24 kHz) with range information given on a moist- or dry-paper recorder. At 18 kHz the transducer (total radiating area 1600 square cm) produces a 10.5 × 12 degree beam. Peak power is 4 kW (8 kW optional, with a second transmitter). Maximum instrumented range (with a scale divided into six ranges) can be chosen between 3500 and 9000 m, and there is also an audio channel for watch-keeping. The sonar's center frequency is set to one side of the receiving filter band, leaving more room for positive (approaching) than for negative (retiring) doppler. There is also an optional PPI, which can pulse the sonar at very short range (75 or 150 m), out to a maximum of 500 m, for high-resolution survey work.

SU-R is identical but lacks stabilization in pitch and roll.

◆ SX220

This navalized SX200 fish-finder operates at 24 rather than 57 kHz and, therefore, has a larger transducer. The upper part of the CRT is a normal sonar display; the lower part is the output of the sonar acting as a multibeam side-scanner. SX220 became available late in 1983.

UNDERWATER FIRE-CONTROL SYSTEMS

◆ MSI-70U

Kongsberg's Multi-Sensor Interface for the *Kobben*-class submarines, MSI-70U was one of the first systems to employ Kalman filtering to assist in associating data from different sensors to form a fire-control solution.

◆ MSI-90U

Development of Kongsberg's automated submarine command/control system began in 1980, for new Norwegian and German submarines (*Ula* class and Type 211). The initial study was completed in 1982, and a Norwegian-German MoU signed in December 1982. The prototype multifunction display was completed in mid-1983. MSI-90U will form a common-core (federated) combat system, with each partner supplying its own sensors, and will communicate with the consoles via a new BUDOS data bus. The central computer is a KS900F. Because both navies expect to operate in target-rich environments, MSI-90U is designed to support multiple engagements in quick succession. It can track 12 targets simultaneously and can handle 8 weapons.

There are four consoles. Each console is powerful enough to take over nearly the entire load normally borne by the central computer. Each console provides two side-by-side color CRTs. The central command-and-information unit includes a digital scan converter for the submarine's radar and is near the steering console and plotting table on the starboard side of the boat. The other three are on the port side, next to the sonar consoles.

SWEDEN

SONARS

◆ Bottle Cap

A joint SAAB-Simrad very high frequency sonar, for harbor defense, hull mounting, or helicopter dipping, Bottle Cap was announced in 1987. Bottle Cap's square-plane receiving transducer is trainable, and the beam is scanned electronically across the transducer in both elevation and azimuth. The projector is a line array below the receiver. Targets are detected automatically, out to a range of 1000 m, and several can be tracked simultaneously. The transducer can be tilted, and the sonar incorporates a compass. Bottle Cap can be bottom-mounted or used as a dipper. Pulse length is 0.1–10 msec, and the horizontal beamwidth is 1.9 deg. Vertical beamwidth is adjustable (6, 12, 18, or 36 degrees), and angular resolution is 0.225 degrees (mechanical step size is also 0.225 degrees). Scan rate is 15 deg/sec at 200-m range (range scales are 0–5, 10, 20, 50, 100, 200, 500, and 1000 m). For automatic target designation at a range of 500 m, resolutions are about 1 degree, 2 meters, and 1 kt. In the zoom mode at 500 meters, resolution is about 1 meter. In a typical application, the sonar might scan over a 275-degree arc using a 1000-meter range scale, scanning every 20 seconds. Display resolution is 512 × 512 pixels (128 colors). The scan pattern can shift range scale every 7.2 degrees, providing 50 different ranges over 360 degrees, and 100 such patterns can be stored. The range changes are necessary to allow for the irregular contours of a harbor bottom. The very high frequency was apparently chosen in hopes of detecting small submarines.

FIRE-CONTROL SYSTEMS

◆ AI-FCS

AI-FCS is Datasub Communications's Action Information–Fire-Control System for A 17–class submarines. It uses two identical consoles, each of which can show any of four plots: contact-evaluation plot (CEP), operational plot (OP), tactical plot (TP), and fire-control plot (FCP). CEP is used mainly when TMA would be unsuitable, e.g., when a contact can be detected only sporadically, or at very long range. Collected information is shown in time-bearing (waterfall) form, covering all 360 degrees and up to two hours vertically. The OP (in effect, a navigational plot) is used during transit to the patrol area. OP shows features such as own and enemy minefields, mission information, coastal radars (with their parameters), the route, and the operational area itself. The OP can show 50 internally generated points, ten target channels for TMA, up to 240 plots received externally by data link, and 32 ESM emitters or emitter modes. Normally the TP is used for TMA, while the submarine is preparing to attack; up to ten targets can be analyzed simultaneously. In the TP, own-ship is at the center, and there are no navigational displays, although eight reference points can be used to show, e.g., the boundaries of the patrol area. Up to 50 internally generated plots can be shown, and also a list of which sensor is tracking which target. For longer ranges, the OP is better because it shows chart information and true motion. Finally, the FCP is optimized for rapid automatic multiple engagements, controlling up to 12 torpedoes simultaneously. It normally shows relative motion (own-ship at center), but it can be centered on a torpedo. Typically one console is used as command station (showing CEP or OP or TP), and one is fire-control station.

The computer's storage capacity is 512K (32-bit words), with a storage cycle time of 750 nanosec (clock speed 1.3 MHz) and an average execution time of 2.5 microsec.

A reduced form of this system has been installed in Swedish *Sjoormen*-class submarines during their mid-life refits.

◆ NEDPS

Nacken Electronic Data Processing System, manufactured by Datasaab, is the computer-driven combat system of the Swedish *Nacken*-class submarines. Requirements were formulated in 1966–67; they included passive fire control (by target-motion analysis, which the Swedes call target-factor calculation, or TFC) on several targets simultaneously. That capability clearly required a computer. The same computer could also be used for other shipboard tasks, such as machinery control and depth-keeping, and the system evolved from weapons and sensor control to overall submarine control. A simulator, ordered in 1970, was used in 1971–74 to test and develop the requisite software. The system is built around two Censor 932 64-kbyte computers, feeding a pair of consoles with CRTs: a tactical plot (TP) and a fire-control plot (FCP). Between them is mounted a torpedo status board (the torpedo fire-control display, or FCD), and there is also an alphanumeric display, the general communication unit (GCU), manned by the ship's electronics officer. The consoles are equipped with keyboards and trackballs. Calculated target tracks are displayed on the TP, which replaces the conventional paper plot; it can also display the signal-to-noise ratios of various targets being tracked. The system can carry up to 50 targets, and it can automatically provide simultaneous target-motion analysis (for fire control) for up to ten of them. Up to twelve torpedoes can be controlled simultaneously.

This system is also used in the *Vastergotland* class.

◆ TORCI

PEAB's torpedo fire-control system for surface ships uses a search radar. TORCI can engage two targets simultaneously with long-range wire-guided torpedoes.

USSR

The NATO reporting designations listed below were published in 1986, and many are presumably no more than older systems renamed. Because the only list thus far published associates sonar code names only with ships or classes, some of the identifications below may be incorrect. No detailed characteristics of modern Soviet sonars have been published. Moreover, this list may well be incomplete. For example, early Whiskey- and Zulu-class submarines probably had wartime-developed HF passive arrays (MARS-12) that seem not to have received postwar code names. The first modern sonars, Feniks and Hercules, appeared only in 1958.

During and immediately after World War II, the Soviets had access to British and U.S. high-frequency searchlight sonars and to German wartime surface-ship and submarine sonars, including the low-frequency arrays that were developed further in Britain and in the United States. Presumably, the parallel development of Pegas and Tamir reflects parallel work along both U.K./U.S. and German lines for surface ships; it is interesting that the Soviet equivalent of the passive array for big submarines (presumably Trout Cheek) apparently took so long to develop.

No code designations for Soviet helicopter dipping sonars have been published. There are probably at least two types, a high-frequency unit in Hormones (see Rat Tail) and one medium-frequency type in, presumably, Helix and Haze (see Foal Tail/Lamb Tail). There is no published indication of whether these dipping units are searchlights or scanning sonars (sector or omnidirectional).

In 1989, the U.S. Director of Naval Intelligence reported that the Soviets had short-range fixed acoustic sensors in the Northern Fleet operating area, and longer-range planar arrays (code-named Cluster Lance) in the Far East, where geography is more favorable to such devices. Presumably, the devices in Northern Fleet waters are, in effect, acoustic fences that indicate that a submarine has actually passed through them. Such fences could be used to cue nearby aircraft or other ASW platforms and could form part of bastion defenses. The sensors would probably use reliable acoustic path propagation and thus could function even in relatively shallow water. The DNI also stated that the Soviets were testing a towed surveillance array similar in concept to the U.S. SURTASS, and that within a few years they were expected to deploy surveillance platforms equipped with the new array.

None of these systems is likely to be particularly effective. The current (1989) argument within the U.S. defense community is that submarines such as Akula can defeat U.S. long-range passive systems such as SOSUS. SOSUS is likely to be more sophisticated than the Soviet systems, and U.S. submarines are quieter than current Soviet types, including even Akula.

◆ Buck Toe

See Pegas below.

◆ Bull Horn

The hull sonar of the *Sovremennyy* and of the Modified Kashin class is presumably a smaller and less effective equivalent to the bow-mounted Bull Nose of the Krivaks, as these former ships require only a self-defense capability. The sonar is associated with 21-in (533-mm) homing torpedoes. Bull Horn is probably, therefore, broadly comparable to the U.S. SQS-56. Some ships have Bull Nose instead.

◆ Bull Nose

This medium-frequency bow sonar is associated with SS-N-14 in the Krivak, Kara, and Kresta-II classes, and with ship-launched ASW torpedoes in the Kanin, *Sovremennyy*, and *Slava* classes. Bull Nose is also the sonar installed on board Grisha. Bull Nose is probably broadly comparable to SQS-23. The associated VDS is Mare Tail or Elk Tail. Bull Nose is probably the 7.5-kHz sonar reported in 1960, using a 7500-yard keying interval (corresponding to its expected maximum range). Bull Nose succeeded Wolf Paw (Hercules) and, presumably, was substantially improved before it could be used to direct SS-N-14.

◆ Elk Tail

Variable-depth sonar for the Grisha class, Elk Tail is associated with the Bull Nose hull sonar. The associated ASW weapon is a 533-mm (21-in) homing torpedo or an RBU-6000.

◆ Feniks (Pike Jaw)

Feniks is the standard Soviet diesel-electric attack (searchlight) sonar of the past. Feniks (Phoenix) is apparently the Soviet name. It first appeared in 1956 and was, typically, combined with Tamir-5L onboard submarines. Feniks is in a dome atop the bow of a submarine. Early examples showed only a single dome. In later units, a narrower stalk, Fez, is visible above the main dome.

Feniks is probably the same as Pike Jaw. At least some of the submarines equipped with Pike Jaw have keel sonars; the standard arrangement may well be a pair of transducers, top and keel. The keel sonar is needed to protect the submarine when it runs on the surface. That protection was important for early Soviet missile-firing submarines, which had to fire while surfaced. Moreover, those submarines firing the antiship version of SS-N-3 had to remain on the surface to provide mid-course guidance.

A Foxtrot displays Trout Cheek, Feniks, and Fez, and also a row of hydrophones in the sail proper, Fin Teeth, which ONI assumed was a sonar-intercept system. The extended mast is for radio. (U.S. Navy)

◆ Fez

Fez is the high-frequency system found in a tall narrow dome atop the Feniks domes on Soviet submarines. Fez is almost certainly an underwater telephone.

◆ Foal Tail/Lamb Tail

These Mirka-class variable-depth sonars are associated with Bull Horn and Wolf Paw hull sonars and with the Steer Hide sonar. The VDS of Mirka-II–class corvettes is a helicopter dipping sonar rather than a towed body; the connection, if any, with Rat Tail is not clear. It seems likely that the dipping sonar associated with Wolf Paw matches Rat Tail, and that the sonar associated with the medium-frequency Bull Horn is a later medium-frequency type, presumably carried by the later Helix or Haze helicopters.

Helicopter-type dipping sonar deployed from a Mirka-II–class frigate. (U.S. Naval Institute)

◆ Hercules (Wolf Paw)

This standard Soviet sonar for surface ships and submarines appeared in 1957. It operated at high frequency and probably introduced scanning technology to Soviet practice; thus, Hercules was presumably roughly comparable to the U.S. QHB or SQS-10 family. Hercules, apparently the Soviet name, survives on board Soviet-supplied Foxtrots (e.g., to Libya). The standard combination of the late 1950s (and on export units) is a Hercules search sonar plus a Feniks attack sonar. Hercules was also used as a sonar for surface ships, e.g., on board Petyas exported to India. The NATO Wolf Paw code name applies only to the surface-ship version.

Soviet Foxtrot-class submarines show a bulbous sonar bow, reportedly containing Hercules. Given the probable dimensions of this sonar, it seems likely that the bulb contains an active transducer inside a larger-diameter medium-frequency passive transducer, like the U.S. BQR-2/BQS-4 combination. Foxtrots generally also have a sonar in their sails, indicated by the series of bright metal windows about halfway up.

Hercules was the standard Soviet hull sonar of the early 1960s, e.g., on board *Kynda*-class missile cruisers (as built) and some *Sverdlovs* (replacing Stag Hoof), and on board Kashin- and earlier class destroyers, replacing Buck Toe. Wolf Paw is the sole sonar on board Poti-class corvettes.

◆ Horse Jaw

A large low-frequency hull sonar, in the *Kirov* and *Udaloy* classes, Horse Jaw is associated with the SS-N-14 missile and with the Horse Tail variable-depth sonar.

◆ Horse Tail

This variable-depth sonar is associated with the low-frequency Horse Jaw hull sonar. Unlike earlier Soviet VDS fish, this one is saucer-shaped. Horse Tail operates at low frequency.

◆ Mare Tail

The variable-depth sonar, the first in Soviet service, is associated with the Moose Jaw hull sonar in the *Moskva* and *Kiev* classes, and with Bull Nose in frigates and destroyers. Mare Tail is a medium-frequency type, and it was tested in 1966 onboard a Petya-I type trials ship.

Variable-depth sonar "fish" of a Krivak-class frigate. (U.S. Naval Institute)

◆ Moose Jaw

This enormous low-frequency hull sonar was first installed on board the *Moskva*. Moose Jaw is also on board the *Kiev*. In the *Moskva*, Moose Jaw is probably associated with the FRAS-1 stand-off ASW rocket and, presumably, was intended to achieve convergence-zone capability. In the *Kiev*, Moose Jaw is, presumably, associated with SS-N-14. The successor sonar in the *Kirov* is Horse Jaw. The associated variable-depth sonar is Mare Tail.

◆ Pegas (Buck Toe)

The successor to Tamir, Pegas was installed on board Soviet surface combatants from the Riga class up from 1955 onward. This searchlight sonar is probably code-named Buck Toe. In larger ships it was succeeded by the Hercules scanning sonar. Compared to Tamir, Pegas was credited with better bearing accuracy and with a maximum active range of about 5000 yards. Pegas could maintain passive contact on a cavitating submarine out to about 12,000 yds and could determine a target's depth (which was essential for using the new ballistic ASW rocket launchers then coming into service). Maximum listening speed was about 20 kts, and the sonar could automatically pass its data to the approach-and-attack computer.

◆ Perch Gill

This sonar appears mainly on board Whiskey- and Zulu-class submarines, some of which lack Pike Jaw (Feniks). Perch Gill, a higher-frequency searchlight attack sonar, is probably a submarine version of Tamir, the predecessor of Feniks.

◆ Pike Jaw

See Feniks above.

◆ Rat Tail

A variable-depth sonar for Petya-class corvettes, Rat Tail is associated with the Wolf Paw high-frequency hull sonar. Rat Tail is a helicopter-type dipping sonar, rather than a towed body, located in a temporary installation amidships. Presumably, the sonar is that of the Hormone helicopter. The relationship with Lamb Tail/Foal Tail is not clear.

The dipping sonar of the Hormone-A helicopter operates at 14–16 kHz, with a maximum range of 4000–6000 yds.

◆ Sail Plates

Presumably, Sail Plates is the array of small transducers around the sail of Foxtrot and some later classes of Soviet submarines.

When first observed, these transducers were identified as torpedo-warning devices (intercept receivers).

◆ Seal Skin

This sonar appears only on board Romeo-class diesel-electric submarines and Echo-I–class nuclear attack submarines (ex–strategic-cruise-missile submarines).

◆ Shark Fin

This sonar array, reportedly medium frequency for torpedo fire control, is found in the sails of many Soviet nuclear submarines. Typically, Shark Fin is combined with Shark Teeth; although in Echo-II Shark Fin is combined instead with Pike Jaw, Trout Cheek, and Perch Gill. Tango, which is a contemporary of this generation of nuclear submarines, is also equipped with Shark Fin/Shark Teeth.

Shark Fin first appeared on board Echo-II– and Charlie-class missile submarines. Presumably, it is required to control long-range antiship weapons, such as nuclear torpedoes and the SS-N-7 missiles of the Charlie.

◆ Shark Teeth

This low-frequency sonar bow array is found in many Soviet nuclear submarines. Compared to Trout Cheek, Shark Teeth is much more completely faired into the curving bow of the submarine. In a November-class nuclear submarine, Shark Teeth is combined with Sail Plate and Pike Jaw, both of the latter presumably faired into the sail. This system is probably associated with the much longer attack range provided by the first Soviet nuclear torpedoes, which, presumably, were designed in tandem with the November class. The submarines had sufficient speed to get into position to attack U.S. aircraft carriers, and the torpedo had sufficient lethal radius to make such attacks profitable even without very precise targeting data. Presumably, November was equipped with a shorter-range attack sonar, Pike Jaw, so that the submarine could also use short-range straight- or pattern-running antiship torpedoes. Pike Jaw, in turn, lacked the range to control the much longer range antiship homing torpedoes of the 1960s; hence the advent of Shark Fin.

◆ Steer Hide

This variable-depth sonar is found in the *Kiev*, *Kashin*-II, *Sovremmennyy*, and at least one *Mirka*-class corvette.

◆ Tamir (Stag Hoof and Stag Ear)

This Soviet sonar was a copy of British wartime searchlight sets. It operated above 24 kHz. Tamir-5N (Stag Hoof) was introduced in 1947–48 and appeared on board large surface ships up through the *Sverdlovs*. Tamir-5L, for submarines, was introduced in 1950, followed by Tamir-11 and -11M (Stag Ear) in 1952. Tamir-5N was the sonar originally carried by *Skoryy*-class destroyers. In many cases it was replaced by an improved searchlight, Pegas. Stag Ear remains in service on board many smaller combatants, such as minesweepers.

◆ Trout Cheek

This sonar is presumably the large passive array in the bows of Soviet diesel submarines from the Foxtrots on. The prototype was tested on board a pair of Whiskey-class submarines about 1958. Trout Cheek probably corresponds very broadly to the U.S. BQR-2, i.e., by reflecting the use of German wartime low-frequency array technology. When this array first appeared, the U.S. interpretation was that the Soviets had adopted the U.S. SSK (antisubmarine submarine) mission, for which the U.S. Navy had adopted BQR-2 in the first place.

◆ Victor Sonar (No Code Name Known)

Soviet Victor-class submarines have a large chin sonar, first revealed publicly when a Victor-I suffered severe bow damage in a collision in the Straits of Gibraltar. Presumably, this sonar is associated with the SS-N-15 weapon, just as the big U.S. spherical bow sonar, BQS-6, is associated with SUBROC. Presumably, too, the Soviets obtained at least some details of the U.S. sonar when the Soviets obtained details of the SUBROC system (from which they developed SS-N-15). In contrast to the U.S. system, the Soviet sonar cannot easily exploit sonar propagation paths above the submarine, e.g., the bounce path off the surface. That limitation may mean that the Soviets do not expect to fire SS-N-15 at any great depth, i.e., at any depth at which such paths would be worthwhile.

This Victor-class submarine collided with a merchant ship near the Straits of Gibraltar in October 1985. Under emergency repair, she shows the upper line of transducers of her chin sonar (just at the waterline), as well as her characteristic torpedo tube arrangement: two above, four below. (U.S. Navy)

♦ **Wolf Paw**

See Hercules above.

UNITED KINGDOM

SONARS

♦ **Type 162 and 162M**

"Cockchafer" bottom-profile sonars detect bottomed submarines. Type 162 sweeps a narrow beam across the seabed and detects the shadow of an object. Three quartz-strip transducers, each producing a fan beam, are mounted horizontally, flush with the hull near the bow: one on the keel and one on either side, tilted down at a 25-degree angle. The shadow is shown on a conventional chemical range recorder. Frequency is 50 kHz. Range scales are 300 and 600 yards (Type 162M has a third, 1200-yard scale). The three fan beams are about 3 × 40 degrees, and range accuracy is better than 2 percent.

Cockchafer entered service in 1948. In 1951 it successfully located the wreck of the submarine *Affray*. Type 162 remains in British (and foreign) service and is currently manufactured by Kelvin-Hughes.

SQS-501 is the Canadian version of this sonar.

♦ **Type 164B**

Type 164 was the first postwar British production sonar, based on the experimental 160X tested in HMS *Scorpion*. 164 combined two transducers on separate shafts in a 100-inch dome: a 144 for passive listening and, aft, a second 144 with Q2 attachment (secondary beam tilted downward) for attack and Squid control. The former could rotate rapidly to give all-around coverage on a PPI. In Type 164 the passive set (144) was replaced by 174, and the range and bearing recorders and captain's and helmsman's bearing indicators were improved. A "ship's component mechanism" removes from the range and bearing recorders the effects of the attacker's movement across the tar-

get's track, so that correct bearing can be passed to the Squid ASW mortar. That mechanism also assisted in maintaining contact with a fast submarine. Frequency range is 14–22 kHz. Depth determination limit is 1500 ft. Range scales (for search) are 1.5 and 3 kyds.

This sonar entered British service in 1950 and currently equips Chilean *Almirante Williams*–class destroyers.

♦ **Type 170B**

This set was the "four square" attack sonar associated with the Limbo mortar. The transducer was square, arranged as a diamond, the four beams being compared to keep the sonar pointing at the target both in bearing and in elevation. Type 170 was conceived as part of an automated underwater fire-control system, analogous to an automatic tracking radar. The transducer was stabilized, and depth settings for fire control were derived from the tilt angle. Frequency was about 15 kHz.

Production of Type 170 began in 1952. The modified 170B provided information for acoustic torpedoes and allowed visual and radar information to be used for Limbo control (to allow detection of a shallow submarine either just submerging or showing a periscope). 170 entered production in June 1954. Type 170B remains in service on board British and ex-British *Leander*-class frigates.

A solid-state version, Type 170M, entered service in 1974. Ships already fitted with Type 170 could be converted to 170M during their normal refits, as the transducer was not changed.

A version of this sonar, Type 171, was planned for submarines, but it was canceled.

♦ **Type 174**

Type 174 is the secondary listening set for Types 164 and 170, in British destroyers and frigates.

♦ **Type 177**

This set was the first British scanning sonar. Unlike U.S. cylindrical-transducer types, 177 used a flat transducer to scan a sector. This use was practical because the British transducer scanned electrically rather than mechanically, using electronic delay networks. In effect, then, 177 used preformed beams similar to those of the wartime German GHG (which in turn was the basis of the U.S. postwar BQR-2).

Frequency was 7.5 kHz, to achieve a range of 8,000–10,000 yards. The sector-scanning solution was chosen in preference to a large cylindrical transducer or a long keel array. The transducer was about 4 ft square, and it produced 10-degree beams over a 40-degree sector. Transmission consisted of five 150-msec pulses, followed by five 20-msec pulses at a second frequency, and then a 5-msec pulse (for short range and high definition) at a third frequency. In each case, it appears that the five pulses covered a 50-degree sector in five beams. This sequence was processed to give four channels to cover the 40 degrees, and the receiver consisted of sixteen channels (4 × 4 beams). Range scales were 5, 10, and 20 kyds. Each channel fed a separate recording stylus, as well as a channel for the head set.

Type 177 was accepted for service in 1957, the first tests having been conducted in 1951 using a scaled-up Type 170 transducer. This sonar was roughly comparable to the U.S. SQS-4 series. No longer in Royal Navy service, Type 177 survives on board some ex-British ships.

♦ **Type 181**

The towed asdic repeater target (TART) responds to all sonar frequencies. TART simulates a real sonar reflection. Since its position is known (it is towed), it can be used to compare a given sonar's measurement of range with actual range. Presumably TART's signals show the appropriate doppler shifts, and it can, therefore, be used to calibrate the doppler features of sonars, since its own speed through the water (on the end of a towing cable) is known and is measurable. In theory, TART might decoy an active-pinger torpedo seeker. However, antiship torpedoes generally use passive seekers. The TART towed body generally resembles that of the Type 182 decoy. The Graseby G 733 SLUTT (Ship-Launched Underwater Transponder Target) would seem to be an expendable version of TART.

◆ Type 182

See countermeasures below.

◆ Type 183

This emergency underwater telephone operates at 8–9 kHz. Range is about 1000 yards. Type 183P was a portable version.

◆ Type 184 and 184M/Graseby G750

Type 184 was the first operational British sonar to use a cylindrical transducer, in this case 4 ft in diameter and 46 in high, with 32 staves. Operating frequency is 7.5 kHz; Type 184 originally used Type 177 transducers. The display is a pair of CRTs, one for doppler and one a PPI. There is also a separate torpedo-warning CRT display. Two targets can be marked and automatically tracked simultaneously on the PPI. The doppler display uses four beams forming a 45-degree searchlight arc for active search; target doppler can be measured for speeds up to 40 kts. The passive CRT shows a 360-degree arc, and an audio beam can be trained to any selected bearing. In 1985 Graseby was reportedly supplying a modification kit that replaced the existing eight-sector display with a sixteen-sector display, for greater accuracy. Transmission is at dual frequencies. The dome, which can accommodate Type 177 as an alternative, is 157.25 in long, 64 in in maximum width, and 61 in deep. It is retractable.

The Graseby G750 is an export version of the solid-state Type 184M, providing data directly to a fire-control computer. As of 1985, nine had been exported, six to India and three to New Zealand. G750 could be supplied in both LF/MF and MF/HF versions, in each case with a 32-stave array.

By 1976 Graseby was advertising G1750, an improved solid-state version with such features as autotracking. G1768 was a smaller-ship version, presumably operating at higher frequency but with a similar architecture.

◆ Type 185/Graseby G1732

An underwater telephone (8–9 kHz), the Graseby G1732, advertised about 1976, is a modernized version for high-speed data transmission. This system may have been associated with British work on having nuclear submarines provide direct support to surface ships, the submarine acting, in effect, as a variable-depth sonar and passing its data to a nearby surface ship. Reportedly, British experiments using HMS *Dreadnought* preceded U.S. interest in the direct-support mission.

Type 185 was superseded by Type 2008.

◆ Type 186

This passive medium-frequency sonar for submarines ("Knout"), introduced in 1956, was an adapted German GHG. It was, therefore, analogous to the U.S. BQR-2. One pair of arrays was on each side of the submarine, operating at about 1 kHz. Targets were sought by circling at slow speed or by following a sinuous course. With beam steering, this system became Type 2007.

◆ Type 187

An active-passive sonar for submarines (low to medium frequency), Type 187 is an adapted Type 718, with an added low-power mine-detection sonar. The sonar consists of a 5-ft-wide flat transducer rotated mechanically inside a streamlined dome with a maximum diameter of 72 inches (length 192 inches, height 57.5 inches). Using split-beam techniques, this system can achieve a bearing accuracy of about half a degree.

In the Canadian SOUP refit program, the mechanically trained transducer head was replaced by a phased array.

Type 187 trainable sonar transducer with its sonar dome removed, on board a British *Oberon*-class submarine, 1988. The individual spot transducers can just be distinguished; the sonar is trained broadside. (A. Wetback)

◆ Type 189

Type 189 is a cavitation indicator.

◆ Type 193

See the Mine Warfare section under countermeasures.

◆ Type 195/2069

The standard British helicopter dipping sonar was manufactured by Plessey. Type 195 entered service in 1966 and was exported to Australia, Argentina, Canada, Egypt, India, the Netherlands, and Pakistan. Some were modernized in the mid-1970s, and production ended late in 1985, the final version being 195M. This sonar was a building block of Plessey's PMS 26 and 27.

The flat sector-scanning 45-lb transducer (120-lb fish) was on an 800-ft cable, covering a 90-degree sector before having to be turned. On-board electronics dead reckoned between dips so that the helicopter could maintain contact as it approached its target. A doppler display was used for initial detection. The fish included a BT to measure the sound-velocity profile. Maximum instrumented range was 8000 yds.

Type 2069 is an upgraded 195M, capable of operating at a greater depth and of being integrated with the AQS-902 acoustic processor. The successor to Type 195 is tentatively designated Type 2095.

◆ Type 197

This sonar-intercept gear (French Velox system) consisted of a hydrophone atop the sail. Claimed accuracy was a few degrees, but in service this set could reportedly determine the direction of an active sonar transmission only to within a 90-degree quadrant.

◆ Type 199

A variable-depth sonar, Type 199 is the British version of the Canadian SQS-504. The Canadian sonar was based on Type 170 in a towed version of the British 100-inch dome. Development began in 1956, the first prototype being completed in 1961. Type 199 entered Canadian service in 1962. Although the Admiralty bought Type 199 in 1960, it did not enter British service until 1968; and all units were gone by the late 1970s. Type 199 is now used by the Indian Navy, on board three *Leander*-class frigates.

◆ Type 718

This postwar low-frequency (2.5 kHz for slow submarine speed, 10 kHz for high submarine speed) hydrophone is designed to obtain accurate bearings. Typically mounted topside, it is a split-beam. See also Type 187 above.

◆ Type 719

This postwar azimuth scanning hydrophone for submarines was designed for torpedo detection. Type 719 consisted of a hydrophone and a parabolic reflector. Originally to have been mounted in the keel, Type 719 was eventually installed in submarine sails, pointing aft. It was introduced in the postwar streamlined "T" and *Porpoise* classes.

◆ Type 2001

This British first-generation bow sonar for nuclear submarines was developed by Plessey. Type 2001 introduced conformal-array techniques. It was characterized as a bottom-bounce (rather than convergence-zone) set. Type 2001 was succeeded by Type 2020.

◆ Type 2002

Type 2002 was a low-frequency long-range sonar, presumably abortive.

◆ Type 2003

This bottom-bounce sonar was possibly the large array tested on board HMS *Matapan* in the late 1960s. The British did not proceed with development of this sonar.

◆ Type 2004

Type 2004 is a submarine hull-mounted sound velocity meter, for sonar performance prediction. Such predictors are used to help sonar operatives choose optimum operating modes. They also help in the interpretation of sonar data, since the predictor can estimate ray paths.

◆ Type 2005

Type 2005 is the French DUUX 2A passive range-finder.

◆ Type 2006

Type 2006 is the U.S. AN/BQQ-3 LOFAR detector/classifier (see U.S. sonars below).

◆ Type 2007

This low-frequency passive flank array for submarines is a replacement for Type 186. Type 186 used fixed beams, but 2007 can steer them electronically. It operates at 1–3 kHz and is used for initial detection, bearing resolution, and limited TMA. This system can also use a towed array, and existing 2007s are being converted to towed-array use. 2007 is otherwise now leaving service.

The requirement was stated in the late 1960s, and the array was developed by British Aerospace; the first unit entered service in 1971. Later units were manufactured by Graseby Dynamics. Type 2007 was bought for Australian, Brazilian, Canadian, and Chilean *Oberon*s. The addition of a TAPS processor converts Type 2007AA to Type 2007AC, with greater sensitivity and better target discrimination.

When the submarine is moving so fast that noise drowns out the flank array, the Type 2007 display can be connected to the towed array.

◆ Type 2008

This high-frequency underwater telephone replaces Type 185. This set is also used as a short-range passive sonar. Many navies apparently use their underwater telephones this way, since they provide wide-band omnidirectional reception.

◆ Type 2009

Type 2009 is an underwater IFF and multitone simplex communications set (UARS, underwater acoustic recognition, IFF).

◆ Type 2010

Type 2010, also named ACUTE, is an underwater RATT teletype.

◆ Type 2011

Type 2011 is a noise target.

◆ Type 2012

Type 2012 is a passive sonar-classification set, presumably replacing 2006.

◆ Type 2013

Type 2013 is a bathythermograph.

◆ Type 2014

An Acoustic Ray Trace Indicator (ARTI, sonar ray path predictor), this set was intended to guide ships using variable-depth sonars (Types 195 and 199) in setting sonar depth. Type 2014 is now obsolete.

◆ Type 2015

Type 2015 is an expendable bathythermograph (XBT).

◆ Type 2016/2020/2028

Type 2016, a medium-frequency hull sonar introduced in the Type 22–class frigates, was the first British sonar with substantial computer assistance. In the Falklands 2016 was credited with the ability to overcome multiple reflections, and thus to distinguish an Argentine submarine on the bottom. The Type 184 equipping other British frigates seemed to have no such capability. On the other hand, 2016 was criticized for its lack of direct output, in the form of headphones, and thus presumably for its poor passive performance.

The replacement for 177 and 184M, Type 2016 uses two transmitters operating at 5.5, 6.5, and 7.5 kHz; the broad variation in frequency helps avoid intership interference. Operating modes are ODT (omnidirectional transmission) and SDT (steered directional transmission). Capabilities include automatic target detection and tracking. There are three side-by-side displays: from left to right they are classification/tracking (doppler B-scan as well as A-scan for target details); surveillance (PPI); and passive (all-around torpedo warning). There is also an auxiliary display on which data can be logged, and such information as bottom conditions and sound speed displayed. Normally the operator sits at the center (surveillance) PPI, supported when necessary by an operator at the left-hand (tracking) display.

Type 2016 was manufactured by Plessey, although Ferranti is responsible for signal processing (which uses an FM 1600B computer). Ferranti began research into computer-aided sonar in 1967, working with the Admiralty Underwater Weapons Establishment (AUWE): the objective was to improve the operator's detection performance and the quality of sonar data passed to the computer combat system. Work on the associated sonar began in 1971, a prototype running sea trials on board HMS *Matapan* in 1971–76. An operational prototype was tested in 1978 on board HMS *Broadsword*. A total of 34 were built for Type-22 and Batch-3 *Leander*-class frigates, for later Type-42 destroyers, and for the *Invincible*-class aircraft carriers. 2016 is to replace Type 184 on board retrofitted Type-42 destroyers. Type 2016 in turn will be replaced by Type 2050. Three of four Type-42 Batch-3 destroyers were completed with 2016, and it has now been back-fitted in two Batch-1/2 ships.

Type 2020, a second-generation sonar for nuclear attack submarines, is the submarine version of Type 2016. 2020 is in the *Trafalgar* class, replacing Type 2001. 2020 uses steered preformed beams (DIMUS). Reportedly, active frequencies are 5.5–5.7 kHz, and passive operation is at 2–16 kHz. Type 2020 is designed primarily for passive detection, including the use of bottom-bounce and convergence-zone modes. Features include automatic tracking for reduced workload. There is a manual override.

The upgraded version of Type 2020 is designated MODEX. It uses two Ferranti universal raster-scan (i.e., television-like) displays for both passive and active data, replacing the earlier cursive PPIs. Reportedly the universal screens make for faster operator reactions during close contact or in torpedo evasion. The original hard-copy (paper) displays are retained for mission analysis. In addition, plasma touch-panel displays replace the earlier keyboards.

The Type 2020 requirement, for *Trafalgar* class, was stated in 1976–77, Plessey receiving a contract in 1977. 2020 was tested in 1981/82, the first production delivery following in October 1982 for HMS *Tireless.*

Type 2028 was a smaller version of 2016 but was not procured.

♦ Type 2017

Type 2017 was a spectral analyzer (now obsolete).

♦ Type 2018

Type 2018 is a digital spectral analyzer.

♦ Type 2019 (PARIS)

This sonar intercept gear was developed under the British/French/Dutch PARIS (Passive/Active Range-and-Intercept Sonar) program. 2019 covers up to 360 degrees at 2–14 kHz. It is installed in modern submarines, including *Upholder* class (in which an active pinger is added). The project began in 1965, a prototype being built in 1968–69. Thomson-CSF was prime contractor. The Royal Navy placed its contract in 1973, testing a prototype in 1974–75 and ordering its first sets in 1977.

In *Trafalgar*-class submarines, Type 2019 is located forward of the sail, in a small sonar dome on deck.

♦ Type 2021

Type 2021 is an expendable bathythermograph (XBT).

♦ Type 2022

Type 2022 is an acoustic beacon.

♦ Type 2023

This towed array for ballistic missile submarines is based on the U.S. BQR-15. 2023 uses a British array and U.S./British electronics and is retrievable, the array being stowed in the ballast tankage. The requirement was stated in the late 1960s, Plessey receiving the R&D contract early in the 1970s, roughly simultaneously with 2024. Arrays were installed during major overhauls. In the early 1980s TAPS, a towed-array broad-band processing system, was added. Reportedly it reduces the stern null, i.e, allows the sonar to form narrower beams. This array also has a three-dimensional heading-reference sensor (by Ameeco).

Reportedly Type 2062 was developed as a replacement, the cost of BQR-15 wet-end spares proving very high.

♦ Type 2024

A clip-on towed array for nuclear attack submarines, 2024 is installed on board *Valiant-* and *Swiftsure-* class submarines and on board the first two *Trafalgars*. 2024 in turn is being replaced by Type 2026. Existing arrays are being fitted with the new broad-band TAPS processor. Because 2024 is a clip-on array, at least one has been lost to underwater obstructions. In the Falklands War, HMS *Conqueror* reportedly used her array to track the Argentine cruiser *Belgrano* from beyond the horizon, keeping station for 2½ days.

The contract was let in 1970, followed by preprototype tests in 1974 and service in 1975.

♦ Type 2025

Type 2025 is an expendable bathythermograph (XBT).

♦ Type 2026

This British/Dutch second-generation towed array for attack submarines uses a stronger cable, more sensitive hydrophones, and improved reception. 2026 has a new broad-band low-frequency processor and an updated narrow-band processor. A photograph of the display shows three large CRTs, a configuration that suggests that three octaves are covered. Type 2026 was developed in tandem with 2031(I) to replace Type 2024. As of 1986, five British and five Dutch arrays were on order.

Marconi Underwater Systems received the R&D contract for this array in 1977–78, the Royal Navy specifying a clip-on with a stronger array. 2026 was tested in 1983–85. Meanwhile the Royal Netherlands Navy negotiated for five (concluded late 1985). The array was approved for service use early in 1986. Type 2026 entered British service in 1987.

Type 2026 normally employs a clip-on array attached to the port stern plane. However, recently HMS *Turbulent* tested a reelable array, the winch for which was housed in a hump visible aft, above the waterline. Presumably the array itself was stowed in the narrow space between pressure and outer hulls. The Type 2026 processor can be used to classify signals from the intercept sonar and the Type 2008 underwater telephone.

Reportedly the Dutch version, for the *Walrus* class, uses a Signaal display processor, a Marconi beam-former, and an Ameeco wet end.

This sonar is described officially as Integrated Sonar Phase I.

♦ Type 2027

The acoustic processor for Type 2020, 2027 is a prototype passive-ranging sonar.

♦ Type 2029

Type 2029 is automatic digital sonar-intercept gear.

♦ Type 2030

Type 2030 is classification equipment: Spectral Dynamics's two-channel spectrum analyzer with waterfall display (U.S. AN/BQR-22).

♦ Type 2031

Type 2031 is the British towed-array sonar for surface ships. Unlike the U.S. Navy, the Royal Navy uses its towed-array frigates not only tactically but also for surveillance; the RN, therefore, requires greater ranges, achieved by a combination of lower frequency (presumably longer arrays) and more processing. There are two versions: 2031(I) for four frigates operates at low speed and has relatively simple processing; 2031Z, for Type-22 frigates (Batches 2 and 3) operates at a higher tow speed. All combine broad- and narrow-band processing.

Reportedly 2031 is a five-octave system. Type 2031Z incorporates the newer (ca. 1983) Curtis processing architecture, which drastically cuts computer requirements. The Curtis processor is a very fast special-purpose digital computer with a fixed program and over 100 Mbytes of memory. In 1987 it was reported that 2031 is normally trailed more than 1600 m astern, at speeds of 8–10 kts down to 2–3 kts; reported range is "over 100 nm," which presumably means at least three convergence zones (105 nm in the Norwegian Sea).

The initial R&D contract was awarded to GEC Avionics in 1971/2, followed by trials on board HMS *Matapan* and *Lowestoft* in 1978/81, four 2031(I) being installed on board modified *Leanders* in 1982. A fifth was built as a spare. Thirteen 2031Z were purchased.

The associated processor was the GEC Avionics JASOND (1976), the first British digital 360-degree towed-array processor. It was first tested on board a British submarine. JASOND was based on the earlier Sonalyzer (1974), used as a four-channel sonobuoy mission replay unit.

Type 2031Z reportedly embodies a new (Curtis-architecture) processor, developed by AUWE, which drastically reduces weight (by 60 percent) and power requirement (by 80 percent) and is also much less expensive than its predecessors. The equivalent submarine sonar is Type 2046.

♦ Type 2032

This add-on package to extend the capability of a submarine's bow sonar includes a special transducer and beam-former; 2032 complements Type 2020.

◆ Type 2034/2053/Sonar 3000 PLUS

Waverly's dual (left- and right-hand arrays) sidescan sonar has been in British service since 1976. The current version of the towed body ("towfish") is Mk 3. Sonar frequency is 110 kHz (100-msec pulse), and range scales are 75, 150, and 300 m (PRFs of 10, 5, and 2.5 pps). Over 50 units are in current use by the RN Hydrographic Service.

Sonar 3000 PLUS is a family of side-scan devices developed from 2034, and Sonar 3010 has been proposed as a mine locator (analogous to the U.S. Klein Mk 24; see the Mine Warfare section). Sonar 3010 adds a higher-frequency (300-kHz) mode for short range and high precision (37.5-m scale) and can mark a target.

Type 2053 is the British designation for Sonar 3000.

◆ Type 2040

This sonar for new British diesel submarines (*Upholder* class) is based on the French Thomson-CSF "Argonaute" passive system. 2040 was a British/French/Dutch development of the French Eledone (DSUV 22). The Dutch system is called Octopus.

The system as a whole consists of a circular bow transducer with a separate active transmitter (usually in the sail), plus a passive sonar interceptor (PARIS, Type 2019).

There are three types of bow transducers, with 32, 64, or 96 staves; but only the 64-stave version is in service in the three navies. The 32-stave version was proposed for the abortive CA-type French export submarine. The passive mode uses 128 preset low-frequency channels. It can track 12 targets simultaneously, and it interfaces with the submarine's fire-control system. The fire-control system uses Type 2040 data for its TMA solution.

The original Thomson-CSF system was a new passive/active commercial venture intended for the French submarine program of the late 1960s and early 1970s. The French *Agosta*-class sonar requirement was issued in 1971, Thomson-CSF offering its Eledone system and receiving an update contract (development 1971–76, tests 1975–76, approval for use 1976 as DSUV 22). Octopus was developed specifically for the Dutch *Walrus* class, and a further development won the British competition in 1982 for Batch-I *Upholder*-class submarines. Octopus was ordered in 1984.

As installed in an *Upholder*, Type 2040 has a 64-stave (3-meter diameter) cylindrical passive array on the bow forward of the torpedo tubes, and a smaller-diameter cylindrical active sonar in the sail (mechanically rather than electrically trained). The bow array differs from that of the original French system in having three, rather than two, tiers of staves. 2040 requires four processing cabinets for its four operating modes (adaptive, active, passive, and intercept). There are also flank arrays and a towed array. Up to twelve targets can be tracked simultaneously, data from each of the twelve threat channels feeding into the automated combat system for target-motion analysis. By using combinations of the twelve channels, the sonar can determine direction to within 0.1 degrees.

The display uses a color CRT to display signals from different sensors (or from different operating modes) simultaneously, for correlation and, therefore, classification. For example, the display can easily distinguish between a helicopter's sonar (which shows up only on the intercept sensor) and a ship's hull sonar (which will be accompanied by propeller sounds, visible on the combined display).

◆ Type 2043

An active/passive bow sonar for Trident submarines, Type 2043 is part of Type 2054. The Type 2043–45 designations are no longer used.

◆ Type 2044

This towed array for Trident submarines is part of Type 2054.

◆ Type 2045

This sonar-intercept system for Trident submarines is part of Type 2054.

◆ Type 2046

This core processor/display for submarines' towed arrays embodies Curtis architecture. See Type 2031Z and Ferranti FMS 12. This designation has also been applied to the submarines' towed arrays themselves, the replacements for Type 2024s. As of 1987 a total of 27 had been ordered, the first having been delivered that year.

◆ Type 2047

Plessey's wide-band hard copy (pen output) analyzer covers 5 Hz to 3.2 kHz and produces up to 12 LOFARgrams simultaneously.

◆ Type 2048 (PMS 75)

Plessey's Speedscan is a display that allows a conventional Type 193M minehunting sonar to function in side-scanning mode. The transducer is trained 90 degrees on the beam, and Speedscan records the echoes obtained. Its beam-former transforms that data into a map of a strip of the bottom, using three pings for each point in the map.

◆ Type 2050

Ferranti's bow dome sonar for Type 23 frigates is the successor to Type 2016 and reportedly uses the same transducer but a different signal processor (although the new bow location suggests a larger and lower-frequency sonar). 2050 is credited officially with an excellent software-based ability to reject bottom echoes, for good performance over the continental shelf.

2050 is an upgraded version of the Ferranti FMS 21 export sonar. Operating at 4.5–7.5 kHz, with 64 5.5-degree beams, 2050 should be capable of bottom-bounce and convergence-zone operation. Four electronic cabinets replace the twelve of 2016. The requirement included digital operation and simpler (more maintainable) electronics.

Unsuccessful competitors were the Plessey PMS 46 export sonar and a Marconi sonar.

Trials of a hull-mounted version began in 1986 on board HMS *Jupiter*, followed by sea trials in 1987 on board HMS *Scylla*. As of 1987, a total of 17 Type 2050s were on order, the first production unit having been delivered in mid-1987.

◆ Type 2051 (Triton)

Type 2051 is a new sonar for the modernization of diesel-electric submarines. Plessey (with Ferranti and GEC Sonics) won the contract in 1985. 2051 is a partially integrated sonar using an active/passive bow array in a new streamlined bow dome, a broad-band bow processor, two conformal flank arrays (narrow-band processor), an intercept sonar, and a clip-on towed array. The bow array has 32 preformed beams in a new low-noise dome. 2051 is a full upgrade rather than a simple replacement of Type 186 by Type 2007. 2051 was developed to compete with a system offered by Thomson-CSF. The R&D contract went to Plessey/Ferranti/GEC Sonics for an upgraded FMS 12, leading to R&D in 1982–84.

The prototype was tested in HMS *Opossum*; the first production set was in HMS *Otter*. Triton is the commercial name, Plessey acting as design authority. Triton 1 is the *Oberon* suite, and Triton 2 has been offered for follow-on Type 2400s. The manufacturers claim that Triton 2 is 15 percent less expensive than Argonaute and 10 percent less expensive than the German CSU 3-4 used for Australian and Canadian *Oberon* upgrades.

◆ Type 2052

This interim clip-on towed array for nuclear attack submarines is intended as an upgrade for older units; it is derived from Type 2024. This Type number has also been used for the Marconi

TAPS (towed-array processing system) broad-band signal processor.

♦ Type 2053

Waverly's hydrographic side-scan sonar has advanced digital processing (naval version of Sonar 3000); see Type 2034.

♦ Type 2054

Plessey's sonar suite (active/passive/towed passive) is for British Trident strategic submarines. The requirement was issued in 1983, proposals following in 1984; Plessey was chosen early in 1985. 2054 includes a Sub-Harpoon missile capability. Signal processing is entirely digital, the signals being transformed to digital form before being passed to the beam-former. That process may be unusual among modern sonars. This system employs a Type-2043 active/passive sonar, a Type-2044 towed array, and a Type-2045 intercept sonar. These subdesignations are no longer used.

Plessey is responsible for the bow sonar, the beam-former, and the signal processor; Marconi for the intercept sonar; and Ameeco for the towed array. There will be five consoles, each with two display screens.

The associated sonar-activated fire-control system is SAFS 3. The tactical-data handling system is DCC(BN).

♦ Type 2057

This towed array is in development to replace 2031Z on surface ships (Plessey/GEC). This array is much longer than 2031Z, to operate at lower frequencies.

♦ Type 2058

Thorn-EMI's towed sound source for acoustic ranges is proposed as a component of Vosper-Thornycroft's Sea Serpent multi-influence towed mine-countermeasures array. The free-flooding towed body is based on that of the Type-182 decoy, and Type 2058 is towed from the Type-182 winch.

♦ Type 2059

See the Mine Warfare section under countermeasures.

♦ Type 2062

The replacement for the Type-2023 SSBN towed-array sonar, Type 2062 uses a Waverley dry end based on that of Type 2031Z and an Ameeco wet end.

♦ Type 2068

Sonar-environment prediction-and-display system (SEPADS) is used specifically with towed arrays. 2068 incorporates a library of oceanographic information on a 50-Mbyte hard disk and a series of sound-propagation loss models (each taking about 1.5 seconds to run) to predict ranges and to estimate the optimum array depth. The associated computer is a commercial Digital PDP-11/44, and the prediction is updated every 4 to 6 hours.

♦ Type 2069

See Type 195, of which 2069 is an updated version.

♦ Type 2073

Type 2073 is an emergency underwater telephone (rescue pinger) for submarines, made by A.B. Precision (Poole), Ltd.

♦ Type 2074

This fully integrated active/passive bow-array sonar, for new nuclear attack submarines, is to replace Type 2020/2027. Plessey received the development contract in February 1988. Type 2074 is derived from Type 2054.

♦ Type 2075

This hull sonar for Batch-2 *Upholder*-class diesel-electric submarines (for delivery from 1991) is to replace Type 2040. The array locations would match those of Type 2040. Tenders for this contract were invited 24 August 1987, due 25 February 1988.

♦ Type 2078

This integrated sonar suite is being developed for the next-generation British nuclear attack submarine, SSN 20.

♦ Type 2093

Type 2093 is a replacement for Type 193. See the Mine Warfare section.

♦ Type 2095

Type 2095 is the generic designation for the successor for the Type 195 helicopter sonar. Cormorant (see below) may be chosen as the basis for Type 2095, but the choice had not yet been made when this book went to press.

♦ SIU

The Sonar Interface Unit federates the existing British submarine sonar suites that were designed as combinations of discrete units. The SIU allows any one console to display and process data from any of the arrays. As mounted in HMS *Turbulent*, the SIU connects Types 2007AC, 2008, 2019, 2020, and 2026. This combination is presumably a standard suite.

♦ AS360

The UDI sonar for remotely controlled underwater vehicles was selected (MS1/1 version) by the Royal Navy for PAP 104 Mk 5. The sonar is mechanically scanned, with an effective range of 100 m. Frequency is 500 kHz (700 kHz in MS5 version). Beamwidth is 1.4×27 deg (1.5×50 deg in MS5 version). This sonar is used in Japanese and U.S. deep-submergence rescue vehicles.

AS360MD2 is a dipping sonar, nine of which have been supplied to the Swedish Navy as self-contained units (200 kg). Range is about 150 m.

♦ AS370

UDI's bottom harbor-surveillance sonar is designed to detect swimmers and small submersibles. Range on swimmers (sea-state 3) is 500 m; on submersibles, up to 1 km. The beam pattern is 4×6 deg, and scanning can be either by sector or continuous.

♦ AS380

AS380 is UDI's dipping sonar for small ships or for helicopters. It scans a 60-degree sector electronically, with a maximum range of 3 km. Because the frequency is high (50 kHz), the sonar can provide some information on the size and shape of a target. Beamwidth is $? \times 10$ (vertical) deg; displayed resolution is 5 deg; bearing accuracy is 1 deg. Both FM and CW pulses are used. One example was supplied to the Swedish Navy in 1986.

♦ ATAS

Active towed-array sonar, developed by British Aerospace, consists of a flex-tensional transducer towed up to 900 meters astern of a ship, with a 20-meter (88-mm diameter) towed-array receiver another 300 meters further aft. Transmission is omnidirectional (in the horizontal plane), with a beamwidth of 25 degrees in the horizontal. The resolution of received bearings is 0.5 degrees in the broadside beam. British Aerospace claims that the usual port/starboard bearing ambiguity of linear arrays is automatically resolved, presumably by having the receiving array swing left and right relative to the transducer. As received, echoes would, then, be distorted by the sideways motion of the receiver; and this distortion could be used to break the inherent symmetry of a totally passive towed array.

The entire system can be streamed from a ship of 250 tons or more, at a depth as great as 200 meters. Operational speed is 5–20 kts, and the array can survive towing at 30 kts.

The transmitter requires a peak power of 25 kW and is 1.2 m high, 0.7 m long, and 0.3 m wide (weight 200 kg). Frequency is probably about 3 kHz (based on the relative sizes of BAe flex-tensional transducers). On-board electronics weigh 280 kg, and the handling system weighs 7 metric tons. The 900-meter cable is 23 mm in diameter and weighs 1.5 metric tons.

Several ATAS were reportedly procured by the U.S. Navy early in 1987 to support the development of an active surveillance towed array, presumably a future SURTASS system (see the Surveillance and Control section).

◆ COMTASS

Plessey's Compact Towed-Array Sonar System is available both for surface ships and for submarines. There are three versions: COMTASS 1, which gives broad-band surveillance in three frequency bands; COMTASS 2, which adds narrow-band surveillance and classification; and COMTASS 3, which adds automatic detection. The array is 97 or 129 m long, with a diameter of 63 mm, and is towed on a 1000- or 1500-m cable (diameter 25 mm). Total wet-end weight is 2600 kg, and overall weight is 6 tons. Plessey claims that contacts can be detected at convergence-zone range, about 30 nm.

This system was evaluated by the Royal Swedish Navy in 1986, and reportedly COMTASS will be ordered for at least eight Swedish submarines.

◆ Cormorant/Guillemot

The development of Plessey's low-frequency helicopter dipping sonar, the first of its kind, began as a private venture in 1978. The dipping body has now (1988) completed development and can, therefore, be incorporated into a production sonar. Cormorant has been selected for evaluation by Canada, the United Kingdom, and the United States, in the latter country under both a NATO Comparative Test Program and as part of the U.S. ALFS program (see below). Cormorant is the wet end of the Canadian AQS-503 (HAPS).

The sonar body is streamlined enough to be flown while trailing below a helicopter, yet in the water Cormorant is large enough to provide useful sonar beams at low frequencies. This capability is achieved by placing the stave transducers on arms that deploy outward, like gates, from the dipped body. The arms are long enough (vertically) to provide a useful degree of beam forming in the vertical plane. As a result, in shallow water the beam can be focused more or less horizontally and, thus, can be kept clear of both the surface and the bottom, avoiding ex-

Cormorant (PMS 122) lightweight dipping sonar, with its transducer array extended. (Plessey)

cessive scattering and reverberation. This solution cannot substitute for a large low-frequency transducer, but Cormorant should achieve much better ranges than current small medium-frequency types.

The transducer can operate in both the active (CW and FM-slide pulses) and passive (broad-band) modes. Power is provided by transmitter modules, each of which generates 2.2 kW.

In its ALFS form, the entire system weighs only 640 lbs. It operates at 1500 ft in depth (2000-ft cable), with three selectable frequencies and five selectable pulse lengths. The streamlined body sinks at 15 ft/sec (and retracts at 25 ft/sec) so that dipping time is not excessive even at great depth. Bearing accuracy reported in 1988 was 2 deg active and 5 deg passive.

Guillemot is an enlarged Cormorant, similar in size to Type 195M, for the EH-101 program. Guillemot operates at about 2.5 kHz (Cormorant operates at 5 kHz).

◆ Dolphin 1000 Series

Marconi's sonar processors, both broad- and narrow-band, are to upgrade submarines' existing arrays or to be installed as part of the systems of new construction submarines.

There are four main processors: a broad-band processor fed by either conformal or cylindrical arrays; a broad-band line processor; a signal analyzer; and an intercept processor. The broad-band processor provides HF or LF waterfall displays (time vs. bearing, with up to 20 minutes shown). Several targets can be autotracked simultaneously. The broad-band line processor, which can take signals from flank, bow, or towed array, displays either the combination of these signals or else the output of separate arrays. The analyzer provides spectral data and can also apply DEMON (demodulated noise) to retrieve spectral data from broad-band noise. The intercept processor provides bearing, time, pulse parameters, and a list of intercepts.

◆ Ferranti FMS 12

This two-octave narrow-band passive-sonar processor was chosen as part of the Triton (Type 2051) program (*Oberon*-class update) in 1985, to work with flank and towed arrays. The digital signal processor embodies the new Curtis architecture (see Type 2031). The reported frequency range is 10–384 Hz and 384–768 Hz. The system operates on 32 preformed beams. There is a simple multiple-beam (waterfall) display for surveillance, and a high-resolution vernier (frequency) display for classification. Self-noise can be processed out. Optional improvements are automatic target detection and classification, automatic communication with a submarine's tactical system, hard copy output, and a color display.

The FMS series was announced at RNEE 1983, and trials of FMS 12 were conducted in 1984.

FMS 12 is the basis of Type 2046.

FMS means Ferranti Modular Sonar.

◆ Ferranti FMS 15

FMS 15 is a five-octave narrow-band passive-signal processor.

◆ Ferranti FMS 20

FMS 20 is an active hull sonar with VDS option. The transducer has a diameter of 4 ft. FMS 20 uses both FM and CW pulses and has 32 preformed beams. This system incorporates a passive torpedo alarm and a ray trace predictor.

◆ Ferranti FMS 21

The export version of Type 2050, FMS 21 has a transducer 6 ft in diameter and is compatible with a VDS. FMS 21 uses CW and FM pulses and has 64 preformed beams. The system incorporates a passive torpedo alarm and a ray trace predictor.

◆ Ferranti FMS 30

FMS 30 is a passive broad-band system with a 3-ft array.

◆ Ferranti FMS 31

FMS 31 is a passive broad-band system.

◆ GETAS

Marconi's passive towed array uses a wet end from Geophysical Company of Norway (GECO A/S). Versions for both surface ships and submarines are available, and the array can also be laid on the bottom for surveillance.

◆ Graseby GI777

This medium-range active/passive sonar for patrol craft was useful for craft down to 100 tons. GI777 could track two targets simultaneously, the output being digital fire-control information. GI777 was being advertised about 1976–1980.

◆ Graseby GI780

This passive sonar for small submarines was advertised about 1976.

◆ Graseby Type 850

This medium-range scanning sonar was announced in 1979 to replace G750 (Type 184M). Type 850 was specified for the abortive Type-24 export frigate. The sonar is designed to connect to a computer combat system. Transmission is both CW and FM coded (for long range), and three targets can be automatically tracked simultaneously. 850 has 32 preformed beams, with separate doppler processing. Resolution: range, 100 m (accuracy, 10 m); bearing, 0.175 degrees (accuracy, 1 degree); doppler 2.3 kts. Dome size is 4623 × 1956 × 2085 (depth) mm. Maximum instrumented range is 24 km. This sonar can be operated by one operator under normal conditions, but a second is needed for an attack; the display is probably similar to that of the contemporary Type 2016.

◆ Marconi Small-Ship GP Sonar

This short-range sonar is for detecting submarines and mini-submarines, for minehunting, and for navigating underwater. The sonar consists of a towed or dipped body containing the projector and an array of 100 plastic elements sweeping a preformed beam rapidly through 360 degrees. The display is a PPI. The operator selects 83.3 kHz (3.3-deg beam, maximum range about 800 m) or 250 kHz (1.1-degree beam, about 150-m range). The plastic polarized transducers are a proprietary Marconi development, and they can operate over the range from 1 kHz to 1 MHz. The towed body is 32 cm × 1.2 m and 150 kg. Range resolution is 90 mm, and vertical-beam coverage is 15 deg. The body can be towed at speeds of up to 5 kts. The data rate is 2.5 frames/sec at 300 m range. Processing is entirely digital; there are no moving parts.

This technology has also been applied to fixed harbor-surveillance sonars (Marconi 360-degree Surveillance Sonar) and also to a 360-degree area-defense sonar (23, 33, or 68 kHz, for 4.6-, 3.4-, or 1.6-degree beams, capable of detecting a diver at, respectively, 200, 300, and 500 meters, or a submarine at 3.0, 1.5, or 1 km). The area-defense sonar, suspended from a float and tethered to the bottom, uses the same console as the others. In theory this sonar could be laid by a ship in harbor, used for protection against hostile swimmers, and retrieved when the ship went to sea.

◆ Plessey PMS 26/27

Sector-scanning sonars (ODT), for medium and small ships, these units are closely related to the Type-195 helicopter dipping sonar. They cover 360 degrees in four steps and can depress their beams for MCC. The transducer is 44.5 cm wide × 99.6 cm high × 53 cm deep and weighs 100 kg. Theoretical range is 7.5 km, but effective range is about 4.5 km. PMS 26 is in a retractable dome.

PMS 26 is in the Danish *Peder Skram*– and *Nils Juel*–class frigates and in the fishery-protection vessel *Beskytteren*, on board the Iranian destroyer *Damavand*, and in the Nigerian *Erin'mi* class. In all, 55 of these sets were exported, and in 1987 42 or 43 were still in service.

PMS 27 is the same sonar using a different hull outfit suited to ships down to 750 tons.

PMS 56 was intended as a more modern and less expensive replacement; it uses the same transducer. See below for details.

◆ Plessey PMS 32

PMS 32 was a frigate sonar with a 2000-kg array (transducer diameter 1220 mm, height 1000 mm). Peak power was about 5 kW.

Torpedo warning was offered as an optional feature.

Development began in 1967, the prototype being completed in 1971.

◆ Plessey PMS 35

This digital search-and-attack sonar for frigates of 600–1500 tons was announced in 1975. Operating modes include ODT and a 30-degree sector search. The operator can call up an expanded sector covering a limited range bracket. Doppler classification can be applied to any one of the preformed receiving beams. Operation can be at one of two selectable frequencies, and there is an optional torpedo-alarm feature.

◆ Plessey PMS 40 Series

A new private-venture hull-sonar series, PMS 40 was announced in 1983. There are three versions, PMS 42, PMS 44, and PMS 46, to cover the full range of ship sizes, from patrol craft up through destroyers. PMS 42 employs a single electronics cabinet and a 27-inch (diameter) transducer; PMS 44 has two cabinets and a 44-inch transducer (corvettes and above); PMS 46 has three cabinets and a 78-inch transducer.

These sonars are extensively automated to reduce manning, each having only a single operator. Multiple transmitting elements provide redundancy. Presumably that redundancy means that much of the transmitting function is concentrated in the individual staves, rather than in a centralized power source. The operator selects such pulse transmission characteristics as long/short mode (which can be interleaved) and frequency. It appears that the primary operating modes are ODT and passive, and for larger ships the beam itself can be electronically stabilized.

Simultaneous computer-aided tracking is provided for up to ten active contacts, and there is an automatic torpedo alarm. A scanning audio channel locks onto the sources of such alarms to assist in classifying them.

PMS 46 is on board the Danish fishery protection frigates of the *Hvidbjørnen* class.

◆ Plessey PMS 56

This solid-state replacement for PMS 26 has improved signal processing. PMS 56 can operate either alone or in combination with a COMTASS towed array. Operating frequencies are 9.5, 10, and 10.5 kHz; pulse widths are 250 msec and 1 second (modes FM and CW). Range scales are 3, 6, 12, and 18 kyds.

In fixed-dome form this sonar is suited to ships of up to 3000 tons (speeds up to 30 kts); there is an alternative version with a retractable dome, for ships up to 1000 tons (18 kts with dome extended, 30 with dome retracted). Existing PMS 26/27 sonars can also be updated to PMS 56 standards.

◆ Smiths Industries Hi-Scan Sonar

This high-definition scanning sonar is primarily for remotely controlled vehicles. The sonar operates at 300 kHz (600 kHz in production sonars). It transmits at high frequency and scans very rapidly over a limited sector to receive. The beam (2 degrees wide) is scanned electronically over a 30-degree sector; range resolution is 7.5 cm. Vertical beamwidth is 7 deg, and the transducer can tilt through 90 deg. In the 600-kHz version, beam dimensions are 1.6 × 10 deg (but claimed resolution is better than 1 degree), the beam scanning at 15 kHz and using a 75–400 microsecond pulse (source level 214 dB); PRF is 4, 8, 16, or 32 kHz. Range resolution is 5 cm. Instrumented ranges are 5, 10, 20, 40, 80, and 160 m. The transducer is a 16-element receiving array and projector, 120 × 45 × 60 mm (2 kg). The display is a standard 16-color television monitor (raster scan), display information being held in a frame store and updated on a frame-by-frame basis. This scheme avoids flicker and, thus, makes the display easier to view.

Smiths Industries Hi-Scan 600 was developed to meet an MoD requirement for a mine-clearance sonar for remotely controlled underwater vehicles.

♦ SP2110

SP2110 is a GEC Avionics towed small-ship export array based on Type 2031 I and Type 2026 technology. The manufacturer claims that SP2110 will be less expensive than those earlier systems and that its modular design makes for relatively simple expansion. Basic options include DEMON (i.e., extraction of low-frequency spectra from higher-frequency signals); narrow-band surveillance, classification, and tracking; and broad-band surveillance. Autodetection and autotracking can be provided. This system was announced in 1988.

♦ SWS 35/40

This streamer array sonar for small boats is made by Ameeco Hydroscience. The wet end is 92 mm long, carrying clustered hydrophones operating in the 25–3200 Hz range, plus two high-frequency hydrophones. The array is towed on a 150-m cable. The processor forms broad-band beams using the hydrophones; and the two high-frequency hydrophones (which are intended as sonar-intercept receivers, primarily against high-definition navigational sonars) have a separate display.

SWS 40 adds a vertical array that can be steered to exclude surface reflections. The vertical array produces five beams, over a broad frequency range (seven octaves).

Ameeco also makes a seabed horizontal array, SWS 45, intended primarily to protect offshore oil rigs. Early in 1989 it was reported that Ameeco was developing an experimental Royal Navy array using fiber optics both for data transmission and for the hydrophones proper. In theory, a fiber-optic hydrophone would detect sound by measuring the change in the length of an optical fiber wrapped around a deformable body. The phase of a light signal sent through this fiber would vary as it stretched or contracted. This same signal could be amplified and sent back up the information-transmission cable. In theory, such information might be much less subject to electrical noise than the usual electrical signals. In addition, optical fibers should be able to carry vastly more data than conventional cables. Advances in optical computers, which are particularly well adapted to the sort of parallel processing required for ASW, might make an optical array particularly attractive. Ameeco is not alone in working on optical hydrophones, but no other projects have become public.

Underwater Fire-Control Systems

♦ TCSS 9/TDHS (DCA)

Torpedo control system (submarine)/tactical-data handling system is installed in HMS *Splendid* and later British nuclear attack submarines (DCA is the designation of the tactical-data system). TCSS 9 was the first (1973) fully computerized British submarine action information organization (AIO). It could manage 25 tracks simultaneously, carrying out target-motion analysis (TMA) on all of them to present tactical officers with a full passive picture of nearby contacts. The displays are a pair of consoles flanking the central sonar PPI, each with a twin CRT (with light pens for operator interaction). The single Ferranti FM 1600B computer is used for TMA on 24 targets, a great improvement over manual methods that (even with a large attack team) were limited to two or three targets (and which even then took considerable time).

TCSS 9 is being phased out of service in 1988. It was originally conceived as a fire-control system for submarines, upgraded with a torpedo control unit Mk 2 to control Mk-24 (Tigerfish) torpedoes. In this case the computer was used only to display target and weapons information. TDHS represented the fusion of fire control and AIO functions, the computer being used also for TMA, and the automated AIO being connected to the torpedo fire-control device.

DCA first went to sea in 1973 on board HMS *Swiftsure.*

♦ DCB

The automated submarine AIO (1978) succeeds DCA/TCSS 9, requiring fewer operators. The usual command team for a TCSS 9 submarine is thirteen, reduced to eight for DCB. This system is based on two Ferranti FM 1600B computers.

DCB was originally designed for the *Swiftsure* class. DCB can engage two targets simultaneously and can track 20. It is currently being upgraded through installation of a peripheral processor, the Gresham-CAP DCG (see below). This addition enlarges DCB's memory to 128 kbyte. There have also been considerable software improvements, reportedly five in the last three years. DCB was originally developed to fire wire-guided torpedoes as well as air-flight missiles (single-shot or salvo); Gresham Lion is now updating DCB to fire Spearfish.

DCB equips all British nuclear submarines other than HMS *Swiftsure.*

♦ DCC

DCC is the automated command/control system of the British *Upholder*-class attack submarine, developed by Ferranti (with Dowty-CAP as subcontractors for consoles and fore-end hardware). Two FM 1600E computers drive the three consoles (one on standby). Each of the three equivalent operator positions can be used for either command/control or fire control.

KAFS (see below) is an export derivative of DCC, with considerable commonality with other Ferranti AIO systems. This system employs a single FM 1600E computer in the base of its console, for both AIO and FCS. Automatic TMA can be conducted on up to 35 tracks simultaneously. Interaction is via light pen and keyboard, and the tactical picture can be presented either as a PPI or as a vertical display. Two or more wire-guided torpedoes can be controlled simultaneously against two targets. A special navigational program can be run for minelaying.

COMKAFS (DCH) (see below) is a variant, used in the RN to update existing *Oberon*-class submarines. COMKAFS is built around the Argus Compact computer.

DCC(BN) is the tactical-data handling system for British Trident submarines.

♦ DCG

An add-on processor for DCB, made by Gresham-CAP, DCG is a PDP 11/44 with an array processor intended to improve TMA capability. However, DCG is also used for simulation (for onboard training), for environmental analysis (e.g., sonar ray path prediction), and as a command tactical aid.

♦ DCH

DCH is a replacement for TCSS 10/11 in the British *Oberon* class (Ferranti COMKAFS D). The first of twelve was delivered in 1987.

♦ SMCS

Submarine Multiscreen Command System by Gresham-CAP, to replace the existing DCB/DCG for all future British submarines (SSN, SSK, SSBN), was under development in 1988. SMCS uses a dual-redundant fiber-optic data bus connecting four multifunction consoles, a main tactical display, two sensor input nodes, two common-service nodes, and two remote terminals. SMCS is a fully integrated submarine control system, the same computers being used both for information processing and for weapons control. All consoles are identical, and all are software-configured, for maximum redundancy and flexibility. For example, in one role all the consoles may be devoted to sonar data; at periscope depth, one or more may display ESM data; in another role, one or more may function as fire-control or countermeasures consoles. SMCS is a federated system using eleven computers incorporating Intel 80386 32-bit processors plus special parallel processors. They are linked by a high-capacity fiber-optic data bus. The entire system is programmed in ADA (OCCAM for the transputers of the parallel processors).

SMCS is the first announced dedicated military application of the transputer (parallel computer), and the first naval use of the new standard ADA language. Gresham-CAP claims that SMCS has more than 20 times the processing power of current (1988) submarine combat systems, at lower acquisition and ownership costs (and with better than 99.9-percent availability). This sort of improvement is probably a natural and virtually universal consequence of recent improvements in computer hardware, paralleling well-known civilian experience.

The common-service nodes store bulk information and carry out high-speed computation (each has eight processing cards, each of which carries eight transputers; and each node can process information at the rate of 50 Megaflops).

Development of SCMS began with the award of a contract in December 1986 after a three-year competition, and delivery is scheduled for 1992, for installation in all submarines other than surviving *Oberon*s.

◆ FISCS

FISCS is the Ferranti Integrated Submarine Combat System, developed primarily for export. There is a single six-operator console, all operator positions being identical and interchangeable. Two wire-guided torpedoes or two missiles can be fired simultaneously at one or two targets; the system can be expanded to control six torpedoes or four missiles. FISCS provides sonar performance prediction and is linked directly to the submarine's bathythermograph. Oceanographic analysis is possible because the system can store so much background data.

◆ KAFS/COMKAFS

Ferranti's submarine action information and fire-control system was announced in 1981. KAFS stands for SSK AIO and Fire-control System, and COMKAFS is compact KAFS. KAFS was first ordered to equip Brazilian Type-209 submarines. Derived from the AIO designed for the British *Upholder* class, KAFS uses a single Ferranti FM 1600E computer (192K expandable to 256K). The prototype KAFS (1982) was a cannibalized WSA-420 surface-ship AIO/FCS console. COMKAFS D will replace TCSS 9 in the *Oberon* class.

This system was designed to handle 35 target tracks (expandable to 50), performing TMA on all of them. KAFS has two operator positions, the computer fitting into the bottom of the console. Each position carries two CRTs, a tactical display on the left and a tote (alphanumerics) display on the right; only one display is operated in the patrol condition. The displays are canted rather than upright so that the lengthy use of light pens will be less fatiguing.

The tactical display can switch between PPI, time-bearing (waterfall), and vertical display formats, with tactical aids including calculated closest point of approach, rendezvous, estimated time of arrival, and angle on the bow. The tote provides 37 pages of material, including weapons-control data. The operator calls up pages by applying his light pen to a menu at the bottom of the page, and he also uses the pen to designate tracks to fire control. Although most commands are made by software, some critical ones, such as the firing command, are made by special buttons and switches on the control panel.

KAFS can control four wire-guided torpedoes firing at four separate targets, and it can also fire unguided torpedoes or lay mines. In addition, the system can preheat up to 12 stowed battery-driven weapons simultaneously, monitoring their condition so that they can be loaded and fired more quickly.

◆ Series 4

The Plessey Marine combat/integrated sonar systems were announced in 1986; the name reflects the use of fourth-generation, i.e., distributed, computer architecture and data busing. Plessey claims that by using high-capacity memories and fast processors, it can radically reduce the number of different components in a typical sonar system. For example, a complete sonar suite might be built up from ten types of electronic cards (such as a 32-bit processor and an 8-Mbyte memory), compared to about 300 different cards in Type 2020. The first Series 4 suite was Pisces 4, offered for the Royal Australian Navy's new submarine.

◆ TIOS

Tactical Information Organization, Submarine, by Ferranti/Vickers/Gresham-Lion, was developed in parallel with DCB and exported to Brazil (for *Oberon*s) and to Israel (for the three Vickers 540s). TIOS was an early example of the use of a digital fire-control computer for some AIO tasks, such as target-motion analysis (TMA), applied to one or two targets.

TIOS-B is fitted to Brazilian *Oberon*s. It is based on the Ferranti FM 1600B.

TIOS-C is for IKL 500/1000-ton submarines, based on the Ferranti FM 1600B.

TIOS-D is based on the Ferranti FM 1600D.

TIOS-E uses the FM 1600E computer, but differs from KAFS by using privately developed software; and -E has one rather than two CRTs at each of the three operator stations, the same display showing both graphics and alphanumerics.

UNITED STATES

HELICOPTER SONARS

◆ AQS-13

An AQS-13 transducer suspended from a Sea King helicopter. (U.S. Navy)

The standard U.S. dipping sonar is employed primarily on carrier-based inner-zone ASW (SH-3) helicopters. AQS-13 is manufactured by Bendix and is a development of the AQS-10 of 1955.

The original AQS-13 was a medium-frequency sonar (9.25–10.75 kHz, operating at 5 kW, with a 3.5- or 35-msec pulses and with range scales of 1, 3, 5, 8, 12, or 20 thousand yards). The typical pulse was 180 degrees wide, and the sonar scanned on reception. The dip cycle, from transducer launch to recovery, was 2–3 minutes; and with the helicopter hovering 50 feet up, the transducer was 450 ft below the surface. Typical range was 4000 yds, and installed weight was 775 lbs. AQS-13B (625 lbs) had sixteen preformed beams; 200 lbs was saved by using hybrid microcircuits, and a single 360-degree omnidirectional ping was adopted to speed scanning. Built-in test equipment was also added. AQS-13C added a sonobuoy interface.

AQS-13E added APS (adaptive processing sonar) for better shallow-water performance through fast-Fourier-transform narrow-band analysis of the coded sonar pulse. In effect AQS-13E traded poorer range definition for much tighter frequency definition and, thus, for much better measurement of doppler shifts against a reverberation background.

AQS-13F was originally a lighter version (615 lbs) with a longer cable (1500 ft) and higher power, saving weight by reducing all data to digital form. Two prototypes failed their U.S. tests partly because greater pressure badly distorted the beam patterns at depth. The West German Navy persisted with a modified version, AQS-18. Recently the AQS-13F designation has been revived for the dipping sonar of the new SH-60F helicopter.

All versions of AQS-13 provide for voice communications; -13A added keyed (coded) communications as well, for greater range.

An SH-60F carrier inner-zone ASW helicopter dips its AQS-13 sonar. (Sikorsky)

◆ AQS-14

See the Mine Warfare section under countermeasures.

◆ AQS-18

This Bendix helicopter dipping sonar was developed from the abortive AQS-13F specifically for the West German Navy. AQS-18 weighs 600 lbs (194 lbs for the fish alone), including a 450-m cable (allowing operation down to 440 m), operating at 9.23, 10, and 10.77 kHz (3.5- and 35-msec CW pulses, 200- and 700-msec FM pulses, range scales the same as AQS-13). Source level is 217 dB. Modes include passive and moving-target indicator. Like AQS-13F, AQS-18 uses a separate transmitter and receiver. A lead-acid battery pack is carried in the sonar "fish," but there is no capacitor to store energy between pings. Instead, the helicopter recharges the battery between transmission cycles. The power level is reportedly twice that of the original AQS-13B, and the high-speed winch (22 ft/sec average) limits the dip cycle to no more than that of the earlier sonar, although the depth can be much greater.

These data are for the current AQS-18(V) version, which is available with both 1000- and 1500-ft cables.

◆ ALFS (Airborne Low-Frequency Sonar)

ALFS is a Naval Air Systems Command project for a next-generation helicopter dipping sonar, to replace the existing AQS-13 series. The new sonar will be installed on board SH-60F carrier inner-zone helicopters (which are replacing the existing SH-3) and, perhaps, on board future LAMPS helicopters. The weight target is 700 lbs, and the associated signal processor is UYS-2. Proposals have been submitted by Allied Signal (Bendix), Gould/Plessey, Martin-Marietta (with Diagnostic/Retrieval Systems and Breeze Eastern), Sanders, and Thomson Sintra. The

Allied Signal, Martin-Marietta, and Sanders systems are described separately in the three entries immediately below.

The Gould-Plessey proposal is a development of the Cormorant low-frequency helicopter dipper that Plessey has developed as a private venture since 1978. See the Plessey Cormorant entry above for details of the proposed towed body. The Gould-Plessey ALFS would achieve very long sonar ranges through a combination of low frequency and great depth (1500 ft, with 2000 ft available as an option). A fast winch would maintain a quick dip cycle (deploy to depth and recover to fly at trail in 180 seconds). This ALFS would concurrently process active sonar and helicopter-deployed sonobuoy data. Cormorant has been accepted for the demonstration phase of the Canadian HAPS project, for the new Canadian ASW helicopter (NSA, or New Shipborne Aircraft).

Thomson Sintra has offered its FLASH (Folding Light Acoustic System for Helicopters).

The flextensional transducer (projector) of the Sanders-GEC dipping sonar. (GEC)

The dipping body of the Sanders-GEC low-frequency helicopter sonar. It is the only one of the ALFS alternatives not to use extending arms for more directional reception. (GEC)

◆ HELRAS

An Italian Sea King deploys the Allied Signal (Bendix) HELRAS long-range dipping sonar. (British Aerospace)

HELRAS is Bendix's (now Allied Ocean Systems) low-frequency/long-range sonar developed specifically for the Anglo-Italian EH-101 helicopter. Like Cormorant and the Martin-Marietta ALFS entry, HELRAS employs a series of stave transducers on extendable vertical arms. The projector is a stacked array of 8 or 10 low-frequency (presumably flex-tensional) transducers, 16.3 or 20.5 ft long. It extends vertically in the water; in the air, the projector is folded inside the sonar fish, the individual transducers stacking closely one above the other. Above the projector is a receiving array consisting of vertical staves on extending arms. When unfolded, the dimensions are 9.2-ft diameter and 4.2-ft height. The entire fish weighs either 380 or 410 lbs (depending on the number of active transducers) and is 16 in in diameter and 53 or 56 inches long. Total system weight, including a lightweight reeling machine, is 662 or 692 lbs, depending on the number of active transducers. This weight is light enough for HELRAS to be accommodated on board an SH-60 or NH-90 (NATO Lynx successor) helicopter. Accommodation on board the SH-60 makes HELRAS a candidate for the future LAMPS or inner-zone CV helicopter.

The long array of active transducers produces a beam omnidirectional in the horizontal plane but narrowly defined in the vertical, so that, for example, it can avoid multipath in relatively shallow water by grazing both bottom and surface at a very shallow angle (and at a great distance). Very low frequency makes for long potential range; Bendix claims that HELRAS's range is about seven times the conventional dipping sonar's range, which implies convergence-zone performance. Given such long sonar range (and the blank zone that range implies), Bendix proposes to fuse all other available sensor data (e.g., radar and MAD) with the active and passive data picked up by HELRAS. Bendix also claims that the necessary signal processor is powerful enough to process sixteen active or passive sonobuoys simultaneously.

Compared to the Plessey Cormorant, which was probably the first such low-frequency extending-array sonar, the chief differ-

ences shown by HELRAS seem to be the much lower frequency and the very long transmitting array (to focus the beam in the vertical plane).

HELRAS flew for the first time in December 1987 on board an Italian Navy SH-3D.

◆ HIPAS

Martin-Marietta's High-Performance Active Sonar is a competitor for ALFS. HIPAS uses a five-arm array in umbrella shape, each arm containing 30 receiving transducers, with a diameter of 2 m.

HIPAS has also been offered for the Canadian NSA competition and for the British EH-101 helicopter; for the latter application Martin-Marietta is teamed with Dowty Maritime Systems.

◆ Sanders Advanced Dipping Sonar

This private-venture sonar was announced in 1988, and the prototype was tested in July. It can operate at four frequencies, with diverse pulse lengths, types, and shapes, and can also provide broad-band passive capabilities, acoustic intercepts, and fathometer readings. This sonar can operate at depths of 1500 ft or more, with a dip cycle of 180 seconds, trail-to-trail, and a duty cycle of 10 percent. Total system weight is 650 lbs. Reportedly this sonar operates at about 3 kHz, using a DICASS-like cylindrical array of flex-tensional transducers. Sanders's system is the only ALFS competitor that does not employ a fold-out array.

Processing would be by the standard U.S. UYS-1 (as in LAMPS-III helicopters) or by British GEC AQS-903, which has been selected for the Anglo-Italian EH-101 helicopter.

SUBMARINE AND SURFACE-SHIP SONARS

◆ BQG-4 (PUFFS)

The submarine *Wahoo* shows three vertical PUFFS hydrophones. MicroPUFFS and WAA use two-dimensional hull arrays instead. (U.S. Navy)

This passive-ranging device for submarines measures range by the curvature of the wave front of the detected sound, comparing times of arrival. The typical installation consists of three vertical transducers: bow, amidships, and aft; and range accuracy depends on the ratio between the range and the length of the installation. The original concept was for three equally spaced 6-ft (vertical) hydrophones along a 250-ft baseline, operating at 200 Hz–8 kHz, to get a range accurate to within 2 percent against a snorkeling submarine at 10–15 thousand yards. Feasibility studies began in 1953, and the first prototype was tested in 1960. PUFFS means "Passive Fire-Control Feasibility Study."

In U.S. service, PUFFS was associated with the now-extinct Mk 45 nuclear torpedo. The torpedo had no seeker, and the firing platform had to detonate the torpedo at the appropriate range. Target-motion analysis using a single sonar was not precise enough, but PUFFS could provide a good enough range. Adoption of Mk 45 was actually predicated on the success of the PUFFS tests.

A few of these devices remain in service, mainly on board submarines transferred abroad by the United States. Sperry manufactures a Micro-PUFFS for installation on board modern diesel submarines (see separate entry below). The current Martin-Marietta wide-aperture array (WAA) is a lineal descendant.

◆ BQG-5/WAA (Wide-Aperture Array)

This official sketch of the new U.S. *Seawolf* shows the three panels of her Wide-Aperture Array (WAA) distributed along her side.

WAA is the successor, in effect, to PUFFS and Micro-PUFFS, consisting of three large flat arrays on each side of a submarine. Larger array size should enable both lower-frequency operation and directivity both in depth and in azimuth, so that WAA should be able to exploit bottom- and surface-bounce paths and the convergence-zone propagation path. The concept was first tested on board the experimental submarine *Baya* in FY71 and on board USS *Barb* in January–April 1980, presumably as part of Micro-PUFFS. By 1980 WAA was considered an essential element of any post–*Los Angeles*–type submarine. For example, in January 1977, the then secretary of defense described WAA as capable of providing bearing and range data "out to the limits of present weapons capabilities." The current manufacturer is Martin-Marietta, and WAA was tested on board the submarine *Augusta* about 1985. WAA will be fitted as a stand-alone system in *Los Angeles*–class submarines beginning with those authorized in FY89, and some will be backfitted to earlier ships. WAA will also be part of the BSY-2 system of the new *Seawolf* class.

[*Below*] BQQ-2 sonar system, as installed in a *Sturgeon*-class attack submarine. The conformal array is BQR-7, and the three spot arrays (forward, amidships, and aft) are part of BQQ-3. The PUFFS ranging arrays, which were narrow vertical retractable arrays of transducers (and which were rarely fitted) are not shown. They had to be retractable because otherwise they would have spoiled the streamlining of the submarine hull; they had to be straight because they were being used to measure the precise curvature of an incoming wave front. (From *Principles of Naval Weapons Systems*, fourth edition, by the Weapons and Systems Engineering Department of the U.S. Naval Academy)

As of early 1988, two BQG-5s were planned for FY89, and the total program consisted of nine BQG-5s (plus units integrated into BSY-2 for the new *Seawolf* class).

◆ BQQ-2

The integrated sonar system designed for the *Sturgeon/Permit* class consists of a bow spherical transducer (BQS-6), a conformal array of low-frequency transducers around the bow (BQR-7), and a BQA-3 computer-indicator group. In some versions there are also BQG-4 (PUFFS) transducers for passive ranging.

The bow sphere operates at about 3.5 kHz and was initially credited with a peak power of 170 kW (compared to 100 kW for SQS-26). The sphere is 15 ft in diameter and operates in ODT, RDT, and tribeam modes. The conformal array receives at 50 Hz–2 kHz.

The spherical transducer is the submarine equivalent of the roughly contemporary SQS-26 surface ship's sonar; the transducer permits the submarine to exploit all possible underwater propagation paths and is associated with the new SUBROC antisubmarine rocket. The low-frequency conformal array was intended primarily for target classification, using LOFAR techniques. It was soon discovered, however, that the array is a superior long-range detector.

Because it can operate so directionally, the bow sphere was also considered a means of secure acoustic communication with nearby surface ships, but this communication seems not to have been very successful.

BQQ-2 has been replaced by BQQ-5 in many cases. As of 1988, funding for the program to replace BQQ-2s with BQQ-5 was reported complete. Reported procurement of BQQ-5 in recent years: FY83, 4 systems; FY84, 8; FY85, 9; FY86, 9; FY87, 8; FY88, 2; FY89, 9. Existing BQQ-5s will be brought up to -5D standard.

◆ BQQ-3

BQQ-3 is the passive classification system associated with BQQ-2, using three groups of hydrophones. The display is a series of four strip charts (chart recorders): a group of three LOFAR displays in a very low frequency band (bow, bow plus midship, and midship plus stern); LOFAR data in a slightly higher frequency band (using the bow hydrophones or the steered beam of BQR-7); a LOFAR display based on the demodulation of higher-frequency signals; and wide-band low-frequency noise level. The first chart gives no directional data because it operates at very low frequency and requires extreme silence. The second gives poor directional data but can be used to cue other, more directional, sensors. Both of these charts are useful primarily against noisy targets. The third chart is used against targets with continuous noise spectra modulated by line sources.

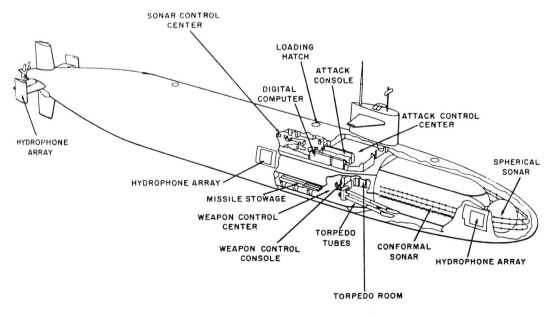

SONAR CONTROL CENTER
LOADING HATCH
ATTACK CONSOLE
DIGITAL COMPUTER
ATTACK CONTROL CENTER
HYDROPHONE ARRAY
SPHERICAL SONAR
HYDROPHONE ARRAY
MISSILE STOWAGE
WEAPON CONTROL CENTER
TORPEDO TUBES
CONFORMAL SONAR
HYDROPHONE ARRAY
WEAPON CONTROL CONSOLE
TORPEDO ROOM

◆ BQQ-5

A U.S. *Sturgeon*-class submarine, in drydock, displays the drogue at the end of her towed array, the object on the end of her port stern plane. Also visible is her highly skewed propeller, adopted as a silencing measure. Submarine propeller noise is generated when a blade cuts through the wake of the sail or of a horizontal or vertical plane; otherwise the flow through the propellers is symmetric, and thus the blades do not encounter anything that will create noise. Skewing makes the entry of the blade more gradual and, thus, reduces noise. In 1983 U.S. Chief of Naval Operations Admiral James Watkins stated that the quietest Soviet submarines, the Victor-IIIs, were being detected primarily through radiated propeller noise (blade tonals). Two years later it was revealed that the Soviets had bought computer-controlled blade-cutting machines through Toshiba of Japan and Kongsberg of Norway, allowing the Soviets to mass-produce propellers optimally shaped to reduce just those tonals to which Admiral Watkins had referred. Skewed propellers are common in Western submarines, but the details differ from navy to navy. (G. Arra via *Ships of the World*)

The improved submarine sonar suite developed for the *Los Angeles* class incorporates DIMUS for reduced internal noise; in effect, BQQ-5 is a digital replacement for BQQ-2. DIMUS permits the sonar to track many targets simultaneously. In contrast, the bow sphere of BQQ-2 is limited because there are only two commutators (beam-formers) inside; it can perform TMA on only two targets simultaneously. BQQ-5 includes the BQS-13 DNA (DIMUS narrow-band accelerated active search) and BQS-14 transmitters. Compared to BQQ-2, BQQ-5 has better displays, DIMUS, improved active search, passive classification, an on-line performance monitor, and automatic fault location for quicker repair. Concept formulation began in January 1969, and BQQ-5 was approved for service use in April 1979. An improvement program began in FY80.

BQQ-5A has improved computer capacity (in the form of an additional UYK-7) and a towed-array broad-band processor (ICC/TABP).

BQQ-5B incorporates SHAB, a steerable hull-array beamformer. Beam forming presumably applies to a hull (flank) passive array rather than to the spherical bow array. The displays are improved, and the system is less expensive than BQQ-5A.

The major improved version is BQQ-5C, an upgraded -5B, with expanded DIFAR reception (multiple interface unit/digital spectrum analyzer with three UYK-44 computers in one cabinet). BQQ-5C(V) passed operational evaluation in June 1984. BQQ-5D, with thin-line array, is operational in 1988. Successful operational trials of the thin-line array were conducted in FY85. BQQ-5D is to be approved for full production in FY89. Techeval was completed in October 1988. BQQ-5D incorporates some BSY-1 technology. BQQ-5E will incorporate TARP, a new thin-line array (TB-12X) for passive ranging. The BQQ-5E contract was awarded in December 1988. System design is focused on the localization process. A varient is to be installed on board later Trident submarines. BSY-1 technology in this system includes sonar for under-ice operation and mine avoidance (MIDAS).

BQQ-5 is associated with the WLR-9 acoustic intercept receiver, sometimes referred to as AERP (active emission receiver). The thin-line array, TB-23, is replacing the earlier TB-16 (approved for service use in FY84).

◆ BQQ-6

The integrated sonar for Trident missile submarines differs from BQQ-5 primarily by lacking any active element in the bow transducer. There are also a towed array and two flank arrays. The bow sphere includes 944 transducers. About 73 percent of BQQ-6 components are common with BQQ-5.

◆ BQQ-9

Rockwell International's towed-array signal processor can operate either as a stand-alone system or as an auxiliary to a federated submarine combat system. Rockwell claims that its advanced software and data-processing techniques allow an operator easy access to all system capabilities, with minimum training. The result, according to the company, is increased passive detection range. BQQ-9 incorporates built-in test equipment, and as of 1984 the system had passed all of its sea trials and operational evaluations.

◆ BQR-2B

BQR-2B was the passive sonar for early U.S. postwar fast attack submarines, presumably remaining on board some ex-U.S. Guppies. BQR-2B operated over the 0.5–15 kHz band. -2B originally had no time-bearing (waterfall) recorder, but that feature became standard in the BQR-2E version. Bearing-time information was recorded for the 0.7–1.4 kHz band, and a bearing-deviation indicator (5–9 kHz) was accurate to within about 0.1 degrees. Modes were MTB (maintain true bearing), GTT (generate target track), ATF (automatic target following), and automatic on-target slewing. There were two consoles (stacks) for simultaneous acquisition and processing of multiple targets and independent, continuous recorder scanning. Sweep rates were manual or 4 rpm for one beam (recorder beam 1 or 10 rpm).

The array consisted of 48 staves (43-inch line hydrophones) in a 68-inch diameter circle. Signals were filtered to limit them to the 0.5–15 kHz band; then beams were formed by phasing 24 adjacent signals, forming right and left signals (12 each), the phase difference being maintained for BDI use. At 5 kHz, the beam was about 18 × 30 deg.

About 1960 BQR-2B was credited with a range of 15–20 nm against a snorkeling Guppy in the deep Atlantic; it was estimated that a quiet platform would be able to increase this range to 50 nm.

◆ BQR-3

This directional hydrophone occupies a small deck sonar dome on board many former U.S. submarines. BQR-3 is a trainable 5-ft line array with a 22-degree beam (but with sum/difference bearing-deviation indication for accurate direction). Typical range on a snorkeling submarine was given in 1956 as 18,000 yds.

◆ BQR-4

BQR-4 was the passive sonar for U.S. ASW submarines (SSKs) and is also found in early U.S. nuclear submarines. Operating over the 0.15–5 kHz range, BQR-4 includes a bearing-time recorder (waterfall chart) for the 0.7–1.4 kHz range. There is also a PPI. There is no bearing-deviation indicator; nominal long-range bearing resolution is 10 deg. The beam is manually controlled for continuous target contact, and at the same time the system can search at 4 rpm.

The array consists of 58 staves (10-ft line hydrophones) in a 10 × 20 ft conformal (horseshoe) array. Beams are formed by phasing 29 adjacent signals; the delay lines can be adjusted for the speed of sound (4750–5100 ft/sec).

BQR-4 was based on the wartime German GHG and as such is related to several contemporary postwar passive sonars.

In 1960 it was estimated that a quiet submarine equipped with BQR-4 would be able to detect a snorkeling Guppy at 65 nm.

◆ BQR-7

This conformal passive array, found, e.g., in BQQ-2, covers a 270-degree arc around the bow and scans at 1 or 20 rpm. A bearing-deviation indicator permits tracking with an error limited to about 0.1 degree, sufficiently accurate for fire control. The frequency range is 50 Hz–5 kHz. The associated bearing-time (waterfall) recorder operates in the 0.5–2 kHz band. Overall system accuracy is about 1 degree (but bearings may have to be offset about 3 degrees to take account of signal integration over time).

The array consists of 52 hydrophone groups (each consisting of three hydrophones vertically), running back about 45 ft down the length of the submarine from the bow.

In 1960 it was estimated that, on a quiet submarine, BQR-7 would be able to detect a snorkeling Guppy at 75 nm.

◆ BQR-15

This towed array for ballistic-missile submarines (SSBN-608 and -616 classes) was introduced largely to give them an ability to detect targets aft, hidden in the baffles of the bow sonars. BQR-15 was the first U.S. towed array for tactical submarines and led directly to installations for attack submarines. BQR-15 incorporates the BQR-23 signal processor.

◆ BQR-19 (Top Hat)

Raytheon's mast-mounted short-range navigational sonar for SSBNs is designed for evasion while surfacing.

◆ BQR-20

Interim Spectral Dynamic's signal processor for improved narrow-band detection and classification is found in *Los Angeles*–class and earlier U.S. attack submarines. BQR-20 is also in British service. Work began in the late 1960s, based on the SQQ-23 passive receiver, with added passive classification equipment. The parent firm, Atlanta Scientific, has proposed that BQR-20 be replaced by the more capable BQR-23.

◆ BQR-21

This DIMUS passive array is for attack and ballistic-missile submarines lacking BQQ-series systems (i.e., SSBNs prior to the *Ohio* class and submarines prior to the *Thresher*). BQR-21 replaces the earlier BQR-2 for broad-band detection and can track as many as five targets simultaneously, with accuracy sufficient for weapons delivery. BQR-21 uses the BQR-2 hull-mounted array. Honeywell received the development contract in June 1972, with sea trials of the first engineering-development model following in 1974. This system includes BQR-15, BQR-19, and BQQ-9. Procurement ended in FY82, a total of 66 having been purchased (59 tactical units, 6 trainers, and 1 configuration-control unit).

◆ BQR-23

The STASS (Submarine Towed-Array Sonar System) signal processor is used with BQR-25 in SSN-688 and SSBN-726 classes. The current version is BQR-23A.

◆ BQR-24

Raytheon's array (parallel) processor is used with BQR-21.

◆ BQR-25

See BQR-23. The array "wet end" is made by Gould. The tow cable is about 1000 ft long, with a diameter of 1 inch; and the array itself is 298 ft long, with a diameter of 2 inches. This array is used in SSN 594 and 637 and SSN (ex SSBN) 598 classes.

◆ BQS-4

The successor to SQS-4 for submarines, BQS-4 consists of seven vertically stacked cylindrical transducers inside a passive sonar (BQR-2C) that acts as receiver. Vertical stacking permits beam movement in the vertical plane. BQS-4 operates at 7 kHz, and typical range is 6–8 kyd. BQS-4 is found in older U.S. diesel and nuclear submarines.

◆ BQS-6/11/12/13

The bow sphere sonar in BQQ-2, replaced by BQS-11, then -12 and -13 in later submarines, BQS-6 transmits at about 3.5 kHz (i.e., about like SQS-26/53) and listens between 0.5 and 5 kHz, with bearing-deviation indication in the 1–2.8 kHz band. The passive capability supplements that of BQR-7, replacing it when own-ship flow noise blanks out the lower-frequency bands of the conformal array. Two independent passive beams are available for search and detection. Rated output in the original BQS-6 was 75 kW, and transmission (and reception) could be ODT, single beam, or tribeam (beams spaced 6 degrees). Sphere diameter is 15 feet.

BQS-11 was a replacement, with a peak power of 196 kW (but capable of transmitting between 1.45 and 3.2 kHz). BQS-12 was another replacement for BQS-6, but BQS-13 was chosen for the new BQQ-5 system. In April 1983, Raytheon received a contract to update BQS-11/12 to BQQ-5 standards.

BQS-13 is Raytheon's DIMUS narrow-band accelerated active search (DNA) sonar, used in the BQQ-5 system. Like BQS-6, BQS-13 uses a spherical transducer.

◆ BQS-14/15/18/20

Under-ice and mine-avoidance sonars, these high-frequency sets are part of BQQ-2, -5, and -6. MIDAS, Mine Detection-and-Avoidance Sonar, is sometimes linked with SADS, Submarine Active-Detection Sonar, as SADS/MIDAS. The MIDAS test ship was SSN 687, USS *Richard B. Russell*, about 1986; MIDAS may, therefore, have occupied the large dome mounted aft at that time. However, any operational MIDAS system would occupy a forward-facing position, e.g., in the forward edge of the sail. Released paintings of the new *Seawolf* show a sonar window in the appropriate position at the upper forward part of the sail.

◆ BQS-15

BQS-15 is the under-ice sonar for the *Los Angeles* class.

◆ BSY-1 (SUBACS)

The submarine integrated combat system was originally designated BYS-1 and apparently redesignated as the result of a typographical error; BSY-1 is now pronounced "busy-one." It appears to have been conceived as a submarine equivalent of the SYS series of systems on board AAW ships: a system that would automatically detect targets on a variety of arrays and meld this data (obtained in various frequency ranges) into a single usable tactical picture. One advantage of such automatic detection would be the ability to range passively on a target detected simultaneously (in different frequency ranges) by several arrays, e.g., by a towed and a flank array. That capability no longer seems to be a program objective; apparently automatic detection and classification of passive signals is still extremely difficult, beyond the current state of the art.

IBM was responsible for overall system design, with Hughes developing combat system displays, Raytheon the combat control system (CSS Mk 1) and the wide-aperture array, and Rockwell the own-ship data-set group. The two basic elements of the system were a multipurpose console incorporating a new densely packaged electronic card, and a high-capacity fiber-optics data bus tying the consoles together. A submarine would have eleven such consoles arranged side by side, but only four would be required for operation. Thus, it would be unnecessary to perform maintenance during a patrol: any console that failed could be taken out of line and replaced by one of the others. One consequence of the adoption of multipurpose consoles was the elimination of the fire-control system as such in favor of a fire-control system (CCS 1) embedded in the system's software. In practice, the dense packaging was apparently much more difficult than expected, and the data bus also encountered difficulties. The consequence was that BSY-1 had to be recast; it now employs special-purpose consoles.

As of 1985, the program had been split into three versions:

SUBACS Basic, for FY83 submarines (scheduled for delivery 1987): distributed acoustic processing, UYK-44 computers, thin-line towed array, and SADS/MIDAS active sonar for submarine and mine detection.

SUBACS A (FY86 submarines for delivery 1989) added an enhanced modular signal processor (EMSP), distributed combat control, a piloting and combat system (PACS), a combat-system display console (CSDC), and common displays. SUBACS A employs a new bus interface unit and is an application of VHSIC technology. The term PACS suggests some measure of automatic maneuvering, presumably for torpedo evasion or perhaps for faster and more precise TMA.

SUBACS B (FY89 submarine, the new *Seawolf* class) added the wide-aperture array (WAA) and improved ESM and external countermeasures (presumably antitorpedo decoys).

In fact, as noted, this program could not be met and had to be split between BSY-1 (which IBM retained) and BSY-2 (which went to GE).

The first BSY-1 was delivered in July 1987, for installation on board the attack submarine *San Juan* (SSN 751). BSY-1 represents an improvement in passive sonar capability and in some weapons control. A further post-completion upgrade, for the *San Juan* and the next four *Los Angeles*–class submarines, will be installation of new UYK-43 computers, new software, active sonar improvements, under-ice capability, and new weapons capability (presumably Sea Lance). This two-phase approach was chosen when the SUBACS program was restructured in May 1985. From SSN 756 on, submarines will be completed with the full BSY-1 suite.

BSY-1 uses distributed processing to support a combat-control subsystem and an acoustic subsystem. This integrates BQQ-5, SADS/MIDAS (see below), the thin-line array (TB-23), and CCS Mk 1 (Mk 117 plus over-the-horizon targeting). The system will initially use the improved control-display consoles (ICDC) and Mk 81 WCC (weapons-control console) of the BQQ-5/CCS Mk 1 system, the UYK-7(V) computer of BQQ-5/CCS Mk 1, tri-advanced signal processors (TRIASPs), and the active emission-receiver processor (sonar-intercept receiver) of BQQ-5. New features are the weapons-launch system (WLS), the common beam-former cabinet (CBC), and a modified plotter Mk 19.

IBM describes BSY-1 as the first military application of distributed architecture on a large scale. BSY-1 employs one UYK-7 and one UYK-43, supported by two UYK-44 minicomputers; presumably the retention of the older UYK-7 reflects commonality (in some software) with earlier *Los Angeles*–class systems. There are also five linear beam-formers, two digital (DIMUS) beam-formers, and six advanced signal processors (in the form of two TRIASPS). Overall, the system has 30 MCOPS in raw general-purpose computing power, supported by 60 Mbytes of on-line RAM storage and 400 Mbytes of disk storage. The computer power required for signal processing dwarfs general-purpose power: 120 MCOPS of signal processing, 800 MCOPS of linear beam-forming (for towed arrays, presumably), and 2 GCOPS (giga-COPS) of DIMUS beam-forming. All of this power requires about 4,519,000 lines of instruction code. Total weight is 32 tons, and total power requirement (aside from the transmitter) is 142 kW. The system occupies 117 units with 11.5 miles of wiring. Presumably, the enormous amount of wiring reflects the failure of the optical-fiber data bus originally planned.

Improvements over BQQ-5 include much better fault detection, and a greatly reduced number of logic cards.

As of November 1988, a total of 21 BSY-1s were on order or delivered: 20 for submarines, 1 as a trainer. Techeval and opeval are scheduled for 1990.

BSY-1 is to be upgraded with a new CCS Mk 2, a program awarded to Raytheon/General Dynamics in September 1988. See below.

BSY-1 replaces BQQ-5.

◆ BSY-2

BSY-2 is the combat system of the new *Seawolf*-class submarine. The program was split from BSY-1 when the latter encountered severe problems in 1985–86. At present the FY89 combat system (for *Seawolf*) employs, among other items, WAA (BQG-5), the long thin-line array TARP (the towed-array range processor), a transmitting group (TG), a multi-array signal conditioner (MASC), multipurpose consoles (MPC), combat-system display consoles (CSDC), a horizontal plotter (HP), and a tactical-situation display (TACSIT). The shift from individual sensors to various sensors all feeding a common beam-former and MASC suggests integration, different sensors seeing different elements of the same target signature.

◆ QCU-2

This World War II searchlight sonar is still in use in a few U.S.-built ships of that period and in some small patrol craft transferred postwar. Frequency is 17–27 kHz (centered on 25 kHz). Range scales are 1, 2, 4, and 6 kyds (associated pulse lengths 25, 75, 75, and 200 yds, respectively).

◆ SQQ-14

See the Mine Warfare section under countermeasures.

◆ SQQ-23

See SQS-23 below.

◆ SQQ-25

This high-definition 3-dimensional sonar is found on board the submarine rescue ships *Ortolan* and *Pigeon*. SQQ-25 uses a 7-kHz chirp. Active range is 2500 yds; passive, 1000 yds.

◆ SQQ-28

The LAMPS-III shipboard processor is the successor to SQS-54. SQQ-28 was later extended to LAMPS-I support, for *Perry*-class frigates assigned to Naval Reserve units. SQQ-28 can process all buoys up to and including VLAD (SSQ-77).

◆ SQQ-30

See the Mine Warfare section under countermeasures.

◆ SQQ-32

See the Mine Warfare section under countermeasures.

◆ SQQ-35

See the Mine Warfare section under countermeasures.

◆ SQQ-89

General Electric's integrated surface-ship sonar suite is analogous to the submariners' BQQ series. The different surface-ship systems share two common displays (UYQ-21s), and data are handled by computer. Passive and active data can be shown simultaneously, for correlation and localization. Contact data are transmitted directly to the Mk-116 fire-control system.

SQQ-89 includes the UYQ-25 and -26 Sonar In-Situ Mode Assessment System (SIMAS), a performance predictor.

Current versions are the following. (V)1, for the *Spruance* class, consists of SQS-53B hull sonar, SQR-19 towed array, Mk-116 Mod-5 ASW control system (ASWCS), UYQ-25 SIMAS, and SQQ-28 (LAMPS Mk-III processor). (V)2, for *Perry*-class frigates, is the same as (V)1 but without a long range-active sonar ((V)2 has only SQS-56) and without a Mk-116 fire-control system ((V)2 uses a Mk-309 fire-control panel for lightweight torpedoes). (V)3, for the *Ticonderoga* class, is the same as (V)1 but with Mk-116 Mod 6 fire-control system. (V)4, for the *Arleigh Burke* (DDG 51)–class, is the same as (V)1 but with SQS-53C sonar and with the UYQ-25 function embedded in the new Mk-116 Mod-7 software. Each version includes an on-board trainer, SQQ-89T(V). The first ship fitted with SQQ-89 was the *Spruance*-class destroyer *Moosebrugger*, which also had the prototype SQR-19 towed array (1985); she was followed in 1987 by *Fife, Fletcher,* and *Spruance,* five more ships following in 1988. The first FFG 7–class frigate to receive the new system was *Curts* (1985), followed in 1986 by *Elrod* and *Simpson* and then by five ships in each of 1987 and 1988. From *San Jacinto* (CG 56) on, newly completed Aegis missile cruisers will have SQQ-89 as initial equipment.

In 1989 two industrial teams are competing to develop SQQ-89(I) (improved), the next-generation surface-ship ASW system. This will be a two-phase program, the first being improvements to *Perry*-class frigates (beginning in FY90); the second is improvements to battle-group escorts, which already have long-range hull-mounted sonars. Requirements include a multiline array and a low-frequency active adjunct sonar.

The teams are:

—General Electric (leader and integrator), using Presearch for ASW mission analysis, Martin-Marietta for the towed array and low-frequency active adjunct, Raytheon for the hull active sonar and trainer, AT&T for the signal processor, EDO for towed array handling and stowage, and Unisys for advanced software (including data fusion and expert systems applications).

—Westinghouse (leader), with Bendix, Honeywell, Link-CAE, Norden, and Singer-Librascope.

See also SSATS, below.

◆ SQR-13

PADLOC (Passive-Action Detection and Localization), the first U.S. multi-array (and microcircuit) system, uses two arrays in separate domes. SQR-13 is incorporated in SQQ-23. PADLOC is a technique rather than a specific device; it was first tested using an SQS-29 and a submarine-type BQR-2B on board the destroyer *Glennon* in 1959, and PADLOC variants were proposed for use with SQS-26 during the 1960s.

◆ SQR-14/15

These very long range towed arrays are for surveillance. SQR-14 was designated the interim towed-array surveillance system (ITASS). SQR-15 was an improved version, intended as a backup to SOSUS. Instead, the U.S. Navy procured a longer-range SURTASS system. Both SQR-14 and -15 were produced by Gould. They are similar to, but not interchangeable with, BQR-15. Compared to SQR-18/19, SQR-14/15 use much longer arrays and operate at either much lower frequencies or with much narrower beamwidths.

The first SQR-14 was produced under the FY68 program. Tests were run in the early 1970s, and systems upgraded to SQR-15 configuration in 1974. SQR-14 was manufactured by Chesapeake Instrument Co.; Gould bought the company in 1975 and manufactured SQR-15 (last under the FY78 program). A total of six (plus one trainer) were produced, the first in FF 1037 and FF 1038 in 1975, then six in the FF 1040–class frigates. One unit was lost in 1983 (when a Soviet Victor-III–class submarine cut through the towing cable with her propeller). The arrays were removed from their original platforms in 1983/4 and moved onto new ones, reportedly *Spruance*-class destroyers (including DD 966). SQR-14 is no longer in service.

SQR-16 was a proposed improved version of SQR-15, using a Gould wet end. -16 was unsuccessful; only one was made.

◆ SQR-17

This family of shipboard sonar processors evolved from the SQS-54 LAMPS-I processor. SQR-17(V)1 is a four-channel sonobuoy processor for the LAMPS-I, working with LOFAR, active, and BT buoys. SQR-17 can also process data from buoys dropped

over the side of a ship, and from hull-mounted sonar. Acoustic data are displayed in either A- or B-scan and also in standard hard-copy form (e.g., LOFARgrams). SQR-17(V)2 is an upgraded version to process towed-array data via an interface kit. The latter includes a digital multiplexer encoder/decoder (DMED) that converts the 32 channels of towed-array data, plus own-ship course, speed, and track bearing, into high-density digital format for tape recording. SQR-17(V)3 adds frequency domain adaptive line enhancement (FDALE), an adaptive filter that makes weak lines more detectable within broad-band noise. FDALE was the first adaptive line enhancer in a fleet ASW processor. All of these systems were followed by SQR-17A(V)1 and (V)2, which add more sophisticated sonobuoy capabilities: eight LOFAR channels or two DIFAR/DICASS channels. These versions can process VLAD array buoy data. Adaptive line-enhancement software is embedded in the system, which can also conduct target-motion analysis (MATE/MLE).

Subsystems are the SKR-4 link receiver, AKT-22 link, ARR-75 sonobuoy receiver, and UYS-1 processor. In 1988 this system was being modified to include a torpedo-warning capability.

These systems, which equip every LAMPS ship, are all manufactured by Diagnostic Retrieval Systems (DRS), Inc.

◆ SQR-18

The interim escort towed-array surveillance system (IETASS) was developed under the escort towed-array sensor (ETAS) program. SQR-18 was conceived as a simpler alternative to SQR-14/15. Work began under the FY68 program. One Patterson experimental array (PEA) was bought in FY72, leading to a specific operational requirement in FY73. IETASS was tested on board *Knox*-class frigates and a minesweeper, leading to the ETAS (program established FY75) and then to the TACTASS (tactical towed-array sonar) programs. Contracts for two IETASSs were awarded in August 1974. In FY80, 12 were retrofitted into *Knox*-class frigates, four more following in FY81.

The original SQR-18 was towed at depths of up to 366 m, at the end of a 1706-m cable. SQR-18A was the original production version, towed from an SQS-35 fish at the end of a 1524-m cable. SQR-18A(V)1 is an improved version deployed on board *Knox*-class frigates, towed from their SQS-35 VDS fishes on a 730-m cable. A modified version, SQR-18A(V)2, which does not require a sonar fish, uses a special depressor and a 5300-foot cable. -18A(V)2 is towed by those *Knox*-class frigates that were never fitted with variable-depth sonars, and by some *Perry*-class frigates. SQR-18(V)2 uses the same array-handling system, OK-410, as does SQR-19. The array itself consists of 32 vibration-isolated hydrophones (eight modular hydrophone sections), with preamplifiers in the fish; it is 222.5 m long and 3.25 in in diameter. SQR-18 is towed at depths up to 366 m on a 1706-m cable.

SQR-18A(V)2 can use an Edo-developed short-scope tow, an alternative to a critical-angle tow requiring much less towing cable. The longer critical-angle tow is generally needed to isolate the noise of the towing ship from the array. However, Edo developed an own-ship noise canceler that can subtract the measured self-noise of the towing ship from the output of the array. The array is held down by a special depressor, a low-drag winged body with a V-tail and trailing-edge flaps on the tail fins, weighing 265 lbs. The array passes through the depressor shell, for easy handling. This device was tested at sea in July 1981 on board the research vessel *Athena*, a former fast motor gunboat, at up to 34 kts, and then on board the surface-effect craft JEFF-A in August 1981 (at over 40 kts).

Compared to SQR-18, -18A has a low-noise array, an interference canceler, and an improved tracker. Production of SQR-18A began in the spring of 1978, and an improvement program began in April 1981. The Dutch (2) and Japanese (6) Navies have bought this system.

Produced by EDO, and also now manufactured by Gould, SQR-18 was initially to have been replaced altogether by the superior SQR-19; but development continued as insurance against any problems in the -19 program, and the -18 is now an alternative standard.

SQR-18 was first tested on board USS *Moinester* in 1975; -18A was tested in 1978. The initial results were that -18 was effective (but unreliable) in the first convergence zone, and that -18A corrected the demonstrated deficiencies. Only two SQR-18 were built, virtually all arrays being SQR-18A.

◆ SQR-19

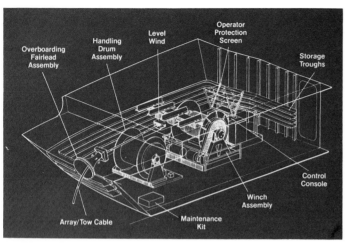

Typical towed-array handling gear (OK-410/AN/SQR-19). (Gould)

The tube running down one side of the submarine *Olympia* houses a towed array; there is no space within the single hull for anything so massive. Such stowage in turn limits the maximum length of the array. (U.S. Navy)

SQR-19 was intended as the ultimate standard U.S. Navy tactical towed array, but development was protracted. Produced by Gould, this array is now (1988) in service. Unlike SQR-18, SQR-19 does not appear to require a fish or other depressor.

The array originally consisted of three nested acoustic apertures formed by eight acoustic modules, each of which contained 48 equally-spaced hydrophones and was 12 m long (4 low-frequency, 2 medium-frequency, and 2 high-frequency modules). Experience in 1983 reportedly showed that it was necessary to go to much lower frequencies to meet the silencing of new Soviet submarines, so the aperture was doubled and a fourth aperture (8 VLF modules) added. The original array was 150 m long altogether and weighed 1700 lbs. It included a separate heading, depth, and temperature module monitoring ambient water conditions; and the array proper was isolated from its 5600-foot (3.25-inch diameter) tow cable by three vibration-isolation modules. Each hydrophone module contained its own

amplifier, and the data was multiplexed for transmission, by the towing cable, up to the towing ship. The on-board electronics included a pair of UYQ-21 computer display terminals.

SQR-19 is operable in sea-states 0–4 at high speeds and can be towed at depths as great as 1200 feet, to achieve ranges that cover multiple convergence zones. Because SQR-19 consists of multiple hydrophones, it can continue operation (by reconfiguring itself without shutting down) if several hydrophones fail. Operational availability is 0.993 (i.e., available all but 3.5 hours in a 210-day operating year), with a mean time between failure greater than 600 hours, a maximum fault detection time of one minute, and a mean time to repair of less than 20 minutes. The system is built out of standard electronic modules (SEMs). Electronic features include automatic contact alert and automatic tracking and track keeping.

The engineering-development contract for SQR-19 was awarded in December 1977, the first ship installation following in November 1981 (DD 980). The array was evaluated in November and December 1982, and approval for limited production was granted in March 1983. Full-scale production was approved on 26 December 1984 after a 2000-hour array MTBF had been demonstrated. SQR-19(2X), a lengthened array to detect lower-frequency tonals, was tested in FY87.

◆ SQS-4/SQS-29 through -32/SQS-39 through -42/SQS-43 through -46/SQS-49 through -52

SQS-4 was the first major U.S. low-frequency sonar, the earliest type operating at 14 kHz with three alternative pulse widths: 6 msec (50 kW), 30 msec (30 kW), and 80 msec (10 kW). Operating frequency was further reduced in three variants: Mod 1 (8 kHz), Mod 2 (10 kHz), and Mod 3 (12 kHz), the original 14-kHz version becoming Mod 4. Nominal range was about 5000 yds, and there was a passive mode. SQS-4 scanned mechanically at 150 cycles/second. Although the first units had range scales at 1, 2, and 5 kyds, demonstrated long-range performance led to recalibration, and the maximum range scale was set at 15,000 yards. Other improvements were RDT and DMCC (dual maintenance of close contact), the latter permitting depression of the sonar beam to maintain contact on a nearby target. MCAR (multiple-channel aural reception) was a modification for broader-beam reception to improve capability against fast targets (three beams 7.5 degrees apart instead of the single receiving beam that was 10 degrees wide).

SQS-4 versions were transferred to many Allied navies during the 1950s and 1960s. The sonar was first tested in 1951, and it entered fleet service in 1954. Some were installed on board submarines.

SQS-29 through -32 were modified SQS-4 Mods 1 through 4, respectively, with RDT and passive-search capability. Pulse lengths were 2, 7, 30, or 120 msec (4–50 kW); and range scales 1, 2.5, 5, 10, 15, and 30 kyds. This series introduced ASPECT (Acoustic Short-Pulse Echo-Classification Technique: a burst of short steered pulses gives an indication of a target's shape) and built-in test equipment.

SQS-39 through -42 were modifications of SQS-29/32 with steered-directional transmission (SDT) and improved maintainability and reliability.

SQS-43 through -46 were SQS-29B or -29C through -32B or -32C modified with RDT and SDT and capable of operating a variable-depth sonar off the same sonar stack. These units equipped U.S. FRAM-II destroyers, which were widely exported. The VDS fish and hoist are designated SQA-10.

SQS-49 through -52 were SQS-4 Mods 1 through 4, respectively, with improved maintainability and reliability (MARK).

◆ SQS-10/11

These sonars were modernized postwar versions of the late-war QHB scanning sonar, the first scanning sonar in U.S. service. One QHB may survive; all known examples of this series are SQS-11s. SQS-10 was initially designated QHB-3; it was, in effect, a higher-frequency (20-kHz) SQS-4. SQS-11 was a 25.5-kHz equivalent. SQS-10 produced 6- (50 kW), 30- (10 kW), and

80- (3 kW) millisecond pulses, scanning at 150 cycles/sec with a 19-deg beam (range scales, respectively, were 1000, 3000, and 6000 yds). SQS-10A had a capacitor to provide a peak power of 30 kW at a pulse width of 35 msec. SQS-11A was analogous to -10A, also with the boost capacitor. Typical SQS-11A performance was 1600 yds/800 yds for targets in/below the layer (probability of detection 0.25) at 15 kts, and 1300/800 yds at 18 kts. These sonars were specified for U.S. destroyers and frigates in the mid-1950s, to replace QHBs installed from about 1950 on. SQS-4 was generally used instead.

SQS-11A survives in the Japanese target service ship *Azuma*, the former patrol boats of the *Mizutori* and *Umitaka* classes, and the Thai frigate *Pin Klao* (SQS-11 version).

◆ SQS-17

A scanning sonar for small ships, SQS-17 was tested for service in 1954 and exported to Allied navies. It operates at 12, 13, and 14 kHz, with 16, 35, and 60 msec pulses (peak power 1–6, 22, or 30 kW). Range scales are 1.5, 3, 4.5, 6, and 12 kyds; and source level is 134 dB. SQS-17 is the search sonar of the French *Commandant Rivière* class.

◆ SQS-23/SQQ-23/PAIR/PADLOC

SQS-23 installed as a bow dome, USS *Barry*, 1959. This ship was the test installation. (U.S. Naval Institute)

SQS-23 was the low-frequency replacement for SQS-4, associated with the ASROC stand-off weapon. SQS-23, was first installed in 1958 both in FRAM-I destroyers and in new construction, and it was also built under license in Italy and in Japan.

Base frequencies are 4.5, 5, and 5.5 kHz; and the operating frequency can be varied around a base frequency to limit intership interference. Pulse lengths are 2 (later 5), 30, and 120 msec, with range scales of 1, 2.5, 5, 10, 20, and 40 kyd. The mechanical commutator scans at 150 cycles per second. The cylindrical array consists of 48 staves, each containing 2 transducers, for a total of 96 channels; and the sonar beam can be depressed electronically. In the long-pulse, wide-sector RDT mode, SQS-23H transmits 60 kW for 4.3 seconds. Current versions employ both fixed-frequency and FM-slide pulses.

Numerous SQS-23s have been modernized by the addition of Raytheon's solid-state transmitters (SSTs); see the entry for the Raytheon DE 1191 below.

Recent development work has emphasized improved reliability as well as noise reduction for longer range. Thus, current SQS-23s are credited with bottom-bounce and convergence-zone performance in the Mediterranean, though not in the Atlantic or Pacific, where the convergence zone is further away.

SQQ-23 (PAIR, performance and integration refit) is a modified version that incorporates passive tracking by a second transducer and PADLOC (passive-active detection and localization). Compared to SQS-23, PAIR adds a second operator console, as well as built-in test equipment. Output is 160 kW for 160 msec in ODT mode and 60 kW for 5.6 seconds in RDT mode at 4.3–5.7 kHz, using 48 channels (1 per stave rather than 2 per stave, as in SQS-23). SQQ-23A uses simplified solid-state equipment (three solid-state cabinets for transmission rather than 21 vacuum-tube cabinets and 10 motor generators). SQQ-23B integrates both transducers into a single sonar dome and is the version in the cruiser *Long Beach* and in the *Leahy* class. The two-dome version is in four *Adams*- and two *Mahan*-class missile destroyers.

SQQ-23 uses a rubber rather than a steel dome, for better sonar transmission. Rubber domes were also applied to SQS-26, and they were credited with helping that sonar to achieve its designed range.

◆ SQS-26/53

SQS-26 was the culmination of U.S. low-frequency sonar development, operating at about 3 kHz. Feasibility studies began in 1955, the prototype XN-1 model being installed in 1961. SQS-26 and its solid-state successor SQS-53, are the current standard U.S. long-range sonars.

The engineering development model, SQS-26 (XN-2), was delivered for installation in USS *Wilkinson* in November 1961. The pilot production models were delivered in August 1962, for the *Bronstein* class. Three alternative versions of SQS-26 were built: -26AX by General Electric; -26BX by Edo; and -26CX by General Electric, which produced all later units to that standard. The AX system deliveries began in May 1963 (*Garcia, Brooke,* and *Leahy* classes). The BX version was installed in FF 1047–1051, in FFG 4–6, and in CG 28–35. These AX and BX sonars were not altogether successful, and a series of major modifications was approved in January 1965. CX system deliveries, for the *Knox* and *California* classes, began in December 1967. General Electric also modified existing -26AX sonars to -26XR standards. The sonar itself was approved for service use only in November 1968, after considerable difficulties; and for some years SQS-26 was not credited with being able to achieve its theoretical performance, so that in service SQS-23 could often achieve better results. Major improvements included much higher power, a rubber (rather than steel) sonar dome, and

Installation of an SQS-53 sonar dome. (U.S. Navy)

increased reliability. By the mid-1970s, SQS-26 was reliably achieving the bottom-bounce and convergence-zone performance for which it had been designed.

The transducer is about 16 ft in diameter and 5½ ft high and weighs about 60,000 lbs; the sonar dome is generally described as comparable in size to a 60-foot personnel boat. Operation is at about 3.5 kHz, and the transducer forms 72 beams (5-degree coverage). Each of 72 staves consists of 8 elements; and the beam can be electronically elevated and depressed, both for stabilization and for bottom-bounce and convergence-zone operation.

The next major version, SQS-53, began delivery in October 1972 (for the *Spruance* and *Virginia* classes). SQS-53A is a solid-state version of SQS-26C with greater reliability and better signal processing (using a Proteus acoustic processor, UYK-20 computers, and UYQ-21 displays). -53A has digital output to interface with a Mk-116 fire-control system.

SQS-53B (Phase I of the SQS-53 Improvement Program) has multiple-target tracking-and-classification aids and reduces manning by 60 percent. Claimed reliability: 2000-hour MTBF (the goal was 500 hours) and 30-minute MTTR. -53B passed technical evaluation on board USS *Moosebrugger* in August and September 1982; an associated narrow-band passive capability was successfully demonstrated in November 1982.

SQS-53C has improved active performance (partly due to greater power), multiple-target capability, automatic target tracking, simultaneous active/passive modes, greater bandwidth, and shorter reaction time; -53C incorporates a UYH-1 mass memory. This version will appear on board *Arleigh Burke*–class destroyers. The first engineering development model was tested on board USS *Stump* (DD 978) in 1986. Compared to SQS-53B, -53C saves 50 percent in electronics space and weight. The remaining 1960s electronic technology of the -53B is replaced by new standard digital equipment. The transmitter is now modular, one power amplifier for each transducer element. A production version of SQS-53C was tested on board USS *Stump* in March through October 1987.

This sonar incorporates SIMAS, the Sonar In-Situ Mode Assessment System, which helps the operator monitor the sonar's performance. In 1978 SQS-53C was expected to enter service in FY86, with a 750-hour MTBF.

◆ SQS-35/36/38

SQS-35 variable-depth sonar fish. (U.S. Navy)

The standard U.S. independent variable-depth sonar, found on board some *Knox*-class frigates, is now significant primarily as the depressor for SQR-18 towed arrays. SQS-35 operates at 13 kHz, with a peak power of 30 kW, and uses 12 preformed RDT beams and a total of 24 reception beams (the transducer has 24 staves). SQS-35V is a solid-state version.

This sonar, developed by Edo under a 1966 contract, was derived from SQS-17. SQS-35(J) is a version license-built in Japan (by NEC).

SQS-36 is a hull-mounted equivalent of SQS-35. SQS-38, which equips U.S. *Hamilton*-class coast guard cutters, is a solid-state version. It operates at 11.9, 13, and 14.1 kHz and has an MCC mode, the last two (lowest of 9) transducers on each of its 24 staves being depressed to turn the beam down when desired. Nominal range is 12,000 yds.

◆ SQS-54

The shipboard processor for the LAMPS-I helicopter (1969) is built by Diagnostics Retrieval Systems, Inc. The helicopter itself carries no sonobuoy processor, acting merely as a sonobuoy and torpedo dropping platform and as a relay for acoustic data. Thus, the helicopter's effective range depends, not on its fuel capacity, but on its ability to transmit data back by digital link to the deploying or controlling ship. LAMPS-I ships, therefore, have characteristic data-link antennas as high as possible, for maximum range. SQS-54 evolved into SQR-17(V)1 (see above).

◆ SQS-56 (DE-1160B)

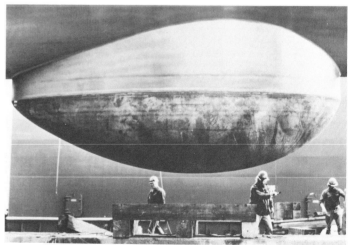

SQS-56 transducer and its sonar dome.

The hull-mounted direct-path sonar of the *Perry* class is built by Raytheon. SQQ-23 was originally chosen for these ships. Then the Canadian SQS-505, whose performance was not much worse but whose cost was much less, was chosen. SQS-56 was conceived as a solid-state duct sonar whose weight, performance, size, and cost would roughly match those of

SQS-505. Engineering design was completed in October 1977. Production began in 1979, following tests in 1975 and then in 1978.

The sonar is entirely digital in both active and passive modes. Operation is at 5.6, 7.5, and 8.4 kHz (36 kW).

DE-1160B is the export version. DE-1160C provides more power (with an extra electronic cabinet). Spain has upgraded her DE-1160Bs to 1160C standards. DE-1164 is the corresponding variable-depth sonar, which can be trailed at depths as great as 600 ft.

♦ **SQS-58**

See Raytheon's DE-1167 below.

♦ **LAMPS**

An SH-60B LAMPS III helicopter. The sonobuoy rack is on the side, above the empty torpedo rack, and the flat ESM arrays are in the nose. (Sikorsky)

The U.S. Light Airborne Multi-Purpose System is carried by a helicopter. LAMPS is listed here because it is conceived as a direct extension of a surface ship, rather than as a stand-alone device. All LAMPS sensors feed directly into the parent ship's CIC. There are two versions: LAMPS-I and LAMPS-III.

LAMPS-I, on board an SH-2F helicopter, carries an LN-66 radar and four sonobuoys. Sonobuoy processing is done by an SQS-54 processor on board ship, the data being passed back by one-way AKT-22 data link. The requirement for shipboard processing limits operation to the first convergence zone. The helicopter carries MAD for final attack confirmation before dropping torpedoes. LAMPS-I is the redetection/prosecution system associated with the SQR-18A towed array.

As of 1987, projected LAMPS-I improvements included a better engine (T-700), an on-board acoustic processor, TACNAV-to-TACNAV data transfer (secure ship-helicopter link), and a 99-channel sonobuoy receiver.

LAMPS-III is the redetection/prosecution system associated with the SQR-19 towed array. Because the array may be able to detect targets beyond the first convergence zone, i.e., beyond radio range, the helicopter requires an independent prosecution capability. However, LAMPS-III is still essentially an extension of shipboard systems.

LAMPS-III, an SH-60 helicopter, carries an APS-124 radar, an ALQ-142 ESM system, and 25 sonobuoys (although 12 would be used in a typical mission). The data link is two-way, and the helicopter can do some on-board processing, although the ship is still required for more detailed analysis (both helicopter and ship each carry a UYS-1 Proteus processor). Moreover, because the helicopter is controlled by the ship, the helicopter's sonobuoys form, in effect, an over-the-horizon supplement to shipboard sensors such as a towed array. Normally the helicopter and its sensors are controlled by four individuals on board ship: an acoustic-sensor operator (ASO) in the sonar room; a remote-radar operator (REMRO) in CIC (who receives the helicopter's radar output via data link; he can directly control radar range and operating mode); an electronic-warfare operator (EWO) in CIC; and the air-tactical-control officer (ATACO). The helicopter itself carries a pilot, an airborne tactical officer (ATO) who also functions as copilot, and a sensor operator (SO). The ATACO

takes over from the ATACO as directed, e.g., when the helicopter passes out of radio range.

LAMPS-III incorporates an acoustic target tracker (ATT) developed by IBM to automate the manual tracking process of the past. Past sonobuoy tracking was based on bearing fixes generated by pairs of buoys and on the tacit assumption that the submarine was not maneuvering. IBM's goal was to reduce localization time and the operator's localization work load by 50 percent, and also to provide a real-time solution even if the submarine maneuvered.

In the manual system, contacts are manually updated as the submarine runs through the buoy field (ideally, down a lane of buoys). The bearings are converted into fixes that then become a course and speed determined by least-squares fit. Because the LAMPS-III system was automated, IBM could add doppler information from the buoys, measuring a submarine's radial speed relative to them. The tracker maintains a real-time estimate of a target's position by filtering both frequency and bearing measurements from the buoys; there is no least-squares fit and, therefore, no need to assume straight-line motion. The algorithm begins with a crude estimate of submarine location based on bearings. Once that has been made, data are fed into parallel bearing and frequency trackers, which feed the target tracker.

Tests showed that the automated tracker could reach a consistent target-location solution very quickly, reaching attack criteria about twice as fast as the least-squares tracker and compensating automatically for the target's maneuvers. Often the least-squares tracker took as much as ten minutes merely to come within 90 degrees of the target's course, whereas the automated tracker could come within 15 degrees in that time.

The LAMPS-III Block-I upgrade (1987) includes the Mk 50 torpedo, a 99-channel sonobuoy receiver, GPS, and provisions for the Penguin missile (which was not bought). A projected Block II, which should appear in the 1990s, will provide a stand-off classification sensor (presumably ISAR applied to the APS-124 radar), cockpit night vision, basic self-defense, and acoustic improvements.

♦ **ALOFTS/LFAS**

EDO's experimental Active Low-Frequency Towed Sonar was first tested in 1983. It is interesting as a harbinger of future low-frequency systems. EDO used a standard 13/7-kHz fish carrying a flextensional transducer, and a multiline towed array was used as receiver. The system was tried on board a Second Fleet ship (using a single-line array) about 1984, then revived by NUSC New London in 1986 (with the three-line array).

The projected Low-Frequency Array Sonar would be a production version of ALOFTS, perhaps using a larger fish, suitable for ships such as Knox-class frigates. A drawing of this system was displayed at the U.S. Navy League show in 1989.

See also SSATS/LFA/RMES below, and SQQ-89.

♦ **BGMSS**

EDO's Battle Group Multi-Static Sonar is a NUSC New London program. A drawing of the active element, a towed vertical body carrying an array of flextensional transducers, was displayed at the U.S. Navy League show in 1989. This type of system is one way of overcoming Soviet silencing.

♦ **SSATS/LFA/RMES**

Surface-ship advanced tactical sonar is a generic term for the next-generation U.S. surface-ship sonar. It will probably be an active/passive suite, consisting of a multiline towed array (for greater gain/discrimination) and a low frequency transmitter, probably in the hull; there will probably also be a hull receiving array. The towed array will be the primary receiver for the low-frequency pinger. For a time this sonar, under preliminary design by Martin-Marietta, was associated with the U.S. FFX next-generation escort project.

LFA is the low-frequency active test array, installed in FY88 in the bow of USS Glover, a three-line SQR-18 being used for reception. This system was later described as an FY88 new start, in collaboration with Britain, which will furnish a test ship and the instrumentation. The goal is a shallow-water (presumably continental-shelf) capability. Canada may join this program.

RMES is the Gould reconfigurable multiline towed-array evaluation system (contract awarded April 1987), a means of testing future towed-array configurations. Parallel lines of arrays provide increased gain without the geometric distortion associated with a single very long array, and can also help solve the left-right ambiguity problem. However, it is not clear that these arrays can easily be handled at sea: hence the need for a test device.

Gould is supplying both the wet end (including a tow body) and the shipboard processor/beam-former.

See also SQQ-89 (improved).

◆ SURTASS (UQQ-2)

See the Surveillance and Control section.

◆ TARP

Towed-Array Range Processor is a term that apparently applies both to a form of signal processing and to a new long array used for passive ranging. In principle, an array can be used either as one leg of a triangulation device (the hull or bow array forming the other) or can be divided into elements and those elements used for triangulation. During FY87 a TARP model (presumably a processor using an existing array) was developed for at-sea testing, and a developmental TARP array was scheduled for tests during FY89. TARP is part of BQQ-5E, which is described officially as a quantum improvement in long-range detection and localization.

TARP system-processing capabilities were reduced and full vernier and target-motion analysis capability delayed because of reductions in FY88 funding.

◆ TB-12

TB-12 is a towed array for submarines. In the new *Seawolf*, TB-12X will be combined with TB-16D.

◆ TB-16

This thick array is a component of BQQ-5. TB-16 is 82.5 mm (3.25 in) in diameter and is towed on an 800-meter, 9.5-mm cable. The acoustic module is 240 ft long. Typically TB-16 is stowed in a tube running outside the pressure hull, the reel, cable, and winch being located in the forward main ballast tank. The array is streamed out of a tube leading from the port horizontal stabilizer. This installation was originally designed for SSN 637–class submarines, the early 688s being fitted with a permanently streamed (clip-on) array. The 688s were later provided with reelable arrays using tube stowage, operational experience having shown that the fixed array could be damaged during high-speed runs.

TB-16 is now associated with a towed-array range processing (TARP) unit. Approximately 1973 technology, TB-16 is to be replaced by the long thin array (TB-23).

Gould received a contract for 24 TB-16s in August 1982 (for BQQ-5 and -6 installation), and late in 1982 the company received a contract to integrate this array and the mine detection-and-avoidance system (MIDAS) into BQQ-5. In FY84 a total of 27 TB-16s were authorized (three-year procurement).

◆ TB-23

This long thin-line array was introduced in FY83 *Los Angeles*–class submarines. TB-23 was tested in 1987. Current plans call for this system to be installed not only in *Los Angeles* but also in *Sturgeon* (SSN 637) and *Ohio* –class submarines. Development of the *Sturgeon* class's thin-line handling equipment (THLE) was completed in FY88.

◆ EDO 610 Series

This low-frequency (6-, 7-, or 8-kHz) hull sonar is for frigates and larger ships. 610 uses preformed 10-degree beams both for reception and, in directional-transmission modes, for transmission. Modes are ODT, search (120-degree sector), and attack (50-degree sector). Maximum instrumented range in 32 kyds, and 610 can measure target doppler up to 40 kts. There is also a passive display for long-range detection. Beamwidth is 10 degrees vertical and horizontal, and range scales are 2, 4, 8, 16, and 32 kyds.

The hull transducer is 1245 mm in diameter and 1067 mm high (weight 2500 kg).

This sonar is designed so that it can be used in conjunction with the EDO 700/701 VDS. An improved 610A appeared in 1972. EDO 610E is a solid-state version incorporating SQS-38 experience.

Development began in 1963, specifically for the Royal Netherlands Navy, of the first EDO sonar designed specifically for a foreign customer. A prototype was completed in 1966; the first production model completed its sea trials in 1969. This work incorporated EDO's experience with SQS-26. The sonar, either in its 610 or its 610E form, is on board the two Dutch *Tromp*-class destroyers and was fitted to Dutch (some now Indonesian) *Van Spejk*–class frigates when they were modernized; the sonar is also on board the Italian *Audace*-class destroyers and on board some *Lupo*-class export frigates. In Dutch service this sonar is designated CWE-610.

◆ EDO 700/701

This variable-depth sonar was developed in parallel with the 610-series hull sonar, also for the Royal Netherlands Navy; 700 can be used in combination with the 610. Model 700E is a solid-state version incorporating SQS-35(V) technology (1972). Dutch *Van Spejk*–class frigates modernized with EDO 610 hull sonars were also fitted with this variable-depth sonar, designated PDE-700. The Brazilian Vosper-Thorneycroft frigates are fitted with the related EDO 701 variable-depth sonar. EDO 700/701 technology was incorporated in the U.S. SQS-35(V) sonar.

The transducer is 495 mm in diameter (787 mm high) and weighs 397 kg. The hoist and towed body together weigh 8250 kg. Frequency is probably 13 kHz.

◆ EDO 780 Series (780, 786, 796, 795, 7860, 7960, 7950)

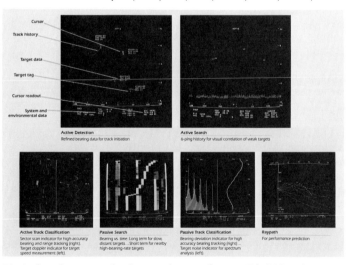

Typical modern sonar displays, in this case from an Edo 780 series sonar. The passive search display is a waterfall. At right in the passive track classification display is a time-integrated LOFAR (a spectrogram). (EDO)

This modular series of hull and variable-depth sonars ranges from a lightweight VDS (780) up to a large low-frequency hull sonar (795/7950). Each model uses the same basic console, transmitter, receiver, and data-storage and control unit. Given this modularity, any hull sonar in the series could be supplemented by a VDS, or vice versa. The original EDO 780 was a small VDS; 786 was the same sonar in a hull-mounted version. 796 and 795 were lower-frequency hull sonars.

EDO/780 Series Characteristics

	MODEL			
	780	*786*	*796*	*795*
Frequency	11.9/13/14.1 kHz	11.9/13/14.1 kHz	6/7/8 kHz	4.3/5/5.7 kHz
Source Level	(Higher Level was available as an option):			
SRDT	232 dB	226 dB	231 dB	232 dB
TRDT	226 dB	226 dB	225 dB	226 dB
DT	224–232 dB	218–226 dB	223–231 dB	224–232 dB
ODT	217 dB	217 dB	216 dB	217 dB
MCC	199 dB	201 dB	210 dB	210 dB
Weight:				
Inboard	2188 kg	2176 kg	2436 kg	2436 kg
Outboard	7300 kg	1365 kg	3045 kg	5000 kg

EDO's 7860, 7960, and 7950 are all combinations of a 13-kHz VDS and, respectively, a 786, 796, and 795 hull sonar.

The standard display has a dual CRT, and display data are all stored internally, so that alternative displays can be called up at will. Tracking is by ball-located cursor on a display. Alternative displays are: ray-path predictor; active detection (range vs. bearing); active search (6-ping history to make weak targets stand out visually), active track classification (sector scan range vs. bearing and target doppler side by side); passive search (bearing vs. time waterfall; either long-time for slow targets or short-time for fast ones); and passive track classification (bearing-deviation indication for high-accuracy tracking and target spectral analysis side by side). All of these displays show processed, rather than raw, video.

All sonars in the series have 24 preformed beams, and all employ 10-, 30-, and 60-msec CW pulses and 60-msec FM pulses. Each sonar provides its operator with the choice of 8 acoustic-intercept bands. Accuracy is $\frac{1}{2}$ percent of the range scale, 1 degree in active bearing, and 0.5 degrees in passive bearing. Range scales are 2, 4, 8, and 16 kyds, with 32 kyds added in the two lower-frequency sonars.

For the two high-frequency sonars, the passive band is 5.8–10.6 kHz; for the two lower-frequency sonars, it is 2.8–5 kHz.

The original EDO 780 was derived from the company's experience with SQS-35 and appeared in 1976; 780 is installed on board four Israeli *Sa'ar*-II–class missile boats, controlling lightweight torpedoes. EDO 786 (1979) is derived from EDO's experience with the corresponding hull sonar, SQS-38. 786 is installed on board Korean KCX-class frigates. EDO 7867 and 7957 are improved versions of 786 and 795 (1984).

The EDO 780-series displays were based on experience with BQQ-5. Compared to SQS-56, they show more attention to passive detection, with waterfalls (time vs. bearing displays).

◆ EDO 787

This compact 7-kHz variable-depth sonar uses the same fish as the 13-kHz EDO 780. The electronics are common to, and compatible with, Models 786, 795, and 796.

The transducer operates at 6, 7, or 8 kHz, with source levels as follows: ODT, 215 dB; DT, 219–226 dB; TRDT, 220 dB; SRDT, 226 dB. Pulse widths are 10-, 30-, or 60-msec CW, or 104-msec long FM (pulse-compressed). The active receiving bandwidth is 500 Hz, and the passive bandwidth is 2.8–5 kHz. The operator can specify 8 acoustic intercept bands. There are 24 preformed beams. Instrumented ranges are 2, 4, 8, 16, and 32 kyds. Accuracy: active range, 1/2 percent of range; active bearing, 1 deg; passive bearing, 0.5 deg.

Transducer dimensions: diameter 22 in, height 31 in. Unlike most cylindrical transducers, 787 is not constructed of a series of vertical staves. Instead, square spot transducers are arranged in a spiral over its face. EDO claimed that this new transducer design was what made it possible to provide a 250-ton patrol boat with a useful low-frequency sonar.

Model 787 was announced together with a new EDO Advanced Modular Signal Processor, which could be used by other 780-series sonars. That processor, in turn, was the basis for a linear FM coherent signal processor that was expected to improve performance substantially in the face of noise or reverberation. Signals were linearly broken down into pulse compressed signals and displayed in a clutter-free computer-driven display.

◆ EDO 814

A lighter-weight sonar based on the 780 series, 814 is acoustically equivalent to the 786 and was announced about 1980. 814 can carry out simultaneous active search, tracking, and classification; it has a built-in autotracker (for up to three targets) and a selectable passive mode. Transmission and reception are electronically stabilized. Fire-control provisions are built in.

The single CRT can be switched between a passive-search display (waterfall) and an active display (B-scan rather than PPI). The latter shows a track history (with target data displayed alongside the track in alphanumeric form). Readouts include system data (operating mode, frequency, pulse width) and cursor data (range, true and relative bearing).

The sonar operates at 11.9, 13, or 14.1 kHz, with source levels of 226 dB for SRDT and TRDT, 218–226 dB for DT, 217 dB for ODT, and 201 dB for MCC. There are 24 preformed beams. Pulse lengths are 10, 30, and 60 msec in CW and 60 msec in linear FM (slide) mode (to reject reverberation clutter). Accuracy in active mode is 0.5 percent of range scale in range and 1 degree in bearing.

Options include a coherent processor (for better performance in reverberation) and an acoustic-intercept threat-detector.

◆ EDO 900/910

These units are underwater-object locators and mine-detecting sonars for submarines. The difference between the two models is that in Model 900 the scanning head is above its drive mechanism, whereas in Model 910 the scanning head is below; Model 910 is a 900 adapted as a minehunting sonar. Dimensions and the display (a 7-inch ship-centered CRT) are identical. The signal is a continuously transmitted FM slide, which gives a clear audio presentation. The transducer is 368 mm in diameter.

◆ EDO 1102/1105

These passive/active sonars for submarines are derived from BQS-4 and BQR-2 experience. Models 1102 and 1105 appeared in 1976. In the passive surface-ship detection mode, processing prior to display shows ranges up to 30,000 yds and bearing accuracy to within 0.5 degrees. In the active mode the operator can obtain a precise range and target doppler. Visual display modes are bearing vs. time (waterfall), range vs. radial speed (doppler), and self-noise.

Details of operation are not available, but these sonars are single-dome systems, so passive ranging is probably done by target-motion analysis, target speed being estimated automatically by blade count. The hydrophone assembly is 1244 mm in diameter; the active transducer, 330 mm in diameter. The dome is 1524 mm wide and 4140 mm long (2032 mm deep). Given the ancestry of the system, it probably contains an active transducer inside a circular array of vertical passive transducers.

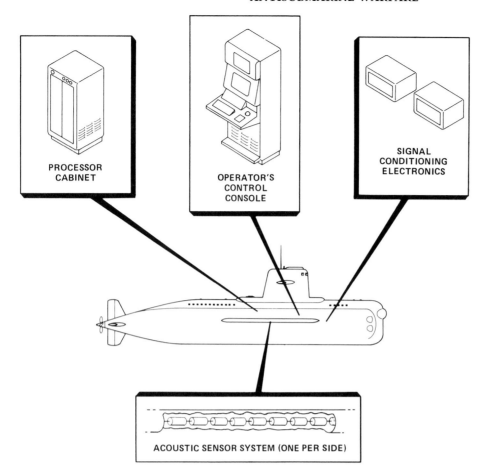

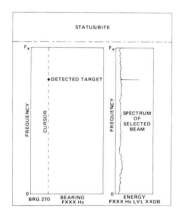

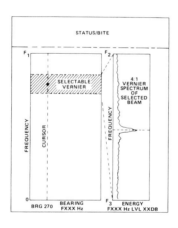

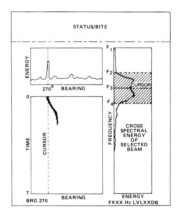

(*Above*) EDO 1110 submarine flank-array sonar. (EDO)

◆ EDO 1110

Model 1110 is a flank sonar for submarines, consisting of a linear transducer array. 1110 is intended as an adjunct to existing sonar, combat, and fire-control systems. This sonar uses low frequency beam-preforming, split-beam correlation (for accurate pointing), and spectral analysis; and 1110 can track more than fifteen targets simultaneously, using broad- and narrow-band processing interpolation. Selected targets can be assigned to "high quality" track processors for improved positional accuracy, and these tracks can be maintained even when targets cross the submarine's path (passing from the field of view of one array to the other). The operator initiates track by using a cursor at his console.

There are two high-resolution color displays, options including frequency vs. bearing and bearing vs. time.

This system appeared in 1985. EDO describes 1110 as based on operational experience in the U.S. and foreign navies, so the capabilities above may be typical of existing passive hull arrays.

◆ Micro-PUFFS/PASRAN/BQG-501

Sperry's passive ranger for submarines is a micro-circuited version of the earlier BQG series, using baffled hydrophone arrays. Because Micro-PUFFS employs three transducers along the hull, it is inherently much quicker than TMA; on the other hand, range is limited by the length of the baseline. PUFFS itself was developed by the U.S. Navy and by Sperry in 1956–60 (and Sperry produced 54 units in 1960–66). Micro-PUFFS was developed specifically for the Royal Australian Navy (1972–76), and in 1979 Sperry began work on a similar system for the Royal Navy. As BQG-501, Micro-PUFFS was incorporated in the Canadian *Oberon* upgrade program (SOUP), Micro-PUFFS electronics replacing that of the earlier Type-719 sonar. In the Canadian ships, Micro-PUFFS is visible in the form of six red-outlined soft patches along the sides of the upper casing (Stations 15 to 18a–19a, 64b to 69a, and 103 to 110, all port and

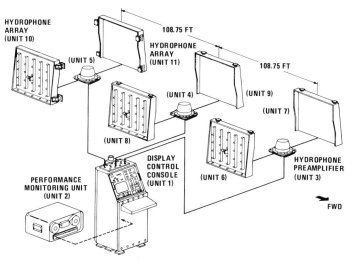

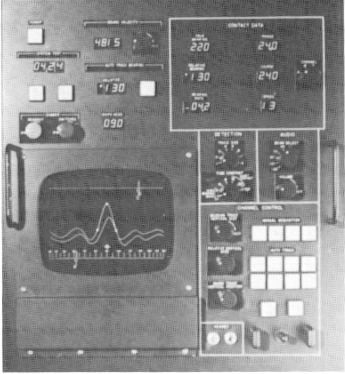

MicroPUFFS arrays. (Sperry)

MicroPUFFS display. The CRT shows two correlograms, one for each pair of adjacent arrays on one side. The upper line shows 150 degrees of bearing on the starboard side; the lower, 150 degrees on the port side. Targets appear on one or the other, and a control stick can be used to position a cursor on the target. When the operator aligns the peak of a correlogram with three dots on the display and presses a button, the system begins to track the target automatically in bearing. He can begin to track automatically in range when the peaks of the two correlograms are aligned (i.e., when he is triangulating on the same target). Contact data are displayed in the upper right-hand side of the panel, including true bearing, relative bearing, bearing rate, and range. Target's course and speed are indicated continuously through target-motion analysis. (Sperry)

starboard). This sonar was also installed on board the USS *Barb* (tested 1980).

The three hydrophones on each side of the submarine form five continuously processed preformed beams (five beams per array); targets are tracked automatically. Ranging is by cross correlation of the same signal as received by the three arrays, the two time differences being converted into bearing and range data. The range solution is, therefore, both instantaneous and continuous. Each triplet of hydrophones covers a 150-degree sector. In an Australian *Oberon*, the hydrophones are 108 ft 9 in apart. Each hydrophone is a square array (five staves, each carrying five spot hydrophones). Sperry estimated that the range

error on a target directly abeam at 6000 yds would be about 2.5 percent, rising to about 11 percent 60 degrees off the beam. The error would be about 5 percent at 12,000 yds (directly abeam).

Sperry claimed that Micro-PUFFS could more efficiently reject background noise because it used correlation and preformed-beam techniques. Early sea experience suggested that MTBF might be as great as 3600 hours, with 30 minute (or less) MTTR.

PASRAN (Passive Ranger) was a modified Micro-PUFFS delivered to the U.S. Navy in 1979 and tested on board the nuclear submarine *Haddock* from July 1979. The arrays are larger than those of Micro-PUFFS, and the system can track quieter targets at greater ranges. Presumably, PASRAN was an alternative to WAA.

◆ Raytheon DE 1160 Series

DE 1164 fish shown after it had been streamed and recovered by the Italian frigate *Maestrale*, March 1982. (Raytheon)

As of 1988, over 100 of these Raytheon export sonars are in service. All share common computer hardware and software, common displays, common transmitter amplifiers and power supplies, common circuit cards, and common interface units.

DE 1160 is a medium-range direct-path sonar for corvettes and larger ships. See the entry below for DE 1160B details.

DE 1160C is the standard U.S. SQS-56 frigate sonar (see above). 1160C weighs 12,800 lbs, compared to 11,600 for DE 1160B; and peak power is 90 kW (average 10 kW) rather than 30 kW (10 kW average). Both B and C have the same transducer and the same sonar receiver, but DE 1160C adds an additional transmitter (unit 13) and a dummy load (unit 14). Both sonars provide simultaneous active and passive detection.

DE 1160LF is a larger low-frequency version.

DE 1163 is a variable-depth sonar version of DE 1160. Peak power is 35 kW (average 7 kW).

DE 1164 is an integrated hull-mounted VDS variant, combining DE 1160 and DE 1163. In hull sonar form 1164 equips the Italian carrier *Giuseppe Garibaldi* and the new *Animoso*-class destroyers. In VDS form, 1164 is installed on board Italian *Maestrale*-class missile frigates. Peak power is 35 kW (average 7 kW).

DE 1165 (see entry below) is an integrated submarine sonar.

DE 1167 is the latest version, smaller and lighter for fast patrol craft and similar types. 1167 exists both in hull and in VDS versions (and also in a hull/VDS combination version). Total weight of the hull version, including the dome, is 1460 kg; total weight of the VDS version is 10,260 kg. There is also a low frequency version for larger ships that cannot accommodate DE 1160 B/C. DE 1167 (MOD) is used to modernize existing SQS-23s: the receiver and console and a new 48-kW solid-state transmitter (SST) are added to the existing dome and transducer, adding a minimum of 10 dB in performance.

DE 1190 is a new solid-state transmitter suitable for SQS-23 modernization.

DE 1191 is a convergence-zone sonar for large frigates and destroyers (see entry below).

◆ Raytheon DE 1160B

Raytheon's hull sonar has an optional VDS extension. 1160B operates on 6.7, 7.5, and 8.4 kHz, with a bandwidth of 400 Hz (FM or CW). The beam can be depressed/elevated at 12.5 or 25 degrees. Operating modes (active) are ODT (5.0–160 msec pulses, source level 218 dB), Single RDT (5.0–2180 msec pulses, source level 232 dB, over a 20–120 degree sector), Triple RDT (5.0–1940 msec pulses, 227 dB), and wide (5–700 msec pulses, 30–120 degree sector, 225 dB). Reception modes (600-Hz bandwidth) are search (36 fixed beams, 12.5-degrees depression/elevation, 2-degrees resolution in azimuth, 2-yds resolution in range on 2.5-kyd scale, 16-yds resolution at 20 kyd) and tracking (two steered independent 20-degree beams, range gates 625 and 1250 yds using a sector-scan indicator and target doppler indication; one 14-degree independent audio beam, accuracy 0.5 degrees in azimuth, 1.1 yds in range, and 2 kts in doppler). The sector-scan indicator (SSI) and target doppler indicator (TDI) are target-following aids, respectively comparing the phase differences on either side of a beam and showing target doppler.

There is also a passive mode using 18 fixed beams (18 × 21 deg) at 3–6 kHz, with audio on one selected beam. This mode uses a DIMUS processor (signals are clipped, processed digitally, and then filtered through short-term averaged and long-term averaged smoothing filters). The displays are all B-scans; active track data are presented on an expanded B-scan (20 degrees in bearing × 625 or 1250 yards), and both long- and short-term averaged data can be presented separately, in waterfall form.

Peak power is 30 kW (7.2 kW average). The hull transducer is 121.9 cm (diameter) × 96.5 cm (weight 2268 kg). Total system weight is 5302 kg.

◆ Raytheon DE 1165

Raytheon's integrated submarine sonar uses a large passive transducer and an active transducer similar to that of the DE 1160 series surface-ship sonars. The active transducer is used for fire control. Peak active power is 10 kW (average 2.5 kW).

◆ Raytheon DE 1167 (SQS-58)

Raytheon's hull and variable-depth sonar for smaller ships (hull, fish, or combined) operates in a 2-kHz band around 12 kHz, and there is also an 18-kHz version. The passive-search band is 2 kHz wide, centered on 4.5 kHz. Reception is on 36 preformed beams, with a selectable 10 × 13 degree sum beam for listening. Comparison of half-beams allows a tracking accuracy of 2 degrees. Range resolution is 8–64 yds. The active display operates on 256 range cells and 180 bearing cells (2 degrees each), with two intensity levels. Pulses are FM slides covering 1 kHz (6.25, 50, 100, 200 msec). Source levels are 225 dB (triple beam) and 215 dB (ODT). The ODT mode is limited to 5-kyd range, to maximize data rate on the most urgent threats. The more concentrated triple beam is necessary to provide enough energy for greater ranges. The display can show a three- or six-ping history. Range scales are 2, 4, 8, and 16 kyds.

In search operation, the sonar interlaces tribeam and ODT ping modes, the tribeam mode consisting of twelve transmissions in sequence to cover the full 360 degrees. In this mode the sonar usually transmits 200-msec pulses, although it can use 50-msec pulses. In the evaluation mode, the sonar transmits ODT pulses, with lengths of 6.25, 50, and 200 msec. There is a listening (passive) mode and an optional passive mode, which can operate simultaneously with the active mode (at lower frequency).

The display is a CRT that can be used in various formats: a B-scan (with over 300 lines of sonar data) for active search, a restricted B-scan for sector scanning (showing target doppler), a passive waterfall (which shows both short- and long-term averaged data), and a variety of alphanumerics.

The variable-depth sonar weighs 10,260 kg (6.4 square meters). The hull sonar weighs 4375 kg (12 kHz) or 3920 kg (18 kHz). Only one operator is required. MTBF: one hour of service is required for sixty days of operation. MTTR is 30 minutes. The sonar uses built-in test equipment.

Another version, DE 1167LF, operates at 7.5 kHz (and can support a 7.5- or 12-kHz VDS). The 7.5-kHz hull array is 48 inches in diameter, compared to 28.2 inches for the 12-kHz array. The 7.5-kHz VDS fish weighs 50,300 lbs; the 12-kHz fish, 23,550 lbs. As of 1985, two DE 1167LF/VDS had been sold to Egypt, to equip *Descubierta*-class frigates. As of 1986, a total of 25 DE 1167 had been sold. Some parts are made in Italy by Elsag.

SQS-58(XN-1), on Raytheon's test ship *Sub Sig*-II, is a DE 1167. The U.S. Navy uses the DE 1167 engineering model to track nuclear submarines on their sea trials; Raytheon claims that the model has operated for more than 8000 hours and that it has "perhaps more 'ping time' against live submarines than any other surface ship system anywhere." Raytheon currently refers to the hull version of this sonar as DE 1167HM. It incorporates the operating techniques and processing power of the larger DE 1160/1164 series but can be installed on board ships displacing as little as 200 tons.

◆ Raytheon DE 1191

Raytheon's hull sonar combines features of the DE 1190 transmitter, the DE 1160 receiver and display, and a new low-frequency transducer. The solid-state transmitter (DE 1190 SST) is sold as an SQS-23 upgrade, 71 having been sold as of FY85. They included 48 for the U.S. Navy and 12 for Taiwan (GRC). DE 1191 includes a 48-kW transmitter (14-dB improvement over SQS-23) and eliminates 40 cabinets and boxes of vacuum tubes and 10 motor generators, saving 450 cubic feet. DE 1191 requires five cabinets. It uses the same dome and transducer as SQS-23, so no drydock work is required for installation. Typically the SST is installed first, then the more expensive receiver/display. Features include memory-refreshed B-scan and multi-ping storage.

DE 1190 is offered in 12-, 24-, 36-, 48-, 72-, and 96-kW versions, using 1-kW transmitter modules. Peak power is 28–56 kW. DE 1191 peak power is 120 kW (average 10 kW).

◆ TAVA

The transducer "fish" of the Gould TAVA (towed active vertical array), showing the vertical column of sixteen flex-tensional transducers in two vertical struts (for left/right patterns; the beam could also be steered vertically). When not in use, the column could swing back into its recess to reduce drag. (Gould)

Gould's Towed Active Vertical Array is for a joint NATO SACLANT/NAVSEA/NUSC program. TAVA was tested in the Mediterranean in October–November 1986. The transmit array was 16 Sanders Model 30 flex-tensional transducers in two vertical struts, providing left/right cardioid patterns. The beam could also be steered vertically. Signal strength was 226 dB at 1125 Hz. The receiver was towed separately, using a critical-angle tow. The first two weeks of the sea trial were spent on acoustic and hydrodynamic tests; the third was spent operating with a *Glavkos*-class (Type-209) submarine, and the fourth week was spent acquiring environmental data.

This program was established in January 1986.

◆ WQRSS

Whitehall's Quick-Reaction Surveillance System is a containerized towed array proposed by Whitehall Corp. about 1985. The navy leased three units under its FY86 program, operating them very successfully; this system was, in effect, SURTASS without the command/control aspects. Whitehall manufactures the "wet end" of the SURTASS sonar (UQQ-2) and has made numerous hydrophone arrays for oil exploration.

UNDERWATER FIRE-CONTROL SYSTEMS

◆ ASWCCS

ASW Command-and-Control System, a small-ship variant of NTDS developed specifically for ASW, was installed only on board the two frigates *Koelsch* and *Voge*. The project was begun in 1962 as the U.S.-Canadian SSCDS (Small-Ship Command-and-Control System); much of it was based on a 1959 Canadian study. SSCDS consisted of a single USQ-20A computer (64k 30-bit words) connected with six SYA-3 displays. SSCDS employed Links 11 and 14, and the project initially also included a UHF link (tentatively designated Link 12). Inputs included both sonar and radar (required for helicopter control), and the Naval Electronics Laboratory developed a digital sonar signal extractor (SPADE, for the SQS-23 sonar) specifically for this system. An electronic warfare (ESM) processor, SINEWS, was also planned, since under some circumstances submarines might be detected by their RF emissions.

SSCDS system design and software specifications were completed by 1963, and joint U.S.-Canadian trials were planned, using three stations: a *St. Laurent*–class frigate, a FRAM-I destroyer, and the Antisubmarine Development and Experimental Center (ASDEC) of NEL, the system developer. SSCDS would have equipped the original Canadian "Tribal"-class general-purpose frigates, but they were canceled in 1964, and the projected tests did not take place. SSCDS then evolved into a purely U.S. program, redesignated ASWCCS. It was tested in 1967, on board the two frigates and the carrier *Wasp*. Although no further U.S. frigates were fitted (the *Knox* class all integrate their sensor data entirely manually), ASWCCS did lead to the ASW tactical data system implemented in the *Spruance* class.

SSCDS was a development of the Canadian Datar system and provided essential experience for CCS-280 (see the Surveillance and Control section). Datar was conceived about 1950 as a digital data system, at a time when both the Royal Navy and the U.S. Navy were still concentrating on analog systems (CDS and the Cambria ASW system in the Royal Navy, EDS in the U.S. Navy). Datar incorporated the world's first digital data link, demonstrated in 1950, as well as the ball-tracker used in NTDS and analogous NATO tactical data systems to take target positions off radar displays. The original system capacity was 64 targets (within an 80×80 nm area, with a resolution of 40 yds). The Canadians were led to adopt digital technology because analog systems tended not to resolve ambiguities between neighboring targets, and because analog systems were difficult to tune even to minimize these ambiguities). Datar was a vacuum-tube system, and it occupied nearly the entire stern of a fleet minesweeper. Its successful demonstration in 1953 (employing the fleet minesweepers *Digby* and *Granby* on Lake Ontario) led directly to the British and U.S. decisions to abandon analog systems in favor of the digital ADA and EDS.

Datar was conceived as a small-ship system (the Canadians operated mainly frigates and destroyers, with only one carrier), but in 1955 a proposal to fit Datar in both the carrier *Bonaventure* and the new *St. Laurent*–class frigates was rejected. The argument was that the new British or U.S. systems would be superior. A 1957 proposal to fit Datar to the new *Restigouche* class was also rejected. However, Datar led directly to SSCDS and then to ASWCCS, and so is worthy of description here. It did demonstrate that a small-ship equivalent of NTDS was viable.

In 1960 the Canadian Navy began a study of a new Action Data and Control System (ADACS) for the general-purpose frigate then planned (but ultimately canceled). This project merged with the U.S. SSCDS then under development by NEL San Diego, and there was some hope that the result would meet a NATO Basic Military Requirement for a destroyer/frigate tactical data system. SSCDS as conceived at this time was somewhat too elaborate for the NATO requirement, as both the Canadian and U.S. Navies planned highly automated ships (the abortive Canadian general-purpose frigate and the abortive U.S. Seahawk ASW destroyer). Both ship projects died in 1964. However, ADACS/SSCDS ideas survived in the Action Information System (AIS 240) developed for the ASW hydrofoil (HMCS *Bras d'Or*) the Canadian Navy was then developing. As in both earlier systems, AIS 240 included both sonar and radar data as digital inputs.

◆ Mk 101

The first U.S. post–World War II submarine fire-control system was found in new-construction submarines and full Guppy conversions only. Developed by Arma, Mk 101 entered service in 1952. It used the new Mk 55 computer-analyzer (also in contemporary surface-ship ASW systems) and an automatic plotter (which replaced the dead-reckoning tracer of earlier submarine fire controls). Mk 101 could handle relative target speeds of up to 45 kts, ranges of up to 20,000 yards (depths as great as 1000 ft), and travel times as great as 15 minutes. Mk 101 could apply curved courses for target-motion prediction. Maximum target range was 34,000 yds. In its ultimate form, Mk 101 could control wire-guided torpedoes such as Mks 37 and 45.

◆ Mk 106

This postwar fire-control system was for older submarines that could not accommodate the full Mk 101. The system was built around the earlier Torpedo Data Computer Mk 4 and analyzer Mk 7. Like Mk 101, Mk 106 was designed to track targets at ranges up to 30,000 yds, and it could provide initial gyro angles and enable ranges for torpedo travel up to 15,000 yds. Maximum target depth was 1000 ft, and maximum target speed was 40 kts. Total system weight was 7300 lbs (compared to 9340 lbs for Mk 101), and the system required a total of 6 men (compared to 7 for Mk 101). Mk 106 was not initially intended to control wire-guided torpedoes, but the latest version, in Guppy-III submarines equipped with PUFFS, could control the Mk 45 (Astor) wire-guided nuclear torpedo as well as the nonnuclear Mk 37.

◆ Mk 111

This digital solid-state ASROC and torpedo/hedgehog fire-control system (using the digital Mk-38 attack console) was widely installed in the late 1950s and early 1960s, e.g., on board FRAM destroyers. The early digital system was considerably less reliable than the analog computer of the somewhat later Mk 114, which replaced 111 in later U.S. warships.

◆ Mk 112

Mk 112 was the replacement for Mk 101, in *Tullibee* and *Ethan Allan* classes (also in the *George Washington* class, now defunct). Mod 1 controlled Mk 37 and Mk 45 torpedoes; Mod 2 controlled Mk 48 torpedoes as well. This system was replaced by Mk 113. Digital technology made for a considerably more compact unit than Mk 101; Mk 112 weighed only 3500 lbs and required only 5 operators. Since it used a better sonar, Mk 112 was designed for a maximum target range of 70,000 yds (torpedo running range of 35,000 yds). Target speed could be up to 50 kts, and torpedo speed 10–80 kts (the latter figure presumably represents expectations for future torpedo development, as of about 1955, when Mk 112 was conceived). These figures all describe the standard system as of about 1958, and they are interesting mainly for comparison with Mk 101 and Mk 106 performance of that period.

Like all earlier submarine and surface fire-control systems, Mk 112 was a computer whose dials showed relative target and own-ship bearing, in the form of ship hull symbols. Targets would be tracked passively, and their courses automatically fed into the computer, but the final range would be obtained from a single sonar ping. Such techniques became less satisfactory as much longer tracking ranges became available via the new generation of lower-frequency sonars, mainly bow spheres, and as submarine speeds increased. By about 1960 target-motion analysis (TMA) had become the primary ranging tool. A classic fire-control computer presented only part of the data needed for TMA, and the actual analysis had to be done on a paper plot, using data assembled from several sources in a submarine attack center. This type of data fusion was unsatisfactory because it did not immediately present the information needed to maneuver to improve the TMA solution. The problem was not solved until, in later versions of Mk 113, a CRT replaced the old dials. The CRT could still display representations of the old pair of turning dials, but it could also present, in one place, a full TMA plot.

The CRT was first introduced during Poseidon refits of SSBNs, and then it was extended to later versions of Mk 113.

◆ Mk 113

The Librascope Attack fire-control system for submarines was compatible with the BQQ-2 sonar. Even-numbered mods were installed on board attack submarines; the odd-numbered mods were scaled-down versions for ballistic-missile submarines. Mod 2 incorporated SUBROC capability. Mk 113 incorporated the first submarine digital fire-control computer, Mk 130, with Mk 129 for leveling and for SUBROC calculations. Although the system itself was digital, it could control analog-set weapons, particularly SUBROC. Mk 113 was also the first use of a cathode ray tube (CRT) display in a submarine ASW system (analyzer console Mk 78). This interactive display was intended to increase the number of targets the system could handle simultaneously. Work on a Mk-48 torpedo capability began in 1964 (improvements to Mods 2 and 5).

Typically the fire-control portion of the system was a console consisting of two analyzers Mk 51 Mod 3 next to an attack-control console (Mk 50-4), two torpedo-control consoles (Mk 66-2), and two attack directors (Mk 75-4). The consoles were fed by the leveler and the fire-control computer, as well as by the sonar, electromagnetic log, dead-reckoning analyzer, and gyro.

Mod 1 could track four targets and engage two simultaneously. Mod 2 was limited to two targets at a time, and Mod 3 (not used) to one. Mod 4 (not used) could track two targets and engage one at a time (because it had one rather than two attack directors Mk 75). Mod 5, in SSBN 616 and 640 classes, was limited to a single attack director. Mod 6 added Mk-48 torpedo capability. Mod 8, in later Sturgeon (SSN 637)-class submarines, has four attack consoles. Mod 9, a modified Mod 5 or Mod 7, has a better target-motion analyzer (Mk 78 rather than Mk 51); Mod 9 is installed in strategic submarines. Mod 10 adds Harpoon capability and has increased computer capacity for surveillance and analysis of target/objective acoustic horizon (two attack directors). Mod 12 is fitted for Mk-48 TELCOM guidance and has a new computer-driven CRT display. Mod 12 is to be used with BQS-13 under a shipboard-requirements improvement program (SHRIMP) for 31 SSN 594/637–class submarines. The remaining submarines will be fitted instead with Mod 11.

This system has been succeeded by Mk 117 in newer submarines but may still exist on board older ones not yet fully modernized. It has almost certainly been retained on board SSBNs.

◆ Mk 114

This analog solid-state ASROC/torpedo fire-control system replaced the digital Mk 111. Mk 114 is now widely used in navies that obtained destroyers and frigates from the United States. Mk 114 employs attack console Mk 53. An additional unit, position-keeping computer Mk 143, which would have controlled surface-launched wire-guided Mk-37 torpedoes, was not fitted to U.S. Knox-class frigates. That computer probably has been fitted to Spanish Baleares-class frigates, which do incorporate fixed torpedo tubes in their transoms.

The shift from digital technology back to analog was made because the digital computers of the late 1950s and early 1960s were still expensive, slow, and relatively unreliable. The underwater ASW problem was well enough defined to make an analog computer attractive. As digital technology improved, it became overwhelmingly more attractive, particularly because a digital system was much easier to update to match new weapons, sensors, and target characteristics. For that reason the U.S. Navy adopted the digital Mk 116 to succeed the analog Mk 114.

◆ Mk 116

This all-digital surface-ship fire-control system, made by Librascope, uses the SQS-53A sonar. Unlike earlier ASW fire-control systems, Mk 116 uses a standard UYK-7 digital computer, for simplified logistics. Mod 1 is in Virginia-class cruisers and Kidd-class destroyers. The weapons-control panel is Mk 329 Mod 1, controlling two missile-setting panels (Mk 330) and a torpedo-setting panel (Mk 331). The main input is an SQS-53A, fed into the UYK-7 computer. Its output goes through a fire-control switchboard, which also feeds the sonar PPI console. Mod 1 was approved for service use in October 1980. Mod 4 is Mod 1 adapted to Aegis. Mod 6 is in CG 56 (which has vertically launched ASROC). Mod 7 is the version for CG 65 and the Arleigh Burke–class destroyers. It introduces the sonar supervisor console and the UYK-43B computer.

Mods 5 and 6 add capacity to exploit the increased number of contacts obtained by the new SQQ-89 (SQS-53B and SQR-19) as well as active/passive fire control (plus contact management, localization, and correlation). Mod 5 was evaluated on board USS Moosebrugger, August through November 1982.

The system is designed to accept all the contacts (and associated data) generated by SQS-53B, correlating them with each other and with manually entered data inputs from the combat direction system (CDS) to generate track files with at least a 70-percent probability that all contacts reported back to the CDS are unique. Mk 116 aids the operator in target classification and annotates the contact range after the first tagged active contact is returned to the ASW control system.

In the passive mode, Mk 116 estimates contact range and recommends maneuvers for TMA to improve that estimate. 116 creates track files accurate enough for fire control. The test requirement is that, using up to four pings to determine a contact's course and speed, 116 must obtain track files of sufficient quality that the CO/TAO can determine that the threat is within active sonar range (as predicted by SIMAS, the sonar performance monitor). The attack that follows is based on active confirmation of the estimated range.

These requirements were met in the 1982 trials.

UYK-43B in Mod 7 adds integrated acoustic-performance prediction and sensor supervision.

◆ Mk 117

This system (and probably earlier U.S. submarine fire-control systems) is as much a command-integration as a pure fire-control device. The individual sensors all feed the central computer, which forms the integrated picture of the volume around the submarine, much as NTDS integrates the radar and sonar picture around a surface ship. For example, Mk 117 can actually produce a picture similar to that of NTDS or of a radar PPI.

Mk 117 was the first all-digital fire-control system, first tested on board Narwhal, for installation on board SSN 700 and later

U.S. attack submarines. The all-digital attack center (ADAC) employs three computer-driven CRT displays. Mod 0 is for SSN 700 through 715; Mod 1 is a backfit for SSN 594–596, 603–607, 612–615, and 621. Mod 2 equips SSN 637–639, 646–653, 660–670, and 672–677. There are no separate attack directors, only three weapons-control consoles Mk 81. Mod 5 (Tomahawk capability), to replace Mod 1, also adds a digital navigation system, DMINS. Mod 6 is Mod 2 plus digital navigation (ESGN) for Tomahawk; Mod 7 is Mod 3 plus ESGN and Tomahawk, for SSN 671 and 678–687. Mod 8 provides for SUBROC as well as Tomahawk (SSN 716–720) and includes a submarine integrated attack center (SIAC) and four Mk-81 attack consoles. Presumably SUBROC capability was reflected in the inclusion of a digital-to-analog converter.

The decision to buy all-digital systems made the analog SUBROC obsolete. Although there were some efforts to retain it (e.g., Mod 8), the weapon is being retired as this book goes to press. However, Congress demanded that the navy keep SUBROC in service and modify fire-control systems to match. Presumably that demand means that SUBROC will remain in service, albeit in small numbers, until Sea Lance becomes operational.

Combat-control system (CCS) Mk 1 was begun in FY73 to support development of the new digital Mk 117, beginning with SSN 700 (backfit into SSN 688–699). CCS was approved for service use in 1980. Mod 1 adapts Mk 117 to control Tomahawks against over-the-horizon targets and was approved for service use in July 1980. Mod 2 supports the submarine vertical-launching system.

◆ Mk 118

The Trident (*Ohio* class) all-digital defensive fire-control system has provisions for real-time data processing, conversion, and display.

◆ Mk 119

The proposed digital underwater fire-control system for surface ships incorporates some submarine technology (e.g., attack console Mk 81). The first Mk 119 was installed at NUSC San Diego.

◆ Mk 309

A fire-control panel, not a complete fire-control system, Mk 309 controls lightweight torpedo tubes on board frigates.

◆ CCS Mk 2

Raytheon's Combat Control System Mk 2 is the successor to the CCS Mk 1 embedded in the BSY-1 system. Both are successors to the earlier stand-alone Mk 117. From a hardware point of view, the basis of the system is a standardized multifunction workstation, one of the Raytheon SC-2000 series. The workstation is derived from a commercial design, the Silicon Graphics 4D/20 Personal IRIS. Probably much more important is the modular software design, which permits Raytheon to offer versions of CCS Mk 2 for all four current U.S. submarine classes: the three versions of the *Los Angeles* class (Mod 0 in SSN 688–718 and Mod 1 in SSN 719–725 and 750, which have vertical launching tubes; and Mod 2 in SSN 751–779, which have BSY-1) and the *Ohio* class (Mod 3). One requirement is sufficient computing power to support a powerful emulation mode, so that the workstation can replace several current consoles without any impact on existing interfaces.

In each case, the submarine is fitted with a block of three of the new workstations (common display consoles), supplemented by a new attack-control console Mk 92. The existing weapons-launch console, weapons-data converter, and torpedo-tube control panel (all located in the torpedo room) are retained (in BSY-1 they are replaced by a new weapons-launch-system console). Mods 1 and 2 add a UYK-43B computer (plus a random access storage set) to interface with the submarines's sonars; it is already present in BSY-1 and in Trident submarines. Submarines with vertical tubes but without BSY-1 have an additional set of Tomahawk control panels and interface consoles

in a separate missile control room (not required for Tomahawks loaded in standard torpedo tubes).

The workstation incorporates special-purpose processors to convert analog PPI data to raster-scan, to convert sonar data to LOFARgrams, waterfalls, and A-scans, and to superimpose synthetic data on raw video. The displays can be color or monochrome, with 1280×1024 pixels (12 bits per pixel, for color or shading).

◆ Combat Control System (*Los Angeles* class)

The *Los Angeles* was the first U.S. submarine to have a combat system built around digital computers. It employs a central computer complex (CCC) with a UYK-7 computer to conduct a variety of combat-system functions. The CCC processes attitude signals (converted into digital form). It receives raw velocity data from the inertial navigation system and computes own-ship velocity north and east. There is also an underwater log and an analog dead-reckoning analyzer/indicator (DRAI). The CCC conducts TMA using primarily sonar inputs and navigational data, under control of the fire-control system. The BQQ-5 sonar transmits data directly to the CCC, which then provides this information to the fire control–signal data converter (FC–SDC) for use by fire-control system analog devices. The BQS-15 active sonar transmits analog target data directly to the fire-control analog devices and to the CCC computer for TMA. The CCC computer combines the target and own-ship data through target localization and TMA computations and, thereby, allows ship's personnel to evaluate the tactical situation. Simultaneously with target and own-ship data entry into the CCC, the fire-control system digital display subsystem (DDSS) provides the computer with the operational program control necessary to perform target localization and TMA. The DDSS also provides various display techniques, such as numerical, geographic, vectorial, or tabular display and analysis, during the target localization and TMA process. Manual TMA calculations may also be performed by fire control and sonar system operators. These calculations are primarily performed at the navigation/sonar (NAV/SONAR) plotting station. They may also incorporate ECM bearing data and periscope range data.

Classification is usually by target acoustic or electromagnetic characteristics; and BQQ-5 can conduct automatic classification. This data is routed directly to the CCC.

Weapons and tactic selection are by the weapons order subsystem (WOS), supported by the CCC computer. The system includes two attack directors, two torpedo control consoles, one firing console, one own-ship data console, and one leveling computer. WOS programs the Torpedo Mk 48 for launch. The assigned attack director uses analog TMA solutions from FC–SDC to compute torpedo orders. The attack director also computes and transmits the torpedo gyro angle to the torpedo. The torpedo control console monitors attack director functions and generates additional preset data as required. For SUBROC, the attack director provides target parameters and own-ship data to the leveling computer. The latter processes this data and transmits ballistic preset signals to SUBROC; the leveling computer also provides prelaunch alignment signals.

The WOS firing console initiates launch of preselected weapon(s). In the case of Mk 48, WOS continues to guide the torpedo. For SUBROC, WOS provides post-launch position-keeping calculations, for evasion or re-attack.

◆ SUBACS

See BSY-1 above.

◆ Rockwell Combat System (ACS)

The combat system of the Australian Type-471 submarine was developed by RSSA (Rockwell Submarine Systems Australia). Reportedly Rockwell is also responsible for the combat systems of the projected Israeli diesel-electric (German Type-209) submarines and *Sa'ar*-V–class corvettes. Presumably all three share some of the same technology. Singer-Librascope is supplying the multifunction consoles, which are the same as those of the SFCS described below.

As in the SFCS, ACS is based on multifunction common consoles (MFCC) and one command-plotting (CP) console. The ESM cell is, however, separate to maintain its security. Each of the seven MFCCs is capable of handling all combat-system functions, primarily surveillance (detection, classification, contact-data management) and threat prosecution (including review of surveillance data). Each console contains two 19-inch touchscreen color CRTs. The CP, which is horizontal, has a 39-inch color CRT, for tactical analysis or for reproduction of one of the MFCC displays. There are also four supplementary plasma displays, two for supplementary alphanumeric data, such as weapons status, and two used as remote presetting, testing, and control panels for the port and starboard sets of torpedo tubes.

The entire system is tied together by a Rockwell fiber-optic Expanded-Service Ship-Data Multiplexing System (ESSDMS), derived from the new U.S. Navy USQ-82(V) multiplexing system.

Reportedly the Advanced Combat System (ACS) can detect more than 1000 targets, initiate tracks on 200, and localize 25 or more; and engagements are limited only by the nature of the torpedo tubes.

◆ SEAS/Seawitch

Unisys's privately developed expert data-fusion systems are for ASW data analysis. Seawitch is the overall in-house program, and SEAS is a Submarine Expert Analysis System using techniques developed for Seawitch. Presumably these prototypes represent technology being offered as part of SQQ-89(I).

Different sensors have different ranges of errors and, thus, present somewhat different pictures of the same tactical situation. Moreover, it is not always possible to determine what is happening in a complex tactical situation in which, for example, tracks cross (track identity is easily lost). Seawitch presents the operator with several different possible scenarios for actual tracks based on the variety of available data from the different sensors and on probabilities assigned to different possible interpretations of the data (e.g., alternative identifications for tracks emerging from a crossing). A multiple-hypothesis algorithm is used to determine the most probable interpretation. Seawitch can show uncertainty ellipses around the actual correlated track and also around the hypothesized track.

Data fusion becomes increasingly important as the variety of available sensor inputs (e.g., sonars at different frequencies, offboard sonar data, sonobuoys) increases. Moreover, tactical decisions must be made more rapidly because targets can move very rapidly and, more importantly, because they can suddenly fire very high speed weapons. SEAS takes the output of Seawitch, which is a traditional plot, and analyzes the situation (using expert systems methods) to provide a list of target intents and future actions. Unisys plans to extend the system to provide

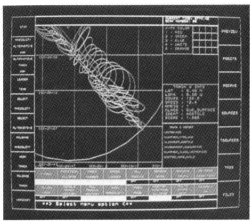

Seawitch can present the operator with uncertainty limits (ellipses) around the alternatives it hypothesizes. (Unisys)

recommended actions; SEAS then becomes the Unisys ASW Tactical-Decision Aid (ASWTDA). The company plans to test SEAS, using actual ASW data inputs, during 1989. This application of data bases to recommend action is somewhat analogous to the extension of NTDS to ACDS Block 1 described in the Surveillance and Control section.

◆ Singer-Librascope SFCS Mk I

The Librascope SFCS (submarine fire-control system) Mk I is a digital fire-control system that is in service in the Australian and Canadian Navies and that is now (1988) being installed on Indian Navy Type-209 submarines. The company claims that SFCS Mk I was the first all-digital submarine fire-control system. It reflects the company's experience in U.S. Navy systems such as Mk 113 (see above) and presumably reflects some U.S. Navy practice. Librascope described SFCS Mk I as closest in technology to Mk 118. In 1977, the U.S. Navy stated that SFCS Mk I had proven much less expensive than a comparable system purchased under standard Defense Department procurement rules.

Design objectives were automation (reduction of operators from ten to three), integration (all sensors can be coordinated by one operator using a multifunction console), improved availability, and adaptability to new weapons (torpedoes Mk 8, Mk 23, and Mk 48-3). The system uses computers to perform target-motion analysis (TMA) and to generate firing orders. It can detect 20 targets, track four, and engage two. The three manned positions are the command-display console in the control room (which must be manned continuously) and the two fire control consoles, each with its own CRT. The latter are manned only in action and standby conditions. Normally, one of the fire-control consoles provides contact motion analysis, the other controlling weapon and torpedo-tube status. Input into these consoles is by both light pen and keyboard.

The system is based on a command-display console. It contains a sensor-data converter (SDC) that accepts data from 15 sensors and that has nine passive sonar tracking channels. The display itself is a 20 × 24 inch paper plotter. Sonar operators can designate sonar bearings by means of one of the three sonar-assignment units at each sonar console, or the operator may designate one of the nine sonar-data channels. Such designation causes the system to store all data from that channel (for the most recent 30 minutes) in the computer's memory. Any four of the nine channels may be designated threats and, therefore, be subject to TMA. Typically a tactical analyst at the CRT of a fire-control console carries out threat assessment (e.g., TMA), normally at the right-hand console (with the left-hand console — which is functionally interchangeable — reserved for weapons control).

For TMA, passive sonar measurements are sampled every second and averaged over 20-second intervals. The submarine can maneuver to improve TMA ranging, and both automatic and

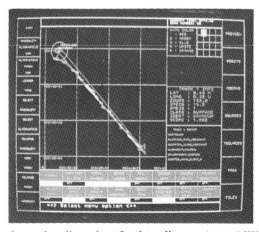

Seawitch shows the effect of artificial intelligence in an ASW combat system. Here it presents the operator with several possible interpretations of target track data. (Unisys)

manual target solutions can be obtained. There is also an acoustic environment display (ray path predictor).

The basic computer is UYK-20 (64K, 16-bit words, 1.3-MHz clock rate, with a 400K hard disk, average access time 18.4 msec).

Claimed MTBF is 400 hours (98-percent on-line availability).

Before the merger of Librascope into Singer, this system was called LFCS Mk I (Librascope submarine fire-control system Mk I). Development began after Librascope won a design competition in September 1974. The first system was delivered in mid-1978. SFCS I was also supplied to the Canadian Navy, to modernize Canadian *Oberons*.

◆ Singer-Librascope SCCS Mk II

Submarine combat-control system Mk II is a developed SFCS Mk I. SCCS Mk II consists of up to eight multifunction consoles fed by a 5-MHz fiber-optic combat data bus, a single command (summary) display, a sensor-data converter/processor, and a weapons-data converter/processor. The system is federated: all processing associated with the sensor-data converter/processor is carried out in that unit. Each combat-control display has two separate screens: an upper plasma screen with an IR touch overlay and a lower 19-inch CRT with a light pen. The display also includes a keyboard and a joystick. The summary display is identical with the plasma display of the combat-control console.

Because all the control consoles share the same data stream (which includes data from all available sensors and from any data link to which the submarine can have access), individual operators can be assigned to concentrate either on particular targets or on overall surveillance. All sensor data is automatically entered into a combat data base for processing and recording. For example, data can be selected for up to 25 simultaneous target-motion analyses.

Four targets can be engaged simultaneously with wire-guided torpedoes, and the system can also support submarine-launched missiles such as Sub-Harpoon.

All elements of the system are sized to fit through a standard 650-mm hatch, so that existing submarines can be upgraded with the system without having their hulls opened.

Singer-Librascope's work on the Australian submarine combat system (in collaboration with Thomson-CSF and Rockwell International) is based on SCCS Mk II. The Australian project began late in 1985.

◆ Rockwell International

Rockwell has reportedly been selected to develop the combat system for the West German Type-209 submarines Israel is to build under U.S. Foreign Military Sales grants. Reportedly, similar systems are to be provided to South Korea, for the Type-209 submarines to be built for that navy.

SONOBUOYS AND AIRBORNE SIGNAL PROCESSORS

Most Free World sonobuoys are built to a standard "A"-size ($4\frac{7}{8}$ in × 36 in) to fit the buoy ejectors of such aircraft as the Nimrod, P-3 Orion, and Atlantique. "B"-size is $6\frac{7}{8}$ × 60 in (ERAPS size); "C"-size (9 in × 60 in) was used only by Britain; and "D"-size is 3 in × 15 in (projected for submarine underwater signals). "E"-size probably refers to a projected D-size sonobuoy. "F" is a dwarf (A/3) size ($4\frac{7}{8}$ × 12 in) now used by the Royal Navy and for some French buoys. The U.S. Navy is considering an A/2 size ($4\frac{7}{8}$ × 16.5 in), which may be designated "F." "G" is A/2 size ($4\frac{7}{8}$ × 18 in), but it was discarded because a filler was needed between two buoys in a launch tube: hence the choice of the 16.5-in length.

In 1973, the Space Development Corp. announced that it had developed a smaller-diameter (conventional length) equivalent of SSQ-41, several of which could be loaded side by side into a standard A-store tube and which, therefore, could be launched in any order, unlike Dwarfs. See the entry for SSQ-41 below.

The other major factor in sonobuoy operations is the number of available radio channels (for the link with the airplane), typically either 31 or 99. As sonobuoy range decreases because of submarine quieting, the number that must be laid to gain contact (or to search an area) increases; therefore, more channels are needed. About 1984 the major improvement was the increase from 31 to 99, as reflected (in the U.S. Navy, for example) by replacement of the 31-channel ARR-72 receiver with the 99-channel ARR-78.

In these notes, LOFAR (low-frequency analysis and recording) is spectral analysis using time integration to pick up stable narrow-band signals amid the surrounding noise. CODAR is a correlation-display analyzing recorder, which measures the time difference between reception of the same signal by two buoys. As in the PUFFS passive ranger for submarine fire control, CODAR can obtain the direction of a signal relative to the two-point hydrophones that pick it up, given knowledge of the spacing of the buoys (which were dropped at specified points by intervalometer). If the time of the signal's origination is known, CODAR also gives a range. The system of dropping a signal depth charge and then using CODAR to pick up the echoes of the explosion off a submarine is code-named Julie. Originally Julie was developed by the U.S. Navy as a way of using existing passive buoys despite silencing of Soviet submarines in the late 1950s. [Reportedly the name Julie honored a stripper who could "make a passive buoy active."] It was largely abandoned in favor of a new passive technology, LOFAR (code-named Jezebel). The necessary signal processing technology has survived, however, and Julie probably has not been altogether abandoned.

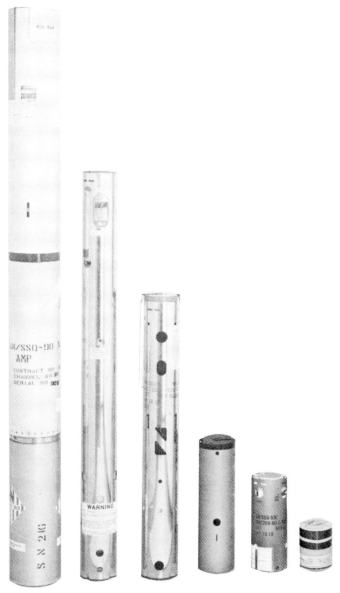

B-size   Stretch A   A-size   G-size   F-size   A/6

The range of sonobuoy sizes. (Sparton)

Standard A-size sonobuoys being loaded. The vanes protruding from their heads are rotochutes, which slow the buoys as they descend. (U.S. Navy)

AUSTRALIA

SONOBUOYS

◆ Barra (SSQ-801/SSQ-981)

Barra is an A-size (914 mm × 123.8 mm, 12.7 kg) broad-band (10–2000 Hz) array sonobuoy, employing 25 hydrophones in a horizontal configuration (planar array consisting of five out-stretched arms). The sixty beams formed by the array can be steered horizontally, and bearing data is provided by an internal magnetic compass. Because the beams can be quite narrow, the manufacturer, Sonobuoys Australia, claims that a single Barra can provide detection, classification, and unambiguous bearing information. Two units should, therefore, provide rapid passive localization.

Array depth is either 21.5 or 128.5 meters, and operating life is 0.5, 1, 2, or 4.5 hours. Fifty VHF channels are available; data are transmitted at 136–173.5 MHz (channels are spaced 0.750 MHz apart), the data-sampling rate being 8.29630 kHz.

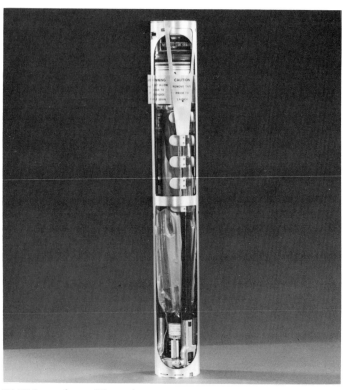

BARRA sonobuoy. (Plessey)

Processing is done by either an AQS-901 (RAAF Orion or RAF Nimrod) or by the combination of a UYS-503 sonobuoy processor and an AQA-801 side processor in a helicopter (RAN Sea Hawk).

SSQ-981 is a version for the U.K. Ministry of Defense, developed by Plessey, which claims that its manufacturing techniques reduce unit cost. Dimensions match those of the original SSQ-801, but weight is reduced to 11 kg. Alternatives for the operational life span are 1, 2, 3, or 4 hours; and the operating depth is 21.5 or 121 meters. Compass resolution is 0.36 degrees, and accuracy is 1.0 degrees at less than 65 deg in latitude.

The program began in 1969 as Project Barra, full development being approved late in 1974. Initial production was completed by Amalgamated Wireless late in 1981. A total of 25,000 units had been manufactured through 1986.

BARRA array deployed underwater, looking down. (Plessey)

CANADA

SONOBUOYS

◆ Sparton Miniature Buoys

Sparton, the Canadian sonobuoy manufacturer, has developed two types of miniature buoys: the Microbuoy, $\frac{1}{20}$ the size of the standard "A" type (for passive omnidirectional use), and the Miniature Sonobuoy, $\frac{1}{12}$ of "A" size, a passive omnidirectional buoy providing digital transmission of real-time or processed data (as commanded by UHF channel). The Microbuoy was developed in 1984; it is pie-shaped and 18 cm high, so that five stacks of four units each can be placed in a standard "A"-size container. The Miniature buoy is 28 cm tall, and Sparton claims that its buoy's performance is broadly comparable to that of the SSQ-41B (LOFAR) buoy in low sea-states. Sparton suggests that reductions in sonobuoy size and unit cost make it practical for small aircraft and even large RPVs to carry out searches, the buoys being carried in external pods rather than inside the aircraft. There is also an A/3 DIFAR buoy.

Sparton has designed a variety of seeder magazines for these buoys.

◆ SSQ-512 and -520

Julie buoys (for explosive echo ranging) are A-size, with a lifetime of $\frac{1}{2}$ hour or $1\frac{1}{2}$ hours. The hydrophone depth is 60 or 600 ft, and the buoys have 31 radio channels.

◆ SSQ-517 and -518

These passive A-size LOFAR/CODAR buoys operate omni-directionally (10 Hz–10 kHz). SSQ-517A has a lifetime of 1 or 3 hours; -517B lasts half an hour or $2\frac{1}{2}$ hours. Both have a hydrophone depth of 100 ft. SSQ-518 and -518A are much longer lived, respectively, 13½ and 8 hours. All report on one of 31 radio channels.

◆ SSQ-519 and -521

These passive A-size LOFAR/CODAR buoys are for ships' use; SSQ-521 has a 13.5-hour lifetime, -519 over 2½ hours. Hydrophone depth is 100 ft. Reporting is on one of 31 channels.

◆ SSQ-522

This active range-only buoy, manufactured by Sparton of Canada, Ltd., is equivalent to the U.S. SSQ-47B. More than 175,000 had been delivered by FY85, and production was proceeding at 5000–7000 per year for export. SSQ-522 is license-manufactured in Japan, Norway, and the United Kingdom; and the buoy is also used by Italy, the Netherlands, South Korea, Spain, and Taiwan (GRC).

Lifetime is half an hour, with the hydrophone at 80 or 600 ft, and there are twelve radio channels. Acoustic frequencies are 13.0, 14.2, 15.4, 16.6, 17.8, and 19.0 kHz.

◆ SSQ-523

The CANCASS command-activated sonobuoy has six high-frequency sonar channels (short, medium, long CW pulses, linear FM sweeps) and is controlled by a 12-channel UHF radio. Dimensions are 5 in × 3 ft. Depth is 60 or 800 ft. Sparton received a contract for an enhanced version in 1973, and 20,000 were ordered through 1986.

This buoy is roughly equivalent to the U.S. SSQ-50.

◆ SSQ-525

SSQ-525 is the Canadian equivalent of the U.S. SSQ-77 VLAD.

◆ SSQ-527 A/B

This passive omnidirectional A-size buoy is manufactured by Sparton of Canada. Weight is 21 lbs, and hydrophone depth is selectable (98, 328, or 984 ft), with a lifetime of 1, 3, or 8 hours. The buoy uses 31 RF channels.

These buoys are equivalent to the U.S. SSQ-41B.

◆ SSQ-529 (DICANCASS)

This active directional command-activated buoy is made by Sparton of Canada. SSQ-529 is broadly equivalent to the U.S. DICASS buoy (2.4 lbs, 5 in × 3 ft). Depths are 65, 330, and 820 ft. SSQ-529 was developed beginning in March 1981, with pre-production tests in 1984/85; and 2500 were ordered in 1986, the first year of full-scale production.

◆ SSQ-530

This passive directional LOFAR buoy (DIFAR), made by Sparton of Canada, is equivalent to the U.S. SSQ-53B.

◆ SSQ-531

This passive line-array directional buoy is made by Sparton of Canada.

SIGNAL PROCESSORS

◆ UYS-502

Emerson Electric's CALYPSO (computerized acoustic analyzer processor) sonobuoy processor is for helicopters. It has 32 time-multiplexed channels and uses parallel multiple arithmetic units for pulse compression, digital translation and filtering, FFT, display scaling, and other post-processing functions.

◆ UYS-503

Computing Devices Co.'s airborne signal processor is used by Australia, Canada, and Sweden. UYS-503 uses denser memory components than its predecessors. This processor suffices for all buoys except the complex broad-band Barra; that buoy requires a Side Barra Processor, SBP 1-1. This combination is part of the Australian RAWS (role-adaptable weapons system) of the Seahawk helicopter.

UYS-503 stores 20 minutes of LOFAR data from each buoy (4 DIFAR or 8 omnidirectional) in four modules (one unit). Alternatively, each module can be used with one DICASS or one range-only buoy (the former with CW or FM pulses, the latter CW only). UYS-503 can also process expendable bathythermograph buoys or a dipping sonar (one "slice" per 90-degree sector). Each 44-lb unit includes 8 standard buoy receivers.

UYS-503 and AQS-902G were tested in April 1987 as alternative processors for the SH-2F LAMPS-I helicopter; there was no U.S.-produced alternative. Late in 1988 UYS-503 was selected for new-production SH-2G helicopters. It will be installed on board existing SH-2Fs as they go through a SLEP program.

Computing Devices Co. was formerly Computing Devices of Canada.

◆ HIPADS/HAPS

Helicopter integrated processing-and-display system/helicopter acoustic processing system is the Canadian next-generation sonobuoy processing system. HIPADS is being developed by Canadian Marconi, Computing Devices Co., and Litton Canada. HAPS is being developed by Computing Devices Co. and uses the Plessey Cormorant dipping sonar.

◆ SBP 1-1

The Barra processor works with the UYS-503 processor. SBP 1-1 can also function as a stand-alone processor, consisting of four subprocessors. Each subprocessor can handle eight omni-directional buoys or four DIFAR or DICASS. In the passive mode, SBP stores 20 minutes of LOFAR data on each frequency channel; the operator can call up and display the stored data on the CRT. The unit includes a patented demultiplexer that allows digital sonobuoys to be used with a standard analog receiver. A second SBP 1-1 can be connected in parallel to double the processing capacity.

The first SBP 1-1 was delivered in the summer of 1984, and the unit was bought for Canada and Sweden (and for Australia, in conjunction with a UYS-503).

FRANCE

SONOBUOYS

◆ DSTA-3

CIT-Alcatel's active buoy operates at depths of 65 or 330 ft; it transmits at 9, 10, or 11 kHz and reports on one of 16 radio channels. DSTA-3 works with a DSAA-4 processor, which can handle two buoys simultaneously.

Development began in the late 1950s, with trials in the mid-1960s and service in 1968–70. There were large orders in the 1970s and early 1980s, and later buoys were modified for better sensitivity. Reported production through 1986 was 15,000. The current version is DSTA-3E (123 mm × 914 mm, 16 kg, depth 30 or 135 m, 4 sonar and 8 VHF channels, lifetime about 20 minutes).

◆ DSTV-4L/M (MSR-810) (TSM 8010)

Thomson-CSF's passive buoy (124 × 914 mm, 8 kg or less) is also produced in Italy by Misar as MSR-810. DSTV-4L, the passive counterpart to DSTA-3, operates at 65 or 330 ft (with an additional 990-ft option in the -4M version), is omnidirectional (10 Hz–20 kHz), and has a lifetime of 1, 3, or 8 hours. DSTV-4L/M reports on one of 31 radio channels. The -4M version is more reliable and more sensitive.

DSTV-4L was developed in the early 1960s, trials following in the late 1960s. The -4L version was procured in 1963 and 1968. In all, 20,000 DSTV-4 series buoys have been procured. The successor is DSTV-7Y.

This buoy, which replaced DSTV-2K, is broadly equivalent to the U.S. SSQ-41A/B.

◆ DSTV-4N

This ambient-noise measurement buoy is analogous to the U.S. SSQ-57.

◆ DSTV-7 (TSM 8020)

An A/3-size (124 × 305 mm, 4 kg) version of DSTV-4M, DSTV-7 incorporates a radio-frequency synthesizer so that buoy radio channels need not be set before flight. Instead, they can be set manually on the airplane from among a preselected 34 of the total of 99 channels, separated by 375 Hz, ranging from 136–173 MHz. Frequency range of the buoy is 10 Hz to 20 kHz (optimally 5 Hz to 20 kHz); the hydrophone depth is 20 or 100 m (with an optional 300-m setting). Lifetime is 1, 3, or 8 hours. The buoy can be dropped from 150–10,000 ft, at 80–250 kts.

DSTV-7 is probably a LOFAR buoy. It entered production in 1986. In 1986 the French Navy decided to develop a DIFAR buoy. A DICASS was moving into production, and studies of low-cost sonobuoys were beginning.

DSTV-7X mini-Jezebel (LOFAR) buoy. (Thomson-CSF)

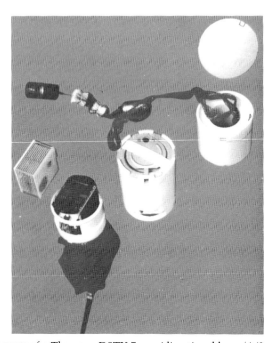

Components of a Thomson DSTV 7 omnidirectional buoy (A/3 = size). (Thomson Sintra)

◆ TSM 8030

Thomson Sintra's A-size (124 × 915 mm, 17.6 kg) DICASS buoy operates at 6.5, 7.5, or 9.5 kHz with either CW pulses (0.1–0.5 or 1 second) or 1-second FM pulses; pulses can repeat with intervals of less than 1 second. Beam modes are ODT, cosine, or sine. Depth, remotely selectable, is 20 m or 150 m (450 m optional). The buoy reports on one of 31 VHF channels, and it is controlled by UHF (291.4 MHz). Power is supplied by a lithium cell, with an operational life of 30 minutes at 20 m, 20 minutes at maximum depth (50 seconds of emission).

Production began in 1986.

◆ TSM 8050

Thomson Sintra's A-size range-only buoy will enter production in 1989. Weight is 17.69 kg. Acoustic frequency is 6.0, 6.71, 7.5, 8.4, 9.4, or 10.5 kHz. The buoy emits either CW pulses (4 pulses in a train, total duration 100 msec) or FM pulses (1 pulse lasting 320 msec), in each case with an 11-second recurrence rate. The hydrophone is at a depth of 20 or 150 meters (TSM 8050A) or at 20 or 450 meters (TSM 8050B). Total operational life is 30 minutes, using a lithium cell and a magnesium/lead-chloride battery. The buoy reports to the launching aircraft by VHF on one of 12 possible channels spaced 750 kHz apart (162.25–170.50 MHz), at a power level of 0.25 watts (compared to one watt for the passive DSTV 7). Presumably the lower power level corresponds to the planned tactical use of the buoy, as a means of localizing a submarine detected by a relatively large field of passive buoys (some of which might have to be monitored from a considerable distance).

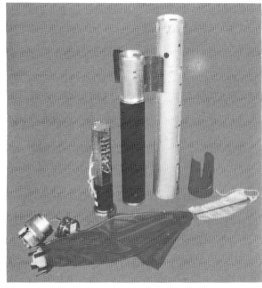

Components of a Thomson TSM 8050 range-only buoy, showing its parachute, its electronics, and its transducer. (Thomson Sintra)

◆ Low Cost Buoy

As of 1986 Thomson-CSF was beginning work on a future low-cost sonobuoy, presumably comparable to the U.S. LCS.

SIGNAL PROCESSORS

◆ DSAX 1 (SADANG, TSM 8210)

DSAX 1 is the signal processor of the Atlantique-2 maritime-patrol aircraft. SADANG means *Système Acoustique de l'Atlantique Nouvelle Génération*. This system is oriented toward processing omnidirectional buoys. It has two operators and can process 16 sonobuoys simultaneously (each processor has eight LOFAR channels, equivalent to two DIFAR channels). Processing capability includes DEMON (recovery of low-frequency lines by demodulating broad-band noise). This processor uses CODAR (discrepancies in amplitude, frequency, time, or phase between two or more buoys) to determine lines of bearing and range.

TSM 8210, the export version, is lighter and has one processor and one operator. Total weight is about 140 kg.

◆ TSM 8200 (SECBAT)

Thomson Sintra's airborne signal processor for the Atlantic-1 works with active or passive buoys, with ambient-noise buoys, and with XBTs. TSM 8200 uses a 99-channel VHF receiver and a UHF transceiver for active-buoy control. There are two operators.

◆ TSM 8220 (Lamparo)

Thomson Sintra's acoustic-signal processor for small maritime-patrol aircraft or helicopters is derived from DSAX 1. Lamparo employs one operator and can simultaneously process 4 or 8 sonobuoys. This processor can also be integrated with an HS 12 dipping sonar. Processing techniques are LOFAR, CODAR, DEMON, and range-only. TSM 8230 is a modified version that can support a dipping sonar as well as sonobuoys.

Lamparo has been adapted to the AS 332F Super Puma and to the AS 365F Dauphin-2 helicopter (as in the Saudi frigates).

A new system is under development: FLASH (Flexible Lightweight Acoustic System for Helicopters).

Lamparo LOFARgram display. The curved white area is a reflection from the pilot's helmet; the display proper shows the usual vertical lines, spread out over the frequency spectrum. The operator seeks lines that remain stable over time. (Thomson Sintra)

GERMANY (WEST)

◆ DSSQ-12

This LOFAR/DIFAR buoy, made by Atlas Elektronik, was planned for Atlantic maritime-patrol aircraft (with AQA-1 processor) but was dropped in favor of the U.S. SSQ-53 because of cost.

INDIA

In 1978 Hindustan Aeronautics, Ltd., reported that it was producing a sonobuoy for the Indian Navy, based on a design by the Naval Physical Oceanographic Laboratory at Cochin. The buoy is retarded by rotochute, and it lowers its transducer to a depth of 30 m. Lifetime is $8\frac{1}{2}$ hours, power being provided by a nickel-cadmium battery; and data is transmitted by VHF (162.25–172.5 MHz). Presumably the buoy is A-size, to fit West-

ern-supplied helicopters and aircraft, and its long life suggests fully passive operation.

ITALY

◆ BI Series

The BI series are Olivetti's buoys. BIT-3 is a 5 in × 36 in omnidirectional buoy, operating on 31 channels, at 65 or 330 ft; lifetime is 1–3 hours. BIT-8 is similar but adds 10 more channels. BIR is intended for light helicopters (4.5 in × 24 in, 1-hour lifetime, 65-ft maximum depth).

Work on these buoys began in the mid-1970s to replace U.S. types. After trials in the late 1970s, the buoys entered service in 1979–80; about 12,000 were manufactured through 1986. They were intended specifically for the Mediterranean, with its shallow surface layer.

An earlier Julie-Jezebel buoy, BI 68, was announced about 1974. Dimensions were 91 × 1220 mm (weight 8 kg), and the manufacturer, USEA, claimed that BI 68 could operate on twice the usual number of channels. Maximum depth was 60 m. Presumably this buoy never entered service.

JAPAN

◆ HQS-3D

Japanese Julie (explosive echo-ranging) buoy, manufactured by Oki, is equivalent to the U.S. SSQ-23.

◆ HQS-5

This bathythermograph buoy is equivalent to the U.S. SSQ-36. HQS-5D operates down to 1500-ft depth, and -5E down to 4000 ft.

◆ HQS-6B

Oki's LOFAR buoy is equivalent to the U.S. SSQ-41.

◆ HQS-12

Oki's DIFAR buoy is equivalent to the U.S. SSQ-53.

◆ HQS-21B

Oki's acoustic-reference buoy is equivalent to the U.S. SSQ-57.

◆ HQS-31

NEC's active buoy is equivalent to the U.S. SSQ-47.

◆ HQS-32

NEC's active buoy is equivalent to the U.S. SSQ-50 CASS (omnidirectional).

USSR

It is very unlikely that the following catalog is complete; rather, it is an indication of past progress and of past design practice. Soviet warships are equipped to receive sonobuoy data.

◆ RGB-56/64

RGB-56/64 were the first Soviet sonobuoys, the numbers presumably indicating dates of design. RGB-64 was a somewhat miniaturized version of RGB-56 (which was approximately 8.75 × 48 inches, with a total weight of 60 lbs). Both buoys are omnidirectional, with detection ranges of about 2000–4000 yds. RGB-56 operates over the 4.4–6.4 kHz range; RGB-64 operates between 3 and 11.5 kHz. The data link is 18-channel AM (49.2–53.45 MHz), each buoy being preset before launch.

RGB-56 was first seen in September 1959. It was dropped at low altitude (500–1000 ft) and low speed (150 kts) and was parachute-retarded (lanyard activated). This procedure helped avoid drift. The hydrophone's beam was 17 degrees wide in the vertical.

In each case, the buoy does not transmit unless target noise (in effect, integrated over its bandwidth) exceeds one of seven (RGB-56) preset threshold levels. The monitoring helicopter, therefore, continuously tunes over the 18 channels, automatically locking onto a transmitting buoy and locating it using a

VHF/DF built into the sonobuoy receiver. The operator can listen, e.g., for a turn count, and then resume tuning, or he can hand-tune. He can obtain a rough fix by comparative listening, or he can try to estimate a submarine's speed by turn-counting.

The threshold procedure also extends the buoy's life, which (in RGB-56) could be as great as 4 to 5 days (given battery strength); the buoy was designed, however, to scuttle in 24 hours).

U.S. observers compared RGB-56 with the first U.S. postwar broad-band buoy, SSQ-2, and also noted that RGB-56 had the beam pattern appropriate to bistatic operation with an active sonar, the transmission biasing necessary to prevent transient interference, and the center frequency (5 kHz) and band pass well suited to such operation. Presumably the wider bandwidth of RGB-64 showed that the Soviets did not intend to use their buoys that way, at least at the time.

There were also marker buoys (RBM-100 and -200).

By 1962 U.S. naval intelligence was reporting that the Soviets had stated a requirement for a directional buoy to replace RGB-56. RGB-56 components had appeared, by that time, in a variety of old mine, buoy, and paravane casings, presumably to monitor U.S. and NATO exercises.

◆ BM-1

This passive omnidirectional sonobuoy was manufactured about 1966–1970. BM-1 uses a line hydrophone. Dimensions are 6 in × 50.5 in. The 29-channel FM-radio data link is at about 171 MHz (channels separated by 150-kHz intervals). Internally, this buoy uses printed circuits and transistors, but it has no integrated circuits.

Because BM-1 was associated with the Wet Eye radar (used on board May ASW aircraft), the buoy may not have been back-fitted into Hormone shipboard helicopters.

◆ Type 75

In 1988 the U.S. Department of Defense released a photograph of a Soviet Type-75 sonobuoy that had electronics similar to those of the U.S. SSQ-41B, albeit in a much larger package. The

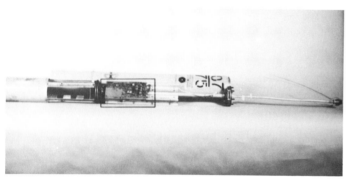

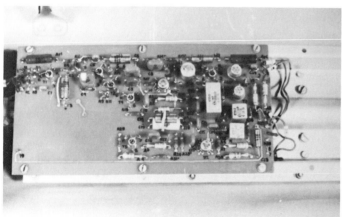

In 1988 the U.S. Department of Defense released these photographs of the Soviet Type 75 sonobuoy, which was described as similar to the U.S. SSQ-41B, i.e., to a LOFAR buoy. (*Soviet Military Power*, DoD)

conclusion seems to be that, since 1975, the Soviets have had LOFAR buoys. This conclusion would be consistent with sightings of Soviet listening devices, short cylinders covered with spot hydrophones, from about that date onward. LOFAR or LOFAR-like techniques, in distinct contrast to earlier passive techniques, operate on the basis of the detailed structure of the submarine's signature. They, therefore, entail an intelligence effort to obtain such signatures and then to match them against particular types of submarine. That effort would account for the bottom-laid devices, which are generally near NATO-submarine operating areas and bases. These devices are not themselves surveillance devices but rather are a means of collecting the information required to make the surveillance devices, such as LOFAR buoys, effective. The existence of such buoys also implies that the Soviets have the necessary signal processors, which in turn could be adapted to monitoring towed passive arrays.

UNITED KINGDOM

SONOBUOYS

Until the 1980s, British-manufactured sonobuoys were designated in a T-series rather than in the standard NATO A/N-series. These earlier buoys were probably exported to various Commonwealth countries and may still be in service. Some were presumably redesignated in the NATO series. Early British developments are interesting in retrospect because they illustrate the limitations imposed by a lack of any processor (aside from the operator's ears). Work began about 1948, at which time the British were using U.S. AN/CRT-1 buoys of wartime type. Stocks of these simple buoys were expected to run out in 1950, and a Mk 1 system was developed.

Mk 1 consisted of a passive omnidirectional buoy (T 1945) that could be laid in twelve-buoy barriers and a complementary directional passive buoy (T 1946) for tracking. An active buoy was planned as an attack aid. The main requirement, which reflects the lack of a signal processor, was that an operator receive enough audible signal from each buoy to detect a submarine trying to penetrate the twelve-buoy barrier. The directional buoy used a rotating searchlight transducer. The operator had to be able to recognize (classify) a submarine's signature during the available processing time, i.e., while the searchlight beam was focused on the submarine. Experiments showed that an operator needed 1.5–2 seconds for recognition or detection, and T 1946 was designed to rotate its 30-degree beam three times per minute. Its hydrophone was suspended at a depth of 40 feet. Staff requirements were formally stated in 1949, and ideal buoy dimensions were set at 10 × 50 in (50 lbs); the prototype T 1946 was 8 × 59.5 in (72 lbs; lifetime 3–4 hours). These figures became the British standard size (C-size), which was larger than the U.S. standard of A-size.

A relatively high frequency, 12 kHz, was chosen to provide good directional information via a relatively small array, a 12-in cruciform unfolding from the directional buoy. Initial tests showed that a submarine running her main motors at 3 kts could be detected at 5000 yds (8000 yds at 5 kts). These figures suggest what can be done with very simple buoys without real processing and may be somewhat like those achieved by Soviet pre-LOFAR systems.

The active buoy that would have been associated with the Mk 1 system never materialized. However, in May 1955 an active directional buoy, TX 1901, was tested at Malta, achieving an average range of 1900 yds (maximum range 3600 yds).

High frequency was not altogether satisfactory, and a Mk 1B system, operating at 160 Hz, was planned, with an active buoy. Mk 1B was planned for service about 1959 but was dropped about 1955 in favor of Mk 1C, also operating at 160 Hz, which was expected to enter service in 1959. Mk 1C buoys were still in service two decades later. This system did include active buoys.

As of 1977, the standard types (used alongside Canadian and U.S. buoys) were

T 17053 C-size (9 × 60 in), passive (160-Hz band), 1-hour lifetime, hydrophone depth 60 or 180 ft, 16 RF channels. T 17053 was the passive element of the Mk 1C system.

T 17054 C-size; active element of the Mk 1C system; 1-hour lifetime; hydrophone depth 60 or 180 ft, 16 RF channels; acoustic channels 20.4, 21.7, and 23.0 kHz (each assigned 4 RF channels)

T 17164 A-size active (Mk 1 CAMBS, Command Active Multibeam Sonobuoy), part of the Mk 1C system, with acoustic channels as T 17054, lifetime 1 hour, hydrophone depths 60 or 180 ft, 16 RF channels

T 24501 A-size passive (LOFAR/CODAR), lifetime 1 or 8 hours, hydrophone depth 95 ft, 31 RF channels

T 24866 A-size passive (LOFAR/CODAR); lifetime 1, 4, or 8 hours; hydrophone depth 95 ft; 31 RF channels

T 24923 A-size passive (LOFAR/CODAR); lifetime 1, 4, or 8 hours; hydrophone depth 60 or 300 ft; 31 RF channels

T 24953 (calibrated version T 30067); A-size passive (LOFAR/CODAR); lifetime 1, 4, or 8 hours; hydrophone depth 60 or 300 ft; 31 RF channels

T 30059 (calibrated version T 30068); A-size passive (LOFAR/CODAR); lifetime 1, 4, or 8 hours; hydrophone depth 60 or 450 ft; 31 RF channels

◆ SSQ-904

This mini- (5 in × 12 in) Jezebel (LOFAR buoy) is made by Dowty. SSQ-904 operates at 10 Hz–6kHz, at a depth of 60, 300, or 450 ft, with a lifetime of 1, 4, or 8 hours. SSQ-904 can signal on one of 31 or 99 channels, operating with an AQA-5 or an AQS-901, -902, or -903 processor. This design resulted from MoD studies of the late 1970s, followed by field tests in 1979 and production in 1980; reportedly 12,000 buoys had been ordered through 1986.

In 1983, Ultra, which then manufactured SSQ-904, was reportedly working on a short 11-element vertical-line-array buoy for better shallow-water performance.

As of mid-1987, Dowty had manufactured a total of 550,000 sonobuoys for the RN, the RAF, and overseas customers, making the company the largest manufacturer in Europe. Customers that year included India and Sweden.

Two new passive sonobuoys were introduced in 1988, SSQ-906 and an enhanced F-size SSQ-904 Jezebel. The latter has 99 RF channels, selectable depth, and selectable lifetime (one, four, or eight hours).

Dowty claims that its passive buoys operate at significantly lower frequencies than do any others within NATO. That capability might be increasingly important as submarines become quieter.

◆ SSQ-905

This mini- (5 in × 12 in, 10 lbs) Jezebel (LOFAR) buoy operates at 10 Hz–6 kHz; at a depth of 60, 300, or 450 ft; with a lifetime of 1, 4, or 8 hours; and on 31 or 99 channels. SSQ-905 is a calibrated version of SSQ-904.

◆ SSQ-906 and -907

These F-size (4.875 × 12 in) miniature Jezebel sonobuoys (weight 9.5 lbs) have selectable lifetimes of 1, 4, or 6 hours; their hydrophones are carried at a preselected depth of 30 or 140 m (other combinations can be provided). The operating range is 4 Hz to 6 kHz, buoy response being shaped to an inverse ambient sea noise curve to overcome average sea noise. Dowty describes this buoy as providing the lowest-frequency coverage in NATO. Buoys report by VHF radio on any of 99 channels (minimum output power 1 watt). The buoy can be dropped from altitudes of 150–30,000 feet and at speeds of 60–300 kts.

SSQ-907 is a calibrated version of SSQ-906.

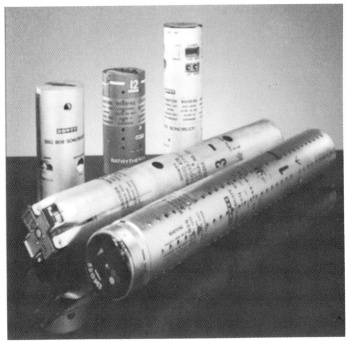

Dowty sonobuoys, with three miniatures in the background and standard A-size buoys in the foreground. The buoy on the left is the SSQ-906 omnidirectional passive type; it is flanked by a bathythermograph buoy and by SSQ-954B. The two buoys in the foreground are a Dowty-made SSQ-47B and SSQ-963A CAMBS. (Dowty)

◆ SSQ-937

SSQ-937 is an F-size expendable bathythermograph buoy. Lifetime is 5 minutes, and the buoy gives temperature down to 1000 ft (sink rate is 5 ft/sec). SSQ-937 operates on one of three preselected channels.

◆ SSQ-947B

This British version of the U.S. SSQ-47B range-only buoy is omnidirectional. Frequency range is 13–19 kHz, and SSQ-947B reports on 12 channels.

About 1985 Plessey received a study contract for a new active buoy.

◆ SSQ-954

Plessey's G-size DIFAR buoy was announced in 1985. The hydrophone depth and operational lifetime of SSQ-954A can be remotely selected. Dowty describes the improved SSQ-954B as an Autonomous Function Selection (AFS) sonobuoy using a microprocessor to control the fully synthesized VHF transmitter, the operational lifetime (1, 4, or 6 hours), and the hydrophone depth (30, 140, or 300 m). Commands are transmitted via multifunction push buttons, and choices are indicated by light-emitting diodes (LEDs) when a "verify" button is pressed. Output power is 1 watt, and shelf lifetime is 5 yrs. The buoy can transmit on one of 99 channels, spaced 375 kHz apart. DIFAR compass accuracy is within 5 deg, and the buoy can also function in omnidirectional mode. The buoy can be dropped at speeds of 50–300 kts from altitudes of 150–30,000 feet.

◆ SSQ-963

Dowty's Command A-size Active Multi-Beam Sonobuoy (CAMBS III) is currently in production for the RAF and Royal Navy. CAMBS uses 31 radio channels. Both the transmitter and the receiver are directional, and the transducer's depth can be varied on radio command. The buoy can operate either in directional passive or directional active modes; in the latter case it emits an omnidirectional pulse and receives with a separate directional array. Dowty describes SSQ-963A as representing an unspecified radically different but proven technical approach, compared to two earlier generations of CAMBS buoys. The buoy can be launched from altitudes of 200–8000 ft and at speeds of

60–300 kts. There are three selectable depths, and lifetime is one hour, with automatic or command scuttling. Shelf life is five yrs.

In 1985, in connection with a proposal to equip Lynx helicopters with sonobuoys (to localize submarines detected by towed array), GEC Avionics claimed that a three-CAMBS pattern would enable a helicopter to cover more than two-thirds of the area swept by a dipped sonar. The Lynx, however, could accommodate only nine A-size buoys, and CAMBS could not be miniaturized because it depends on large batteries.

♦ SSQ-981

SSQ-981 is Barra: see the Australian SSQ-801.

AIRBORNE SIGNAL PROCESSORS

♦ AQS-901

GEC Avionics's signal processor for British Nimrod and Australian P-3 aircraft is adapted to Barra buoy processing. AQS-901 replaces the U.S. AQA-5. The full installation consists of two sets, each capable of processing eight sonobuoys, connected by a data bus. The associated computer is Computing Devices Co.'s 920 ATC with up to 256K words, capable of performing a fast fourier transform on 2048 points in 11.25 milliseconds.

The associated receiver is tunable to 99 channels, and there is a command system to operate active buoys (it controls pulse width, pulse type, and PRF). The displays are CRTs and hard copy chart recorders. The system can be set to alert an operator automatically when a target has exceeded a preset threshold.

AQS-901 was first delivered in March 1979.

♦ AQS-902 (LAPADS)/AQS-920

Lightweight Acoustic Processing-and-Display System, in British Sea King helicopters, uses some AQS-901 technology but is only about 20 percent as large. LAPADS can also process dipping sonar data. AQS-902 entered service in 1980 on board Sea King helicopters, and in 1983 DIFAR processing capability was added. In 1985 GEC designed a new CRT to replace the paper recorder, to save another 20 kg and allow the processing capacity to be doubled.

As displayed in 1984, LAPADS was a passive analyzer for the 0–3.2 kHz band, with both LOFAR and A-scan displays. The main stated advantage was LAPADS's ability to combine wideband (surveillance) with narrow-band (LOFAR, target classification/tracking). AQS-902 has 12 verniers (800, 400, 200, 100, and 25 Hz wide) that can be positioned anywhere in its displays, and it can display twelve LOFARS simultaneously. A harmonic cursor allows the operator to compare a line with its harmonic. Up to 1.5 hours of LOFAR history can be stored, for line enhancement.

Variants: 902A, for passive omnidirectional buoys and hard-copy display; 902B, similar, but with a CRT display; 902C, passive, with omni- and directional buoys and a hard-copy display; 902D, passive, with omni- and directional buoys and a CRT display; 902D-DS, passive, with omni- and directional buoys and a CRT, plus dipping-sonar processing and display; 902F (4 LOFAR, 1 bathythermograph, 4 ranging buoys, 4 DIFAR, 2 DICASS, or 4 VLAD); 902G (for SH-2F LAMPS-I helicopter, see UYS-503 above). AQS-902C can process 4 LOFAR and 1 bathythermograph or 4 DIFAR buoys; total weight is 112 lbs.

In 1987 GEC won a contract to modify existing AQS-902C processors on board Royal Navy Sea King helicopters to the AQS-902G-DS standard. The original processor handled only sonobuoys, the accompanying Type 195 sonar operating independently. AQS-902G processes both sonobuoy and sonar data, substituting digital electronics for the analog system of the sonar. 902G also replaces the current hard copy output with a CRT providing a wide variety of possible displays. One of them, the acoustic localization plot, allows the sonar operator to check the validity of his data before passing it to the observer's tactical plot. This tactical plot of the range and bearing information derived from the sonobuoys provides current and predicted target position and track. In all, 112 processors are to be modernized.

The Italian Navy is updating its Atlantics with AQS-902 and Iguane radar. Pakistan is expected to do a similar modification. AQS-902 is also used by the Royal Swedish Navy. The lightweight AQS-902 export variant is designated AQS-920. It equips Royal Navy and Indian Navy Sea Kings, and is being retrofitted to Italian Navy Atlantics (in some cases under 902 designation).

The AQS-920 series is typical of modern practice. A detailed description is available; the reader should assume that other current airborne processors are broadly comparable (e.g., in integration time).

The two current versions of AQS-920 are AQS-924 and -928; their maximum buoy-processing capabilities are

	AQS-924	AQS-928
LOFAR/DIFAR/VLAD (Omni)	4	8
DIFAR/VLAD (Cardioid)	4	4
Calibrated Buoys	1	1
DICASS	2	2
Range Only	4	4
BT	1	1

Passive processing modes are LOFAR/DIFAR/VLAD omnidirectional, DIFAR/VLAD pseudo-omnidirectional, DIFAR/VLAD single cardioid, DIFAR/VLAD triple cardioid, CODAR, DEMON (demodulated noise), BT, ambient-noise measurement (ANM), and signal-to-noise ratio (SNR). Active modes are DICASS (CW/FM), range-only (CW), and dipping sonar (CW/FM/BT/Depth). The processor can display passive buoy data either in LOFARgram form or in automatic line integration (ALI) form (i.e., integration can be either by eye or by machine). The advantage of using a LOFARgram is that the eye may detect an intermittently transmitted but fairly regular signal, whereas line integration may show little indication above the surrounding noise. Active formats are range/doppler/bearing, range/time history, bearing/time history, and range correlogram (using FM signals).

For detection, the system can perform simultaneous wide- and narrow-band analyses, cardioid detection gain, and automatic alerts. For classification, the system provides harmonic multipoint dividers, so the operator can compare the same line in several harmonic forms. For localization, the system can provide narrow-band frequency/bearing trackers, semiautomatic closest point of approach (CPA)/doppler fixing, and an acoustic localization plot (ALP).

The system has 4 or 8 channels to handle buoys in the 10–2400 Hz frequency range and can handle ten narrow bandwidths or resolutions. The display covers a time history of up to 64 minutes, and integration time (for ALI) is selectable at 3.75, 7.5, 15, or 30 seconds. The maximum number of analyses processed is 8 BBAs (broad-band analyses: 688 cells) plus 24 VWs (vernier widths, i.e., narrow-bandwidths: 180 cells).

Total system weight, excluding the sonobuoy receiver itself, is 52.5 kg. That weight includes one or two 625-line CRTs and a hard-copy unit (for passive buoys only, to print out LOFARgrams).

♦ AQS-903

AQS-901's successor, made by GEC Avionics, employs VHSIC technology, for the EH-101 Merlin helicopter. AQS-903 can process Barra and CAMBS sonobuoys. This processor weighs about 160 kg, about one-third lighter than AQS-902, with up to five times the processing power. With one man, AQS-903 can handle as many buoys (16) as the three-man AQS-901 and can provide each buoy with eight times the processing power (e.g., to handle much more bandwidth).

The distributed processing architecture employs "pipelines," each of which handles a certain number of buoys. The manufacturer claims that four such lines give eight times the power of an AQS-901 at a quarter of its weight.

GEC's AQS-930 series is presumably related to AQS-903 as the AQS-920 series is related to AQS-902. The announced versions are AQS-932, -934, and -938, the differences presumably being in the number of "pipelines." Announced maximum processing capabilities are

	AQS-932	AQS-934	AQS-938
LOFAR/DIFAR/VLAD (Omni)	16	32	64
DIFAR/VLAD (Cardioid)	8	16	32
Barra	2	4	8
DICASS	4	8	8
Calibrated Buoys	1	1	1
CAMBS	3	6	6
BT	1	1	1
Weight	66.5 kg	74.5 kg	82.5 kg
(including APU)	32.0 kg	40.0 kg	48.0 kg

Here APU is the acoustic processing unit; all of the other components (acoustic control unit, two 12-inch 625-line acoustic display units, a common control unit, and a roller ball control/stiff stick control) are common to all versions.

Processing modes are as in AQS-924/928, except that the 930-series uses DIFAR/VLAD four cardioid rather than triple cardioid, and a Barra broad-band option is added.

Added detection aids (compared to AQS-924/928) are narrow/broad-band AGC (automatic gain control), broad-band power/bearing (DIFAR/Barra), and display enhancement. The additional classification aids are predictive (ratio) dividers and recorded data recall. Added localization/tracking aids are broad-band bearing trackers, automatic/manual CPA/Hyfix, and a coordinated tracker for multiple contacts. The LOFARgram display can show up to 60 minutes of history. No data are provided concerning maximum integration time.

Both the AQS-930 series and the AQS-920 series can process dipping sonar data.

UNITED STATES

SONOBUOYS

◆ MCSS

The active moored buoy (moored CASS) is deployed over the side; the hydrophone is deployed at a depth of 20–700 ft. MCSS is rechargeable for continuous operation and is tunable to one of 3 channels.

◆ SSQ-15

Although obsolete, this buoy is included for comparison with its successors. SSQ-15 was a B-size active pinger (100 lbs) operating at 28.4–38 kHz (peak power 40 watts), with a transducer 40 ft below the surface. SSQ-15 appeared in 1952 and was initially eclipsed by Julie but was then revived in view of the failure of the CODAR processor required by the Julie system. Compared to Julie, SSQ-15 suffered from its very short range but was considered a more reliable attack aid. Its use led in turn to the development of SSQ-50 (CASS) and then SSQ-62 (DICASS), both of which are described below.

These buoys were developed as better alternatives to a simple miniaturized active pinger, proposed by GE about 1957, which would have used passive buoys as its receivers. Sparton proposed the first of the CASS series, SSQ-47, in 1959, and the buoy appeared in 1966, followed in the early 1980s by SSQ-50. At this writing (1989), however, the pendulum is swinging back, and interest in a simple pinger is reviving. The advantage of the pinger is that more energy can be concentrated in a buoy that has neither signal receiver nor transmitter. Pings would be picked up by a field of passive buoys. No designation has been announced, but it seems likely that some such device will soon enter production, as a modern form of Julie.

◆ SSQ-23

Although no longer in U.S. service, SSQ-23 is produced in Japan by Oki as HQS-3D. It is an A-size (16 lbs) passive omnidirectional buoy, covering the acoustic range between 400 Hz and 6 kHz, used for Julie explosive echo ranging. The Julie system became operational about 1957.

◆ SSQ-28

Although obsolete, this buoy is included for comparison with its successors. SSQ-28 was the first U.S. Jezebel (airborne LOFAR) buoy, used with the LOFAR-CODAR processor (AQA-3). SSQ-28 entered service in 1960–65. There was also an SSQ-38 (1964), now obsolete. These buoys were superseded by SSQ-41 (1965). SSQ-28 used a spot hydrophone; SSQ-41 used a line hydrophone instead and combined Julie and Jezebel capability (i.e., SSQ-23 and -28 functions). The combination was important because tactics called for conversion of a long-range (Jezebel) contact into a short-range (Julie) contact before an attack could be conducted.

The early omnidirectional LOFAR buoys were not altogether satisfactory because they achieved such great ranges that Julie could not be used to find the detected submarines. The solution was crash development of directional LOFAR buoys (SSQ-53) with which a submarine could be localized much more quickly. In theory, the omnidirectional buoys are used for initial detection, with some direction obtained by techniques such as CODAR. Then DIFARs are used for initial localization, with an active pinger (DICASS) dropped for localization before the final attack pass with a MAD.

The original SSQ-28/LOFAR was so promising that early S-2 carrier-based ASW aircraft were fitted to carry the buoy. They could not accommodate the processor, so they had to send their buoy data back to their carriers by data link, for processing there. This practice, which began about 1958, was repeated with the LAMPS-I helicopter more than a decade later (with more sophisticated buoys).

The first LOFAR buoy prototype was tested on board a P-5 seaplane in 1954, and the system was sold on the basis of a 95-nm detection. Design of an operational system began in 1957, and Jezebel became operational in 1959.

◆ SSQ-36 (XBT)

This expendable bathythermograph is designed to establish acoustic conditions in a sonobuoy field. SSQ-36 has a cable probe down to 1000 ft and is A-size (18 lbs). Although the XBT is not a sonobuoy, it is essential to sonobuoy-field operations and, therefore, is listed here. Lifetime is 5 minutes, and SSQ-36 reports on one of 3 RF channels.

◆ SSQ-41

The standard U.S. A-size (14 lbs) omnidirectional LOFAR buoy is a line hydrophone operating at 10 Hz up to 20 kHz at a depth of 60 or 300 ft, with a lifetime of 1, 3, or 8 hours. SSQ-41B (Jezebel wide-band) operates at up to 10 kHz (with improved dynamic range) at a depth of 60–1000 ft, reporting on one of 31 channels between 162.250 and 173.5 MHz or 99 channels between 136 and 173.5 MHz. Weight is 14 or 15 lbs. SSQ-41B can be launched at up to 370 kts and at altitudes as high as 30,000 ft. SSQ-41A's maximum weight is 21 lbs; -41B's, 29 lbs.

In 1988 the U.S. Department of Defense published a photograph of a Soviet Type-75 sonobuoy that was said to resemble SSQ-41B, albeit in a larger envelope.

SSQ-41 replaced SSQ-28, the first LOFAR buoy (1960), in 1965. SSQ-41 had sufficiently broad response to be usable in Julie and was described as a Julie-Jezebel buoy. SSQ-41 is the most widely used Western buoy.

◆ SSQ-47B

This active A-size sonobuoy (29 lbs) uses a hydrophone at a depth of 60 or 800 feet and has a life of 30 minutes. SSQ-47B is tunable to report on one of 12 channels, so that up to six buoys can be used simultaneously in a single field. SSQ-47B is a deep-operating version of the SSQ-15, incorporating solid-state electronics, controlled transducer beam, and VHF antenna patterns. Command is possible from 0–10 nm and from 500–10,000 ft, at up to sea-state 5. The operating mode is automatically keyed CW; because this buoy is not command-activated, its life is so short.

The last U.S. Navy production orders were in 1982; in 1988 this buoy was manufactured only for foreign military sales.

♦ SSQ-50

Command-Activated Sonobuoy System (CASS) is now superseded in U.S. service by SSQ-62 (DICASS). The signal is omnidirectional. Lifetime is one hour (half an hour for SSQ-50B), and the hydrophone depth is 60 or 1500 ft. There are 31 radio channels. Acoustic frequencies are 6.5, 7.5, 8.5, and 9.5 kHz.

♦ SSQ-53/SSQ-73

The directional LOFAR buoy (DIFAR) operates at a depth of 90 or 1000 ft, with a lifetime of 1 or 8 hours, at a frequency of 10 Hz–2.4 kHz. SSQ-53 is A-size, weighing 26 lbs, and was standardized in 1969. SSQ-53B, the current version, weighs 22 lbs (Sparton version), and its hydrophone operates at a depth of 100, 400, or 1000 ft; lifetime is 1, 3, or 8 hours, and reporting is on one of 99 RF channels. SSQ-53B reduces the low-frequency mechanical noise found in SSQ-53A, and the operating parameters are chosen by push button (verified by light-emitting diodes on the buoy). The sonobuoy can be launched at up to 370 kts and from as high as 40,000 ft. The first SSQ-53Bs were delivered early in 1984.

SSQ-53C is a full-function DIFAR buoy in Dwarf (G) size (16.5 in long but with an A-size diameter), fully equivalent to SSQ-53B (but launchable only from 30,000 ft or below). Weight is 11 lbs.

SSQ-53D is a dwarf version with its frequency range extended to lower frequencies.

SSQ-73 was an experimental deep DIFAR buoy (A-size). It was described as the deep suspended DIFAR (DSD), and it was superseded by VLAD.

Sparton has developed a Dwarf DIFAR (A-size diameter but 12 in long; 10 lbs). Operating depth is 90 to 1000 ft, and operating life is 1 or 4 hours; the buoy is tuned to one of 99 channels. No standard designation has been released.

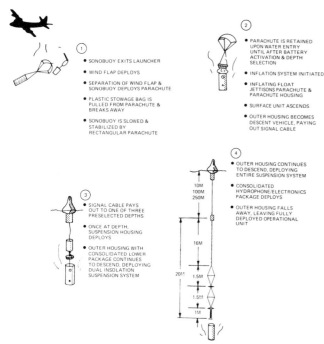

Typical deployment sequence of an SSQ-53 sonobuoy. (Sparton)

♦ SSQ-57A

This low-cost passive A-size buoy (14 lbs) operates at 60 or 400 ft; lifetime is 1, 3, or 8 hours. SSQ-57A operates on one of 31 channels. The hydrophone is Sparton-designed, the company claiming smooth response up to 20 kHz. The company claims that the buoy is effective at ranges of up to 10 nm and is launchable from 100 to 30,000 ft at 45–370 kts, into seas up to sea-state 5.

This buoy is used either for calibrating ambient sea noise (which is why smooth response is important), for monitoring exercises, or for collecting acoustic intelligence (where a smooth response can reproduce an unknown submarine signature, a narrower-band buoy might miss important parts of the spectrum). SSQ-57A is similar in mechanical design to SSQ-41. FY88 procurement was 11,947; FY89, 12,378. SSQ-57A has been sold at least to Australia.

♦ SSQ-58A (MIUW)

SSQ-58A buoy for mobile inshore underwater warfare. (Sparton)

This special moored buoy for Mobile Inshore Undersea Warfare is an element of a movable surveillance system. MIUW consists of a 36-in diameter, 24-in deep, foam-filled fiberglass float, from which are suspended its mooring and its hydrophone assembly, and from which projects its antenna. MIUW is deployed over the side of a boat or small craft, typically in depths between 40 and 110 ft (an optional deep mooring kit allows for a depth of 600 ft). Minimum hydrophone depth is 20 ft. There may also be a deeper-mooring version, since earlier literature listed MIUW with a maximum hydrophone depth of 700 ft. The buoy can survive in tidal currents of up to 3 kts and in surface currents of up to 6 kts. Frequency range is 50 Hz to 10 kHz, and the hydrophone is omnidirectional (with a flow shield). Operation is continuous because the buoy carries a 12-volt commercial rechargeable lead-acid battery; lifetime between recharging is 100 hrs. The buoy reports on one of 31 VHF channels, and it carries a radar reflector atop its quarter-wave antenna. There is also a navigational warning light, which can be enabled or disabled as required. MIUW is currently (1989) in limited production by Sparton.

The SSQ-58 designation originally applied to a LOFAR buoy

that could be anchored in up to 500 fathoms of water (3000 ft) and had a 30-day lifetime, to operate in currents up to 5 kts and in sea-state 5 (and which could survive 40-kt seas in sea-state 6).

◆ SSQ-62 (DICASS)

Directional command-activated active sonobuoy (DICASS) is used for localization of a submarine detected by passive buoys. On command, DICASS can determine a submarine's range, bearing, and speed (from doppler). SSQ-62 uses FM or CW pulses; their lengths and intervals can be chosen via one of four preset acoustic channels. Transmission is ODT but reception is directional. DICASS operates at 60 or 1500 ft and weighs 39 lbs. The feasibility contract was let to Sparton in 1968.

The current SSQ-62B weighs 34 lbs and has a lifetime of 30 minutes. SSQ-62B adds a third depth: its transducer operates at 89, 396, or 1518 feet (as commanded), and -62B reports on one of 31 RF channels. The surface unit employs a seawater battery; the submerged pinger uses a lithium battery. SSQ-62B replaces the SSQ-48B Miniature Range-Only Buoy and is a follow-on to SSQ-50. Current procurement: FY88 is 12,229; FY89 is 17,464.

Raytheon, the developer, claimed that SSQ-62 was the first of its kind to be compass oriented, providing aircraft with true bearing on a target.

◆ SSQ-71

See submarine communications systems in the Surveillance and Control section.

◆ SSQ-75 (ERAPS)

Expendable RAP active sonobuoy was developed by Bunker Ramo. ERAPS is command-activated, uses 2- or 5-second pulses, and has a 3-hour life. SSQ-75 uses a low-frequency pinger and a volumentric (circular) receiving array. Depth could be 60 down to 16,500 feet (typically 15,000 ft in the Atlantic, 6000 ft in the Mediterranean). Maximum range is about 15 nm. Power is provided for 100 ping-seconds.

The preliminary design was reviewed in FY82; airdrop mechanical tests and over-the-side acoustics tests were conducted in FY83; 315 ERAPS buoys were obtained for operational tests in FY84/85, and an airdrop succeeded in FY85. Congress directed that the program be restructured (to reduce costs) in FY87. Tests were scheduled for completion during FY88, with production to follow in FY89.

◆ SSQ-77

VLAD, a vertical-line-array DIFAR buoy (A-size, 29 lbs), uses nine omnidirectional hydrophones and two geophones in place of the single DIFAR hydrophone of its predecessor, SSQ-53B. A conventional DIFAR hydrophone mounted at the array's phase center provides bearing data, and the other hydrophones are used to detect bottom-bounce signals and to discriminate against shipping noise from the surface. The entire array is carried in a faired cable, the fairing reducing cable noise ("strum"); and the array is held vertical by a terminal weight and is stabilized in direction by a 15-foot drogue, a water-filled plastic bag acting as a sea anchor. Depth is 1000 ft; lifetime is 1 or 8 hours; and frequency range is 10 Hz–2.4 kHz. Each buoy can be preset to one of 99 radio channels.

The signal format is identical to that of the SSQ-53B DIFAR, so that the buoy is compatible with existing AQA-7 processors, found on board P-3s. All beam-forming is performed within the buoy. Apparently the vertical orientation of the beam is preset; a sketch provided by Sparton shows a buoy adjusted to detect bottom-bounce signals, rejecting surface noise and horizontal signals.

During the mid-1970s, VLAD was chosen for production instead of the alternative DSD (SSQ-73) buoy. Both buoys reflect the ASW concepts of the late 1960s and were attempts to overcome the improved silencing then expected of the new generation of Soviet submarines (Charlie, Victor, Yankee) and their

successors. Sippican acquired rights to manufacture SSQ-77A, a modified version, from Hazeltine in March 1984. Modifications made for production included redesign of the surface float. Pilot production began in May 1984, full-scale production following in 1986. Sippican's description involves eleven omnidirectional hydrophones (and no geophones) and alternative lifetimes of 1, 4, or 8 hours, but it is not clear whether these are changes specific to SSQ-77A.

In FY76, 2000 SSQ-77 service-test models were bought; operational evaluation was successful, and the buoy was approved for service use late in FY78. Production began in FY80 with 1000 units, followed by 7,000 in FY81 and by 23,000 in FY82. Recent procurement: FY87, 98,812; FY88 request, 51,663; FY89 request, 34,874.

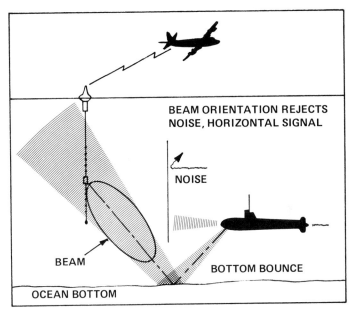

Operating geometry of the SSQ-77A VLAD buoy. (Sparton)

◆ SSQ-79

This steerable vertical-line array (SVLA), in A-size, operates at 1000 ft, for a 4- or 8-hour lifetime. This buoy is also called the Passive Advanced Directional Sonobuoy (PADS). Hazeltine received the advanced development contract in FY76 and began work in FY77. SSQ-79 uses a third-generation sensor, VLADFA (VLAD Frequency Analysis), with a digital uplink. Developmental test and evaluation (Phase II) was completed in FY83. In FY86 (ca. March 1986) the estimated requirement was 480 prototypes and 2000 initial-production buoys for completion of tests through FY87.

This buoy was developed under a Passive Advanced Detection System program begun in FY70.

◆ SSQ-83

SSQ-83 is a SAR (sea-air-rescue) up-link buoy (ULC).

◆ SSQ-86

SSQ-86 provides down-link communications, DLC. See submarine communications systems in the Surveillance and Control section.

◆ SSQ-90

An active multiple ping (AMP) B-size (103-lb) buoy, SSQ-90 is currently in limited production.

◆ SSQ-101

A buoy with a horizontal-line array (HLA), SSQ-101 was initially dropped in favor of vertical-line arrays. However, in mid-1986 the navy sought bids for full-scale engineering development, including production of 400 buoys.

♦ **SSQ-102**

Hazeltine/Sippican or Boeing/Magnavox/TRW (competitors) are developing this tactical-surveillance sonobuoy (TSS) for completion by February 1994. SSQ-102 is to be a long-duration, large-area surveillance buoy (A-size). A processor in the buoy selects and records signals of interest, which are played back at high speed upon interrogation by an airplane. TSS should be a force multiplier because, by using the buoy, one aircraft will be able to cover a very large area. System definition was completed in FY86, and the Hazeltine-Sippican full-scale engineering-development contract was let in September 1987. From a functional point of view, TSS would appear to be equivalent to RDSS.

♦ **SSQ-103**

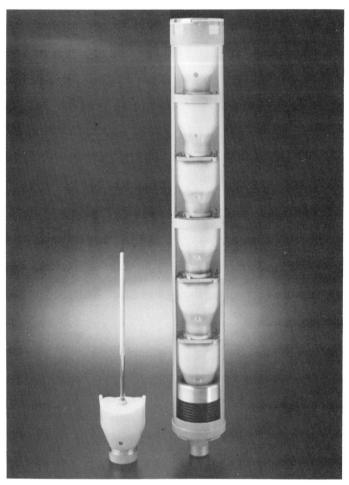

Low-cost sonobuoys (SSQ-103), individual and stacked in an A-size casing. Not shown is the array deployed 300 ft below the buoy. (Sippican)

This low-cost sonobuoy (LCS) may replace earlier LOFAR types. In Sippican's version, SSQ-103 is one-sixth of A-size and is intended for deployment in dense fields. Unlike a LOFAR buoy, which measures a detailed acoustic spectrum for analysis on board a monitoring airplane, a low-cost sonobuoy measures gross (broad-band) noise nearby, integrating (in effect) over much of the spectrum. That scheme cannot match the range sometimes achievable with LOFAR, but LCS should be able to detect the noise of water flowing over the hull of a nearby submarine, a noise that is essentially impossible to eliminate. Because detection range is likely to be very limited, a detection by a low-cost buoy should indicate that a submarine is quite close, and that indication in turn may be a sufficient attack criterion. Alternatively, a detection may lead to a second phase during which more sophisticated buoys can be dropped. Ironically, the low-cost sonobuoy brings sonobuoy operation back to the early 1950s, when passive buoys were all broad-band. At that time, simple silencing measures (such as intermittent snorkeling) seemed likely to overcome such buoys, and active al-

ternatives (Julie) were proposed. LOFAR made passive buoys viable, and only now, more than three decades later, does the potential of passive operations seem about to be exhausted.

LCS does differ from the primitive buoys of the 1950s, which were not nearly sensitive enough to detect flow noise at useful ranges (and which relied on the noise of snorkeling). LCS deploys a passive multi-element array down to a depth of 300 ft and continuously compares the received energy level in the water to a measured figure, thus reducing the effect of background noise. Each buoy is 4.5 in × 5.5 in long, and six are packaged in each A-size launcher. The cost limit is one-tenth the cost of a conventional passive buoy, and the projected production rate (from the late 1980s) is 500,000 units per year.

Both Sippican and Sparton have developed alternative versions of SSQ-103. Sippican's is coffee-cup shaped; Sparton's is cylindrical. Each is essentially A/6-sized, and each is designed for laying in a very dense field. Sippican's can be tuned to any one of 330 channels. Sparton's can be tuned to one of 66 channels and, presumably, is intended to come in any one of five versions (a smaller number of tunable channels would mean a simpler and, therefore, less expensive frequency synthesizer in the buoy).

Quite aside from the need for new tactics to counter very quiet submarines, the LCS project is sometimes justified on the grounds that existing buoys cannot be bought in sufficient numbers for protracted operations. One fear is that submarine surveillance during a lengthy crisis, which might or might not lead to war, would exhaust stocks of the sophisticated buoys, leaving nothing for the war emergency. In theory, LCS might be a way of doing surveillance (as opposed to tracking up through an attack) at a lower cost, the better buoys being reserved for wartime. In this view, LCS cannot in itself provide sufficient localization for attack. In wartime, then, the more sophisticated buoys might be used for localization after area detection by LCS.

These projects seem to have been outgrowths of an Advanced Passive Sensors project for wide-area buoy search and advanced means of localization. LCS was intended as a follow-up to VLAD, using either a horizontal-line array (HLA) or STRAP (Sonobuoy Thinned Random Array Processing). A low-cost sonobuoy field would be a particularly simple form of STRAP, involving simpler, rather than more complex, processing. The problem in STRAP is that buoys cannot be laid in a precise pattern amenable to conventional acoustic processing. Therefore, the beam-former must adapt to the buoy's position, and that position must be precisely known. The technique in STRAP was to provide four of, say, 20 buoys with low-power emitters that could be picked up both by the airplane and by the other buoys. Each buoy would, then, transmit a mixture of acoustic and positional data, and the airplane could locate each one. Given this data, a powerful computer (UYS-1) could develop appropriate beams. Lockheed conducted the first feasibility demonstrations, and sea trials followed in 1986.

STRAP was initially a broad-band buoy field evaluated first with SSQ-53 buoys. The effort then shifted to advanced manufacturing technology for the low-cost buoy needed to make STRAP practicable. The low-cost effort began in earnest in FY84 but was shifted to other projects in FY85.

Specific programs have included long-life commandable (LLC) VLAD (FY80); HLA packaging and acoustic tests (FY81); LLCVLAD field tests (FY81); HLA over-the-side tests (FY82); advanced localization buoy tests (FY83); shallow-water improvements (FY83); LCS high-density design (FY83); HLA over-the-side performance tests (FY84).

The advanced localization buoy used an ERAPS receiving array to evaluate the performance of a baseline high-gain array.

These titles suggest that development initially emphasized better signal processing and greater array gain. However, it would appear that work was redirected about 1983 (when ASW policy was reviewed), the expensive high-gain buoys being abandoned in favor of a relatively dense field of short-range buoys. Presumably the current LCS program represents a further retreat from the ideal, of increased range through signal processing, that was represented by a DIFAR (SSQ-53) buoy: i.e., a further acknowledgment of the effect of submarine silencing.

As of January 1989 LCS had been deleted from the program, described as canceled. Reportedly, neither manufacturer could meet the very low cost requirement imposed by the program. However, LCS is a major part of the P-3C UPDATE IV program and is virtually certain to survive in modified form.

♦ **Advanced Buoys**

Several advanced buoys have been announced:

AA Active Adjunct. This device is a modernized Julie, in which a sound source is dropped in a field of passive buoys.

ADAR Horizontal-Line Array (HLA) active receiver. This device uses an HLA buoy as a multistatic receiver of shipboard and deployed acoustic sources, for detection and location. This system should be ready for evaluation about FY92 and should be introduced in service by 2000.

AE Active Enhancement. Program demonstration is scheduled for FY89.

AI Acoustic Intercept System. System integration began development in FY88.

ITSS Improved Tactical Surveillance Sonobuoy.

TAS Tactical Arctic Sonobuoy. A conventional sonobuoy is encased in a bomb-shaped chemical ice penetrator, which reacts with the ice, eating it away. Eventually the buoy falls into the vertical position and sinks through the hole made by the chemical penetrator, guided by fins in the penetrator's tail. The usual inflatable retarder keeps the buoy afloat in the water crater left by the penetrator. The U.S. program employs a solid lithium compound penetrator; the U.S. Navy signed a prototype contract with Sparton in mid-1987. A parallel Canadian program, using a nonlithium penetrator, began officially on 1 January 1988. The penetrator-encased buoy was first displayed at the 1989 U.S. Navy League show.

♦ **SDC Buoys**

In 1984 the Space Development Corporation announced a new small-diameter (54-mm) LOFAR buoy equivalent to SSQ-41B; see the comments at the beginning of the entries on sonobuoys for SDC's claimed advantages. The buoy was conceived about 1972, to be fired by destroyers using Loki rockets (to ranges of about 60 nm); but although 1973 tests were successful, no orders followed. However, the small-diameter buoy became more attractive as smaller and smaller aircraft were proposed for maritime patrol. Early in 1984 Beech Aircraft took a sonobuoy on tour with the patrol/ASW version of its B200 Super King Air.

AIRBORNE SIGNAL PROCESSORS

♦ **AQA-1**

This sonobuoy indicator uses a CRT. AQA-1 was conceived for directional listening buoys (British-supplied SSQ-20s of 1954–56 vintage) but used for early active ones. The earlier ASA-20 and -26 used fast-moving paper readouts. These devices may survive on board some S-2s and P-2s. This indicator had a relatively broad frequency response, and signals did not persist for very long: they were difficult to see above a noisy trace on the CRT. The width was needed to pick up doppler-shifted signals, but it admitted a great deal of noise around the signal itself. Because they used paper traces, ASA-20 and -26 (a smaller version of -20) had, in effect, some memory and permitted some visual integration of signals to pick them out of the noise.

♦ **AQA-3/4**

These LOFAR (Jezebel) signal processors for, respectively, S-2D and -2E Tracker aircraft are no longer in U.S. service but are used in several Allied navies. Earlier versions of the S-2 lacked any Jezebel capability. They had, at best, an AQA-1 sonobuoy indicator. S-2E introduced a coordinated tactical navigation system to solve tactical problems, combining memory, display, and automatic computation.

AQA-3 and -4 were also carried by P-3A Orions.

These processors used paper displays and could process four buoys simultaneously. AQA-3/4 could also carry out CODAR (correlation detection) analysis: the time of arrival of the same sound at two buoys could be used to give a line of bearing, so that two pairs of buoys could give a cross-fix.

LOFAR spectra were obtained by time compression. The sonobuoy signal had to be subjected to a series of matched narrow-band filters, the output of each filter appearing as a darker or lighter spot on the LOFARgram. It was impossible to apply the filters in sequence as the sonobuoy signal was received: each filter imposed a finite analysis time, and it would have been impossible to follow changing signals. The solution was time compression. The incoming signal was tape-recorded and transferred to a secondary analog memory that could be scanned very rapidly. In AQA-3, the secondary memory was a round magnetic tape about 5 inches in diameter, which rotated slowly past an erase head and then past a recording head on its outer side. Pickup heads for analysis rotated rapidly on the inside; Bell claimed that this system was the earliest example of having recording on one side of a medium and pickup on the other side.

The compression ratio was the ratio of recording speed to pickup speed. Effective analyzer bandwidth is the full bandwidth of the fixed-frequency filter divided by this ratio. The faster the pickup rotational speed (which is fixed by strength of material), the narrower the bandwidth per filter and thus the greater the signal-processing efficiency of the system as a whole. The fixed-filter bandwidth cannot be shrunk.

The next step, then, was to go from a mechanical to a solid-state system, Deltic (Delay-Line Time Compressor). Deltic was incorporated in AQA-5. It was proposed at the Scripps Institution of Oceanography and initially implemented by Bell Labs, the basic patents being filed in 1956. A Deltic contains a digital memory and a delay line. Incoming acoustic data are digitized and recirculated. On each pass back through the analyzer, the oldest digit is dropped and another added. The product of clock rate and delay-line length is the multiplication factor. Greater multiplication factors could be applied both to multibuoy operation and also to better resolution in the analysis of each buoy. AQA-5 introduced Deltic. Compared to AQA-3 and -4, AQA-5 enjoyed an increased compression factor of about 17.

The LOFARgram paper printing mechanism corresponds to these electronic techniques. A single fine stylus sweeps across a paper, marking frequencies detected in the signal under analysis. Its sweep rate across the paper corresponds to the rate at which the signal is analyzed. The paper itself moves to indicate changes over time. The darkness of the marks corresponds to the strength of the frequency components in the signal, and clearly there is a tacit assumption that all or most of the signal remains steady over the time interval it takes the stylus to move across. The more resolution the system requires, the further the stylus must move in a given time (to provide enough indication per channel). Targets are detected by visual integration.

In contrast, a CRT display created by a digital analysis technique (FFT) will create the entire LOFARgram essentially instantaneously, all frequency components being developed at the same time rather than in sequence.

Deltic was still fundamentally an analog device, in that the time-compressed signal still went through a series of narrow-band filters. The next step was a fully digital device, a digital analyzer using FFT techniques. FFT was introduced in the OL-82 of the S-3A and probably also in the AQA-7 of the P-3C.

AQA-3 and -4 could handle a maximum of 4 buoys (4 LOFAR or 2 CODAR in AQA-3, 4 LOFAR or 2 LOFAR and 2 CODAR in -3A and -4).

AQA-4 was made by Western Electric.

♦ **AQA-5**

The signal processor for P-3B aircraft was later installed in British Nimrod, French Atlantic, and Japanese PS-1 aircraft.

AQA-5 was a development of AQA-3/4. AQA-5 had an improved DELTIC (delay-line time compressor) processor and somewhat greater sensitivity and used surface-wave processing. A P-3B carried two AQA-5s. Compared to AQA-3/4, AQA-5 achieved improved classification by using a narrower effective bandwidth, a wider display, and better frequency resolution. AQA-5s were also used ashore, in ASW analysis centers (ASCACs) and on board aircraft carriers, to analyze sonobuoy data collected by ASW aircraft.

AQA-5 could handle up to 8 buoys: 8 LOFAR or 6 LOFAR and 1 CODAR, or 4 LOFAR and 2 CODAR, or 2 LOFAR and 3 CODAR, or 4 CODAR.

An improved AQA-5, WAP II (Wide-band Acoustic Processor II), was used on board some frigates to process SQR-15 towed-array data. WAP III is used by IUWGs (Inshore Underwater Warfare Groups) in TSQ-108 vans.

These processors were built by Western Electric and Emerson. In British service they were replaced by AQS-901; in French, by SADANG (TSM 8210). Emerson Electric delivered its first AQA-5 in 1964 and produced a total of 650. A modified version was delivered to Australia, Britain, and Germany.

◆ AQA-7(V)/IPADS

AQA-7 was the basis of the P-3C, which carried two of these processors. S-2G Trackers (which are still operated by many navies as shore-based patrol aircraft) carry one.

AQA-7 introduced DIFAR (directional LOFAR) processing (SSQ-53 buoys). Compared to AQA-5, AQA-7 is more sensitive and has an expanded frequency coverage. AQA-7 incorporates ALI (automatic line integration), which presumably enables the processor to compensate for doppler line broadening. There are both paper and CRT readouts. AQA-7 can simultaneously process up to eight channels of passive (LOFAR), two channels of active omnidirectional (CASS), and one of active directional (DICASS) sonobuoys.

One-side of an AQA-7, showing both the CRT screen and the paper (hard-copy) display. Each can be used to interpret LOFAR buoy data. The screen can show data integrated over time, frequency interval by frequency interval. The hard-copy printer provides a record of sound at each instant of time, the operator deciding that a line is present by what amounts to visual integration. (U.S. Navy)

AQA-7 was first delivered in 1969. Between then and 1987, five generations were produced, all within the same space and with the same power requirements. Major improvements were:

single vernier (1975)
triple vernier (1979)
DICASS (1980): AQA-7(V)8/9
passive tracking (1984): AQA-7(V)10/11/12

Single and triple vernier presumably refer to finer calibration of sound spectra; triple vernier may mean that three portions of the overall spectrum are examined simultaneously. This modification was requested by the Operational Test and Evaluation Force and was added from January 1979 onward, converting (V)4 to (V)6/7.

AQA-7 has also been modified recently to provide CODAR processing; this modification suggests a reemergence of Julie or of some similar active-passive system.

IPADS (Improved Processing-and-Display System) is a sixth-generation improvement package; the development contract was issued in July 1987, for delivery by May 1990. It will provide expanded channel capacity, improved compatibility with improved sonobuoys (such as array buoys), and improved ability to detect quiet submarines (presumably by increasing integration time).

Broad-band algorithms were tested in AQA-7(V)13/14/15 between 3 January 1983 and 16 July 1985.

These systems are manufactured by Magnavox.

◆ OL-82/OL-5004

OL-82 is Sanders's fast-Fourier-transform (FFT) sonobuoy processor for S-3A aircraft. OL-82 differs from its predecessors in lacking any paper printout, and frequencies are presented logarithmically rather than linearly.

OL-5004 is a modified OL-82 for Canadian Aurora aircraft. It adds vernier displays and can measure ambient sea noise.

Both OL-82 and OL-5004 represent the beginning of a new generation of narrow-band systems, using FFTs to determine the spectral content of an acoustic signal. Incoming signals are converted into series of points (signal intensity at closely spaced time intervals) in digital form, and the spectrum is read off in digital form for further representation or analysis. FFT is now the standard means of spectral analysis in passive sonar applications, including those on board ships and on board submarines. Spectral analysis should be particularly well adapted to data-bused systems, in which data passes from one console to another in digital form.

◆ UYS-1

IBM's Advanced Signal Processor (ASP), the first and current standard U.S. Navy acoustic-signal processor, is intended to replace a variety of special-purpose devices. Therefore, like many other current systems, it emphasizes programmability and can be upgraded by changes in software rather than by rewiring.

Production began in 1981, the 250th unit being delivered in October 1984. The initial requirement, as stated in 1981, was for 500 units.

UYS-1 is a very high speed linear-flow computer, currently used in aircraft (P-3C UPDATE III, S-3B, SH-60B), submarines (BQQ-5C, BQQ-9, SUBACS), and surface ships (SQS-53B/C, SQR-19, UQQ-2 SURTASS); this computer is also used by the air force and army. The current version has a program memory of 128K 32-bit words, expandable to 256K with an engineering change. Bulk storage is up to 1024K 32-bit words, organized in 64-bit double words with 8 error-correction code bits.

Processing rate is 10–20 Megaflops (million multiplications/second), with a total input/output rate of 1.25 million words/second. Demonstrated MTTR is 12 minutes; predicted MTBF is 775–1100 hours, depending on configuration.

Input/Output is organized in up to eight programmable channel pairs (combination of NTDS and Proteus).

In its aircraft form, UYS-1 is $57.32 \times 23.44 \times 11.19$ in, weighs 240 lbs, and requires 1530 watts of power.

Three ASP are packaged together as TRIASP, for the BQQ-5C Expanded DIFAR.

The UYS-1 was designed for upgrading, given the very rapid evolution of computer technology. For example, as of 1984 ASP memory technology was already in its fourth generation, having evolved from 4K (bits per chip) to 64K. Improvements between the start of production, in 1981, and 1984 included doubling the central processor's control memory (2K to 4K 32-bit words), doubling the arithmetic processor's storage (2K to 4K 64-bit words), doubling the arithmetic processor's working storage (2K to 4K 32-bit words), doubling the program's storage (128K to 256K 32-bit words), and improving programmability using distributed program architecture microcode. Many of these improvements resulted from the replacement of 1K static memory by 4K read/write memory, cutting the net number of modules.

In November 1983 IBM completed its first VHSIC chip, capable of 100 Megaflops, ten times more than any previous reported chip, with 37,000 circuits on 64 square millimeters of silicon. Applied to an acoustic brassboard (VHSIC acoustic brassboard, May 1984), this type of chip permitted DIFAR signal multiplexing for twice as many sonobuoys as are currently available. A brassboard is not, of course, a working airborne computer, but this type of performance must have been important for the massive dwarf sonobuoy fields envisaged under the low-cost sonobuoy program (see SSQ-103 above).

◆ UYS-2

The advanced modular signal processor was developed by Bell Labs (AT&T). UYS-2 is intended for use by air, surface, submarine, and shore platforms, in acoustics, radar, electronic warfare, image processing, and communications. However, because UYS-2 was conceived as an ASW signal processor, it is included here. The design concept called for a family of processors, with varying volumes and burst multiplication rates:

        EMSP A 35 cu in, 400 Megaflops
        EMSP B 30 cu in, 200 Megaflops
        EMSP C 25 cu in, 150 Megaflops
        EMSP D 15 cu in, 100 Megaflops
        EMSP E 5 cu in, 25 Megaflops

High net speed is achieved by parallel processing (which AT&T called "multithread control architecture"). The EMSP is designed around six functional elements (FE), each consisting of a group of standard electronic modules (SEMs): a scheduler; a global memory (intelligent memory providing storage and memory management, in 2-, 4-, 6- or 8-Megaword modules); a data-transfer network; a command program processor; an arithmetic processor; and an input/output processor. Words are 16 bits long.

Predicted MTBF is 1250 hours for the largest configuration or 4000 for the smallest; predicted MTTR is 0.25 hours. The computer design can exploit future VHSIC or VLSI technology.

◆ ASPRO (CP-1469)

The Goodyear (now Loral) Associative Parallel Processor is designed for the E-2C. The first prototype was delivered to Grumman in mid-1982.

ASPRO was derived from a series of Goodyear computers embodying a patented multidimensional access memory, leading to the announcement, in 1972, of STARAN, the first commercially available parallel-processing computer. This work derived from a series of studies requiring high-speed searches of existing data files. Goodyear's approach was to associate incoming data with data already on file, and this association or correlation could be done most rapidly using a parallel processor. In 1979 a later version of STARAN was demonstrated as the most efficient means of upgrading the E-2C tactical-data system.

Although not primarily an ASW device, ASPRO is listed here for comparison with UYS-1 and -2. ASPRO is designed to handle more than 4000 computations simultaneously, for functions such as track-to-track correlations. It can perform arithmetic operations, such as coordinate transformations or dead-reckoning, on numerous tracks simultaneously.

ASPRO is conceived as an add-on to a larger host computer. In a volume of 0.44 cubic feet (8 × 10 × 9.5 in, 37 lbs), ASPRO contains 1792 processors with 896K words of associative storage. Program memory is 32K words (32-bit words) with a read/write rate of 5 Mbyte/sec. No net processing rate, e.g., in Megaflops, is available, but the associative processor multiplies two 16-bit words in 108.5 nanoseconds (194.5 nanoseconds for the 1792 items in parallel). The power requirement is 200 watts.

◆ P-3C UPDATE Programs

The series of P-3C UPDATE programs parallels drastic improvements both in sonobuoys themselves and in the computers processing their data. Many navies (and many U.S. naval reservists) still operate P-3B Orions updated to some approximation of the P-3C. Late production P-3Bs had a strengthened airframe (135,000 rather than 127,500 lbs as a maximum take-off weight), and improvements included a fourfold increase in acoustic processing capacity, a better tactical navigation system, and, in 1981, an IR detector and a Harpoon-missile capacity.

All P-3Cs have the strengthened airframe and a new avionics system developed under the A-NEW program (1962–68), begun during P-3A production. The original P-3C sensors and processors were linked together by a general purpose digital computer, the first such on board an ASW aircraft (65K words). Data was automatically extracted rather than manually logged, as in earlier aircraft. There were also automated ESM, dual inertial-navigation systems, and data-link communications. Each airplane carried 84 A-size sonobuoys, 48 preset in chutes and 36 internally (and, therefore, set in flight).

As an indication of the increased computing power of the original P-3C, it was said that the electronics part count in one P-3C equalled the total in all 144 P-3Bs. The P-3C could process sixteen buoys simultaneously, compared to eight in a P-3B and four in a P-3A. The P-3C had 48 externally loaded sonobuoy chutes (plus 4 reloadable in flight), compared to nine chutes in a P-3A or -3B. The P-3C also introduced the dual-antenna APS-115 radar, for full 360-degree sea-surface coverage, and used a low-light television instead of the searchlight of the predecessors. The 43rd production P-3C introduced the ASQ-81 MAD.

The UPDATE I program was begun before the first aircraft joined the fleet and entered service in 1974. UPDATE I increased the computer's memory sevenfold (by adding a 393K auxiliary magnetic drum) and added an additional tactical display for acoustic sensor operators, acoustic processor improvements, a crash locator (beacon), and the Omega navigation system.

UPDATE II doubled the capacity on the acoustic tape recorder (ATR) and added a sonobuoy reference system, the Harpoon antiship missile, and an infrared detector to replace the earlier low-light-level television. The sonobuoy reference system consists of antennas, located around the fuselage, that locate buoys by recording the phase differences in the signals received by adjacent antennas; the airplane no longer has to overfly buoys to locate them. This system was developed for the S-3A Viking. UPDATE II entered service in 1978 (the first such aircraft joined the training command in September 1977).

UPDATE II.5 replaced some systems with more reliable equivalents (INS, Doppler, VHF, VOR/ILS, TACAN, ESM); it integrated aircraft-to-submarine acoustic communications (via buoy); it added a MAD compensation group adapter and a tactical coordinating officer (TACCO) auxiliary IR display; it standardized wing pylons and improved fuel-tank venting.

UPDATE III added an advanced sonobuoy receiver (the 99-channel ARR-78 in place of the 31-channel ARR-72), a single advanced signal processor (ASP: UYS-1), transparent logic units (XLUs), and an acoustic test signal generator (ATSG). An extra lower UHF antenna was added, plus environmental improvements (better cabin-air distribution, a heat-exchanger water spray system, and increased-capacity engine-driven compressors for air conditioning). In this version the airplane has three sensor stations (displays) plus a TACCO display. The airplane can monitor 16 different sonobuoy signals on 99 channels. The XLU designation refers to lighter-weight logic units that are functionally equivalent (i.e., transparent) to their bulkier predecessors, using integrated circuit technology. These logic units leave space for later installation of an AYK-14 computer. The general-purpose UYS-1 (Proteus) computer replaces the earlier hard-wired AQA-7. UYS-1 is heavier than its predecessors, and some reduction in the airframe's weight (such as lightweight floorboards) was needed to compensate. On the other hand, improvements in hardware made it possible to dispense with one of the two computers originally planned.

The ASP displays buoy data (either analog or digital) on two CRTs, each of which can show eight buoy channels. Each channel can be broken down into three narrow-band (vernier) windows.

Continuing work on ASP includes integration with passive tracking algorithms (PTA—see the entry on LAMPS above), broad-band capability, 32-channel half-bandwidth capability (channel expansion), 99-channel on-line capability, and provisions for advanced buoys (using modular software).

UPDATE IV introduces a high-speed data bus (maximum capacity 192 Mbps, using 32-bit words) and a distributed processing system. The data bus allows for easy system expansion and modification, and the distributed architecture should be fault-tolerant. This system is expected to have sufficient computing capacity to permit some measure of automatic classification of passive signals. The acoustic subsystem uses the new standard UYS-2 processor with increased sonobuoy-channel capacity, presumably to handle both future array buoys and large numbers of low-cost sonobuoys (LCS). Other sensors will be an APS-137 ISAR imaging radar, an AAS-36 IR detector, an ALR-77 ESM, and more precise navigation (inertial/Omega/GPS). The UPDATE IV contract went to Boeing; Lockheed, the manufacturer of the P-3C, was responsible for all earlier UPDATEs.

UPDATE IV is to be applied to all existing UPDATE II aircraft. With retirements of earlier P-3s, that modification should reduce the P-3 fleet to two configurations, UPDATEs III and IV.

Compared to UPDATE III, UPDATE IV has 2.5 times the acoustic data throughput, 8 times the bulk memory, 30 times the display memory, and 5 times the MTBF. Increased display memory presumably allows the operator to sample the multiple beams available from new array sonobuoys such as HLA and ERAPS. UYS-2 can handle 54 DIFAR buoys simultaneously. The associated high-volume data recorder can accept 30 Mbits/sec for 7.4 hours.

The five operator stations are derived from the UDACS (universal display-and-control system) developed by Boeing for the Royal New Zealand Air Force's P-3B modernization program.

UPDATE IV was approved by the Navy Acquisition Review Council in November 1984, and in November 1985 Boeing received a contract for demonstration and validation, in competition with Lockheed. The Boeing avionics demonstration began in October 1986, and in July 1987 the company was awarded a full-scale engineering-development contract (with an option for production sets). The first aircraft is to be delivered in mid-1990. The successful Boeing proposal incorporated avionics which had been developed for the Royal New Zealand Air Force's P-3s.

Aircraft are continually updated, so that earlier UPDATEs often receive equipment developed for later ones.

NONACOUSTIC ASW SENSORS

For ASW radars (for periscope or snorkel detection), see the Strike/Surface Warfare section. Virtually the only current non-acoustic ASW sensors are Magnetic Anomaly Detectors (MAD). However, in the past some ASW aircraft have carried chemical detectors of snorkel exhausts ("sniffers," code-named AUTO-LYCUS in Britain); and Sweden is currently interested in the Australian LADS described below.

Reportedly, although the Western powers use MAD as a final-attack confirmation sensor, it is Soviet practice to use MAD instead as a search sensor, flying a tight pattern over the narrow strait through which a submarine is expected to pass. No details of Soviet MAD systems are available.

It is also possible that some nations use magnetic loops for harbor protection; this technology dates from before World War II. The Crouzet MAD buoy would seem to be a current application.

AUSTRALIA

♦ LADS

Not conceived as an ASW system, the Laser Airborne Depth Sounder is an underwater survey system developed to help map the Australian continental shelf. LADS is said to be able to penetrate 50 meters of water under all sea conditions, and the device has flown in a Fokker F-27. Reportedly Sweden has been interested in LADS as a means of detecting small submarines in very shallow water under poor acoustic conditions. LADS was developed about 1975–80 by the Australian Electronics Research Laboratory (of the Defense Research Centre, South Australia), and tested in 1981, in 3.25–164 feet of water.

In April 1988 it was reported that a Larsen 500 airborne Ladar (Laser Radar) bathymeter had been tested by the U.S. Navy Coastal Systems Command, Panama City, and by the U.S. Naval Systems Center at San Diego, and that the device would be tested as a mine detector in the Persian Gulf. This Ladar was developed by Optech Systems of Downsview, Ontario, and it has demonstrated detection of mines down to about 100-ft depth. It uses a pulsed beam and backscatter to determine the position of the water's surface. The Larsen 500 was developed for the Canadian hydrographic service and has been used for coastal surveys since about 1985. Reportedly the Ladar has been tested against submarines, torpedoes, nets, mines, and submarine wakes.

There is a long (and unhappy) history of attempts to use blue-green lasers for submarine detection, beginning with the discovery, about 1962, that such lasers could indeed penetrate sea water to a considerable depth. For example, a primitive laser radar figured in advanced U.S. ASW development in the early 1960s; and in the late 1960s such a device, UDACS, manufactured by Kollsman, was publicly described. By that time it was fairly clear that, although the beams were good enough for one-way communication down to a submarine (albeit not down to great depths), there was not enough of a back-scattered signal for useful detection or tracking. Even so, lasers remain attractive in really shallow water.

See also the Northrop ALARMS in the Mine Warfare section.

CANADA

♦ ASQ-502

CAE Electronics's cesium magnetometer is typical of the optically pumped total-field type that replaced the earlier saturable-core magnetometers from the late 1960s on. The newer devices use a nuclear magnetic resonance (NMR) technology, exploiting basic atomic structure. The external magnetic field determines the precise energy levels of the atoms involved, and those atoms resonate upon passage of a signal whose frequency corresponds to the difference in energy levels. Thus, the frequency of the signal gives the magnetic field's strength. Because frequency can be measured very exactly, such a system is quite sensitive. Sensitivity is 0.01 gamma, and total weight is 38 lbs. At the time of its introduction, ASQ-502 was ten times as sensitive as any other MAD.

♦ AIMS (ASQ-504)

The Advanced Integrated MAD System was devised by CAE Electronics, Ltd., of Canada. Unlike other helicopter-borne MAD gear, AIMS is carried on board the helicopter; CAE claims that this arrangement frees the crew of the operational restrictions associated with towing a conventional MAD body. Moreover, because the MAD detector is not towed, it is very easy for the helicopter to shift from dipping sonar to MAD operation. The company also claims increased detection range, with a sensitivity of 0.01 gamma in flight. Total weight is 50 lbs.

The integration in AIMS is between a very sensitive magnetometer and an advanced compensator to take into account the magnetic field of the aircraft (as well as geological magnetic noise). CAE has been developing sensitive compensators since the 1960s; CAE's AN/ASA-65 is currently the Free World's standard MAD compensator, with 900 units in service.

Detection is by optical pumping of directionally oriented cesium, and interference from the helicopter is canceled out by compensating upon take-off, the compensating terms being computed in 8 minutes using an on-board vector magnetometer.

Users include Britain (242 units for Sea King and Lynx helicopters and for Nimrod MR 2 aircraft), and a total of 75 others for Canadian CP-140s, Australian SH-70s, and Australian S-2 Trackers.

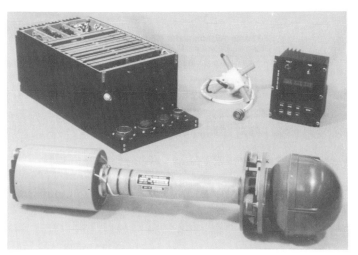

ASQ-504. (CAE)

FRANCE

◆ DHAX-1/DHAX-3

DHAX-1, the MAD that is found in the Atlantique Mk 1, uses four cesium-vapor paramagnetic resonance cells. DHAX-3 is an improved towed version, for helicopters. It uses six rather than four cesium-vapor cells.

◆ Crouzet MAD Systems

Crouzet uses electronically pumped NMR, in contrast to the optically pumped U.S. and Canadian systems that are based on electron spin resonance. The company claims extreme simplicity and reliability for this approach: there is no optical exciter; and the system uses a liquid rather than a gaseous medium, so there is no vapor to be created before the MAD can operate. Moreover, the output is easily read as a resonant frequency. Crouzet also uses a distinctive signal processing technique. Instead of threshold detection, the system compares the received signal with a model of the expected target signal, a method the company calls MAD-SADE (Self-Adaptive Detection/Estimation). A simple dipolar model of the target suffices, and the SADE method gives both a confidence level and a fix of the target's position. Experiments both in the Mediterranean and in the English Channel in 1979–80 showed that MAD-SADE improved net detection probability and that, for a given probability, the method increased detection range, so that in about 60 percent of cases the airplane detected the submarine before passing over it.

The current version is Mk 3, which equips the Atlantique Mk 2 maritime-patrol aircraft and has been tested in Lynx helicopters. The detector is 125 × 1250 mm and weighs 5.5 kg. The entire system weighs 15–20 kg. Sensitivity is within 0.1 gamma. In the Atlantique, twin sensors are used in tandem, to detect any change in the aircraft's signature, canceling it out.

This system was tested in 1983, and production began early in 1985. In helicopters, it is towed on a 70-m cable.

Crouzet is currently (1989) developing a MAD buoy, seen as a replacement for current passive buoys in the face of future very quiet submarines. The company argues that, even if the Soviets build their craft of nonmagnetic titanium, no submarine can avoid having a large mass of magnetic material, e.g., in the power train. The counter argument is that magnetic detection generally depends on the motion of the submarine relative to the detector. That motion is considerable with an airplane but much less so in the case of a submarine passing a static buoy at low speed. Even so, it is worth recalling that magnetic loops were the standard means of harbor defense before World War II. A submarine passing over the loop generated a current, and that signal could be picked up by a shore station. Controlled mines could be detonated in response. Presumably Crouzet can do much better in terms of range, given modern highly sensitive techniques of magnetic detection (loops detected at very short range, which was just what was needed to activate the right controlled mines).

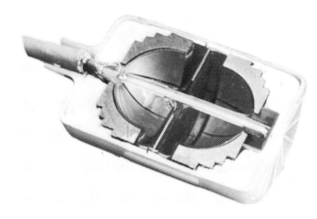

Crouzet MAD sensor, cut away to show its cavity. (Crouzet)

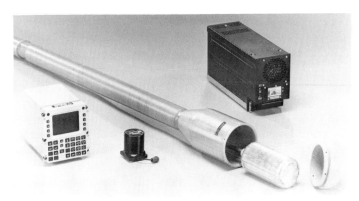

Crouzet MAD Mk 3, showing the probe and its casing. (Crouzet)

INTERNATIONAL

There is an ongoing NATO nonacoustic ASW project, listed by the U.S. government as an FY88 new start. Participants, with expected contributions, are Canada ($2 million), Germany ($6 million), Norway ($10 million), the United Kingdom ($28 million), and the United States ($50 million over five years). The first at-sea experiments, in Norway, were conducted in July 1988, with British experiments expected in the summer of 1989. The Norwegian and German Navies are presumably particularly interested in nonacoustic ASW because acoustic conditions in the fjords and in the Baltic are so very bad. The brief published description of the program suggests that it is basic physical research, the U.S. government finding it useful to be able to estimate the effect of particular sensor characteristics on submarine detection without having to carry out experiments with actual submarines. That arrangement would, for example, permit a measure of nonacoustic development without having to reveal the sensors and their performance.

UNITED STATES

◆ ASQ-10

The MAD in early P-3 and late-production S-2 aircraft, ASQ-10 is a saturable-core magnetometer that was introduced about 1960.

◆ ASQ-81

Texas Instruments's MAD is currently the standard U.S. Navy system. ASQ-81 uses optically pumped metastable helium. There are two configurations, a towed MAD for helicopters and a fixed tail MAD for airplanes. Both have been in use since 1970. In 1979 it was reported that ASQ-81 had triple the effective range of earlier MADs, about 3000 vs. 1000 ft. However, other reports suggest that the range of the earlier MAD was only doubled. ASQ-81 incorporates an improved means of maintaining alignment with the earth's magnetic field and has automatic target detection, which ASQ-10 lacks.

Versions are (V)1 for the P-3C, (V)2 for the SH-3H and SH-2D helicopters, (V)3 for the S-3A, and (V)4 for LAMPS-III helicopters.

The helicopter version can be towed at 10–140 kts and can be reeled at 50 or 200 ft/min, the limiting length of the cable being 80–180 ft. ASQ-81 can typically be turned on in 1.5 minutes, and sensor noise in-flight is generally about 0.24 gammas. Gain can be set at 0.1, 0.2, 0.4, 1, 2, 4, 10, 20, or 40 gammas full-scale.

Users are U.S. and foreign operators of the P-3C and SH-3; the U.S. Navy for the S-3, SH-2, and SH-60; Britain and the Netherlands for the WG-13 Lynx helicopter; Japan for the HSS-2 helicopter; and Taiwan for the H500 helicopter.

Texas Instruments is proposing a digital version of ASQ-81, as yet undesignated, which will use a microprocessor to compensate for the aircraft's magnetic field and will have a three-channel filtered display and threshold processing. Existing ASQ-81 wiring would be retained, but signal recognition would be improved. As in the existing unit, targets would be automatically detected. However, a range/confidence estimate would be provided. Both in-board and towed versions would be available, and aircraft electronics would be simplified.

ASQ-81 MAD stingers on a line of P-3 Orions. The radomes below the MAD boom carry the rear antenna of the APS-115 radar, so that a 360-degree search can be maintained without the drag associated with hanging a radome below the airplane. (U.S. Navy)

MISSILES

AUSTRALIA

◆ Ikara

Dimensions: length 3.43 m, span 153 cm; overall height 157 cm (135 × 60.2 × 60.8 in)
Weight: about 1300 lbs (stated as less than 600 kg)
Warhead: homing torpedo (Mk 44 or Mk 46)
Propulsion: dual-thrust (boost-sustain) Murawa solid-fuel rocket
Speed: subsonic (about Mach 0.75)   **Range:** approx 20,000 yds

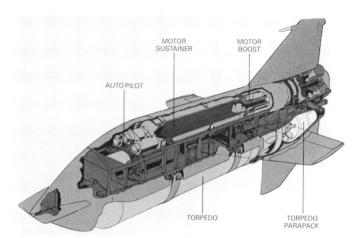

Ikara. (British Aerospace)

Ikara in flight. (British Aerospace)

Ikara is a radio-controlled rocket-powered glider carrying a lightweight torpedo, adopted by the Royal Australian Navy, the Brazilian Navy, and the Royal Navy, and sold to the Royal New Zealand Navy. The existing systems employ a single launcher (55-degree launch angle in all cases) and a magazine of reloads. The missile's transponder is tracked by the launching ship, and the missile is commanded to drop the torpedo. The missile then continues in flight, diving into the sea far enough away so as not to interfere with the torpedo's search pattern. To maintain stability after the torpedo has been dropped, the missile deploys two small fins at its rear end. The guidance receiver/decoder is housed in the missile's upper fin. The manufacturer claims that hit probability is substantially improved because Ikara continues to receive sonar update information as it flies towards its target. Flight altitude of 300 m (about 1000 ft) is maintained by barometer.

In the British ships, one of which is now in New Zealand service, missiles are stowed in two parallel rows, without their wings and tails. Each is on a shock-mounted stool, is extracted manually by an overhead grab on a monorail in the magazine's roof, and is lifted onto a trolley running between the rows. The missile is raised by hoist to an assembly room on the upper deck immediately forward of the bridge and then finned before being moved tail-first onto the launcher. Since the missile has no de-icer, it cannot be stored on the launcher for very long, but missiles can be stored in the assembly room.

The Australian requirement was stated in the late 1950s, and prototype development began in 1959. U.S.-British-Australian trials were conducted on board HMAS *Stuart* in 1963–64.

In British service Ikara is designated GWS.40. It is being phased out of service (it was removed from HMS *Bristol*, and only two of the Ikara-converted *Leanders* are left). The Brazilian designation is BRANIK (Brazilian Ikara). It employs a lightweight semiautomatic launcher. A boxed version, Basset, with folding wings, was announced in 1981. Unlike Super Ikara (below), Basset would use the original Ikara missile (except that the wings would fold to fit within the box launcher). Boxed Ikara did use lighter-weight electronics than the original Ikara system.

There are several versions. The original Australian Mk 1 and British Mk 2, neither of which entered service, were designed to carry the abortive British Mk 31 lightweight torpedo. Mks 2 and 3 (British and Australian, respectively) carry the U.S.-supplied Mk 44, and Mks 4 and 5 the U.S.-supplied Mk 46. One objective of the Ikara redesign program (see below) was to simplify the missile so that it could carry a wider variety of lightweight torpedoes with less variation. The thousandth Ikara was delivered in 1977.

In 1989 it was reported that the Royal Australian Navy planned to deactivate all its remaining Ikara installations during 1989–90. The Royal Navy will discard its two remaining Ikara ships during 1989. If these reports are accurate, then neither navy will retain an all-weather stand-off ASW capability beyond 1990; each will rely entirely on helicopters. Reportedly Ikara is being dropped because of maintenance problems inherent in the launcher and loader design; presumably the proposed boxed Ikara would have solved such problems.

Ikara on board the Australian destroyer *Brisbane*, on the small launcher on the side amidships. The main radars are SPS-40 (foremast, with SPS-10 below it) and SPS-52 (the flat plate aft), with two SPG-51 missile-guidance radars below. The big radome atop the bridge is the Ikara guidance link. (U.S. Naval Institute)

◆ Super Ikara

In April 1982 Australia asked OTO-Melara to collaborate in a new Ikara system, to produce a missile that could be stowed with folding wings and that could be box-launched. This missile would have used an Otomat guidance system. OTO-Melara abandoned this project in 1986 in favor of a new joint OTO-Melara/Sintra missile (see the French MILAS, below). Australia then began a new Super Ikara project, with British Aerospace, and a prototype flew in September 1986. In July 1987 the Australian partner, Government Aircraft Factories, was dissolved in favor of a new company.

Super Ikara is described as 3.42 m (11.22 ft) long with a 1.52-m (5-ft) span and a weight of 600 kg (1320 lbs). The power plant will be a small turbojet (either Microturbo TRI-60 or Teledyne CAE J402) rather than a rocket sustainer, for a range of 60+ nm. Speed is Mach 0.75.

The long range is really long endurance, so that the missile can be launched to loiter over a possible submarine contact while the contact is prosecuted. Control can be passed to a helicopter over the contact area, and the missile can be cued to attack as soon as the target is properly localized or as soon as the target reveals its position by trying to run at high speed. Thus a helicopter can devote its entire payload to sensors, which it may need to detect a new-generation quiet submarine. Current helicopters, carrying both sensors and weapons, are limited in the number of re-attacks they can mount. A Super Ikara/helicopter combination would be limited only by the capacity of the firing ship, and this missile would provide a ship that had a very limited helicopter capability with a useful stand-off ASW weapon.

CHINA (PRC)

◆ CY-1

Dimensions: 41 cm × 5.5 m (16.1 × 216.5 in)
Weight: 700 kg (1540 lbs) **Propulsion:** rocket
Range: 5–18 km (5500–20,000 yds)

This ballistic antisubmarine missile was first displayed at ASIANDEX in November 1986. No details were given, other than that CY-1 will be fired from a multicell launcher on board surface ships. Externally the missile resembles ASROC, and CY-1 is credited with ASROC-like performance. However, unlike ASROC, CY-1 reportedly may be carried by helicopters and maritime-patrol aircraft. It is not clear how the missile would be targeted in that case: perhaps the Chinese expect to operate aircraft in cooperation with submarines that would provide target data. Nor is it clear whether the Chinese currently have a medium-frequency sonar suited to such a weapon, and no Chinese warship carries the requisite launcher. However, drawings of a destroyer offered for export do show a pepperbox launcher. In 1988 the Chinese displayed two new sonars, perhaps operating at lower frequencies, at ASIANDEX in Beijing (ESS-1 and -2).

FRANCE

◆ Malafon

Dimensions: 651 × 5877 mm; span 3190 mm (booster: length 2135 mm, span 1800 mm) (25.6 × 231.4 × 125.6; 84.1 × 70.9 in)
Weight: 1000 kg (2200 lbs) after booster separation; booster: 330 kg (727 lbs) **Warhead:** L 4 homing torpedo
Propulsion: glider, after boost; booster burn time 2.8 sec, impulse 35,000 kg-sec (77,140 lb-sec)
Speed: at end of boost, 280 m/sec, decreasing to 100 m/sec during flight (918 ft/sec, decreasing to 328 ft/sec)
Range: 3,000–15,000 m; maximum 20,000 m (3300–16,400 yds; maximum 21,900 yds)

Malafon is a ship-launched standoff weapon carrying an L 4 homing torpedo and using a gun direction radar for guidance. The missile is tracked using two flares in its wingtips. Malafon is a glider gyro-stabilized in roll and pitch; at the end of its flight (800 m short of the predicted position of the submarine), the missile is commanded to level off, the torpedo is unlocked, and the missile is braked by parachute. The torpedo continues on and enters the water.

Malafon is stowed without its wings and tail fins, the booster fins being folded. One missile is usually held on the launcher, ready to be fired, and the missile can be launched within 30 seconds. A second launch can follow 60 seconds later, and then the firing rate can be up to one every 90 seconds. Typically a ship carries 13 missiles; the launcher proper weighs 10,500 kg.

Malafon's development began in 1956, and the missile was first tested in 1958, with sea trials following in 1962 on board the experimental destroyer *La Galissonière*. Initial operational tests were conducted in 1964. As of about 1978, it was reported that 370 Malafons were in service and that further missiles were being manufactured to replace those expended in training. Eight ships now carry Malafon, the last system having been installed over a decade ago. With Masurca, Malafon is a survivor of the French post–World War II naval missile program.

Malafon's guidance systems were modernized in 1986–87 by Sfena and now use solid-state components vice vacuum tubes. As a result, Malafon should remain in service to the end of the century.

Malafon on its launcher. Reloads are stowed in the deckhouse on the right. (U.S. Naval Institute)

♦ **Malafon Replacement (MILAS)**

> **Dimensions:** 460 mm (1060 mm with boosters) × 6 m (18.1 [41.7] × 236 in) **Weight:** 800 kg including torpedo (1760 lbs)
> **Warhead:** Murène or A290
> **Speed:** 300 m/sec at 20m in altitude (984 ft/sec at 66 ft)
> **Range:** 40 km (time from launch to splash at about 20 nm is less than three minutes) (44,000 yds)

In 1986 two teams competed to produce a replacement for Malafon that would carry the new Murène lightweight torpedo (and, for export, a variety of equivalent foreign weapons). The basic requirement was formulated in the late 1970s, after the French naval staff had decided to abandon such weapons in favor of helicopters. Tactical experience showed that a helicopter's reaction time was about 15 minutes, and the French Navy asked for a convergence-zone stand-off missile.

Matra and OTO-Melara offered a modified Otomat Mk 2, with a range of over 40 km, designated MILAS. The missile's warhead is replaced by a lightweight torpedo. Like Otomat, MILAS can receive mid-course guidance instructions. Recent accounts of MILAS mention a Franco-Italian requirement formulated in 1985, but it is not clear whether this formulation was the beginning of the OTO Melara–Matra project or an official decision.

MILAS, a torpedo-carrying derivative of the Otomat missile, is to replace Malafon. (Matra)

Aerospatiale offered a torpedo-carrying Exocet, about 6.38 m long, which could be launched from a submarine as well as from a surface ship. With a suitable booster, this Exocet could be fired by ASW helicopters and airplanes.

MILAS was chosen in the summer of 1987, and a French-Italian development MoU was signed in September 1987. Given its limited dimensions, MILAS will probably be carried in a deck container (canister launcher) rather than in the magazine used for Malafon. The first production MILAS is to be delivered in 1992, and the French and Italian Navies have both indicated an initial requirement for 200.

Maximum range is nearly 60 km in a straight line. For a flight of 35 km, the elapsed time is less than 3 minutes. Cruise altitude is 200 m. It is estimated that in-flight course corrections can increase the probability of target acquisition by as much as 15 percent at long range. After turbojet cutoff, the delivery system, retarded by a parachute, separates from the torpedo, and another parachute lowers the torpedo into the water.

MILAS will arm French F67-class destroyers (probably 12 launch units each), replacing Malafon; MILAS will also arm seven C70 during mid-life refits (six to eight launch units each) and will be added to Italian *Maestrale*s and other major Italian warships during their mid-life updates. All future French and Italian ASW warships will be armed with this weapon.

USSR

♦ **SS-N-14 (Silex)**

> **Dimensions:** length 7.6 m (25 ft) **Warhead:** homing torpedo
> **Propulsion:** solid-fuel rocket **Speed:** Mach 0.95
> **Range:** 30 nm (4 nm minimum)

A Krivak-class frigate shows her quadruple SS-N-14 launcher, with a pair of RBU-6000s just abaft it. The two shrouded antennas on lattice mast above the bridge are the Eye Bowls controlling the SS-N-14 missiles; above them is a Don Kay surface-search radar, with Head Net C at the masthead. The shrouded object immediately over the bridge is Pop Group, to control SA-N-4 antiaircraft missiles. (U.S. Naval Institute)

The Soviet equivalent of Malafon or Ikara, SS-N-14 is a powered missile that carries a homing torpedo. SS-N-14 might be considered the direct nonnuclear successor to FRAS-1, arming most Soviet ASW ships of destroyer or greater size. Except for on the *Kirov* (which has a unique reloadable twin launcher), SS-N-14 is carried in four-missile sets.

When the launchers first appeared, in the Krivak class, this missile was identified as a short-range antiship missile and designated SS-N-10. No such weapon exists, although SS-N-14 has a secondary antiship capability that uses an explosive charge in the airframe. In 1983 it was reported that SS-N-14 carries an alternative nuclear warhead, presumably a nuclear depth bomb, of about 5-kT yield.

The missile is command-guided, either by a special antenna (Eye Bowl) or via a set of Head Lights SAM control radars. Flight altitude is reportedly about 80 m (about 260 ft). Krivaks have a medium-frequency sonar, which is unlikely to provide data sufficiently accurate for attack beyond about 10,000 yds (as in the case of the U.S. ASROC). Ships equipped with lower-frequency sonars should be able to mount attacks at about twice that range. If these ships detect targets at convergence-zone range (20–35 nm, depending on water conditions), then probably helicopters with sonobuoys or dipping sonars must reacquire the target before the ship fires.

◆ SS-N-15 (Starfish)

The Soviet equivalent of the U.S. SUBROC is armed only with a nuclear warhead. SS-N-15 was copied from the U.S. weapon, reportedly compromised about 1964, and was probably intended as the primary weapon of the Victor-I–class submarine. Maximum range is 21.6 nm.

◆ SS-N-16 (Stallion)

This missile is a dual-capable successor to SS-N-15. Because all Soviet homing torpedoes are substantially larger and heavier than the U.S. lightweight torpedo that SUBROC could carry, SS-N-15 is almost certainly much larger than a 21-inch tube and is probably responsible for the adoption of the 65-centimeter torpedo tube in recent Soviet submarines. The shift from SS-N-15 to -16 may be responsible for the greater length of the Victor-II–class submarine, to accommodate a better combat system.

Maximum reported range is 54 nm, far beyond any usable acoustic range. This figure may have two quite different significances. One is that a missile capable of flying 54 nm will reach tactical ranges (perhaps of the order of 10 nm) quickly enough to keep the prospective target within torpedo-acquisition range. The other would be that the weapon might have an alternative antiship or even shore-attack role.

Both of these possibilities would mirror U.S. Navy experience of the 1960s and 1970s. A nonnuclear torpedo alternative proposed for the U.S. SUBROC missile (see below) was dropped because the target, alerted by the sound of the missile's launch, would have been able to escape the original datum before the torpedo, a Mk 44 with a rated acquisition range of only 600 yds, arrived. By the late 1960s it was no longer clear that the nuclear SUBROC would lightly be used, and a new dual-use weapon, STAM (the submarine tactical missile), carrying a new heavier torpedo with much greater acquisition range, was proposed. STAM would have had a diameter of 30 in, much greater than the 21 in of the standard torpedo tube. Within two years, STAM had developed into a dual-use (antisubmarine/antiship) missile, and in its antiship version it might have flown as far as 200 or 300 nm. STAM was incorporated into a proposed U.S. submarine design, APHNAS (the Advanced High-Performance Nuclear Attack Submarine) projected for the mid-1970s. Part of the cancellation of the submarine was the cancellation of STAM in favor of the antiship version of Tomahawk. No conventional ASW missile was developed at the time, but Sea Lance (see below) might be seen as the STAM idea using a lightweight torpedo (hence making for a torpedo tube–sized weapon). Pre-

sumably the Soviets cannot fit the requisite performance into a small torpedo; hence their choice of 65-centimeter diameter.

UNITED KINGDOM

◆ Ikara (GWS.40)

See the Australian Ikara above.

◆ SUGW

A British staff requirement formulated about 1986 called for an Ikara successor (Surface-to-Underwater Guided Weapon), a weapon that could exploit towed-array detection and that was, therefore, capable of attacking out to the second convergence zone. In the fall of 1987, however, the Ministry of Defense announced that this program had been shelved for at least three years because of a lack of funds.

The two alternatives under consideration in 1986 were Super Ikara and Tarpon (McDonnell-Douglas/Marconi), the latter using Harpoon to project a Stingray torpedo. Tarpon has also been suggested (in the United States) as an ASROC or SUBROC successor. Reportedly Dowty and McDonnell-Douglas were also proposing a vehicle that would lay sonobuoys at long range, making it possible for a surface ship to prosecute contacts at or beyond the convergence zone even if she could not launch a manned helicopter.

UNITED STATES

◆ ASROC (RUR-5A)

The only full-scale test of nuclear ASROC, fired by the destroyer *Agerholm* (in the foreground), 1962. (U.S. Naval Institute)

Dummy nuclear ASROC on a Mk-26 launcher, White Sands Missile Range. (U.S. Navy)

Dimensions: 13.25 × 177.4 in (33-in fins)
Weight: Mod 3, 949–957 lbs; Mod 4, 1071–1073 lbs
Warhead: Mod 3, Mk-44 torpedo; Mod 4, Mk-46 torpedo; Mod 5, Mk-17 Depth Bomb (nuclear: W44 warhead)
Range: maximum about 10,000 yds (minimum range is 900 yds for the torpedo version and 3500 yds for the nuclear version).

The Antisubmarine Rocket is the current U.S. standoff ASW weapon for surface ships; ASROC has also been transferred to many Allied nations, in many cases on board ex-U.S. ships. It carries either a Mk-46 torpedo or a Mk-17 nuclear depth bomb; existing ASROCS will probably be upgraded to carry Mk-50 lightweight torpedoes.

ASROC was conceived as part of a system including a reliable 10,000-yard sonar, SQS-23. The later SQS-26 has higher performance; and an extended-range version, ERA, was designed to exploit its greater direct-path range (nominally about 20,000 yards). Although ERA was tested in 1967, it was never produced, presumably because it had too low a priority in the face of severe fiscal problems during the Vietnam War. VLA is, in effect, a vertically launched ERA, although the technical details are very different.

The usual Mk-112 launcher is trainable, but it fires at a fixed 45-degree elevation, two of the eight cells elevating together. Range is determined by fixing the point of booster separation.

ASROC can also be fired from the Mk-10 launchers of *Belknap*-class cruisers and of the *Truxtun*, and from the Mk-26 launchers of *Virginia*-class cruisers and early Aegis cruisers; these launchers, too, fire the rocket at a fixed angle of elevation. In *Knox*-class frigates two cells of the ASROC box were modified to fire Standard surface-to-surface (later Harpoon) antiship missiles.

About 12,000 ASROCs were manufactured between 1960 and 1970, when production ended.

As of mid-1989, it was reported that the nuclear version of ASROC would be retired on an accelerated basis, perhaps as early as the end of the year.

◆ Vertical Launch ASROC (VLA)

VLA is ASROC modified for firing by the new vertical-launching system (Mk 41). The initial units will be produced by Loral, with Martin-Marietta as the designated second source. Compared to the original ASROC, VLA has increased range (to exploit the greater direct-path range of SQS-53, compared to SQS-23) and can carry a somewhat heavier payload (Mk-46 or Mk-50 homing torpedo). VLA or some equivalent is essential because ships fitted with vertical launchers generally cannot accommodate the earlier ASROC box launchers; without VLA these ships would not have any all-weather standoff weapon.

Dimensions are 14.1 × 200 in, and weight is 1650 lbs. These figures are still within the limits imposed by the existing

A torpedo-carrying ASROC being fired. (U.S. Navy)

A standard ASROC box launcher on board the Japanese destroyer *Haruyuki*, 1989. (W. Donko)

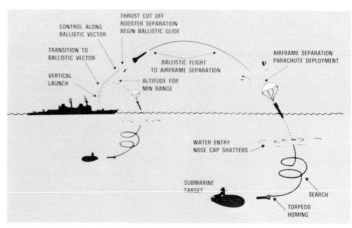

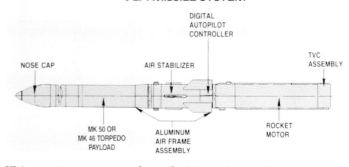

VLA operating sequence and missile. (Martin Marietta)

ASROC and Mk-26 launchers. As of 1987, the navy demanded a minimum range of about 5 kyds and a maximum range of at least 15 kyds. The first all-up demonstration/validation shot was fired at China Lake in July 1984.

The basic design was carried out by the navy, with development by Goodyear (whose naval division was later sold to Loral). The missile is pitched over into its ballistic trajectory by autopilot-controlled thrust vectoring. As in ASROC, trajectory is controlled further by ejecting the booster at the appropriate moment, the torpedo payload continuing on a ballistic path into the water.

This weapon had been expected to enter service in 1989, but Congress authorized none in either FY88 or FY89, the FY89 request for 340 being deferred to FY90. There were reports in mid-1988 that the navy wanted the program reunited with Sea Lance as a common ASW standoff weapon. Later Congress ordered the navy to buy 300 as interim weapons until a surface-launched version of Sea Lance could be made ready, presumably in the mid-1990s.

◆ SUBROC (UUM-44A)

Dimensions: 21 × 252 in **Weight:** 4000 lbs
Warhead: W 55 nuclear warhead
Propulsion: two-stage solid-fuel rocket
Speed: supersonic **Range:** approx 50,000 yds

SUBROC (UUM-44). (Goodyear)

SUBROC (Submarine-launched Rocket) is a torpedo-tube–launched ballistic ASW weapon, a contemporary of ASROC. SUBROC was initially conceived as a short-range shore bombardment weapon; but work was reoriented to the ASW mission about 1955, and SUBROC entered service in 1962. SUBROC is associated with the big spherical active bow sonar, BQS-7 (of the BQQ-2 or -5 system).

The original concept was for alternative payloads, either a nuclear depth bomb or a homing torpedo (as in ASROC). However, SUBROC travels much further, and it was appreciated quite early that aiming errors would often bring the missile outside the homing envelope of a Mk-44 or even a Mk-46 torpedo. Moreover, a prospective target, hearing the ignition of the rocket's motor, would probably be able to clear the torpedo's homing envelope. The alternative was the nuclear depth bomb, which is presumably more powerful than that of ASROC (i.e., SUBROC's has a much larger lethal envelope). The active bow sonar is essential because it is U.S. doctrine not to fire a nuclear weapon without a positive datum: passive contacts are just not accurate enough. Typical practice was to track a target passively, then find an accurate range with a single powerful ping. The spherical bow sonar reliably provided a much greater tracking range than its predecessors because it could exploit all possible acoustic paths, including bottom bounce and surface bounce.

The rocket motor is fired in the torpedo tube, the missile being propelled up through the surface and onto a precomputed ballistic flight path.

SUBROC is an analog weapon. In 1983, as submarines were being fitted with new all-digital fire-control systems (and as existing SUBROC motors were aging), it appeared that SUBROC would be discarded. However, in 1983 Congress directed that the submarine fire-control systems be altered to accommodate it; to abandon the last U.S. submarine tactical nuclear system

would have had major symbolic as well as practical consequences. Now the system will be replaced by the nonnuclear Sea Lance.

This system was reportedly compromised during development (i.e., about 1964), and the Soviet SS-N-15 is often described as a Sovietized equivalent.

◆ Sea Lance (UUM-125A)

Dimensions: 16.0 × 228.0 in (capsule: 20 × 244.23 in)
Weight: 2282 lbs (total with capsule: 2793 lbs)
Warhead: Mk-50 torpedo
Range: probably comparable to SUBROC

Sea Lance capsule being loaded onto an attack submarine. The submarine's high-frequency sonar transducer is in the forward edge of the sail, and the surface-search radar is atop the sail. (Boeing)

Sea Lance in flight. (Boeing)

The digital replacement for SUBROC, Sea Lance was developed as the ASW standoff weapon (SOW). For a time, it appeared possible to combine SOW with the VLA requirement, to produce a Common ASW SOW; but this approach proved impractical, and the two programs were separated in 1982. In 1988, however, the two programs were again being merged. Stated requirements included the ability to launch at up to 80 percent of a submarine's test depth, as well as stealthy operation. It was decided, therefore, that Sea Lance would be launched in a capsule, like the Tomahawk cruise missile, emerging only after reaching the surface. Such buoyant launch is much quieter than the use of a rocket motor underwater.

Flight characteristics have not been released, although ranges as great as 105 nm (three convergence zones in the Norwegian Sea) have been reported (e.g., by the developer, Boeing, in a brochure). These ranges are almost certainly aerodynamic rather than effective tactical ranges. It is much more likely that the effective tactical range is much like that of SUBROC, dictated by a submarine's ability to track a target (i.e., by direct-path range). The long reported range would correspond to the very energetic rocket motor required to minimize the flight time to the targeted submarine.

Sea Lance has a role very different from that originally envisaged for SUBROC. As Soviet submarines become quieter, it becomes less and less likely that they will be tracked at very long ranges. However, U.S. submarines will operate in or near Soviet waters in wartime. Soviet submarine commanders will know that, if they run at high (loud) speed, or if they use their active sonars, they will provide the necessary targeting data. Thus, the existence of a submarine standoff weapon may in itself inhibit Soviet submarine commanders from running out into their patrol areas at high speed, or, for that matter, from seeking out U.S. submarines by active sonar search. Given this mode of operation, Sea Lance had to be usable without high-level authorization, i.e., the weapon had to be nonnuclear. In December 1986 the development program was reversed, the primary version switching from a nuclear depth bomb to a Mk-50 torpedo payload. Presumably, this choice was justified, at least in part, by the demonstrated lethality of the Mk-50 warhead and by the longer acquisition range associated with Mk 50, as compared to Mk 46.

Boeing received the Sea Lance contract in April 1981. Current plans call for 2400 Sea Lance missiles. The program was delayed in FY89. Sea Lance is currently being procured as a dual-use (submarine/surface ship) weapon, with consequent program delays.

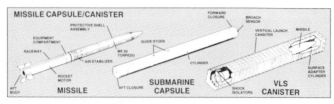

SEA LANCE WEAPON SYSTEM

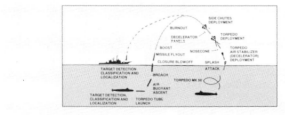

MISSION SEQUENCE

Sea Lance (UUM-125) configuration and operational sequence. (Martin-Marietta)

TORPEDOES

CHINA (PRC)

The current production antiship torpedoes are designated Yu (Fish) 4A and 4B. They are officially described as derived from foreign torpedoes, most likely Soviet types. Development was conducted by Xian Independent University, and these weapons

were standardized in February 1984. There has been no public mention of any PRC submarine-launched antisubmarine torpedo.

In 1988 it was reported that the PRC program to manufacture the U.S. Mk 46 Mod 5 has been delayed because of difficulties in translation to metric units.

FRANCE

An indication of the current production rates of torpedoes for the French Navy is that the 1984–88 budget called for orders for 70 torpedoes (presumably all heavy) in 1984/85 and for an additional 190 in 1986–88, with 278 torpedoes delivered in 1984–88, and another 170 after 1988. Presumably these figures are all heavy torpedoes, since Murène is not yet in production. Reportedly, the initial production rate for Murène is 20 per year.

◆ E 12/E 15

	E 12	E 15
Dimensions:	550 mm × 7.0 m (21.7 × 276.0 in)	550 mm × 5.9 m (21.7 × 232.3 in)
Weight:	1650 kg (3637 lbs)	1387 kg (3057 lbs)
Speed/Range:	25 kts/12,000 m (13,000 yds)	25 kts/12,000 m (13,000 yds)
Warhead:	330 kg (727 lbs)	300 kg aluminum tolite or HBX-3 (660 lbs)
Power plant:	battery	nickel-cadmium battery, 50-kW motor

E 15 is the export version of E 12 . E 12 was developed on the basis of wartime German technology (such as the T-5 homing torpedo) that fell into French hands in 1944–45. Both E 12 and E 15 are CIT-Alcatel's submarine-launched passive-homing torpedoes, for use against surface ships or submarines at periscope depth (target depth down to 18 m [59 ft]). The torpedo has a contact or magnetic fuze. A fire-control solution is required to bring the torpedo within about 700 m (770 yds) of its target. The E 15's homing system duplicates that of E 14; the hull is a lengthened form of that of the E 14.

This torpedo was placed in production after another submarine torpedo development program, V (for *vitesse*) 11, had been abandoned in 1958. V 11 was a fast straight-running oxygen-alcohol torpedo intended for a range of 15,000 m (16,400 yds) at 55 kts.

See the E 14 entry for a modification program.

◆ E 14

Dimensions: 550 × 4279 mm (21.7 × 168.5 in)
Weight: 927 kg (2043 lbs)
Speed/Range: 25.5 kts/5000 m (5500 yds)
Warhead: 200 kg tolite (440 lbs)
Power Plant: nickel-cadmium battery (40 kW)

The submarine-launched passive-homing torpedo by CIT-Alcatel is in effect a smaller version of E 12, designed primarily to arm the small French antisubmarine submarines, now extinct. E 14 uses contact or passive magnetic proximity (range about 4 m) fuzing. This weapon is intended for use against surface ships or shallow submarines (e.g., submarines at periscope depth), using settings of 6–18 m (20–60 ft) for the depth of its run; E 14 can run at depths as great as 300 m (984 ft). Compared to E 12, E 14 trades endurance for a more powerful warhead.

This torpedo has the same propulsion and hull as L 3, but E 14 homes passively, using a bank of four transducers operating by phase comparison within a 1-kHz bandwidth. Enable range is 350 m (383 yds); average acquisition range is 500 m (550 yds). The battery has 76 cells (E 15 has 120).

E 14 was introduced in 1960, and about 100 were made.

DCN is developing a modification kit for the E 14, E 15, and L 3 torpedoes. The existing nickel-cadmium battery is replaced by a silver-zinc battery (which doubles the range); the propulsion system is improved (to add 10 kts); and the homing system is replaced (AH 8 vice AH-7, for 50 percent greater acquisition range).

E 18

Dimensions: 533 × 5230 mm (21 × 205.9 in)
Weight: 1230 kg (2711 lbs)
Speed/Range: 35 kts/18,000 m (19,700 yds)
Power Plant: battery

E 18 is a dual-purpose torpedo for surface ships. E 18 has passive homing (i.e., usable against a noisy submarine) and a maximum depth of 500 m (1640 ft).

F 17

Dimensions: 550 mm × 6 m (21.7 × 236 in)
Weight: 1410 kg (3108 lbs)
Speed/Range: 35 kts/18,000 m (19,700 yds)
Warhead: 250-kg HBX-3 (equivalent to 500-kg TNT) (551 [1100] lbs) **Power Plant:** zinc-silver oxide battery (contraprops)

F 17 wire-guided torpedo. (Thomson Sintra)

F 17 torpedo tubes on board the Saudi frigate *Al Madinah*. Western navies have found it is easier to operate a surface-launched wire-guided torpedo from stern tubes, the wire running out as the ship steams away. That arrangement applies also to several U.S. attempts to combine wire guidance with surface ships (surviving in the Spanish *Baleares* class) and to the Italian A184. (Thomson Sintra)

This wire-guided dual-purpose torpedo was introduced in 1973 by DTCN. F 17 has active-passive terminal homing (active for antisubmarine, passive for antiship). There is a special shallow-water mode that can be preset before launching (sonar scan is limited in elevation). The stated diving limit is 600 m.

F 17 Mod 1 has dimensions of 550 × 5900 mm (21.7 × 232 in), has a speed/range of 35 kts/22,000 yds, and can run at depths as great as 500 m (1640 ft). This torpedo is launched from both submarines and surface ships.

F 17 Mod 2, in service 1988, has dimensions of 533 × 5406 mm (21 × 212.8 in), a weight of 1360 kg (2997 lbs), and a speed/range of 40 kts/20,000 m (22,000 yds) (because of its more powerful—85 kW—motor). Mod 1 is a dual-purpose submarine torpedo. Maximum operating depth is 600 m (1968 ft).

F 17P Mod 2, in service 1985, has dimensions of 550 × 5620 mm (21.7 × 221 in), a weight of 1320 kg (2909 lbs), and a speed/range of 35 kts/32,000 yds. 17P Mod 2 is launched from submarines only, against surface ships.

L 3

Dimensions: 550 × 4320 mm (21.7 × 170.1 in)
Weight: 910 kg (2006 lbs) **Speed/Range:** 25 kts/5000 m (5500 yds)
Warhead: 200-kg HBX-3 or TNT (440 lbs)
Power Plant: nickel-cadmium battery (40-kW motor, 2 contraprops)

L 3 is an active acoustic-homing submarine-launched antisubmarine torpedo (for target speeds up to 20 kts) that uses a contact or active-acoustic (range 20 m) fuze. L 3 is usable in depths down to 300 meters (984 ft). The torpedo's angle of pitch is limited to +10 to −40 degrees. Acquisition range is 1000 m (1100 yds), using a 32-kHz active seeker. The torpedo runs at 30 m (98 ft), executing a sinuous (snake) search after reaching its enable point.

This torpedo was introduced in 1960, and it was first displayed in 1968. L 3 was manufactured by DCN, which now offers a modification package (see E 14 entry above) including a new homing device, AS 15 instead of the earlier AS 3. A 21-inch (533-mm) version was designed but never entered production. This version was 4318 mm (170 in) long and weighed 900 kg (1983 lbs). About 600 L 3s were made.

L 3 replaced an earlier antisubmarine torpedo, the straight-running K 2 (oxygen-alcohol propulsion, speed/range 50 kts/1000 m [1090 yds], maximum depth 300 m [984 ft]). K 2 was a straight-runner, launched in salvos of three with preset tune (i.e., depth) fuzing. It was the equivalent of such contemporary rocket-fired depth charges as the British Limbo, the Italian Menon, and the U.S. Weapon Alfa, using a torpedo power plant instead of a rocket to propel the torpedo to the desired point. Dimensions were 550 × 4400 mm (21.7 × 173 inches); weight was 1104 kg (2433 lbs) with a 280-kg warhead (617 lbs). K 3 entered service in 1956, and it remained in service until about 1976.

French surface ships generally carry a combination of L 3 (short range) and L 5 (long range) torpedoes, both launched by compressed-air catapults rather than from torpedo tubes (two in an A69, four in a larger ship).

L 4

Dimensions: 533 mm × 3.13 m (21 × 123 in)
Weight: 525 kg (1157 lbs)
Speed/Range: 30 kts/5000 m (5500 yds)
Warhead: 150 kg (331 lbs) **Power Plant:** battery

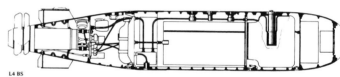

L 4 BS torpedo. (Direction des Constructions Navales)

This French lightweight antisubmarine torpedo is designed to attack submarines running at or below 20 kts. L 4 is used by aircraft and as the warhead of the Malafon missile. The torpedo uses active acoustic homing with an AS-4T seeker, at 32 kHz, with an average acquisition range of 1000 m (1094 yds); L 4 has a circular (helical) search pattern. This torpedo is produced by DTCN and entered service in 1964.

A modernized version can operate in shallow water, and another version is suitable for launching from surface torpedo tubes (3.3 m long, 570 kg [130 in, 1256 lbs]).

L 5

Dimensions: 533 mm × 4.4 m (21 × 173 in)
Weight: 935 kg (2061 lbs)
Speed/Range: 35 kts/7000 m (7700 yds)
Warhead: 150 kg (330 lbs) **Power Plant:** silver-zinc battery

L 5 was a response to the major increase (approximately quadrupling) in sonar range associated with the new standoff weapons of the 1960s (such as ASROC, Malafon, and Ikara). The program began in 1960; compared to E 14, L 5 was expected to have twice the capability both against surface ships and submarines. In the same volume, L 5 achieves ten more knots and greater range, partly by adopting a silver-zinc battery and a two-rotor electric motor (of twice the power). This torpedo is also more difficult to countermeasure. L 5 was initially conceived as two torpedoes, one primarily ASW and one, of greater range, primarily to attack surface ships.

Mod 1 is a ship-launched antisubmarine or antiship weapon. Mod 2 did not enter service. Mod 3 (5500 mm long [216.5 inches], 1300 kg [2865 lbs]) is submarine-launched against submarines; it was a direct replacement for E 12 and E 14. However, Mod 3 was deemed insufficiently effective against surface ships, and that led in turn to the wire-guided F 17. Mod 4 can be launched either by submarines or by surface ships, to attack fast submarines. It is a simplified version of Mod 1. Mod 4P is dual-purpose. The data above refer to Mod 4. Produced by DTCN, all versions are active-passive. Mod 4 has both acoustic and contact fuzes. Maximum operating depth is 500 m (1640 ft). L 5 entered service in 1971.

L 7 is a major modification of L 5, a dual-purpose torpedo with a heavier warhead, for submarines. L 7 appeared about 1980.

◆ L 6

Dimensions: 400 mm × 2.6 m (15.9 × 102 in)
Speed/Range: 45 kts/22,000 yds **Warhead:** 70 kg (154 lbs)
Power Plant: closed-cycle thermal

L 6 was an abortive active-passive homer, a lightweight air-dropped torpedo developed about 1970 as an alternative to the U.S.-supplied Mk 46.

◆ R 3

Dimensions: .324 m × 2.44 m (Mod 1) or 2.57 m (Mod 2) (12.75 × 96.1/101.2 in)
Weight: Mod 1: 210 kg; Mod 2: 235 kg (462.8/517.9 lbs)
Speed: 32 kts
Warhead: Mod 1: 50 kg; Mod 2: 70 kg (110/154 lbs)
Power Plant: battery

DTCN's lightweight antisubmarine torpedo was primarily for use from small surface craft; R 3 could also be dropped by aircraft. The French Navy adopted Mk 46 instead. Maximum depth was 600 m (1968 ft). Reported acquisition range was 1500/1800 m (1640/1970 yds).

◆ Z 13/Z 16

Dimensions: 550 × 7120 mm (21.7 × 280 in)
Weight: 1715 kg (3780 lbs)
Speed/Range: 30 kts/10,000 m (10,900 yds)
Warhead: 300 kg (660 lbs) **Power Plant:** battery

This submarine-launched pattern-runner was based on captured German technology (particularly that of the LUT torpedo). Z 13 has contact and magnetic fuzes. Running depth, set prior to launch, can be as deep as 18 m (59 ft), and the torpedo can be fired from depths as great as 180 m (590 ft). Made by DTCN, Z 13 entered service in 1960; Z 16 is the export version of Z 13. These torpedoes are now obsolescent.

◆ Murène (NTL-90)

Dimensions: 324 mm × 2.6 m (12.75 × 102.4 in)
Weight: 250 kg (551 lbs)
Speed/Range: 38 kts search, 53 kts attack; endurance over 10,000 yds at maximum speed (6 minutes at maximum speed, or 12 min at mixed speeds, gives approximately 10,000 yds at 53 kts and probably about 12,000 yds at mixed speeds)
Warhead: 50-kg shaped charge (110-lbs)
Power Plant: aluminum-silver oxide battery (two-speed 136-HP engine-driving pump jet)

This lightweight torpedo was conceived as a replacement for the current Mk 46, for the L 5 shipboard self-defense weapon, and for L 4, the Malafon warhead. Homing is active/passive using multiple frequencies. Murène is expected to enter service in 1992. Early in 1988 the manufacturer, DCN, was claiming that this torpedo was five times as cost-effective as existing ASW torpedoes; presumably that statement refers to existing Mk 46s.

Information released thus far is that the torpedo is intended to be effective against targets at depths of 40–1000 meters (approximately 130–3300 feet), and that it relies on a large on-board computer to vary the size of the active-sonar beam during search, confirmation, acquisition, and attack. The sonar consists of a flat nose transducer and two flank (sideways-looking) arrays. The search pattern is rectilinear when Murène is dropped from a ship and circular when the torpedo is dropped from a helicopter or missile. The published statement that the torpedo tends to find its target during a single 360-degree circular pass suggests that the side-looking arrays are used for long-range acquisition (presumably at relatively low frequency). Although they are spot transducers, with substantial computer power, they can presumably be used to form a synthetic aperture like that of a side-looking radar. The nose array is presumably used for terminal homing.

Murène is said to be capable of tracking twelve targets simultaneously, the on-board computer predicting the target's course and estimating hit probability. The computer selects the two most promising targets. The warhead is a shaped charge, and the standard attack maneuver is to overhaul the target and then attack from the beam, for maximum shaped-charge effect. One account suggests that the purpose of the flank arrays is to maintain contact with the target while coming abeam. In trials, a Murène warhead striking at an angle of 50 degrees to a simulated pressure hull cut through 20 mm of outer hull, 2 m of water ballast, and then 40 mm of pressure hull, and the torpedo would still have cut through another 300 mm of steel.

This torpedo began in 1976 as an Anglo-French project, but Britain withdrew in 1982 to develop Stingray independently. The French Navy had bought U.S. Mk 46s in 1981 as interim weapons.

About 1000 Murènes are to be bought for the French Navy, at a total program cost of 10,000 million French Francs, about $1.8 billion, or about $1.8 million each. Sea trials late in 1988 demonstrated that the torpedo could effectively attack targets at depths of less than 30 m.

Murène. (Thomson Sintra)

GERMANY (WEST)

Krupp-Atlas makes an AWD wake-detector for heavy torpedoes. It is not clear for which German-built torpedo(es) the wake-detector is built.

◆ DM1 Seeschlange

Dimensions: 533 × 4150 mm (4620 mm including wire reel) (21 × 163.4 [181.9] in) **Weight:** 1370 kg (3020 lbs)
Speed/Range: 33 kts/6000 m; maximum range 12,000 m (6600/13,100 yds) **Warhead:** 100 kg (220 lbs)
Power Plant: silver-zinc battery (contraprops)

This wire-guided (two-way link) ASW torpedo entered service in 1975 after tests in 1972–73. DM1 has much in common with Seal, but only about half the battery capacity, so that a three-dimensional active sonar can be accommodated. Moreover, Seeschlange is much shorter than Seal and so can be accommodated in a small Type-206 submarine.

The initial design concept was a single universal homing head, suited to both active and passive homing, and realized in the later SUT (see below). Fuzing in both torpedoes is combined impact and proximity. Both Seeschlange and Seal have preset search programs to be used in the event the guidance wire breaks before the target is acquired, as well as re-attack logic (e.g., circular search in the event of target loss).

Wire guidance was adopted specifically to suit Baltic conditions, especially the shallow water and the very long detection ranges provided by modern radars and sonars. Torpedoes had to be fired at such great ranges that they could not be expected to home until well into their run; similar logic explains the wire-guided version of the U.S. Mk 37.

The name means Sea Serpent.

◆ DM2A1 Seal

> **Dimensions:** 533 × 6550 mm (6080 mm in the original DM2) (21 × 257.9 [239.4] in) **Weight:** 1370 kg (3020 lbs)
> **Speed/Range:** 33 kts/20,000 m (22,000 yds); also a lower-speed setting **Warhead:** 250 kg (551 lbs)
> **Power Plant:** silver-zinc battery (contraprops)

Seal is the antiship equivalent of Seeschlange, in service in 1969. Like Seeschlange, Seal is wire-guided, but it homes passively; and it has a larger warhead suited to antiship attack. The range is long so that the attacking platform can remain out of re-attack range, and the wire is a two-way link. Fuzing is a combination of impact and proximity. When fired from surface platforms, these torpedoes are launched back over the stern, the tail pointing forward, the wire reeling out over the stern.

◆ DM2A3 Seehecht

> **Dimensions:** 533 × 6600 mm (21 × 259.8 in)
> **Weight:** 1370 kg (3020 lbs)
> **Speed/Range:** 35 kts/20,000 m (22,000 yds)
> **Warhead:** 260 kg (573 lbs) **Power Plant:** battery

Seehecht is a joint AEG/Elsag program to upgrade existing Seal/Seeschlange torpedoes. The seekers were upgraded first (DM2A3), then the propulsion (DM2A4). Selenia is responsible for the new homing head (as subcontractor to AEG). This torpedo entered service in 1987, initially for German Type-206A and Type-211 submarines and for the Norwegian *Ula* class. DM2A4 is scheduled to replace Seehecht in 1998.

◆ DM3

DM3 is the German designation for the U.S. Mk 37. The original armament of German submarines was Mk 37 for ASW and the British Mk 8** for antiship work. Mk 37 may have received a special German designation because of having been modified to German requirements.

◆ SST-3/SST-4 Seal

> **Dimensions:** 533 × 6080 mm (6550 mm including wire reel) (21 × 239 [260] in) **Weight:** 1414 kg (3116 lbs)
> **Speed/Range:** 35 kts/24,000 yds; 23 kts/56,000 yds
> **Warhead:** 260 kg (573 lbs) **Power Plant:** battery

This antiship homing torpedo is fired by surface ships and submarines; SST-3 can be fired from a depth of 100 m (330 ft). This torpedo entered service in 1972. The improved SST-4, with approximately the same characteristics, entered service in 1980. SST-4 was the torpedo carried (and fired) by the Argentine submarine *San Luis* in the Falklands. SST-4 differs from SST-3 in having three speeds (35 kts/12,000 yds; 28 kts/22,000 yds; 23 kts/40,000 yds). SST-4 can be fired by both submarines and surface craft.

◆ SUT

> **Dimensions:** 534 × 6390 mm (21 × 252 in)
> **Weight:** 1414 kg (3116 lbs)
> **Speed/Range:** 34 kts/12,000 m; 23 kts/28,000 m (13,100/30,600 yds)
> **Warhead:** 260 kg (claimed equivalent to 500-kg TNT) (573/1100 lbs)
> **Power Plant:** battery

This dual-purpose (surface and underwater target) wire-guided torpedo has active/passive terminal homing. SUT combines the features of the earlier Seeschlange and Seal. In 1978, AEG claimed that active acquisition range was 2000 m (2200 yds) and that passive acquisition range was 4000–6000 m (4400–6600 yds). The seeker/control incorporates re-attack logic. Torpedo attitude is controlled by a free gyro acting directly on the control surfaces.

SUT was the result of a series of export developments. Seal (above) led to the export SST-4 antiship torpedo, which in turn inspired the dual-purpose SUT. SUT was announced in 1975, ran trials in 1976, and entered service in 1980. In 1986 Indonesia signed a contract for license production. An earlier dual-purpose torpedo, NIXE, was canceled in 1972 because of excessive cost. NIXE characteristics: dimensions 534 × 7200 mm (21 × 283.5 in), weight 1545/1800 kg with a 300-kg warhead (3405/3967 lbs, 660-lb warhead), speed/range 50 kts/20,000 m (22,000 yds) with eight-cylinder Otto motor.

In 1978 it was reported that AEG was developing a light-weight SUT, as an alternative to Mk 46. This development never entered service.

INDIA

◆ NST-58

In 1986 India announced that this torpedo, developed by the Naval Science and Technology Laboratory in Vishakhapatnam, was in production to replace the lightweight A-244/S in Indian service. No details were provided.

ITALY

◆ A-184

> **Dimensions:** 533 mm × 6 m (21 × 236 in)
> **Weight:** 1265 kg (2788 lbs)
> **Speed/Range:** 36 kts/10,000 m or 24 kts/25,000 m (11,000/27,300 yds)
> **Warhead:** 250 kg (550 lbs)
> **Power Plant:** silver-zinc battery

The Whitehead-Motofides A-184 replaces "Kangaroo" (Cangaro), a shipborne antisubmarine torpedo consisting of an ex-German G6e, wire-guided, which in turn launched a Mk-44 homing torpedo upon approaching the submarine target. A-184 can be fired both from submarines and from surface ships.

A-184 is wire-guided, with digital active and passive terminal homing using two semicircular arrays, one in the vertical and one in the horizontal plane, for wide sector coverage. The torpedo employs contraprops and can be fired from both surface and submerged torpedo tubes.

The G6e/Kangaroo replacement requirement was issued in 1971, and the A-184 prototype tested in 1973. It entered service the following year. This torpedo has been exported to both Peru and Taiwan (GRC), the latter in 1986.

Whitehead was the only pre-1943 Italian torpedo producer, and it is likely that some of the company's old straight-running 18- and 21-inch torpedoes were exported postwar, e.g., for torpedo boats. It seems unlikely that any of these weapons have remained in service. Postwar, Whitehead either built or reconditioned German G6e electric torpedoes and developed Cangaro, which was the first postwar Italian torpedo. G6e was apparently the standard Italian submarine torpedo until A-184 replaced it.

◆ A-244 and A-244/S

> **Dimensions:** 324 mm × 2.75 m (12.75 × 108.3 in)
> **Weight:** 220 kg (235 kg for A-244/S) (485/518 lbs)
> **Speed/Range:** 30 kts/6000 m (6600 yds)
> **Warhead:** 34 kg (blast) (75 lbs)
> **Power Plant:** lead-acid battery

A-244 was conceived as a replacement for Mk 44 Mod 2; this torpedo is sometimes described as an improved Mk 44-2. A-244 entered service in 1971, and the improved A-244/S in 1984. A-244 homes passively/actively using a single frequency. A-244/S homes actively/passively using triple-frequency pulses and a programmable seeker (search patterns and standard maneuvers). A-244/S's new CIACIO-S seeker may differ from that

(Elsag AG70) of A-244 by using multiple preformed beams, the shape of which can be changed to suit acoustic conditions (spatially adaptive beam patterns). The pulses are coded FM slides. The manufacturer claims that its computer analyzes the structure, doppler, shape, and time-space coherence of returning echoes to reject clutter, multipath or mirror effects (from the surface or the bottom), and echoes from the bottom, and even to detect submarines (as opposed to natural formations) on the bottom. Mod 1 is for helicopter launch, Mod 2 for aircraft.

The A-244 requirement was issued in 1968; research was completed in 1973; and production began in 1975.

Work on CIACIO began in 1964, after Selenia gained experience with the Mk-44 seeker during license production. The company described the seeker as using principles not previously used in underwater detection and called the seeker compatible with future light- and heavy-weight torpedoes. A 60-kHz CIACIO 60 was completed in 1966, using the transducer of the Mk 44 (but with new operating principles). CIACIO 30, operating at 30 kHz, was completed in 1968; and it led to CIACIO-S, which appeared in 1972. CIACIO-S was tested in the laboratory in 1973, with static sea trials following in 1974 and live trials (using Mk-44 torpedoes) in 1975. Very shallow water trials were carried out in 1977–78.

A-244/S Mod 1 was ready for delivery in 1987. Export customers are Argentina, Ecuador, Greece, India, Indonesia, Iran, Iraq, Libya, Nigeria, Pakistan, Peru, Singapore, Turkey, and Venezuela.

Before developing A-244, Whitehead developed A-243 (presumably a replacement for Mk 43), which did not enter production. The company also made about a hundred Mk 44s under license.

◆ A-290

> **Dimensions:** 12.75-in diameter
> **Speed/Range:** 40–45 kts (also reported as 50 kts goal)
> **Power Plant:** battery

The A-244 replacement, A-290 is to enter service in the 1990s. This torpedo will incorporate some A-244 technology including the CIACIO-S seeker; subsystem tests began in 1987. Development began in 1981. Improvements will include greater power (for a speed of 40–45 kts), a pump jet, improved tracking range, better passive capability, and a greater ability to classify shallow targets in warm water. The manufacturer, Whitehead, states that the design emphasizes improved signal processing (for greater acquisition range) rather than greater speed.

In 1988 the major question in the A-290 program is reportedly which of several alternative computers to use.

JAPAN

Japan currently uses Mk-44 and Mk-46 lightweight torpedoes and Type-80 heavy torpedoes.

◆ Type 54/55

> **Dimensions:** 533 mm × 7.5 m (21 × 295 in)
> **Weight:** 1600 kg (3526 lbs)

A heavy submarine-launched electric passive-homing torpedo, Type 54 has a speed of 30 kts to attack surface ships and snorkeling submarines. Type 54 was the first postwar Japanese torpedo. There was also a Type 54A, which could be ship- or submarine-launched, with a silver-zinc or lead battery. Type 54 replaced the U.S. Mk 23. Mod 1 did not enter service. Mods 2 and 3 had improved homing heads. There was also a Mod 3 Kai, an improved Mod 3, which was canceled. Type 54 was superseded by Mk 37 Mod 0.

Type 55 was a modified Mk 37; Type 55-2B (G 5B) was a Mk 37 with a new internal-combustion engine. There was also a two-stage version, reminiscent of the Italian Kangaroo.

◆ Type 72

A heavy straight-running 21-inch torpedo, Type 72 was comparable to the U.S. Mk-16 Mod-8 hydrogen-peroxide type (50 kts, 533 × 7200 mm [21 × 283 inches]), with somewhat better performance.

Type 72 was derived from the experimental G-5, which had been developed from JFY54 on. Type 72 was a submarine and PT boat weapon intended to attack surface ships and snorkeling submarines. Propulsion was by reciprocating engine derived from that of the wartime Type 93. Reported speed was better than 50 kts. Homing was passive.

G-5 was in development for almost a decade. G-5B, which became Type 72 Mod 1, began development in 1965. B is the first modification in Japanese practice. The G-5B basic specification was established in 1967.

This torpedo was carried by PT 11-15 and also by submarines from the *Natashio* class onward (from JFY80), alongside Mk 37-0 (and then Type 80). Because PT construction ended in the mid-1980s, production of this weapon was discontinued. On board submarines, Type 72 was replaced by submarine-launched Harpoon. The antisnorkeler role is apparently no longer important, as modern submarines tend to snorkel intermittently.

◆ Type 73

Type 73 is a 12.75-in electric antisubmarine torpedo for ship or aircraft use. Type 73 indicates the year of completion, 1973. This torpedo is sometimes mentioned as a possible load for ASW standoff weapons.

Type 73 is an improved version of the U.S. Mk 44 Mod 1, designated G-9 while under development. Performance is between that of Mk 44 Mod 1 and Mk 46 Mod 5. Existing Type 73s have been upgraded to Type 73 Kai standards. R&D on Type 73 Kai began in JFY78, but further upgrades were interrupted by license production of Mk 46 Mod 5.

◆ Type 80

Type 80 is a wire-guided ASW torpedo comparable in size to the U.S.-supplied Mk 37, but with better performance; speed is over 30 kts. Type 80 is about the same size (19-inch diameter and short length) as Mk 37. Type 80 was developed from the GRX-1 experimental torpedo, but it also drew on data from the ongoing GRX-2 program. Research began in JFY65, the designation Type 80 being applied in JFY80. Production began in JFY84. At that time the equipment designator G-11 was applied.

This torpedo is carried by the *Uzushio* and *Ushio* classes. Type 80 replaced the Japanese version of Mk 37, Mk 37-0-N.

◆ GRX Series

These torpedoes of various types are experimental. GRX-1 was an electric torpedo with a silver-zinc battery. GRX-2 was a 21-inch thermal torpedo, reportedly with a maximum speed of 70 kts and a range of 30,000 m (32,800 yds), roughly equivalent to the U.S. Mk 48, developed in parallel with GRX-1. As of 1983 it was to have been ready for designation in JFY85, but apparently development has been more protracted than expected. Despite this failure, Japan has not sought license production of either Mk 48 or Mk 48 ADCAP. As of 1988, GRX-2, the heavy torpedo, was scheduled for standardization in JFY89 (it would become Type 89).

GRX-4 is a new lightweight torpedo broadly comparable to the U.S. Mk 50, with a shaped-charge warhead, a SCEPS power plant, and a propulsor. A development contract for this torpedo was awarded to Mitsubishi Heavy Industries in March 1987. GRX-4 is apparently being developed as an alternative to a Japanese production program for Mk 50. GRX-4 supersedes GRX-3, an earlier experimental air-launched electric lightweight torpedo developed as an alternative to Mk 46. Begun in 1975, GRX-3 was abandoned as too large and too heavy.

The two current developmental torpedo programs are GRX-5 and -6.

SWEDEN

◆ Type 42 Series

> **Dimensions:** 400 × 2440 mm (2620 mm with wire dispenser) (15.75 × 96.1/103 in) **Weight:** 250/298 kg (550/657 lbs)

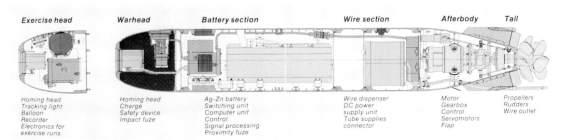

Exercise head — Warhead — Battery section — Wire section — Afterbody — Tail

Homing head	Homing head	Ag-Zn battery	Wire dispenser	Motor	Propellers
Tracking light	Charge	Switching unit	DC power	Gearbox	Rudders
Balloon	Safety device	Computer unit	supply unit	Control	Wire outlet
Recorder	Impact fuze	Control	Tube supplies	Servomotors	
Electronics for		Signal processing	connector	Flap	
exercise runs		Proximity fuze			

(*Above*) Type 43 torpedo. (FFV)

Speed/Range: 25 kts/20,000 m (10,000 m at high speed) (22,000/10,900 yds) **Warhead:** about 50 kg (110 lbs)
Power Plant: battery (2-speed motor)

Type 42 is a lightweight electric ASW torpedo (with secondary antiship capability) that can be launched by submarines, surface ships, and helicopters. It was originally designed for direct homing (using a passive sonar scanning both in depth and in azimuth), but it is adapted for wire guidance. In this form Type 42 is unique among modern lightweight weapons in being wire-guided; that guidance is necessary to assure homing under difficult acoustic conditions (e.g., in shallow water). Type 42 has both impact and proximity fuzes.

Type 42 entered production about 1976, succeeding Type 41, which had similar dimensions and performance (400 × 2440 mm, 250 kg, 25 kts/20,000 m [22,000 yds]). Presumably Type 42 introduced the two-speed motor, for a higher-speed attack.

Current versions are the following:

Type 422 (298 kg, ranges as above), 1983. Compared to the original Type 42, this version has a better wire data link and a better signal processor.

Type 423 (290 kg [639 lbs], 400 × 2850 mm [15.75 × 112 in]).

Type 427 is the current export version of 422/423 (400 × 2600 mm [15.75 × 102 in], 298 kg, silver-zinc battery). Total weight is also given as 310 kg (683 lbs), length as 2.85 m (112 in). This version has been in service since 1982. It incorporates some Type 617 technology.

There is a special "incident" version of Type 42 with a less lethal warhead, to force a submarine in Swedish waters to surface. This development parallels that of Elma and Malin (see unguided weapons below).

Type 43 is descended from Type 41, a homing (dual-purpose) weapon introduced about 1960. Type 41 was developed into Type 411, for the *Abborren*-class submarines (now discarded), which were then being rebuilt for ASW, and then into Type 412, for the *Sjoormen* class. A projected Type 413 was not pursued. Instead, a new series was begun with Type 42. Type 421 was a specialized ASW torpedo carried by the *Nacken* class, and the wire-guided Type 422 was carried by helicopters. The abortive Type 423 was intended specifically for the *Vastergotland* class. The next series, Type 43 (described below), introduced data programming at transmission, an autopilot, and a three-speed motor. Type 431 is designed for use by both the *Vastergotland* class and the corvettes. Type 43X0 is the export version. A new lightweight torpedo is expected about 1990. It should

have improved performance and better counter-countermeasures features, within smaller dimensions.

FFV claims that a lightweight torpedo suffices for ASW because the tamping effect of the water surrounding a submarine will amplify the effects of its 30–70 kg warhead. FFV considers at least a dual-speed motor necessary because the same torpedo may have to deal with moderate-speed (diesel) and high-speed (nuclear) targets. The company considers wire-guidance, for three-dimensional maneuvers, essential, even though other lightweight ASW torpedoes are entirely self-guided.

◆ **Type 43X0/Type 431**

Dimensions: 400 × 2850 mm (15.9 × 112 in)
Weight: 350 kg (280 kg in helicopter version) (771 [617] lbs)
Speed/Range: range 32,000 yds
Power Plant: silver-zinc battery; 3-speed motor

Type 431 is an improved Type 427 optimized to attack very quiet submarines in shallow water. Development was ordered early in 1984. The new digital computer is smaller than its predecessors, and the guidance wire carries more information in both directions. There are two types: one with a heavier battery for surface ships and submarines, and one with a lighter battery for helicopters. In both types, the battery is more durable than that of Type 42, capable of 30 rather than 10 exercise firings between overhauls. This torpedo has a new three-speed motor (speed can be varied up and down during the run), for a maximum range of about 30 km (presumably in the heavy-battery version).

The first Swedish Navy order for Type 431 was announced early in 1986. This torpedo entered service in 1987.

◆ **Type 61**

Dimensions: 533.4 × 7025 mm (21 × 288 in)
Weight: 1765 kg (3890 lbs)
Speed/Range: 45 kts/20,000 m (22,000 yds) (some sources claim maximum speed is over 60 kts)
Warhead: 250 kg (551 lbs)
Power Plant: hydrogen peroxide/alcohol (350 kW 12-cylinder engine)

This long-range wire-guided antiship torpedo is fired from both submarines and surface ships. The manufacturer, FFV, claims that the HTP propulsion system provides two or three times the range of conventional thermal or electric torpedoes. This torpedo is also wakeless. Course and speed are maintained within 0.3 percent during the run to the target. Wire guidance is necessary to exploit the very long range of the torpedo; Sweden was one of the first countries to employ submarine-launched wire-guided torpedoes operationally.

Later versions (613/617), capable of longer ranges, have terminal acoustic homing (wake homing in at least some cases). Two alternative fuzes (inertial or acoustic proximity) are available.

(*Below*) Type 617 torpedo. (FFV)

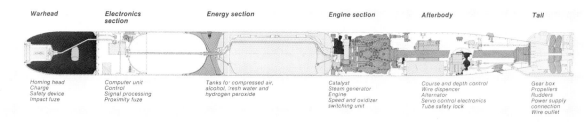

Exercise head — Warhead — Electronics section — Energy section — Engine section — Afterbody — Tail

Homing head	Homing head	Computer unit	Tanks for compressed air,	Catalyst	Course and depth control	Gear box
Tracking light	Charge	Control	alcohol, fresh water and	Steam generator	Wire dispenser	Propellers
Balloon	Safety device	Signal processing	hydrogen peroxide	Engine	Alternator	Rudders
Releasable ballast	Impact fuze	Proximity fuze		Speed and oxidizer	Servo control electronics	Power supply
Data recorder				switching unit	Tube safety lock	connection
						Wire outlet

Type 61, whose data are listed above, entered service in 1968. The prototype was Type 611; Type 612 was the first production version (dimensions 533 × 7500 mm [21 × 295 in]).

Type 613 is the current Swedish Navy service version (533 × 7025 mm, 1765 kg [21 × 277 in, 3890 lbs]). It incorporates a digital computer that can be programmed to suit particular environmental and threat conditions. This version increased range from 20,000 to 30,000 m (22,000 to 32,800 yds), partly as a result of adopting a two-speed motor, the additional range being exploited by the introduction of terminal homing and, therefore, two-way wire guidance. Production began in 1983, with first deliveries following in 1984.

Announced in 1982, Type 617 is the export version of 613. 617 entered service in 1984. Length is 6890 mm (271 in); weight is 1860 kg (4099 lbs); and estimated performance is 60 kts/ 30,000 m (33,000 yds). The warhead weighs 240 kg (529 lbs).

This torpedo has been exported to Denmark and Norway.

Swedish work on heavy HTP torpedoes began about 1955, with the surface-launched Type 14, from which were derived a straight-running Type 141 and a wire-guided Type 142. About 1960 a corresponding submarine torpedo, Type 27, was introduced. From it were derived Types 271 and 272, the latter entering service about 1964. About 1970 a single torpedo, Type 61, for both surface and submarine launch, was produced. Type 611, a wire-guided HTP weapon, was derived directly from Type 272. From 611 evolved Type 612 (swim-out launch; about 1975); from Type 612 were derived the noisy fast Type 618 (about 1980) and then the homing Type 613, with data transmission along its guidance wire and with a two-speed motor. Type 617 is the export version of Type 613. A new heavy torpedo is expected about 1990.

FFV expects the next-generation heavy submarine-launched torpedo to operate at greater depths and at higher speeds than Type 613. The company selected a semiclosed cycle, using HTP and diesel oil. HTP at 85-percent concentration is fed into a catalyst chamber, producing a mixture that is 60 percent steam and 40 percent oxygen at a temperature of 620 degrees C. Diesel oil and water recycled from the condenser are added in a steam generator, and the combustion product is 82 percent steam, 17 percent carbon dioxide, and 1 percent oxygen at 700 degrees C. This product runs a steam engine. The exhaust product (at 200–300 degrees C) is condensed and the water extracted, leaving a mixture of carbon dioxide (96 percent) and oxygen (4 percent), which is compressed so that it can be exhausted against the ambient back pressure. This exhaust is wakeless, and FFV claims that ambient pressure has little effect on performance.

The engine itself is a new 7-cylinder swashplate design, the pistons driving against a cam with a sinusoidal double-rise shape. Each piston is linked to a compression piston so that engine compressor output is proportional to the torpedo's depth. Each cylinder has a 70-mm bore and a 70-mm stroke, and the prototype engine produces up to 300 kW (400 BHP). The entire power section is quite short (2 m for the unit including tankage for 60 kW-hours), and FFV claims that a torpedo of this design would be about a meter shorter than a more conventional one.

◆ Angler

Angler is a projected Swedish hand-launched torpedo, designed to counter intruding mini-submarines. Announced in 1987, Angler is intended to fill a gap between conventional torpedoes and the Elma depth charge. Weight would be 16–100 lbs, and control would be exercised through a fiber-optic cable, though the torpedo could also self-home. The project is being conducted by the Swedish National Defense Research Institute, which hopes to have Angler in service in the 1990s.

USSR

Data below are necessarily incomplete. Information on torpedoes deployed since about 1958 is unofficial, from a few recent publications. Material on earlier Soviet torpedoes is taken from a mix of Soviet official sources and declassified Western intelligence data. All Soviet torpedoes reported in service since be-

The Soviet Union was unique in developing a series of torpedoes specially adapted to be dropped from high altitude and long range. One example, this rocket-propelled torpedo has a special nose break to reduce the impact of hitting the water. Although the torpedo has a tail shroud, it has no propeller. This torpedo is the conceptual ancestor of the long-range antiship missiles of the AS series. Although this photograph is dated 1971, it was probably taken in the late 1950s; the airplane is an IL-28T. (TASS from SOVFOTO)

Quintuple torpedo tubes, on board the cruiser *Kerch*, 1989. The loading trolley is under the muzzles of the tubes. (Eric Grove)

fore World War II are listed, because some of those no longer used by the Soviet Union may have been exported, or perhaps license-manufactured (e.g., in the PRC or in Yugoslavia). At the outbreak of war in 1941 the standard weapon was the 53-38.

For thermal (e.g., steam) torpedoes, the standard designation indicates the caliber and the year of origin, e.g., 53-39 is 53-cm caliber and originated in 1939. Designations of electrical torpedoes vary; the earliest was ET-80. More recent types appear to follow thermal torpedo practice, with the prefix E. There are also other special designations (see below).

Information on the most recent Soviet torpedoes listed here comes from a 1987 publication, but the reader is cautioned that none of the torpedoes there described came into service later than 1981. It is quite likely, then, that new types in some or all four calibers (40, 45, 53, and 65 cm) have appeared since that time. Because there is no formal NATO system of publishing Soviet torpedo designations, the absence of such information in the unclassified literature proves very little. Nor is the list below likely to be complete as of, say 1980.

Moreover, the 1987 article did not list surface-ship torpedoes. Most Soviet surface combatants, from light frigates up, carry 53-cm antisubmarine and antisurface torpedoes. There is now a 53-cm wire-guided ASW torpedo: the evidence is that Grisha-V–class corvettes, which entered service from 1985 on, have had their torpedo tubes lengthened to allow for the wire dispenser.

◆ Type 65

Dimensions: 650 × 9140 mm (25.6 × 359.8 in)
Speed/Range: 50 kts/54,000 yds; 30 kts/109,000 yds (50,000 and 100,000 meters, respectively)
Warhead: 900 kg approx (1980 lbs)

This torpedo, which is probably an enlarged 53-65, became operational in 1981; the Soviet designation is, therefore, probably something like 65-80. Type 65 has attracted very considerable attention in the West because it has the sort of warhead required to sink a carrier and because wake homing is virtually impossible to counter by means of a towed or thrown decoy. Presumably the torpedo is fired on a gyro course toward the expected target position, the wake-homing feature considerably enlarging the effective target length and thus making very long firing ranges (as indicated above) useful. In this sense Type 65 might be regarded as an underwater cruise missile, supplementing antiship cruise missiles flying through the air.

This torpedo marks a drastic change in Soviet torpedo size and, therefore, can be fired only be recent submarines. It seems likely that Type 65 was designed because 65-centimeter tubes had already been selected for Victor-II and later submarines, to fire the SS-N-16 ASW cruise missile. The SS-N-21 also seems to use this tube.

Victor-III–class submarines are fitted with four 65-cm and two 53-cm torpedo tubes, the two smaller-diameter tubes mounted over the four larger ones. The continued use of smaller-diameter tubes suggests that some special 53-cm weapon, which cannot be fired from the larger tube (i.e., using a liner), is carried. The most likely candidate would be a nuclear torpedo that would be carried more or less permanently in the tube for security reasons. That possibility in turn would refute reports that the 65-cm torpedo has a nuclear warhead. Alternatively, the smaller-caliber tubes might be reserved for wire-guided ET-80A (1980) ASW torpedoes, for close-in defense, or for large-caliber decoys.

A nuclear version of the 65-cm torpedo has been reported. From Victor-II onward, most Soviet submarines have tubes with 65-cm diameters, so it would be reasonable to imagine that the Soviets have produced 65-cm weapons in all three major torpedo categories: antiship (as here), nuclear, and electric antisubmarine. To limit the arsenal to existing smaller-caliber weapons (fired, presumably, using unwieldy tube liners) would be to disregard the considerably greater volume (e.g., for endurance, guidance, or both) offered by the larger torpedo caliber.

◆ 53-27L

Dimensions: 21 in × 23 ft   **Weight:** 3800 lbs
Speed/Range: 43.5 kts/4570 yds   **Warhead:** 550–600 lbs
Power Plant: air-steam

This torpedo was carried postwar by North Korean motor torpedo boats, and it may have been exported to other Soviet client states. The L may have indicated manufacture at Leningrad. Running depth was 16–40 ft.

◆ 53-38/53-38U

	53-38	53-38U
Dimensions:	533 × 7200 mm (21 × 284 in)	533 × 7450 mm (21 × 293 in)
Weight:	1615 kg (3560 lbs)	1725 kg (3800 lbs)
Speed/Range:	44.5 kts/4000 m; 34.5 kts/8000 m; 30.5 kts/10,000 m (4400; 8700; 10,900 yds)	
Warhead:	300 kg (661 lbs)	400 kg (882 lbs)
Power Plant:	HPT, 2-cylinder horizontal engine	

These two were the standard surface and submarine torpedoes in service at the outbreak of World War II; 53-38U was a reinforced version of the basic weapon. There were several major wartime modifications. A proximity fuze (NVS) entered operational service about 1943. Running depth was 16–40 ft.

At the outbreak of war the Soviets were also working on jet or rocket torpedoes both for air and for surface use (the latter was designated RT-45). The air-launched rocket torpedo apparently entered service postwar, probably in the early 1950s; it was photographed together with a modified Il-28 bomber.

In 1938 work began on a homing acoustic torpedo (SAT).

◆ 53-39

Dimensions: 533 × 7488 mm (21 × 294.8 in)
Weight: 1780 kg (3923 lbs)
Speed/Range: 51 kts/4000 m; 39 kts/8000 m; 34 kts/10,000 m (4400/8700/10,700 yds)
Warhead: 317 kg (699 lbs)
Power Plant: HPT, 2-cylinder horizontal engine

An improved 53-cm (21-in) torpedo, 53-39 entered service in July 1941. 53-39 had a more powerful engine and greater air, kerosene, and oil capacity. This weapon introduced a new MO-3 gyroscope permitting angled fire (from 0–90 degrees port or starboard).

◆ ET-80

Dimensions: 533 × 7488 mm (21 × 294.8 in)
Weight: 1800 kg (3970 lbs)
Speed/Range: 29 kts/4000 m (4400 yds)
Warhead: 400 kg (882 lbs)
Power Plant: battery; 80-kW motor.

The first Soviet electric torpedo, ET-80 was introduced in service in September 1942.

◆ 53-47D

Dimensions: 21 in × 236 in   **Speed/Range:** 45 kts/20,000 yds
Warhead: 1000 lbs TNT
Power Plant: steam (hydrogen peroxide)

These estimated data were reported by U.S. Naval Intelligence in 1959. 53-47D was listed as recently developed, an interim-service type.

◆ 53-51

Dimensions: 533 × 7800 mm (21 × 307 in)
Speed/Range: 51 kts/4000 yds; 39 kts/10,000 yds
Warhead: 400 kg (882 lbs)

53-51 was the postwar Soviet submarine torpedo, a straight or pattern runner. Maximum launch depth was 106 m (348 ft); maximum operating depth was 14 m (46 ft). The exploder was impact or magnetic (proximity).

◆ 53-56

Dimensions: 533 × 7740 mm (21 × 305 in)
Speed/Range: 51 kts/9000 m; 39 kts/18,500 m (9800/20,200 yds)
Warhead: 400 kg (882 lbs)   **Power Plant:** HTP/fuel (open cycle)

53-56, the first operational Soviet torpedo with an unconventional engine, was a modified 53-51.

◆ 53-?

Dimensions: 533 × 7200 mm (21 × 283.5 in)
Speed/Range: 50 kts/11,000 m; 32 kts/21,000 m (12,000/23,000 yds)
Warhead: nuclear, approx 15 kT
Power Plant: HTP/fuel (open cycle)

The nuclear version of the 53-56 carries a 15-kT warhead. This torpedo became operational in 1959 or 1960, so the designation is presumably 53-59 or 53-60. This torpedo was almost certainly the weapon element of the November-class SSN weapons system, the submarine being fast enough to reach a firing position off the bow of the fast target (e.g., an aircraft carrier). The torpedo did not home; it exploded at a set range as indicated by the propeller turn count. The propeller count was also used to arm the warhead after the torpedo passed a set enabling range. There was an anticircular turn mechanism to protect the firing submarine.

At one time it was suggested that this torpedo was also the first Soviet naval strategic nuclear weapon because it could be delivered to enemy harbors.

There is some evidence that Soviet nuclear torpedo warheads were unsafe. In February 1972 a Soviet submarine off the North American coast suffered crew casualties due to radiation leakage from torpedo warheads. The two nuclear torpedoes on board the Whiskey-class submarine that grounded in Sweden in 1981 had noticeable radiation signatures.

◆ ET-80A/SAET-50/SAET-60

Dimensions: 21 × 307 in **Speed/Range:** 23.3 kts/8000 yds
Warhead: 600 lbs TNT
Power Plant: 46-cell lead-acid battery; 56-HP motor with contra-props

ET-80A was the first Soviet homing ASW torpedo, a modified version of the earlier ET-80. ET-80A was fired only by submarines.

ET-80A could acquire a cavitating submarine (21 dB at 24.8 kHz) at about 700 yards. The torpedo could be set to run as deep as 325 ft, although it could dive to 500 ft when homing and could attack a target either above or below its set depth. The exploder was a modified version of the wartime German TZ-5 (with two additional horizontal receiving coils), with a range of 20 ft (above, below, or alongside).

ET-80A first appeared about 1961. As of 1962, the U.S. evaluation was that it was an interim weapon pending the use of the same passive-homing device in a smaller and more modern torpedo with greater maneuverability. That torpedo was presumably the earliest version of the 40-cm torpedo described below. A passive homer of this type could be used against surface ships as well as against noisy submarines.

As applied to this weapon, ET-80A was an ONI, not a Soviet, designation.

The Soviets have published details of SAET-50, which they describe as their earliest homing torpedo and which may correspond to ET-80A. Dimensions are 530 × 7454 mm (20.9 × 293.5 in); weight is over 1600 kg (over 3520 lbs); warhead is 375 kg (827 lbs); and performance exceeds 40 km/hr over 7000 m (21.6 kts/7650 yds).

SAET-60, which entered service in 1965–66, has been described as the first Soviet antiship homing torpedo. Its dimensions match those of the ET-80A listed above: 533 × 7800 mm. However, performance is higher: 35 kts/15,000 m (16,400 yds). The warhead is 400 kg (882 lbs). The power plant is a silver-zinc battery. Operation is passive at 25 kHz. The exploder is impact or acoustic proximity.

◆ ET-80(66)

Dimensions: 533 × 7700 mm (21 × 303 in)
Speed/Range: 35 kts/10,000 m; 20 kts/40,000 m (11,000/43,700 yds) **Warhead:** nuclear: 20 kT
Power Plant: silver-zinc batteries

A quieter (but slower) nuclear antiship torpedo, ET-80(66) replaced the nuclear version of 53-56. Maximum running depth was 305 m. A deep run would tend to increase the area affected by the nuclear burst, thus reducing the effect of any aiming error by the submarine.

◆ SET-65

Dimensions: 533 × 7800 mm (21 × 307 in)
Speed/Range: 35 kts/10,000 m; 24 kts/20,000 m (11,000/22,000 yds) **Warhead:** 272 kg (600 lbs)
Power Plant: battery

SET-65 is a submarine-launched torpedo, operating down to 400 m. It became operational in 1967.

◆ 53-65

Dimensions: 533 × 7800 mm (21 × 307 in)
Speed/Range: 55 kts/14,000 m; 40 kts/24,000 m (15,300/26,200 yds) **Warhead:** 400 kg (882 lbs)
Power Plant: HTP/fuel using new multipiston engine

This torpedo reportedly introduced both a new power plant (probably semi–closed-cycle, reusing exhaust gas) and wake-homing into Soviet practice. 53-65 was the first Soviet thermal torpedo capable of homing, and it became operational in 1968.

◆ 53-68

Dimensions: 533 × 7200 mm (21 × 284 in)
Speed/Range: 45 kts/15,000 yds **Warhead:** nuclear: 20 kT
Power Plant: HTP/fuel closed-cycle (wakeless)

This torpedo, a modernized nuclear version of 53-65, became operational in 1970. 53-68 can be launched from as deep as 106 m (348 ft), and it can run down to 300 m (984 ft). As in the earlier thermal nuclear torpedo, 53-68 is a straight-runner using propeller turn count to measure the distance to a preset detonation.

◆ 53-VA

The standard Soviet export antiship torpedo, 53-VA reportedly had a 562-kg (1240-lb) warhead and a magnetic influence fuze.

◆ ET-80A

Dimensions: 533 × 7800 mm (21 × 307 in)
Speed/Range: 35 kts/15,000 m; higher speed for 12,000-m range (16,400/13,100 yds) **Warhead:** 272 kg (600 lbs)
Power Plant: battery

The ET-80A designation has already been used; this torpedo presumably has some other designation, as yet unpublished. This torpedo was probably a modernized SET-65; it was the first Soviet wire-guided torpedo. It also had an improved power plant. Submarine-launched, ET-80A can operate down to 400 m.

This torpedo became operational in 1977.

◆ 45-12AV

Dimensions: 18 in × 18.7 ft **Weight:** 1900 lbs
Speed Range: 38 kts/3282 yds; 28 kts/6564 yds
Warhead: 250–300 lbs TNT **Power Plant:** air-steam

45-12AV was a pre–World War I torpedo (probably 1912) still in use for aircraft launch (using a parachute) after World War II.

◆ 45-36NU/45-36ANU

Dimensions: 18 in × 18.7 ft
Weight: 2000 lbs (2101 lbs in 45-36AV air version)
Speed/Range: 45 kts/4400 yds (air version: 41 kts/3280 yds, 39 kts/4370 yds, and 32 kts/6560 yds)
Warhead: 440 lbs TNT **Power Plant:** air-steam

45-36NU was the standard World War II motor torpedo boat/air-launched torpedo. The reinforced ANU version could be dropped at up to 360 km/hr, and in the Northern Fleet torpedoes were typically dropped from 1500–3000 m (5000–10,000 ft) altitude, gliding in from beyond the enemy's antiaircraft range. In theory, a pattern of such weapons could achieve a very high probability of hitting any target. This concept, which was unique to the Soviet Navy, was the direct precursor of the current family of standoff missiles.

◆ 45-44 AN

45-44 AN is a small air-launched torpedo.

♦ **Rocket Torpedo**

For some years after World War II the Soviets developed and deployed rocket-propelled torpedoes designed to be dropped by aircraft at high speed. These weapons were the direct descendants of the wartime high-altitude torpedoes. No details have been published; in a functional sense these torpedoes were replaced by the air-to-surface homing missiles.

♦ **E45-70A**

Dimensions: 450 × 3900 mm (17.7 in × 153.5 in)
Speed/Range: 28–30 kts/10,000 m (11,000 yds)
Warhead: 90 kg (198 lbs)

E45-70A is the payload of the SS-N-14 missile. This torpedo executes an up-and-down helical search, down to 305 m (1000 ft).

♦ **E45-75A**

Dimensions: 450 × 3900 mm (17.7 × 153.5 in)
Speed/Range: 38 kts/9000 yds **Warhead:** 90 kg (198 lbs)

E45-75A is a missile- (SS-N-14 and -16) and aircraft-delivered weapon, an updated E45-70. -75A became operational in 1973. Maximum operating depth is about 300 m.

♦ **E45-75A Mod**

Dimensions: 450 × 4600 mm (17.7 × 181.1 in)
Weight: approx 840 kg (1851 lbs)
Speed/Range: 38 kts/8,000 m (8700 yds)
Warhead: 90 kg (198 lbs)

A lengthened, modernized E45-75A, Mod is reportedly used as the payload of SS-N-14 and -16.

♦ **SET-40**

Dimensions: 400 × 4500 mm (15.9 × 177 in)
Speed/Range: 28 kts/10,000 m (11,000 yds)
Warhead: 100 kg (220 lbs) **Power Plant:** silver-zinc batteries

SET-40 was the first Soviet lightweight torpedo, for firing from small surface ships (light frigates and corvettes). It may also have been delivered by aircraft, though that delivery seems unlikely in view of the development of the 45-cm series. Maximum acquisition range was 585 m (640 yds: from the seeker ping rate), and maximum operating depth was about 300 m (984 ft). This weapon used an active acoustic proximity fuze (frequency reportedly 650 kHz) similar to that of the contemporary French L 3.

This torpedo caliber first appeared in the Soviet fleet in the early 1960s on board Petya- and Mirka-class corvettes.

♦ **E40-75A**

Dimensions: 400 × 4500 mm (15.9 × 177 in)
Speed/Range: 30 kts/14,000 yds **Warhead:** 100 kg
Power Plant: battery

The 400-mm torpedo is not nearly as ubiquitous in Soviet service as is the lightweight (324-mm) torpedo in the West. This torpedo is carried only by small corvettes (Poti and Pauk classes) and by the older light frigates (Mirka and Petya). The newer light frigates (Grisha and Parchim classes) carry 53-cm weapons. That allocation may imply that the 40-cm torpedo has never been altogether satisfactory.

UNITED KINGDOM

♦ **Mk 8****

Dimensions: 21 × 264.85 in **Weight:** 3452 lbs
Speed/Range: 45.5 kts/5000 yds or 41 kts/7000 yds
Warhead: 805 lbs (torpex)
Power Plant: burner-cycle (steam torpedo)

Although this straight-running antiship torpedo is no longer in British service, it was probably supplied to many other countries as the antiship torpedo to supplement a homing antisubmarine torpedo. Like the U.S. Mk 14, therefore, Mk 8 may still be in service in some smaller navies. This weapon sank the Argentine cruiser *Belgrano* in the Falklands War in 1982, the guided Tigerfish not having a reliable antiship mode at that time. Current Tigerfish are dual purpose, so Mk 8** is no longer in British service. Moreover, the Royal Navy feels that Sub-Harpoon is a superior antiship weapon.

Normal depth setting is 40 ft; maximum depth is 200 ft.

Mk 8** first entered service in 1927, although the version used in the Falklands was improved. By 1927, torpedoes were fitted with magnetic proximity fuzes (compensated coil rod or CCR). After World War II the Royal Navy planned to use a modified Mk 8 propelled by hydrogen peroxide (HTP): Ferry, later called Fancy, which was issued in 1954. However, the basic torpedo design was ill-adapted to HTP, and the project was abandoned after the loss of the submarine HMS *Sidon* in 1955. The HTP documentation was sold to the Swedish Navy, where the design became the basis of the Type-61 torpedo. In addition, a Trumper active-homing torpedo was begun using Mk 8's components, but work ceased at the end of World War II.

♦ **Spearfish**

Dimensions: 21 in × approx 19.5 ft **Weight:** 1850 kg (4077 lbs)
Speed/Range: see below **Warhead:** 300 kg (661 lbs)
Power Plant: HAP-Otto fuel (pump-jet propulsor, turbine engine; HAP is hydrogen ammonium perchlorate)

Spearfish. The pumpjet has a shroud. (Marconi)

Spearfish is a heavy dual-purpose wire-guided torpedo selected by the Royal Navy as the successor to the current Tigerfish, in preference to the U.S. Mk 48/ADCAP. Spearfish, being developed by Marconi Underwater Systems, reportedly incorporates some Stingray technology. Spearfish reportedly achieved a speed of 70.5 kts in a trial in a Scottish loch, but reportedly speed at depth is substantially less. Back pressure at depth substantially reduces turbine output (compared to the output of a swash-plate engine as in the U.S. Mk 48); therefore, the torpedo is designed to make its maximum speed at depth and naturally runs much faster at shallower depths. Reports suggest that the engine operates at two speeds, search and run-out/attack. An endurance of 21,000 m has been reported.

Reportedly the seeker uses multiple receivers some distance from the acoustic transmitter, for better directivity. That report suggests that the receivers are arranged around the sides of the torpedo's nose. In 1981 it was reported that Spearfish accommodates five times the computing capacity of Stingray.

Feasibility studies were conducted in 1977–79, leading up to Naval Staff Target (later Requirement) 7525. Reported requirements were a maximum speed of 55 kts; a diving depth of 3000 ft; and significantly improved self-noise, acquisition range, and lethality compared to Tigerfish. Very broadly, the new torpedo combines Stingray's seeker technology with a new thermal power plant for high performance. As no such power plant had been developed in Britain, the U.S. firm of Sundstrand was approached to provide a monofuel turbine. Reportedly early in 1980 Marconi decided to increase Spearfish's speed to meet the problem posed by the Soviet Alfa-class submarine. In 1981 Spearfish was competing with the U.S. Mk 48/ADCAP, which was then credited with a speed of 60+ kts; Spearfish's maximum speed is, therefore, probably somewhat higher, i.e., about 63 kts. This uprating was achieved by replacing pure Otto-II fuel with the current HAP-Otto combination, output increasing from 550 to 1000+ HP.

In 1981 it was reported that a typical Spearfish would run out at 28 kts (to avoid alerting the target) at a depth of about 50 m (launch at 200 m) under wire guidance, then would enter a low-speed glide (passive search). The torpedo might opt to attack the first target detected or to continue searching. The torpedo, once it has found a target, can switch to active mode and accelerate to high speed to attack. Marconi claimed in 1981 that in the active mode the torpedo would typically be able to measure the size and aspect of the target, and that this capability would make Spearfish very difficult to decoy, since a real target would not suddenly change size and shape. Such sonar imaging would also, presumably, make it possible for the torpedo to choose to hit at an optimum point along the submarine's length.

The decision in favor of Spearfish was made in 1980–81 (announced September 1981). It appears that Marconi offered a considerable savings if the Stingray and Spearfish programs were combined into a single British torpedo program. As of mid-1988, the production contract for Spearfish was being delayed because of proposals to include Dowty and British Aerospace as competitors.

◆ Stingray

Dimensions: 325 mm × 2.6 m (12.75 in × 102.4 in)
Weight: 267 kg (588.5 lbs)   **Speed:** 44 kts
Warhead: 45-kg (99-lb) shaped charge
Power Plant: silver-zinc seawater battery (pump jet)

Stingray. This torpedo uses a pumpjet rather than propellers. (Marconi)

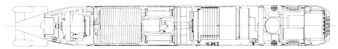

The Marconi-Dowty Lightweight Test Vehicle (LTV), for a chemical propulsion system for a Stingray successor. Presumably the nest of tubes near the tail of the torpedo constitutes the lithium-filled boiler, feeding the steam turbine just abaft it. The object forward of the boiler is the sulfur hexafluoride tank and pump. The front half of the torpedo is occupied by a computer, instrumentation (which replaces the warhead), and the sonar transducer in the nose. (Dowty)

The British replacement for license-built Mk 46s, Stingray was purchased in preference to the U.S. Mk 50. The manufacturer, Marconi, claims that Stingray is the first lightweight torpedo to incorporate a programmable general-purpose computer rather than a hard-wired special-purpose device. Stingray can, therefore, be software-modified for different water environments and for different targets.

Homing is active acoustic, using dual frequency FM pulses and preformed beams. The torpedo can decide to switch between active and passive homing, using the latter mode, for example, if the target speeds up. The manufacturer, Marconi, emphasizes this ability to switch modes depending on circumstances, contrasting Stingray with a conventional torpedo that shifts between passive and active modes (if at all) using a preset homing criterion, or at a preset point. The seawater battery differs from most in recirculating its water internally, so that there is no external water scoop to make self-noise. The onboard computer selects a search mode. Target data can be compared to characteristics stored in the on-board computer, which calculates an interception path that takes into account the target's speed and maneuverability.

The seeker apparently uses preformed beams to search a considerable water depth very rapidly. Search is probably a snake pattern (rather than the helix of earlier torpedoes) at a single depth, since it is stated that the seeker can sweep the total water volume, from the surface down to maximum depth.

Stingray runs at a single speed (approximately equal to Mk 46's maximum speed), so Stingray can optimize its acoustic signature for a combination of maximum speed and maximum acquisition range. In March 1981 the torpedo was credited with depth performance equal to that of an Alfa-class submarine, presumably about 800 m. The torpedo is negatively buoyant: to avoid crashing into the bottom, Stingray must achieve substantial speed (for maneuvering) very early. The torpedo, therefore, starts up quickly upon hitting the water, and the rudders are located in the wash of the propeller for immediate effectiveness. Reportedly Stingray can pull out of its initial (air-drop) dive in less than 4–5 seconds, to avoid hitting the bottom in shallow water. There are alternative search patterns for deep and shallow water, and alternative broad- and narrow-band active ping options, presumably corresponding to long-range narrow pulses vs. shorter-range doppler.

When Stingray was offered in 1981, the U.S. Navy found the torpedo's speed unacceptable. Gould offered an alternative electric variable-speed power plant with a maximum speed of 62 kts. That figure may indicate the sort of performance expected of the current U.S. Mk 50.

Stingray came into service after the purchase of a long series of U.S. lightweights. The Royal Navy designed a heavy airdropped torpedo, Mk 30 (Dealer B), but had to abandon it when the Gannet airplane was dropped in favor of ASW helicopters, which could not lift so heavy a weapon. Instead, the U.S. Mk 43 (now extinct) was bought, while a Mk 31 lightweight (proposed 1970) was developed. Mk 31 in turn was canceled in 1971, and the Royal Navy bought Mk 44 and Mk 46 Mod 2. At present the Royal Navy uses Mk 44 for shallow water and the Mk 46 for deep water.

Stingray studies began in 1964, the NSR 7511 staff requirement being issued in June 1968. It included shallow-water (presumably for the continental shelf of the North Sea) capability. Marconi received a contract for a seeker feasibility study in August 1969. The company apparently proposed something more, a torpedo that would modify seeker operation as it ran and that would be adaptable to a very wide range of water conditions. A design contract followed in 1977, and a production contract was expected in 1980. However, at that time the British defense budget was under pressure, and Mk 46 Mod 5 (NEARTIP) was suggested as an alternative. Stingray was selected instead; the stated reasons were that the U.S. torpedo had less effective homing, that its blast warhead was less effective than Stingray's shaped charge, and that Mk 46 Mod 5 could not operate in shallow water.

Production began in April 1981, with orders for 280 and then for 550. Some Stingrays were sent to the South Atlantic in 1982 (HMS *Antelope* had four on board when she was sunk), but they were not used. The torpedo officially entered service in 1986; the British government placed an order for 2500 Stingrays in January 1986. On 19 October 1985, in its first live-warhead test, a Stingray dropped from a Nimrod aircraft destroyed a double-hulled submarine, HMS *Porpoise,* moored at a depth of 65 m in the Mediterranean. Total running time to the target was about three minutes. The extent of damage to the submarine seems to have been surprising. The torpedo was expected to cut a small-diameter (albeit fatal) hole in both hulls, after which the submarine would have been raised for examination. Instead, it was so completely destroyed that it could not be raised. This result may indicate the power of all current lightweight torpedoes equipped with warheads made of modern explosives.

Several improved versions have been suggested. In 1981 a possible Mk 2, incorporating Spearfish's seeker technology, was mentioned. More recently a new version powered by the sort of closed-cycle engine used in the U.S. Mk 50 (Barracuda) has been proposed. There have also been suggestions that the Torpex warhead be replaced by PBX 104, a more powerful plastic-based explosive used in U.S. weapons.

About 1988 a U.S. estimate of the unit cost of this torpedo was $440,000. Current export customers are Egypt and Thailand.

Toward the end of Stingray's development program, Marconi analyzed a variety of alternative propulsion systems, both electric and thermal. The company proposed construction of a series of Fast Lightweight Test Vehicles (FLTVs), to be powered by the type of closed-cycle SCEPS plant employed in the U.S. Mk 50. In 1985 the British Ministry of Defence placed a contract with Dowty Fuel Systems for a land-based demonstrator, and by 1989 construction was well advanced; completion of a plant packaged for torpedo use is scheduled for 1991. The Ministry then asked Dowty and Marconi to submit a proposal for a torpedo test unit, and a development cost plan was submitted on 26 August 1988. Marconi proposes a Lightweight Test Vehicle (LTV), presumably using a modified Stingray hull.

♦ **Tigerfish (Mk 24)**

Dimensions: 533 × 6464 mm (21 × 254.5 inches)
Weight: 3420 lbs **Speed/Range:** 35 kts/23,000 yds; 24 kts
Warhead: 750 lbs (magnetic proximity fuze for surface targets; impact fuze for submarine targets)
Power Plant: twin silver-zinc batteries (2-speed motor)

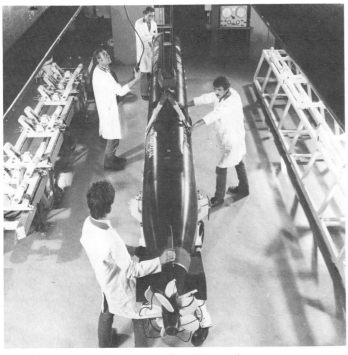

Tigerfish. This torpedo uses propellers. (Marconi)

Tigerfish began in 1959 as Project ONGAR, for a faster and more sophisticated antisubmarine torpedo. An order for 100 was placed in 1967 with the Royal Navy Torpedo Factory (RNTF). ONGAR was a two-speed electric torpedo with wire guidance and a passive terminal sensor. Because the torpedo was heavier than water, it used retractable wings to provide lift at low (search) speeds, and also to improve roll control. Acceptance trials in 1969 were so unsuccessful that a special Torpedo Project Executive was established, and the contract transferred to GEC. The wide-beam seeker (which had large nulls in its beam pattern) was the major problem. Marconi was asked to design a new narrow-beam seeker and a more powerful on-board computer that could take over more of the guidance role. Marconi was also asked to develop a second version, Mod 1, with an antiship seeker. This effort also encountered problems, this time in the interfaces with the shipboard tactical-data systems and with actual torpedo control. RNTF was closed, and production passed to Plessey.

In 1973–74 a second series of trials showed that the weapon could perform as expected but that overall the system's reliability varied wildly, from 20 to 80 percent (40 percent average). The torpedo depended very heavily on data provided by the submarine but tended to dip and snap its guidance wire after being launched. In 1974 the overall production contract passed to Marconi, since the major problem was not the hull of the torpedo but rather its control system (which had been Marconi's responsibility from the start). A redesigned Mod 1 passed trials in 1978, but the main version, Mod 0, was still unsatisfactory. It failed provisional fleet acceptance trials in 1979 but was issued to the fleet beginning in August 1980.

In 1982, two of three Mod 1 torpedoes fired at the burnt-out hulk of the LSL *Sir Galahad* did not hit because their batteries failed.

In 1983 the controller of the navy awarded Marconi a contract for a Mk-24 Consolidation [i.e., get-well] Program. In 1985 test shots showed a satisfactory 80 percent reliability. Part of the get-well program was replacement of the existing wire dispenser with a pair of dispensers, one on board the submarine. Demonstrations have shown that, with this dispenser, the submarine can evade after firing without breaking the guidance wire. Some Stingray technology has also been incorporated into the modified weapon, Mk 24 Mod 2, and all 600 war-stock Mk 24s had been modified by 1987.

This weapon replaced the earlier Mk 20E (Bidder), a dual-purpose passive-homer that entered service in the mid 1950s on board both frigates and submarines (1810 lbs, 196-lb warhead, 20 kts/12,000 yds). The surface version was abandoned because its preset attack data system proved unreliable. No British surface ASW torpedo was available until 1964, when Plessey began to deliver license-built U.S. Mk 44s. Mk 20E remained in submarine service through 1970. Mk 22 was an abortive wire-guided version of Mk 20; VSEL produced a private-venture version in 1970. Mk 23 (Grog) was a modified Mk 20 with a wire-guidance section between the battery compartment and afterbody, issued from 1970 onward as an interim torpedo pending the appearance of Mk 24 (2000 lbs, 28 kts/8750 yds).

Tigerfish typifies the European type of antisubmarine torpedo, operating passively at relatively low speed to avoid alerting the targeted submarine. For example, in 1981 it was reported that Tigerfish was 15–20 dB quieter (in self-noise) than Mk 48. Passive approach died because many submarines themselves became too quiet to be detected passively. Once torpedoes approached actively, they had to be able to catch an alerted target: hence the high-speed Spearfish.

Tigerfish Mod 1 (dual-purpose) has been supplied to Brazil. Mod 2 is the improved British version currently under development.

UNITED STATES

♦ **Mk 14 Series**

Dimensions: 21 × 246 in **Weight:** 3209 lbs
Speed/Range: 31.1 kts/9000 yds or 46 kts/4500 yds
Warhead: 643 lbs **Power Plant:** steam turbine

Mk 14 was the standard U.S. submarine torpedo of World War II, remaining in use through the 1970s. Mk 14 was probably supplied to many Allied navies on board ex-U.S. submarines, and some of these torpedoes may remain in service. Although early Mark 14s had magnetic exploders, all surviving examples are contact-exploded.

About 13,000 Mk-14 torpedoes were manufactured during World War II (with others built prewar), together with 9700 of the simpler one-speed Mk-23 version (46 kts only). Mk 14 was declared obsolete in the late 1950s or early 1960s, when U.S. submarines were all assigned to the ASW role, and when the hydrogen-peroxide Mk-16 became available in quantity to provide the few antiship weapons required. However, Mk 14 was reactivated in 1969 and was withdrawn again only as dual-purpose Mk 48s became available.

Mk 16 was never exported. Over 1700 were made postwar and remained in service until 1975. Mk 16 was the same size as Mk 14 (though it weighed 4000 lbs), but hydrogen-peroxide propulsion enabled Mk 16 to achieve 11,000 yds at 46.2 kts and to carry a 746-lb warhead. The final version was Mod 8.

◆ Mk 15 Series

Dimensions: 21 × 288 in   **Weight:** 3841 lbs
Speed/Range: 26.5 kts/15,000 yds or 33.5 kts/10,000 yds or 45 kts/6000 yds
Warhead: 825 lbs
Power Plant: steam turbine

Although no longer carried by U.S. destroyers, Mk 15 is probably the torpedo fired from surviving ex-U.S. quintuple surface tubes in ships transferred abroad.

About 9700 Mk-15 torpedoes were manufactured in 1940–44.

◆ Mk 32

Dimensions: 19 × 83 in (25.4-in fins)   **Weight:** 700 lbs
Speed/Range: 12 kts/9600 yds (endurance 24 minutes)
Warhead: 107 lbs   **Power Plant:** battery

The first U.S. lightweight torpedo, developed in 1950, Mk 32 was also the first U.S. homing torpedo with an active seeker. Given its very low speed, Mk 32 was effective only against slow submarines, and it is now obsolete. The search pattern was a descending helix, beginning at a depth of about 20 ft, the torpedo seeker emitting 50-kHz pings. Because the fins were much larger than the diameter, Mk 32 could not be tube-launched and instead had to be catapulted over the side or dumped over the stern, like a depth charge. About 330 were made through 1955, when Mk 32 was superseded by the first of the modern small-diameter torpedoes, Mk 43. The last users were Japan and Spain, but Mk 32 may survive as a war-reserve weapon.

◆ Mk 37 and NT37 Series

Dimensions: 19 × 135 in   **Weight:** 1430 lbs
Speed/Range: 24 kts/8000 yds or 16 kts/18,000 yds
Warhead: 330 lbs   **Power Plant:** battery

Mk 37 torpedo. (U.S. Navy)

Data apply to Mk 37 Mod 1.

Mk 37 was the standard U.S. submarine-launched antisubmarine torpedo of the 1960s; Mod 3 was a refurbished Mod 0 and was a passive/active homer. Mods 1 and 2 (1690 lbs, 161 in long) were wire-guided; enable range was 300–9500 yds, and acquisition range was 700 yds.

Mk 37 was also intended for surface use, fired aft from torpedo tubes in ships' transoms. This arrangement seemed to be necessary to allow the guidance wire to pay out properly; attempts to fire the wire-guided version of the weapon from forward-firing tubes angled outboard were, apparently, failures. At present only the Spanish Navy fires this torpedo from surface ships.

Mk 37's operating modes are predicted-intercept, corrected-intercept (i.e., mid-course corrected run), and bearing-rider. In the bearing-rider mode the torpedo points continuously toward the target (as in pursuit-course interception). As fired by a surface ship Mk 37 has the following operating limits: outside range limits 8,000 yds for high speed, 18,000 yds for low speed; minimum range 300 yds; minimum depth 4 ft; max depth 1000 ft. Homing can be active or passive or a combination. The torpedo follows a preset horizontal search pattern to circle left or right or to snake. Vertical search can only be upward from the running-depth ordered, within preset limits. Speed is preset as high (approx 24 kts) or low (approx 16 kts).

Mk 37 is no longer in U.S. service, but this torpedo was widely exported to Allied navies; for example, the Argentine submarine commander in the Falklands fired a Mk 37 at a supposed (and almost certainly false) British submarine contact.

In 1968 Northrop Corporation began work on improvements to Mk 37, in cooperation with the Naval Torpedo Station at Keyport, Washington, replacing the existing silver-zinc battery with the Otto fuel engine of a Mk 46-1. Speed increased by 40 percent, and range by 150 percent. For a service modified torpedo (NT37C), the published figures are 40 percent greater speed, 125 percent more range, and about 80 percent more endurance.

Northrop carried the Mk 37 conversion program through about 1980, when this activity was transferred to Honeywell. The designation of the modified torpedo, NT37, still reflects the company's involvement.

The program was approved in 1968, and acoustic improvement tests began in 1969. Tests of the NT37C systems were conducted in 1970, followed by tests of the submarine systems in 1971, preproduction and production verification in 1972, and certification of readiness for service in 1973 (NT37C version). Improvements included not only the enormous increase in speed and range but also true dual-purpose capability: because NT37C was so fast, it could duplicate the straight run of, say, a Mk 14. NT37C can be set in three modes: (i) straight running at high speed with depth control; (ii) delayed homing, the torpedo running straight but searching if it misses (or beginning its search at a preset range); (iii) full passive homing, as in the original Mk 37. By 1977, NT37C was in service in several NATO and South American navies, and in February 1976 Norway ordered kits for conversions of her Mk 37s.

The next step was a new homing head. NT37C plus the new acoustic system is designated NT37D.

NT37D plus a new guidance system, the fully modernized torpedo, is NT37E. It incorporates a self-noise–reduction nose assembly (with baffling to protect the transducer from engine and hull noise, and with a new nose shape to reduce flow noise), a solid-state acoustic panel (to replace the vacuum tubes of the original Mk 37), and a new digital (vice analog) autopilot. In one version, the autopilot can be programmed to navigate the torpedo to specific geographical coordinates. Honeywell claims that these modifications double the active detection range and nearly double the passive detection range against fast targets, partly because with less flow noise the acoustic system can be made more sensitive (the company cites test results that showed an improvement of 50–90 percent in the active target-acquisition range, and of 100–200 percent in the passive target-acquisition range). The company also claims better performance at higher speed and in shallow water, in both cases thanks to noise reduction. On a subtler level, Mk 37 tactics are fixed; NT37 tactics are programmable and, thus, less easily predicted.

The new nose and acoustic panel were first tested in 1980, developmental and operational tests of NT37E following in 1982 and 1983. In 1980, Canadian/Norwegian/Dutch trials on the Nanoose acoustic range showed a 71-percent success rate in 17 runs; an operational evaluation in the North Atlantic showed 88 percent success in 8 runs. Operational demonstrations in 1981 showed 100 percent success in 18 runs. Canadian guidance-and-control trials in 1982 (Nanoose range) showed 100 percent success in 5 runs.

Given the large number of Mk 37 produced, Honeywell (which currently has rights to NT37) has offered foreign customers a variety of modified versions in an NT37 series; these modifications could be applied to existing torpedoes. Honeywell also offered a modified Mk 37 for the abortive U.S. requirement for an inexpensive surface-only torpedo (see Surface Torpedo below). By late 1983, about 500 torpedoes in five navies had been upgraded to NT37C configuration.

Mk 37 was supplied to at least 16 navies. As of 1986, NT37C was in service with the navies of Canada, Israel, the Netherlands, Norway, and Peru.

Mk 37s have also been rebuilt both as Submarine-Launched Mobile Mines Mk 67 and as Standoff Weapons Mk 32. For details of Mk 67, see the Mine Warfare section. The standoff weapon is intended for use from SEAL Swimmer-Delivery vehicles Mk IX, to attack surface ships in harbors. The standoff weapon was introduced into fleet service during FY87. (The SEALs also have both limpet mines and Underwater Demolition Weapon EX-33, a 1200-lb charge that can be laid under major or nested ship targets in harbor.)

◆ Mk 43

> **Dimensions:** 10 × 91.5 in (13.4 in across fins)
> **Weight:** 260 lbs **Speed/Range:** 15 kts/4500 yds
> **Warhead:** 54 lbs

Although Mk 43 is obsolete, it probably remains as a war-reserve weapon in the Canadian and Japanese Navies. Unlike later U.S. small-diameter lightweight torpedoes, Mk 43 had fins larger than its body diameter and, therefore, could not be launched from a tube. Instead, Mk 43 was thrown over the side mechanically.

Data are for Mod 1. Mod 3, 265 lbs, had a speed of 21 kts (4500-yd range), with an endurance of 6 rather than 9 minutes. Its fins were clipped for an overall diameter of 10 inches. This torpedo was replaced in U.S. service by Mk 44 from 1957 on, about 5000 having been manufactured.

Mk 43 Mods 1 and 3 have no runout feature; they search in depth using a helical pattern.

Mod 1's depth limits are 75 and 650 ft; Mod 3, 50–1000 ft. Sink rates are 12.5 and 17.5 ft/sec, respectively. Initial search depth is usually set at 150 ft but can be 75–500 or 50–850 ft, respectively. Acquisition zone is 500 yds. Acquisition zone is defined by the cylinder within which a submarine will be detected; this zone is not acquisition range. Acquisition zone is acquisition range plus the turning circle's radius; e.g., for Mk 43 Mod 1 it would seem to be 140 ft plus the acquisition range. The search circle's diameter is 280 and 480 ft, respectively. Mk 43 and Mk 44 both initially dive at 30 degrees, making a flat turn at the initial search depth, then sinking while turning and circling to port.

◆ Mk 44

> **Dimensions:** 12.75 × 100 in **Weight:** 425 lbs
> **Speed/Range:** 30 kts/6000 yds **Warhead:** 75 lbs
> **Power Plant:** seawater-activated battery (30-HP motor)

Mk 44 torpedo. The shroud is forward of the propellers. (U.S. Navy)

Mk 44 was formerly the standard NATO lightweight homing torpedo, the payload for which ASROC and Ikara were designed. Development began about 1952 and was completed in 1956. Data are for Mod 0; Mod 1 was 101.3 in long, 433 lbs, with a 73-lb warhead. This torpedo was a pure active homer. Search pattern was helical. Mk 44 was replaced by Mk 46 from about 1967 on, but a great many Mk 44s remain in service in foreign navies, and the U.S. Navy probably retains a stockpile.

In 1986, Honeywell offered a modernization kit for Mk 44. The existing nose was replaced by a new one incorporating ceramic rather than magnetostrictive transducers, in a planar array (rather than using an acoustic window). The planar array incorporates a preamplifier, and the analog transmitter and receiver of the existing Mk 44 are replaced by digital devices. Claimed improvements include an increase in mean time between failure from 160 to 3000 hours and a 75-percent increase in detection range; minimum shallow-water search depth is reduced by 47 percent. Volume search rate is tripled. Honeywell claims that the addition of a notch filter reduces boundary-layer attacks. A new range gate reduces acoustic false alarms. A new search mode is added for intermediate water depths.

Mk 44 Mod 0 has no runout feature. Mk 44 Mods 1, 2, 3, and 4 have a limited range runout (about 1000 yds) before spiral search. These torpedoes have an azimuth snake search pattern.

Mk 44's depth limits are 50–1000 ft. The sink rate is 25 ft/sec. Search ceiling is 50 ft, and the search depth is preset at 50–900 ft. The acquisition zone has an 800-yd radius. The search circle has a 440-ft diameter.

◆ Mk 45F (Freedom Torpedo)

> **Dimensions:** 19 × 225 in **Weight:** 2555 lbs
> **Speed/Range:** 40 kts/11,000–15,000 yds; the warhead is disabled for the first 1000 yards
> **Warhead:** 650-lbs H6 (equivalent to 975 lbs of TNT)
> **Power Plant:** seawater battery (160-HP motor with contraprops)

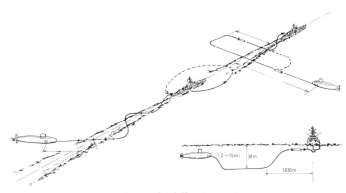

Mk 45F Freedom Torpedo's wake-following action.

These torpedoes were converted by Westinghouse from Mk 45 nuclear torpedo shells, the weapon having been withdrawn from U.S. service in 1976. There are two versions, the straight-running Mod 0 and the homing Mod 1, sale of which requires the approval of the U.S. government.

Mk 45F Mod 1 uses a wake-homing mechanism developed by Westinghouse as an alternative to conventional passive antiship homing techniques. The sensor is presumably an upward-looking high-frequency sonar. The torpedo is generally fired toward a point abaft the target (aft bias). The wake-homer is enabled at a point 2000 yds short of the predicted impact. Upon crossing the target's wake, the torpedo turns toward the target, the desired crossing angle being 30 degrees (for a net speed of advance of 35 kts toward the target). If the torpedo misses on its first pass (i.e., fails to redetect the wake after turning more than 315 degrees), it keeps turning to re-attack. If no wake is detected in the first place, the torpedo turns back at a preset distance and comes back along its initial path, turning back and forth until the target crosses the torpedo's path.

Attack depth is selectable between 6 and 50 ft, depending on the target's draft. It is not clear whether an under-the-keel exploder is provided, although the upward-looking wake sensor itself might be used as such. There is also a deep-run-out mode, in which the torpedo runs at 125 ft until it reaches the enable point 2000 yds from the predicted position of the target.

The torpedo can also be fired as a conventional straight-runner, with or without wire guidance (which was provided in the original nuclear version). Under wire guidance, the predicted impact range can be adjusted in 100-yard steps, and heading can be adjusted in 2-degree steps.

◆ Mk 46

Dimensions: 12.75 × 102 in **Weight:** 568 lbs (dry)
Speed/Range: 45 kts/12,000 yds (at 50 ft) or 40 kts/6000 yds (at 1500 ft)
Warhead: 96 lbs (PBXN-103)
Power Plant: internal-combustion engine (Otto Fuel/Oxidizer)

Data are for Mod 0. Depth is 20–1500 ft.

Mk 46 is now virtually the standard NATO lightweight torpedo. In U.S. service it replaced Mk 44 from about 1967 onward. Compared to Mk 44, Mk 46 is much faster, dives deeper, and can be dropped at up to 500 kts. The United States offered Mk 46 to the Chinese (PRC) Navy, but it is not clear whether the Chinese will adopt this weapon.

Development began in 1958, following a December 1956 feasibility study of a lightweight torpedo fast enough to deal with nuclear submarines. The Mk 46 Operational Requirement was issued in November 1960, and production of Mod 0 began in 1963 (it entered service in 1964).

The initial version, Mod 0, was credited with an acquisition range of 1600 yards, a 60-percent improvement over Mk 44 in 1964. Few such torpedoes were built; these figures are, however, indicative of the performance of later versions. The turbine-powered solid-fuel Mod 0 was superseded in production by Mod 1, which used liquid monopropellant (Otto) fuel in a swash-plate engine and weighed 508 lbs. Mod 1 also incorporated simplified steering. The first production contract was issued in 1965, and Mod 1 was tested in 1966. Both versions could be fired by surface ships, and both, therefore, incorporated runouts to escape own-ship interference.

Mk 46 snake-searches after it runs out, in contrast to earlier torpedoes that helix-search (sinking or rising as they turn). That search pattern presumably reflects Mk 46's longer sonar-acquisition range, which provides a wider field of view at any given depth.

Mod 2 was intended for helicopter use (HATS, the Helicopter Attack Tactical System) and, therefore, required no run-out before a circular search. Prototypes were tested in 1968–69, and production for the U.S. Navy ended in FY69; but the line was reopened in FY72 to provide 950 torpedoes for the Royal Navy.

Mods 1 and 2 equip numerous foreign navies, including those of Australia, Brazil, Canada, France, Greece, Israel, Italy, New Zealand, Spain, the United Kingdom, and West Germany. These versions were manufactured from 1965 through 1981.

Mod 3 was an unsuccessful version, not manufactured.

Mod 4 is a torpedo built specifically as a payload for the CAPTOR (Mk 60) mine.

NEARTIP (Mod 5, the Near-Term Improvement Program) was very nearly a completely new torpedo, employing either entirely new or greatly modified seeker (sonar transducer, transmitter, and receiver), guidance, and propulsion. Sonar improvements were intended specifically to counter submarines with anechoic coverings, specifically Soviet boats. The correlation channel used to determine whether sounds detected by the sonar were in fact echoes of the pulses it sent was improved, to make up for the reduction in signal-to-noise ratio caused by the anechoic coverings. The transmitted waveform was changed to make better use of target doppler for signal processing. Signal processing logic was improved, particularly to reject false targets. At the same time, reverberation effects in shallow water were reduced, so that self-noise could better be measured and disregarded. All operation is now digital, with improved stability and precision. A second gyro was provided to improve diving control.

Finally, the torpedo's motor was modified to provide a second (lower) search speed. The lower speed reduced self-noise and, thus, increased the available signal-to-noise ratio at the torpedo's sonar processor. The slower speed also increased the total torpedo endurance (in terms of time) by 30 to 50 percent. Once the torpedo has locked onto its target it still attacks at the same sort of high speed provided by the original Mk 46. The fuse was revised to function even if the torpedo struck the target at a shallow angle.

The U.S. Navy introduced the first of two shallow water modifications in 1984, to improve performances against slow submarines at periscope depth in both deep and shallow water. Normally such targets are difficult to engage because they provide little doppler (which the torpedo uses to distinguish them from background noise) and because the torpedo has difficulty dealing with reflection (both of its pulses and of its self-noise) from the surface. The modification apparently consisted of a more coherent transmitter and better steering logic.

Honeywell, the manufacturer, developed a further shallow-water modification of its own. The success of the program is presumably demonstrated by a photograph, recently published, of a surfaced submarine target hit by a Mk 46 Mod 5. The target may have been fitted with some noise source, but even so it presented all the problems of a surface-ship target. The torpedo's success suggests that it can be used in an alternative anti–surface ship mode so that, for example, torpedo-carrying missiles like ASROC can be employed against surface targets. Although these missiles are generally far slower and far less efficient than their specially designed antiship counterparts, torpedo-carrying missiles have one interesting potential advantage: they may be able to drop their weapons outside the effective range of close-in weapons. These points would apply more strongly to fast submarine-borne weapons such as Sea Lance.

The warhead was also improved; it was a Mk 103 with PBXN-103 explosive.

NEARTIP began in October 1972, technical evaluation being completed in November 1977 and operational evaluation in February 1978. Production release was in May 1979, the initial contract being awarded in July 1979 (and the last in February 1987). Some Mod 5's were manufactured for the Dutch and British Navies, and Mitsubishi manufactures this torpedo under license in Japan (coproduction approved July 1982).

About 1986 the U.S. Navy's reported objective was a total of 5500 Mk 46-5 and 3000 Mk 46-4 torpedoes. Total production, for FY80 and previous years, was 11,646 torpedoes. Purchases in later years were: 253 in each of FY81 and FY82, 440 in FY83, 1200 in FY84, 1565 in FY85, and then 500 each in FY86 and FY87. These figures do not include the torpedoes used in CAPTOR mines and may not include some export torpedoes. In FY87 the price per torpedo was $195,322. In 1985 the navy proposed to end production of Mk 46 in FY88 (500 torpedoes). At that time procurement of 1521 had been scheduled for FY86, and that figure was cut to 500.

In 1987 it was reported that total Mk 46 production, including export weapons, had been over 17,000. That figure included about 1252 Mod 0 of 1963–65 (by Aerojet) and about 9200 Mod 1 manufactured 1965–69 by Honeywell.

It was announced in November 1988 that Brazil is buying Mk 46 Mod 5 torpedoes for delivery in 1988 and 1989, and kits to update existing Brazilian Mk 46 Mod 2s. Mk 46 is currently operated by 23 navies.

Mk 46 torpedo, showing its propeller shroud and parachute pack. (U.S. Navy)

◆ Mk 48/ADCAP

Dimensions: 21 × 230 in **Weight:** 3480 lbs
Speed/Range: estimated 55 kts/35,000 yds
Power Plant: 500-HP Otto fuel swash-plate engine

Mk 48 began as a development of the RETORC II (Research Torpedo Re-Configuration) research program, which had been underway since 1956. Development characteristics for a new torpedo (at that time designated EX-10) were set in 1960, and

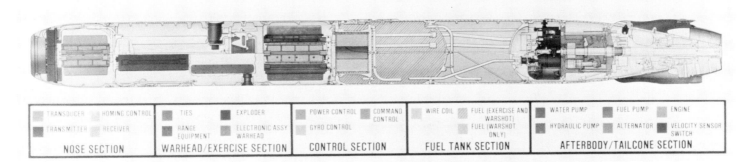

NOSE SECTION	WARHEAD/EXERCISE SECTION	CONTROL SECTION	FUEL TANK SECTION	AFTERBODY/TAILCONE SECTION
TRANSDUCER HOMING CONTROL	TIES EXPLODER	POWER CONTROL COMMAND CONTROL	WIRE COIL FUEL (EXERCISE AND WARSHOT)	WATER PUMP FUEL PUMP ENGINE
TRANSMITTER RECEIVER	RANGE EQUIPMENT ELECTRONIC ASSY WARHEAD	GYRO CONTROL	FUEL (WARSHOT ONLY)	HYDRAULIC PUMP ALTERNATOR VELOCITY SENSOR SWITCH

(*Above*) Mk 48 Mod 4. (Westinghouse)

Mk 48 torpedo, showing the pump jet. (Westinghouse)

tenders requested in May 1962. A project definition contract was awarded to Westinghouse in 1964, with Sundstrand providing propulsion and Clevite (later renamed Gould) the acoustics; Clevite also received a back-up contract for a separate homing system. At that time the existing Mk 37 was credited with only 10-percent effectiveness against a 20-knot submarine. The proposed Mk 48 was credited with 40-percent effectiveness against a 35-knot submarine, and work was accelerated after system tests on board the submarine *Permit* in the Pacific in 1964. In 1967–68 further contracts were awarded to modify the basic torpedo for antiship as well as antisubmarine use, the single-purpose Mk 47 antiship torpedo project having been abandoned. Mk 48 entered service in 1971.

Mk 48 is the current standard U.S. heavy torpedo, credited with dual-purpose (antisubmarine/antiship) performance. Mod 1 and Mod 2 were competitive prototypes; Mod 2 (rejected) had a turbine engine, Mod 1 a swash-plate piston engine using Otto II (nitrogen ester with oxidant) fuel. Mk 48 differs from many other torpedoes in using a pump-jet rather than conventional propellers for propulsion, a choice presumably made to provide very high speed without so much noise that the weapon would be unable to home, or that the target would be alerted soon enough to escape easily. Published illustrations of the new Mk 50, which is also very fast, show a similar pump jet.

The performance listed here is based on congressional testimony (in the 1970s) to the effect that Mk 48 has a range of 20 miles (presumably statute, not nautical) at "nearly twice the speed of Mk 37." Published figures more than a decade old suggest an acquisition range of 4000 yds (compared to 1000 for Mk 37) and a diving depth of 2500 ft. Mk 48 has also been

described officially as the only U.S. torpedo capable of reaching the Alfa's depth, reported as 800 meters (2624 ft).

Aside from the active and passive homing modes, there is a nonacoustic mode, presumably a straight or pattern-running shot at a surface target, the only intelligent element of the torpedo being its fuze. Numerous published photographs showing Mk 48s blowing substantial ex-warships in half strongly suggest that the torpedo uses a standoff (proximity) fuze for under-the-keel explosion.

Mk 48's design emphasizes maintainability, with unit replacements (functional item replacements) to minimize repair time.

Mod 3 (1977) adds a two-way (rather than one-way) wire link (TELCOM), allowing the torpedo operator to exploit the torpedo's own sonar. TELCOM transmits 14 torpedo and target parameters once each second.

Mod 4 incorporates TELCOM as well as a fire-and-forget mode. Mod 4 was a transitional step toward ADCAP, and as of 1984 the U.S. Navy planned to buy 144 Mod 4s in both FY85 and FY86, ending procurement in FY86, and to begin production of all-up ADCAPs in FY87. Costing studies led to the decision to end Mod 4's production with 108 torpedoes in FY85 and to begin ADCAP production that year with 30 torpedoes (with 123

(*Below*) Mk 48 ADCAP's guidance section. (Hughes)

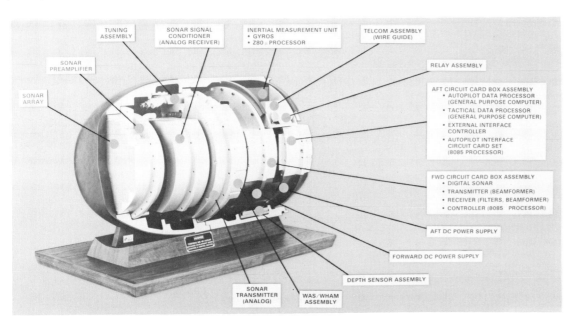

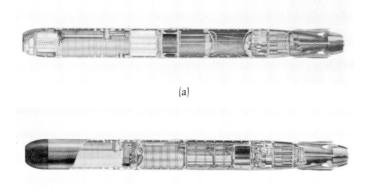

(a)

(b)

Mk 48 Mod 4 (a) and ADCAP (b). ADCAP has much greater fuel stowage, made possible by shrinking the size of the computer between the warhead and the fuel tank. (Westinghouse)

in FY86 and 280 in FY87). However, Congress disagreed, and ADCAP's production was actually slowed, so many conversion kits were procured instead.

Mod 5, a modification kit for existing Mk 48s, is an interim step toward the new ADCAP version.

ADCAP (Advanced Capability) is an extensively modified version capable of greater speed and endurance and incorporating a new homing device. When ADCAP was first developed, there was speculation that it should have received a new Mk number. It appears that Mk 49 was reserved for this purpose but that the Mk 48 ADCAP designator was preferred for political reasons. The swash-plate engine is retained; but the torpedo's shell is stronger, and more fuel is carried. ADCAP has a new active sonar, electronically steered so that the torpedo need not maneuver nor lose as much as net forward speed as its predecessors as it approaches a target.

In 1981, in connection with the competition for the British heavy torpedo, ADCAP's speed was reported as over 60 kts. As a rule of thumb, a torpedo should be about 50 percent faster than its target. Thus the torpedo speed associated with a 42-knot Alfa-class submarine would be 63 kts (ADCAP has often been associated with the requirement to attack Alfas).

The ADCAP Request for Proposals was issued in November 1978, and the program went into advanced development in October 1979. Initial procurement was in FY86. At that time the reported navy objective was 4659 Mk-48 torpedoes, of which 4000 had been funded through FY87; the cost per Mk 48 was then $2,239,515. The currently stated objective for ADCAP modification kits (for Mk 48 Mod 5) is 1062 (March 1988).

Production of Mk 48: 3059 were procured through 1980, then 144 in FY80, and the same number in each of FY81–84. Mk 48 procurement ended in FY85 (108 that year). Mk 48 has been exported to the Australian, Canadian, and Dutch Navies; reported numbers are, respectively, 127 (1979), 48 (1985), and 100 (1980). The first near-term upgrade Mk 48 Mod 4 was delivered to the U.S. Navy in December 1980. ADCAP procurement: 30

(Below) Mk 50 torpedo. (Honeywell)

in FY85, 123 FY86, 50 FY87, 100 FY88, 320 FY89, 320 FY90, 320 FY91. Technical evaluation of ADCAP began in August 1986.

Westinghouse bought Gould's Mk 48 production division in January 1988. The first ADCAP warshot (which sank a decommissioned destroyer) was reported in July 1988.

The Westinghouse version was powered by a Sundstrand turbine; Gould's, by Gould's own swash-plate engine. Reportedly the turbine was much quieter, but Gould's engine was more efficient, particularly at maximum depth, where the combustion products are ejected against considerable back pressure. Torpedo noise was not the determining factor at this time, as the United States enjoyed both the sonar and the weapons advantage, and Gould was chosen. The Sundstrand engine was adapted for the British Spearfish. The engine's power was doubled, and the thermal efficiency of the Otto fuel enhanced by 40 percent by mixing with an oxidant, HAP (hydroxylamine perchlorate).

As of 1988, there is a U.S.-U.K. Memorandum of Understanding on cooperative development of the next-generation heavy torpedo, to replace both ADCAP and Spearfish.

◆ Mk 50 Barracuda

Dimensions: 12.75 × 111.5 in (total length may grow to 115.5 in)
Weight: 771.2 lbs   **Warhead:** shaped charge
Power Plant: closed-cycle thermal (SCEPS)

Mk 50 was developed specifically to counter Soviet Alfa-class submarines and future deep-divers, which were beyond the reach of the existing lightweight torpedoes. Mk 50 will be carried by aircraft, fired from surface ships' torpedo tubes, and fitted as the warhead of the Sea Lance and Vertically Launched ASROC missiles. The 1986 decision to develop Sea Lance primarily as a conventionally armed missile has been read as an indication of the success of the Mk-50 warhead against simulated submarine targets; proponents of the alternative nuclear version have suggested that no lightweight torpedo can reliably attack a large double-hulled submarine.

No performance or homing details have been released. However, if Alfa is credited with a speed of over 40 kts, then the usual requirement for a 50-percent speed margin equates to a maximum Mk-50 speed of about 60–63 kts. Homing is both passive and active (FM active), and it was officially stated in 1987 that Mk 50 homes at twice the range of Mk 46.

The unusual thermal power plant, SCEPS (Stored Chemical Energy Power System), incorporates a block of solid lithium and a tank of sulfur hexafluoride. When the torpedo is fired, electric squibs melt the lithium, and it is allowed to react with the sulfur hexafluoride, creating both heat and a solid ash. The heat in turn is used to produce the steam that propels the torpedo. This system was adopted because the combustion product, the ash, has less volume than the reactants, and so does not have to be dumped outside the torpedo during its run. The torpedo's engine, therefore, does not have to fight increasing water pressure as the weapon dives toward its target. Garrett, which developed the system, says that it is actually easier to produce than the Otto-fuel power plant of a Mk 46.

Development began with a technical-assessment phase (February 1972 through September 1978). The first series of com-

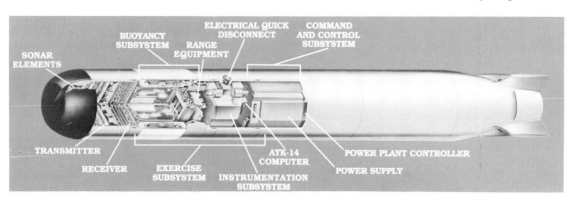

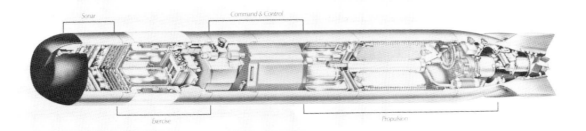

(Above) Mk 50 Barracuda torpedo: the exercise version. (Honeywell)

petitors (Gould/Hughes, Westinghouse, McDonnell-Douglas/ Raytheon, and Honeywell/Garrett) began work in 1978, following a 1975 technology assessment. Two winners were selected in 1979 for a swim-off: McDonnell-Douglas/Raytheon and Honeywell/Garrett. The Honeywell/Garrett design won in 1981, and full-scale engineering development began in 1983.

The McDonnell-Douglas design, Mk 51, reportedly used Raytheon's side-looking linear or flank sonar arrays and may, therefore, have incorporated more of a passive capability. Mk 51 also had a GE silver-oxide electric battery. Published drawings of the Mk 50's nose show clearly that it has only a forward-looking sonar array.

As of 1988, the reported objective for production of Mk 50s was 7743 torpedoes plus 160 for research and testing. Estimated unit cost is $250,000, compared to $180,000 for Mk 46 at a high production rate. Procurement: 39 in FY87, 16 FY88, 140 FY89, 200 FY90, 270 FY91.

◆ Surface Torpedo

Given the very high cost of the dual-purpose Mk 48, the navy proposed a less expensive surface-only weapon. This was partly inspired by the success of the British Mk 8** (which sank the *Belgrano* in the Falklands); there may have been some hope that a single-purpose Mk 48 would be less expensive. Ironically, the success of the dual-purpose seeker in Mk 48 had led, about 1964, to the decision to abandon a single-purpose antiship torpedo (Mk 47) then very early in development. The goal was to achieve a range of 6000 yds at 35 kts at one-tenth the cost of Mk 48 ADCAP, i.e., at roughly the cost of a Mk 46 NEARTIP. The main objection was that the more different types of weapons a submarine carries, the fewer of any one type she can accommodate within her very limited capacity. Moreover, the really important Soviet naval targets can probably outrun a short-range 35-knot torpedo. On the other hand, in the course of a lengthy war, U.S. submarines would presumably have to attack numerous lower-performance targets. World War II provides a precedent: when the Mk-14 submarine torpedo proved too difficult to manufacture, a somewhat simplified (one-speed) Mk 23 was placed in production.

An operational requirement for this Low Cost Antiship Torpedo (LCAT) was published in December 1985. The main competitors were Honeywell (MAKO, a modified NT37 without wire guidance), Marconi (modified and shortened Tigerfish), and Whitehead (A-184).

A trials program begun in 1986 led to a contract award to Whitehead Motofides (13 February 1987) for a modified A-184. However, after the change in the administration of the navy, the secretary tried to end the program late in 1987. A total of 34 trials torpedoes were authorized in FY86, and 2000 were planned for FY88–94. However, none were included in the FY89 budget, and the program was killed.

UNGUIDED WEAPONS (MORTARS AND DEPTH CHARGES)

CHILE

Cardoen, the Chilean explosives manufacturer, produces a fast-sinking depth charge, AS-228, externally similar to the U.S.

"tear drop" of World War II. Depth of burst can be set at any of nineteen figures between 100 and 1600 feet.

Cardoen also manufactures miniature antidiver depth charges that can be set to explode between 4 and 12 meters.

CHINA (PRC)

250-mm Rocket Launcher

Although similar in concept to Soviet RBUs, this weapon seems to differ in detail. As employed on board *Luta*-class destroyers, it has twelve tubes: an outer shallow horseshoe layer of seven, with five inside (two on each side, one in the middle). The mount elevates and trains. A five-tube version (the Soviet RBU-1200) is carried by *Jianghu*-, *Jiangdong*-, and *Jiangnan*-class frigates. The tubes resemble those of the Soviet RBU-1200 (see entry below), and this weapon is probably a modification of the Chinese version of the earlier Soviet system.

This weapon became operational in 1972. The Chinese commercial designation is EDS-25A.

FRANCE

◆ 305-mm Mortar

This four-barrel automatic-loading mount is found only on the *Commandant Rivière* class (French and Portuguese Navies). Its ASW projectile weighs 230 kg and has a range of 400–2750 m (507 lbs, 440–3000 yds), and there is also a 100-kg (220-lb) shore-bombardment round with a 6000-m (6600-yd) range. Usually four illuminating rocket rails are mounted on the sides of the mount.

The ASW round is time delay fuzed, the fuze being set inside the launch tube. The barrels fire at the rate of one round/second, reloading through their muzzles (continuous firing rate is one four-round salvo every 25 seconds). Rounds are stowed in four carousels, one feeding each of the four hoists.

Typical weights are 22.2 tons (metric) for the mortar, 18.75 tons for 72 rounds of ammunition, and 4.7 tons of fittings.

Control is by a DUBA 3 attack sonar.

305-mm ASA mortar between bridge and forward gun, *Commandant Rivière*. The mortar is in the loading position. (Stefan Terzibaschitsch)

◆ Depth Charge

The standard air-dropped depth charges, carried by both the carrier-based Alizé and the land-based Atlantique, weigh 175 kg

(386 lbs). The Alizé was originally built to carry a 160-kg (353-lb) depth charge.

ITALY

♦ Menon Mortar (K 113)

This single-barrel automatic-loading 305-mm (12-inch) mortar is fired at a fixed 45 degree elevation. Range is varied (400–900 m [440–980 yds]) by adjusting gas vent valves on three powder chambers. The depth charge weighs 160 kg (353 lbs). The barrel, which is 4.6 m (181 in) long, loads automatically from a 7-round cylinder, firing a 7-round pattern. An earlier three-barrel version, Lancia Bas, is no longer in service. It fired a 21-round pattern in 70 seconds, covering an area of about 80 × 180 yds.

There is no associated depth-determining sonar; ships carrying these mortars carry scanning sonars.

The Italian frigate *Carlo Margottini* shows a single-barrel Menon (K 113) ASW mortar between her No. 2 3-inch gun and her bridge. The guns are predecessors of the OTO-Melara 76 mm/62. The fire-control radar is RTN-10X, and the air-search set is SPS-12; above it is SPQ-2 (at the masthead). (U.S. Naval Institute)

NORWAY

♦ Terne III

This rocket-fired depth charge was introduced about 1960 in its Mk 3 version for the *Oslo*-class frigates and the *Sleipner*-class corvettes. Terne III is now in a Mk 8/10 version.

The Norwegian frigate *Narvik* shows her prominent enclosed Terne III launcher between her forward twin 3-in/50 gun and her bridge. The radar above her bridge is a French DRBV 22, with a Signaal WM-24 above it. The radar aft is a Mk 91 controlling NATO Sea Sparrow missiles. (U.S. Naval Institute)

The system was developed by the Norwegian Defense Research Establishment with assistance from the United States under the Mutual Weapons Development Program. The system uses a stabilized searchlight sonar to search for, detect, and track the target in depth. As fitted to U.S. ships Terne III was triggered by the SQS-31 or -32 search sonar. In this application the sonar had a maximum depth of 1000 ft (maximum depression angle 35 degrees). The U.S. designation for the Terne rocket was Rocket Thrown Depth Charge Mk 3. The launcher was designated Mk 117 Mod 0. The typical salvo pattern consists of weapons 20 yds apart in a line perpendicular to the target's course. Fuzing modes are time and proximity, the latter using a sonic doppler signal to detonate 20 ft from the target (or upon contact). In the time mode, the depth charge explodes 0.3 seconds after water entry.

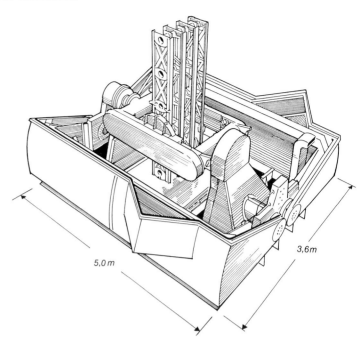

The Terne launcher. (Kongsberg)

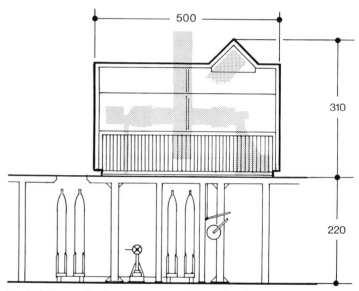

Typical Terne reloading arrangement. (Kongsberg)

For the Mk 3 version, air range at 70 deg F is min 400 and max 920 yds. Corresponding air-flight time is, respectively, 18.2/13.3 seconds. Depth limits are 50 and 700 ft. In U.S. service Terne was part of ASW Weapons System Mk 1. For Mk 8/10, range is 400–5000 m; total weight is 120 kg (explosive charge equivalent to 70 kg); dimensions are 21 cm × 2 m. The launcher has six barrels and elevates to 47–77 degrees to fire. It can be reloaded in 30 seconds, and six salvos are available in ready-use stowage. The deck opening, which is covered by two weather hoods, is 3.6 × 5.0 m.

SWEDEN

♦ Bofors 375-mm Rocket Launcher

This weapon is widely used both in the original four-barrel and in a later two-barrel version. However, this launcher is no longer used by the Swedish Navy, that service having abandoned the use of large surface ships.

The usual installation includes a power-driven four-barrel launcher vertically (for minimum ship impact) power-loaded from below. Initially Bofors offered only the four-tube weapon with either long or short hoist, but in 1967 the company added two types of two-barrel launchers.

Bofors 375-mm Rocket Launcher

	ROCKET TYPES			
	M/50	*Type E*	*Type F*	*Type N*
Weight (charge)	100 kg (220 lb)	107 kg (236 lbs)	107 kg[a] (236 lbs)	80 kg[b] (176 lbs)
Min Range	370 m (405 yds)	670 m (732 yds)	1400 m (1530 yds)	1530 m (1670 yds)
Max Range	875 m (957 yds)	1660 m (1815 yds)	2230 m (2439 yds)	3600 m (3940 yds)
Terminal Sinking Speed	10.9 m/sec (35.8 ft/sec)		10.2 m/sec (33.5 ft/sec)	9.2 m/sec (30.1 ft/sec)

a Total weight of Type F is 242 kg (533 lbs).
b Burster weight. Total weight of Type N is 230 kg (507 lbs).

The associated ERIKA-type ASW rocket has a maximum velocity of 205 m/sec (672 ft/sec). Range (300–3600 m [330–3900 yds]) is adjusted by selection of one of four types of rocket (for varying velocity) and by elevation. Rockets have two concentric (inner and outer) motors, and velocity can be further varied by firing one or both. Depth of burst is set either by time (STIDR) or by acoustic proximity (ZAMBO) fuze; there is also a combined impact (direct acting) and time fuze (STIDAR). The lethal radius of each round is about 15 m (16 yds). Rockets weigh 250 kg (550 lbs); they vary in bursting charge. Types are M/50, Type E (for ERIKA), and Type F (for Flora). The mounting trains and elevates at 18 deg/sec. Elevation limits are +15 and +90 degrees. Rocket characteristics are as shown above.

The long-hoist four-rocket launcher weighs 7.3 tons exclusive of flame guard, and normally eight rockets (2 more salvos) are carried on the rocket table below. Rockets can be fired at intervals of 1 second, and it takes 3 minutes to reload all four tubes. The short-hoist version weighs 7.6 tons, and there is no intermediate hoist stage between magazine and launcher.

The two-tube launcher Type A (3.2 tons, 4 rockets on rocket table) fires M/50, Type E, and Type N rockets. Elevation limits are 0 to +90 degrees, but the launcher can fire only between 0 and 60 degrees. Launcher Type B employed a power hoist that loaded from a rotating loading table, itself replenished by push-button operated trucks, each moving two rockets at a time from storage tables in a magazine. The loading table held eight rockets, but each storage table held another six. This version trained and elevated at 30 deg/sec.

Against a submarine at 100-m (328-ft) depth, times of flight at min/max range for M/50, Type E, Type F, and Type N are, respectively, 14.2/19.4, 16.0/25.3, 19.3/28.5, and 24/36 seconds. Nonrecoverable training rockets are Types L (Lilli, for M/50) and M (Mimmi, for ERIKA) (both 80 mm). The recoverable practice rockets are M/53, Type H, Type K, and Type P for, respectively, M/50, E, F, and N.

A French version, built by Creusot, has six barrels and usually carries six rails for illumination rockets. It is Model 1964, and it can be reloaded in less than 60 seconds. The French had previously used the Swedish four-barrel launcher. Maximum rated range is 1600 m, the French Navy using rounds with 100 kg of explosive. Total system weight, including remote control, is 16,000 kg. The French version weighs 7,700 kg (5,700 kg for the mount proper), typically with another 10,100 kg of ammunition (36 rockets).

The Bofors 375-mm system was originally developed for the Royal Netherlands Navy, which placed it in service in 1954.

◆ Elma

This lightweight ASW mortar is designed to attack midget submarines in Swedish coastal waters. Development began in mid-1983, and first deliveries came a year later. Elma is to arm the Swedish fast patrol craft and *Landsort*-class minesweepers.

The system, produced by FFV and Saab, consists of four nine-barrel mortars firing 100 mm × 267 mm, 4.2-kg (3.9 × 10.5 in, 9.3-lb) shaped-charge contact-fuzed grenades. The grenades sink nose-first, and the shaped charge was developed from that in the Carl Gustav 84-mm antitank rocket. The barrels are mounted at a fixed 30-degree elevation, and range is about 250–300 m (267–330 yds).

In theory hits from these grenades will force a submarine to the surface without sinking it instantly, thus enforcing Swedish sovereignty in the least lethal possible way. The shaped charges should be able to penetrate the inner hull of a double-hulled submarine (at least one of moderate size), and thus a submarine

The ELMA ASW launcher on deck

The French version of the Bofors 375-mm rocket launcher. The flare-launching racks are alongside the rocket tubes. The guns are twin 57 mm/60s, also a French version of a Bofors original. (L & L Van Ginderen)

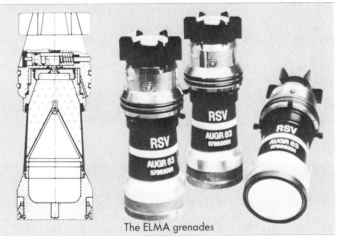

The ELMA grenades

Elma. (FFV)

commander choosing not to surface will have to risk the loss of his craft.

The LLS-920 launcher is nonmagnetic, and it was modified from an earlier design that had been proposed by Saab for launching of Philax chaff grenades. A hand lever adjusts the splay of the tubes, for the desired dispersion. Grenades are launched by charges fitted into the rear of the launch tubes. The firing of a nine-grenade salvo is spread over 2 seconds to limit deck loads.

In January 1985 the system was ordered modified to allow it to engage targets in water only 10 m (33 ft) deep. Later the bombs were further modified so that they armed upon hitting the water, so that they could engage even shallower targets. In addition, Saab modified the system so that it could fire chaff/IR decoys.

◆ Malin

This "incident weapon," announced in 1983, is a magnetic limpet mine that attaches itself to a submarine, emitting a traceable signal until removed. Malin makes tracking easy, and it is a nuisance that cannot be removed unless the submarine surfaces and sends a man out to find the mine on the hull. Malin is reminiscent of the U.S. "clicker" of the 1950s, a magnetized noisemaker that could be dropped on a submarine and that could generally be removed only if the submarine surfaced. Malin was devised to counter supposed Soviet midget submarines operating in Swedish waters.

◆ SAM 204

SA Marine's helicopter-dropped depth charge has a hydrostatic fuze (variable from 15–80 m [49–262 ft] in depth) and a variable charge (50–250 kg [110–550 lbs] of high explosives). The fuze is unusual in being immune to transient pressure waves due to other explosions, so that depth charges can be dropped in salvo. Unlike the fuzes of other air-dropped depth charges, this fuze is set in the cockpit.

USSR

RBU is the Soviet designator (*Raketnaya Bombometnaya Ustanovka*, or Rocket Depth Charge). Former MBU designators reflect an earlier, erroneous Western belief that these weapons were mortars like the British Limbo.

◆ MBU-900

This weapon entered service about 1954 and may survive on board *Kronstadt*-class subchasers transferred abroad. The 25-kg solid-fuel rocket (warhead about 2 kg [55/4.4 lbs]) has a range of about 900 m (980 yds)—hence the designation—and a speed of about Mach 0.5. The Soviets call this system a "jet-propelled depth-charge thrower." It is similar in configuration to the U.S. Mousetrap (Mk 20/22).

This weapon was also manufactured in China.

A Soviet equivalent of Hedgehog, MBU-600, survives on board two Bulgarian Rigas. The Soviets replaced this weapon in their own ships with RBU-2500s; the East Germans used RBU-1200s.

◆ RBU-600

This six-barrelled rocket launcher survives only on board Modified Kotlin-class destroyers. It was formerly designated MBU-4500 (by NATO, not the Soviets). The 30-cm (11.8-in), 90-kg (198-lb) rockets, with 55-kg (121-lb) warheads, are mounted in two vertical rows. Each barrel is about 1.5 m (59 inches) long. The launcher trains to fire all rockets simultaneously.

Range is 600 m (660 yds).

RBU-600 was introduced in 1962–63.

◆ RBU-1000

This launcher employs 30-cm rockets (as in RBU-600), but the barrels are longer, about 1.8 m (71 inches). Presumably the warhead is the same but the rocket is longer, with more propellant, to achieve the greater range reflected in the new designation. The barrels are arranged in a horseshoe, and they load auto-

matically, barrel by barrel, vertically; the barrels fire in sequence. RBU-1000 is in many modern Soviet large combatants (Kara, Kresta-I/II, Kashin, and *Sovremmennyy*; also the large underway replenishment ship *Berezhina*). Range is 1000 m (1100 yds).

Except in the case of the *Berezina*, RBU-1000 is mounted on a ship's quarter. In this position it is more likely an antitorpedo than an antisubmarine weapon, projecting a noisemaking decoy. The Soviets also have a towed noisemaker, but there is always the possibility that a torpedo attracted to the decoy will continue onward to the towing ship. Several navies, therefore, have investigated rocket-thrown noisemakers, which can be projected further from a ship. The only current Western example is under development by the French Navy.

RBU-1000 may also be a barrage antitorpedo weapon, relying on concussion to destroy or disable oncoming homing torpedoes. Again, similar devices have been projected in the past by the U.S. and Royal Navies. In each case, the project has died for two reasons: first, the rate of false alarms was so high that

RBU-1000 launcher. (U.S. Navy)

RBU-1000 rocket launcher on board the cruiser *Kerch*, 1989. This device is mounted on the ship's quarter, firing aft. Kresta-II– and *Sovremennyy*-class ships carry RBU-1000s in similar positions, which would be very reasonable if the weapon had a secondary antitorpedo (e.g., deployed noisemaker) role. The U.S. Navy experimented with a rocket-launched antitorpedo noisemaker, NAE, about 1948, ultimately discarding it because the launcher, Mk 31, presented too many hazards. Towed noisemakers were preferred. Other Soviet classes engaged in ASW lack any equivalent to RBU-1000 aft. Most carry a towed torpedo decoy. (Eric Grove)

excessive weights of antitorpedo charges had to be carried; second, it was never clear just how much explosive was needed to be sure of killing the oncoming weapon. These problems still beset the U.S. SSTD program (see below).

Although the first two *Kirov*-class cruisers lack any RBU-1000, the third ship of the class, *Kalinin*, carries two examples of an RBU-1000 follow-on, with six tubes of greater size.

The earlier NATO designation was MBU-4500A.

◆ RBU-1200

RBU-1200 has two horizontal rows of 25-cm (9.8-in) barrels, three above two. Barrel length is 1.4 m (55 in). The launcher elevates for range but is fixed in train. The 70-kg (154-lb) rockets carry 34-kg (75-lb) warheads. Range is 1200 m (1300 yds). This launcher is found on board T 58 patrol ships, Natya-class minesweepers, and Pauk-class ASW craft. The weapons in Pauks train for loading, but all these weapons fire dead ahead.

A PRC-manufactured equivalent uses 40-kg (88-lb) rockets with 3-kg (6.6-lb) warheads, to achieve a range of about 2000 m (2200 yds). This version is carried on board *Jianghu*- and *Jiangdong*-class frigates, *Hainan*- and *Haiju*-class escorts, *Kronstadt*-class subchasers, and *Shanghai*-class motor gunboats. The latter use suggests that there is an alternative shore-bombardment round.

RBU-1200s on board an SO-1–class subchaser, 1968. (SOVFOTO)

◆ RBU-2500

RBU-2500 rocket launchers on the quarterdeck of a Petya-class ASW corvette. The gun is a twin 76.2. On the foremast, the main radar is Slim Net, with two Square Head IFF interrogators below it, and two Guard Dog ESM radomes below. The mine rails cut into the ship's transom. (SOVFOTO)

RBU-2500 being loaded. (TASS)

This standard Soviet ASW projector of the early 1960s was introduced in 1957–58. RBU-2500 has two horizontal rows of eight 20-cm barrels (21-kg [46-lb] warheads) each, capable of train and elevation. Maximum range is 2500 m (2730 yds).

◆ RBU-6000

This launcher consists of twelve 1.6-m (63-inch) barrels arranged in a horseshoe, automatically loaded when they are elevated into the vertical position, barrel by barrel. The barrels fire in sequence, by pairs. RBU-6000 was introduced in 1960–61 and is very widely used in the Soviet fleet. Maximum range is 6000 m (6600 yds). The old NATO designation was MBU-2500A.

In 1987 the new carrier *Baku* introduced a large new RBU, presumably the replacement for RBU-6000. The new launcher has ten larger-diameter tubes in the familiar horseshoe arrangement. The same launcher appears on board the new cruiser *Kalinin*. No NATO designation has been released.

The carrier *Baku* introduced a new RBU launcher, seen here. The cylindrical vertical launchers immediately abaft the breakwater are for SA-N-9, and the big tubes are for SS-N-12. (U.S. Naval Institute)

RBU-6000 on board a Soviet warship in the Black Sea. (TASS from SOVFOTO)

A Kashin-class destroyer shows an RBU-6000 in upright (loading) position, on the superstructure abaft the saluting gun. (U.S. Naval Institute)

RBU-6000 forward, on board the cruiser *Kerch*, 1989. This is the standard Soviet long-range ahead-thrown ballistic weapon, supplementing missiles such as SS-N-14. (Eric Grove)

♦ **SUW-N-1**

Dimensions: 0.55 × 9.00 m (21.7 × 354 in)
Weight: approx 2300 kg (5070 lbs)
Warhead: nuclear   **Range:** 70,000 m (77,000 yds)

An unguided nuclear ASW missile, SUW-N-1 is a navalized version of the FROG-7 Army weapon. Unlike the U.S. ASROC, SUW-N-1 apparently has no provision for control in range. It is carried only on board the helicopter carrier/cruisers of the *Moskva* and *Kiev* classes, which presumably rely on Hormone helicopters, using dipping sonars, for final target localization. FRAS might be considered the ultimate development of the RBU idea, substituting a single massive explosion for the multiple small explosions of the RBU rounds.

This weapon was formerly called FRAS-1 (Free Rocket Over Sea) in analogy with the land-based FROG (Free Rocket Over Ground).

The details above refer to FROG-7A, which entered service in 1965. References to SUW-N-1 generally give its range as about 16 nm, but the 70 km given for FROG-7A would be more logical if the weapon was adopted to exploit possible convergence-zone performance by the big low-frequency hull sonar of the *Moskva* class. For the land-based weapon, reaction time to fire is typically 15 to 30 minutes.

FROG-7 fires to a fixed range determined by the elevation of its launcher. It is analogous to the old U.S. Honest John nuclear-armed rocket. A later version, which probably is not the one modified as SUW-N-1, has air brakes that open at a preset range.

Recently it has been suggested that SUW-N-1 has an alternative torpedo-carrying version.

♦ **Depth Charges**

Many ships still carry depth charges and throwers, and similar equipment was widely exported to Soviet client states. There are two standard depth charge mortars: BMB-1, now largely gone, was a spade-and-arbor type with the arbor fitting inside the barrel. In BMB-2, the entire depth charge fits within the mortar barrel. All Soviet depth charges are cylindrical. Standard internal and external rack capacity is ten charges per rack.

The standard types are B-1, 4VB, M-1, and 4VM. Characteristics are as follows:

	Dimensions	Weight Total	HE	Settings
B-1	44 × 72 cm	166 kg	135 kg	20–210 m
	(17 × 28 in	366 lbs	298 lbs	66–689 ft)
4VB	46 × 73 cm	163 kg	115 kg	15–210 m
	(18 × 29 in	359 lbs	254 lbs	49–689 ft)
M-1	26 × 43 cm	35 kg	25 kg	10–50 m
	(10 × 17 in	77 lbs	55 lbs	33–164 ft)
4VM	19 × 63 cm	22 kg	16 kg	10–25 m
	(7.5 × 25 in	49 lbs	35 lbs	33–82 ft)

All charges are designed to be launched either by a surface ship or by an airplane.

There is probably also a nuclear depth bomb, carried by helicopters and aircraft as an alternative to a homing torpedo. It is not known whether this bomb is the same weapon used as an FRAS-1 or SSN-15/16 warhead.

UNITED KINGDOM

♦ **Air-Launched Depth Charge Mk 11**

Dimensions: 11 in × 4 ft 7 in (body section is 3 ft 2 in long)
Weight: 320 lbs   **Warhead:** 176 lbs

Mk 11 is one of very few surviving Western air-launched depth charges; the details describe Mod 3, a new modified version with a stronger outer case to withstand high-speed drops and helicopter vibrations. The U.S. Navy abandoned conventional depth charges on the grounds that they had only a very small chance of killing a fast submerged submarine in deep water. However, modern homing weapons are generally unable to deal with a surfaced or near-surfaced submarine. For example,

Mk 11 Depth Charge. (Sperry)

in the Falklands British helicopters attacked the surfaced Argentine submarine *Santa Fe* with Sea Skua radar-homing missiles, but the weapons passed through the submarine's sail without damaging her pressure hull. A pair of Mark 11s forced the submarine aground in sinking state. The advantage of depth charges is that, because they are hydrostatically fuzed, they cannot home accidentally on an irrelevant portion of the submarine. On the other hand, unless the submarine is caught at the surface, the depth charges will almost inevitably miss.

♦ **Nuclear Depth Bombs**

The Royal Navy uses nuclear depth bombs, popularly referred to as Lulus, which is the U.S. code name for Mk 57 (see below); it is not clear whether some or all British depth bombs are of U.S. type. The U.S. weapon was designed as a dual-purpose land-attack bomb and depth bomb. The British weapon may have similar characteristics, making it suitable for dual-purpose ships: that is, the British light carriers may find themselves used either for ASW or for ground support (as in Norway).

The British official reply to those proposing abolition of this weapon is that it is the only certain counter to fast deep-diving submarines, that existing air-dropped torpedoes either lack sufficient performance or else cannot be relied upon, particularly in the presence of countermeasures.

♦ **Limbo**

As originally completed, the Australian frigate *Yarra* shows two Limbo triple-barreled mortars aft. (U.S. Naval Institute)

Limbo is a triple-barreled hand-loaded mortar (Mk 10). Range is varied (between 400 and 1000 yards) by opening gas vents, and the barrels are aimed by a combination of roll and pitch (which is also used to stabilize the mounting). The appropriate spacing between rounds is achieved by a short time delay in firing. The weapon is designed so that its shells always enter the water at the same angle (for any ship's speed): their underwater trajectory is easily predictable, for effective fire control. The shells are time-fuzed, to explode at a preset depth. Each projectile weighs 390 lbs, including 207 lbs of Minol.

The usual installation was two Limbos, to form a pair of triangular patterns above and below the estimated position of the submarine. In many cases, however, one of the two Limbos had to be eliminated to save weight. The total weight, for one Limbo mounting and a magazine holding 17 salvos (51 bombs), is about 35 tons. Lethal range is about 5 yds; however, at ranges up to 50 yds, light fittings will be shattered and pipes cracked. Serious psychological effects can be expected at even greater ranges.

Limbo was the ultimate development of World War II British ahead-thrown ASW weapons, beginning with Hedgehog. The associated sonar is Type 170. In 1988, only four Royal Navy ships retained Limbo.

♦ **Squid**

This triple ahead-thrown mortar (Mk 6) was introduced in 1943. Unlike Hedgehog, Squid fires depth charges that explode at a preset depth. Although Hedgehog entered service first, both Hedgehog and Squid were conceived simultaneously and were developed in parallel, and Squid outlasted Hedgehog in postwar British service. Squid was the first ASW weapon to be fully integrated with a sonar, its depth pistols being set automatically by a depth-determining sonar (usually Type 147 in World War II). Each 394-lb projectile (11.93 × 56.5 inches) carries 207 lbs of Minol II and sinks at about 44 ft/sec. The pattern for each projector is a triangle with 120-ft sides, and the standard installation is a double Squid producing a double layer with charges about 60 ft apart vertically, the hope being that the submarine is sandwiched between them. The mountings are designed to fire dead ahead, but they can tilt about 30 degrees to compensate for roll and yaw, and also for minor course errors. The middle barrel's splash range is set at 270 yds (mortar 9 ft above water; for each additional 3 ft of height, the range increases a yard). The firing interval is 0.28 seconds.

There is also a shallow setting (20 ft), introduced late in World War II, that can be used against a submarine detected either on the surface or just below (e.g., by radar detection of a periscope). In such a case, radar data is fed directly into the sonar's range and bearing indicators.

Squid is still in service on board one Bangladeshi frigate, two Chilean destroyers, two Ghanaian corvettes, and one Iranian and one Pakistani "Battle"-class destroyers. In these ships the projectors are well above the water line, and range is 380 yds.

SQUID. (A. Wetback)

UNITED STATES

♦ **Hedgehog (Projector Mk 10/11)**

This World War II standoff mortar was installed on board all U.S. World War II escorts and on board many U.S. destroyers during the 1950s, and Hedgehog survives on board some units in foreign navies. Existing units are fixed in train and elevation, although the mortar spigots can be rolled back and forth to stabilize them against the roll of the ship and to move the point of impact in train (by up to 25 degrees).

Hedgehog fires 24 impact-fuzed fast-sinking rounds from spigots, the bombs forming an elliptical (Mk 10) or circular (Mk 11) pattern in the water. The standard post–World War II installation is two Mk 10s or Mk 11s that fire together. Typical pattern dimensions for the double Hedgehog: Mk 10, 195 ft wide and 168 ft in range at an average range of 283 yds; Mk 11, 267 ft in diameter at a range of 267 yds. Maximum bomb velocity is 175 ft/sec, and a typical flight time is 10 seconds, plus 18.2 seconds to sink to 200 ft. Total installation weight, including the usual six reload salvos, is 28,720 lbs.

Fixed MK11 Hedgehog on board USS *Cassin Young* (museum ship), 1986. (A. Wetback)

♦ Hedgehog (Projector Mk 15)

The trainable Hedgehog spigot mortar is found on board post-war-built U.S.-designed 173-foot patrol craft in the Turkish and Chilean Navies. In these cases the weapon is controlled on the basis of SQS-17A sonar data. The mortar is stabilized and power-trained; total weight is 17,425 lbs (26,785 lbs including the standard allowance of six patterns). The typical pattern was a 279-ft circle at a range of 265 yds, the bombs taking a total of 29 seconds to reach a depth of 200 ft (10.4 seconds in flight, 18.6 in the water).

Hedgehog Mk 15. (Author)

♦ Mousetrap (Projector Mk 20/22)

Mousetrap is a World War II–designed rocket standoff weapon for small craft, installed on board many patrol craft supplied to U.S. allies through the early 1970s. Rocket propulsion was adopted to avoid the weight penalty (in deck strengthening) associated with Hedgehog. Mark 20 consists of two sets of four rails, which can be folded down to lie flat on deck; Mk 22 has two sets of eight (four rails on top of the original four). The warhead was that of Hedgehog, but with a rocket motor (i.e., with a slower-burning propellant). The sixteen projectiles of a Mark 22 formed a pattern about 80 yds wide at a range of 300 yds. Mousetrap probably survives on board patrol craft built in the United States for foreign aid during the 1950s and early 1960s.

Mousetrap. (National Archives)

♦ Depth Charges

The U.S. Navy currently uses only nuclear depth bombs. The standard nuclear depth bomb is based on the B57 weapon and is designated bomb Mk 101 or "Lulu" (18 × 92.4 in, 1200 lbs). B57 can be used either as a depth bomb or (in a streamlined casing) as a lay-down bomb against land targets. B57 can be delivered both by LAMPS helicopters and by fixed-wing aircraft. Mk 17 is the nuclear depth bomb used as the ASROC warhead (W44 weapon).

Many conventional depth charges formerly used by the U.S. Navy probably survive in Allied navies and, therefore, deserve description here.

The standard air-dropped weapon was the Mk-54 depth bomb (13.8 × 52.5 inches, total weight 354 lbs, charge 250 lbs of Torpex or HBX). A new depth bomb is being developed, in the form of a hydrostatic fuze (SAM-104) for Mk-82 bombs, to give SH-3s and other helicopters the ability to attack surfaced and

U.S.-type streamlined (teardrop) depth charge, on board USS *Cassin Young* (museum ship), 1986. (A. Wetback)

near-surfaced submarines. The SAM-104 program was inspired by the successful depth-bomb attack on the *Santa Fe* in the Falklands (see the U.K.'s Mk 11 above).

The standard shipboard depth charge was the fast-sinking (teardrop-shaped) Mk 9, provided with fins that spun it to stabilize it while it sank. Mk 9 carried 200 lbs of explosive and sank at 22.7 ft/sec (settings 30 to 300 or 600 ft). Overall dimensions were 17.7 × 27.6 in; total weight, 340 lbs. The initial version, Mod 0, sank at 14.5 ft/sec. Mk 14 is an influence-fired version of Mk 9, using an acoustic pistol.

Some earlier cylindrical depth charges (Mk 6) may survive. Dimensions are 17.7 × 27.6 in; total weight is 420 lbs, including 300 lbs of explosive. Burst depth can be set at 30–1000 ft. Sinking rate is about 8.5 ft/sec.

COUNTERMEASURES

Underwater training targets are, in effect, submarine simulators and are, therefore, viable decoys, although they are not generally so described. Some of them are listed in the U.S. systems below.

FRANCE

In 1984 the French Navy funded studies by Lacroix and Thomson-CSF of thrown torpedo countermeasures, with preliminary trials between December 1984 and January 1985. The grenades would be fired from SAGAIE countermeasures launchers (see the AAW section for launcher details). Three alternatives were considered: a pyro-acoustic noisemaker, a gas generator that would produce a bubble curtain to hide a ship (just like an underwater chaff cloud), and an expendable jammer. The bubble cloud would tend both to hide the noise of the ship and also to reduce the ability of an active homing torpedo to detect a ship. The expendable jammer might be used to monitor the approach of the torpedo and communicate with the ship, which in turn would order the jammer to produce noise or deception signals.

As described in 1986, the jammer would be deployable about 20 seconds after alerting, 3800 m (4160 yds) from a ship, to operate for four to eight minutes. As of 1988, Lacroix was designing a 130 × 780 mm (5.1 × 30.7 in) round (50 kg [110 lbs]), operating in less than 3 seconds, at ranges of 10 to 200 m (11 to 220 yds), carrying a 25-liter payload of bubble generators, pyro-acoustic noise sources, or an active decoy that would respond to the torpedo's sonar and emit doppler-shift-compensated false echoes. Safare-Crouzet and Thomson Sintra are developing an electro-acoustic decoy.

Reportedly a self-propelled antitorpedo direct-kill (kinetic-energy) weapon is under consideration.

ISRAEL

◆ ATC-1

Rafael's Acoustic Torpedo Countermeasure (decoy) for the Israeli Navy was announced in 1986; ATC-1 is also usable by merchant ships. Dimensions of the towed body are 30 × 120 cm (12 × 47 in), and it weighs 25 kg (55 lbs); launch and recovery gear weigh 800 kg (1760 lbs), and the electronics cabinet onboard ship weighs another 190 kg (419 lbs), with a 10-kg (22-lb) remote control unit.

UNITED KINGDOM

◆ Bandfish (Amulet)

Dowty's expendable submarine self-protection countermeasure is designed to float in the water while transmitting active pulses to confuse an oncoming active-homing torpedo. Bandfish is programmable before launch. Bandfish, which won a competition against a Marconi countermeasure, is named Amulet in British naval service. Dimensions are 102 × 995 mm (4 × 39.2 in), and weight is 12 kg (26 lbs). Shelf life is 5 years.

◆ Foxer/Unifoxer

These towed torpedo decoys were developed during and immediately after World War II. They emit broad-spectrum noise

and reportedly were retained in storage because they could simulate the noise of, for example, a convoy. They were used as countermeasures by merchant ships and some auxiliaries during the Falklands War.

Derived from a wartime acoustic mine sweep, Foxer consisted of two steel pipes held loosely in a frame. When towed, they hit each other to produce the noise. Escorts towed a string of two Foxers 100 yards apart (this distance was maintained by minesweeping kites), on the theory that the German acoustic torpedo had only a limited field of view and might miss a single decoy. The devices were towed 200 yards astern. Foxer weighed about three tons and could not be towed at speeds over 14 kts. It tended to break up under tow (average lifetime was 25 hours) and to interfere with sonar (asdic). Foxer's production began in July 1943.

It turned out that the German torpedo had a very wide field of view, so a single noisemaker, Unifoxer, could suffice. Unifoxer was issued beginning in February 1944. It was towed 350 yds astern at 10 kts (maximum tow speed was 20 kts), and it covered the 5–50 kHz band.

◆ TALISMAN

This British project for an antitorpedo project later became a joint U.K.-U.S. project.

◆ Type 182/Graseby G738

This tunable narrow-band noisemaker uses a magnetostriction transducer. Wartime experience showed that the broad-band units, such as Unifoxer, jammed escort sonars. It was soon discovered that acoustic homing torpedoes themselves operated on fairly narrow bands; given sufficient intelligence, a noisemaker could be tuned to the appropriate frequency so that it could operate without jamming a sonar operating on a different one. Work began late in 1944, leading to Type 155 (Cheater), a decoy embodying a frequency-modulated (FM) noise source, to be towed 350 yds astern. Although Cheater was not ready in time for wartime use, it appears that the current standard British decoy, Type 182, was an extension of the same basic idea.

The Type-182 fish is 21 inches in diameter and 79 inches long and weighs 163 lbs. Typically two towing drums are arranged side by side at the stern, the decoy itself being handled by davit. The decoy is designed to be streamed 400 m astern. In its present form the decoy can either simulate the noise characteristics of a ship or produce sonar-like pulses (CW) that can jam or confuse an active-homing torpedo. Both modes can be transmitted simultaneously. Shipboard signal generators are duplicated so that the system can continue to operate even in the event one fails.

Graseby G738 is the export version of Type 182, and GI738 is a solid-state version. As of 1983, GI738 had been exported to both Argentina (for MEKO frigates) and India.

Type 182 handling gear on board the frigate *Andromeda*, 1988. Although the "fish" are not shown, their size can be estimated from the size of their handling crane. (A. Wetback)

◆ ATAAC

The DBE Technology (Ferranti subsidiary) antitorpedo acoustic countermeasure is a noisemaker designed to be fired from a standard British or U.S. chaff launcher (there are both 3- and 4-inch versions). ATAAC was announced in 1987. Rounds are programmed immediately before launch, to produce broad-band highpower noise. ATAAC can also be produced in 8-inch diameter form, for ejection from standard submarine countermeasures tubes; and reportedly a 21-inch self-propelled wire-guided version, for firing from submarine torpedo tubes, was developed in 1987–88.

In 1987 it was reported that Graseby was developing a similar software-controlled decoy, actuated directly by a ship's sonar.

UNITED STATES

◆ ADC Mk 2

Acoustic Device, Countermeasure, produced by Emerson, was introduced in 1978. By 1987, when ADC was first shown publicly, over 2800 had been manufactured. It uses a small propeller to hover, emitting signals after being ejected. Diameter is 8 cm (3.1 inches).

◆ CSA Mk 1

Librascope's Countermeasure Set, Acoustic, is an externally mounted submarine-sonar countermeasure launcher, apparently for strategic submarines.

◆ Fanfare (T.Mk 6)

The standard U.S. towed torpedo decoy of the 1950s and 1960s is fitted on board FRAM destroyers. The characteristic installation includes a small spray shield protecting the towing winch. Two decoys are provided per installation. In U.S. service, Fanfare was replaced by Nixie, but many Fanfares probably remain in service in other navies.

Fanfare replaced the U.S. wartime FXR.

Fanfare on board the destroyer *Cassin Young*, showing the dual winches, each with its fish, and the spare fish between. (A. Wetback)

◆ Nixie (SLQ-25)/SLQ-36

This towed noisemaker, made by Aerojet, was first produced in 1974. A total of 180 have been procured for the U.S. Navy, and many have been exported. The usual installation is a pair of winches with two Nixies, the decoys trailing through ports in the transom. They do not generally operate together; rather, one is available if a torpedo destroys the other. Nixie is about half the size and weight of Type 182; approximate towed body dimensions are 6 × 31 inches.

SLQ-36 is a combined torpedo countermeasure, an improved Nixie.

◆ SLQ-33

SLQ-33 is a towed acoustic simulator for escort battle groups. SLQ-33 is used for cover and deception and is van-mounted. Specifications for a product-improved version were completed in FY87.

◆ SLR-24

This passive acoustic-threat sensor is a torpedo detector designed as part of the new (ca. 1985) U.S. antitorpedo program. SLR-24 would trigger either defensive maneuvers or an antitorpedo weapon, perhaps a converted torpedo.

◆ SSTD

Surface Ship Torpedo Defense is the current U.S.-British program. The two competing consortia are: General Electric, Honeywell, Marconi, Plessey; and AT&T, Librascope, Dowty, Ferranti. No details have been released, but logos displayed at the U.S. Navy League show in 1989 show a surface ship launching an undefined single object at an incoming threat torpedo. That representation suggests that SSTD will employ a homing antitorpedo weapon. Such a development, which is presumably possible with modern forms of torpedo homing, would solve a major problem of earlier antitorpedo weapons, the excessive amount of ordnance needed to deal with each incoming torpedo. The other central problem, a drastic reduction in the false-alarm rate, might be solved by better on-board signal processing. The problem remains difficult, particularly in the face of intense sea noise in rough weather. On the other hand, beyond some particular sea-state, the sea noise will make passive homing against surface ships virtually impossible, and the roughness of the sea will probably make wake-seeking torpedoes ineffective.

SSTD follows several false starts. Renewed interest in hard-kill torpedo countermeasures was inspired by the appearance of the big Soviet wake-following torpedo (Type 65), which would not respond to conventional noisemakers, no matter how sophisticated. By 1987, two separate programs, Antiship Torpedo Defense and Surface Ship Torpedo Defense, had both died. Under the Nunn Amendment, effort shifted to a joint U.S.-U.K. program, SSTD.

◆ WLR-9A/9B/12/17

These acoustic intercept receivers (AIRs) for submarines are manufactured by Norden. The system typically consists of a sail-mounted sonar hydrophone, a receiver-processor, and a display group. WLR-9A provides some localization, intercepting low- and high-band signals of active sonars. The receiver-processor obtains frequency, bearing, and signal strength. WLR-9A is also used to detect enemy homing torpedoes using active seekers. Work on these systems began in the late 1960s. The current versions are automatic, presenting both CRT (raster scan) and digital readouts and identifying threats by comparison with libraries of ship, submarine, and torpedo sonars. These versions may also detect important transients such as those associated with torpedo and other weapon firings. Part of SAWS, the Submarine Acoustic Warfare System, which also includes submarine-launched countermeasures.

WLR-5 was an earlier acoustic intercept receiver.

◆ Mk 30

Mk 30 is a torpedo-sized acoustic target used primarily to test deep-diving torpedoes, but it is also usable, in theory, as a particularly realistic decoy. Mk 30 is capable of about 30 kts. Mk 30 is the current standard U.S. submarine simulator, to be used as a target. Its characteristics suggest what sort of performance a torpedo-sized decoy can provide, although there has never been any indication that Mk 30 itself is considered a viable decoy (it would displace a torpedo, and submarines have too little torpedo stowage to afford such a decoy). Manufactured by Goodyear, Mk 30 was approved for service use in 1978, with a procurement objective of 60 units by FY86 (for 2400 runs per year). Mk 30 operates at the three main underwater ranges:

Barking Sands in Hawaii, AUTEC in the Bahamas, and the Atlantic Fleet range at St. Croix in the Virgin Islands.

The target is 21 inches in diameter and 20 feet (245 inches) long, weighing 2700 lbs; it can be launched from a surface ship or helicopter. Mk 30 tows a 300-foot array consisting of a hydrophone, a projector (to simulate submarine sounds), and a magnetic source (to trigger MAD gear). Speed is 7 kts (endurance 4 hours) to 30 kts (endurance 30 minutes), and operating depth is 25–2000 ft. Turn rate is 0.25–8 deg/sec, depending on speed; and the target can climb at 2–20 degrees.

A new target is being developed to test the new generation of high-performance torpedoes (ADCAP and Mk 50). The new Fast/Deep Prototype Target will be a Mk 48 shell and structure with an advanced SCEPS power plant.

◆ EMATT (Mk 39)

Expendable Mobile ASW Training Target is an air- or ship-launched submarine simulator manufactured by Sippican for the Naval Sea Systems Command. The vehicle is the size of an A-size sonobuoy ($4\frac{7}{8} \times 36$ in) and weighs 21.1 lbs. Run speed is 10 kts (duration 3 hours), and maximum depth is 700 ft. EMATT acts as an echo reporter for active sonars, produces signals for passive sonars, and acts as a transponder for the Mk-46 torpedo. EMATT can also deploy a 100-foot wire to produce a recognizable MAD signature. This target replaces an earlier Mk 38.

◆ SPAT

Self-Propelled Acoustic Target is a torpedo-sized submarine simulator manufactured by Gould. Although normally considered a training device, SPAT might also be considered a long-lived decoy. The vehicle carries an echo repeater (4–85 kHz, nominal target strength 25 dB, towed on a 12-m coaxial cable) and a broad-band noise generator simulating a submarine (800 Hz–85 kHz). SPAT operates for two hours. Maximum speed is 11–13 kts (for up to 10 minutes), and cruising speed is 6–8 kts. Dimensions are 10×129 in; weight is 330 lbs; depth limits are 16–787 ft; maximum dive/climb angle is 15 deg.

SPAT was in production about 1980. It was based in part on experience with an earlier submarine countermeasure, the BLQ-2 beacon of the 1950s.

◆ Mobile Submarine Simulators (MOSS)

MOSS are submarine decoys; Gould manufactures Mks 57 and 70. In 1984 an Advanced Submarine Countermeasure was under competition, to replace MOSS. The advanced device was to be battery powered and to have a quarter the volume of a MOSS; and the new countermeasure would be carried externally rather than projected through a countermeasures tube.

MOSS Mk 70 is a relatively large decoy; the one published photograph suggests a diameter of about 10 in. All U.S. ballistic-missile submarines are fitted with four large-diameter countermeasures tubes on each side, just below the sail, presumably to launch MOSS. Attack submarines probably swim it from their torpedo tubes.

MINE WARFARE

This section includes both mines (antiship and antisubmarine) and mine countermeasures. Mines in current service include some types developed as long ago as World War I, and the influence explosion mechanisms developed during World War II still seem to dominate the field. It is difficult to say which old types remain in service; for example, the United States reportedly distributed Mk-6 moored antenna mines to many Allies after World War II.

The major current mine mechanisms are contact, acoustic, magnetic, and pressure, although others may exist. The simplest contact mines are set off by an electric current produced when a ship breaks open the batteries formed in the "horns" of the mine. The U.S. Mk 6 of World War I was a more sophisticated alternative: a ship touching or nearing an antenna formed one element of a simple battery, closing a firing circuit. The advantage of the antenna, which is a very primitive application of the underwater electric potential (UEP) principle, is that the target need not actually touch the mine, so that the mine's lethal radius is increased.

The other major mine types are described as influence weapons, exploding at a distance from a ship. Influence mines on the seabed were the first weapons attacking ships from under the keel.

An acoustic mine listens for the characteristic signature of its target. World War II acoustic mines simply listened for an increase in broad-band sound, but it should be possible to set a modern acoustic mine for a particular characteristic frequency or set of frequencies.

Magnetic mines detect the magnetism of a ship's steel. The early magnetic mines had to rest on the sea bottom, but after World War II the U.S. Navy developed a new three-axis magnetometer that could compensate for the tidal movement of a moored mine.

Pressure mines respond to the decrease in water pressure under a ship. Such mines necessarily lie on the bottom, and they must be protected against mistaking the change due to the turn of the tide for the change due to the passage of a ship. One solution is to combine the pressure sensor with one or more sensors of the target's characteristics (e.g., acoustic or magnetic), so as to eliminate the problem.

Contact mines must generally be moored. The main limitation on their design is the requirement that the combination of mine body and mooring chain be buoyant. The weight of the mooring chain limits the potential weight of explosive. For example, some have suggested that Iranian contact (moored) mines in the Persian Gulf often broke their moorings because the Iranians tried to load them too heavily and used chain that was too weak. Acoustic and magnetic mines may be moored, or they may sit on the bottom. Generally a bottom mine can be effective in depths as great as 80 feet. Presumably mines can lie in greater depths if they are intended to damage very large merchant ships, which may draw that much water.

There is a difference between a mine's case depth and laying depth. Case depth is the depth at which the mine itself lies or floats. A floating mine will have an anchor at a far greater depth, which will be the laying depth.

Pressure mines are inevitably bottom mines, since they measure the absolute drop in pressure associated with the difference between water depth and the depth of water under a ship. Thus they are only an inshore hazard.

For very deep water, there is a further category, the rising mine. The mine case may lie close to the bottom, but when it detects a passing ship or submarine it launches a projectile or torpedo. The U.S. Captor (Mk 60) is the best known, but not the only, example. Depending upon the speed and endurance of the projectile, a rising mine may be laid in extremely deep water. Moreover, it may be able to hit a target at some distance. That capability requires a long-range sensor unlike that used in any other mine category.

The only available sensor is an acoustic one. A bottom mine must rely on passive detection of its target, recognizing the target's signature. The mine then uses an active acoustic sensor for fire control. In principle, then, deep rising mines can generally be countered either by silencing (which denies them the initial detection) or by some form of active deception (which ruins the fire-control solution). However, the mine, even if it is quite deep, is probably functioning far closer to its target (e.g., within about a thousand feet) than any sonar (and far closer than virtually any sonobuoy), so the mine may be able to rely on a high-frequency signature that is lost at normal ASW ranges.

As an example of such a mine, Captor relies on a long-range passive sonar for initial detection and then on a long-range active sonar for target tracking. Presumably, this mine requires the long-range initial detection for two reasons. First, there is a substantial time lag between the weapon's launch and the weapon's arrival near the target, so the target has to be detected early. Second, because the torpedo can maneuver as it rises, the mine can engage fairly distant targets, if it can detect them. In contrast, an unguided rocket mine (such as the abortive U.S. PRAM or, probably, the Soviet Cluster Bay/Gulf) travels straight up. Its required detection range is set by the time to rise and by the decision time required to classify the target. Such a weapon cannot rely on any kind of impact fuze because the projectile may be near, but not at, the target. Instead, the active sonar is probably used to fuze the projectile.

A rising mine's case depth is probably fixed by the crush depths of the mechanism and the projectile. In really deep water, then, the mine must be moored, and its case must be buoyant enough to support a considerable weight of cable. Consequently, the mine must be large, and the laying rate will be limited. In contrast, in shallower water, say down to a thousand feet or more, the mine case might well lie on the bottom, unsweepable by mechanical means (i.e., by any device that would cut the mooring cable). Very deep minehunting sonars, such as are now being developed, are presumably intended to detect just such bottom mines.

The effect of the existence of deep-water rising mines is to extend the mineable area of the world significantly. Countermeasures are very expensive because the mine may cover a substantial lethal area (the projectile may maneuver to one side or the other) and because any attempt to destroy mines or mine mooring requires very deep operations. Examples of such expensive countermeasures probably include not only the British EDATS but also the U.S. Mine Neutralization System. However, because bottom mines must use passive acoustic detectors, these mines are (at least in theory) subject to sweep by acoustic devices simulating target signatures.

There are several mine countermeasures, in two categories. One is self-protection, for a ship passing through an area that may be mined. The other is mine clearance, either sweeping (wholesale mine neutralization) or minehunting. In the latter, the bottom is examined foot by foot, and suspicious objects are examined and, if they are mines, destroyed individually. Sweeping means either cutting mine-mooring cables (and thus bringing the mines to the surface, where they can be destroyed by small-arms fire) or providing a false signature that causes influence mines to detonate without damaging real targets. Minehunting is necessary because some mines, such as pressure types, cannot be induced to explode by anything short of a real ship, since the signatures in question cannot be duplicated.

When virtually all mines were contact weapons, the chief self-protection measure was the paravane, a towed float whose wire pushed moored mines away from the ship. Paravanes were standard in both world wars but were largely abandoned with the advent of large bow sonar domes (which paravanes could damage) and also with the advent of influence mines (which paravanes could not counter). The only modern self-protection measures are silencing (against acoustic mines) and degaussing (in effect, magnetic silencing). The only protection against pressure mines is to move so slowly that the pressure change is not quick enough to detonate the mine. In World War II, for example, tables were constructed to show appropriate speeds for ships of particular tonnages.

Most current mine-countermeasures work goes into sweeping and hunting. Moored mines may be swept by means of a cable carrying small explosive-driven cutters. Moored or bottom acoustic and magnetic mines are generally swept by towed acoustic or magnetic noisemakers. Mine designers have produced two counter-countermeasures. One is a ship counter, which allows several potential targets to pass before the mine is armed. The ship counter was invented by the Germans during World War II, and by 1944 many mines could let at least 15 targets pass before exploding. In theory, a counter protects the mine against sweepers accompanying a high-value target. A second counter-countermeasure is arming delay, which appears in many of the mine descriptions below. The presence of delay-armed mines forces influence sweepers to go back over a field. This idea also applies to moored mines, for which the mine's release from its anchor can be delayed.

Many current mines are described as microprocessor-controlled. They can be programmed to seek particular ship signatures, are extended in space (i.e., in time, as the ship passes over), and so will force the minesweeper to use more and more complex ship simulators. The British Sea Serpent and the French Sterne I exemplify the counters to this type of mine. Compared to earlier hard-wired mine sensors, a microprocessor can very easily be reset to any desired set of target characteristics or counter-countermeasures.

Pressure mines cannot easily be swept. If they distinguish between the turn of the tide and a ship by using a known auxiliary (acoustic or magnetic) sensor, they should be vulnerable to an appropriate towed noisemaker. However, that relatively desperate measure is much dependent on detailed knowledge of the threat mine. In any case, a pure pressure mine can be designed to avoid detonating at the turn of the tide.

Minehunting employs a high-definition (very high frequency) sonar to identify suspicious objects, and then some means of examining and destroying those objects. The simplest such system employs divers, but modern Western navies tend to employ remotely controlled submersibles equipped with even higher definition sonar and underwater television (such as PAP 104 or the Honeywell MNS) instead. The great problem of hunting is that most harbor bottoms are covered by the detritus of industry (cars, refrigerators, bodies in concrete, etc.), much of it vaguely resembling mines (which need not be neatly packaged as cylinders with markings like "Mine—do not handle"). The very high false-target rate explains the need to examine each suspicious object, rather than destroying it immediately from the minehunter. To the extent that friendly harbors must be protected against mining, detailed bottom surveys of the routes merchant ships are expected to take can be used for comparison, to find out which suspicious objects are new.

Even then, there is a serious problem in silty harbors, as mines dropped on the bottom tend to bury themselves. Depending on their trigger mechanisms, they may still be lethal in that state. This problem probably applies more to magnetic than to other mine mechanisms.

Mine-countermeasures vessels tend to be small because their small signatures tend not to set off influence mines and because sweepers and hunters are needed in substantial numbers and, therefore, cannot be allowed to grow too expensive. If they are built on conventional lines, then, these craft are relatively slow. They may be effective in home waters, but they cannot easily deploy with the fleet. If territorial waters are extensive, moreover, and if the sweepers are expensive (because they have to be sophisticated), then their low speed may be a problem even at home. Norway faces this problem, for example, and it explains current Norwegian interest in surface-effect minesweepers. An alternative is to develop a mine-countermeasure suite that can be fitted to extemporized craft of opportunity, but it seems less and less likely that any such craft will be quiet enough (acoustically or magnetically) to avoid setting off special antisweeper inshore weapons. One alternative, adopted by the U.S. Navy, is the helicopter sweeper or hunter. Helicopters can be carried abroad with the fleet, and they can tow special sweeps or hunting sonars. They are clearly limited, but they make up for that limitation with extreme mobility. Experience in the Persian Gulf seems to show that conventional surface sweepers and hunters are, of course, still essential.

Small remotely controlled submersibles are commonly used by the offshore oil drilling industry. Most of these devices may be too small to carry useful mine-disposal charges (or, for that matter, useful mine-classification sensors), but these submersibles may be usable under mobilization conditions. In 1985, Gould marketed one such vehicle, the Sea Rover, in the United States; it was small enough to travel as excess luggage on most airlines. The vehicle itself weighed 45 to 55 lbs.

Many mines of pre– or World War II origin probably remain. The section that follows lists only the older Soviet and U.S. weapons, but before World War II France (Breguet and Sauter-Harle), Norway, and Sweden all produced a variety of contact and, in some cases, influence mines. Some probably still exist. Vickers produced a variety of commerical mines, some of which were reported in Argentine service during the Falklands War. Some wartime German mines may have survived, as German wartime coast-defense guns have. Similarly, Japanese contact mines may have survived in the Far East. The key point is that mines, particularly contact mines, do not become obsolete. No details of which weapons are used by which navies are available. Similarly, no details of controlled mines, used for harbor defense, have appeared, apart from the data below concerning the U.S. Mk 51. It is unlikely to be unique. Finally, U.S. mine exports almost certainly included plans and production assistance, so that various countries have manufactured U.S. mines (perhaps in modified form) under local designations.

The United States supplied specially converted minelayers (and, presumably, mines) to Denmark, Greece, Norway, and Turkey during the mid-1950s, before the Mk-52 series entered full production. The principal available surface-laid mines were, then, probably Mk 6, Mk 16, and Mk 18.

MINES

Navies rarely indicate their own capacity for naval mine warfare. In 1988 the U.S. Office of Naval Intelligence stated that 21 countries could deploy mines capable of damaging major warships. In the Falklands, Argentina was credited with a serious mining capability, although it appears that she did not make use of it. In the past, the United States has provided allies near strategic straits with minelaying ships and, presumably, with U.S. mines.

FRANCE

The principal prewar surface-laid mines were all contact types: the Breguet B4, B4M, and B5B, and the Sauter-Harle H5, H5P, and H6. The Breguets were relatively small horned mines, with total weights of 1168 lbs (B4/B4M) and 2535 lbs (B5); explosive weights were, respectively, 176 and 485 lbs. B5B was an antenna ASW mine analogous to the U.S. Mk 6, with 25-m upper and 30-m lower antennae. These mines entered service in the late 1930s, the mines lying at a depth of 90 m (about 300 ft) with alternative water depths (mooring depths) of 225, 300, or 400 m (respectively, about 740, 1000, and 1310 feet). The Sauter-Harles were antiship mines. H5 and H5P were horned mines (4 horns) with a total weight of about 2550 lbs (485 lbs of TNT). Some versions had antennae. These older mines were introduced in 1928. Prewar versions, which may have been experimental, were designed for greater depths (e.g., H5UM1, moored in about 3000 ft of water to float at 600 ft (1935)). H6 was a horned mine with a heavier explosive charge (about 660 lbs of TNT). These mines apparently survived World War II, and some probably still exist.

Postwar, the French Navy developed a wartime German project for a bottom mine triggered by cosmic radiation. In principle, the layer of water over the mine reduced the level of radiation by an amount proportional to its depth. The water

under a ship would be less, so the radiation level would rise and the mine would be triggered. In theory, such operation would be analogous to that of a pressure mine. In practice, the problem was that levels of cosmic radiation fluctuated naturally, so the mine had to use an array of detectors to make instantaneous comparisons between the average radiation level and that immediately overhead. This concept was reportedly the main French mine research project of the mid-1950s; by that time the U.S. Navy had given up on the idea (which had been quite exciting about five years earlier). No such mine appears to have entered service, and it seems likely that the cosmic-ray mine fell victim to the massive French research budget cuts associated with the Algerian War. The types described below were probably the only fruits of later French work.

◆ FG 29

FG 29 uses multi-influence sensors and is designed for localized laying from submarine torpedo tubes. Dimensions are 52 cm × 3 m, and weight is 1000 kg (600 kg of tritonal explosive). FG 29 can operate down to 300 m in depth. FG 29 has an arming delay, and it is an antisweep device, explosion-resistant to defeat explosion-based minesweeping. Fuzing is magnetic, acoustic, or pressure. This mine is very sensitive, so it can be used against ships with very low magnetic moments. The acoustic sensor operates on several low-frequency channels. The main contractor is DCN; Thomson-Sintra makes the sensors. The development of FG 29 began in the early 1970s, and the first batch was delivered to the French Navy in 1988.

◆ TSM 3510 (MCC 23)

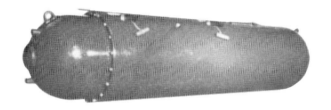

MCC 23 (above) and MCT 15 (below). (Thomson Sintra)

This magnetic/acoustic ground mine is designed to be triggered by any ship displacing over 1000 tons. TSM 3510 can be launched from a torpedo tube, so the diameter is 533.4 or 550 mm (21 or 21.7 in); the length is 2.525 m (99.4 in). Weight is 850 kg, including a 530-kg warhead (1873/1168 lbs). The mine can be set to wait for up to 30 days before arming, and there is a ship counter. Thomson Sintra is the manufacturer. An earlier version (ca. 1978) was 530 × 2368 mm (20.9 × 93.2 in), with a 650-kg (1432-lb) warhead.

There are also practice mines: a submarine-laid mine, EP 30C (533.4 mm × 3 m, 900 kg [21 × 118 in, 1984 lbs]), which can be laid in depths of 10–50 m; and sweeper/laying training mines, ED 28B (TSM 3500) and MCED 23 (TSM 3517)/MCEM 23 (TSM 3515). The latter is intended to train minelayers, and it lacks the magnetic and acoustic detonator scoring system of the former. ED 28 is laid by surface vessels.

Thomson-CSF began work on mines in the late 1960s, beginning with exercise mines for surface ships and submarines.

◆ TSM 3530 (MCT 15)

TSM 3530 is an air-dropped, parachute-retarded mine. Dimensions are 1.2 (diameter) × 1.1 m (47.2 × 43.3 in); weight is 1500 kg, including a 1000-kg warhead (3306/2204 lbs). Fuzing is acoustic/magnetic. 3530 is almost semispherical in shape. Like MCC 23, 3530 arms after a clock-set delay. Thomson Sintra is the manufacturer.

GERMANY (WEST)

The postwar German Navy used stocks of wartime and postwar mines, presumably of U.S. and British origin. A new generation of ground and moored mines (and antisweep devices) was developed under a Seemine 65 program. It resulted in the FG 1 described below. Germany and Denmark collaborated in two more recent programs, Seegrundmine 80 (SGM 80) and Seemine Anti-Invasion (SAI).

German World War II mines were all designated by letters, the first two indicating the function and the third the type within that category. The EM series (e.g., EMC) were horned contact mines, EMC and EMD being the most common. The KM series were anti-invasion mines, typically with a single horn protruding. RM indicated a controlled mine. UM mines were ASW contact weapons. There were also mines for torpedo-tube laying (MT and TM series) and for air laying (BM and LM series), but these are unlikely to have been suited to the requirements of current users. Likely users of German prewar and World War II mines would include Finland (which was a German ally during much of World War II, and which received little military hardware postwar), Spain (which would have received considerable aid during the civil war and afterward, and which operated some German submarines, torpedo boats, and aircraft), and Yugoslavia (which retains a few German coast-defense guns).

◆ FG 1

This submarine-launched ground mine is built of nonmagnetic material, with a 535-kg (1179-lb) warhead. Dimensions are 534 mm × 2310 mm: 710 mm for the control section, 1600 mm for the charge section (21 × 91 in: 28 in/63 in). Total weight is 770.5 kg (1698 lbs). Maximum effective depth is 60 m (197 ft). FG 1 is built by the Faun-Werke.

◆ SAI

Seemine Anti-Invasion, developed by Germany and Denmark, is laid by landing craft. Procurement began in 1982.

◆ SGM 80/IGM 10

This cylindrical ground mine was developed by Dornier, for launch from a cradle on board a fast attack craft. SGM 80 was part of a German-Danish program, and procurement began in 1984.

IGM 10 is an SGM 80 derivative, to be laid by submarines with exterior mine belts. IGM 10 can be laid in deep water. It uses a programmable microprocessor with acoustic (low and audio frequency), magnetic, pressure, or a combination of signatures. IGM 10 can be programmed immediately before leaving the ammunition depot.

SGM 80. (Dornier)

ITALY

The principal mine manufacturer, Misar, was formed in 1977 by a group of technicians who joined the Italian SEI (Societa Esplosivi Industriali) and the French SAEPC (Société Anonyme d'Explosifs et des Produits Chimiques) to develop and sell both naval and land mines.

◆ EPR Series

Tecnovar's anti-invasion mines are essentially flat disks (like land antitank mines) in form. The number indicates the weight of explosive, 1.2, 3.6, or 6 kg (e.g., EPR 3.6). Fuzing is electronic.

These mines were announced about 1981.

An EPR 2.5 limpet mine advertised in 1984 weighed about 6 kg (13 lbs) and carried a 2.5-kg (5.5-lb) charge. EPR 2.5 was described as an electronic underwater mine, which might be laid by aircraft or else magnetically/mechanically attached to the hull of a ship. Dimensions: 26-cm diameter × 9-cm height (10.2 × 3.5 in). In tests, EPR 2.5 blew a 250-mm (9.8-in) diameter hole in a steel plate 30 mm (1.2 in) thick.

◆ MAL/17 and MAS/22

Tecnovar's anti-invasion mine was advertised in 1984. MAL/17 is a contact mine with three horns in its top and a stabilizer extending down from its spherical body. Total weight is 22 kg, and it carries a 17-kg charge (48.5/37.5 lbs). Dimensions: 38-cm diameter, 110-cm height, including stabilizer (15 in × 4.3 in). Case depth is about 3 m (10 ft).

MAS/22 is an alternative version of the same mine, with three sharp stakes at its bottom so that it can be driven into a beach

Tecnovar mines (left to right): MAL/17, MAS/22, and EPR 2.5. (Tecnovar)

(just below the water line) or into a river bed. Total weight is about 22 kg, and charge weight is about 17 kg. MAS/22 is hemispherical (virtually identical to the upper hemisphere of MAL/17), with a diameter of 38 cm and a height (including spikes) of 63 cm (24.8 in).

◆ MANTA

Misar's anti-invasion (shallow water) mine, for depths of 2.5–100 m (8–330 ft), has an effective lifetime of over a year. It uses magnetic and acoustic fuzes and can be laid by ships, helicopters, or frogmen. The warhead is 140 kg of TNT or 170 kg of HBX-3 (309 or 375 lbs). Dimensions: diameter 980 mm, height 470 mm (38.6 × 18.5 in). Total weight is about 220 kg or 240 kg depending on loading (485 or 529 lbs). The form of the casing is intended both to avoid movement due to currents and to avoid visual detection.

Manta, with MRP-80 in the background. (Misar)

◆ MR-80/MP-80/MRP

Misar's antiship and antisubmarine mine is usable in depths from 5 m to 300 m (15–100 ft), with a maximum transport depth of 500 m (1640 ft) and a submerged life of up to two years. There are three versions, A, B, and C. Characteristics are as follows:

	A	B	C
Dimensions	533 × 1650 mm (21 × 65 in)	533 × 2096 mm (21 × 83 in)	533 × 2750 mm (21 × 108 in)
Total Weight	656 kg (1446 lbs)	820 kg (1807 lbs)	1070 kg (2358 lbs)
Explosive	460 kg (1014 lbs)	630 kg (1389 lbs)	870 kg (1917 lbs)

Available fuzes are magnetic, pressure, and acoustic (high or low frequency), and they can be used in any desired combination. Arming and neutralization delays can be set at up to 999 days, for a useful life of 500–1000 days. MR-80 can be laid by torpedo tube but also by aircraft or surface ship. The casing is made of fiberglass impregnated with epoxy resin, carrying explosives in the nose and the controls in the tail.

Reportedly MR-80 has been sold to several Middle East countries.

MP-80/MRP is a similar mine with an updated firing mechanism and a better (digital) target recognition device. This mine has four microprocessors, which compare the target's signature (magnetic, pressure, and/or acoustic) with entries in a threat library: thus, mines can almost be assigned to particular targets. MP-80 is the Italian Navy/NATO version; MRP, with software not subject to NATO restrictions, is the export version (Misar's Advanced General-Purpose Sea Mine).

The initial MR-80/1, announced in 1978, was the first Misar mine. It could be laid in water 10–200 m (33–660 ft) deep. In 1978 it was being evaluated by the Italian Navy, probably as an alternative to the Valtec SM 600; it seems to have been the successful competitor.

About 1986, at the request of the Italian Navy, Misar conducted a feasibility study of the modernization of Italian stocks of U.S. mines. The conclusion, that the mines themselves were in good condition but that their firing mechanisms needed replacement, led the company to study the export market for such modernization. Presumably this program competes with the British Aerospace modernization programs described under the United Kingdom entries below.

In mid-1985 Misar signed an agreement with Aerojet to market the U.S. Mk-65 Quickstrike mine with a Misar Target Detection Device (TDD) related to that of the MP-80/MRP.

◆ SB-81

Misar's mechanical mine for coast defense, also usable as a depth charge, was displayed in 1980.

◆ SB-MV

Misar's anti-invasion mine with a shaped-charge warhead was displayed in 1980.

◆ TAR 6/TAR 16

These multicharge (string) ASW mines are made by Whitehead. TAR 6 can be used against surface targets and is intended to bar passage from the surface down to a depth as great as 820 ft. A typical barrier consists of four rows of mines carrying their vertical strings of charges at different depths; the numbers in TAR 6 and 16 are the number of charges. Each charge carries three switch (not chemical) horns. Because the detonation of any one charge in the string generally sets off the others, a single string cannot effectively cover the entire depth to be blocked.

TAR 6 consists of a buoy, itself carrying a charge, five cylindrical charges, and an anchor, the charges being spaced about 13 ft apart. Thus a buoy at a depth of 16 ft carries a string that reaches down to 92 ft. The buoy carries 110 lbs of explosives, and each cylinder carries another 55 lbs. TAR 16 is similar, except that it has more charges and its buoy is not explosive. TAR 16 covers a total length of 225 ft, the buoy floating 39 ft above the shallowest charge. A typical field might consist of a row of TAR 6s, their deepest charges at 92 ft, then a row of TAR 16s, with buoys at 65 ft and charges extending down to 330 ft, then another row of TAR 16s (buoys at 65 ft, but shallowest charges at 348 ft and deepest at 572 ft), and then a third row of TAR 16s (buoy at 65 ft, charges between 590 and 812 ft).

Typical assembled dimensions of TAR 6 are 6 ft 5.5 in (high) × 3 ft 6 in (wide) × 3 ft 11 in. Weight is 2435 lbs. Analogous figures for TAR 16 are 7 ft 6.5 in × 3 ft 8 in × 3 ft 11 in and 3240 lbs. TAR 16 can be laid in water depths as great as 1520 ft.

TAR means *Torpedine Antisom Rosario*, or antisubmarine rosary mine. It was conceived in the early 1950s, and by October 1954 test fields had been planted in depths as great as 400 ft.

◆ VS-RM-22 and -30

Valtec's anti-invasion or shallow-water mines are exploded by trip-wire. The number indicates the weight in kg.

◆ VS-SM-600

Valtec's ground mine can be laid in water 10 to 150 m deep (33 to 490 ft) by a surface ship, a submarine, or an airplane. The four sensors are magnetic, high-frequency acoustic, low-frequency acoustic, and pressure. There are also a ship counter, an antitamper device, and a long arming delay. The mine can be remotely controlled. Dimensions are 533 mm × 2.75 m (21 × 108 in). Weight is 780 kg (1719 lbs), with a 600-kg (1322-lb) charge.

◆ VS-SS-22 and -30

VS-SS-22, a limpet mine made by Valtec, is intended to sink ships of up to 400 tons and to disable ships up to four times that size. -22 carries about 12 kg of RDX/A10 explosive. The mine is attached to its target by two rubber suckers, by two pins driven in by rivet guns, or by a removable clamp. Dimensions are 200 × 650 × 360 mm (7.9 × 25.6 × 14.2 in). Weight is 20 kg, including 10 kg of explosives (44/22 lbs), and the standard arming delay is 15 minutes, after which antihandling devices switch on. The explosion delay can be between one and ten hours.

◆ WP 900

Whitehead's modular ground influence mine is laid by submarine or surface ship. There are three versions, containing one, two, or three charges; and fuzing can be a combination of magnetic, acoustic, and pressure. Designed shelf life is 30 years.

WP/E 900 is an exercise version.

JAPAN

The principal wartime moored mine was Type 93, which carried an explosive charge of 220 or 243 lbs. Net buoyancy (which determined how much mooring cable could be used) was 265 or 243 lbs (depending on explosive load), and total weight, including anchor, was 1543 or 1565 lbs. Using thin cable, a Type 93 mine could be laid in water as deep as 586 fathoms (3250 ft). These mines were provided with 4, 7, or 9 contact (Hertz) horns. Stocks in Japan in 1945 were presumably destroyed, but stocks in Japanese-occupied territory probably survived the war.

Japan currently uses mines either identical to, or externally similar to, U.S. types. Japan's current mines are designated in a K-series during their development period, after which they receive Type numbers. The types are: K-1, K-2, K-3, K-4, K-5, K-13, K-15, K-16, K-21, K-22, K-23, K-24, K-52, and K-55. K-15 is the Type 56 moored contact (antenna) mine, similar to the U.S. Mk 6. K-21, K-22, K-23, and K-24 are Type 70 bottom influence mines similar in appearance to the U.S. Mk 36. K-33 is a moored contact mine. There is also a Type 55 horned moored mine (710 kg total, including 100 kg of TNT, with total buoyancy of 60 kg to support the mooring wire; diameter is 86 cm; there are seven Hertz horns). The K-X moored mine, an air-dropped mine, and a rising mine are under development.

SWEDEN

◆ GMI 100 Rockan

This anti-invasion ground mine, for shallow water, was announced in 1984; Rockan can also be laid in deeper water as an ASW mine. The unusual shape causes the mine to glide through the water, typically to twice the depth of the water in which the mine is laid (5–100 m depth). The mine's low profile makes sonar detection difficult, and the irregular shape and GRP casing tend to camouflage Rockan's purpose. Dimensions are 1015 × 800 × 385 mm; weight is 190 kg (105 kg of explosive); minimum distance between mines is 25 m.

Rockan (left) and MMI 80 (right). (Bofors)

The Rockan sensor will not react to any sweep that creates a homogenous magnetic field; this sensor is also being incorporated into the moored MMI 80.

◆ LYDIA

This rising antiship mine was placed in production about 1956. LYDIA is laid as a bottom mine and is influence (passive acoustic) actuated. When it detects a ship, the mine rises by changing its buoyancy (its hydraulic mechanism pushes water out of the lower mine chamber). LYDIA then floats at a predetermined depth and is contact fired. If the sound source recedes without contact, the mine sinks to the bottom to await another ship, when it will again rise in a new cycle. Operational life is limited only by the battery (life 3 months, or about 60–90 cycles). Operation is limited to shallow water by the small negative buoyancy of the mine, which limits its resistance to currents and also limits the speed with which it can rise to meet a potential target.

◆ MMI 80

This moored influence mine, announced in 1984, has an operational depth of 20–200 m. The buoyant body is made of plastic, and the sensors are similar to those of the Rockan mine. Dimensions are 1125 × 660 × 1125 mm; total weight is 450 kg; charge is 80-kg hexotonal; sinker weight is 240 kg. Minimum distance between mines is 25 m.

◆ Mobile Mine

In 1985 it was announced that FFV, Bofors, and Ericsson were cooperating in the development of a submarine standoff mine, probably a converted torpedo. The principal changes would be a new influence sensor and a modified propulsion system for a long/slow rather than a short/fast run.

◆ Type 74

This moored mine is made by SAB Industri AB. Total weight is 205 kg, and the body is cylindrical. It can be laid in depths as great as 110 m and operates over a radius of 3–70 m.

◆ Type 77

SAB's pressure mine weighs 470 kg. It is to be laid in depths from 20–200 m.

SWITZERLAND

◆ Telemine

In 1983 the Swiss company Tek Sea announced that it was developing the Telemine remotely controlled torpedo to meet an Argentine Navy requirement. The mine body is 55 cm × 5 m, with a maximum weight of 650 kg (170 kg of explosives). Powered by a 4.5-kW electric motor (up to 10 km at 20 kts), Telemine would be laid on the sea floor (at depths of up to 150 m), remaining dormant for up to two years, and then being activated by acoustic signals from a distance as great as 4 km. Upon being activated, the mine releases its ballast and rises to near the surface. A sensor pod on Telemine's back carries an antenna, which penetrates the surface, for radio control by airplane, ship, or submarine. The sensor pod itself surfaces 500 m from the target, to provide the controller with a television picture of the target.

Tek Sea claimed that Telemine is almost undetectable by minehunting sonars because its acoustic density is so close to that of sea water.

TAIWAN

Taiwan uses a variety of domestic and foreign-produced mines. There are still large stocks of ex-U.S. antenna and contact mines, as well as magnetic (and probably pressure) bottom influence mines. There are also air-dropped cylindrical bottom mines (designated WSM-110), and Manta-like anti-invasion mines (WSM-210). WSM-110 resembles World War II influence mines, with slight tapering at one end for an appropriate trajectory, and two holes in the side for sensors. WSM-110 may be an adapted U.S. type.

USSR

Reports of total Soviet mine reserves vary. In 1987 the U.S. Department of Defense claimed a total of 300,000 mines, including about 100,000 moored contact mines. These figures greatly exceed World War II usage (40,000 mines for the Soviets, 44,000 for the United States). Many of these mines have been exported to Soviet client states and allies, but it is often claimed that the Soviets do not export their pressure mines. Much of the data that follows dates from the early 1950s, in many cases from mines confiscated during the Korean War. Very little information has been released on more modern types, and information given here should be taken as representative rather than complete. For example, it seems likely that there are moored acoustic and magnetic mines, but no data or designations have been published.

Many of the designations given are no more than Western applications of standard Soviet mine categories, such as AMD; it is not always clear how the Soviets designate their equipment. Moreover, the historical record, even that part the Soviets have declassified, is not particularly clear. It is entirely possible that some of the descriptions below are really somewhat different references to the same weapon, or to versions of the same weapon.

The old Imperial Navy was an enthusiastic supporter of mine warfare, but the expertise vanished with the revolution. A special technical bureau for mine development was established in 1921 and a mine testing center in 1924. However, stocks of earlier mines remained, and their designs were repeated in new production batches. M26 was the first entirely Soviet ship-laid mine. There was also a PLT series of submarine-launched mines.

It is reported that the Soviets have submarine-launched mines, one with a range of about 1 km.

◆ AGSB

Development of this antenna mine began in the early 1930s; it entered combat early in World War II. AGSB had two 35-m steel antennae (above and below) and the charge of an M-26, but AGSB could be laid in water four times as deep as M-26 (about 560 m).

◆ AMD/KMD/KMK Series/MKD

Respectively, these devices are air/surface/submarine-laid ground mines, the number (-500 or -1000, but -1000 only in the case of submarine mines) indicating the weight in kg. For 500 and 1000 kg, respectively, maximum case depths (antiship) are reportedly 24.4 and 54.9 m (80 and 180 ft); charge weights, 300 and 699 kg (660 and 1540 lbs); and minimum distance between mines, 69 and 137 m (226 and 449 ft). If these mines are used against submarines, they may be laid at greater depths, up to 200 m (660 ft) for a -1000. Known influence mechanisms are (i) magnetic (horizontal or vertical component of target field), (ii) acoustic (high or low frequency), (iii) pressure, and (iv) combination. There may also be others; what appears to have been a Libyan-laid KMD was recovered in the Red Sea in 1984, with a new type of influence mechanism. Approximate dimensions were 21 × 120 in. KMD reportedly incorporates a ship counter (up to eleven ships) and a delayed-arming mechanism (up to ten days). The 1984 mine may have had a modular electronic firing mechanism to replace the earlier plug-in type.

Two KMK-1000 can be carried in lieu of a torpedo.

AMD, KMD, and KMK may be no more than generic designators.

The original AMD was the air-dropped version of the MKD magnetic induction ground mine. Dimensions were 21 × 114 in. Weight was 2167 lb total with 1725 lbs of modified torpex. Maximum effective depth was 120 ft. MKD could be laid by aircraft, surface ships, and submarines; and it had an arming delay clock and a ship counter. MKD was the first modern Soviet ground mine.

The original AMD-500 appeared in 1942. It is sometimes suggested that the KMDs, which first appeared in the early 1950s, were derived from captured German mines. These mines were exported from the early 1960s on.

◆ Cluster Bay/Cluster Gulf

Cluster Bay is a rising ASW mine, reportedly for use on the continental shelf. This mine is, therefore, comparable in concept to the Anglo-U.S. Crusader/Hammerhead. The rising body is a rocket, and it is fired on the basis of passive/active acoustic sensing. The rocket is presumably unguided, probably exploding when it reaches the expected target depth (as measured by the active sonar). The Soviet term for such a mine is Reaktivno-Vsplyvayushchaya Mm, and it would presumably have an RVM designation. Reportedly the charge is 500 lbs, and typical case depth is 2000 ft.

The advent of this mine led to U.S. and other Western interest in very deep hunting/sweeping. The name is a NATO designation.

Cluster Gulf is reportedly a similar mine for use in deep water beyond the continental shelf. Recently, a Soviet torpedo mine broadly comparable to Captor has been reported.

◆ KB-1/M-31/MAV/KB-3

These mines are improved versions of M-08. KB-1 was a special five-horned moored contact mine for use in icy water, the mine casing releasing a protective shield after laying. KB-1 could be laid down to a mooring depth of 160 m and carried a charge of 230 kg of TNT. KB-1 probably appeared in the early 1930s, and the aircraft-laid M-31 was very similar. Some of these mines were fitted with antenna firing mechanisms. There was also an aircraft-laid MAV moored mine of about this vintage.

KB-3 (MA-39) was introduced in 1941. It carried horns, a 35-m antenna, and a 250-kg explosive charge. Its relation to KB-1/M-31 is not clear.

◆ KRAB

This moored influence mine is ship-laid, has a case depth of 18.3 m and a bottom depth of 272 m, and carries 230 kg of explosive. Minimum distance between mines is 41 meters.

◆ M-08

This contact mine, developed before World War I (1908), is currently manufactured in North Korea; this mine is currently being used by Iran in the Persian Gulf. M-08, a spherical moored

M-08-4 mines, of Soviet design and North Korean manufacture, seized in the Persian Gulf in 1987 on board the Iranian ship *Iran Ajr*. (U.S. Navy)

mine, carries five chemical horns. Diameter is 34.5 in, and explosive charge is 253 lbs of TNT. Total case weight is 500 lbs, and the anchor weighs about 700 lbs. Laying depth is 34–360 ft, and case-depth settings are 4–20 ft. Minimum distance between mines (to avoid countermining) is 120 ft.

North Korean–made M-08 mines in the Persian Gulf have sometimes broken from their moorings. That breaking may mean that the North Koreans have used a heavier explosive charge, compensating by using a lighter and flimsier mooring chain.

◆ M-12 and M-26

These moored mines have inertia-impact firing devices. M-12 is spherical (34.5-in diameter, 220 lbs of TNT, 1320 lbs total). M-26 adds a parallel midbody between two spherical caps (total length 52 in, 528 lbs of TNT, 1210 lbs total case weight plus 990 lbs anchor). M-12 can be laid in 30–432 ft of water, with a case depth of 4–20 ft; M-26 in 30–456 ft of water, with the same case depths. M-12's minimum spacing is 100 ft; 180 ft for M-26 (because of the more powerful charge).

KB was a modified M26, a bomb-shaped mine for aircraft delivery, dropped without a parachute. Maximum mooring depth was 270 meters, and the explosive charge was 230 kg of TNT. The horns were moved into position by springs after dropping. This mine was also described as Type Geiro, and possibly as AMG.

There is also an M-16 moored contact mine suitable for a maximum bottom depth of 366 m, carrying 115 kg of explosive, with a minimum spacing of 36 m.

◆ MIRAB

This ground magnetic induction mine was shaped in the form of a half-teardrop. Dimensions were 40.5 in (long) × 27.5 × 27.5 in. Charge was 141 lbs of TNT in a 616-lb case. Minimum spacing was 200 ft. The mine was originally intended to be airdropped; but its case was not strong enough, and it was surface-laid.

MIRAB was the first Soviet aircraft-laid bottom influence mine; it entered service in 1941. Soviet histories of their sea mines claim that MIRAB's induction firing mechanism had been developed as early as 1928. However, the histories also state that the first Soviet influence mines entered service only in 1945.

◆ MKB/MKB-3/MAG/AMG-1

MKB was the standard Soviet surface-laid contact mine of the 1950s. Like M-08, MKB used five chemical horns. Diameter matched that of M-08 (34.5 in), but the case was larger (length 52 in) and thicker. The charge was 506 lbs of TNT; case weight was 984 lbs, and the anchor weighed 1415 lbs. Laying depths were 34–894 ft, and case depths 8–30 ft. Minimum separation was 115 ft.

MKB-3 was similar, but with a shorter parallel midsection (length 47 in); charge weight and case weight were similar to those of the MKB.

The basic design was repeated in the MAG and AMG-1. There were two types of charge container, and the horns might be distributed irregularly over the body of the mine.

MAG was a moored ASW antenna mine, otherwise similar to MKB (diameter 34.5 in, length 52 in, case weight 984 lbs, anchor 1415 lbs). Maximum laying depth was 1490 ft. Case-depth settings were 8–146 ft, and minimum spacing in a field was 115 ft. The mine could be used with or without horns. The lower antenna was 35 m long (diameter 11.6 mm); the upper, 24 m (6.3-mm diameter wire).

AMG-1 was a moored contact mine, laid like a bomb by aircraft (no parachute) from low altitude (5–25 m). Dimensions were 37 in (diameter) × 141 in; 572 lbs of TNT in a 1080-lb case (with a 1200-lb anchor). Laying depths were 43–327 ft; case depths, 8–28 ft. Minimum spacing was 145 ft. Planting heights and speeds were 100–160 m at 260 kts and 160–600 m at 180 kts. AMG-1 appeared in 1939.

◆ MYaM (YaM)

This small ellipsoidal moored contact mine had three chemical horns. Dimensions were 21 in (diameter) × 22.8 in. Weights were 44 lbs of TNT, with a 142-lb case and a 243-lb anchor. Laying depth was 9–167 ft; case depth, 2–9 ft. Minimum distance between mines was 66 ft. MYaM was probably an anti–small-craft mine (e.g., antisweeper). It was first reported in Korea in 1952, and both Iran and Iraq used MYaM in the Gulf War.

◆ Nuclear Mines

The Soviet Union reportedly has small stocks of nuclear ASW mines (yield 5–20 kT). The virtue of a nuclear mine is that it can destroy submarines at any depth, whereas a conventional moored or ground mine has only a very limited lethal volume around itself. The other simple solution to the depth problem, the string mine, is relatively cumbersome, the only known Western example being the Italian TAR. The nonnuclear solution to this problem is the rising mine (see Cluster Bay/Cluster Gulf above).

◆ PLT/PLT-3

This cylindrical moored contact mine (inertia-impact fired) was to be laid by special submarine minelayers; no current Soviet submarines have tubes of sufficient diameter. Dimensions were 31.5 in (diameter) × 70 in. Total weight was 1850 lbs, with 506 lbs of TNT. Maximum laying depth was 450 ft; case depth, 13–30 ft. Minimum spacing was 262 ft.

PLT-3 was a moored contact mine laid from a submarine torpedo tube; it was fired by four galvanic horns. Dimensions were 21 in (diameter) × 94 in. Total weight was 2220 lbs, with 220 lbs of TNT. Maximum laying depth was 470 ft; case depths, 8–30 ft.

There is a submarine-laid moored sectional influence mine, carrying 500 lbs of explosive; it can be moored in depths as great as 1600 ft.

◆ PLT-G/EP-G

These moored mines were introduced early in World War II, both of them for torpedo-tube laying by K-class cruiser submarines. Designed for upright laying from special tubes, EP-G was a deep-laying version of the PLT-G, introduced by the end of 1941. There is also reference to EP-SA, a wartime submarine-laid mine with a 200- or 300-kg explosive charge and 130 m (420 ft) of mooring chain. Shell diameter was 90 cm (35 in). Reportedly the torpedo-tube mine was not satisfactory, at least initially.

◆ Type R

This moored ship-laid contact mine has a case depth of 1.8 m (6 ft) and a bottom depth of 35 m (115 ft). It carries 10 kg (22 lbs) of explosive, and the minimum distance between mines is 15 m (49 ft). R was a U.S. designation; the Soviet designation was not known.

◆ R-1

This small moored contact mine for shallow water is fired by two chemical horns. Dimensions are 19.5 in (diameter) × 6.5 in. Weights are 88 lbs of TNT, 253 lbs for the case, and 352 lbs for the anchor. Laying depth is 3.5–115 ft; case depth is 1.5–5 ft. Minimum spacing is 66 ft. In very shallow water the mine does not separate from its anchor.

R-1 was a U.S. designation, indicating a mine whose Soviet designation was not known (R for Russian unknown).

◆ UEP

At least some recent Soviet mines reportedly exploit the underwater electric potential (UEP) of submarines as their fuzing mechanism. UEP is inherently very short ranged, and it is a direct consequence of the use of rotating machinery, such as propellers. Therefore, it is very difficult to silence.

◆ YaRM

This small shallow-water contact (anti-invasion) mine carries a 3-kg charge.

UNITED KINGDOM

◆ Continental Shelf Mine (Crusader/Hammerhead)

Continental Shelf Mine is a joint U.K.-U.S. program for a mine to operate in medium water depths, down to about 100 fathoms (600 ft). For the U.S. Navy, this program fulfills the former intermediate water depth mine (IWDM) requirement, replacing the abortive propelled rapid ascent mine (PRAM, EX-68) of the 1970s. In the 1984 competition, Marconi (MUSL) offered a Captor-like mine based on the Stingray lightweight torpedo. BAe

British Mk 5 bottom mine (in Australian service). (Klein)

British Mk 17 moored mines with Mk 18 bases (in Australian service). (Klein)

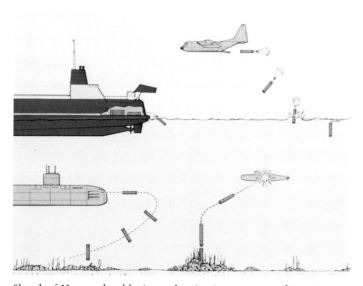

Sketch of Hammerhead laying and activation sequence: this mine uses a rising body to attack, and the body can maneuver. Drawings of Crusader show a similar sequence. (Marconi)

offered a rocket-propelled weapon similar in principle to PRAM. Ferranti offered a cluster of 10 or 12 rockets firing upward in a predetermined pattern from a box launcher. The two emerging contenders are Crusader (British Aerospace/Plessey/Honeywell) and Hammerhead (Marconi/Loral). Because the mine must be able to deal with submarines passing over the continental shelf at a variety of depths, as well as with surface ships, the mine must be a rising vehicle. The published sketch of Crusader suggests buoyancy (passive) propulsion; sketches of Hammerhead suggest the use of a propeller. Both mines will be deployable by submarine (torpedo tubes), by surface ships, and by air. The meager details thus far released suggest search by passive sonar and then prosecution by an active sonar built into the mine's rising body, in rough analogy to the deeper-water Captor. At least in the case of Crusader, the manufacturer claims that the mine will be effective beyond the continental shelf. That capability would certainly be true of a buoyancy-propelled weapon, which would actually gain speed (hence range as well as controllability) as it rose through the water.

This program is sometimes called the Advanced Sea Mine.

As of 1988, the Continental Shelf Mine was scheduled to enter service in the mid-1990s. In January 1989, however, the U.K. MoD canceled this program. The U.S. Navy had provisionally canceled its Advanced Sea Mine program as part of the FY90 cuts, although in the United States such cuts are often provisional pending congressional action. At the time of cancellation, the U.K. contribution to the program was reported to be about 19 percent of the total cost.

◆ Existing Mines

In connection with mine modernization programs, it is often suggested that Britain has manufactured no mines since World War II. However, there were several postwar programs, begun about 1953. Information is somewhat fragmentary.

In the past, there were three mine series: moored mines with Mk numbers, air-launched mines (A numbers), and special magnetic ground mines (M series). The principal mines, at the end of World War II, were the following:

A Mk 6 was an aircraft-laid ground mine (1800 lbs; 960- or 1040-lb charge; magnetic, acoustic, combination, or pressure). Minimum depth was 40 ft. Dimensions were 18.45 in × 8 ft 6 in (9 ft 4 in including parachute). In 1949, 5707 were on hand.

A Mk 7, 7*, and 7** were 1100-lb ground mines (555- or 610-lb charges). Fuzing was magnetic or acoustic. Minimum case depth was 40 ft. Dimensions were 15.8 in × 7 ft 6 in (6 ft 11 in without parachute). In 1949, 4502 were on hand.

A Mk 9 was an 1850-lb ground mine carrying a 960- or 1060-lb charge. Fuzing was magnetic, acoustic, combination, or pressure. Minimum case depth was 40 ft. Dimensions were 18.5 in × 8 ft 6 in (9 ft 4 in with parachute). In 1949, 1427 were on hand and another 400 were on order. This mine was renumbered in 1955 and is probably still in service.

M Mk 1 was the standard buoyant magnetic mine, ship-laid in up to 1000 fathoms of water. It carried a 320- or 500-lb Amatol charge. A total of 8948 were on hand in 1949.

M Mk 2 was a 1760-lb ground mine (1020-lb Amatol charge), laid by submarine or coastal forces in 5–20 fathoms. 1310 are on hand.

M Mk 5 was running sea trials. It was a 1930-lb ground mine (1030-lb charge, with magnetic, acoustic, or combination fuzing) laid by submarines or coastal forces in 6.5–20 fathoms.

Mk 15 was a buoyant contact mine carrying 320 or 500 lbs of Amatol; it could be laid in water as deep as 1000 fathoms. A total of 1972 were on hand.

Mk 17 was a similar buoyant mine, which could be laid in 500 fathoms of water; 14,933 were on hand.

A Type S and A Mk 12, developed in 1953–56, were the new

air-delivered ASW ground mines. Weights were 1000 and 2000 lbs, respectively. Both mines used combination acoustic-magnetic-pressure mechanisms. At the time of development, the standard air-drop requirements were 450 kts/5000 ft (Royal Navy) and 35,000 ft in altitude (RAF). Minimum water depths (which determined the shock level the mine had to survive during laying) were 12 and 40 ft.

Mk 10 was a postwar aircraft-laid buoyant ASW mine, and its development began during World War II. Mk 10 used a contact mechanism, and the length of its mooring cable had to be adjusted before flight. Mk 10 was intended to be as simple and as inexpensive as possible, and it was the only means of mining deep water not accessible to surface ships and submarines. Total weight was 810 lbs (100 lbs of Minol charge). Maximum case depth was 600 ft.

Mk 28 and Mine "H" Type "T" As of 1956, two new surface-laid ASW mines were under development. Mk 28 was an antenna mine, said to be more reliable (i.e., less subject to premature detonation) than others. Mine "H" Type "T" was a small moored mine, under trial in 1956. Presumably it was intended for laying from small fast attack craft. There were also a variety of experimental mines, including buoyant UEP (antenna) mines tried from about 1944 on.

These programs almost certainly died in the major post-1957 British defense reorganization, so that they probably represent the high point of British mine production prior to the 1980s.

Unfortunately, the reported postwar Mark numbers do not correspond to the three reported Mark numbers of existing British service mines. Presumably, existing mines were renumbered some time after 1956, the three series merging into one. The three current types are:

Mk 5 Submarine- and ship-laid ground mine.

Mk 12 Air-laid ground mine.

Mk 17 Moored acoustic mine.

In 1982 the Royal Ordnance Factories proposed a modernized version of Mk 5, Mk 5N, with a microprocessor-controlled fuze (target designation module) that used a BAJ Vickers mine circuit emulator (MICE). This device could also be applied to existing stocks. Mk 12 is now being modernized by British Aerospace. Finally, it was reported in 1986 that Mk 17 mines have been fitted with a new acoustic sensor.

◆ Dragonfish

Dragonfish is the current production Marconi 85-kg [?] (80 kg of explosive) anti-invasion mine for use in shallow water (down to 30 m). Dragonfish uses two types of influence sensors. It has a 200-day operational lifetime. The technology used is similar to that in the Marconi Stonefish, which is designed to be laid in deeper water.

◆ Sea Urchin

This family of modular advanced multi-influence ground mines was developed by British Aerospace Naval Weapons Division. The warhead is built out of one or two charges (150, 300, or 600 kg each), for a warhead weight of 150–1200 kg. There is also a standard sensing-and-processing unit (SAP) using the target's acoustic, magnetic, or pressure signature, or a combination. There is also a selectable ship counter. All units have an outside diameter of 21 in, for launch from a submarine's torpedo tubes. The manufacturer claims that microprocessor control provides a high level of target discrimination, so that the mine can ignore countermeasures and can choose the highest-value target.

There is also a Sea Urchin moored mine, usable down to 200 m in water depth; the mine floats at 75 m. Buoyancy requirements limit it to a 150-kg warhead in a barrel-shaped float, which also carries the SAP. Finally, there is a Sea Urchin Exercise Mine.

In October 1984 Sea Urchin cost £10,000 to £20,000 each.

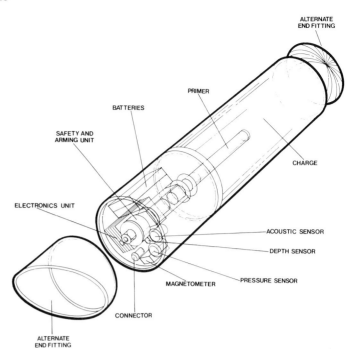

Sea Urchin, a typical ground mine. (British Aerospace)

◆ Mine Modernization Program

Britain has not manufactured naval mines for some years, probably since the mid-1950s, but she has retained large stocks of these weapons. British Aerospace has received a contract to modernize existing ground mines. The existing units required lengthy prelaunch preparation and could make little or no target selection. British Aerospace designed a new microprocessor-based sensor- and -processing unit (SAP) that solves both problems, while retaining as much of the original mine as possible. A new safing- and-arming system can be added if desired, and high energy batteries make for a long shelf life. The mine can be programmed before it is launched.

As described in 1982, the SAP had only magnetic and acoustic sensors, the pressure sensor being built into the software (which covers frequencies down to O Hz). Acoustic signals would be analyzed in three bands, to cover sonar, engines, and propellers themselves, and thus to provide a high degree of target identification.

The modernization program was announced in 1982. It applied to about 1500 mines, some of them reportedly dating from the 1950s (and presumably of World War II type). In 1984 it was reported that the entire program might be abandoned because at least some mines were suffering from deterioration of their TNT or RDX filling. Some of it crystallized, causing at least two mines to explode prematurely. Such deterioration is quite common in civilian explosives such as dynamite and may limit the shelf life of existing mines, an important consideration for a country, such as the Soviet Union, with a very large stockpile, much of which must be elderly. Modern formulations are more stable, but reportedly the existing fillings cannot safely be steamed out once they have begun to deteriorate. In 1984 the reported solution was to X-ray each mine and to discard those whose fillings showed cracks or crystallization.

Thus far mine modernization has, apparently, been applied only to surviving World War II Mk-12 mines.

Although the SAP was developed specifically for British mines, British Aerospace claims that SAP is adaptable to many other types. Presumably it is either identical to, or closely related to, the SAP of the Sea Urchin mine.

◆ Stonefish

This medium-depth modular magnetic/acoustic/pressure (either single- or multiple-influence) mine replaces earlier British types. Launched by airplane, ship, or submarine, Stonefish is suitable for water depths of 30–200 meters. Dimensions are 53 cm (21 in) × 2.4 m (1.9 m exercise); weight is 990 kg (600-kg warhead). The training version weighs 440 kg. Shelf life is 20 years, and life in the water is 700 days.

In March 1988 Marconi completed delivery of a Stonefish order (placed in 1985) to Finland. The exercise version has been delivered to the Royal Australian Navy, and other navies have evaluated the weapon.

◆ Versatile Exercise Mine System (VEMS)

VEMS is a British Aerospace system designed to evaluate the performance of mine-countermeasures forces, both for exercises and for the development of new countermeasures. Each VEMS body can be programmed to simulate any known mine firing device, and VEMS can be recovered (and on-board test tapes removed) up to six months after laying. The manufacturer claims a twenty-year service life.

Dimensions are 533 mm × 2.71 m, and weight is 560 kg; the body includes a buoyant section that is released for recovery.

VEMS is currently in service with the Royal Navy and has been ordered for the U.S. Navy, the Thai Navy, and the Royal Australian Navy.

UNITED STATES

◆ Destructors

Destructors (DST) were standard streamlined bombs converted into shallow-water mines during the Vietnam War. Mks 36, 40, and 41 were, respectively, conversions of bombs Mks 82, 83, and 84. The Destructor's firing mechanism was developed very rapidly, and at the end of the war it was stockpiled. However, these mechanisms cannot have met the usual standards for reliability or shelf life: hence the development of the Quickstrike Mines (Mks 62–65, see below). It is not clear how many, if any, Destructor mechanisms remain in U.S. war stocks.

As disclosed to the North Vietnamese in 1973 (as part of Operation End Sweep), the DST uses a thin-field magnetometer with selectable sensitivity. There is also a version using seismic (acoustic) fuzing against small and medium craft.

DESTRUCTOR (DST) MARK 36

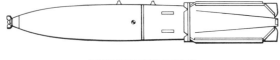

DESTRUCTOR (DST) MARK 40

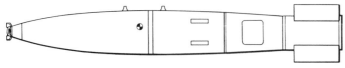

DESTRUCTOR (DST) MARK 41

Destructors (converted Mk 80–series bombs).

◆ Mk 6

This antenna mine was developed during World War I for the North Sea antisubmarine barrage and subsequently became the main U.S. surface-laid contact weapon. Mk 6 was used during World War II and was probably distributed to U.S. allies postwar. It was a 34-inch sphere containing 300 lbs of TNT (1400 lbs total, including sinker) and could be moored in up to 3000 ft of water. Mod 3 had a 100-ft lower antenna, and Mod 4 a 50-ft lower antenna.

Mk 6 practice mine being launched. (U.S. Navy)

◆ Mk 13

Mk 13 was an aircraft-laid magnetic mine, delivered without a parachute. This mine could also be used as a bomb. Total weight was 1048 lbs, including 640 lbs of TNT, or 1118 lbs, including 710 lbs of Torpex explosive. Mods 1 and 2 were redesignated Mk 26 Mods 0 and 1 (which was not produced); Mod 3 (with a parachute) was not issued; Mod 4 was designed for shallow water. Mod 5 (990 lbs, including 640 lbs of TNT, or 1060 lbs, including 710 lbs of TNT) had an acoustic exploder. Mod 6 (1020 lbs, including 640 lbs of TNT, or 1090 lbs, including 710 lbs of TPX) had an acoustic exploder and was fitted with a parachute.

Mk 36 might be considered a development of Mk 13, via Mk 26. Prior to development of the Mk-52 series, Mks 13/36 were the primary U.S. lightweight aircraft-laid bottom mines, and Mk 25 was the primary heavy equivalent. All were probably exported to U.S. allies postwar.

◆ Mk 16

Mk 16 is a contact (Hertz horn) mine, ovoid in shape (Mk 6 is spherical). Mk 16 carries 1130 lbs of HBX-1, total weight being 2070 lbs. Possibly exported postwar, Mk 16 was originally conceived as a successor to the Mk 6 antenna mine. A magnetic influence version was not manufactured, and there was an acoustic version.

◆ Mk 18

Mk 18 is a surface-laid bottom magnetic mine, cylindrical in shape (with the cylinder axis vertical), with a prominent vertical post protruding from it. The mine is provided with wheels beneath the cylinder so that it can be run down a track on board the laying ship. Total weight is 2140 lbs, including 1440 lbs of HBX-1. Mk 18 was probably exported to U.S. allies in the 1950s, to be used to mine shallow strategic straits. There is no other U.S. ship-laid bottom magnetic mine of the same vintage.

◆ Mk 25

The standard U.S. World War II aircraft-laid bottom mine was used during the Vietnam War. Weight was 2000 lbs total (1274 lbs of TPX or 1200 lbs of HBX). Mod 1 was acoustic; Mod 2, pressure; Mod 3, acoustic. Depending on the flight gear used, Mk 25 was 22.4 in × 87.2 in to 93 in (i.e., roughly the size of the contemporary aerial torpedo Mk 13). In 1980 new flight gear was being issued to permit this mine to be carried at high speed. Mk 25 was probably provided to U.S. allies postwar.

◆ Mk 36

Mk 36 was an air-laid bottom influence mine with a slanted nose for optimum underwater trajectory. The basic version was acoustic, but there was also a magnetic version. Mods 2 and 3 were special, with low-frequency acoustic (A-5) or pressure (A-6 or A-8) firing. Weights for the acoustic version were 1024 lbs total, including 570 lbs TNT, or 1082 lbs total, including 638 lbs TPX. For the magnetic version, 940 lbs total, including 570 lbs TNT, or 1008 lbs total, including 638 lbs TPX. This mine was probably exported.

◆ Mk 39

Mk 39 was an aircraft-laid high-altitude magnetic bottom mine, delivered without any parachute. Total weight was 2000 lbs, including 800 lbs of explosive.

◆ Mk 49

Mk 49 is a submarine-laid bottom mine. Mod 0 is the magnetic version, Mod 1 the acoustic version, and Mod 2 the pressure/magnetic version. Mod 0 weighs 2000 lbs, including 1180 lbs of HBX-3. Mod 1 weighs 1890 lbs, including 1180 lbs of HBX-3. Mod 3 weighs 1960 lbs, including 1180 lbs of HBX-3. All three types can be launched at depths as great as 125 feet. These mines have probably been exported.

◆ Mk 51

This controlled mine for harbor defense is typically laid in groups of thirteen. Mk 51 is a vertical cylinder (62 × 37 in), carrying 3275 lbs of TNT (total weight is 6200 lbs). It is fired either from shore or by magnetic induction. Associated equipment may include a pair of hydrophones attached to anchors on the sea bottom. Mk 51 resembles Mk 18, but Mk 51 is substantially larger. This weapon was probably exported after World War II.

◆ Mk 52

The first of a postwar series of modular antisubmarine mines, Mk 52 was the 1000-lb–class air-laid weapon. Mod 1 was acoustically fuzed; Mod 2, magnetic; Mod 3, combined pressure and magnetic; Mod 5, combined acoustic and magnetic; and Mod 6, all three mechanisms combined. Dimensions were 18.8 in × 70.2 in. Weights were 1130, 1170, 1190, 1200, and 1235 lbs, in each case with a 625-lb HBX-1 charge. All mods used identical mine cases and removable instrument racks. The abortive Mk 59 was a submarine-laid version of Mk 52 (800 lbs with a 70-lb charge; Mod 2 weighed 1500 lbs with a 100-lb charge).

As disclosed to the North Vietnamese in 1973 (as part of Operation End Sweep), Mk 52 Mod 2 used a two-look, reverse polarity, magnetic induction fuze, with selectable magnetic sensitivities, interlook, dead periods, intership dead periods, ship counts, and preset self-sterilization/self-destruction time.

Mk 52 was part of the U.S. Long-Range Mine Program begun in 1948 and was released for production in January 1954 (it became operational in 1961). Mk 52 was also produced in West Germany. In FY60, each of 2500 Mk 52 mines cost about $4900.

Mine Mk 52. (U.S. Navy)

◆ Mk 53

Mk 53 is a 500-lb sweep obstructor (to protect mine fields against sweepers).

Mine Mk 53. (U.S. Navy)

◆ Mk 55

Mk 55 is the 2000-lb–class air-dropped bottom mine. Mods 1 through 6 corresponded to Mk 52 Mods 1 through 6; Mod 7, unique to Mk 55, used an improved dual-channel magnetic firing mechanism. Weights are 2039, 2110, 2120, 2119, 2128, and 2118 lbs. Dimensions are 23.4 in × 89.9 in, or 142.6 in if faired for high-speed carriage. These mines can be laid by surface ships, using portable rails.

Mk 55 was the 2000-lb equivalent of Mk 52; Mk 55 was released for production in November 1955 and became operational in 1961. In FY60, each of 1400 Mk 55 mines procured cost about $5500.

Mine Mk 55. (U.S. Navy)

Mines Mk 55 under a P-3. (U.S. Navy)

◆ Mk 56/57

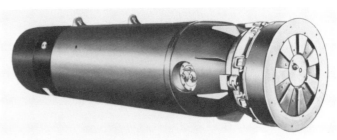

Mine Mk 56. (U.S. Navy)

Mk 56 is a 2000-lb aircraft-laid moored mine (22.4 in × 114.3 in), with a 360-lb charge (HBX-3). Mk 57 is a similar submarine-laid magnetic moored mine (2059 lbs, 340 lbs of HBX-3, 21 in × 121.1 in), for water up to 200 fathoms deep. Mk 56 uses a total-field magnetic exploder and has a stainless-steel nonmagnetic case.

Mk 56 was released for production in 1960 and became operational in 1966; Mk 57, the submarine-laid version of Mk 56, with a fiberglass case, was released for production at the same time and became operational in 1964. In each case, the delay was caused by a lack of funding for production at the time.

Mine Mk 56 as carried on the centerline of an A-4 Skyhawk, 1965. The control unit in the tail of the mine is marked Mk 66. (U.S. Navy)

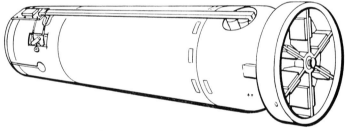

Mine Mk 57.

2000-lb–class mine being loaded onto a P-3. (U.S. Naval Institute)

♦ Mk 60 (Captor)

This deep-water ASW mine was conceived about 1960 and developed at the Naval Surface Weapons Center at White Oak. A tentative specific operational requirement was issued in November 1962, the name Captor being selected for a specific operational requirement issued in May 1964. At that time it was hoped that Captor would reduce mine barrier costs by a factor of 100 (and barrier numbers by a factor of 400). The first production contract (for Techeval/Opeval) was awarded to Good-

year Aerospace (now a division of Loral) in 1972. Technical evaluation began in February 1974 and operational evaluation in June. Initial operational capability was achieved in September 1979 and approval for service use granted in February 1980. This very protracted development testifies to the complexity of the system. In fact, reliability problems prompted a suspension of production in 1980, procurement being resumed in FY82.

Captor (the encapsulated torpedo) is a Mk-46 Mod-4 torpedo encapsulated in a mooring/sensing body that passively detects and tracks submarines passing overhead. When a supposed track is sufficiently attractive, Captor begins active tracking and then launches the torpedo upward. This mode of operation will work in almost any depth because it utilizes reliable acoustic path (RAP) sound propagation. Determination of the target's initial bearing is by passive acoustic correlation and low-power digital processing, using techniques originally developed for the PUFFS (BQG-2/4) submarine sonar project. The mine body can be air-, surface-, or submarine- (torpedo-tube) launched, and it can moor in water at least 1000 ft deep. Lifetime is several weeks or months. Dimensions (weights) for the air/surface-launched versions are 21 × 145 in (2370 lbs); for the submarine-launched version, 21 × 132 in (2056 lbs).

Mod 1 (conversion kit) incorporates an improved target detection device. Mine Mk 66 is the practice version.

Procurement began in FY78, the FY78–80 budgets including 1810 Mk 60s. None were bought in FY81, but FY82 included a request for another 400 Captors. Subsequent procurement: FY83, 500; FY84, 300; FY85, 300; FY86, 150 (unrequested). As of 1985, plans called for 475 in FY85, 600 in FY86, 493 in FY87, and none in FY88. Unit cost in FY86, the last year of procurement, was about $377,000. In comparison, the unit cost of Captor was $113,000 in FY78.

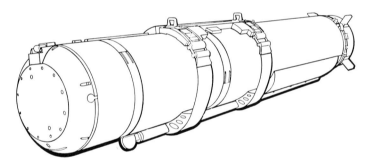

Mine Mk 60 (Captor).

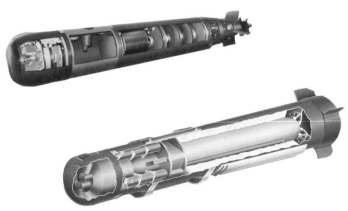

Mk 60 mine and its Mk 46 torpedo payload. (Goodyear)

♦ Mk 62/64

These conversions of standard streamlined bombs (Mks 82, 83, 84, respectively: 500, 1000, 2000 lbs) supersede Destructors EX-52 through -54. The Destructors were magnetic-fuzed. These weapons can be dropped either on land (where they can be exploded by the magnetic signatures of vehicles) or in shallow water. Assembled very quickly using stored fuzes, Mk 62/

64 are called Quickstrikes. All have standard thick-walled bomb casings, and their tails are adaptable to parachutes.

These weapons use two alternative target-detection devices (TDDs): Mk 57 (magnetic-seismic) and Mk 58 (magnetic-seismic-pressure). Presumably seismic is, in effect, an acoustic sensor using sound as transmitted through the sea floor rather than directly through the water. These units are to be replaced by new Mk-70 and Mk-71 TDDs.

The great advantage of this program is that the United States need not stockpile large numbers of bottom mines. Instead, it can stockpile an equivalent number of specialized exploders. The logic is much the same as for the standard U.S. guided bombs, which are assembled by adding special modules to standard Mk 80–series streamlined bombs.

Mk 62 was approved for service use in 1980. As of about 1986, plans called for procurement of 39,804 Mk-70/71 TDDs, plus 8000 Mk 57 and 2500 Mk 58. Actual TDD procurement: Mk 57: 1575 in FY83 and 1753 in FY84. Mk 58: 75 in FY84, 165 in FY85, 400 in FY87, 300 each in FY88 and FY89.

Mk 62 may be an alternative designation for DST-36; Mk 63, DST-40; and Mk 64, DST-41. In each case there are Mods 0 to 5, depending on TDD.

The development of the Quickstrike series and its associated target detection devices is justified on two grounds. First, the existing devices, as well as the Mk-52 series ground mines, were all compromised in Vietnam. Second, they are all becoming difficult to maintain and are no longer being manufactured. For example, their batteries must be stored under refrigeration. Quickstrike's design emphasizes ease of maintenance and also ease of mine preparation for use. All the Quickstrikes are air-delivered. The corresponding submarine-delivered bottom mine is Mk 67; there is no corresponding ship-delivered bottom mine.

Mk 65 Quickstrike being prepared for flight. (U.S. Naval Institute)

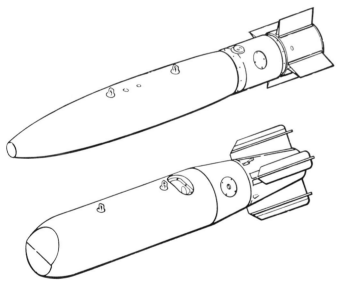

Quickstrike Mines (Mks 64 above and 65 below).

◆ Mk 65

A 2390-lb modular mine (29 in across fins × 128 in), Mk 65 is the only Quickstrike not converted from a standard bomb. Unlike Mk 64, Mk 65 has a special thin-walled casing and a special arming device. Aerojet received the Mk 65 contract on 15 April 1982. Mod 0 uses a Mk-57 TDD; Mod 1 uses a Mk-58 TDD.

In 1985 Aerojet, the U.S. manufacturer, and Misar of Italy agreed to allow Misar to market Mk 65 in Europe. A new family of microprocessors developed by Misar will replace the U.S. Mk 58 multisensor TDD (trigger unit).

Mk 65 was approved for service use in 1983. Procurement: 307 in FY82, 579 in FY83, 600 in FY84, 524 in FY85, 1445 in FY86, 500 in FY88, and 524 in FY89, for a total of 4479 against a planned total of 4500. As of 1985, plans called for 559 in FY85, 743 in FY86, 743 in FY87, and 777 in FY88; the new schedule bought out the planned production run early. Actual procure-

ment was 1445 in FY86; as of late 1986, plans called for 500 in FY88 and 524 in FY89 (none were bought in FY87).

◆ Mk 67 (SLMM)

The submarine-launched mobile mine was converted from a Mk-37 torpedo and was designed to be fired into a mine field from a distance. Advanced development was completed in FY78, and Mk 67 Mod 2 was approved for service use in FY83. At that time plans called for 2421 such mines, up from an earlier projected level of 1729. Procurement: 101 in FY82, 266 in FY83, 242 in FY84, 280 in FY85. As of 1985, planned procurement (which was not carried through) was 290 in FY86, 284 in FY87, and 266 in FY88.

This weapon uses TDDs Mk 70 and Mk 71.

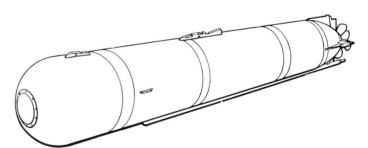

Mine Mk 67 (Submarine-Launched Mobile Mine).

◆ Universal Laying Mine

Universal laying mine is a mine development project. Procurement was 3500 in FY86, at a total cost of $3.7 million. None were bought in FY87, but late in 1986 the navy hoped for 2400 in FY88 and 3600 in FY89. Engineering evaluation was completed during FY86, and approval for full production was expected late in FY87. Details have not been published, but presumably the universal laying mine is a new moored mine to replace Mk 56/57. The new mine is included in the same program element as the Quickstrike series of new bottom mines. No Mark number has been announced.

This mine may be associated with a new parachute flight-gear Mk 16 for 500-lb mines.

◆ MOWAM

EDO's private-venture mobile mine project is designed for use principally against amphibious vehicles in shallow water. MOWAM would be deployed from helicopters or small patrol craft. MOWAM would appear to be a bottom-laid rising mine, triggered acoustically, that would use a rocket motor and a magnetic proximity fuze. These data were published in 1986.

YUGOSLAVIA

◆ SAG-2b

This locally produced contact mine, with a total weight of 600 kg (115 kg of explosive), can be laid in 110 m of water. This mine must date to the 1950s or before.

In the mid-1960s Yugoslavia acquired Soviet KMD-500 and KMD-1000 influence mines. In 1975 the Yugoslav government announced that it had two new acoustic mines in production, *Koral* (coral) and *Biser* (pearl).

MINE COUNTERMEASURES/MINEHUNTING SONARS

Very precise navigational systems are essential to mine countermeasures because the sweeper must be able to identify the position of the cleared channel. Examples include the Racal Hyperfix (accuracy 5 m at 250 km) and the U.S. Precision Navigation System. Raydist, which was used to control the U.S. sweeping of Hanoi/Haiphong in 1973, was an extemporized civilian system using antennas on shore. Minesweeper navigation also requires high-definition surface-search radars, many of which are listed in the Antiaircraft Warfare section.

CHINA (PRC)

◆ Type 312

This remotely controlled magnetic and acoustic minesweeper is similar in concept to the German Troika system. Type 312 can also operate manned. Displacement is 46.95 tons fully loaded (dimensions 20.94 × 4.20 × 1.30 m), and propulsion is by a 300-BHP diesel. Radio control is effective to about 3 nm, and the craft is electrically driven at 1–5 kts. All equipment is shock-mounted, and the hull form is intended to reduce the shock effect of the mines the craft detonates. These craft have a lasar precision navigation system. They are limited to coastal waters because the hull form is not suited to heavy seas.

Type 312 became operational in the early 1970s, and by 1986 60 were in service. Reportedly this class was inspired by successful conversion of several 400-ton *Lienyun*-class auxiliary sweepers (trawler type) to remote control.

FRANCE

◆ French Sweeps

(i) Oropesa (Wire Sweeps)

OD 1 on coastal sweepers.

OD 2 on inshore minesweepers.

(ii) Magnetic

MB 1 through MB 4 symmetrical loops for coastal sweepers.

MB 5 and MB 6 asymmetrical loops for ocean and coastal sweepers. MB 5 uses a 225-kW or 364-kW sweep generator.

(iii) Acoustic

AM 1 and AM 2 hammer (*marteau*) sweeps.

AM 3 and AM 4 medium-frequency hammer sweeps for coastal sweepers. AM 3's dimensions are 856 × 520 × 340 mm; weight is 45 kg.

AP 1 and AP 2 piston sweeps for low frequency. AP 1's dimensions are 1130 × 558 × 380 mm; weight is 105 kg.

AP 4 acoustic sweep, announced in 1972. It combines the capability of older low- and medium-frequency towed loop systems in a single body without any surface float. Total weight is about 2 tons. This device is to equip the next-generation French minesweeper, the BAMO (*Bâtiment Anti-Mine Océanique*), and AP 4 was tested in that role in 1980–84. Compared to the British Osborn, AP 4 is said to cover a wider frequency range by using an electrodynamic (rather than hydraulic) noise generator.

AE 1 explosive sweep.

AP 4 acoustic sweep, covering both the low and intermediate frequency ranges. (Direction des Constructions Navales)

◆ DUBM-20 (TSM 2020)

The first French minehunting sonar incorporates both search and classification sonars. The entire dual transducer is stabilized, and the console shows both radar and sonar coordinates superimposed, for accurate mine location. Typical performance gives detection at 300 m and classification at 130 m. The detector's frequency is about 100 kHz (variable within 20 kHz, 7.5 kW), and the classification frequency is about 400 kHz (variable within 30 kHz, 4.5 kW).

A DUBM-20A upgrade program, announced in 1984, incorporated four main improvements: coherent processing (for better range in noisy conditions), sweep-to-sweep integration (for a clearer display), a performance indicator (to measure bottom reverberation), and a multi-image memory (to make classification easier).

Work began in 1963, and a DUBM-20X prototype was tested on board the ocean minesweeper *Narvik* in 1967. As a result of the success of these trials, the *Circe* class was built and equipped with DUBM-20A. The first such sonar was installed in 1970 (trials 1971).

◆ DUBM-21 (TSM 2021)

Derived from DUBM-20, DUBM-21 is the successor sonar. It was first installed (as TSM 2021A) on board five French ocean minesweepers converted to minehunters, a program begun in 1974. Compared to DUBM-20A, DUBM-21 is much smaller and more reliable. This sonar (TSM 2021B version) plus the TSM 5730 doppler sonar log (for position keeping) are the standard sensors of the Tripartite (French, Belgian, Dutch) minehunter. This sonar is also the basic element of the IBIS III minehunting system. DUBM-21 uses two arrays to provide simultaneous detection and classification. This technology led in turn to the U.S. SQQ-32. As of 1988, the program called for the production of 40 DUBM-21s.

Mine classification is by two methods, shadow and direct echo. Echo classification alone cannot be sufficient because the signatures of many mines are unknown (and the echo classifier generally does not provide an image immediately recognizable as a mine). Moreover, an irregular seabed may mask the echoes of a small mine. Shadow classification can reveal the shape of a mine, even if it has been designed to be nonreflective. On the other hand, it is not clear whether a shadow sonar can reliably detect deep ground mines. DUBM-21 is, therefore, designed to provide both echo and shadow classification: a conventional

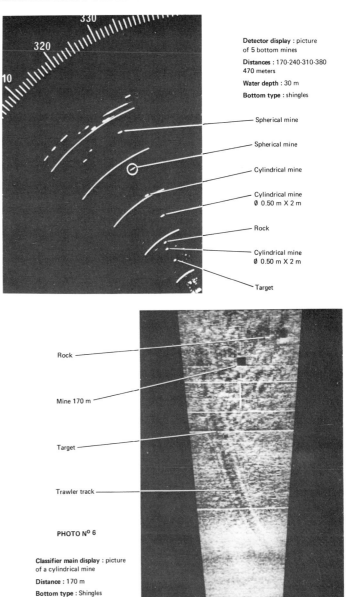

Detector display : picture of 5 bottom mines

Distances : 170-240-310-380 470 meters

Water depth : 30 m

Bottom type : shingles

Spherical mine

Spherical mine

Cylindrical mine

Cylindrical mine Ø 0.50 m X 2 m

Rock

Cylindrical mine Ø 0.50 m X 2 m

Target

Rock

Mine 170 m

Target

Trawler track

PHOTO Nº 6

Classifier main display : picture of a cylindrical mine

Distance : 170 m

Bottom type : Shingles

Detector and classifier displays (DUBM-21 sonar). (Thomson Sintra)

DUBM-21B (TSM 2021) array (*Eridan* or Tripartite class). (Thomson Sintra)

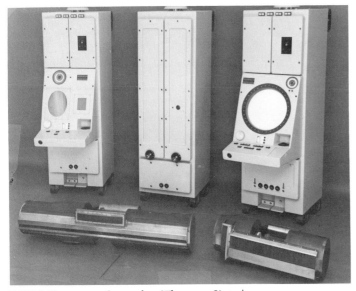

DUBM-21 arrays and consoles. (Thomson Sintra)

echo detector with a range of 100–500/600 m; and a shadow classifier imaging the seabed at 100–170 m, providing images even at 200 m, and having the capability, in theory, of identifying 0.2 square-meter objects. Both transducers are roll- and pitch-stabilized. They are not dome-housed, to avoid any distortion of the beam; at low hunting speed (4 kts), it was believed that cavitation around the transducers would have only a negligible effect.

Both transducers used preformed beams. The long-range beam (100 kHz) is 1.5 degrees wide and can sweep through 30-, 60-, or 90-degree sectors. The beam uses FM pulses 0.2 or 0.5 msec

long; and the range scales are 400, 600, and 900 meters. Source level is 110 dB (120 dB at maximum power). The transducer has 32 staves (each of 6 elements), and it produces 20 preformed reception beams. Their output is shown on a 16-inch PPI showing a 30-degree sector, with 100-m range markers.

The shadow (classifier) beam covers either a 3.5- or 10-degree arc and is 0.17 degrees wide. The beam can be depressed from −5 to −30 degrees. It operates at 420 kHz (plus or minus 15 kHz), using the same pulse widths as the search sonar, with 200- and 300-m range scales. Source level is 122 dB at maximum power. There are 80 preformed reception beams (from 64 staves, each of 6 transducers). Data is presented on a rectangular CRT, and the operator can mark mine images.

◆ DUBM-40A (TSM 5420)

This small towed mine-detection sonar is for use from standard naval launches and has an 80-meter (262-ft) cable. DUBM-40A emits 100-microsecond pulses at 735 kHz (1 kW power). Range scales are 40, 80, and 120 m. The transducer rotates at 3, 6, or 9 deg/sec, either continuously or by 5-, 10-, or 15-degree sectors. There are two displays: panoramic (PPI) and rectangular. Directivity: in bearing, 22 minutes; in elevation, 45 degrees. The standard naval launch that tows DUBM-40A is 14.87 × 4.14 × 1.18 m, weighs 18 tons, and is capable of 9 kts on diesel power. The sonar fish and cable weigh 196 kg (432 lbs), and the console inside the launch weighs another 185 kg (408 lbs).

A modified version, DUBM-40B, was designed for use by launches, hovercraft, and hydrofoils; it can also be used for wreck surveys. Total weight is 2055 kg, which compares to 4500 kg for DUBM-21A.

◆ DUBM-41

This towed side-scan sonar displays its data in real time on board the ship. The French Navy towed this sonar from U.S.-supplied MSO-class minesweepers equipped with the UQS-1D search sonar; DUBM-41 functioned as a classification sonar. The French view was that such a combination was much inferior to a single integrated sonar such as SQQ-14 or DUBM-20.

The sonar fish is 3.7 m (146 inches) long and weighs 350 kg (771 lbs). It emits 200-microsecond pulses at 735 and 785 kHz (750 watts), and range is 45 or 75 m to each side. If two fish are used (50 m [164 ft] apart), a total sweep width of 200 m (220 yds) can be achieved. The fish is held at a depth of 5–60 m (16–197 ft), and speed is 5 kts. The towing cable is 115 or 120 m (377 or 394 ft) long, each fish being held down by a kite. The height of an object can be determined within 0.5 meters. Directivity of the beam is 35 degrees vertically, 15 degrees horizontally.

The display is either a persistent-image CRT (TEI) or a pen-marked paper (ALDEN). Typical mine classification range is 60 m.

This sonar is very similar to the U.S. Shadowgraph of the 1960s, except that DUBM-41 has three bottom-looking sonars to keep it clear of underwater obstacles.

The DUBM-41B fish. (Direction des Constructions Navales)

◆ DUBM-42/IBIS 42

This side-looking sweep replaces DUBM-41, for future French minesweepers (BAMO). Tow speed is greater (10 vs. 4 kts), maximum depth is greater (300 vs. 100 m), and maximum detection range is increased (150 vs. 50 m). Unlike DUBM-41, DUBM-42 uses multiple preformed beams, and one rather than two vehicles are required. DUBM-42 can cover almost ten times the area in a given time.

The system built around DUBM-42 is IBIS 42. IBIS 42 is described as a surveillance system, mapping Q-routes in peacetime so that any changes (i.e., bottom-laid mines) can be de-

tected rapidly in an emergency. The fish carries a TSM 2051 sonar, for shadow classification of objects in its path, and a multibeam side-looking sonar (TSM 2054). The latter can cover a 200-m track at 12 kts, providing a high-resolution (20 cm × 10 cm) picture of the sea bottom. An associated hull sonar, TSM 5421, is used to detect moored mines, so that the hunter can avoid them. IBIS 42 feeds its Q-route data into a land-based processing center, which compares each survey with previously held data. A minehunting map is created in two steps. First the sonar image is updated, then the image is used to generate a synthetic map. Processing consists of bottom-image processing, extraction of any new echoes, location, correlation, and updating of the reference picture.

◆ DUPM-1

This hand-held minehunting sonar for divers operates in both active and passive modes and enables a clearance diver to find a mine in disturbed or muddy water. DUPM-1 uses a conical reflector with the controls on its back. Power is provided by nickel-cadmium batteries (good for 50 hours), and range is about 200 m. Overall diameter is about 12 inches, for a 9-degree beam (FM slides at 50–90 kHz). The operator listens to beats between the transmitted and received beams; the beat frequency is proportional to the time difference and, therefore, to the range, since the returning signal comes from a different portion of the FM slide. Range scales are 2–22 m, 20–90 m, and 60–200 m. In each case the audio frequency range is 250–2500 Hz. This sonar can also listen for a sonar beacon that is laid to mark either an area to be cleared or a suspicious object (37–41 kHz, tuned manually). The beacon, operating at 38 kHz, lasts for 500 hours and can be detected at 500–1000 m (550–1090 yds).

◆ Buried-Mine Hunting

Two alternative sonars to detect buried mines were shown at Bourget Navale in October 1986. They are the fruit of discussions among British, French, and Dutch companies begun about 1982; and at the time of the show a trilateral MoU was expected.

British Aerospace and Thomson Sintra proposed a low-frequency towed sonar, which might be accommodated in a DUBM-41 body, and which would use a flex-tensional transducer. To some extent this approach was proven during the hunt for the *Titanic*, a low-frequency sonar on board the SAR vehicle giving an image of the composition of the ocean's floor down to 1000 ft.

DRET (*Direction des Recherches, Études, et Techniques d'Armement*) is supporting a project using a 10–50 kHz sonar, which is suggested as a compromise between low frequency (which penetrates deeply but has poor definition) and high frequency (no penetration, high definition for mine classification). The array shown consisted of eight staves in star formation, each carrying three spot transducers, and the electronics would concentrate the beam on the bottom. Maximum penetration would be about 3 m.

◆ SAR

Thomson Sintra's advanced towed imaging sonar is effective down to 6000 m. This sonar was used to locate the *Titanic*. SAR would have naval applications in deep minehunting, and its characteristics give some idea of what really deep sonar imaging requires. The sonar, which is positively buoyant, is towed by a heavy (2.5-ton) depressor. In survey configuration, the towed body (1 × 5 m [39.4 × 197 in], 2.3 tons) carries a pair of side-scanning sonars (range 600 m to either side) and a bottom-penetrating echo sounder. The sonar operates at high frequency (190 kHz port, 170 kHz starboard) with a 0.5 × 80 degree beam; the transducer is 914 × 63 × 43 mm (36.0 × 2.4 × 1.7 inches).

◆ TSM 2022

Thomson Sintra's single-array hull-mounted commercial minehunting sonar is designed to detect mines at ranges of 500–600 m and to classify them at up to 250 m; this performance is achieved at water depths of 10–90 m. The sonar can also measure the depth of moored mines and can conduct channel searches in the side-scan mode. For minehunting, TSM 2022 is part of the IBIS V system with the TSM 2060 automatic plotter.

The single array, which is stabilized in roll and pitch (15 degrees in pitch, 5 degrees in roll), feeds one console; detection and classification must, therefore, be carried out consecutively. For detection, the sonar covers sectors of 14, 28, or 60 degrees, the latter requiring mechanical rather than electronic scanning. These sectors can be steered plus or minus 175 degrees from the bow. Range scales are 50–500 or 50–1000 meters. For classification, the range scales are 50–150 or 50–250 meters, and a 7-degree sector is covered, steerable plus or minus 175 degrees from the bow. Classification is either by shadow or by direct echo.

The transducers are arranged in a horizontal linear array, which can be tilted into the vertical position for depth-finding (e.g., of moored mines). The array has two beamwidths, 0.37 degrees for search and 0.17 degrees for classification. Either the search or the classification mode can be used for depth finding. The array can be turned broadside to an expected mine position; or turned to look down, the array can be used to profile the bottom over a 14- or 28-degree arc.

Minehunting is possible at up to 6 kts; mine avoidance, at 10 kts; and side-scanning, at 10 kts. The sonar is credited with a mine-position accuracy of 1 meter (3.28 ft). In the classification mode, resolution is 0.16 degrees, and range resolution is 0.15 meters. Thomson Sintra claims a 90-percent probability of detection of a 1 square-meter target (ground or moored mine) at ranges from 100 to 500 meters. With the array vertical, a moored mine 5 m (16.4 ft) below the surface can be detected at 300 meters (about 330 yds). Objects as small as 0.5 square meters (1.6 square ft) can be classified at up to 170 meters (about 186 yds).

TSM 2022 is the minehunting sonar of the Swedish *Landsort* class. Compared to DUBM-21, TSM 2022 was designed for smaller ships: hence the reversion to a single array.

TSM 2022 array. (Thomson Sintra)

◆ TSM 5420

Thomson Sintra's small-craft dipping search sonar is capable of displaying and classifying small seabed objects at depths as great as 300 m (984 ft).

◆ PAP 104

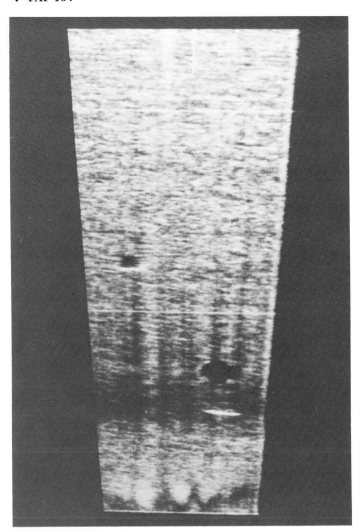

A mine and the PAP 104 vehicle on the main mine hunting sonar (classifier) display of a French minehunter. (Thomson Sintra)

PAP 104. (Direction des Constructions Navales)

PAP 104 (*poisson auto-propulsé*) was the first of the modern series of unmanned minehunting/minekilling submersibles. PAP was developed by ECA for the French Navy, to a requirement set by GESMA (*Groupe d'Études Sous-Marines de l'Atlantique*). GESMA wanted a mine-disposal device that could operate up to 500 m from a ship, in water between 10 and 100 m deep, for up to 20 minutes on station. The device had to be silent and almost entirely nonmagnetic to avoid setting off influence mines, and it had to be small and inexpensive so that

PAP 104 on the crane of a Dutch Tripartite Minehunter. (van der Giessen–de Noord).

(*Below*) PAP 104 Mk 5 modular design alternatives. Key: (1) central body; (2) standard or user-chosen head; (3) reacquisition sonar heads; (4) near-field identification sonar head (KAE AIS 11 sonar); (5) two moored mine cutters, one each side; (6) standard destruction charge (100 kg); (7) exercise charge; (8) high-capacity cutter; (9) manipulator with TV/searchlight; (10) ballast; (11) standard variable-pitch propellers; (12) MG motors (electronic commutation); (13) vertical thrusters; (14) standard blue wire; (15) new green wire (1000 meters); (16) alternative red (fiber optics) wire; (17) sealed battery; (18) high-capacity battery; (19) power down the cable; (20) standard guide rope with variable-length control; (21) manipulator guide rope with variable-length control. (ECA)

it could be used in large numbers by small minesweepers. Because PAP 104 replaced the usual mine-clearance divers, it had to be able to operate in conditions too severe for them, particularly in water with 4-knot current and in a force-4 wind. Finally, because the device was unmanned, it had to transmit back to the controller on board ship sufficient information to make the identification of a supposed mine reasonably certain, by means of some type of image.

The fish was, therefore, designed to carry an underwater television camera and an associated floodlight. Propelled by on-board batteries, the fish had sufficient energy for five 20-minute operations before recharging. The fish's speed, about 5 kts, was set by the requirement to operate despite a 4-knot current, and propulsion was by two podded electric motors. Because they could be controlled independently, the fish could turn sharply. There was no depth control as such. However, the fish, which was slightly heavier than water, had a guide rope hanging from it. When the rope hit bottom and began to drag, the weight that must be supported by the buoyancy of the fish was reduced enough to allow it to hover. Similarly, when the operation was over, the guide rope was dropped and the fish, which was now positively buoyant, surfaced. An onboard gyroscope kept the fish on course.

PAP was tracked by the shipboard minehunting sonar, using an on-board transponder in the sail atop the hull. Once PAP had been guided into position, the operator on board the minesweeper could fly the device into place, examine the supposed mine, and set a 100-kg demolition charge. In very poor visibility the destruction charge could be dropped by sonar alone; the sweeper's sonar would probably give an accuracy within 2 m (6.6 ft). After all, the purpose of the fish was not so much to ensure accuracy as to identify the object to be destroyed, so that ammunition (and time) was not expended wiping out bottom junk. The demolition charge was fired from deck, by acoustic signal (a small grenade), after the fish had been retrieved (typically 15 to 30 minutes after the charge had been laid).

Launching took about five minutes, and refitting between operations (replacement of guide rope, new guidance wire, new charge, battery replacement) took about fifteen.

The original version had a radius of action of 500 m (550 yds) and could run at either 80 m ("GESMA," i.e., French Navy,

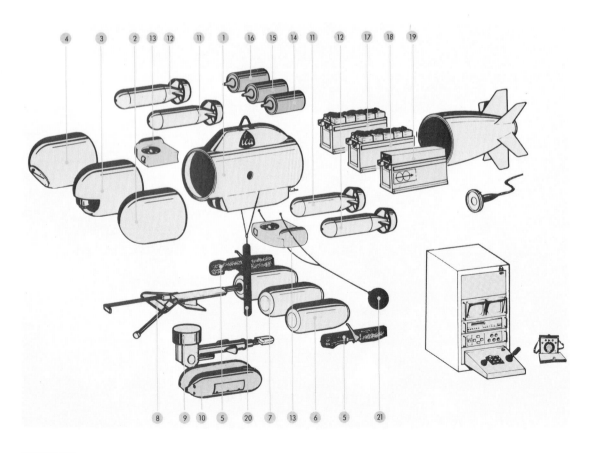

version: 262 ft) or 300 m ("civil" version: 984 ft). Speed was 2, 4, or 6 knots; and weight was 700 kg. Endurance was 3 hours at 2 kts. This version was intended solely to attack ground mines; it had no cutters to deal with mine mooring cables.

The first production version, for the French Navy, was Mk 2 (1975), made of formed aluminum rather than the sheet metal of the Mk-1 prototypes. Production cost was reduced by using standard car-type batteries and a commercial television camera.

Mk 3 was designed for reduced magnetic and acoustic signatures, as well as reduced corrosion. Mk 3 was the first export model. Mk 3s for the Royal Navy were built of nonmagnetic materials (other Mk3s are degaussed).

PAP Mk 4 (1983) could operate at depths of 300 m rather than the 120 m of earlier models. Although the Mk 3's hull could withstand the greater pressure, the earlier motors could not; Mk 4 has new motors (which can operate at a greater depth, using electronic commutation rather than brushes) for a speed of 5 kts. The principal sensor is either a high-resolution short-range sonar or a low-light television. Mk 4 was developed specifically for the Malaysian Navy, which wanted to be able to hunt mines at a greater depth.

Mk 4 has a high-data-rate cable developed for the German Navy, which wanted to use a Krupp-Atlas AIS 11-104 high-resolution short-range sonar instead of the usual television camera (for poor visibility). The sonar can acquire targets at up to 20 m, beyond television range. Although the Royal Navy also operates under conditions of low visibility in the water, the RN has preferred the low-light–television version of PAP 104.

Finally, Mk 4 introduced a cable-cutter, to attack deep-moored mines.

PAP Mk 5 is the current version. Maximum speed is 6 kts, and maximum depth is 300 m. Maximum distance from the launching ship is 600 m, and endurance is five 20-minute missions. The fish is modular, carrying alternative heads (user's sensors; a long-range relocation sonar; or a short-range classification sonar, the Krupp-Atlas AIS 11); alternative payloads (two moored mine cutters, one on either side; the 100-kg mine-disposal charge; a manipulator with a TV; a high-capacity cutter; or ballast for mid-water navigation); alternative forms of propulsion (standard variable-pitch propellers or MG motors with electronic commutation, for increased power and depth and reduced acoustic/magnetic signature; or vertical thrusters); alternative control cables (standard 1000-m [1090-yd] blue wire; a wider-band 1000-m green wire; or a 2000-m [2200-yd] red fiber-optic wire); alternative energy source (sealed battery; high-capacity storage battery; or power drawn through the control cable); and alternative means of depth control (guide cable with variable-length control or manipulator guide cable with variable-length control). Dimensions are 120 cm in diameter × 2.7 × 1.3 m; total weight including charge is 700 kg (800 kg for Mk 5) (47.2 × 106 × 51.2 inches; 1542/1763 lbs).

This system, developed and built by ECA, is currently in service in the Australian, Belgian, British, Dutch, French, German, Indonesian, Malaysian, Norwegian, and Yugoslavian Navies; over 300 PAP vehicles have been sold.

◆ IBIS III

The minehunting combat system of the Tripartite minehunter uses the DUBM-21 sonar. See also Skubermor below.

◆ IBIS V

Thomson-CSF's minesweeper combat system was announced in 1980. IBIS V incorporates the TSM 2022 sonar and the TSM 2060 22-inch four-color tactical display. The action display shows the ship's track and the contact's location; the operator can record and display positions of minelike objects such as obstructions on the bottom. Similarly, the operator can compare the current situation with previously recorded runs. The display shows a 100-meter safety circle around the minesweeper/hunter, so that it does not come too close to a suspected mine while investigating it. Ten previous contacts can be recorded and displayed.

IBIS V minehunting system shows the shadowing effect of mines illuminated by an overhead sonar. (Thomson Sintra)

Typically IBIS V includes a Thomson Sintra doppler bottom log (TSM 5721 or 5730).

Compared to IBIS III, IBIS V weighs 1.4 rather than 6 tons.

◆ IBIS VII

IBIS VII is a self-propelled sonar fish for the *Narvik*-class ocean minehunter (BAMO). Under development by DCN, the fish is

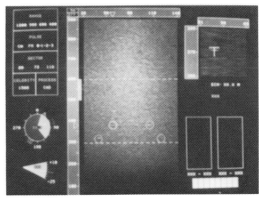

IBIS VII mine detection display, showing synthetic video to indicate mine positions. (Thomson Sintra)

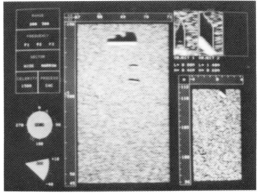

IBIS VII mine classification (shadow image) display. (Thomson Sintra)

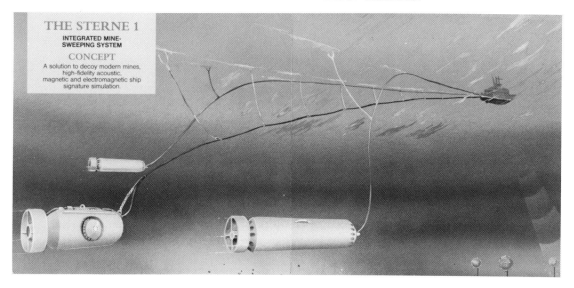

(*Above*) A Sterne I integrated mine countermeasures tow, consisting of a noise-maker flanked by two solenoid fish. (Thomson Sintra).

fitted with TSM 2023. Alternatively, the sonar could be fitted in towed form, to function either as a variable-depth sonar or (housed) as a hull sonar. When towed, the sonar can operate down to a depth of 200 m (about 660 ft) but at a trailing distance of less than 150 m abaft the ship. The sonar can operate at ship speeds of up to 5 kts, and its depth is automatically controlled. In self-propelled form, the fish can operate up to 600 m ahead of the using ship, down to 300 m in depth (about 1000 ft), and at up to 6 kts. The fish's course is automatically controlled. In either form, TSM 2023 can operate in sea-states up to 5. The sonar is designed to detect and classify targets simultaneously, at long range, operating at several frequencies. Classification is either by echo (image) or by shadow, and both detection and classification are computer-aided. Operating mode is selected with the assistance of a performance-prediction system.

Thomson Sintra describes this sonar as suitable, then, both for escort missions in moored fields, where it functions as an evasion aid, and for transit and operations in shallow waters, where it would be faced with bottom mines. DCN–Thomson Sintra–Bertin are the manufacturers, and IBIS VII is to replace DUBM-42. IBIS VII is in the early development stage.

◆ Sterne I

Sterne I is a complex acoustic/magnetic sweep designed to mimic some of the detailed structure of a target's signature.

(*Below*) The linear Sterne I tow, intended to mimic a ship's detailed magnetic signature. (Thomson Sintra)

Sterne I is analogous to the British Sea Serpent. The sweep employs two magnetic bodies (solenoids) and one acoustic body (the standard French Navy AP 4), the two solenoids lying to either side of, and slightly ahead of, the AP 4. Alternatively, a linear configuration, e.g., of six solenoids and one AP 4, can be used against mines so sophisticated that fidelity to the ship's signature is more important than swept width. Solenoid power is supplied by an electronic amplifier that can adjust power to the level and shape of the desired signature. The manufacturer, Thomson Sintra, claims that it can achieve a large magnetic sweepwidth even using low electrical-power levels.

◆ Skubermor

Skubermor is the French series of minesweeping systems; the Breton name means sweeper of the sea. All versions consist of a detection/classification sonar, a means of identification and neutralization, and a means of precise navigation. Skubermor I, in the minehunter *Circe*, uses the DUBM-20 sonar, an EVEC 10 plotting table, radar and Ragep-Toran for navigation, and PAP 104 and divers for mine classification and destruction. Skubermor II, in the converted ocean sweeper *Dompaire* (now discarded), used the DUBM-21 sonar, an EVEC 11 plotting table, and the same means of navigation and mine destruction (plus the American wire sweep originally supplied with the ship). Skubermor III, in the Tripartite Minehunters, uses an EVEC 20 plotting table, radar, Syledis-Toran or Decca (in Dutch and Belgian ships) for navigation, PAP 104, divers, and the lightweight wire sweep OD 3.

The EVEC (*Ensemble de Visualisation et d'Enregistrement de la Chasse Aux Mines*) automated plotting table is installed in the minehunter's CIC. EVEC 20 includes automatic naviga-

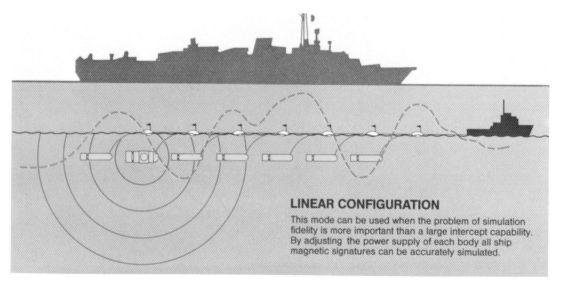

LINEAR CONFIGURATION

This mode can be used when the problem of simulation fidelity is more important than a large intercept capability. By adjusting the power supply of each body all ship magnetic signatures can be accurately simulated.

tional radar input. Toran and Syledis are radio navigation systems using the HF and VHF bands, respectively; the Decca system is Hi-Fix.

FINLAND

◆ Fiskar Sweeps

Fiskars Elesco supplies a magnetic sweep to the Finnish and Swedish navies, and in 1986 the company supplied the sweep for the two modified Tripartite sweepers built for Indonesia. The entire system weighs 2.5 tons and is intended particularly for use against mines on a rocky seabed. The magnetic sweep can be combined with an acoustic sweep to form FIMS (Fiskars Integrated Minesweep System), in which a microprocessor stores a series of waveforms corresponding to different ships, controls both the acoustic and magnetic sweeps, and monitors mine detonation (which shows whether the applied field is sufficient). The manufacturer claims that its system is particularly simple to operate and can be launched by two men in ten minutes.

GERMANY (WEST)

◆ DSQS-11

The current standard German minehunting sonar is also found in the new Australian *Rushcutter* class and on the last four Swedish *Landsort*-class minehunters (replacing the Thomson-CSF TSM 2022). DSQS-11 uses a 90-degree horizontal beam with overlapping sweep sectors to port, starboard, and straight ahead, all 90 degrees wide. The sonar can be depressed to measure a target's depth. DSQS-11 has a variable pulse rate and uses a PPI display whose video is processed to suppress noise returns.

DSQS-11H is a hull sonar in a retractable dome. This version consists of a cylindrical detection array and a flat classification array trainable through 130 degrees in azimuth. Simultaneous coverage of a 90-degree sector (in azimuth) is provided by RDT of 45 pulses, with 45 preformed receiving beams, each 2 degrees wide. The detection sector can be switched to any one of five preset center bearings 72 degrees apart, the sectors overlapping by 18 degrees. Classification is in two stages: first depth, then shape; up to five classification images can be stored. Operating frequency is 103 kHz, using 1-msec FM pulses for detection and 0.1-msec CW pulses for classification. The flat array is square, for a narrow beam; the cylinder is relatively shallow, presumably to form a fan beam. The full array projects 0.9 m below the keel, and the assembly above it is 2.5 m high. The cylindrical array transmits 45 preformed fan beams for detection (search); the flat array transmits 20 vertically stacked beams within a 2-degree horizontal width. This sonar equips the RAN *Bay*-class minehunters, the Thai Navy M48s, and the West German Type 332s.

◆ Pinguin A1

Pinguin A1 was the vehicle from which B3 was developed. A1 is now being used as the basis for a mine search/classification vehicle without mine destruction capability. At present this phase of minehunting takes much longer than actual disposal. The search/classification vehicle can be lighter than a full minehunting device and can operate in tandem with a mine destroyer. Dimensions are 1.0 m (diameter) × 3.7 m × 2.0 m (span) (39.4 × 145.7 × 78.7 inches); weight is about 2 tons; and diving depth (hull strength) is 200 m (656 ft). Propulsion is by a shrouded propeller at the tail, for a speed of up to 7 kts. The vehicle maneuvers with flaps set into the trailing edges of the two delta wings and with a vertical flap in the fin.

Normally Pinguin is powered through a cable run from the minehunter. However, the vehicle can also operate from a catamaran buoy carrying a small motor/generator unit. The fish tows the buoy, and in this form Pinguin can operate for up to ten hours. The buoy is used as one terminal of a radio data link with the minehunter, the vehicle operating much further away than is common in other underwater vehicle systems.

Pinguin A1 is expected to become operational in its role in the 1990s. A1 will probably carry a side-scanning sonar that will replace a similar sonar streamed by a minehunter.

Work on the Pinguin series began in the early 1970s, and at that time layouts for B3 and for B6, for offshore work, were developed. Design of a model of B3 for engineering development began in 1979, based on experience already gained in the Type-331 minehunter program.

◆ Pinguin B3

This mine identification-and-disposal vehicle was part of the Type-343 minehunter program. Like PAP 104, B3 is powered by motors fed by on-board batteries, in this case silver-zinc units giving 150 min of endurance at 6–8 kts. Propulsion is by twin podded units. The high speed was chosen because of the strong currents in German coastal waters; the vehicle can also hover. It turns by controlling the thrust of the two motors, and it climbs and dives by manipulating elevons in the wash and by using a vertical propeller in a tunnel. The gyro-stabilized vehicle is launched along a preprogrammed path to a point selected by the minehunter's combat system, and this degree of self-control reduces the operator's work load. Pinguin is brought into a hover over the location of the presumed mine, then uses television (which looks both ahead and down) or high-definition (2 MHz) sonar. The sonar's range is about 10 m, and the beam is focused using an acoustic lens. Alternatively, Pinguin can be

Pinguin B3. (Messerschmitt-Bölkow-Blohm)

fitted with a Krupp-Atlas high-definition (but lower frequency) sonar. The cable link with the controlling ship carries three sets of signals: a two-way digital data link for commands and feedback, a sonar link, and a television link.

The B3 body is slightly positively buoyant, to facilitate recovery. However, this buoyancy is small enough so that B3 can fly using relatively small control forces. Thus with 30-degrees-down elevon angle, B3 can reach maximum depth (from the surface) in less than a minute.

The manufacturer is MBB-VFW. The first test vehicle was completed in 1979, a second following in 1982, with sea trials in September–October 1982, followed by trials with the minehunter *Minden* in August 1983, and trials with alternative sensors in October–November 1983.

Dimensions are 70 cm (diameter) × 3.5 m × 1.5 m (span) × 1.45 m (height) (29.9 × 137.8 × 59.1 × 57.1 in); weight is 1350 kg (2975 lbs). Pinguin B3 carries two 120-kg (264-lb) charges in tandem so that it can destroy two mines during a single mission. Range from the operating ship is 600–1000 m (660–1090 yds). Diving depth is 100 m (328 ft).

◆ Troika

Troika consists of a control ship (which tows a moored sweep) and three drone sweepers that provide acoustic and magnetic signatures to trigger influence mines. The drones are tracked by stabilized X/C-band radar (the three boats are fitted with Luneberg Lens radar reflectors atop their masts), and the data link is UHF. Courses for both drones and control ship are corrected automatically. Control range is several miles. Typically the control ship carries her own mine-detection/avoidance sonar (DSQS-11A) to detect moored mines not swept by the drones.

Each Troika sweeper is 24 m (79 ft) long and displaces about 95 tons; draft is less than 2 m (6.6 ft). The boat has a blast-resistant steel hull (around which a wooden hull has been built), in which diesel engine, control, power supply, and remote controls are all shock-mounted. The diesel uses a hydraulic drive for shock resistance. Two coils, one at each end, generate a strong magnetic field to explode magnetic mines. For acoustic mines, each Troika carries two medium-frequency sound sources in its bow and tows a low-frequency source.

Krauss MaK is the prime contractor.

Experiments in 1959–60 led to the construction of two remotely controlled sweepers, *Walross* and *Seekuh* I (Manatee), followed in 1965 by two more *Seekuh*, the three constituting the first German Troika. The coastal minesweeper *Niobe* served as control ship. In 1969, under remote control, *Walross* swept a field of World War II mines in the Tegeler Platte shallows so that a lighthouse could be built. Six Troikas (18 remotely controlled craft and 6 controllers) were ordered in the mid-1970s (the controllers were converted in 1979–81).

A Troika boat, *Seehund* 1. (Bundesministerium der Verteidigung)

◆ MWS 80

Krupp-Atlas's minehunter weapons system uses the DQS-11H sonar and the PAP 104 vehicle. As applied to the Australian catamaran minehunters, the operations room itself is containerized so that it can be removed for maintenance without withdrawing the hunter herself, a second operations room being substituted.

INTERNATIONAL

◆ EPMDS

Experimental Parametric Mine-Detection System is a French-British-Dutch program to find buried and disguised mines. EPMDS uses a very stable towed fish carrying sonars, beamformers, some of the processors of the French DUBM-41, and new receiver arrays (with on-board processors) developed by British Aerospace. Trials are scheduled for 1990, on board the Dutch research ship *Tydeman.*

◆ NATO MCM Studies

NATO Project Group 22 is studying technologies for mechanical and influence sweeping in the mid-1990s and beyond, both for the deep sweeps wanted by the U.S. Navy and for coastal waters. The study of mechanical sweeping was conducted between September 1987 and May 1988; the issue was whether the full water column (2 km) could be swept by one system. The conclusion was that no single system could easily handle this volume because the sweep would be so heavy that a ship of destroyer size would be needed to tow it. Instead, two types of sweep would be required: a flying sweep using existing types of cutters, and a rolling or sliding sweep to clear bottom mines. Even so, large sweepers would be required, and the group considered using decommissioned bulk carriers and other merchant ships.

◆ ERMISS

Explosion Resistant Multi-Influence Sweep System is under development by a five-nation consortium within NATO (France, Germany, the Netherlands, the United Kingdom, and the United States) to deal with pressure as well as acoustic and magnetic mines. The first underwater explosion trials were conducted in 1983. The idea of an unsinkable craft that would simulate the usual target dates back to World War II, and in the early postwar era the idea led to the construction of the U.S. XMAP cylindrical countermeasure and to British experiments with strings of Thames barges. In the 1950s and 1960s the United States experimented with explosion-resistant modified Liberty ships, powered either by deck-mounted turboprops or by what amounted to outboard motors.

ERMISS is conceived as an inflated fabric tube surrounding an explosion-resistant body consisting of ballast tanks open at the top and sealed at the bottom by flexible rubber diaphragms. The inflated portion of the hull carries the diaphragms above the water, to form an air space that reduces shock effects. This concept is similar to the abortive U.S. surface-effect minehunter (MSH), and the air cushion also explains why air cushion minesweeping experiments have been so successful. In the case of ERMISS, the problem is to provide a sufficient pressure signature to detonate a pressure mine without coupling the hull so strongly to the water as to destroy it.

Germany, Britain, the Netherlands, and the United States signed an MoU covering the first two to three years of ERMISS development in 1978.

ITALY

The standard wire sweep is designated MIS.4.

◆ P2072

P2072 is FIAR's sonar for *Lerici*-class minehunters: see the U.S. SQQ-14 entry. This sonar is also used by the Belgian Navy. The Plessey Speedscan (see the British Type 2048 in the ASW section) has been integrated with P2072 for route surveillance. A memory has been added to the classification sonar so that up to four pictures can be recalled at will, either singly or together, to assist in classification. Signal processing is largely digital.

◆ MIN 77

This mine-disposal vehicle is designed for the *Lerici* class. Smaller than PAP 104 or Pinguin, MIN is powered, at up to 5 kts, by a single ducted propeller, which can be oriented in two planes for steering. Paired (fore and aft) vertical and horizontal thrusters work in tunnels in the body of the vehicle. For minimum magnetic signature, the body is GRP over an aluminum frame, and the use of pneumatic (actually compressed nitrogen rather than compressed air) motors eliminates the usual magnetic signature of an electric motor. The motors are fed by five oil-nitrogen pressure tanks, which can be topped up by an electric pump in the vehicle. Because the motors can operate at variable speed, the propellers can be fixed pitch, to minimize the acoustic signature. The vehicle can be recharged in 15 minutes and turned around for a second mission in 20 minutes.

MIN carries either a low-light-level television (with underwater light) or a sonar and is powered, in either case, by onboard batteries. The sonar operates at 400 kHz with 0.05- or 0.70-msec (for, respectively, seabed or moored mines) pulses, scanning a 60-degree sector in about 2 seconds. Maximum range is 20 m or 40 m (bottom or moored target). Display modes are raw video (bottom mines), synthetic video (moored mines), or raw video with digital range (moored mines).

The vehicle floats to the surface after it drops its acoustically fired charge.

Dimensions are 105 cm (diameter) × 3.5 m × 1.4 m (41.3 × 138 × 55.1 in); weight is 1300 kg (2865 lbs). Maximum depth is 200 m (656 ft), and maximum operational range is 400 m (440 yds) (the umbilical cable's length is 1000 m [1090 yds]). Endurance is 40 minutes at 3 kts. Hovering control is better than plus or minus 0.5 m, and the depth of the bottom can be measured more accurately than plus or minus 0.25 m. The vehicle can operate in sea-states up to 4 and in currents up to 3 kts (along the hunting line).

The vehicle is built by a consortium, SMIN, formed in February 1978 by Elsag and Riva Calzoni. SMIN received a contract for four vehicles in June 1979. Tests began in 1983.

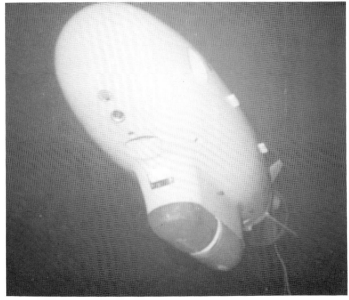

MIN 77. (Selenia)

◆ Pluto

This private-venture minehunting vehicle, designed by Gaymarine, is based on the FILIPPO underwater inspection device. The fiberglass body is mounted on a steel sled frame (for ease of handling). The body in turn consists of a fixed rear section (containing batteries and electronics) and a forward section that can tilt up to 240 degrees, carrying the sensors (200-kHz sonar, with a range of 30 m [98 ft] and 10-degree beamwidth, and television). Propulsion and control are by five electric motors, two, inclined at about 45 degrees, behind the head; two horizontal at the stern, for motion forward or in reverse; and one horizontal at the stern, to turn the vehicle. The operator uses two joysticks. The vehicle carries either explosive cutters or a 15-kg mine-destruction charge. Dimensions are 0.6 × 1.6 × 0.6 m (23.6 × 63.0 × 23.6 in); weight is 160 kg, including a 40-kg charge (353/88 lbs); maximum range is 500 m (550 yds); maximum diving depth is 400 m (1312 ft); speed is 6 kts; endurance is 1–2 hours.

As of 1986, reported purchasers were the Nigerian Navy (for four *Lericis*), the South Korean Navy, the Thai Navy, and the Italian Navy (which had conducted trials with the prototype in 1982–83). The U.S. Navy has bought at least two units.

◆ SSM

Gaymarine's semisubmersible minehunting vehicle operates at periscope depth under remote control (UHF data link), in up to sea-state 4 or 5. SSM carries both search (forty 3-deg preformed beams in a tiltable head, range about 200 m [656 ft]) and classification (mechanically scanned, 2 scans/sec, over a 45-deg sector, at 1.2 MHz, with a 7.5-m [24.6-ft] range) sonars. SSM can release a Pluto mine-disposal vehicle (released and recovered via a stern hatch). The Pluto can be automatically reloaded with mine-disposal charges (SSM carries six). The vehicle is powered by two diesel generators, amidships, and it has two stern propellers (for speeds up to 6 kts) and two vertical and two lateral thrusters (one each at bow and stern) for maneuvering.

SSM was announced in 1986, and construction of a prototype began in the fall of that year. SSM was conceived as a minehunting system for a craft of opportunity, the mother ship having no sonar.

JAPAN

The standard Japanese minehunting sonar is ZQS-2, a license-built version of the British Type 193. The -2B version is in the *Hatsushima* class. The standard acoustic sweep is designated S-2. Japan also uses the U.S. A Mk 4(v) and A Mk 6(b) and the U.S. magnetic sweeps M Mk 5(a), M Mk 6(a), and M Mk 6(h). Japan uses a distinctive Type S-4 remotely controlled underwater vehicle that lays its own mine-disposal charges. S-4 has two thrusters with prominent motor housings, one at each side at the rear end, and a saucer-shaped nose with a flat dome on top. S-4 is carried by the *Hatsushima* class; the earlier *Takami* class carries four divers.

The Japanese FY89 budget includes the first of a new class of deep-water minehunters, to employ the S-7 deep-water minehunting system and the S-8 deep-water moored sweep.

Japan also employs a helicopter minesweeping system, using KV-107s. They are now being replaced by Sikorsky MH-53Es.

NETHERLANDS

The standard sweeps are the MDV/OD.3 wire sweep, the AS.203 acoustic sweep, and the F.82 magnetic sweep. Presumably the wire sweep is a version of the French type.

SWEDEN

◆ SAM

A remotely controlled vehicle for preliminary sweep, SAM uses an integral magnetic sweep and a towed acoustic sweep and carries eight Dan buoys to mark a cleared channel. The hull is a pair of foam-filled GRP pontoons covered by an 18 × 6.1 m platform of aluminum girders, on which sits the engine casing (one 150-kW Volvo Penta TAMD 70D engine and Schottel propulsion unit). Speed is up to 8 kts, and endurance is up to 330 nm. Draft is 0.7 m (1.6 m over propeller).

The SAMs were delivered by Karlskronavarvet in 1983–86.

SAM unmanned craft. (SUTEC)

◆ Sea Eagle

This vehicle, used on board Swedish M80 (*Landsort*) -type minehunters, was developed by the Scandinavian Underwater Technology Group (SUTEC) from the earlier commercial Sea Owl. The Swedish Navy used Sea Owl and underwrote half the development cost of Sea Eagle.

The vehicle is built of aluminum inside a steel frame and is powered by four horizontal (two athwartships, two lengthwise) and three vertical electric thrusters; power is fed through the umbilical, which also passes control instructions and data. The main sensor is a television camera. There is also a telescoping arm, which carries either a small camera or a small destruction charge that is laid directly alongside the mine.

Dimensions are 76 cm (diameter) × 1.45 × 0.58 m (29.9 × 57.1 × 22.8 in); weight is 90 kg (198 lbs) total; range is 350 m (380 yds) from ship; maximum depth is 250 m (820 ft); speed is 2.5 kts.

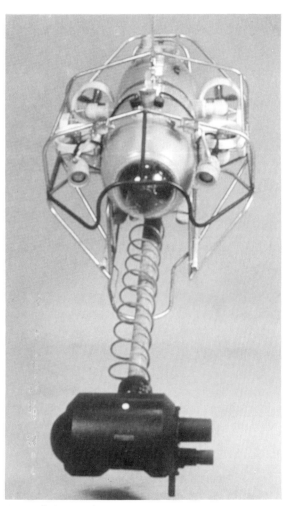

Sea Eagle (SUTEC).

Double Eagle (SUTEC).

◆ Philips 9MJ400

This mine-countermeasures system for the *Landsort* class incorporates a Racal MAINS Minehunting Action and Navigation System and the French TSM 2022 minehunting sonar. This system is related to the 9LV series of combat systems for fast patrol boats. 9MJ400 incorporates a lightweight 9LV100 optronic fire-control system, which uses the minehunting target plot for target detection, designation, and tracking and which controls the 40-mm gun.

Radar and sonar data are presented together on a common display. For minehunting, a search plan can be entered into the system, the operator monitoring the operation.

9MJ400 can control up to three SAMs. During actual sweeping, the ship is under the control of the integrated autopilot, for tracking accurately and for hovering the ship in the appropriate position for mine disposal.

USSR

Four or more Soviet Polnocny-A and -B–class medium landing ships are line-charge layers to clear beach defenses. These ships carry line charges in side troughs, with stern chutes to launch the two small remotely controlled motor boats that tow the charges into place.

As of 1988 the Soviets do not appear to have a mine-disposal submersible in service; their two *Vanya*-class minehunters carry boats, presumably for diver support. The Soviets do use a television minehunting system that lays marker buoys for later investigation of supposed mines. Published reports of a Soviet mine-disposal vehicle (SPA) seem to reflect the inclusion of such vehicles in encyclopedia articles (which describe the general state of the art, not necessarily the state of Soviet mine countermeasures).

The Soviets do have drone minesweepers (analogous to the German "Troikas"), the Ilyusha class. There are also several dozen towed sweep craft, and there is a helicopter-towed version of the Volga-class sports hydrofoil, carrying acoustic and magnetic countermeasures.

UNITED KINGDOM

◆ Towed Sweeps

Type "O" is Oropesa, the sweep to cut mine moorings; Type "A" is acoustic; and Type "M" is magnetic. The current standard British sweeps are the Oropesa Mk 3 Mod 2 (plus a later version with GRP floats, kites, and otters, for reduced weight); the MM Mk 11 magnetic loop sweep; and the Osborn acoustic sweep (see separate entry below). In the mid-1950s the wartime electrode (magnetic) sweeps were supplanted by loop sweeps, which could be towed at relatively high speed and were easier to stream and recover. However, because the loops swept out to both sides of the sweeper, they tended to place a higher magnetic field under the sweeper. Moreover, it was relatively difficult to place a low frequency acoustic sweep inside a loop to trigger combined magnetic/acoustic mines.

Typically, a double "O" sweep (towed by one sweeper, double because one wire is streamed to each side) has a depth of 30 m and a swept path 265 m (290 yds) wide. Team sweep by two ships is with an "A" sweep, with a depth of 90 m (300 ft) and a swept path 350 m (380 yds) wide. A typical magnetic loop sweep clears a path 75 m (80 yds) wide, 400 m (about 1300 ft) abaft the sweeper.

Standard acoustic sweeps use a broad-band noisemaker covering the usual ship frequencies. More recent systems, such as Osborn, can be tuned more precisely to the expected mine-triggering frequencies.

Below are listed the wire and magnetic sweeps in service just after World War II. Although much has changed since then, the figures listed should be typical of modern sweeps. Wire lengths are in fathoms (6 ft each), and other distances are in cables (120 fathoms). Since the wires are not straight, swept paths are much narrower than the lengths of the streamed wires.

(i) Oropesa Sweeps

Mk 1 Ocean sweepers. "O" sweep 300 fathoms (kite to otter), 8/8.5 kts; "A" sweep (two sweepers, 2½ cables apart), 400–450 fathoms between kite blocks, 8/8.5 kts.

Mk 2* coastal sweepers. "O" sweep 300 fathoms, 6–9 kts; "A" sweep, 300 fathoms, 5–7 kts.

Mk 3* coastal sweepers. "O" sweep 250 fathoms, 7–8 kts; "A" sweep, 300 fathoms, 5–6 kts. Mk 3*, rather than Mk 1, is the standard "Hunt"-class sweep.

Mk 7 inshore sweepers. "O" sweep only 60 fathoms, 9–10 kts. This sweep was used by postwar inshore craft ("Ham" class).

These sweeps may be prefixed W, as in W Mk 2 for coastal sweepers.

(ii) Magnetic Sweeps

LL means double longitudinal.

LL Mk 3 for coastal sweeper. Long leg 525 yds, short leg 200 yds, maximum sweep speed 7 kts, 300 yds wide in P formation (108-kW sweep current). Cycle 4.5 secs, double cycle 60 secs.

LL Mk 6* for ocean sweeper. Long leg 575 yds, short leg 225 yds, maximum sweep speed 12 kts, path 300 yds wide in P formation (220-kW sweep power). Cycle normally 3.5–7 secs, special 10 secs, double cycle 28–60 secs.

LL Mk 8 for inshore sweeper. Long leg 500 yds, short leg 175 yds, 7 kts, 200 yds wide (sweep power 35 kW using batteries).

Mod L modified Loop sweep. Three legs (575, 325, 185 yds), maximum speed 12 kts for ocean sweepers, 10 kts for coastal sweepers, 8 kts for trawlers; 125yd-wide path.

The current standard magnetic sweep is MM Mk 2.

(iii) Acoustic Sweeps

There were also acoustic sweeps, using both noisemakers and explosives. The latter, which may still be in use, were intended to deal with mines that could distinguish between the steady build-up of noise from a noise-making sweep and the relatively sharp build-up of the noise of a real ship. Postwar standard British types were AH Mk 4 (hammer), AO Mk 4 (oscillator), and AX Mk 3 (explosive).

See also EDATS below.

◆ Type 193/193M

Type 193 is the current standard British minehunting sonar. It operates at two frequencies: a lower frequency for search and a higher frequency for better resolution for mine classification. The sonar transducer, which is stabilized, is hull-mounted, and it is steerable both in train (270 deg to either side) and in elevation.

The modernized Type 193M entered production in 1976. Improvements include greater reliability and much reduced weight and volume, all consequences of adopting solid-state electron-

ics. The most significant performance improvements were the introduction of a long (600-yard) range scale and a better beam pattern.

Because the variety of objects on the sea floor is immense, the sonar needs an unusually wide dynamic range, in this case 120 dB. However, conventional displays are limited to 20 dB, so that the sonar must be set to operate in a variety of modes: shadow, target shape, or echo structure classification. A very short pulse mode (50 microseconds) shows target highlights without distorting them by overlapping.

In the shadow mode, the sonar illuminates the area behind the mine and then picks up the reflections. This technique is used in Type 162 and in the U.S. Shadowgraph. The shape of the shadow does provide evidence of the shape of the object, but in many cases no shadow can be formed (the seabed is not sufficiently reflective), or there may not be a useful shadow (as in the case of ground mines in deep water). In the target-shape mode the sonar senses the detailed structure of the returning echo. This mode is expected to be particularly effective when the mine has a rough surface, echoes coming from many points on its surface. However, modern mines are unlikely to become very rough even after lengthy immersion. A smooth mine is a poor reflector, and its shape may not show up clearly. The third mode, echo structure, works on discontinuities in the mine's projected surface. The result is only rarely an image resembling a mine, but it does make classification more accurate.

◆ Type 2059

Type 2059 is a high-frequency PAP 104 tracking sonar.

◆ Type 2093

Type 2093 is the Plessey/General Electric replacement for the existing hull-borne Type 193, the first of which will be fitted to the new British *Sandown*-class Single Role Minehunter. The

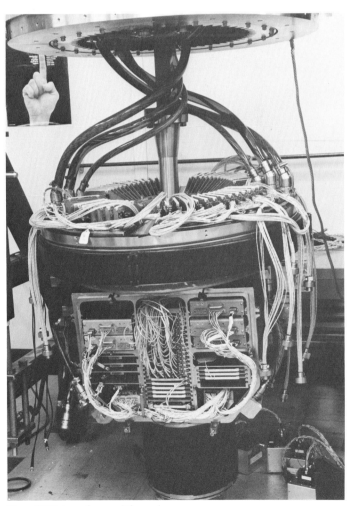

Type 2093 transducers. (Plessey)

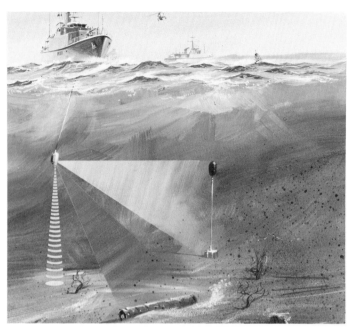

Type 2093 operation, showing the multiple sonar beams. (Plessey)

manufacturer describes 2093 as the first variable-depth multi-mode minehunting sonar. It can operate either as a hull or a variable-depth sonar and has different frequencies for search and classification. The manufacturer claims a range at least twice that of a conventional hull-mounted minehunting sonar and three times the detection depth. Maximum speed of advance is 12 kts, compared to 3–4 kts for Type 193M.

The towed body, 1.054 m in diameter (not including vanes) and 2.521 m high, weighs 2900 kg in all. It accommodates a low-frequency ring array, a VLF ring array, a VHF projector, an HF projector, a VLF projector, and an HF/VHF hydrophone, as well as a depth sounder on the underside. The manufacturer does not define these frequency bands, but even the VLF band is likely to be on the order of 100 kHz. The HF and VHF sonars are used for classification, and they share a common broad-band receiver. They use separate transmitter arrays, generating either wide or narrow beams according to the selected sonar function. The LF height-finder uses a separate fixed-beamwidth array. The VLF transmitter uses its own array of six circular transducer layers, for vertical beamwidth control. The depth sounder operates at VLF.

Alternative operating modes are VLF search and moored mine classification; LF search and moored mine classification; VLF and LF search; search and ground mine classification; and search and route survey. A special height-finding sonar in the system can find moored mines, concurrently with the search

for bottom mines. Two classification frequencies are available, to deal with different bottom and sea conditions.

There are two identical shipboard displays, each fed by a telemetry link and each capable of any of the sonar processing functions (for dual operation). Computer-aided classification circuits take expanded HF or VHF range data and provide images directly to the display consoles.

2093 is credited with twice the range and three times the depth performance of 193, down to the continental shelf. 2093 costs three times as much as the hull-mounted 193. The RN has ordered thirteen units, and the first are now on trials.

Type 2093 was developed under a fixed-price contract at a total cost of £83 million, including delivery of two preprototypes and ten production units.

◆ EDATS

Extra-Deep Armed Team Sweep is found in the current "River"-class steel ocean minesweepers. EDATS, deployed by paired sweepers, is a wire catenary stretched between them. Each sweeper tows a kite to depress its end of the sweep wire, and a sweep monitor pod hangs from the sweep wire just outboard of the kite, to provide an acoustic telemetry link back to the sweeper.

This system is also referred to as BAJ-Vickers Wire Sweep Mk 9 Team Sweep System; the word "armed" presumably refers to the use of explosive wire cutters rather than a serrated wire. The original EDATS used a kite to depress both the sweep wire and the kite wire. WS Mk 9 has only one kite, since the sweep wire is attached to the end of the kite wire, to give a deeper sweep with a given length of kite wire.

Typically, the sweep depth is 200 m and the sweep path is 350 m wide. The ends of the sweep wire are about 1000 m astern of the sweepers, and ideally the wire is towed at 8–9 kts about 2–3 m (in practice, about 10 m) above the seabed, to cut wires of mines with very short tethers. These conditions are difficult to ensure because of the current and the irregular shape of the bottom. The sweep, therefore, incorporates tensionmeters measuring the pull of the wire and kites (to maintain a constant sweep speed). The pair of acoustic monitor pods are intended to maintain depth above the bottom. As of 1983, this stage of development had not yet been attained.

The first "River"-class sweepers were ordered in September 1982, after EDATS trials using the commercial stern trawlers *St. David* and *Venturer*. The British naval requirement is to sweep mines out to the edge of the continental shelf. The sweepers are steel, and in wartime they would approach from the sea to avoid influence mine fields closer inshore.

◆ Osborn (MSSA Mk 1)

Osborn is an acoustic sweep developed and manufactured by British Aerospace. In contrast to earlier broad-band noise

Osborn. (British Aerospace)

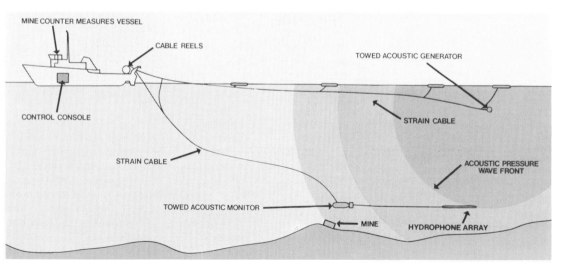

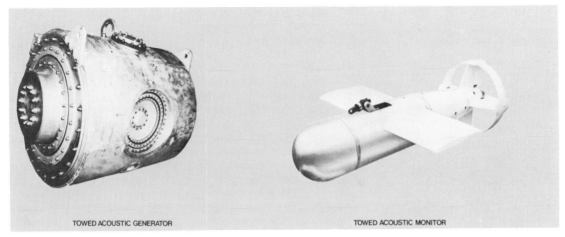

TOWED ACOUSTIC GENERATOR   TOWED ACOUSTIC MONITOR

(*Above*) Osborn. (British Aerospace)

sources, Osborn can simulate specific ship signatures and, thus, can deal with a relatively intelligent acoustic mine. Osborn combines an acoustic generator near the surface with an acoustic monitor towed at greater depth, to ensure that the required degree of signature is supplied near the mine, despite surface layering.

As of 1988, Osborn was in service in the Royal Navy and was being evaluated by the U.S. Navy.

◆ Pilotfish

This agile towed body was developed by the Admiralty Research Establishment as the basis of a future deep single-ship sweep. The sweep would be positioned between two Pilotfish, which would control its depth. Pilotfish could also be used as a maneuverable acoustic decoy. Control is exerted by ailerons (in an X-shaped wing, for roll) and by elevators (in a cruciform tail).

◆ Scarab

This floating mine countermeasure was developed on an urgent basis by the Admiralty Research Establishment, for the Persian Gulf. Scarab was intended to replace the usual technique, shooting at the mines with rifles, since some mines sank instead of exploding and thus remained dangerous. Scarab is a pair of pontoons driven by a BMW yacht engine. Guided visually to within 50 m of the mine, at a speed of about 5 kts, Scarab is then guided closer by closed-circuit television. Scarab carries a hydraulic grab. Once the mine has been secured, Scarab reverses, reeling out a cable by means of which the mine can be either towed away or detonated at a safe distance. Scarab is thus, in effect, a sea-going equivalent of the remotely control mine-disposal vehicles that have existed for some years.

◆ Invasion Sweep

During the Falklands War, AUWE (Admiralty Underwater Weapons Establishment) designed, delivered, and shipped (via Hercules) both magnetic and acoustic influence sweeps intended to protect landing ships in the islands' inshore waters (such as Teal Inlet). The sweeps, which simulated an LSL signature, were towed ahead by smaller landing craft (LCVPs). LCVPs were considered preferable to helicopters because the craft were less easily detected from shore, and thus did not tend to reveal the fact of a planned landing.

The magnetic assault sweep was a towed bar electromagnet in a cushioned wooden box, fed by electronics onboard the towing craft. The acoustic sweep (Go-Kan) was a commercial hydrosounder (a Kango Type-637 hammer, later replaced by a Type 2500 for greater power and more output at low frequency) in an industrial waste-cotton bin. In fact, this sweep was used only once, for an exploratory trip on the north side of East Falkland; no amphibious craft followed on that occasion.

These improvised sweeps worked well enough to encourage postwar work on something more satisfactory. By 1983, AUWE had developed a variable-moment magnet (VMM) that could be air-shipped in a no-field condition, then set at different strengths for different conditions.

In a larger sense, the Falklands demonstrated a need for a covert sweeping capability: otherwise, the sweepers preparing the beach alert the defenders. In 1983 it was reported that AUWE was working on a torpedolike device, carrying a side-scanning sonar, for covert minehunting.

◆ AMMS

Plessey's Advanced Mirror Minehunting System employs a trainable reflector instead of a beam-preformer. The projector produces a broad beam; the reflector focuses the reflected beam. This type of system is usable for minehunting because the target, the mine, does not move and because distances are quite short: there is enough time to send and receive many narrow beams in succession. In ASW, an equivalent system would fail because a sonar waiting to receive on one beam before listening to the next would miss distant, fast-moving targets.

Under Project Kingfisher, Plessey packaged several minehunting mirror sonars into hull domes for use on board U.S. frigates for mine evasion in the Persian Gulf.

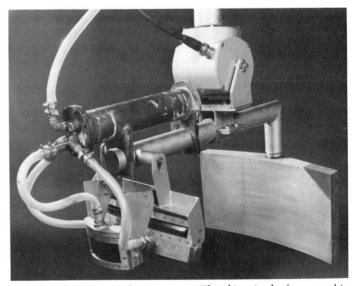

The Plessey mirror minehunting sonar. The object in the foreground is the broad-beam transducer, with a narrow-beam transducer behind it, and the mirror itself in the background. (Plessey)

◆ ARMS

Plessey's Advanced Remote Minehunting System is designed to be carried by ships not intended for minehunting. A remotely operated vehicle (ROV) would swim up to 1000 m ahead of the ship and down to 300 m below it, at a speed of up to 6 kts, clearing a safe channel. The vehicle is fully stabilized, and its automatic operation can be overridden by its operator, who can

ARMS vehicle hunting for mines. (Plessey)

make ARMS hover. The vehicle itself provides a sonar or underwater television picture on a display screen on board the operating vessel. When ARMS identifies a mine, the ROV can lower a mine-destruction charge, which is detonated from the ROV by acoustic link. There is also a cable cutter for use against moored mines.

The ROV is lowered over the side by crane then swims out 20 m and submerges to an ordered depth and heading. The ROV is controlled via a cable tether and has a unique tandem propeller drive that should make for very accurate positioning even in high currents and turbulence. Because the ROV is positively buoyant, it will rise to the surface in the event of failure. The entire system is containerized for rapid deployment, one of three containers carrying the vehicle and its spares.

ARMS was announced in 1987, as a private venture. It may have been inspired by British fears of Argentine influence mines in the Falklands landing areas; there were no British minesweepers fast enough to accompany the invasion fleet, and the British had no minesweeping helicopters. Plessey's claim that the three ARMS containers can fit a standard DC-9 would apply to the Persian Gulf problem: if ARMS had been on the shelf, it could presumably have been deployed very fast. More generally, ARMS can be seen as one ultimate development of the minehunting vehicle idea typified by the French PAP 104 or the U.S. MNS.

◆ Dragonfly

The GEC Avionics/OSEL (Offshore Systems Engineering, Ltd.) modular underwater vehicle was entered in the Royal Navy's competition for an underwater remotely controlled inspection and mine-disposal vehicle (RCIV and RCMDS II). The basic vehicle (hydraulic thruster, electrical power system, control telemetry, navigation equipment, and cameras) carries a variable payload, such as a pair of manipulator arms or cutters.

The umbilical carries both power and a fiber-optic data link with three digital video channels (allowing for both television and sonar) and a high-speed two-way control (and feedback) data link. Up to six cameras can be accommodated. There is a second fiber-optic link for redundancy, and the umbilical carries two

additional cables so that sonar or other payload data can be carried outside the fiber-optics.

The combination of RCIV and RCMDS is to replace the single PAP 104; this combination shows much the same logic as the German choice of Pinguin A1/B3 (see West Germany above).

Two separate requirements for remotely controlled vehicles were formulated late in 1984, with an initial purchase of 20 vehicles planned (and a total of as many as 100 possible). Formal invitations to tender were issued in the summer of 1985, with bids for the inspection vehicle due by 14 November 1985 and those for the mine-disposal vehicle due by 28 November 1985.

The inspection requirement, NSR MER(S) 19/85, calls for a fast inexpensive vehicle, the RCIV, to classify a sonar contact. The RCMDS will actually place the charges. Reportedly both vehicles will have to be able to navigate very precisely to benefit from route surveys so that only objects not previously identified will be investigated. ECA and Honeywell offered PAP 104 Mk 5 for the RCIV, with an enhanced version for the RCMDS; Plessey/Ametek Straza offered a derivative of the Scorpio remotely operated vehicle; Ferranti offered a modified version of the existing Spring 104 designed by Robertson Tritech of Norway; Smiths Industries/OSEL offered a new vehicle; Sutec of Sweden offered a version of its Sea Eagle; Fairey offered Trail Blazer; GEC offered Microv; BAJ and MBB offered Pinguin; Marconi offered Minnow; and British Aerospace also offered a system. High definition sonars were the subject of a parallel competition.

◆ Microv

This vehicle, developed by GEC/OSEL, is teamed with Dragonfly for the Royal Navy RCIV/RCMDS II requirement. Microv is derived from the earlier UFO and ROV oil-field support vehicles, the principal change being a low-drag frame. Power is supplied by an internal battery, and propulsion is by three thrusters.

Dimensions are 1 m (diameter) × 2.1 × 0.6 m; total weight is 150 kg; maximum range is 800 m; depth is 200 m; speed is 8+ kts.

◆ Minnow

The Marconi Underwater Systems, Ltd. (MUSL) mine disposal vehicle is driven by four thrusters. Power is taken from an umbilical, and Minnow carries both a sonar and a television.

◆ RCV225

A competitor with Dragonfly and Microv for RCIV/RCMDS II, RCV225 was developed by Honeywell Leafield, the British contractor for PAP 104. The company developed new modules for PAP 104s on board "Hunt"- and Sandown-class countermeasures ships. RCV225 itself was developed for North Sea oil-field support and was first used in 1974. RCV225 is powered by four thrusters.

A larger RCV150 has manipulators and/or cable cutters.

◆ Sea Pup

British Aerospace Naval Division's mine-disposal vehicle was tested in October 1983.

◆ Sea Serpent

Vosper Thorneycroft's sweep was announced in 1987, to counter sophisticated mines. Two or more bodies, each containing 19 variable-moment magnets, can simulate a real ship, whose magnetic field varies along its length. The usual magnetic countermeasure, whose field is more or less uniform along its length, can be recognized as a decoy by a sophisticated signal processor. Conversely, if Sea Serpent is towed by a potential target, a sophisticated mine will detect and interpret the extended field as a magnetic sweep. The magnets are all permanent; the system requires electric power only for resetting. In effect, Sea Serpent is a huge (and sophisticated) equivalent of the U.S. Magnetic Orange Pipe (see below).

Osborn is the acoustic complement to this system.

◆ Trail Blazer

This joint-venture underwater vehicle is made by Fairey Hydraulics and ISE of Canada. Trail Blazer was designed to fit a standard 747 cargo container and can be deployed from small fishing craft. The vehicle is designed for slight positive buoyancy, using high-density foam (and more foam can be added to balance heavier loads). Propulsion is by five hydraulic thrusters (two at the after end for ahead and reverse, two amidships for lateral movement, and one vertical), the electrical power for the hydraulic pump coming from the controlling vessel through the umbilical. Control is exercised through a single joystick for the four thrusters in the horizontal plane, with a separate control for the vertical thruster. The standard sensor is a television, and the vehicle can carry either four 50-kg (U.S. Navy standard) or one 127-kg (NATO standard) mine-disposal charge.

Dimensions are 64 cm (diameter) × 2.63 × 0.86 m; weight is 772 kg, including a 130-kg charge. Maximum range is 1+ km; diving depth is 500 m; speed is 5.75 kts.

◆ QX3/System 880

Racal MCM's Action Information System, the third-generation, consists of a Racal Integrated Navigation System (RINS) and a Racal Action Display System (RADS). RINS suffices for minesweepers, which need only to know precisely which channel they have swept. RADS is required for minehunters and sweeper/hunters. A typical RADS display shows the known bottom features, the vessel's track, a safety circle around the vessel, the location of a suspected mine (with its danger circle), and the locations of other suspected mines.

In the complete system, RINS and RADS share a common central computer. The RINS inputs are various positioning systems, including the log and gyro; RINS exchanges data with the autopilot. RADS inputs are from sonar and radar; RADS exchanges data with the minehunting vehicle proper and provides data to the chart table and to tactical displays. RINS can be used to guide the helmsman, or it can control the ship automatically for great track precision.

In theory, the minehunter can make an initial route survey using a side-scanning sonar; RADS/RINS can locate any contacts precisely so that the hunter can revisit them later. The system also incorporates a track plotter, so that the results of minesweeping or -hunting can be charted for use by other vessels. These charts also show whether coverage of an area is sufficiently complete.

QX3 is in service in U.S. *Avenger*-class minesweepers. QX3(3) is in service in British "Ton"-class minehunter refits. QX3(1) is on board "River"-class minesweepers. The "Ton"-class version includes an interface with Type 193, and the system can store up to 60 contacts/km. System 880 is the export version.

UNITED STATES

◆ U.S. Towed Sweeps

There are three types: A, acoustic; M, magnetic; and O, Oropesa (wire sweep). All date from World War II. The principal versions are:

(i) Acoustic Sweeps

A Mk 2 parallel pipes or bars, towed broadside-on, in different versions for different frequencies and different towing speeds (4–20 kts). A Mk 2(g) was used by helicopter minesweepers in North Vietnam in 1973. Suspended from a Size 5 O-float, A Mk 2(g) weighs 130 lbs and consists of two parallel triangular plates connected by three pipes, each of which is welded at each end to the vertices of the triangles. Two other pipes are pivoted from one of these plates; as the device moves through the water, the two pivoting pipes strike each other and the other pipes. Water passing between the pipes creates a venturi effect, reducing the pressure between them and thus causing them to collide. The faster the tow, the greater the intensity of the collisions.

A Mk 4 towed hammer box, conceived for small craft in restricted areas but later extended to all types. A Mk 4 consists of a hydraulically driven hammer in a streamlined box, driven by a gasoline engine on board the sweeper. A Mk 4(v) weighs about 1300 lbs.

A Mk 6 very low frequency acoustic sweep, the towed eccentric mechanism, usually towed about 1200 yds astern of a coastal sweeper. A Mk 6(b) uses a diaphragm driven by pistons connected to an eccentric driven by an electric motor. Weight is about 3500 lbs. During Operation End Sweep, the clearance of North Vietnamese waters, A Mk 2(g) was recommended as a replacement for the A Mk 6(b) then in use by the surface sweepers.

There was also an explosive sweep (A Mk 5).

A U.S. acoustic sweep, photographed in 1987. It resembles, but is not identical to, the old A Mk 2. It is streamed suspended from an O-type float. (U.S. Navy)

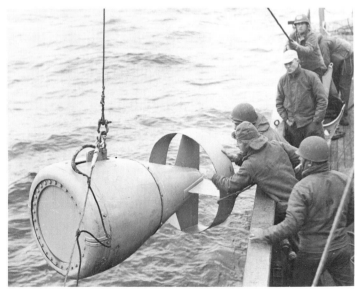

A Mk 4(V) acoustic sweep. (U.S. Navy)

(ii) Magnetic Sweeps

M Mk 1 magnetized iron rail, which could be extemporized. It was not standard after World War II, but a device of this type was used in Vietnam (in the Cua Viet River, after magnetic/

acoustic mines were found there). The MOP (see below) is reminiscent of this device.

M Mk 4(m) small two-ship closed loop.

M Mk 4(i) two-ship single-catenary small-craft sweep, using special tails, the short legs of which are connected by an insulated cable forming the catenary; the long legs stream aft.

M Mk 4(v) postwar variation on M Mk 4.

M Mk 5(c) standard large-sweeper sweep, consisting of two legs (buoyant conducting cables) married together through the 675-foot length of the shorter leg, with the longer leg streaming aft another 900 ft. In some arrangements two or more ships could sweep together, pulsing their tails synchronously.

M Mk 5(a) straight-tail electrode sweep (I-sweep).

M Mk 6(a) J-sweep: the long leg curves around to meet a diverted line towed by the ship and connected to an Oropesa and a kite.

M Mk 6(b) single-ship closed-loop sweep, using Oropesa floats to keep the legs apart.

M Mk 6(h) closed-loop sweep, the two legs meeting at a diverter line streamed from an Oropesa.

(iii) Oropesa (Wire) Sweeps

O Size 1 largest, for ocean sweepers (MSO and MCM). When streamed with 300-fathom wires, the swept path is 500 yds wide (double sweep) at maximum sweep speed, about 8.5 kts for an MSO. A single-side sweep can clear a 250-yd path at 10 kts. Sweep depth is 5–35 fathoms (maximum 40 fathoms).

O Size 4 modified, for coastal sweepers (MSC). With 300 fathoms of wire streamed on each side, the swept path is 420 yds at 8 kts; wire depth is 2–30 fathoms.

O Size 5 small, for minesweeping launches (MSL), etc. This type uses explosive cutters because the craft are too slow for the saw action of the wire to cut mine moorings. Sweep speed can be up to 7 kts. With 250 fathoms of wire streamed on one side, the swept path is 176 yds wide. This sweep could be used as an emergency or shallow-depth sweep, with a wire depth of 2 or 3 fathoms. Size 5-G is used for adapted landing craft, etc., and was modified for helicopters and MSBs. 5-G uses a different otter and depressor and can be streamed at relatively high speed in shallow water, e.g., for assault purposes. Depth control is more precise than in Size 5, so 5-G can operate in 1–7 fathoms, at 6–14 kts. With 150 fathoms of wire streamed on one side, the swept path is 70 yds wide.

S Type C a two-speed high-speed sweep for converted destroyers, but such ships no longer exist. The two-speed feature referred to the ability of the special paravanes to stabilize the sweep in two quite different speed ranges, around 12 and 20 kts.

All the standard sweeps are designed to deal with mines floating close to the surface. When the sweeps were designed, the only exceptions were ground mines (which cannot be wireswept) and antenna mines, the cases of which might be well below the surface. However, the sweep wire could brush the vertical antenna, causing the antenna mine to explode. At present the United States, like her allies, is developing a deep sweep to cut loose the cases of rising mines, which may be over a thousand feet below the surface.

♦ ALQ-141/SLQ-35

ALQ-141 is called DOUBLE ALFA; SLQ-35, a ship-towed version, is ALFA TWO. The designation suggests an acoustic sweep, presumably covering a different portion of the spectrum than ALQ-160. ALQ-141 was described about 1979 as an electronic counter to deep-water rising mines. This sweep is manufactured by Westinghouse. There was also an EDO ALQ-138, probably an unsuccessful competitor.

A helicopter-towed acoustic countermeasure used during the clearance of the Red Sea in 1984. Although labeled Mk 104, it is far more sophisticated than the simple bars used in Vietnam and is presumably ALQ-141 or -160. (U.S. Navy)

♦ ALQ-160

ALQ-160 is a helicopter-towed acoustic sweep using a stable towed body.

♦ ALQ-166

EDO's magnetic minesweeping hydrofoil sled is the successor to Mk 105. ALQ-106 exploits the greater pulling capacity of the new MH-53E helicopter, which replaces the original RH-53D. Unlike the earlier catamaran, ALQ-166 is a monohull and, thus, can carry a heavier load in the same dimensions. The new 1200-HP Avco Lycoming engine is about three times as powerful as the engine of the Mk 105, to drive a more powerful sweep generator. Reportedly 166 quadruples the net sweep rate of the earlier device and can operate at 6–30 kts. A sled-mounted ASQ-182 measures the magnetic environment so that sweep track spacing can be optimized. The second production ALQ-166 was delivered in FY83. EDO began the development of this Lightweight Magnetic Sweep (LMS) with internal R&D funds, to counter the next-generation mine threat; this LMS was then successful against existing advanced projects in a navy trade-off study.

ALQ-166 (EDO)

Reportedly it is possible to use a magnetic sweep of this type in conjunction with a water pressure monitor, so that pressure/magnetic mines can be swept at the turn of the tide. Such mines avoid detonation at the turn of the tide by seeking an accompanying magnetic signature. Similarly, it would be possible to sweep pressure-acoustic mines using a pressure monitor and an acoustic sweep. However, at least some pressure mines avoid this problem by monitoring the rate of pressure change, which is much faster for a ship than for the tide.

◆ AQS-14

AQS-14 is Westinghouse's high-speed helicopter-towed mine-hunting sonar. It is actively controlled for platform stability; the stabilized towed body carries a high-resolution side-scanning sonar. AQS-14 is said to allow sweeping at a rate about 40 percent faster than can be achieved by conventional methods.

The sonar is a Westinghouse-patented multibeam all-range focusing type, providing an operator with a continuous high-resolution television image of objects to either side. The system employs active controls to keep itself clear of both the bottom and the surface and can even right itself if launched upside down. Objects detected by the sonar are marked by the towing helicopter for further investigation.

Westinghouse describes AQS-14 as suitable for installation on board hovercraft and other surface-effect ships.

Production was approved in March 1980, operational evaluation having been completed in September 1979 (and having proceeded since FY76). As of March 1988, 29 units had been made. This sonar operates with ALQ-141. AQS-14 was first used operationally during the Red Sea operation in 1984, marking minelike objects with sonar beacons for subsequent inspection either by remotely operated vehicles or by divers.

AQS-14 helicopter-towed fish, with the towing helicopter in the background. (U.S. Naval Institute)

◆ AQS-20

AQS-20 is a sonar mine detector, formerly the Advanced Mine-hunting Reconnaissance System. No details are available.

◆ Mk 24 Underwater Ordnance Locator/Klein 590

This lightweight side-scanning sonar for minehunting and channel conditioning was developed by Klein Hydroscan. Earlier UOLs were magnetic detectors. Mk 24 can be used on board virtually unmodified commercial helicopters and small craft, and it has been adopted for the U.S. Craft of Opportunity Program. Mk 24 has also been adopted for the seven surviving U.S. minesweeping boats (MSBs), four of which were sent to clear the Persian Gulf in 1987. Mk 24 was used during the clearance of the Suez Canal after the 1973 Mid-East War and has been used extensively since then by U.S. Navy explosive ordnance disposal teams and similar organizations. Foreign naval users include Sweden, Greece, Colombia, South Korea, New Zealand, Norway, Pakistan, Portugal, West Germany, the Netherlands, Indonesia, Thailand, and Canada.

Small size and light weight are achieved by using very high frequency: Mk 24 operates at 100 kHz (beamwidth ¾ degree), but Klein offers an optional very high resolution 500-kHz sonar. In the past, this sort of frequency has generally been associated with very short range, perhaps a swath width of 100 m. However, Klein claims a swath width twice that. There is also an optional 50-kHz fish for large-area sonar sweeps, e.g., for channel surveys.

Total weight, for both recorder and fish, is about 150 lbs, and range is selectable in 13 increments between 25 and 600 meters. The fish can be operated down to 2300 m or, as an option, 12,000 m.

The Klein 100/500-kHz system was supplied in 1988 to the Royal Australian Navy for its COOP program. In 1984 the Royal Swedish Navy bought seven Klein sidescan sonars, with a reported range of about 900 m (which seems too great) for inshore ASW.

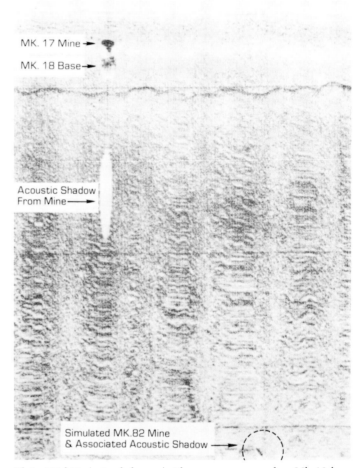

MK. 17 Mine →

MK. 18 Base →

Acoustic Shadow From Mine →

Simulated MK.82 Mine & Associated Acoustic Shadow →

Klein 500-kHz (extended-range) side-scan sonar records a Mk 18 base with a Mk 17 moored mine (both British types) moored about 6 ft above the bottom, and a simulated Destructor (Mk 82 bomb with mine fuze) bottom mine at the bottom. The fish was towed at 2.5 kts, and water depth was 22 meters. (Klein)

◆ Shadowgraph (C. Mk 1)

This side-looking mine-detection sonar was built by Gould; the designation refers to a sweep to deal with combination (as opposed to acoustic or magnetic) mines. Shadowgraph was originally designed during the 1960s for U.S. minehunters operating in shallow water, but the system did not become operational. However, over 100 units were manufactured for the U.S. and French Navies. Stored U.S. units were proposed as COOP (Craft of Opportunity Program) sensors, but the Klein Mk 24 was adopted instead because of its lower cost (modification of Shadowgraphs would have cost more than new Kleins) and greater capability and reliability. Shadowgraph's fish was very heavy, so it would be awkward to handle from small COOP craft.

Total weight (recorder and fish) is about 1500 lbs, and range is fixed at 82 ft. Frequency is 1.4 MHz to port, 1.3 MHz to starboard. Operating depth is 3–30 fathoms. The towed fish, which maintains itself at a preset height above the seafloor, carries two markers that it can drop.

Shadowgraph provided so detailed a picture of the bottom that, in theory, it could be relied upon to classify the objects it saw. It was then practical to use guided weapons to destroy mines, since the rate of false alarms would (in theory) be relatively low. The destruction vehicle was Sea Nettle, a wire-guided torpedo carrying 75 lbs of HBX. Shadowgraph was successfully evaluated in 1962–63, and it and Sea Nettle were included in the new minesweeper designed in 1965–66, but the project died because of the demands of the Vietnam War.

C. Mk 1 was displayed publicly for the first time in 1980, when Gould was hoping to find new customers for a solid-state version. The French DUBM-41 is derived from Shadowgraph.

◆ PQS-1/SQS-37

PQS-1 is a hand-held mine-clearance sonar for divers. It uses continuous FM transmission or passive detection of a sonar beacon. PQS-1 employs a 12-inch conical reflector, which forms a 9-degree beam at 70 kHz. In search mode, frequency is swept over 30 kHz (between 50 and 90 kHz); there are three range scales (20, 60, and 120 yds). Source level is 72 dB. The reflected beam is combined with a sample of the transmitted beam to form a difference frequency in the audio range; the minimum and maximum frequencies in this range correspond to the minimum and maximum ranges of the range scale selected. The lower the tone, the closer the object. The set can also be used to detect 40-kHz marker beacons; the sonar indicates direction but not range.

SQS-37 was PQS-1B modified for riverine use in Vietnam. SQS-37 could easily be transferred from one craft to another. This sonar was also used for helicopter minehunting trials in the mid-1960s. A towed body (Turtle) carried a modified PQS-1 for detection, a television for classification, and a destruction charge. The system was rejected because water was often too turbid for the television.

PQS-1B in use. (U.S. Naval Institute)

◆ PQS-2A

This nonmagnetic portable sonar was announced in 1986 by General Instrument Corp. Modes are active (continuous transmission) and passive (beacon reception, in the 24–45 kHz range). Active range scales are 20, 60, and 120 yards; like PQS-1, this sonar uses an FM slide, so that the tone of the echo indicates the range. Beamwidth is 6 degrees, and a 12-in object can be detected at 120 yds. In the passive mode, a 39-kHz beacon can be detected at up to 2000 yds. The sonar can operate down to 300 ft. Dimensions are 4.5 × 12.5 in (height, with handle, 9 inches); total weight is 8 lbs.

◆ SLQ-35

See ALQ-141 above.

◆ SLQ-37

This modular magnetic/acoustic combined sweep is found in the new U.S. *Avenger* class. Three are being procured under the U.S. FY89 budget.

◆ SLQ-48

See Mine Neutralization System below.

◆ SQQ-14/P2072

The standard U.S. minesweeper/minehunter sonar of the 1960s is also built under license in Italy in a modified version. SQQ-14 equips many minesweepers transferred by the United States to foreign navies. In a license-built form (P2072), SQQ-14 equips Italian *Lerici*-class minehunters. SQQ-14 is basically UQS-1 fitted with CXRP, a copy of the British Type-193 high-resolution sonar, for classification.

SQQ-14 is unusual among variable-depth sonars in that it is carried on a rigid retractable boom rather than at one end of a flexible cable. The reason seems to have been an inherent instability in variable-depth bodies, which tend to swing back and forth at speeds above 5 kts, ruining the accuracy of their narrow beams. In later systems, such as SQQ-30 and the British Type 2093, considerable attention has, therefore, gone into stabilizing the variable-depth body using fins.

SQQ-14 was standardized in 1960. The data that follow are for the Italian-built P2072 version; they are probably also accurate for the U.S. SQQ-14. Maximum depth is 45 m beneath the keel. SQQ-14 consists of an 80-kHz search sonar (which is also used for route surveys) and a 350-kHz classification sonar. The search sonar has a 1.5-degree-wide beam (100-degree field of view); azimuth resolution is 1.5 deg, and range resolution is 1 m (1.0-msec pulses, 15 kW, 126-dB source level). The classification sonar has an 0.3-degree beam (18-degree field of view); azimuth and range resolutions are 0.3 deg and 8 cm, respectively (0.1-msec pulses, 15 kW, 125-dB source level). In search mode the sonar scans a sector at least 82 degrees wide at a speed of at least 15 deg/sec. Once a target has been detected, it is transferred to the classification sonar. Both the search and classification sonars can be tilted between +10 and −30 degrees (elevation). There is also a side-scan mode.

The FIAR version has been completely redesigned for the Italian *Lericis*. Only the mechanical hoist has been retained; the transmitter electronics have been relocated into the towed body, and there are new consoles. FIAR is currently working on a new deep-water sonar for a new class of MHSOs planned for construction from 1993 on. FIAR, GE, and Plessey are jointly offering the 2095, a development of the Plessey/GE 2093, to meet Italian requirements.

A towed version, SQQ-35, is under development.

◆ SQQ-30

Replacement for SQQ-14, SQQ-30 is a much modified solid-state version of the earlier sonar. Unlike the earlier sonar, this one is towed by a conventional cable/umbilical rather than articulated links. SQQ-30 can, therefore, operate at greater depths and can be handled more easily. The towed body is self-stabilizing and reportedly houses three sonars.

SQQ-30 will equip the new generation of U.S. mine-countermeasures vessels until SQQ-32 becomes available.

◆ SQQ-32

Raytheon/Thomson Sintra's minehunting sonar is for later U.S. MCM- and MHC-type countermeasures ships. SQQ-32 was originally designated AMSS (Advanced Minehunting Sonar System). This sonar uses DUBM-21 and TSM 2022 technology for its high-resolution classification sonar, and Raytheon technology for its search component.

SQQ-32 displays search and classification data simultaneously, using separate search and classification transducers in a stable variable-depth towed body. There are two identical display consoles, each of which can display either set of data. Although SQQ-32 normally uses two operators, it can be located in one mode by only one. The search display shows the location of objects of potential interest; the classification display provides images, either of the object itself or of its sonar shadow. Both methods are complementary: the echo mode is most useful for objects clear of the bottom (and for rejecting objects clearly not mines by their apparent shape); the shadow mode, for objects on the bottom (where reverberation is a major problem). A computer is used to help classify the objects detected, so as to reduce the operator's work load. Multibeam operation increases the sonar's search rate.

SQQ-32 can also be used from the hull in shallow water.

◆ UQS-1

This minehunting sonar of the 1950s remains in service on board most ex-U.S. minesweepers. UQS-1 is a short-pulse electronically scanned sonar. UQS-1 has been superseded in the U.S. Navy by SQQ-14. UQS-1D has a total weight of 2126 kg and a frequency of 100 kHz (10-kW pulses). Range scales are 200, 500, and 1000 yards; precision is 5 yds at 200, 25 yds at 500, and 50 yds at 1000. The beam is 20 × 10 (vertical) degrees; but it rotates, and it can scan up and down to cover angles between +5 and −50 degrees. Bearing precision is 30 minutes. The sonar can scan over a 90-degree sector or over all 360 degrees. UQS-1 is not stabilized, and it cannot provide the mine image required for classification.

UQS-1 was derived from the World War II Underwater Object Locator Mk 4 (most UOLs were magnetic); about 150 UQS-1 were built in 1951–54. SQS-15 was a variable-depth version. SQQ-14 was derived from this sonar.

◆ Airborne Mine-countermeasures System Mk 103 and A/N37U

This helicopter-towed moored-mine sweeping system is manufactured by Boeing Vertol. Mk 103 consists of a tow wire, sweep wires (with explosive cutters), floats, a depressor, otters, and float pendants. In operation, the helicopter sits at the extreme end of the flight deck, streams the gear into the water, and then takes off.

The main recent development is A/N37U, a controlled-depth, rapidly deployable sweep for use at greater depths. This deep sweep is now being adapted to surface ships as the single-ship deep sweep (modular). Four engineering-development models are scheduled for procurement in FY88.

◆ Airborne Mine-countermeasures System Mk 104

This helicopter-towed acoustic mine countermeasure consists of a cavitating disk within a venturi tube, driven by a water turbine. Mk 104 was originally developed by American General. For this system the helicopter supplies sweep power. Minimum sweep water depth is 30 ft, compared to 15 ft for an MSL or MSB and 30 ft for an MSO or MSC. Total weight is 180 lbs.

Mk 104 and the other major helicopter-towed mine countermeasures were bought in quantity in response to Project SIXTY Decision 5 (1970, under Admiral Zumwalt), which ordered the mine-countermeasures forces reorganized to emphasize helicopters. In 1971 the navy borrowed 15 Marine Corps CH-53A helicopters to equip the first squadron, HM-12. This squadron swept North Vietnamese waters in 1972–73 and the Suez Canal in 1974–75.

◆ Airborne Mine-countermeasures System Mk 105

Mk 105 is the EDO helicopter-towed minesweeping hydrofoil sled. It carries a power pack (gas-turbine generator) for magnetic sweeping. Mk 105 is being succeeded by ALQ-166. Mk 105 was approved for service use in 1970. The first production models were delivered on 1 July 1972. Mk 105 was first used operationally during the Hanoi-Haiphong sweep at the end of the Vietnam War and was also used for the Suez Canal sweep the following year. Initially the sweep had to be streamed from the helicopter-carrying ship (e.g., an LPH); the sweep was then attached to the sled after having been streamed, and only then did the helicopter lift the sled into the water. The helicopter pilot had to thread his tow ball through the throat of the lifting device of the sled, a very difficult operation. It was discovered during training that the sled could be launched much more safely from the well deck of an LPD. The sled (with its foils up) was positioned at the after end of the well deck, ready for streaming, with the ship ballasted so that the ramp was about 18 inches above water. The helicopter then picked up the tow cable from a small landing craft (LCVP) and carefully pulled the sled down the ramp.

The sled is typically towed at 25 kts, about 450 ft behind the helicopter, the on-board gas turbine powering twin magnetic tails. The sled becomes foilborne at 13 kts, and minimum sweep water depth is 12 feet. The sled trails a conventional open-electrode magnetic sweep 600 ft long.

Six Mk 105 sleds were purchased by the Shah of Iran, and reportedly they were delivered before his fall.

See also EDO Model 819 (MIMS) below.

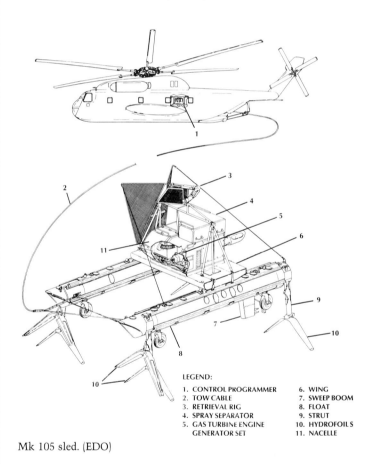

LEGEND:
1. CONTROL PROGRAMMER
2. TOW CABLE
3. RETRIEVAL RIG
4. SPRAY SEPARATOR
5. GAS TURBINE ENGINE
   GENERATOR SET
6. WING
7. SWEEP BOOM
8. FLOAT
9. STRUT
10. HYDROFOILS
11. NACELLE

Mk 105 sled. (EDO)

◆ Airborne Mine-countermeasures System Mk 106

Mk 106 is a combined Mk 104 and Mk 105 for acoustic/magnetic sweeping, the Mk 104 being attached to one of the Mk 105 tails. This device was used extensively during the 1984 Red Sea sweep.

◆ Buried-Mine Hunting System

This system is an FY88 new start, in collaboration with Britain and Germany. It is to use both magnetic and acoustic sensors. The ASQ-81 MAD (on a catamaran) was used to locate buried mines at the end of the Vietnam War, in Operation End Sweep.

◆ Mine Neutralization System (SLQ-48)

SLQ-48 is the current U.S. unmanned minehunting submersible, equivalent in principle to the French PAP 104. The vehicle takes its power from the launching ship, proceeding at a speed of 6 kts. Weight in air is 2500 lbs; the vehicle has 20 lbs of positive buoyancy and rises to the surface in the event of failure. Dimensions are 12.5 × 3 ft, and power is provided by two 12-HP electric motors. There are also two side thrusters. The umbilical cable is 3500 ft long. Including its shipboard components, the mine neutralization system weighs 26,000 lbs and requires a 60-kW power source. Honeywell, the manufacturer, claims that MTBF is 120 hours, with a 4-hour MTTR.

The vehicle itself carries a small high-definition sonar and an acoustic transponder that enables the vehicle to be tracked by the shipboard minehunting sonar. There is also a low-light-level television for examining a mine or minelike object. The vehicle carries MP-1 (Mk 26-0) cable cutters and an explosive mine-destruction charge (MP-2, Mk 57-0).

The Honeywell Mine Neutralization System vehicle. (Honeywell)

Prototypes were tested in 1971–77, with a decision to begin engineering development made in 1977. In 1978 Honeywell was awarded a contract for two prototypes, and operational evaluation of the engineering-development model was completed in September 1982. It was tested on board USS *Fidelity*.

It was announced in 1985 that the mine neutralization system would be supplemented by an advanced remotely operated underwater vehicle (ARDROV) that will help locate and identify objects, perhaps like the projected German Pinguin A3.

◆ Special Acoustic Sweeps

Several special noisemakers were manufactured by the Naval Coastal Systems Laboratory (Panama City) specifically for shallow water mine clearance as part of Operation End Sweep (1973). They had to be simple and were turned over to the North Vietnamese. Although these noisemakers probably would not be precisely duplicated in future, they are interesting examples of extemporized devices:

Drum Sweep a device to sweep magnetic-acoustic mines (DST Mod 4) in canals and rivers too narrow for helicopters or boats. Drum Sweep was a cut-down 55-gallon drum with a 3-HP lawn-mower engine inside, and with permanent magnets and a small paddle wheel outside. The paddle rotated the drum about its vertical axis. This rotation changed the drum's magnetic field and helped free the drum from snags so that it could ride the current down river. The drum's acoustic signature was provided by the engine and by the exhaust, which was vented into the water. Five drums were provided to the North Vietnamese.

Rotating Acoustic Pipe (RAP) a 4-ft section of 10-inch steel pipe with a towing swivel, nose cone, and external vanes causing

RAP to tumble when towed. Scrap iron bars inside tumbled to produce noise. When towed with an MOP (see below), the RAP could detonate a U.S. seismic/magnetic destructor (DST Mod 4, at its most sensitive setting). Twenty were manufactured for the North Vietnamese.

Big Noisy Orange Barrel (BNOB) a towed barrel noisemaker developed in part by the mine force in Vietnamese waters. BNOB was a 55-gallon drum containing scrap iron and fitted with vanes on its outside; it worked much like the RAP. One was built.

Magnetic Orange Barrel (MOB) a horizontal coil of about 400 ampere turns, seven feet in diameter, with a battery at its center to supply current. MOB was towed on a styrofoam float by a boat. This device was experimental only.

Sophisticated Orange Barrel (SOB) (acoustic solenoid barrel) a solenoid inside a 55-gallon drum, energized by a battery inside. As the solenoid was pulsed, it struck the inside of the barrel. The SOB designation differentiated it from BNOB; SOB was not built.

Static Loops static coils used for inland sweeping. Dropped on the bottom or placed on a raft (or suspended from floats), these coils could be pulsed to simulate the signature of a passing boat; they were repositioned after sweeping. Power could be provided either by a battery or by a welding generator. Two such loops were lent to the North Vietnamese.

There was also a drone minesweeping boat developed specifically for End Sweep (and not, therefore, identical to the drone sweepers developed during the Vietnam War). This boat was commercial fiberglass (14 ft 6 in × 5 ft) and could tow RAP, MOP, and the A Mk 2(g) sweep. One problem was that the existing drone sweepers (MSD) had magnetic signatures that would have detonated destructors under them. Ten remotely controlled boats, which could be operated from a range of 2 miles, were provided to the North Vietnamese.

◆ SPU-1/W (MOP)

SPU-1/W is a magnetized pipe filled with styrofoam; MOP means Magnetized Orange Pipe. It was employed during the sweep of Haiphong harbor at the end of the Vietnam War. At that time, it turned out that some of the mines laid in Vietnamese waters were so sensitive that they would have destroyed the sweep sleds. A precursor sweep was needed: the MOP. This procedure was interpreted by some as demonstrating shortcomings in helicopter sweeping, but in fact precursor sweeping was more a commentary on the design of mines sensitive enough to destroy small wooden craft held together by metal fasteners. The MOP was also needed to sweep water too shallow for a Mk 105.

A modern version of the 1940 iron-rail sweep (M Mk 1(m)), MOP was a pipe long enough to provide the magnetic mass of the rail and wide enough to be buoyant (30 ft × 10 in diameter). MOP was sealed at each end, filled with styrofoam, fitted with towing lugs, and magnetized. A helicopter could tow as many as three MOPs in tandem. A total of 150 were manufactured by the Naval Coastal Systems Laboratory (Panama City).

In 1972, when Operation End Sweep was being planned, there was some fear that not enough Mk 105 sleds would be available in time. One proposed solution was to wrap a MOP in coils energized by a generator in the helicopter, increasing the sweep path's width by a factor of 5.

◆ ALARMS

Northrop's Airborne Laser Radar Mine Sensor employs a downward-looking blue-green laser pulsed at 10 kHz. Prompted by reports of moored mines in the Persian Gulf, Northrop proposed the system to DARPA in the summer of 1987 and was awarded a development contract late in November 1987. The first tests were run early in August 1988, at San Clemente Island. Northrop claimed that these tests showed a search rate at least ten times the current visual rate.

The copper-vapor laser scans in a 682-shot circular pattern. The mine targets are detected in real time, the display showing, in effect, the mines directly beneath the aircraft carrying ALARMS. They are displayed as squares, the color of the square showing their depth. The system shows only moored mines; it is range-gated to reject the reflections of the surface and the bottom. Gain is adjusted for sea-state. The Northrop system is built around a Larsen 500 ladar (laser radar) built by Optech Systems of Downsview, Ontario, Canada. Maximum operating depth is reported as about 100 ft.

ALARMS was never actually deployed to the Persian Gulf. It is still a developmental system, housed in a 35-ft container and carried by a big MH-53 helicopter. Northrop is seeking funds for a more compact version.

ALARMS is not the only laser minehunting system proposed; see also the description of the Australian laser system in the ASW section.

◆ **EDO Model 819**

A shipboard derivative of the EDO Mk-105 airborne mine-countermeasures system, 819 is called MIMS (Modular Influence Minesweeping System) by the company. 819 employs a gas-turbine generator and a tow cable for both acoustic and magnetic sweeps, the cable carrying magnetic electrodes and towing an acoustic fish. MIMS is intended to equip craft of opportunity; the towing reel and winch weigh, together, only 5000 lbs (it takes up only about 10 square feet on the ship's deck).

◆ **EDO Model 910**

See the ASW section (Model 900/910).

YUGOSLAVIA

Yugoslavia has the following river sweeps: Type PEAM magnetic and acoustic; Type AEL-1 explosive; Types MDL-1 and -2 mechanical.

INDEX

ADDENDUM

SURVEILLANCE AND CONTROL

SPAIN

◆ Tritan-1

Tritan-1 is a new tactical data system being fitted to Spanish *Baleares*-class frigates, as part of their modernization. The system employs four Selenia tactical and weapons-control consoles, as well as a radar-data integrator (apparently broadly analogous to the U.S. SYS-1), and a Rockwell two-way data link (presumably for at least Links 11 and 4). Modernization of the frigates is to be completed by 1991. The associated electronic-warfare system, Deneb, is also new; it is manufactured by Ceselsa.

UNITED KINGDOM

◆ ADAWS

Ferranti has been awarded a contract for ADAWS system upgrades, for *Invincible*-class carriers and Type 42–class destroyers. Existing FM1600 computers are to be replaced by FM2420s, which can use the same programs but which have more than six times the computer power of the earlier machines.

STRIKE/SURFACE WARFARE

FRANCE

◆ Ocean Master

Ocean Master, the next-generation radar for maritime-patrol aircraft, is now under development and is derived from technology originally developed for the RDX/RDY fighter radars, both of which have programmable signal processors (for variable waveforms). Ocean Master is expected to enter service in 1995–96.

Like the current French radars for maritime-patrol aircraft, Ocean Master employs pulse compression. Ocean Master will also use scan-to-scan and pulse-to-pulse integration to detect periscopes in sea clutter, will incorporate ISAR, and will be capable of tracking numerous targets while scanning. A SAR capability is under development. The radar's RDX/RDY ancestry will provide significant air-to-air performance, for a degree of airborne early warning. As in the fighter radars, the antenna is electronically scanned (the customer can specify either an active or a passive array).

The scan-to-scan and pulse-to-pulse integration and digital processing features are now being tested on board an Atlantique-2 aircraft.

◆ Antiship Missiles

The next-generation ANS antiship missile is to use a high-density liquid fuel. As of June 1989, Aerospatiale hoped that the program would be officially launched during 1989. ANL, the successor to the existing AS 15TT will be powered by a ramjet with solid (boron-doped) fuel. As of mid-1989, ANL was a study program only, albeit with strong interest being shown by the West German Navy. Current performance estimates are a speed of Mach 2.2 and a range of about 30 km; the warhead's weight will be the same 30 kg used in the AS 12 and AS 15TT, a size that Aerospatiale considers sufficient against a small or medium ship. Total weight will be about 200 kg, a figure chosen so that the missile can easily be carried by a helicopter or small maritime-patrol aircraft. ANL will fly a sea-skimming profile.

ITALY

◆ APS-717

APS-717, manufactured by SMA, is a new dual-purpose X-band airborne radar. It combines the functions of navigation and weather radars to provide search and detection in bad weather and clutter (during search and rescue and patrol missions). APS-717 can be integrated with a FLIR.

USSR

♦ AS-7

Rumania and Yugoslavia now manufacture versions of the AS-7 tactical air-to-surface missile. At Baghdad in April 1989, the Rumanians displayed their version of the Soviet AS-7. Its characteristics presumably match those of the Soviet prototype. This A921 was described as a radio-guided command–to–line of sight air-to-surface missile. Guidance is manual as in the U.S. Bullpup. Weight is 287 kg, and dimensions are 275 × 3490 mm (span 785 mm); the warhead weighs 110 kg, and range is 2–10 km. The missile can be launched from altitudes of 100–5000 m, and the maximum G load at launch is 4.6 Gs. Launching speed is 600–1000 km/hr, and maximum flight speed is 600–750 m/sec. The Rumanian manufacturer is Rom Tecnica, and A921 is currently in service.

UNITED STATES

♦ UAV

IAI's Impact RPV, a competitor for the U.S. SR-UAV program, on display at the Paris Air Show, 1989. Impact has twin propellers (push-pull configuration) and an under-body sensor. The vehicle is powered by two 45-HP engines and cruises at 60 kts; maximum speed is 110 kts. Rate of climb is 1000 ft/min, and service ceiling is 18,000 ft. Endurance is up to 12 hours. Gross weight is 1250 lbs, including 150 lbs of useful load and 200 lbs of fuel. Wing span is 26 ft, length is 20 ft, and height is 6 ft. Impact has been under operational evaluation since 1988. (Author)

Development of the U.S. RPV (or UAV, unmanned air vehicle) is now being conducted by a JPO (Joint Project Office) established in mid-1988. The term UAV is now preferred because it encompasses robotic vehicles that are not piloted. A UAV Master Plan was submitted to Congress in June 1988, calling for three categories: short-range, medium-range, and long-endurance. There was some fear of duplication of effort, between UAVs and standoff (but loiter) munitions; Tacit Rainbow falls into the gray area between a classical UAV and a standoff missile.

The U.S. medium-range RPV is to be designated BQM-129. It is now known as JSCAMPS (joint-service common-airframe multiple-purpose system). As of about March 1989, projected procurement (during FY89–94) was 775, including 230 (150 air force and 80 navy) reconnaissance aircraft equipped with ATARS, 120 non-ATARS reconnaissance aircraft, and 425 targets. Teledyne has won the competition for the medium-range version with Model 350, defeating Northrop and Martin-Marietta/Beech.

The version of ATARS to be carried by JSCAMPS will be more compact than that planned for tactical aircraft. The latter carry both electro-optical cameras and an infrared line scanner; the RPV will be designed to carry one or the other.

An RFP for a projected short-range vehicle (SR-UAV) was issued in March 1989, after industry had objected to an earlier draft. Two contractors are to be chosen for an FY91 fly off. Planned procurement (FY89–94) is 308 aircraft and 38 ground stations, with most to be bought during FY93–94. Likely competitors include GEC Avionics/McDonnell Douglas's R4E-50 Skyeye, IAI's Impact, AAI's Guardian, Pacific Aerosystems's Heron 26, Teledyne Ryan's 410, General Atomics's Predator, and California Microwave's CM-44. AAI markets Mazlat's Pioneer in the United States, and Mazlat is now owned by IAI.

Reportedly both Impact and Guardian resemble Pioneer, on a larger scale. Of the UAVs listed, only Skyeye is currently operational, having entered service with Egypt at the end of 1988. Skyeye has also been bought by several other countries.

Current plans call for three versions: Blocks 0, 1, and 2. Block O is a baseline system for the army and marines, with a day/night imaging payload. Block 1 is modified for naval use. Block 2 is to be an improved version, with automatic track/search features and greater survivability; the engine will burn a heavy fuel such as JP-5. Reportedly the main issue in Block 1 is shipboard handling (which proved difficult to engineer with Pioneer). It is estimated that the vehicle itself will account for only 10–15 percent of the overall system cost, a factor that makes a VTOL such as Bell's Pointer attractive for Block 1. To choose such a vehicle, however, would be to reject the congressional desire for a high degree of commonality between all versions of the RPV.

Reportedly the initial short-range concept called for a radius of action of about 30 km and an endurance of 1–6 hours. Early in 1989 it was reported that the JPO would split the SR requirement in two, calling for a very low cost, man-portable, battery-powered, 25-km device and for a more capable 80-km device. As of early 1989, the marines had tested one low-cost device, Aero-Vironment's Pointer. The marines and the army have bought a longer-range very low cost vehicle, Brandebury's Ex-drone (expendable drone), which has a range of 565 miles and a 7-hour endurance.

As of early 1989, 36 Pioneers were on hand, with 28 more scheduled for delivery during 1989. Pioneer, originally a naval system, is to replace the army's more expensive Aquila. As of early 1989, 8 Aquilas were on hand, with 8 more scheduled for delivery during the year.

At the other end of the scale, an RFP for a long-endurance vehicle is expected during FY91. The only long-endurance RPV in current U.S. service is Leading Systems's Amber, six of which were on hand early in 1989. Four more are to be delivered during 1989. This figure covers all the services, and service requirements for (and definitions of) high endurance will vary. For example, the army's concept of a long-endurance RPV or UAV calls for an endurance of about 36 hours and for ranges out to about 300 km. On 7–8 June 1988 an Amber set what its manufacturer called a world endurance record for a UAV, remaining in the air for 38 hours and 27 minutes. This record is still far short of the several days' endurance that a useful long-loiter naval UAV would require.

♦ Shrike

As of 1989, Shrike antiradar missiles reportedly are no longer carried on board aircraft carriers. These missiles presumably survive as war reserves.

♦ Advanced Rocket System

Early in 1989 the U.S. Navy announced a program to develop an Advanced Rocket System to replace the existing 2.75-in weapon, to enter service in FY95. The new rocket motor is to provide a velocity (with a 10-lb warhead) of at least 1000 m/sec (3280 ft/sec) at zero aircraft speed; the motor is to have a low smoke signature (for stealthy operation), and the rocket is to be insensitive (i.e., relatively safe on board a burning carrier). Minimum effective range is to be 10,000 m (15,000 m in a loft mode). The new weapon reportedly will use multipurpose warheads. Initial work is funded under the 2.75-in rocket account, but a new ARS project is to begin formally in FY92. An RFP is scheduled for FY90. Apparently the new rocket, like the current 2.75, would be carried in a 19-weapon pod.

Reported mission requirements are: dry marking (to use a family of different-colored markers other than the current toxic white phosphorus); antipersonnel (one pod to cover 15,000 square meters); antimateriel (to penetrate a minimum of 1.5 in of armor); antiarmor (to penetrate a minimum of 3 in of armor); antihelicopter (four rockets to cover an area of 2500 square meters); anti–coastal shipping (to penetrate 1 in of steel at a range of 4 km, with a delayed-action fuze and incendiary effect); chaff (for self-protection and deception); flare (1 million candlepower for 1.5 min); night marking (2-min marker, observable by FLIR and other night-vision devices); smoke screening (pattern 50 × 400 m; duration 5 min in winds of 5–10 kts; effective in visual, IR, and ER spectra); and training. The requirements stated above are for ranges of up to 10 km (up to 4 km for the antishipping mission) and are to be met from a hovering helicopter.

Work on improvements to the existing 2.75-in rocket is also proceeding. In 1989 the U.S. Navy began testing a Norwegian-developed (Raufoss) antiship warhead (HEISAP, or high explosive, incendiary, semi–armor piercing).

◆ Harrier Radar-Warning System

For FY90 the Marine Corps plans to begin development of a new radar-warning system for its AV-8B Harriers. Unlike the current ALR-67, the new system would automatically begin defensive reaction. In addition, the new system is to be able to detect incoming infrared missiles as well as active and semi-active radar-guided weapons. No designation has been assigned.

ANTIAIRCRAFT WARFARE

FRANCE

◆ Vigil and RDY

Vigil, the X-band airborne early-warning radar for the next generation of French carrier aircraft, is to enter service in 1992. Vigil uses the programmable signal processor and waveform developed for the existing RDY fighter radar, plus an electronically scanned antenna. Total weight, exclusive of consoles, will be 450 kg. The radar will be installed on board refurbished Grumman Tracker aircraft (originally built for carrier-based ASW) in a belly radome; the aircraft will be reengined with turboprops. There will be two operators, and the radar will automatically detect and track targets, automatically computing intercepts. Thomson-CSF, the manufacturer, estimates that Vigil will detect a 5 square-meter target at 110 nm, based on performance already achieved by RDY (using a smaller antenna).

RDY itself is a multifunction (air-to-air, air-to-ground, and air-to-sea) radar, achieving these capabilities by means of a programmable signal processor (as in the U.S. APG-65). For air-to-air operation, RDY can use one of three waveforms (high, medium, and low PRF). It can track 8 targets while scanning, assigning each target a priority label. Simultaneous fire-control solutions can be computed for several targets so that a fighter equipped with RDY can engage several targets simultaneously when using active missiles. Alternatively, the radar can be used to illuminate a target for a semiactive missile. The air-to-ground modes of operation are ground mapping (RBGM) and doppler beam sharpening (DBS), for navigation; and air-to-ground ranging (AGR) and detection and tracking of fixed (HTT) and moving (GMTI/GMTT) targets. The radar is also designed for sea search, using a variety of waveforms to cancel clutter at different sea-states.

RDY is a pulse-compression radar (with a variable compression ratio) that uses two different peak-power levels (dual-mode operation). The transmitter uses a TWT.

GERMANY (WEST)

◆ FL 1800S Step II

AEG's FL 1800S system, now standard in the German Navy, is to be upgraded to FL 1800S Step II standard. The existing omnidirectional and DF antennas are modified, and a Racal SADIE parallel processor is introduced to handle the expected high data rates. For ECM, there are a new tracking processor (to achieve almost pulse-synchronous jamming) and a new switching matrix (to deal with multiple threats). Step II has eight TWTs facing in different directions, rather than employing the more common technique of time-sharing a single signal generator. TWTs

not needed to jam in their particular directions can be switched to the threat directions. Displays are also being modified to provide a clearer color picture. Finally, the German Navy requires some indication of threat range because the ESM system will be used to trigger RAM defensive missiles. Step II estimates range using the amplitude of the received signal.

AEG plans to make Step II the basis of a modular family of systems, for small patrol craft, submarines, and maritime-patrol aircraft. To achieve compactness, the company is combining omnidirectional and DF antennas into a single biconical antenna. AEG hopes to incorporate the signal processor into this antenna so that it will send only digital data into the ship's combat system. As of mid-1989, the company expected to complete development of this 60-kg system sometime in 1990. The associated ECM system would employ a stabilized dish antenna. AEG hopes to reduce the weight of the ECM by using more powerful TWTs, cutting their number from the current eight to six or four.

◆ Octopus

For details of Octopus, a new system for patrol boats, see United Kingdom below (Racal is the main contractor).

INTERNATIONAL

◆ Polypheme-SM

Polypheme-SM emerges from the water, its canister falling away. The after rocket motor is burning. (Aerospatiale)

Aerospatiale (France) and MBB (West Germany) are privately developing a submarine-launched fiber-guided antiaircraft missile, Polypheme-SM. As of 1989, the two companies claimed that the system could be made operational within five years, should either the French or the German Navy fund full-scale development. Range would be 10 km against typical ASW helicopters; presumably the range would be shorter if the missile were fired against higher-performance fixed-wing aircraft. Maximum altitude would be 5000 m (about 16,000 ft). The 43-kg missile (carrying a 3-kg fragmentation warhead) would be carried free of the water in a pressurized 62-kg capsule. The capsule could be fired at a depth as great as 300 m (about 1000 ft), fol-

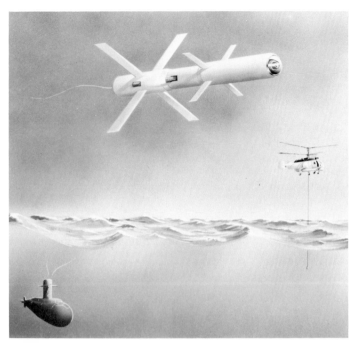

Polypheme-SM in flight, trailing its fiber-optic guidance link. The forward rocket motor is burning. (Aerospatiale)

The fiber-optic guided SS 12 test vehicle for Polypheme-SM. (Aerospatiale)

lowing a preprogrammed underwater trajectory, at a speed of 15 m/sec, and emerging from the water about 1 km from the launch position, to prevent disclosure of the submarine's position.

The missile employs a boost-sustain motor and has two flight speeds: 150 m/sec for target search and 250 m/sec for attack. Polypheme carries two separate rocket motors for the two phases of its flight. The missile has four canard steering fins and four fixed stabilizing fins at its tail.

Like the U.S. FOG-M land-based missile, Polypheme is compact because it contains virtually no guiding intelligence. The seeker is optronic, and the seeker output travels down the optical fiber to the launching submarine. The operator on board the submarine flies the missile to its aerial target.

There are two operating modes. If the target's range and bearing are fairly well known (e.g., if the helicopter is detected by the sound of its blades or by the pinging of its dipping sonar), the missile during its flight can search a path 3 km wide. Alternatively, if the target's position is only approximately known (e.g., by the splash of sonobuoys entering the water), the missile can fly an ascending spiral search pattern, with a radius of 1 km.

Polypheme-SM is interesting because it minimizes the exposure of the firing submarine. However, this missile still limits the extent to which the submarine can escape after firing. The ideal submarine self-protection weapon would deter any close approach (for localization) and would be deployable while the submarine runs. More, rather than less, intelligence inside the missile would seem appropriate (infrared guidance is an interesting option here). Any effective submarine-launched surface-

to-air weapon would greatly reduce the value of current airborne ASW systems. Otherwise, the use of the missile tends to confirm that a supposed submarine contact is indeed a real one.

As of mid-1989, Polypheme-SM is a technology study program. Hardware development to date has been limited to work with optical fibers; an SS 12 missile has flown 8 km trailing such a fiber. Aerospatiale initially used fibers coated with Kevlar, but currently only the hairlike fiber itself is used. Images have been transmitted successfully over a distance of 60 km.

ISRAEL

◆ NS-9000 Series

Elisra exhibited advanced versions of its existing NS-9000 series naval electronic warfare systems at the Paris Air Show in June 1989: the NS-9003 ESM system and the NS-9005 jammer. Elisra claims that the new version of NS-9003 (suffixed PR) can deal with pulse compression, frequency agility, frequency hopping, and wobbulated (jittered) PRF signals. NS-9005 PR can produce both noise and deception jamming, and it can be integrated with a multibeam array transmitter (MBAT). Typically NS-9005/MBAT employs four MBATs and one exciter, each array covering 90 degrees. This system incorporates four trackers, to deceive four threats simultaneously, and can expand to cover more, with up to 16 trackers available as options.

NS-9003 PR covers the 1–18 GHz range. Direction of arrival is measured with an accuracy of 1–3 deg for signals between 2 and 18 GHz. The system employs a total of 60 directional antennas.

Elisra claims that its new proprietary lens technology provides NS-9005/MBAT with high effective power in the 7.5–18 GHz band.

The new systems are the third generation to be produced by Elisra. The company produced its first naval systems about 1978/79, for service in the early 1980s. They were initially ESM devices, integrated with existing ECM. The second generation (NS-9010) entered service in the mid-1980s. It employed new technology in the form of an RKR lens, which was more compact than the earlier spiral antennas. This system was a radar-warning receiver as well as an ESM system. The related ECM system was a conventional mechanically steered antenna, but with a very sophisticated exciter employing deception techniques. The new third-generation features are concentrated mainly in the ECM portion of the system: a multibeam array transmitting antenna, high effective radiated power, and very fast switching for transmission and deception.

NS-9001, an ELINT version of the original NS-9003, falls between the first and second generations.

The associated submarine ESM system, NS-9034, is not yet a real product, but rather a design for using existing NS-9000 series components in repackaged form. NS-9034 is intended to achieve a bearing accuracy of 1 deg for targeting.

◆ GET/RAN-1001, MBAT/RAN-1010, SEWS/RAN-1100

Rafael exhibited three new related electronic-warfare systems at the Paris Air Show in June 1989: GET/RAN-1001, MBAT/RAN-1010, and SEWS/RAN-1100. All are apparently intended for corvettes or larger ships (the brochures show *Perry*-class frigates).

GET/RAN-1001 is an ESM system that uses a broad-band IFM receiver and a broad-band instantaneous direction finder (IDF), the latter employing RKR lens technology. There are separate omnidirectional (IFM) and directional (IDF) antennas, typically two of the latter. Processing is conducted partly in parallel, and Rafael claims that GET can identify such complex signals as chirps, frequency-agile pulses, and staggered or jittered PRFs. Frequency coverage is 1–18 GHz, and accuracy is 2 deg in bearing and 1.5 MHz in frequency. Dynamic range is 60 dB, and sensitivity is better than −60 dBm.

MBAT/RAN-1010 is a multibeam array transmitter for ECM. MBAT employs electronically steered lens antennas and can generate several jamming signals simultaneously.

SEWS/RAN-1100 is a shipborne EW suite combining a receiver (RAN-1001 technology), two high effective radiated power multibeam array transmitters (MBATs), and a distributed data processor that decides which signals to generate.

◆ Chaff Rockets

Rafael's three current chaff rockets (as of mid-1989) are

	Short-Range	Beamtrap	Long-Range
Weight	3.2 kg	6.6 kg	9.4 kg
Chaff	1.75 kg	—	1.3 kg
Diameter	90 mm	115 mm	89 mm
Length	640 mm	804 mm	922 mm
Fin Span	125 mm	115 mm	179 mm

Of these, the short-range rocket is typically fired from a six-rocket launcher on a standard 0.50-caliber machine gun mount, three rockets being carried together in a loading unit. Elevation is fixed at 45 deg. A single firing box controls two launchers. Total weight of the loading unit is 22 kg.

Beamtrap, a newer system that will replace the current short-range rocket, is mounted in a six-tube launcher on the side of the ship's superstructure; the firing unit on the bridge or in the CIC controls 24 rockets. The typical firing interval is 0.5 sec.

The long-range rocket is carried in pairs of fixed tubes, typically two pairs per ship. They are manually reloaded. Long range is achieved by using a dual-thrust (boost-sustain) rocket, and chaff dispersion is triggered by an altitude fuze.

ITALY

◆ Myriad CIWS

The dual-band (Ku and W) radar director of the Myriad weapons system. (Breda)

A model of the new Myriad close-in defensive weapon, at the Paris Air Show, 1989. The canted platform is similar to that employed in the Seaguard system (which Contraves manufactures). As in Seaguard, the director is separate from the mounting. (Author)

The new Myriad CIWS mentioned in the main text employs a pair of Oerlikon seven-barrel 25-mm KBD Gatling guns, which fire the high-velocity ammunition of the Oerlikon KBB gun. KBD is the first application of the Gatling principle to Oerlikon weapons. Myriad is a joint venture of Breda, Contraves Italiana, Elsag, and Selenia.

The logical basis of Myriad is the contention that next-generation antiship missiles will be both supersonic and highly maneuverable and will be able to evade weapons whose fire-control systems would have to predict target motion. Hence it will be impossible to hit an incoming missile at any great range. Myriad's developers argue that, no matter how a missile maneuvers, it must attack a ship through a relatively constricted window close to the ship. Myriad's fire-control system, built by Elsag, uses a missile's known aerodynamic features to predict the location of the window, between 500 and 1000 m from the ship. The very high rate of fire developed by the twin guns, 10,000 rounds per minute, saturates this window. The ammunition is a special AMDS (anti-missile discarding sabot) type, using a tungsten-alloy rod penetrator 14.5 mm in diameter. As in the U.S. Phalanx, the kill mechanism is penetration of the missile's warhead to ensure its detonation; the manufacturer argues that only such destruction will prevent missile fragments from damaging the ship. Muzzle velocity of the AMDS round is 1270 m/sec (1285 m/sec for the APDS-T round). Remaining velocity at 500 m is 1190 m/sec; time to 500 m is 0.41 sec. Remaining velocity at 1000 m is 1113 m/sec (time to 1000 m is 0.84 sec).

The gun itself has a new patented antihangfire safety mechanism, which precludes firing ammunition from an unlocked breech.

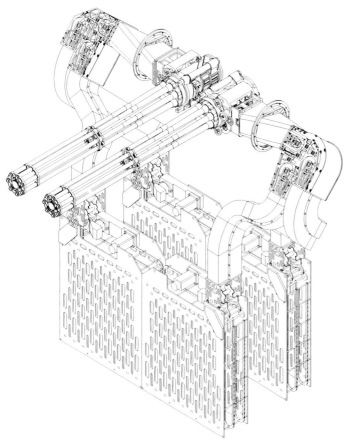

Twin 25-mm Gatling guns of a Myriad mounting, showing ammunition feeds. (Breda)

Like the existing Seaguard weapons, Myriad is mounted on a tilted platform to be able to engage zenith attacks. The mounting carries 2000 rounds in four boxes, two per Gatling (so that each gun can switch between two types of ammunition). Total weight, including ammunition, is 7700 kg. Rate of train (elevation) is 2.5 (3.0) rad/sec. Each of the two guns weighs 1600 kg, including its 1000 rounds of ammunition.

Gun and director are connected to a standard MAGICS console via the standard 10 Mbit/sec data bus (MHIDAS); the system is arranged so that many trackers and many guns can be interconnected via a single bus. The system can accept data from a search radar and conduct a threat evaluation before firing.

◆ Fast Forty

Breda's single Fast Forty mount, on display in 1989. Behind it is the combined chaff and Mistral launcher. (Breda)

The Breda-Oerlikon 25-mm KBB gun. (Breda)

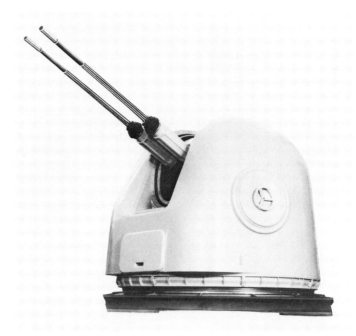

The Breda twin 25-mm mounting. (Breda)

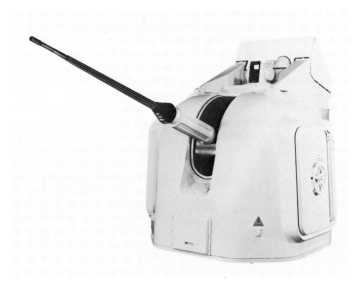

The Breda single 25-mm mounting in locally controlled form. (Breda)

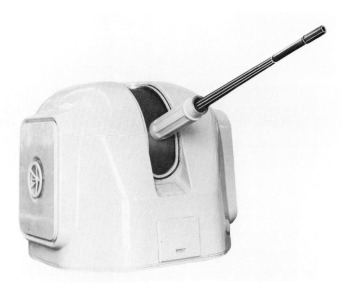

The Breda single 25-mm mounting in remote controlled form. (Breda)

Breda exhibited the prototype of a new single-barreled Fast Forty antiaircraft cannon at the Mostra Navale exhibition in Genoa in May 1989. There are three versions: Type A (remotely controlled) and Types B and C (locally controlled). Type B uses a simple on-mount fire-control system. In Type C the mount is provided with a microcomputer-based fire-control system employing a stabilized television line of sight, independent of the line of fire, and a laser range-finder. Power is provided in part by a converter that accumulates recoil energy as the gun fires. Compared to previous 40 mm/70 weapons, Fast Forty uses a new oscillating mass (designed by Breda) that substantially reduces recoil distance (from 230 to 100 mm) and time, allowing a higher rate of fire (450 rounds/min compared to the previous 300 rounds/min). Changes include a new rammer, which takes the round directly from the feed position to the breechblock closing position. The mount carries two 42-round magazines, and five more rounds are accommodated in the gun feeder and hopper. Elevation limits are +83/−13 deg.

Breda claims that a twin Fast Forty, firing 900 rounds/min and using proximity-fuzed bursts, can kill an incoming supersonic missile that is flying a straight path at a range as great as 3000 m. At such ranges it is probably sufficient to destroy the missile's control surfaces. The mount automatically shifts to the heavier APDS rounds when the missile reaches a range of 1000 m.

Now associated with Oerlikon, Breda has applied the former's 25-mm KBB gun to existing 30-mm and 40-mm mount technology. The results were first displayed at the Mostra Navale exhibition in Genoa in May 1989: single and twin mountings. A single open mounting had already been displayed.

The single mounting employs dual feed (two 80-round boxes) and on-mount buffer batteries sufficient for up to two hundred 360-deg rotations (or the equivalent in elevation and depression). The batteries are charged by the ship's power and permit gun operation to continue in the event ship's power is no longer available. The locally controlled mounting employs Breda's Hawkeye micro fire-control system, with an independently stabilized line of sight. Target tracking is computer-aided (the computer projects a straight trajectory), and range is estimated by using precalibrated reticles (for example, the operator opens fire when the target's image coincides with a circle of predetermined lens magnification). The mount can be fitted with an LLLTV in place of the usual daylight television camera and can be controlled remotely.

The twin 25-mm mounting employs Breda's specially designed cradle, the bore axes being set unusually close together for accuracy. There are three alternative magazine arrangements: Type A (2000 rounds), B (1000 rounds), and C (500 rounds, on the rotating platform).

♦ SCLAR

Breda's combined Mistral missile and SCLAR chaff launcher, 1989. (Breda)

At the 1989 Genoa show, Breda also exhibited a new version of its SCLAR chaff launcher, which carries two sets of tubes on top for a total of six French Mistral short-range missiles. A television camera is mounted between the Mistrals' tubes. Control is exercised from a one-man below-decks console incorporating a television monitor and a joystick. The daylight television can be replaced by a low-light or infrared unit for night operation. Typically the mounting receives target designation from a two-dimensional or navigational radar, the operator slewing the mount onto the designated bearing and then searching in elevation. The launcher begins to autotrack optically when within 0.5 deg of the target.

Long-range chaff can be launched, followed by missiles when the target comes within range, and then followed by short-range chaff in the event the defensive missiles fail. The entire launcher is stabilized and remotely controlled.

Individual Mistrals are locked onto targets before firing; the missiles can home on forward-aspect radiation. Unlike many previous IR-guided missiles, Mistrals employ proportional (rather than pursuit) navigation, using a gyro as a reference. One effect of such navigation is to reject flares ejected from the rear of a target.

Total swept radius of the launcher is 1.380 m; elevation limits are +57/−4 deg. Total weight, including 20 rockets and 6 Mistrals, is 2150 kg (1430 kg empty). Training velocity is 60 deg/sec (elevation rate 30 deg/sec). The manufacturer estimates that the six Mistrals can be reloaded manually in less than 5 minutes.

NETHERLANDS

♦ Radar Developments

SMART has been adopted for the German Type-123 frigate (in preference to the French Arabel, the British Type 996, and the U.S. Target Acquisition System). As a result, the German frigate will have much the same air-defense radar system as the new Dutch M class; SMART will also equip the two Dutch L-class area-defense missile ships. SMART is being adapted for land-based use under the designation Vanguard. The smaller but analogous MW-08 is being adapted for land-based use in the Dutch Army's Skyspy system.

Signaal is offering an upgrade to existing WM 20 series radars, based on an upgrade applied to German WM 27s on board Type 143 fast attack craft. The original Philips spin-tuned magnetron transmitter, which was replaced by a Varian coaxial magnetron in later WM 20 series radars, is replaced by a solid-state coaxial magnetron. The original spin-tuned unit had the virtue of providing great frequency diversity but was not very stable at any one frequency, and lifetime was relatively short. Moreover, as the transmitter degraded, it did so gracefully, and operators could not always be sure that their radars were losing performance. The new magnetron is very stable (for good MTI) and very reliable; when it does fail, it does so catastrophically, so that the operator knows when it has to be replaced. The new magnetron is tuned by a piston, among about six crystal-controlled frequencies, for limited frequency diversity.

At the same time, a slotted-waveguide antenna is being added to the existing one, to search up to about 30 deg in elevation; and new software greatly reduces the multipath problem at low angles of elevation. The new software also improves ballistics and prediction calculations.

For future upgrades, Signaal is offering to replace the existing magnetron transmitter with a TWT (for pulse-compression and coherent operations). The resulting digital radar employs fast Fourier transforms to detect moving targets by their doppler shifts, in place of the earlier analog MTI. Presumably the TWT involved is the same as that now being introduced in production versions of the STIR fire-control radar for the new Dutch and West German frigates (the Canadian TRUMP project employs the earlier magnetron version).

There are two new radar concepts to increase the capability of existing Sea Sparrow missile systems. SIR, a slaved illumination radar, would be controlled by a 3-D radar such as SMART; SIR is similar in concept to the SPG-62 slave illuminator used in the U.S. Aegis system. SIR would be a STIR without the radar components, retaining only the CW illuminator. No prototype has been made.

The alternative is MEMPHIS (multiple-engagement phased-array illumination system). A single director can track four targets within a 90-deg sector, and the director can rotate to cover the full 360 deg. MEMPHIS uses an X-band reflector composed of numerous small pistons, tightly packed, each driven by what amounts to a loudspeaker motor. Each piston has eight alternative positions. The reflector as a whole, then, shows a series of alternative stepped surfaces. It might be termed a Fresnel reflector, in analogy to a Fresnel lens consisting of a series of alternating steps. The direction in which the reflector stares is changed by moving the pistons, and they can move continuously in a ripple. This motion can also be used to distort the beam produced by the reflector. Although the resulting motion is not so fast as that of an electronically driven phased array, MEMPHIS is much simpler and much less expensive. A proof-of-concept reflector has been built, but as yet there is no full prototype. An operational MEMPHIS would be radome-enclosed.

UNITED KINGDOM

♦ Electronic Countermeasures

Existing UAA(1) (Abbey Hill) systems are being upgraded to UAA(2) configuration to deal with denser pulse environments.

Although UAF(1) is being fitted to the new Type-23 frigates, it is no longer considered adequate in view of the large number of high-PRF emitters, such as point-defense systems. The Royal Navy has, therefore, requested a new higher-capability UAF(X) for Type-23 Batch-2 frigates; Racal, Marconi, Thorn-EMI, and Plessey submitted bids in February 1989.

HMS *Trafalgar* shows her ESM search outfit (UAB) atop a telescopic mast. The other two masts are, fore to aft, the snorkel induction (air intake) and the diesel exhaust for her emergency diesel. Forward are a radar mast and two side-by-side periscopes, all retracted. This photograph probably dates from 1985; more recent ones show a much more elaborate ESM array, with at least four monopulse DF antennas (probably spirals) around the broad-band cone visible here, and a short dipole surmounting the cone. These two antenna systems may be part of UA-11/12, the simpler cone being the UAB antenna. (G. Arra via *Ships of the World*)

Racal is offering a UAF(1) modified to use its SADIE VLSI processor; the latter has already been chosen for Royal Navy EH-101 helicopters. The receiver would use filter banks to channelize incoming signals, scanning each channel separately.

Marconi is offering a version of its UAG developed for auxiliaries. This version uses Bragg cells to channelize signals. Marconi's experimental 500-MHz Bragg cell broke incoming signals into 500 parallel frequency channels (each presumably 1 MHz wide, and each having its own detector).

Thorn-EMI is also offering a channelized receiver, claimed to be capable of achieving ELINT precision, and of detecting signals at least as well as a conventional wide-open device. Moreover, the company claims that channelization makes the signal-to-noise ratio in each channel so high that the system can detect the sidelobes of a radar and, thus, can detect a sector-scanning set even if it is not pointing at the receiver. Thorn-EMI also proposes signal analysis by parallel computer (transputer). The faster the analysis, the larger the library that the system can consult. The company's generic Wavefinder ESM system can accommodate a threat library ten to fifteen times as large as that employed by a conventional ESM system.

No details of Plessey's system have been made public.

The first UAG system was delivered for trials in February 1989. It employs an omnidirectional antenna and six DF antennas, covering the 2–18 GHz range. As installed on board the new underway replenishment ships (AOR), the DF antennas are mounted on the sides of the radar platform. Marconi, which developed UAG, claims that it is the only ESM system that can overlay a synthetic picture on raw video. The library contains 2500 radar modes and can be searched in 1 sec, compared to 26 sec for standard Royal Navy systems that list only 200 radar modes. The export versions of UAG are Mentor 1 and 2.

There is a new Early Threat Warning (ETW) program, intended to provide the existing Type 675(2) jammer with its own threat warner, so that the jammer can respond to changes in the target's radar mode. As of June 1989, a contract was expected sometime that summer. Bidders include MEL and Thorn-EMI (the manufacturer of Type 675).

Bids for a Royal Navy off-board active decoy were submitted in February 1989 by Marconi, Thorn-EMI, and Racal. In 1990 two companies are to be selected for project definition studies, and deliveries would begin in 1992 (the decoy would enter service in 1993). The device is to be fired from the standard 130-mm Sea Gnat (U.S. Mk-136) launcher. Reportedly the decoy's role has not yet been defined. A long-range decoy might make do with a 100-watt TWT and a frequency-memory loop, whereas a short-range decoy would need much more power to deny an incoming missile burn-through vision of the ship. Marconi has proposed a rocket, burning for about a second to project itself well clear of the ship. After burnout, the decoy, like Marconi's Siren, would descend by parachute. Racal is using a winged decoy body made by British Aerospace.

◆ Export Systems

There are several new export systems, mainly combinations of existing types.

Octopus is Racal's new system, recently selected by the German Navy to replace Thomson-CSF's DR-2000s on board the Type-148 fast attack boats. Octopus consists of a Cutlass B1 ESM system, a Scorpion jammer, and an AEG threat library. The German Navy has specified two antennas: a wide-beam (40 × 40 deg) horn for area defense, and a steerable carbon-fiber dish for point defense. Scorpion provides 150-kW midband effective radiated power (50 kW minimum) and can jam up to 16 threats.

Another version of the Cutlass/Scorpion combination is designated Type 242. The ESM suite is based on that of the Royal Navy EH-101 helicopter, covering the 0.5–40 GHz range.

Racal is currently delivering Sabre ESM systems for installation on board Danish Stanflex 300 corvettes. The Royal Danish Navy requires 2 deg in bearing accuracy, hoping to use the system to target Harpoon missiles. The processor is SADIE, and the system covers the 0.5–18 GHz band.

MEL is currently delivering its Sceptre XL system to the Royal Swedish Navy, for *Goteborg*-class corvettes. The system operates in three bands, the DF antennas for the bands being mounted in two mast boxes. Frequency range is 2–18 GHz. Elevation coverage is +30/−10 deg, and bearing accuracy is 4.5 deg (with 2 deg available as an option). Sensitivity is −64 dBm, and dynamic range is 60 dB. The system can handle PRFs between 100 Hz and 300 kHz, pulse widths between 50 nanosec and 100 microsec, and scan periods of 0.02–40 sec. It is intended to detect radars with simple or modulated pulses, using frequency and PRF agility. Maximum pulse density is 1 million pps. The associated threat library covers 2000 emitter modes, with 144 emitter modes selected for threat warning; the operator's library consists of 100 emitter modes.

Sceptre XL is the most complex of a series of Sceptre ESM systems. Sceptre X covers the same frequency range but uses a simpler antenna (single arrays of horns and spiral in each direction), is limited to 6 deg in bearing accuracy, cannot deal with complex pulses, and has a threat library containing 1000 emitter modes. Dynamic range is reduced to 40 dB, and sensitivity is −50 dBm. Sceptre O is a much simpler system employing a single masthead antenna array (for both omnidirectional reception and DF), achieving a DF accuracy of 10 deg. The threat library is limited to 144 emitters; dynamic range is 35 dB, and sensitivity is −40 dBm.

UNITED STATES

◆ Terrier

In April 1989 it was announced that the nuclear version of Terrier, the only version of the missile remaining in service, would be retired on an accelerated basis.

◆ Mk-38 25-mm Cannon

Production of Mk-38 25-mm cannons was drastically accelerated in 1987–88 to meet the needs of ships in the Persian Gulf, much of the work being done at NWSC (Naval Weapons Support Center) Crane (which was responsible for the design of the gun's Mk-88 mount).

◆ Mk-26 Mod-15 Gun Mount

Another weapon produced in large numbers for the ships in the Persian Gulf was the Mk-26 Mod-15 (soft recoil) 0.50-caliber gun mount, developed by NWSC Crane. Mod 15 was originally developed after the 0.50 began to appear on board large ships in 1978. It was soon apparent that the hard recoil of the existing version of the Mk-26 mount drastically limited accuracy. Mod 15 was developed in the early 1980s, and limited production was approved about 1985. However, the gun mount's accuracy did not become important until ships in the Gulf began to encounter small attack boats in numbers.

The 0.50 itself gained importance with the introduction of a new explosive round, developed by Raufoss in Norway. Previous attempts to develop such a round for so small a caliber had failed because the 0.50-caliber bullet was too small to admit a mechanical safing and arming device (which was required to ensure safety, e.g., if rounds were accidentally dropped). Raufoss developed, in effect, a chemical safing and arming mechanism. The hard body inside the bullet is surrounded by explosive, and a detonating charge is packed into a cavity in the nose of the bullet. When the bullet hits, the charge bursts and ignites the main explosive charge, while the solid penetrator passes through thin armor. However, if the bullet is merely dropped, the impact is insufficient to set off the detonating charge.

Raufoss describes the round as multipurpose (MP) because it combines armor penetration with explosive effect. This type of construction was originally applied to 20-mm rounds and then to larger calibers up through 40-mm. The first 20-mm MP round was fired in 1968, and the first production batch was delivered to the Royal Norwegian Air Force in 1971. The 0.50-caliber round was a later development; by the end of 1989, about twelve million will have been delivered. There are now three types: MP, MP/T (tracer, production of which began in 1988), and APS (which was first marketed early in 1989). The APS round can penetrate 20 mm of armor at up to 30 deg from the normal, from a range of 400 m. The MP round is credited with penetration of 25 mm of steel at a 45-deg angle.

Rounds originally bought by the U.S. Navy for evaluation were sent to the Persian Gulf in 1987 on an emergency basis. As of 1989 Raufoss is supplying these rounds to the U.S. Navy. The Olin Matheson Company in the United States obtained manufacturing rights to the basic technology in 1981. Rounds were ordered only in 1987, and as of 1989 the company was still experiencing difficulties in production. As of 1989, however, production of both 0.50-caliber and 20-mm rounds was underway in the United States, and 25-mm rounds were undergoing qualification tests.

Compared to conventional 0.50-caliber rounds, the Raufoss round is much more accurate because of its weight and the different location of the center of gravity.

The effect of Raufoss's development is to extend some of the advantages of the 20-mm cannon, until now the smallest that could fire an explosive shell, to the much lighter and more portable 0.50. Presumably this development makes the 0.50 much more attractive as an anti–small boat weapon, to be carried on board both small boats and helicopters. Large numbers of these rounds have been sold (more than 3 million in France, the best customer).

As of 1989, Raufoss was developing a new tracer round based on this technology.

ASW

ITALY

◆ A.290

A MILAS ASW missile, carrying an Italian A.290 torpedo, at the Paris Air Show, 1989. (Author)

The A.290 torpedo was displayed publicly for the first time at the Mostra Navale exhibition at Genoa in May 1989. The torpedo employs a shaped-charge warhead and is 2.75 meters long. A.290 is to enter service in the Italian Navy early in 1992.

UNITED STATES

◆ VLA

The designation of the Vertical Launch ASROC is RUM-139A (ASROC is RUR-5A). One important argument against VLA, and in favor of the extension of Sea Lance to surface ships, is that the latter's long maximum range can be exploited by using a LAMPS helicopter as a targeting platform. The helicopter localizes the targeted submarine within the box defined by the ship's long-range sensor, and the ship can fire multiple rounds into that box. In this way the overall effectiveness of the ship/helicopter weapons system is not limited by the torpedo-carrying capacity of the helicopter, and the helicopter can gain endurance by carrying extra fuel.

Flight trials of the Sea Lance missile began at White Sands in the summer of 1988, and the first all-up round was fired from San Clemente in February 1989.

◆ Nuclear ASW Weapons

In April 1989 it was announced that SUBROC and the nuclear version of ASROC would be retired on an accelerated basis. The only remaining U.S. nuclear ASW weapon, the Mk 57 depth bomb, is expected to remain in service. No decision as to production of the next-generation nuclear depth bomb is likely to be made until 1992 or later, and preliminary work on the nuclear version of Sea Lance is still proceeding.

◆ P-3 Aircraft Systems

In April 1989 it was reported that an upgrade to P-3C aircraft, ASUTAA (acoustic system upgrade to ASW aircraft), would probably be proposed under the FY92 budget. ASUTAA is an attempt to achieve something close to UPDATE IV capability, doubling the DIFAR capability of the P-3C UPDATE III to 32. By way of contrast, UPDATE IV will be able to handle 54 DIFAR buoys simultaneously. An RFP for ASUTAA had originally been expected in FY90 but was reportedly delayed so as not to compete directly with the new UPDATE IV program.

At the same time, the new proposed defense budget for FY90–91 called for retirement of the P-3A and -3B aircraft currently operated by reserve squadrons. These aircraft have very limited sonobuoy-processing capacity, and an upgrade, IPADS (improved processing and display system) had been proposed. IPADS would have doubled the current 16-buoy processing capacity of reserve P-3Bs. If the reserve cuts survive in the budget ultimately adopted, IPADS will presumably be canceled; it may, however, be applicable to P-3A/Bs (and equivalents) remaining in service abroad.

◆ ELCS and ILCS

The Hermes microbuoy at the Paris Air Show, 1989. The extended object is the ballute used to brake the buoy's descent. The buoy is made in two layers, the upper one containing the radio and processor, and the lower the suspension and array. The longer and more elaborate the array, the larger the buoy. (Author)

In the aftermath of the cancellation of the LCS program, the U.S. Navy is considering a program for an enhanced low-cost sonobuoy (ELCS) or an improved low-cost sonobuoy (ILCS). Both would retain the low-cost and automatic-detection features expected of the original LCS. Reportedly the original LCS program died of both excessive cost and problems with the onboard processor. In theory, ELCS should enter service in 1995; ILCS in 1999, probably under a new program name. As of mid-1989, the buoy's characteristics are still ill-defined. The ELCS/ILCS study began with an RFP in June 1988, and in April 1989 work was completed by the four competing teams. As of mid-1989, their reports were being evaluated.

ILCS is likely to employ a command link, which will allow all of the buoy's functions (including operating depth and band) to be reset. Buoys are currently launched with preset parameters, which include the radio frequency, the array's depth, and the listening frequency. The operator on the airplane must, therefore, guess which line or frequency band will be most useful before he launches buoys; he does so partly on the basis of an ambient noise sample. However, as the target runs through the field of buoys, that preliminary estimate may prove faulty. LOFAR buoys are fairly narrowly tuned, so new ones would have to be launched. A command link would solve this problem.

The four competing teams are Magnavox/Boeing, Sparton/Lockheed, Hermes/Lockheed, and Sippican/IBM. Sparton's and Hermes's proposals draw on experience gained in four years of work on a Canadian Microbuoy (contracted for by the Canadian Defence Research Establishment Atlantic, DREA). DREA called for omnidirectional LOFAR buoys and dropped both types from a CP-140 Aurora in the fall of 1988. The standard A-size buoy container carries 12 Hermes or 16 Sparton buoys.

In each case, the buoy converted its acoustic data directly into frequency data (using a fast Fourier transform), greatly reducing the processing load on board the airplane. In theory, such a buoy can be set to automatically detect a particular LOFAR line signal and to contact the airplane only when that line has appeared. Moreover, by reducing the usual acoustic data to frequency data, the buoy can greatly reduce the amount of transmitted information, and the buoys of a pattern can all share the same frequency (using time-division multiplexing).

The next step in the Canadian program is to improve performance by increasing the array's depth (from about 100 ft to about 1000 ft) and also by operating at lower frequency. Since the array and suspension take up much of the volume of the buoy as loaded, this development requires enlargement, to about A/6 size. As of mid-1989 it was uncertain whether this work would be paid for by DREA, by the companies themselves (as part of the work-up towards ELCS/ILCS), or by the U.S. Navy.

The initial version of the Hermes microbuoy had 1500 radio channels, programmable immediately before launch. The second version reduced that number to 500, to provide more channel width (75 rather than 25 kHz per channel) so that the original LOFAR omnidirectional array could later be replaced by a directional (DIFAR) array. On sea trials in 1988, the buoy demonstrated performance comparable to that of a standard A-size LOFAR buoy (SSQ-41) down to about 10–15 Hz, a lifetime of 5 hrs, and a radio output of half a watt. The buoy has two preset detection modes, detection of a preset line or autocorrelation, and the buoy can be set to transmit either continuously or upon detection. Processing is by a 1024-point FFT, providing a resolution of 0.10 Hz and a bandwidth of 250 Hz. The Hermes buoy is A/15 size. These figures are presumably typical of what can now be achieved.

MINE WARFARE

FRANCE

◆ IBIS 43

In 1989 Thomson Sintra announced the IBIS 43 minehunting system, developed from the earlier IBIS 41 (DUBM 41) and IBIS 42 (DUBM 42). The sonar fish automatically avoids underwater obstructions; sonar range is either 50 or 100 m (two beams, one to each side) with a resolution of 10 or 20 cm depending on the range chosen; search rate is up to 5.4 square km per hour.

IBIS 43 has been chosen to equip the Danish StanFlex 300 corvettes in their mine-countermeasures role.

IRAQ

◆ Naval Mines

At Baghdad in April 1989, Iraq displayed a new naval mine system, Sumer, which was said to have been under development since 1985. No details are available, but the weapon is an influence mine that can be laid by aircraft, surface ships, or submarines; it is, therefore, constrained by the usual 21-in torpedo-tube diameter. Sumer is also described as either a ground or a moored mine, controlled by a computer-controlled target-detection device. Sumer is to enter service shortly.

Iraq also displayed two anti-invasion mines, Sigeel and Al-Munthena-45, at least one of which broadly resembles the Italian Manta. A large oil-rig demolition device, Alkaakaa-16, was also on display.

ITALY

◆ Mine Projects

Misar's three new mine projects were shown at the Mostra Navale show in May 1989. Seppia is a private-venture moored multi-influence mine, using a Misar-developed programmable microprocessor. Seppia carries a 200-kg (HBX-1) explosive load and can be laid by ships, aircraft, or submarines. Misar is also developing a moored mine, MEB 90, in a joint venture with two Spanish companies, Bazan and Expal. Finally, Misar is developing the CSM rising continental-shelf mine, in collaboration with Whitehead, for the Italian Navy. The rising body is described as partially self-guided.

◆ Pluto Plus

Gaymarine exhibited a new mine-countermeasures submersible, Pluto Plus, at Mostra Navale in Genoa in May 1989. Compared to the existing Pluto, Plus is longer (1.95 vs. 1.6 m) and heavier (800 vs. 135 kg); Pluto Plus can operate to a depth of 400 m and at a speed of up to 7 kts (with an endurance of about 2 hours). Sensors are a color television camera and three sonars (for search at medium range, for navigation, and for target identification).

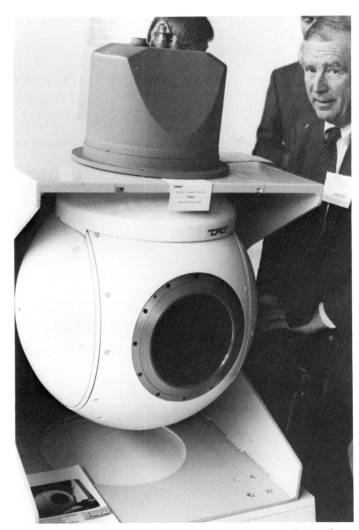

The TANGO IR turret of the Atlantique-2 maritime-patrol aircraft, at the Paris Air Show, 1989. (Author)

APS-705 antenna, line-of-sight stabilized in roll and pitch. This radar is also offered in a podded version, to provide aircraft with an antiship capability, in association with the Marte missile. APS-705 operates in X-band, with peak power of 20 kW (see page 56). (SMA)

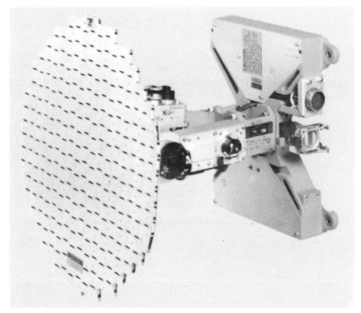

APS-717 antenna. (SMA)

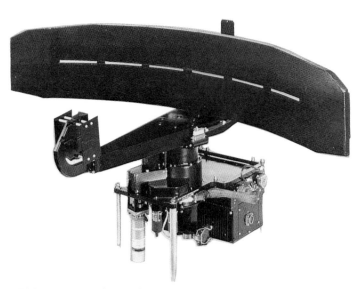

APS-707 antenna, designed to operate at a peak power of 90 kW (see page 56). (SMA)

Penguin being fired by the Norwegian missile boat *Skudd*. (*Ships of the World*)

APS-707 installed on board an Argentine Electra airliner converted for use in maritime patrol. The U.S.-built Orion (P-3) shares much the same airframe. (SMA)

ALARM antiradar missile at the Paris Air Show, 1989, with Active Sky Flash in the background. (Author)

The Dornier version of MSOW, at the Paris Air Show, 1989. (Author)

Chinese missiles manufactured by CPMIEC on display at ASIANDEX 1988. From the top, they are M-1B, C301, C101, C802, C201, M-1, and HQ-61 (SAM). M-1 and M-1B are army artillery rockets fired from multiple launchers; -1B is heavier and achieves a greater range. (CPMIEC)

C801 antiship missile, with booster. (CPMIEC)

Balcom 10 shows the new Soviet antiship missile in its canister launcher. (West German Ministry of Defense)

C101 antiship missile, showing ramjets and boosters. (CPMIEC)

A TALD decoy, at the Paris Air Show, 1989. The decoy can dispense chaff, either continuously or in packages, from its tail. TALD weighs 450 lbs. It achieves a 10:1 glide ratio, so that when it is launched from 40,000 ft at 250 kts it flies for 68 nm. Launched from 2000 feet, at the same speed, it flies 14 nm. The manufacturer, Brunswick, claims that one TALD costs about one-thousandth as much as a combat airplane, which probably means much less than $50,000 each. (Author)

SPN-720 carrier-controlled-approach radar. Search range is about 15 nm; approach-control range is about 8 nm. Aircraft can be detected at altitudes up to 2000 m (about 6600 ft) (see page 133). (SMA)

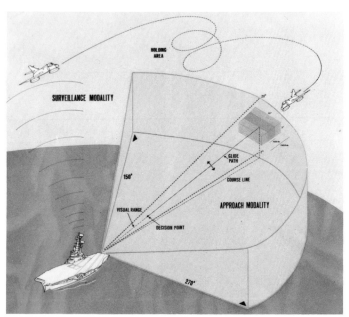

Coverage of the SPN-728 carrier-controlled-approach radar. The only current Western alternative to the U.S. SPN-35, SPN-728 is shown as installed on board the Argentine carrier *25 de Mayo*. (SMA)

SPN-728 antenna, for navigation and surface search. This medium-power X-band radar is supplied with several alternative roll- and pitch-stabilized antennas. There are four alternative pulse widths, and the display is a raster rather than a rotating scan, partly so that the radar can use low-cost television-type monitors as repeaters. Targets are automatically detected (see page 133). (SMA)

OPS-14B radar antenna on board the Japanese destroyer *Isoyuki*, 1989. (W. Donko)

Type 2-21 gunfire-control system director on board the Japanese destroyer *Haruyuki*, 1989. (W. Donko)

The 9LV200 Mk 3 director, with television, laser, and infrared camera on the left. (PEAB)

The ELSA radar associated with the 9LV200 Mk 3 system. (PEAB)

The 9LV100 optronic director, carrying an IR camera and gyro on the left, a laser range-finder on the upper right, and a television camera on the lower right. The most basic version of the director lacks the infrared camera. (PEAB)

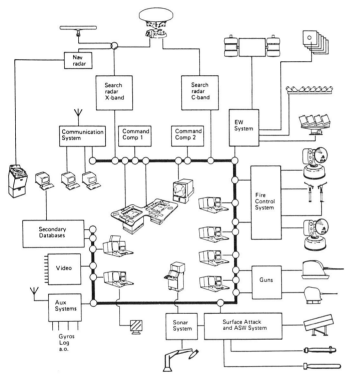

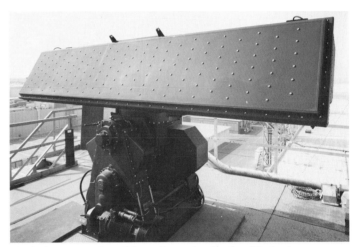

Hughes's Improved TAS three-dimensional radar. (Hughes)

Overall layout of the 9LV200 Mk 3 system, including its interface with a standard CEPLO command-and-control system (with its double horizontal console and its circular vertical display). The two gunlike objects on the right, above the director, are optical target designators. There is no central computer; the entire system employs distributed processors and a data bus (the thick black line). (PEAB)

ASTER in flight. (Aerospatiale)

Sea Archer. (British Aerospace)

ASRAAM (AIM-132) at the Paris Air Show, 1989, with ALARM in the foreground. (Author)

Active Sky Flash at the Paris Air Show, 1989. Sky Flash itself is a modified Sparrow (AIM-7E). British Aerospace has been marketing a proposed X/K-band active version since 1985, originally with a seeker by Marconi. The current seeker's contractor is Thomson-CSF. The missile is being offered to countries that will not be permitted to buy AMRAAM; British Aerospace claims that Active Sky Flash can be in service as early as 1992. (Author)

Mk 29 Sea Sparrow box launcher on board the Japanese destroyer *Amagiri*, 1989. (W. Donko)

The French GIAT Affut 15 mounting for the 20-mm M621 gun. The gun fires 750 rounds/min; the mount carries 160 rounds. Elevation limits are +45/−10 deg, and total weight (without ammunition) is 167 kg. (GIAT)

OTO-Melara compact 76-mm gun mount on board the Japanese destroyer *Isoyuki*, 1989. (W. Donko)

Meroka on board the Spanish aircraft carrier *Principe de Asturias*, with both the radar (PVS-2) and the optical director visible. The cartridge chute is at the side. (G. Arra via *Ships of the World*)

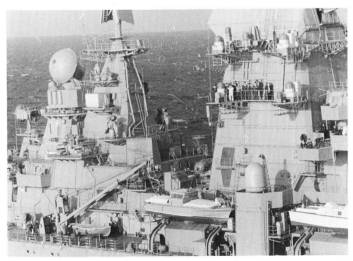

A close-up of the new Soviet cruiser *Kalinin* shows her new gun-and-missile CIWS just below her Top Dome missile director. To the right a Tin Man optronic device is visible. The RBU-1000 follow-on is visible on deck at the lower left-hand corner of the photograph. (West German Ministry of Defense)

アイランド前端の4脚マストの頂部はSPS・52C三次元レーダー（将来SPS・52Dに換装予定）で、その直下の棒状のアンテナはSPS・55対水上レーダーである。艦橋は下部が司令部艦橋、その上が航海艦橋、発着艦指揮所はアイランド内艦側に設けられている。

The Nettunel ECM system, as installed on board the Spanish aircraft carrier *Principe de Asturias*, 1989. Nettunel occupies the boxes at the edges of the two big mast platforms cantilevered over the sides of the quadrupod mast. The intercept/DF antennas occupy the upper box, the transmitter the lower. The two dipoles visible near the port-side transmitter box are part of an unrelated ship-to-air radio system. Radars occupy the platforms projecting forward of the mast, with a U.S. SPS-52C at the top. Floodlights surround two of the mast platforms. The mast is surmounted by a TACAN antenna. The prominent fueling-at-sea hoses are on their booms. The ship acts both as flagship and as afloat support ship for her accompanying frigates. (G. Arra via *Ships of the World*)

A British attack submarine shows the the ESM array mounted atop her periscope (to the right of, and forward of, the telescoping ESM mast). This is a combined IFM and D/F array; in some cases it is carried together with the conical antenna on the ESM mast. The sonar dome forward of the sail covers a Type 2019 underwater telephone; the significance of the two prominent vents on either side of the hull under the sail is unknown. (Plessey)

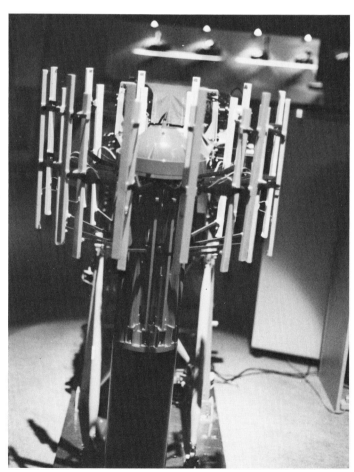

The French FLASH (folding light acoustic system for helicopters) low-frequency helicopter dipping sonar, which has been offered for the U.S. ALFS, the Canadian NSA (New Seaborne Aircraft), and the European EH-101 and NFH90 programs. The associated processor can handle 8 or 16 sonobuoys. In the background is a display of Thomson-CSF A and A/3 size sonobuoys. (Author)

The FLASH dipping body folded and unfolded. The dark object at the bottom is the omnidirectional pinger; the receivers unfold to achieve directional performance. FLASH operates at three frequencies, all below 5 kHz, and its array preforms 24 receiving beams. (Author)

Allied-Systems's HELRAS low-frequency helicopter sonar. (FIAR)

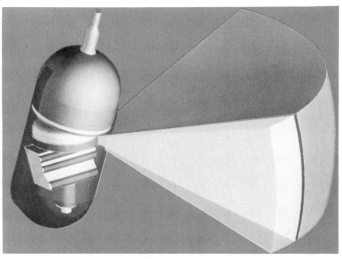

The Plessey-FIAR P2095 minehunting sonar (the towed body is shown). Operational testing is expected in 1992, with installation on board an Italian minehunter by the end of 1993. (FIAR)

The Naval Institute Press is the book-publishing arm of the U.S. Naval Institute, a private, nonprofit professional society for members of the sea services and civilians who share an interest in naval and maritime affairs. Established in 1873 at the U.S. Naval Academy in Annapolis, Maryland, where its offices remain today, the Naval Institute has more than 100,000 members worldwide.

Members of the Naval Institute receive the influential monthly naval magazine *Proceedings* and substantial discounts on fine nautical prints, ship and aircraft photos, and subscriptions to the Institute's recently inaugurated quarterly, *Naval History.* They also have access to the transcripts of the Institute's Oral History Program and may attend any of the Institute-sponsored seminars regularly offered around the country.

The book-publishing program, begun in 1898 with basic guides to naval practices, has broadened its scope in recent years to include books of more general interest. Now the Naval Institute Press publishes more than forty new titles each year, ranging from how-to books on boating and navigation to battle histories, biographies, ship guides, and novels. Institute members receive discounts on the Press's more than 300 books.

For a free catalog describing books currently available and for further information about U.S. Naval Institute membership, please write to:

Membership Department
U.S. Naval Institute
Annapolis, Maryland 21402

or call, toll-free, 800-233-USNI.